3 Ways to Request Information

1 Sponsored Return Postcard.
Some religious communities have placed pre-addressed postcards in this book that may be mailed directly to their vocation office. See index of postcards on reverse side.

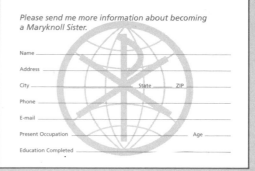

Please send me more information about becoming a Maryknoll Sister.

Name ____________________

Address ____________________

City ____________ State ______ ZIP ______

Phone ____________________

E-mail ____________________

Present Occupation ____________ Age ______

Education Completed ____________________

2 Reader Service Card.
(Postage paid)
Complete and mail one of these cards in order to receive literature from several religious communities active in your area of interest.

I am interested in a life of religious ministry. Please forward information about different religious communities. I am interested in being a:
❑ Priest ❑ Brother ❑ Sister ❑ Lay Minister

My particular interest for ministry in a religious life is in:
❑ Parish Work ❑ Education
❑ Missions ❑ Health Care
❑ Undecided ❑ Social Service
❑ Other: ____________

Type of Community:
Refer to front of A section for a description of each
❑ Apostolic/Active
❑ Contemplative/Cloistered
❑ Monastic

Mr./Ms./Mrs. ____________________

Address ____________________

City/State/Zip ____________________

Telephone ____________________

E-mail Address ____________________

Last Grade Completed ____________ Age

Comments ____________________

3 Direct Return Postcard
(Please apply postage)
These blank cards are provided for you to complete and mail to religious communities you would like to learn more about. See the index of advertisers listed on page A-25 (for Men) and A-97 (for Women).

I read your profile in ***A Guide to Religious Ministries***.
Please send me additional information.

Mr./Ms./Mrs. ____________________

Address ____________________

City/State/Zip ____________________

Telephone ____________________

E-mail Address ____________________

Last Grade Completed ____________ Age ______

Comments ____________________

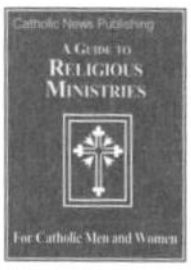
Catholic News Publishing
A Guide to
Religious
Ministries
For Catholic Men and Women

This postcard is a service of
A Guide to Religious Ministries
210 North Avenue, New Rochelle, NY 10801
914-632-1220

D0325521

Index of Postcard Advertisers

Please send me information about The Paulists

Name __________

Address __________

City, State, Zip __________

Age __________

Telephone (   ) __________

Last Year of School Completed __________

Email Address __________

Serving God as a priest, brother, sister or lay minister is a rewarding career. Vocation directors can help you discover if the religious life is for you.

3-A ↑

3-B ↓

Adorers of the Blood of Christ

I saw your ad in *A Guide to Religious Ministries* and would like more information about the *LifeChoices*® Program.

Name: __________

Street Address: __________

City, State, Zip Code: __________

Phone: __________

E-mail: __________

Age: __________ Last grade completed: __________

Comments: __________

PLACE
POSTAGE
HERE

Fr. Edward C. Nowak, C.S.P.
The Paulists
415 W. 59th Street
New York, NY 10019

Sending in these postcards to the vocation director does not obligate you to anything, but it may be the first step towards your life's work.

NO POSTAGE
NECESSARY
IF MAILED
IN THE
UNITED STATES

BUSINESS REPLY MAIL
FIRST-CLASS MAIL PERMIT NO. 5247 WICHITA KS

POSTAGE WILL BE PAID BY ADDRESSEE

ATTN: VOCATION OFFICE
ADORERS OF THE BLOOD OF CHRIST
1165 SOUTHWEST BLVD
WICHITA KS 67213-9890

Please send me information about

The SMA Fathers Missionary Priesthood or Lay Mission Program

Name ____________________

Address ____________________

City, State, Zip ____________________

Last Year of School Completed ____________________ Age ______

Telephone (   ) ____________________

Comments ____________________

____

This postcard is a service of
A GUIDE TO RELIGIOUS MINISTRIES
210 North Avenue, New Rochelle, NY 10801

Serving God as a priest, brother, sister or lay minister is a rewarding career. Vocation directors can help you discover if the religious life is for you.

5-A ↑

5-B ↓

ALEXIAN BROTHERS

A Religious Community of Men in the...
HEALTH CARE MINISTRY

Ordinary Men, Extraordinary Lives.
in Hospitals, Nursing Homes, Retirement Homes, AIDS Houses. **SEND FOR INFORMATION** or call **1-800-556-0332**.

NAME ....

ADDRESS ....

CITY ....

STATE .... ZIP ....

AGE .... EDUCATION ....

Place
Stamp
Here

Vocation Director
SMA Fathers
23 Bliss Ave
Tenafly, N.J. 07670

Sending in these postcards to the vocation director does not obligate you to anything, but it may be the first step towards your life's work.

PLACE
STAMP
HERE

ALEXIAN BROTHERS

Director of Vocations
600 Alexian Way
Elk Grove Village, IL 60007

BECOME A FRANCISCAN FRIAR OF THE ATONEMENT

Please send me information about the Friars of the Atonement.
I am interested in becoming a ☐ Priest ☐ Brother.

Name ______________________

Address ______________________

City ____________ *State* ____________ *Zip* ____________

Last year of school completed ____________ *Age* ____________

Telephone (____) ______________________

Your e-mail address ______________________

"Experimenting with tradition since 1898..."

Return this card today or visit us online at:
www.atonementfriarsvocations.org

This postcard is a service of A Guide to Religious Ministries.

Serving God as a priest, brother, sister or lay minister is a rewarding career. Vocation directors can help you discover if the religious life is for you.

7-A ↑

7-B ↓

The Augustinians

Order of St. Augustine

Eastern Province: James McBurney, O.S.A.
214 Ashwood Rd • P.O. Box 340 • Villanova, PA 19085-0340
Phone: 610-527-3330 ext. 284 • Fax: 610-520-0618

Western Province: Tom Whelan, O.S.A.
108 Cole Street • San Francisco, CA 94117-1116
Phone: 415-387-3626

Midwestern Province: John Merkelis, O.S.A.
20300 Governor's Highway • Olympia Fields, IL 60461-1081
Phone:708-748-9500 • Fax: 708-481-2090

Augustinian Contemplative Nuns:
440 Marley Road
New Lenox, IL 60451
815-463-9662

Please send information about the Augustinian Order.

Name ______________________ Age ____________

Address ______________________

City ______________________ State ________ Zip ________

Education ______________________ Present Occupation ______________________

Area Code ____________ Phone Number ______________________

NO POSTAGE
NECESSARY
IF MAILED
IN THE
UNITED STATES

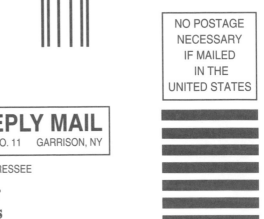

BUSINESS REPLY MAIL
FIRST-CLASS MAIL PERMIT NO. 11 GARRISON, NY

POSTAGE WILL BE PAID BY ADDRESSEE

Vocation Director
Franciscan Friars
of the Atonement
PO Box 300,
Garrison, NY 10524-0300

Sending in these postcards to the vocation director does not obligate you to anything, but it may be the first step towards your life's work.

Place
Stamp
Here

The Augustinians

Director of Vocations

Please fill in the address nearest you from the other side

Serving God as a priest, brother, sister or lay minister is a rewarding career. Vocation directors can help you discover if the religious life is for you.

9-A ↑

9-B ↓

PLACE
STAMP
HERE

Father Meinrad Miller, O.S.B.
St. Benedict's Abbey
1020 N. Second St.
Atchison, KS 66002

Sending in these postcards to the vocation director does not obligate you to anything, but it may be the first step towards your life's work.

NO POSTAGE NECESSARY IF MAILED IN THE UNITED STATES

BUSINESS REPLY MAIL

FIRST-CLASS PERMIT NO. 4 COLLEGEVILLE, MN 56321

POSTAGE WILL BE PAID BY

Saint John's Abbey
Vocation Director
Box 2015
Collegeville, MN 56321-2015

SAINT LOUIS ABBEY

A Benedictine monastery of Catholic priests and brothers

We explore the mystery of God in PRAYER, living a COMMON LIFE and WORKING for the Lord in our apostolates of teaching, pastoral work and other ministries.

◆
Name Age

◆
Street address Phone

◆
City State Zip

◆
College/professional experience

Send in this card for more information, or call 1-800-638-1527

Web site: **www.stlouisabbey.org**

Come and serve the Lord as a monk of the Benedictine Community of Saint Louis Abbey.

Serving God as a priest, brother, sister or lay minister is a rewarding career. Vocation directors can help you discover if the religious life is for you.

11-A ↑

11-B ↓

Please send me information about

Sisters of Saint Benedict

Mount Saint Benedict Monastery

Name ____________________

Address ____________________

City, State, Zip ____________________

Last Year of School Completed ____________________ Age ________

Telephone ____________________

E-mail ____________________

Comments ____________________

This postcard is a service of A GUIDE TO RELIGIOUS MINISTRIES

NO POSTAGE
NECESSARY
IF MAILED
IN THE
UNITED STATES

BUSINESS REPLY MAIL
FIRST-CLASS MAIL PERMIT NO. 2599 ST. LOUIS, MO

POSTAGE WILL BE PAID BY ADDRESSEE

Ralph Wright, O.S.B.
Director of Vocations
Saint Louis Abbey
500 S. Mason Rd.
St. Louis, MO 63141-8500

Sending in these postcards to the vocation director does not obligate you to anything, but it may be the first step towards your life's work.

PLACE
STAMP
HERE

Vocation Director
Mount Saint Benedict Monastery
620 Summit Avenue
Crookston, MN 56716-2799

Please send me more information about the Sisters of St. Benedict

Name ____________________

Address ____________________

City ____________ State ______ Zip ______

Phone ____________________

Best time to call ____________________

E-mail address ____________________

Occupation ____________________

Education level ____________________

Birthdate (day/month/year) ____________________

This postcard is a service of Guide to Religious Ministries.

Serving God as a priest, brother, sister or lay minister is a rewarding career. Vocation directors can help you discover if the religious life is for you.

13-A ↑

13-B ↓

SSS

Nourished by Christ, who gives himself to us totally in the Eucharist, we express, in our form of life, the gift of ourselves.

Rule of Life, No. 15

CONGREGATION OF THE BLESSED SACRAMENT

Yes, please send me information about the Blessed Sacrament Fathers and Brothers.

Name ____________________

Address ____________________

City ____________ State ______

Zip ______ Email ______

Telephone ____________ Age ______

☐ I'm interested in discernment "Come & See" Retreats:
Albuquerque, NM - Cleveland, OH - Houston, TX - New York, NY - San Antonio, TX

NO POSTAGE
NECESSARY
IF MAILED
IN THE
UNITED STATES

BUSINESS REPLY MAIL
FIRST CLASS MAIL PERMIT NO. 3 FERDINAND, IN

POSTAGE WILL BE PAID BY ADDRESSEE

VOCATION OFFICE
SISTERS OF ST BENEDICT
802 E 10TH ST
FERDINAND IN 47532-9971

Sending in these postcards to the vocation director does not obligate you to anything, but it may be the first step towards your life's work.

NO POSTAGE
NECESSARY
IF MAILED
IN THE
UNITED STATES

BUSINESS REPLY MAIL
FIRST-CLASS MAIL PERMIT NO. 3691 CLEVELAND OH

POSTAGE WILL BE PAID BY ADDRESSEE

VOCATION DIRECTOR
CONGREGATION OF THE BLESSED SACRAMENT
5384 WILSON MILLS RD
CLEVELAND OH 44143-9960

Called To make a difference

Please send me further information on the Carmelites

Name ______________________________

Address ______________________________

City/State-Province/Zip ______________________________

Date of Birth ____________ Education Completed ____________

E-Mail Address ________________ Phone: ________________

Me gustaría recibir información vocacional en español: ❑

Serving God as a priest, brother, sister or lay minister is a rewarding career. Vocation directors can help you discover if the religious life is for you.

15-A ↑

15-B ↓

In circles that matter
you could be an insider

THE CLARETIANS

On Fire with God's Love

The Claretians invite you to consider our ministries and community life. Send for more information about joining our circle...

❑ As a priest ❑ As a brother

Please mail this completed card today.

Name______________________________

Address______________________________

City______________ State______ Zip__________ Age________

Tel.____________ E-mail____________ Education____________

I am interested in the (check one):

❑ Eastern Province, states east of and bordering the Mississippi River

❑ Western Province, states west of the Mississippi River

Place
Postage
Here

Carmelite Vocation Office
8433 Bailey Road
Darien, IL 60561

Sending in these postcards to the vocation director does not obligate you to anything, but it may be the first step towards your life's work.

NO POSTAGE
NECESSARY
IF MAILED IN THE
UNITED STATES

BUSINESS REPLY MAIL
FIRST-CLASS MAIL PERMIT NO. 16423 CHICAGO, IL

POSTAGE PAID BY ADDRESSEE

REV. CARL QUEBEDEAUX, C.M.F.
ROOM 2308
205 W. MONROE STREET
CHICAGO IL 60606-9506

Please send information about

Daughters of St. Mary of Providence

(Guanellian Sisters)

Name ______________________________

Address ______________________________

City, State, Zip ______________________________

Last Year of School Completed ______________________ Age ________

Telephone (   ) ______________________________

Comments ______________________________

____

This postcard is a service of
A GUIDE TO RELIGIOUS MINISTRIES
210 North Avenue, New Rochelle, NY 10801

Serving God as a priest, brother, sister or lay minister is a rewarding career. Vocation directors can help you discover if the religious life is for you.

17-A ↑

17-B ↓

I would appreciate more information about the Salvatorians:

- ☐ Sisters
- ☐ Lay Salvatorians
- ☐ Priests and Brothers

Name: PLEASE PRINT

Address:

City/State/Zip:

Phone: (Area code:) —

Birthdate:

Occupation:

Education level:

Please complete and return card or give us a call...

Women please call (414) 466-0810

Men please call (414) 258-1735

This Postcard is a service of A Guide To Religious Ministries

Place
Stamp
Here

Vocation Directress
Daughters of St. Mary of Providence
4200 North Austin Avenue
Chicago IL 60634

Sending in these postcards to the vocation director does not obligate you to anything, but it may be the first step towards your life's work.

PLACE
STAMP
HERE

Proclaiming the Savior – Together in Mission

Salvatorians
1735 N. Hi-Mount Boulevard
Milwaukee, WI 53208-1720

☐ **YES!** I want to make a difference with my life. I am interested in learning more about Divine Word College.

Name ______________________________

Address ______________________________

City/State/Zip ______________________________

Phone Number ______________________________

e-mail address ______________________________

Education Completed ______________ Date of Birth ____________

Complete the response card and mail it or call us toll free: 1-800-553-3321
Visit our web site: www.svd.org
E-mail us at: dwm@mwci.net

Serving God as a priest, brother, sister or lay minister is a rewarding career. Vocation directors can help you discover if the religious life is for you.

19-A ↑

19-B ↓

I would like to know more about

The Dominican Sisters of Hawthorne

Please send information to:

NAME ______________________________

ADDRESS ______________________________

CITY/STATE/ZIP ______________________________

This postcard is a service of **A GUIDE TO RELIGIOUS MINISTRIES** 210 North Avenue, New Rochelle, New York 10801

NO POSTAGE
NECESSARY
IF MAILED
IN THE
UNITED STATES

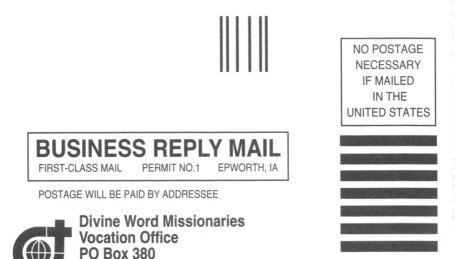

BUSINESS REPLY MAIL

FIRST-CLASS MAIL PERMIT NO.1 EPWORTH, IA

POSTAGE WILL BE PAID BY ADDRESSEE

Divine Word Missionaries
Vocation Office
PO Box 380
Epworth IA 52045-9900

Sending in these postcards to the vocation director does not obligate you to anything, but it may be the first step towards your life's work.

DOMINICAN SISTERS OF HAWTHORNE
Rosary Hill Home (Motherhouse)
Hawthorne, New York

St. Rose's Home
New York, New York

Sacred Heart Home
Philadelphia, Pennsylvania

Our Lady of Good Counsel Home
St. Paul, Minnesota

Holy Family Home
Cleveland, Ohio

Our Lady of Perpetual Help Home
Atlanta, Georgia

PLACE
STAMP
HERE

DOMINICAN SISTERS OF HAWTHORNE
Sr. Teresa Marie Barnaby, O.P.
Vocation Director
600 Linda Avenue
Hawthorne, NY 10532

The Franciscan Friars of the Holy Land

Another Red Cross has been the symbol of International care and service to the poor, suffering and outcasts for nearly eight centuries:

The oldest Province of the Franciscan Order, the Custody of the Holy Land, is anything but "provincial-minded" as its 400 Friars from 29 nationalities minister to the People of God in 12 countries. Faithful to the charge entrusted to them by Francis of Assisi in 1217, the Friars highlight the humanity of Jesus through an intense religious, educational and social apostolate and by serving those places made holy by His life on earth. This is why we need men whose vision has no horizons. **Phone (202) 526-6800**

www.myfranciscan.com

Name ________ Age ________
Address ________
City ________ State ________ Zip ________
Education ________ Phone ________
GFM 04 C

Serving God as a priest, brother, sister or lay minister is a rewarding career. Vocation directors can help you discover if the religious life is for you.

21-A ↑

21-B ↓

FRANCISCAN SISTERS OF LITTLE FALLS MINNESOTA

Please send me more information about the Franciscan Sisters of Little Falls, Minnesota

Name ________
Address ________
City ________ State ________ Zip ________
Phone ________
Best time to call ________
E-mail address ________
Occupation ________
Education level ________
Birthdate (day/month/year) ________

This postcard is a service of Guide to Religious Ministries.

Place
Postage
Here

Director of Vocations

Holy Land Franciscans

1400 Quincy Street, NE

Washington, DC 20017

Sending in these postcards to the vocation director does not obligate you to anything, but it may be the first step towards your life's work.

NO POSTAGE
NECESSARY
IF MAILED
IN THE
UNITED STATES

BUSINESS REPLY MAIL

FIRST-CLASS MAIL   PERMIT NO. 5   LITTLE FALLS, MN

POSTAGE WILL BE PAID BY ADDRESSEE

VOCATION OFFICE
FRANCISCAN SISTERS OF
LITTLE FALLS, MINNESOTA
116 8TH AVE SE
LITTLE FALLS MN 56345-9939

Please send me information about the Joliet Franciscans.

Joliet Franciscans... Women of living faith and loving service.

Name ______________________________

Address ______________________________

City, State, Zip ______________________________

Phone ______________________________

e-mail ______________________________

Best time to contact me is: ____________________

Come visit our website: www.jolietfranciscans.org
You may fax this card to: (309) 820-1677

Serving God as a priest, brother, sister or lay minister is a rewarding career. Vocation directors can help you discover if the religious life is for you.

23-A ↑

23-B ↓

Please send me more information about the:

Franciscan Sisters of the Poor

Name ______________________________

Address ______________________________

City ______________________ State ______ Zip ________

Phone: (   ) ______________________________

E-mail: ______________________________

Best Time to be in Touch: ______________________

Present Occupation: ______________________

Date of Birth ______________________________

Place
stamp
here

Sr. Margaret Kelly, OSF
Director of Vowed Membership
Sisters of St. Francis of Mary Immaculate
801 N. Larkin Ave. Ste. 101
Joliet, IL 60435

Sending in these postcards to the vocation director does not obligate you to anything, but it may be the first step towards your life's work.

Place
Stamp
Here

Sister Arlene McGowan, SFP
Franciscan Sisters of the Poor
60 Compton Road
Cincinnati, OH 45215-5199

"I have called you
by Name;
You are Mine..."
(Is. 43:1)

Please send information about **The Sisters of the Third Order of Saint Francis.**

Name ______________________________

Address ______________________________

City/State/Zip ______________________________

Phone ____________________ Age: __________

E-mail ______________________________

Occupation ______________________________

Education ______________________________

This postcard is a service of A Guide to Religious Ministries

---

Serving God as a priest, brother, sister or lay minister is a rewarding career. Vocation directors can help you discover if the religious life is for you.

25-A ↑

25-B ↓

I want to take a look at Glenmary. Please send me information about Glenmary priesthood and brotherhood.

Name ______________________________

Address ______________________________

City ____________________ State ______ Zip ____________

Phone ____________________ Alternate Phone ____________________

E-mail ______________________________

Birth Date ____________________

GLENMARY
HOME MISSIONERS

DEUS MEUS ET OMNIA

Place Stamp Here

The Sisters of the Third Order of Saint Francis

Vocation Director
1175 St. Francis Lane
East Peoria, Illinois 61611-1299

Sending in these postcards to the vocation director does not obligate you to anything, but it may be the first step towards your life's work.

NO POSTAGE NECESSARY IF MAILED IN THE UNITED STATES

BUSINESS REPLY MAIL
FIRST-CLASS MAIL PERMIT NO. 1 CINCINNATI, OH

POSTAGE WILL BE PAID BY ADDRESSEE

Vocation Department
Glenmary Home Missioners
P.O. Box 465618
Cincinnati, OH 45246-9897

Holy Cross Sisters
USA PROVINCE

"I need sisters who understand the Cross. With them I can accomplish anything."

-- Theodosius Florentini, Founder, Holy Cross Sisters, 1856

Sister Linda:
I want to know more about the Holy Cross Sisters.

Name____________________________

Address____________________________

____

Phone____________________________

E-mail____________________________

Comments____________________________

____

____

Serving God as a priest, brother, sister or lay minister is a rewarding career. 27-A ↑
Vocation directors can help you discover if the religious life is for you. 27-B ↓

SPIRITANS
ONE HEART, ONE SPIRIT

Please send me information about Spiritan community life and mission.

Name ____________________________

Address ____________________________

City ________________ State _______ Zip _______

Phone: ________________ E-mail ________________

Age _______ Education ________________

Comments: ____________________________

____

PLACE
STAMP
HERE

Holy Cross Sisters
USA PROVINCE

Sister Linda Songy
Vocations Director
Holy Cross Sisters
501 S. Center Avenue
Merrill, WI 54452

Sending in these postcards to the vocation director does not obligate you to anything, but it may be the first step towards your life's work.

SPIRITANS
ONE HEART, ONE SPIRIT

Place
Stamp
Here

Spiritans Vocation Office
Laval House
Duquesne University
Pittsburgh, PA 15282-0001

Please send me information about

HOSPITALLER BROTHERS OF ST. JOHN OF GOD

Name ____________________

Address ____________________

City, State, Zip ____________________

Last Year of School Completed ____________________ Age ________

Telephone (   ) ____________________

E-mail ____________________

Comments ____________________

____

This postcard is a service of
A GUIDE TO RELIGIOUS MINISTRIES
210 North Avenue, New Rochelle, NY 10801

Serving God as a priest, brother, sister or lay minister is a rewarding career.
Vocation directors can help you discover if the religious life is for you.

29-A ↑

29-B ↓

Exclusively committed to serving the African American Community

Please send me the information marked below about the Josephite Society.

❑ Priest ❑ Brother ❑ Volunteer

www.josephite.com

Name: ____________________

Address: ____________________

City: ____________________ State: ________ Zip: ________

Telephone: ____________________ Date of Birth ________

Your email address: ____________________

Education: ____________________ **GRM 04 C**

Place
Stamp
Here

Bro. Thomas Osorio, O.H.
Hospitaller Brothers of St. John of God
1145 Delsea Drive
Westville Grove, NJ 08093

Sending in these postcards to the vocation director does not obligate you to anything, but it may be the first step towards your life's work.

NO POSTAGE
NECESSARY
IF MAILED
IN THE
UNITED STATES

BUSINESS REPLY MAIL
FIRST-CLASS MAIL PERMIT NO. 16803 BALTIMORE, MD.

POSTAGE WILL BE PAID BY ADDRESSEE

Rev. Charles P. Moffatt, S.S.J.
Vocation Director
The Society of St. Joseph
1130 North Calvert Street
Baltimore, MD 21297-0306

I wish to learn more about the Little Company of Mary Sisters through:

❑ Quarterly Newsletter
❑ Phone Call
❑ Visit with a Sister
❑ CD-Rom

Name ______________________________ Age __________

Address ______________________________

City ____________________ State ________ Zip __________

Phone ______________________________

E-mail ______________________________

Education Level/Occupation ______________________________

Serving God as a priest, brother, sister or lay minister is a rewarding career. Vocation directors can help you discover if the religious life is for you.

31-A ↑

31-B ↓

The Marianists
PROVINCE OF THE UNITED STATES

Please send me more information about the Marianists.

I am interested in:

__________ brotherhood __________ priesthood __________ sisterhood

Name: ______________________________

Address: ______________________________

City: ______________________________

Age: __________ Telephone: (   ) ______________________________

E-mail: ______________________________

Place
Stamp
Here

Sister Jean Stickney, LCM
Little Company of Mary Sisters
9350 South California Avenue
Evergreen Park, IL 60805

Sending in these postcards to the vocation director does not obligate you to anything, but it may be the first step towards your life's work.

NO POSTAGE
NECESSARY
IF MAILED
IN THE
UNITED STATES

BUSINESS REPLY MAIL

FIRST-CLASS MAIL PERMIT NO. 2769 SAINT LOUIS, MO

POSTAGE WILL BE PAID BY ADDRESSEE

The Marianists
Bro. Charles Johnson, SM
National Vocation Director
4425 W. Pine Blvd.
St. Louis, MO 63108-9833

Please send me information about the
MARIANNHILL MISSIONARIES

Name ____________________

Address ____________________

City, State, Zip ____________________

Education ____________________

Telephone (   ) ____________________ Age __________

Comments ____________________

Interested in: ❑ Priesthood ❑ Brotherhood

This postcard is a service of
A GUIDE TO RELIGIOUS MINISTRIES
210 NORTH AVENUE, NEW ROCHELLE, NY 10801

Serving God as a priest, brother, sister or lay minister is a rewarding career. Vocation directors can help you discover if the religious life is for you.

33-A ↑

33-B ↓

PRO CHRISTO ET ECCLESIA

Marians
of the Immaculate Conception

Please send me information

Name ____________________

Address ____________________

City ____________________ State ________ Zip __________

Age __________ Telephone (______) ____________________

Email ____________ @ ____________

Best time to call ____________________

Comments ____________________

____

Place
Stamp
Here

MARIANNHILL VOCATIONS OFFICE
23715 ANN ARBOR TRAIL
DEARBORN HEIGHTS, MI 48127

Sending in these postcards to the vocation director does not obligate you to anything, but it may be the first step towards your life's work.

PRO CHRISTO ET ECCLESIA

Place
Stamp
Here

Rev. Anthony Gramlich, MIC

Vocation Director

Marians of the Immaculate Conception

515 Belleview Blvd

Steubenville, Ohio 43952

I would like to know more about . . .

The Marians of the Immaculate Conception

Please send information to:

Name ________________________________

Address ________________________________

City ________________ State ____ Zip ________

Last year of school completed ________ Age ________

Telephone ________________________________

Comments ________________________________

This postcard is a service of
A GUIDE TO RELIGIOUS MINISTRIES - 210 North Avenue, New Rochelle, NY 10801

Serving God as a priest, brother, sister or lay minister is a rewarding career. Vocation directors can help you discover if the religious life is for you.

35-A ↑

35-B ↓

MARIST FATHERS AND BROTHERS

Please send me information about your congregation

I am interested in: Priesthood ________ Brotherhood ________

Name ________________________________ Age ________

Address ________________________________

City, State, Zip ________________________________

Education ________________________________

Phone (Area Code) ________________________________

This postcard is a service of
A GUIDE TO RELIGIOUS MINISTRIES
210 North Avenue, New Rochelle, NY 10801

PLACE
POSTAGE
HERE

Father Dan Cambra, M.I.C.
Marian Vocation Office
701 Plainfield
Darien, IL 60561

Sending in these postcards to the vocation director does not obligate you to anything, but it may be the first step towards your life's work.

Place
Stamp
Here

Marist Vocation Office
27 Isabella Street
Boston, MA 02116-5216

Please send me more information about becoming a Maryknoll missioner.
I am interested in becoming a

❒ Priest ❒ Brother ❒ Sister

Name: ______________________________
Address: ______________________________
City ______________ State ______________ Zip ______________
Phone: ______________________________
e-mail: ______________________________
Age: ______
Occupation: ______________________________
Education Completed: ______________________________

GRM04

Sending in these postcards to the vocation director does not obligate you to anything, but it may be the first step towards your life's work.

Missionaries of the Sacred Hearts of Jesus and Mary

Yes, I would like to know more.
Please send information about your community to:

NAME: ______________________________
ADDRESS: ______________________________
CITY/STATE/ZIP: ______________________________
AGE: ______ TELEPHONE: ______________________________
LAST YEAR OF SCHOOL COMPLETED: ______________________________

❑ **Priest** ❑ **Brother**

NO POSTAGE
NECESSARY
IF MAILED
IN THE
UNITED STATES

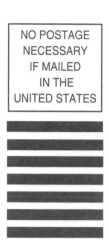

BUSINESS REPLY MAIL
FIRST-CLASS MAIL PERMIT NO. 1 MARYKNOLL NY

POSTAGE WILL BE PAID BY ADDRESSEE

Fr. Michael J. Snyder, M.M.
Vocation Ministries
Maryknoll Fathers and Brothers
P.O. Box 302
Maryknoll, NY 10545-0302

Sending in these postcards to the vocation director does not obligate you to anything, but it may be the first step towards your life's work.

Place
Stamp
Here

VOCATION DIRECTOR
MISSIONARIES OF THE SACRED HEARTS
OF JESUS AND MARY
2249 SHORE ROAD
LINWOOD, NEW JERSEY 08221

Please send me information about Oblates of the Virgin Mary.

☐ Priest ☐ Brother

Name: ______________________________

Address: ______________________________

City: ______________ St: ________ Zip: ________

Telephone: (____) ______________________

Age: ________ Last year of school completed: ____________

The best time to call: ______________________

OVMR2

Serving God as a priest, brother, sister or lay minister is a rewarding career. Vocation directors can help you discover if the religious life is for you.

39-A ↑

39-B ↓

Mercederian Friars

☐ I would like to receive more information

Name ______________________________

Address ______________________________

City ______________ State ________ Zip ________

E-Mail ______________________________

I am Presently:

☐ a high school student

☐ a college student

☐ working

Age ______________

NOTE: We Accept candidates between the ages of 18-40 years of age

Telephone No. ______________

Preferred Time To Call ________

PLACE
POSTAGE
HERE

Vocation Director
Oblates of the Virgin Mary
1105 Boylston Street
Boston, MA 02215

Sending in these postcards to the vocation director does not obligate you to anything, but it may be the first step towards your life's work.

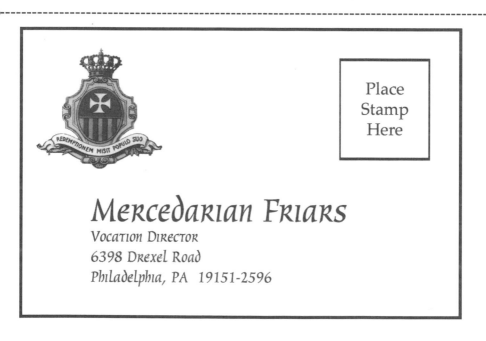

Place
Stamp
Here

Mercedarian Friars

Vocation Director
6398 Drexel Road
Philadelphia, PA 19151-2596

Priests of the Sacred Heart

brothers and priests living, praying and serving
Christ together as a religious community

I'd like information about the Priests of the Sacred Heart and how to respond to the invitation of Jesus to follow him as a brother or priest.

Name ______________________________

Address ______________________________

City, State, Zip ______________________________

Telephone (   ) ______________________________

E-mail address: ______________________________

Last Year of School Completed ______________________ Age ______

GRM 04

Serving God as a priest, brother, sister or lay minister is a rewarding career.
Vocation directors can help you discover if the religious life is for you.

41-A ↑

41-B ↓

Make a Difference!

Sisters of St. Joseph

of the Third Order of St. Francis

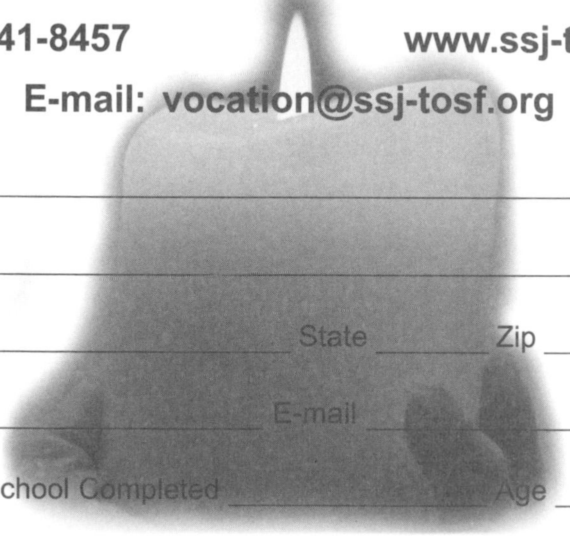

(715) 341-8457 **www.ssj-tosf.org**

E-mail: vocation@ssj-tosf.org

Name ______________________________

Address ______________________________

City ____________________ State ________ Zip ________

Telephone ________________ E-mail ________________

Last Year of School Completed ________________ Age ________

NO POSTAGE
NECESSARY
IF MAILED
IN THE
UNITED STATES

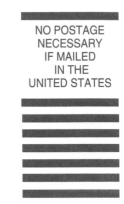

BUSINESS REPLY MAIL

FIRST-CLASS MAIL PERMIT NO. 27 HALES CORNERS,WI

POSTAGE WILL BE PAID BY ADDRESSEE

Vocation Director
SCJ Vocation Office
PO Box 206
Hales Corners, WI 53130-9965

Sending in these postcards to the vocation director does not obligate you to anything, but it may be the first step towards your life's work.

Place
Postage
Here

Sisters of St. Joseph of the Third Order of St. Francis
Vocation Minister
P.O. Box 305
Stevens Point, Wisconsin 54481-0305

Please send me information about

THE SERVANTS OF CHARITY

Name ______________________________

Address ______________________________

City, State, Zip ______________________________

Last Year of School Completed __________ Age __________

Telephone ( ) ______________________________

Comments ______________________________

____

This postcard is a service of
A GUIDE TO RELIGIOUS MINISTRIES
210 North Avenue, New Rochelle, NY 10801

Serving God as a priest, brother, sister or lay minister is a rewarding career. Vocation directors can help you discover if the religious life is for you.

43-A ↑

43-B ↓

The Trinitarians

Please send me your free vocations brochure.

Name ______________________________

Address ______________________________

City __________ State __________ Zip __________

Phone __________ E-mail __________

Age __________ Highest degree attained __________

MAIL TO:

Fr. Damian Anuszewski, O.SS.T.
P.O. Box 5719 Baltimore, MD 21282-0719
410-484-2250 1-800-525-3554

Place
Postage
Here

Father Silvio DeNard, SC
1795 S. Sproul Rd
Springfield, PA 19064-1137

Sending in these postcards to the vocation director does not obligate you to anything, but it may be the first step towards your life's work.

Place
Stamp
Here

Fr. Damian Anuszewski, O.SS.T.
Director of Vocations
The Trinitarians
P.O. Box 5719
Baltimore, MD 21282-0719

❏ ***Yes, I would appreciate more information about The Servants of the Holy Heart of Mary***

Name ______________________________

Address ______________________________

City __________ *State* __________ *Zip* __________

E-mail ______________________________

Phone ______________ *Best time to call* __________

Birthdate ______________ *Occupation* __________

Education Level ______________

I am presently

❏ *A high school student*

❏ *A college student*

❏ *Working*

Please complete and return this card or
call Sr. Myra Lambert, SSCM 630-879-1296

Serving God as a priest, brother, sister or lay minister is a rewarding career. Vocation directors can help you discover if the religious life is for you.

45-A ↑

45-B ↓

Trinity Missions Vocation Department

E-Mail Address: mccann@trinitymissions.org

Please call us-1- 800-298-5602

Yes, please send information today about:

❏ Summer Volunteer

❏ Long-Term Volunteer

❏ Missionary Priest or Brother

❏ Missionary Sister

Name: ______________________________

Address: ______________________________

City: ______________________ State: ______ Zip: __________

Phone (please include area code): (_____) ______________________

Last year of school completed: ____________ Date of Birth _____/_____/______

E-mail address: ______________________________

Me gustaria recibir informacio´n en español: ______________________

Place
Postage
Here

Sr. Myra Lambert, SSCM
Servants of the Holy Heart of Mary
717 North Batavia Avenue
Batavia, Illinois 60510

Sending in these postcards to the vocation director does not obligate you to anything, but it may be the first step towards your life's work.

Place
Stamp
Here

TRINITY MISSIONS VOCATION DEPARTMENT
9001 New Hampshire Avenue
Silver Spring, MD 20903

yes! *I'd like to learn more about the* URSULINE SISTERS OF CLEVELAND.

I'M INTERESTED IN:

__________ VOWED MEMBERSHIP

__________ AFFILIATE MEMBERSHIP

HERE'S HOW TO CONTACT ME:

__________ BY REGULAR MAIL

__________ BY E-MAIL

__________ BY TELEPHONE

NAME

ADDRESS

CITY,STATE, ZIP

( ) DAYTIME PHONE

( ) EVENING PHONE

@ E-MAIL

Serving God as a priest, brother, sister or lay minister is a rewarding career. Vocation directors can help you discover if the religious life is for you.

47-A ↑

47-B ↓

Xaverian Missionaries

Please send me:

- ☐ Information about your community and work.
- ☐ Your "Mission Newsletter."
- ☐ Brochures on your discernment and volunteer service programs.
- ☐ I would like you to come and visit me.
- ☐ Envienme information en Espanol.

Name: ____________________

Birthdate: ____________________

Address: ____________________

____

Phone: ____________________

Education completed: ____________________

Present occupation: ____________________

We are counting on U!!!

Place
Stamp
Here

THE **URSULINE**
SISTERS OF CLEVELAND
VOCATION OFFICE
2600 LANDER ROAD
CLEVELAND, OHIO 44124-9908

Sending in these postcards to the vocation director does not obligate you to anything, but it may be the first step towards your life's work.

Place
Stamp
Here

Fr. Dario, Vocation Office
Xaverian Missionaries
12 Helene Court
Wayne, NJ 07470-2813

I read your profile in ***A Guide to Religious Ministries***.
Please send me additional information.

Mr./Ms./Mrs.______________________________

Address ______________________________

City/State/Zip ______________________________

Telephone ______________________________

E-mail Address______________________________

Last Grade Completed ____________________ Age__________

Comments ______________________________

This postcard is a service of
A Guide to Religious Ministries
210 North Avenue, New Rochelle, NY 10801
914-632-1220

DIRECT RESPONSE CARD

Complete and mail one of these postcards directly to the vocation office of a men's or women's community listed in the "A" section of this Guide.

49-A ↑

49-B ↓

I read your profile in ***A Guide to Religious Ministries***.
Please send me additional information.

Mr./Ms./Mrs.______________________________

Address ______________________________

City/State/Zip ______________________________

Telephone ______________________________

E-mail Address______________________________

Last Grade Completed ____________________ Age__________

Comments ______________________________

This postcard is a service of
A Guide to Religious Ministries
210 North Avenue, New Rochelle, NY 10801
914-632-1220

PLACE
POSTAGE
HERE

COMMUNITY

ADDRESS

CITY/STATE/ZIP

ATTN: VOCATION DIRECTOR

Sending in these postcards to the vocation director does not obligate you to anything, but it may be the first step towards your life's work.

PLACE
POSTAGE
HERE

COMMUNITY

ADDRESS

CITY/STATE/ZIP

ATTN: VOCATION DIRECTOR

I am interested in a life of religious ministry. Please forward information about different religious communities. I am interested in being a:

❑ Priest ❑ Brother ❑ Sister ❑ Lay Minister

My particular interest for ministry in a religious life is in:

❑ Parish Work
❑ Education
❑ Missions
❑ Health Care
❑ Undecided
❑ Social Service
❑ Other: ____________________

Type of Community:

Refer to front of A section for a description of each

❑ Apostolic/Active
❑ Contemplative/Cloistered
❑ Monastic

Mr./Ms./Mrs. ____________________

Address ____________________

City/State/Zip ____________________

Telephone ____________________

E-mail Address ____________________

Last Grade Completed ____________________ Age __________

Comments ____________________

READER SERVICE CARD 51-A ↑

If you would like to receive literature from several religious communities, mail this postpaid card and your requests will be forwarded to you. 51-B ↓

I am interested in a life of religious ministry. Please forward information about different religious communities. I am interested in being a:

❑ Priest ❑ Brother ❑ Sister ❑ Lay Minister

My particular interest for ministry in a religious life is in:

❑ Parish Work
❑ Education
❑ Missions
❑ Health Care
❑ Undecided
❑ Social Service
❑ Other: ____________________

Type of Community:

Refer to front of A section for a description of each

❑ Apostolic/Active
❑ Contemplative/Cloistered
❑ Monastic

Mr./Ms./Mrs. ____________________

Address ____________________

City/State/Zip ____________________

Telephone ____________________

E-mail Address ____________________

Last Grade Completed ____________________ Age __________

Comments ____________________

NO POSTAGE
NECESSARY
IF MAILED
IN THE
UNITED STATES

BUSINESS REPLY MAIL

FIRST CLASS MAIL PERMIT NO. 2121 NEW ROCHELLE, NY

POSTAGE WILL BE PAID BY ADDRESSEE

A GUIDE TO RELIGIOUS MINISTRIES
CATHOLIC NEWS PUBLISHING COMPANY
210 NORTH AVENUE
NEW ROCHELLE, NY 10801-9910

Sending in these postcards to the vocation director does not obligate you to anything, but it may be the first step towards your life's work.

NO POSTAGE
NECESSARY
IF MAILED
IN THE
UNITED STATES

BUSINESS REPLY MAIL

FIRST CLASS MAIL PERMIT NO. 2121 NEW ROCHELLE, NY

POSTAGE WILL BE PAID BY ADDRESSEE

A GUIDE TO RELIGIOUS MINISTRIES
CATHOLIC NEWS PUBLISHING COMPANY
210 NORTH AVENUE
NEW ROCHELLE, NY 10801-9910

A GUIDE TO
RELIGIOUS MINISTRIES
For Catholic Men and Women

"There are many ministries but one Lord."
- Paul to the Corinthians

Published by
The Catholic News Publishing Company

Cover photo courtesy of the Crosiers

A Guide to Religious Ministries **www.ReligiousMinistries.com**
For Catholic Men and Women

25th Annual Edition

Publisher ....Myles Ridder

Editor ....Mari Castrovilla

Advertising Manager ....Virginia Klemm

Web Editor ....Rosemary Ridder

Account Executives ....Stephen Brehl
Chris Kristensen
Robert B. Tennyson
Robert C. Tennyson
Peter Tirro
Gary Williams

Art Director ....Melvin Harris

Editorial Production ....Patricia Korn

Design and Layout ....Mark Ridder

Web Production ....Victor Ridder

Data Management ....Olga Sotire

Production ....Laurie Berman

Circulation ....Karen Ridder Stuart
Nancy Lappin

Treasurer ....Joseph Ridder

$10.00 per copy
International Standard Book Number (ISBN) Number 1-893275-28-0

For information, write to Catholic News Publishing Company, 210 North Avenue, New Rochelle, NY 10801. 914.632.1220 Fax: 914-632-3412, E-mail: info@religiousministries.com

PRINTED IN THE UNITED STATES OF AMERICA

Table of Contents

Section A

A man can have no greater love
then to lay down his life for his friends.
You are my friends,
if you do what I command you.
I shall not call you servants any more,
because a servant does not know
his master's business;
I call you friends,
because I have made known to you
everything I have learnt from my Father.
You did not choose me,
no, I chose you;
and I commissioned you
to go out and to bear fruit,
fruit that will last;
and then the Father will give you
anything you ask him in my name.
What I command you
is to love one another.

John 15:13-17

Pray and Work
for Justice and Peace

The Call to Religious Ministry

The decision to dedicate one's life to the service of God is a much different one than that of choosing a career.

Selecting a career field – in most instances, an occupation – involves decisions about education, personal skills, preferred job characteristics, desired income levels, and often geographic location. The decision impacts on family life, personal interests and long-range goals. A career decision answers the question, "What will I do with my life?"

The more important decision in life is, "What will I be?" Everyone is called to be with God, whether married, single, clergy or religious. Some people are called to be with God as a priest, brother or sister. It is not a calling to do anything, go anywhere, or become something. It is a call to a state of being.

Commitment

Commitment to a religious career often flows from one's whole being. This commitment is rooted in the core of inner being, and it affects and involves the totality of the person. If one is concerned only with external manifestations in a religious career, then that person is making more difficult the acquisition of a deep and inner sense of fulfillment and personal growth to be found in the pursuit of such a career. Religious careers enable persons to express adequately the being they are. External witness touches generally on the demonstrative; it manifests the character of a religious career, but this alone is not enough. When one attempts to justify the rationale and the validity of a religious career in today's society, there is a strong tendency to remain engrossed merely in its circumferential elements such as service to people in need, improvement of the qualitative aspects of human interaction, and the like. However, there is an important pivotal point from which all other elements spring and in which they are resolved. Some are wont to falsify, more or less seriously, the essence of religious careers and their total ecclesiastical dimension, each time they view an external, visible element as the living core of a religious career. The act of feeding the poor or comforting the sorrowful is not in itself the living core of a religious career. When one makes an external manifestation the essence of a religious career, this essence is simply too shallow to subsist.

What then constitutes the being and validity of religious careers, and makes them relevant today? The same mystery that made religious careers relevant in the past and inspired men and women to dedicate their lives is present today.

At this point one may ask: "What then is the essence of a religious career? What constitutes the state of a religious career choice? What makes it what it is? What gives it its particular identity?" That by which the very being of a religious career as a state of life can be distinguished from another state is very simple; it is a very specific consecration, a consecration often contrary to popular belief. It is not a ritual of a self-gift to the Almighty, nor is it man-made. For it is ultimately the Almighty who consecrates and invests a person in a religious career.

The Need for Prayer

Individuals will be aided in a religious career choice through a life of prayer. The prayerful religious person is able to recognize in other persons their intrinsic worth and potential for good. The religious career person is seeking to make visible what is hidden, and touchable that which is unreachable. Prayer, the great power of grace, will help eliminate a behavior which is contradictory to the great principles upon which moral decisions are made. A person embarking upon his career choice must be personally convinced that prayer and faith give purpose and meaning to this life. In this way, that individual can hope to instill the value of religion in others and manifest this value in him or herself.

The style of religious careers for the years ahead may be determined not so much by those who strive toward this ideal and this goal, as by those others who do not. The audience, the object of activity, the persons whom those in religious careers seek to serve, will determine the mode of relevant activity. The religious is, therefore, challenged to tailor the message to the audience, to communicate on terms which the target group can relate to.

Pursuing a religious career involves a great deal of work. The individual pursuing such a career should pray, seeking to know and gain direction in this regard. The individual should think. The power of the mind may be marshalled to think life through. Reading is important. Learn about the particular organization or denomination in which you anticipate pursuing a religious career. "Knowledge is power," said Socrates. The more one knows about a subject the better one can handle it. The more an individual knows about the particulars of the specific religious career of interest, the better that individual will be to handle the necessary decisions involved. Talking it over with persons whom we admire and trust, perhaps someone already living a religious career, can be most helpful. If an individual wants to pursue a religious career, then that individual should do the things early that will aid him or her in such a pursuit.

Personal Characteristics Needed

Those pursuing religious careers should possess self-confidence, the ability to make hard decisions, and a willingness to accept criticism and listen to people. They must be tactful, have personal drive and ambition, but yet be tolerant of other's shortcomings. An ability to work under pressure, to live up to moral standards, and ability to get along with others are the ideals to be striven for.

Whatever the denomination or the particular ministry within that denomination, certain predispositions are generally looked for. Good health is desirable as the religious career makes demands upon a person's physical constitution. A good and healthy body aids in the development of a good and healthy mind. A good mind is necessary, as one must be able to combine the spiritual and the intellectual. One must be able to relate meaningfully the theoretical dimensions of religion to the world of practical realities. The well-trained religious career person is thus aided in thinking – deeply – about important things that are necessary parts of the religious career. The supernatural rests upon the natural, and the religious career person must grow naturally and intellectually.

Choosing a life's career can be one of the most exciting, demanding and yet perplexing experiences one is likely to face. The choice made will determine to a large extent the focus of one's energy, attention, and efforts. That career choice offers the possibility of a genuine measure of satisfaction and fulfillment. That career choice will determine the nature of the role and the contribution the individual will make in today's complex and often impersonal world.

A person pursuing a religious career is also a servant, someone doing something, and doing this in a committed way. Giving oneself to the service of others makes that individual a symbol of concern not only in word and deed, but in all of that person's life as a totality of a human person.

Religious career persons are not supermen or wonder women. They are men and women living among men and women – sometimes wounded men and women whose mission is to heal. Often religious career persons are stammering men and women whose mission is to preach; they are often weak persons whose mission is to conquer evil or console.

Surely the religious career offers the reward of full joy and peace for the individual aware of the call, honest in service, and giving freely for others. Incomparable happiness realized in deep personal fulfillment is often the reward for those individuals who have pursued a life's career in religion.

People caring about people can be manifested in the pursuit of a religious career. Religious careers offer opportunities, challenges, and lifestyles for a role of influence in molding the outlook and design of tomorrow's world.

Discerning a Vocation

What is a vocation? How does one discover it? Where does it lead? What has it to do with free will?

These are puzzling questions to anyone considering what to do with the rest of his or her life. Ordinarily they are questions facing a person in teen-age or early adult life but many reoccur at other times. Many women face such questions after their family is raised. A married man, his wife and family may very suddenly face the unexpected possibility of a vocation to the permanent diaconate.

Vocation, of course, does not refer exclusively to religious life or priesthood: these, however, are so unusual that frequently in Catholic circles they alone are called "vocations."

The word vocation means "a calling". It is extremely important to keep this in mind. We are called by the providential arrangement of circumstances, by the realities of life, by our own limitations and potential, by the historical moment, and by our own emotional, intellectual and psychological needs. If one follows the teachings of the Fathers and Doctors of the Church in this regard, one comes to accept that a vocation is found in the providential arrangement of significant aspects of life and also by the grace which we receive to make the best of these situations.

The loss of awareness of this providential aspect of vocation is one of the things that leads to an immense insecurity in modern life. When people forget the divine and providential element in their lives, they try desperately to find a course through life like a man on a raft with neither rudder nor map.

It has been a consistent belief of Christians that the Lord gives each of us something to do, some work to perform that makes us an essential link in the chain of life. Parents pass on life to their children and, by good examples, instruction, encouragement and membership in the Church contribute to their growth in the life of grace.

Single people, including priests and religious, pass on life in a psychological and spiritual way by being a help to those around them. This passing on of life and grace is the ultimate vocation of the Christian. Cardinal Newman sums it up well when he says: "I am a link in a chain, a bond of connection between persons. God has not created me for nothing. I shall do good; I shall do His work; I shall be an angel of peace, a preacher of truth, in my own place, while not intending it, if I do but keep His commandments."

The idea of God's special purpose in our life is what gives the individual an awareness of his dignity and importance. Among great numbers of people we frequently feel like atoms, little and meaningless. As Newman says, "God has created me to do Him some definite service: He has committed some work to me which He has not committed to another. I have my mission. I may never know it in this life, but I shall be told it in the next."

If one is convinced of being singled out by the Lord for some work in this life, how is that work discovered? First, we quietly discern or observe our potentials and needs and try to fit them into what we can do best. Often in such a process, God leads us by interior inspiration, by an attraction to do this or that work, to follow this person, or to marry that one. We will be attracted by a certain kind of work because it fits our capacity and because it opens to us possibilities of security or fulfillment.

The need for inspiration and divine guidance in any vocation cannot be overstressed. The Lord has led many people in mysterious ways. The only Trappist ever canonized, St. Benedict Joseph Labre, was led to his strange vocation not to be a monk but to be a hobo, by going from one monastery to another, vainly trying to fit in because of psychological difficulties.

St. Catherine of Genoa found herself married to the wrong man as a result of a political alliance of her family. Faced with such a situation, she relied on God and spent the rest of her life working with her husband in the service of the poor and sick.

From such experiences at least two rules emerge for discovering one's vocation. Both come from Holy Scripture: "If today you hear His voice, harden not your heart" (Psalm 95); and Our Lord's own admonition: "He who puts his hand to the plow and looks back is not worthy of the kingdom of heaven."

Apostolic Work

The apostolic works performed by priests, brothers and sisters – also called ministries – encompass a wide range of skills and services. Some religious communities specialize in one or a few types of ministries – health care or teaching, for example – while others have members engaged in many different ministries. The work itself does not constitute a religious "career" but is simply the expression of a religious person's dedication to God.

Some of the most common ministries are:

Parish Work

Home Missions

Child Care

Chaplaincies
- Prisons
- Hospitals
- Military

Education
- Administration
- Teaching
- Coaching

Social Work

Campus Ministry

Foreign Missions

Religious Education

Communications
- Film
- TV & Radio
- Newspapers
- Magazines
- Books

Health Care
- Hospitals
- Nursing Homes
- Visiting
- Nursing

Counseling
- Students
- Families
- Adults

Spiritual Direction

Retreats

Inner City Work

Cloistered, Contemplative and Monastic Religious Orders

Although the terms "cloistered", "contemplative" and "monastic" may vary in meaning due to the founder's differing objectives and the interpretation by different communities in various parts of the world, a generally used and understood meaning of each is as follows:

Cloistered (*clausura*) refers to religious men and women who live in an enclosed space, not accessible to outsiders and who may not go outside the area without permission. Solemn vows are made by those in monasteries and convents where there is *clausura* and simple vows where there is no cloister.

Contemplation – the "loving gaze of the soul upon God" – is, in its widest sense, the goal of every Christian. Its highest earthly fulfillment is applied to those religious men and women who do not engage in active ministries; who live in seclusion, apart from the world; and whose lives are taken up in prayer and meditation. In order to sustain themselves, communities perform such tasks as keeping bees/bottling honey, farming, translation, artistic work, vestment design and production, baking, computer typesetting and Web page design.

Monasticism (or *monachism*, literally the act of "dwelling alone") has come to denote the way of life pertaining to persons living in seclusion from the world, under the religious vows of poverty, chastity and obedience, and subject to a fixed "rule", as monks, friars, or nuns. Eastern monasticism and Western monasticism deal with the monastic order strictly so called as distinct from the "religious orders" such as the friars, canons regular, and other more recent orders whose special work or aim, such as preaching, teaching, liberating captives, etc., occupies such a large place that many of the traditional observances of the monastic life give way to these special works.

For detailed explanations and other information on these terms, see the Catholic Encyclopedia online (http://newadvent.org/cathen/).

The Formation Process

There are several stages involved in the process of becoming a religious priest, brother or sister. Each community has its own rules, but they generally involve four stages.

The first stage involves the time period when a prospective candidate becomes acquainted with the community, and the community with the candidate. This may occur as early as high school or college years. The vocation director is usually the point of contact between the individual and the community. The candidate may spend short periods of time living with the community in order to become exposed to the spiritual and community life of the members.

The second stage begins when the candidate is ready for a more formal relationship. This usually involves full-time residency with the community and gives the candidate the opportunity to experience the life of the community. During this stage, the candidate may be continuing outside studies or employment. This stage may last one or two years.

The next stage occurs when the candidate enters the community's novitiate. This marks the official entry into the community and is a period of one to two years during which the novice spends time in prayer and study to learn more about his or her relationship with God, with the community, and with the decision to make a lifetime commitment to the religious life.

The final stage involves temporary promises. Depending on the community, promises of poverty, celibacy and obedience may be taken for periods of one to three years at a time, up to nine years. Final vows may be taken after as few as three years of temporary promises.

Men studying for the priesthood also must complete seminary training in theology before ordination.

The Diocesan Priesthood

A candidate for the diocesan priesthood must complete four years of high school, four years of college and four and a half years of graduate study in theology before ordination. A candidate may attend the college of his choice or a minor seminary to complete studies for his bachelor's degree. Graduate study is completed in residence at a major seminary.

Most diocesan priests serve in parishes. Many others serve as teachers, administrators, military chaplains, hospital chaplains, prison chaplains, and other ministries.

Educational Requirements

The works performed by members of the religious community usually dictate the amount of education that is required. A bachelor's degree is usually required, and often a master's. Many priests, brothers and sisters earn a doctorate degree, particularly those involved in education.

Most communities prefer candidates to complete their bachelor's degree before entering, although some communities will accept candidates after high school graduation. There are also some high school seminaries for candidates who are prepared to consider a vocation at that age. Some dioceses conduct preparatory seminaries for high school boys who are interested in the priesthood. Generally, the boys live at home while going to school.

Contact A Vocation Director

The people who are in the best position to be helpful to those who are considering a religious career or lay ministry are vocation directors. Their job is to counsel men and women about the requirements for this kind of commitment. They can suggest reading materials, arrange for visitations, answer questions and provide the spiritual guidance candidates need.

Every diocese has a vocation director who can provide information about religious communities for men and women as well as information about the diocesan priesthood. A complete list of diocesan vocation directors is included in one of the following sections in this book.

Most religious communities have one or more members assigned to vocations. Their names, addresses and phone numbers are included in their community's respective listing in the following sections of this book.

Vocations in the Catholic Church

"Then He said to His disciples, 'The harvest is ready but the laborers are few. Ask the harvest master to send out laborers to gather his harvest'."

Mt. 9:37-38

Many influences come together to bring it about that a woman or a man decides to become more fully involved in the ministerial life of the church. This personal commitment can be temporary or permanent, partial or complete. Whatever form this calling may take, a Catholic believes that the Holy Spirit is the source of every authentic vocation. The instruments, the human means, of His work often include the living example of persons in a given church ministry. There is also the home, the classroom, the hospital, retreat houses, religious experience, reading, friends, prayer...the Bible itself. All of these, and other things also, contribute to a church vocation.

The full and permanent commitment involved in the religious life and priesthood has long had its place in Catholic tradition. Yet these callings are by no means the only vocation: in the best sense all Christians are called to a vocation in the community. Marriage itself, for example, is certainly a vocation. We list here not simply priesthood and religious life but other possibilities for ministry in the Church. And there are others not listed here, such as sodalities, covenant communities, etc. Information about these can be secured from local pastors or chanceries, or from the National Religious Vocation Conference.

It is the Spirit that the Father has sent through Christ that is at the center of a church vocation, just as Christ Himself is the head of the Church. Hence this kind of vocation, while it is certainly a matter of professional guidance and consultation on a "career" level, is also far more than that. Here the assistance of a competent spiritual director is invaluable. The work of the Spirit must be discerned. This discernment means, among other things, evaluating the qualities of a person who wishes to follow such a vocation.

The general qualifications for priesthood and the religious life (and similarly for other church-related occupations) include an appropriate level of spiritual life, emotional and physical health, and a level of intelligence and academic accomplishment consistent with the kind of life one seeks. One may enter some form of training as early as first-year high school or as late as "mid" or even later life. Most commonly, however, a man or woman enters a formation program after high school or college. The length of training varies depending upon when one enters a program, the extent of his or her background, and the specific traditions of a given community or diocese. Generally, for example, it takes the same amount of preparation to become a diocesan priest as for any other professional person: four years after college, or eight years after high school. Formal entrance into a seminary or community is often preceded by participation in an associate or affiliate program.

There is no obligation created by seeking the counsel of a trusted, knowledgeable advisor – and it is most important to do so.

A Catholic might wish to serve the Church, the people of God, in a specific, professional manner. This could be done as a diocesan priest, permanent deacon, religious brother, religious priest, religious sister, as a lay person employed in a Church ministry or engaged in volunteer work, as a member of a secular institute or by participation in any number of Church organizations.

Diocesan Priest

A diocesan priest ordinarily serves the people of God in a given area – a diocese – as a parish priest. And yet diocesan priests are also involved in administration, campus ministry, hospital and prison chaplaincy, teaching and sometimes at foreign missions. Beneath the visible surface of these ministries lies an abiding prayerful relationship with the Lord for whose sake and for whose people he ministers. Information about the diocesan priesthood can be obtained from any diocesan priest, by contacting one or more of the diocesan vocation directors listed in the **Diocesan Vocation Offices** section of this book or by contacting:

National Conference of Diocesan Vocation Directors
PO Box 1570, Little River, SC 29566-1570
(843) 280-7191, Fax: (843) 280-0681
E-mail: ncdvd@aol.com; Web: www.ncdvd.org

Permanent Deacon

Recently the Catholic Church restored the order of permanent diaconate. A deacon is a man 35 years of age or older, married or single, who serves the people of God in the ordained diaconal ministry. His ministry is liturgical (preaching), sacramental (except the Eucharist and Penance), pastoral and social. Inquiry about deacons' training programs can be made at the local diocesan chancery office or by contacting one of the following:

United States Conference of Catholic Bishops
Secretariat for the Diaconate, Deacon William Ditwing, Director
3211 Fourth St. NE, Washington, DC 20017-1194
(202) 541-3038, E-mail: wditewig@usccb.org; Web: www.usccb.org

National Association of Diaconate Directors, Gregory S. Urban, Deacon, Executive Director, 2136 12th St., Suite 105, Rockford, IL 61104
(815) 965-2100, Fax: 815-965-1569
E-mail: info@nadd.cc; Web: www.nadd.cc

Religious Brother

As a male religious, a brother is a lay Christian who commits himself to Christ and the Christian community by vows of poverty, chastity and obedience. Not only is he in service to the community, he himself lives in a religious community that centers his life. It is from this root and from his own interior life that he is able to meet the needs of the Church in ministries such as teaching, social work, technical occupations, etc. The ministries of religious brothers are varied and reflect the traditions of a given community.

Flexibility to meet current needs is one of the main characteristics of the brother's life style.

There are many communities of religious brothers as well as communities of priests and brothers. Often a man applies to a community with which he is familiar. Information about the brotherhood may be obtained by writing to one or more vocation directors listed in the **Religious Communities for Men** section of this book or by contacting:

The National Religious Vocation Conference
5420 S. Cornell Ave. #105, Chicago, IL 60615-5604
(773) 363-5454, Fax: (773) 363-5530
E-mail: nrvc@aol.com; Web: www.nrvc.net

The Religious Brothers Conference provides advocacy for the identity and the vocation of brothers; acts as a professional and ministerial resource to its member communities and offers direct services to individual brothers. Contact:

Religious Brothers Conference (RBC)
5420 So. Cornell Ave., Chicago, IL 60615-5604
(773) 493-2306, Fax: (773) 493-2356
E-mail: brothersoffice@ameritech.net; Web: www.brothersonline.org;
Brother Stephen Synan, FMS, Executive Director
1201 W Esplanade Ave., #314, Kenner, LA 70065
(504) 862-9102, Fax: (504) 862-0391, E-mail: swsynan@aol.com

Religious Priest

Some religious communities are "clerical": they include priests. What was said immediately before applies equally to priests living in religious communities. The religious priest takes vows of poverty, chastity and obedience according to the spirit of his own congregation. Being a priest he is a minister, for the Church, of the sacraments. His work generally depends upon the ministry appropriate to his community and may include teaching, overseas ministry, social work, pastoral ministry, chaplaincy, etc. A person who feels called to this life may contact any member of a community with which he is familiar, or one or more vocation directors listed in the **Religious Communities for Men** section of this book, or:

The National Religious Vocation Conference
5420 S. Cornell Ave. #105, Chicago, IL 60615-5604
(773) 363-5454, Fax: (773) 363-5530
E-mail: nrvc@aol.com; Web: www.nrvc.net

Woman Religious

A woman religious is a lay person who commits herself to Christ and to the Church by vows of poverty, chastity and obedience. She lives in a religious community that follows a constantly renewed tradition, patterned on the life and teaching of the founder of the community. The work she generally does will depend upon the particular community as influenced by the needs of the Church and its people, and includes such ministries as pastoral; social service; education (in many forms and ways); hospital/medical; youth/campus; missionary; retreats/conferences/spiritual direction; peace and justice; evangelization/faith formation; creative expression through music, the arts, etc.; work with the poor/elderly/broken/oppressed and distressed and so on.

The role of women in the Church is constantly developing and expanding. A significant part of that renewal is occurring within the faith communities of woman religious. Prayer and work are part of the tradition of all communities yet some are primarily contemplative while others are more active. Information about the vocation of a woman religious can be secured by contacting one or more of the vocation directors listed in the **Religious Communities for Women** section of this book or by contacting:

The National Religious Vocation Conference
5420 S. Cornell Ave. #105, Chicago, IL 60615-5604
(773) 363-5454, Fax: (773) 363-5530
E-mail: nrvc@aol.com; Web: www.nrvc.net

Second-Career Vocations

(Older Men and Women)

Second-career vocations are not a new trend in the Catholic Church; for instance, all the apostles were men who had previous careers before they answered the calling of Jesus Christ.

Today, people from all walks of life, including retired men and women, leave successful careers as nurses, lawyers, engineers, teachers, secretaries, etc. to join or affiliate themselves with a religious community. They become priests, brothers, sisters or lay ministers with contemplative, evangelical or apostolic communities.

These men and women bring a wealth of talent to religious communities whether it be management know-how, a professional background, technical skill, etc.

Most religious communities listed in this publication have their own age restrictions on accepting second-career vocations. There is no set age limit; each community should be contacted to find out what age restrictions apply.

This also applies to men who are interested in becoming diocesan priests. All diocesan vocation directors are listed in this publication and should be contacted directly.

Seminary programs structured to meet the needs of the second-career priestly candidate provide a unique seminary environment with a supportive peer community and experienced faculty. These seminaries are:

Sacred Heart School of Theology
Fr. Tom Knoebel, Director of Admissions
7335 South Highway 100, PO Box 429
Hales Corners, WI 53130-0429
(414) 529-6984, E-mail: tknoebel@shst.edu; Web: www.shst.edu

Holy Apostles College and Seminary
Rev. Bradley Pierce, M.S.A.
33 Prospect Hill Rd., Cromwell, CT 06416-2005
(860) 632-3010, Fax: (860) 632-3030
E-mail: rector@holyapostles.edu; Web: www.holyapostles.edu

Blessed Pope John XXIII National Seminary
558 South Ave.,Weston, MA 02493-2699
(781) 899-5500, Fax: (781) 899-9057
E-mail: popejohn@ziplink.net; Web: www.blessedjohnxxiii.org

Women who wish to enter the religious life as a second-career vocation should contact the individual congregation listed in the **Religious Communities for Women** section of this book. (Some congregations [e.g., Sisters of Loretto] welcome second-career women; other congregations have upper-age limits. Therefore, it is necessary to contact the individual congregation in which you are interested.)

Lay Person

(Church-Related Career)

Examples of this vocation would include service as a director of religious education, campus minister, hospital chaplain, prison minister, pastoral associate, pastoral administrator or teacher. Such a person might be married or single. Someone specifically interested in these kinds of ministries should contact the local diocesan chancery and ask for the diocesan official responsible for the given area of interest. One also might contact Catholic colleges or schools of theology where there are programs in ministry. See the **Religious Study Opportunities** section of this book.

Lay Person

(Volunteer Service)

Usually this service extends for a year or two in a mission of the Church either in the U.S. or overseas. In this ever-expanding group, opportunities are available for people to render service in numerous areas of Church activity. Religious communities affirm that lay extensions actually intensify their charism of service. People representing every type of service are incorporating positions for lay volunteers into the work they give in the Church. Young, old, married and single are responding to this challenge. The benefits often include stipend, room and board, health insurance and some travel allotment. The personal rewards for a lay volunteer begin with the immeasurable gratitude expressed by those who are served. The blessings continue in ways bestowed by the Spirit and unique to each person.

Turn to the **Lay Missionary** section of this book to discover which volunteer mission work holds the most promise for you. And/or contact:

Catholic Network of Volunteer Service (CNVS)
Jim Lindsay, Executive Director,
6930 Carroll Ave., Ste. 506, Takoma Park, MD 20912-4423
(800) 543-5046, (301) 270-0900, ext. 18, Fax: (301) 270-0901
E-mail: volunteer@cnvs.org, jlindsay@cnvs.org; Web: www.cnvs.org

St. Vincent Pallotti Center for Apostolic Development
415 Michigan Ave, NE, Washington, DC 20017
(877) VOL-LINK (877-865-5465), (202) 529-3330, Fax: (202) 529-0911
E-mail: pallotti@pallotticenter.org, Web: www.pallotticenter.org

Lay Person

(Associates)

Associates are men and women who want to enrich their Christian life by an affiliation with a religious community of priests, brothers or sisters. Their occupations vary – each continues to carry out the usual duties of their state of life in whatever their chosen job or profession. Associates may be married, single or widowed. Solemn promises (vows) – usually of commitment – are made with some religious communities.

Associates, also known as co-members, oblates, co-disciples, agregés (companions on the road), etc., choose a particular religious community based on their identification with that community's unique charism, values and mission. By sharing in the spiritual life, prayers and apostolic works of the religious community, associates have the opportunity for personal growth, the sharing of their own gifts and the mutual support of a faith community.

Turn to the **Associates, Oblates, Secular Institutes and Other Communities** section of this book to find a religious community with which to affiliate. And/or contact:

North American Conference of Associates and Religious (NACAR)
Sr. Ellen Rose O Connell, SC, 1720 Metropolitan Ave., Bronx, NY 10462
(718) 918-9420, Fax: (718) 918-9421
E-mail: eocsc@aol.com; Web: www.catholic-church.org/nacar

NACAR is the clearinghouse for all US and Canadian Associates and provides identification and exploration of issues concerning Associate life; assistance in policy and guideline development for Associate groups; networking, mutual support, workshops, annual conferences; and visioning for the future.

Secular Institutes

Over 60,000 Catholic lay men, lay women and secular clergy belong to over 160 canonically erected secular institutes throughout the world. The vocation of a single consecrated secular is a vocation in, and of, the world. Members take vows of poverty, celibacy and obedience, but do not wear distinctive attire or live in community as do members of religious orders. Generally, members live alone or with their families and hold regular jobs. They come together for periodic meetings, retreats and spiritual renewal. For information about secular institutes, contact one or more of the institutes listed elsewhere in this book or write to:

United States Conference of Secular Institutes
Rev. George F. Hazler, President
PO Box 4556, 12th St., NE, Washington, DC 20017-4556
E-mail: gfh141@aol.com; Web: www.secularinstitutes.org

Societies and Other Communities

There are some societies and communities in the Church that have a membership for priests and/or religious together with lay people (married and/or single). Many of these have sprung up in recent decades often in response to the Second Vatican Council's universal call to holiness for not only priests and religious but also for lay people. While married members of these communities generally live in their own homes, the priests and/or religious and/or single lay members often share some kind of common community life. Each individual community has its own particular mission, spirituality and apostolate.

Harvest

Harvest Prayer Association for Vocations wants to bring people to discover prayer as the true solution to the need of vocations in the Church, according to the words of the Gospels: "The Harvest is abundant but the laborers are few. Pray therefore the Lord of the harvest to send out laborers to gather in His harvest." (Mt. 9:37; Lk. 10:2) The goals of the Association are: to make its members aware of their personal Christian vocation in their daily life through prayer and action; to pray every day for numerous and holy vocations to the Church and that those who have accepted God's call may persevere; to offer part of the joys and sufferings of their daily life for vocations and to proclaim, everywhere, the importance of heeding Jesus' command to pray for vocations. Everyone – religious men and women and lay people – can join Harvest. For information, contact:

Harvest Prayer Association for Vocations, Rogationist Fathers
6635 Tobias Ave., Van Nuys, CA 91405
(818) 782-1765, Fax: (818) 782-1794
E-mail: MagazinVOC@aol.com; Web: www.rcj.org

Vocation Discernment

Making **any** decision can be a time of special graces and a vehicle for the Holy Spirit to manifest guidance if approached prayerfully. Considering a life in service to Our Lord, and to our brothers and sisters in Christ, as a professed priest, brother or sister is a significant deliberation. But, it's really no more complex than any vocation choice. After all, decisions have consequences.

St. Ignatius of Loyola offers very wise and practical counsel and spiritual direction for those trying to discern a life choice. He encourages one to project ahead to the time of death, and to look back to this present moment and the current decision to be made. Essentially, St. Ignatius suggests envisioning your deathbed scene. Will you regret making this decision, or not making this decision, from that retrospective? It's an interesting spiritual exercise.

If you find yourself in discernment about a religious vocation to the priesthood, brotherhood or sisterhood, you are on a very special journey. Travelers set a course and gather provisions. Trust that you can rely on the Lord as your compass. As your fare, include the reception of the Holy Eucharist, an active prayer life, and spiritual direction. Visit the tabernacle daily for quiet prayer. Make a directed or non-directed retreat. Stay close to the Lord because God, indeed, is close to you.

The writings of St. Gaspar Bertoni, founder of the Stigmatine community, include this pithy advice, "When things are not very clear, then we must await enlightenment with (full) confidence. Before asking men's opinions, let us put our problems and even the order and manner of solving them, before the Lord."

St. Gaspar himself felt unworthy to respond to the inner prompting he experienced to the call of priesthood, but he determined that the Holy Spirit affirmed his vocation when his parish priest chided him, "Get on with it, Bertoni! You know that you have been called to be a priest!"

Our Lord operates on a "need to know" basis. He will make your discernment clear. Let Him, and on His timetable! Sometimes just "showing up" allows Him to do the rest. Like everything else in this life, discernment unfolds "one day at a time."

Questions to Ask when Discerning a Religious Vocation

Thoughtfully thinking about the questions below can help you in the process of discerning whether you are being called to a religious life as a priest, brother, or sister. Writing down the answers in a journal often helps one to reach clarity, as does discussing your thoughts with your spiritual director.

- Name the two top motivating factors for your interest in a religious vocation.
- What excites you at the prospect of ministering with and for others? Explain each.
- What, in your estimation, is the number one "mission" of the Catholic Church?
- What is the difference between serving God and being in love with God?
- What does a "personal relationship" with Jesus mean to you?
- What major events, changes, or traumas in your life trigger your attraction toward a religious vocation?
- Are you flexible and open to others of different thought, theology, practice, piety or devotion?
- Who has been a mentor or someone you would like to imitate in your ministry and why? If there are several list them all.
- Do you think the Catholic Church needs to address issues that you feel are important? What are your solutions?
- What do you think is the biggest challenge facing the Church in the 21st century and what has given you this impression?
- Please explain your idea of what "collaborative ministry" entails. Have you ever worked in this fashion (give concrete examples)?
- We face obstacles and resistance with any major decision in our lives. Name the obstacles which at present are hindering you from making an informed or a confident decision towards a religious vocation. How have you been addressing these obstacles or areas of resistance?
- Do you prefer to spend time with others or do you consider yourself a private person?
- What is the difference between being alone and being lonely?
- Reflecting on God's Word and prayer will help you with these questions. Here are some passages from Scripture relating to call, vocation, choices and journey on which you can meditate:

OLD TESTAMENT
Genesis 12:1-4a (Abraham)
Exodus 3:10-12 & 4:1, 10-12 (Moses)
Amos 7:14-15 (Amos)
Isaiah 6:8 (Isaiah)
Jeremiah 1:4-8 (Jeremiah)
Ezekiel 3:1-4 (Ezekiel)
1 Kings 10 (Kings)

NEW TESTAMENT
Matthew 16:24-28 (The Cross)
Matthew 22:1-14 (Few chosen)
Luke 4:1-13 (Temptations)
Luke 6:12-15 (Night in prayer)
Luke 9:57-62 (Requirements)
Luke 10:38-42 (Martha, Mary)
Luke 12:22-31 (Seek first)
Luke 18:15-30 (Rich young man)
Mark 3:13-15 (The twelve)
Romans 8:26-31 (All things)

 *To contact the diocese see the listing in the section **Diocesan Vocation Offices**.*

Pope John Paul II on His Priestly Vocation

"I am often asked, especially by young people, why I became a priest. Maybe some of you would like to ask the same question. Let me try briefly to reply. I must begin by saying that it is impossible to explain entirely. For it remains a mystery, even to myself. How does one explain the ways of God? Yet, I know that, at a certain point in my life, I became convinced that Christ was saying to me what He had said to thousands before me: 'Come, follow me!' There was a clear sense that what I heard in my heart was no human voice, nor was it just an idea of my own. Christ was calling me to serve Him as a priest.

"And you can probably tell that I am deeply grateful to God for my vocation to the priesthood. Nothing means more to me or gives me greater joy than to celebrate Mass each day and to serve God's people in the Church. That has been true ever since the day of my ordination as a priest. Nothing has ever changed this, not even becoming Pope." (Los Angeles, USA, September 14, 1987)

"The priestly vocation is essentially a call to sanctity, in the form that derives from the Sacrament of Holy Orders. Sanctity is intimacy with God; it is the imitation of Christ, poor, chaste and humble; it is unreserved love for souls and self-giving to their true good; it is love for the Church which is holy and wants us to be holy, because such is the mission that Christ has entrusted to it. Each one of you must be holy also in order to help your brothers pursue their vocation to sanctity." (Rome, Italy, October 9, 1984)

"Your wish to become priests, or at least your wish to discover if you are really called...And so the question is a serious one, because you have to prepare thoroughly, with clear intentions and an austere formation." (Rome, Italy, October 9, 1984)

"His calling is a declaration of love. Your response is commitment, friendship, and love manifested in the gift of your own life as a definitive following and as a permanent sharing in His mission and in His consecrations. To make up your mind is to love Him with all of your soul and all of your heart in such a way that this love becomes the standard and motive of all your actions. From this moment on, live the Eucharist fully; be persons for whom the Holy Mass, Communion, and Eucharistic adoration are the center and summit of their whole life. Offer Christ your heart in meditation and personal prayer which is the foundation of the spiritual life." (Valencia, Spain, November 8, 1982)

"The world looks to the priest, because it looks to Jesus! No one can see Christ; but everyone sees the priest, and through him they wish to catch a glimpse of the Lord! Immense is the grandeur of the Lord! Immense is the grandeur and dignity of the priest!" (Rome, Italy, October 13, 1979)

"'Pray, therefore, to the Lord of the harvest that He send harvesters into His harvest'...Considering that the Eucharist is the greatest gift our Lord gives to His Church, we must ask for priests, since the priesthood is a gift for the Church. We must pray insistently for this gift. We must ask for it on our knees." (Rome, Italy, March 25, 1982)

"Called, consecrated, sent. This triple dimension explains and determines your conduct and your lifestyle. You are 'set apart;' 'segregated,' but not 'separated.' What would separate you, would be to forget or to overlook the meaning of the consecration that characterizes your priesthood. To be but one more in your profession, in your lifestyle, in your way of living, in your political obligations, would not help you fully carry out your mission. You would betray your own faithful who want you to be priests through and through." (Valencia, Spain, November 8, 1982)

Lord, Are You Calling Me?

GOD'S CALL

How do I know if God is calling me?
How can I tell?
Who can help me?
Where do I go?
When will I know?
What will I do?

Step One

Ask yourself, first of all, how am I doing with my very first vocation: my Baptismal Call.

Am I really a loving and faithful daughter or son of God?
Do I worship God at liturgy, keeping the Lord's day?
Do I use my gifts to pray, to read, to serve, to sing, to play music, to be a greeter, usher, sacristan, etc.?

Is Jesus alive in me? Am I alive in Him?
Am I living His Gospel?
Is my life giving witness to His presence in me?
Do I take pride and find joy in my union with Jesus Christ?

Am I a true dwelling place of the Holy Spirit?
Is prayer important in my life?
Do I really try to love others?
Forgive them?
Speak well of them?
Pray for them?
Do I enjoy learning about my faith and religion?
Am I involved in things that help people?

Step Two

Do I have a desire to serve?

Do I have an attraction to doing something with my life?

Have I always wanted to be like someone I admired and respected in ministry or religious life?

Do I feel driven to help people or to make the world a better place?

What do I see myself doing with my life?

What do other people think I would be good at?

Step Three

Pray over your calling and talk to God about it and LISTEN.

Make a retreat (see listings in the **Retreat Centers** section of this *Guide,* spend a weekend in a seminary, a convent, a monastery, or a vocation awareness program.

Also talk about it with others: friends, parents, your pastor, sisters, priests, brothers, teachers, mentors, your own sister or brother - anyone you trust and who knows you well.

Learn about how other people have found their calling.

Find a spiritual director to help you. Search this *Guide* or the *Online Guide for Religious Ministries* at www.ReligiousMinistries.com to identify communities which best suit your particular talents and abilities.

Step Four

Take a deep breath.
Pray.
Now call, write, or email the vocations director in the religious community or diocese in which you have an interest.

Step Five

Give it a try.
You will never know if you have a vocation to be a priest, a sister, a brother, a deacon, or a lay minister unless you actually test and try it.

Application and acceptance into a diocese, a seminary, a religious order or a formation program is essential to discovering a religious vocation to pastoral ministry or religious community life.

Give it a try.
Do you really want to come to a moment later in your life and ask the question What if God was calling me to serve the Church back then?

There is nothing to lose and everything to gain. The experience, whatever the outcome, will be a rewarding and grace-filled blessing for life.

THE HARVEST IS GREAT.
THE CALLING IS A GIFT.
COME AND SEE AND LIVE.

Reprinted, with permission, from the Diocese of Rapid City, website at www.rapidcity-diocese.org/OFFICES/vocations/page3_17_questions.htm. All rights reserved. To contact the Diocese of Rapid City vocations director, see the listing in the section ***Diocesan Vocation Offices****.*

Lay Associates Share in Mission of Religious Communities

Associate relationship is a way in which women and men outside of the vowed membership can share in the mission and goals of a religious congregation. The relationship is mutually creative; it enriches, supports and challenges both associates and vowed members to a deeper living of the Gospel commitment. The essential element of association is to widen and strengthen bonds with others who affirm the goals and mission of a religious community. Associates do this while maintaining their independent life style.

Associates often go through an official formation or orientation period to learn about the community's charism and mission. Although associates do not take formal vows as religious do, they commit to living the mission and charism of the religious institute within their independent lay life style as married, single, or widowed folk. They strive to balance family life, work, prayer and leisure in a way that puts "first things first." The associate relationship is fostered by regular contact with vowed religious and other associates.

Associates have been a presence in the Church community since the 1970's; today, they number over 27,000 in the United States. Because nearly 50 percent of male associate groups did not begin until the 1990's, women associates outnumber men associates by about seven to one.

Associates say that they are encouraged to participate more often in the prayer life and social activities of the institute than in institute committees, chapters or financial meetings. As they gain familiarity with the religious institute, many associates report a growing desire to serve others and to become involved in various forms of ministry.

The majority of vowed religious support the associate relationship, with age being a variable as to the extent of the support. Older vowed religious are less likely to have relationships with associates in their communities and to be less familiar with the formation and orientation process for associates. Younger vowed religious are much more likely to interact with associates in prayer and faith-sharing, and to be aware of the commitment of associates to live the charism and mission of the institute.

Women and men become associates for varied reasons. Associates in men's communities are greatly attracted by the ministries of the institute and a desire to work with vowed members. There is also a desire for community that draws them. In institutes of women religious, associates are more attracted by a desire for deeper spirituality, especially the spirituality of the institute. They seek opportunities for prayer and faith sharing with other association members and associates. Both men and women associates agree on the main focus of association as living the mission, charism and spiritual tradition of the institute.

The majority of associates make - and renew - a formal commitment to live the mission of the religious institute as associates. This commitment is a strengthening and a mutual support for both associates and the religious community, as well as being a support for the Church as a whole.

Printed with permission of the North American Conference of Associates and Religious (NACAR). All rights reserved. For more information about the goals of NACAR, membership, workshops and its annual convention, contact Sr. Ellen O'Connell, SC NACAR , 1720 Metropolitan Avenue, Bronx, NY 10462, (718) 918-9420, fax: (718) 918-9421, e-mail: EOCSC@aol.com, nacar@erols.com; website at www.catholic-church.org/nacar.

Pope John Paul II to Parents:

When Your Child Is Called by God to a Religious Vocation

"I address parents…May faith and readiness never be lacking in your hearts, if the Lord should bless you by calling a son or a daughter to missionary service. May you give thanks to God! Indeed, see that this call is prepared through family prayer, through education rich in spirit and enthusiasm, through participation in parochial and diocesan activities, through involvement in associations and volunteer work.

"The family that cultivates a missionary spirit in its lifestyle and in education itself, prepares good soil for the seed of the divine call and, at the same time, strengthens the loving ties and Christian virtues of its members." (Rome, Italy, May 22, 1994)

"The Christian family, as the 'domestic church,' forms the original and fundamental school for training in the faith. The father and mother receive, in the Sacrament of Matrimony, the grace and the responsibility of providing Christian education for their children, to whom they bear witness and transmit, at one and the same time, human and religious values. In learning their first words, the children also learn to praise God, whom they feel to be very close as a loving and provident Father. As they learn the first expressions of love, the children also learn to open themselves to others, perceiving in their own self-giving the meaning of human living.

"Here is Jesus, who returns to Nazareth and is obedient to them, to Mary and Joseph. That 'obedience' signifies filial obedience, but also, at the same time, an obedient opening to humanity, which always needs to learn, above all in the family. Parents must behave in such a way that children can find in them a living model of mature humanity - and can, on the basis of this model, gradually develop their own human and Christian maturity." (Rome, Italy, December 26, 1982)

"For man, to generate a child is above all to 'receive it from God' : it is a matter of welcoming from God as a gift the child that is generated. For this reason, children belong first to God, and then to their parents: and this is a truth which is rich in implications for both parents and children.

"To be instruments of the heavenly Father in the work of forming their own children - here is found the inviolable limit that parents must respect in carrying out their mission. They must never consider themselves 'owners' of their children, but rather they must educate them, paying constant attention to the privileged relationship that their children have with their Father in heaven. In the last analysis, as with Jesus, it is His business that they must 'be about' more than that of their earthly parents." (Plato, Italy, March 19, 1986)

"The family is for this reason also the first and fundamental setting in which the Christian vocation sprouts, is formed, and is manifested. Just as Jesus' vocation was manifested in the family of Nazareth, so every vocation today is born and manifests itself also in the family. And when this general vocation is revealed as a particular calling to 'leave everything' then the Christian family is revealed here also, and above all here, as the privileged place where the seed placed by God in the heart of the children can take root and mature; the place where the participation of the parents in the priestly mission of Christ himself is revealed in its most elevated degree. Vocation touches the very roots of the human soul. It is an interior calling of God directed to the person: to the unique and irreplaceable person." (Cainca, Ecuador, January 13, 1985)

Catholic News Publishing Company
A GUIDE TO
RELIGIOUS
MINISTRIES
For Catholic Men and Women

Community Profiles

Men

The following pages contain profiles of men's communities that are sponsors of the 2004 edition of A Guide to Religious Ministries for Catholic Men and Women. These orders have made a special effort to describe their life's work. Review these pages to determine which of these men's orders perform the sort of ministry that may be of interest to you.

If you would like information about becoming a member of a religious order but are unsure of which ones to consider, complete the card below and you will receive literature from several communities.

Sending in this postcard does not obligate you to anything, but it may be the first step towards your life's work.

You may also visit our website, **www.religiousministries.com** to obtain more information about any of these orders.

Request for Information - Men's Communities

I am interested in a life of religious ministry. Please forward information about different religious communities. I am interested in becoming a:

☐ Priest ☐ Brother ☐ Lay Minister

My particular interest for ministry in a religious life is in:

☐ Parish Work
☐ Missions
☐ Undecided
☐ Other: ____________________

☐ Education
☐ Health Care
☐ Social Service

Type of Community:

Refer to front of A section for a description of each

☐ Apostolic/Active
☐ Contemplative/Cloistered
☐ Monastic

Mr.____

Address ____

City/State/Zip ___________________________________

Telephone (Optional) ______________________________

E-mail Address (Optional)___________________________

Last Grade Completed ____________________ Age_______________

Comments ______________________________________

A Guide to Religious Ministries
Index to Men's Profiles

The Gospel

Live, Serve, Discover...
In Africa

BECOME A PRIEST OR LAY MISSIONARY

PLEASE CONTACT
THE SOCIETY OF AFRICAN MISSIONS

Deacon Keith McKnight, Director of Vocations
1-888-250-4333 - email: deaconkm@smafathers.org

Theresa Hicks, Director, Lay Missionary Program
256 North Manor Circle ■ Takoma Park, MD 20912 ■ (301) 891-2037
e-mail: smausa-v@smafathers.org ■ http://www.smafathers.org

SMA

Use the Society of African Missions postcard to request further information.

Use the Alexian Brothers postcard to request further information.

Use the Atonement Friars postcard to request further information.

Community living in service of God's people

The Order of Saint Augustine

BROTHERS AND SISTERS WITH ONE MIND AND ONE HEART INTENT UPON GOD

As Augustinian Friars, we go where the needs of the Church call us — the inner city, rural areas, the campus, the missions. And we serve in many ways: as preachers of the Word and presiders at the sacraments, as missionaries, chaplains and social workers, as teachers and writers, as counselors, musicians and artists.

For more information:

James McBurney, O.S.A.
214 Ashwood Road
P.O. Box 340
Villanova, PA 19085-0340
610.527.3330, ext. 284
vocations@augustinian.org

Tom Whelan, O.S.A.
108 Cole Street
San Francisco, CA 94117-1116
415.387.3626
osacole@pacbell.net

John Merkelis, O.S.A.
Tolentine Center
20300 Governor's Highway
Olympia Fields, IL 60461-1081
708.748.9500
jmerkosa@aol.com

Augustinian Contemplative Nuns
440 Marley Road
New Lenox, IL 60451
815.463.9662

A contemplative Augustinian Nun at prayer

VISIT OUR WEBSITE: WWW.AUGUSTINIAN.ORG

Use the Augustinian Friars postcard to request further information.

We Have A Place For You

We welcome single Catholic men, generally between the ages of 19-55, who *desire* to seek God in the monastic religious life.

Our life of prayer is *rooted* in the daily celebration of the Eucharist and of the Liturgy of the Hours.

The life of a monk is not always easy. It is a life of prayer and work and study. Our life is rooted in *charity* and *service* towards our brothers in community and the people of *God*. All skills, talents and trades are welcome and considered important.

Contact: Vocation Director • St. Benedict's Abbey
12605 224th Ave. • Benet Lake, WI 53102
888-482-1044 • www.benetlake.org

Send one of the postcards in this book for more information.

Benedictine Monks
St. Benedict's Abbey

This message of mine is for you, then, if you are ready to give up your own will, once and for all, and armed with the strong and noble weapons of obedience to do battle for the true King, Christ the Lord.

-From the Prologue to the Rule of St. Benedict

May every Benedictine community present itself with a well-defined identity, like a "city on a hill", distinct from the surrounding world, but open and welcoming to the poor, to pilgrims and to all who are searching for a life of greater fidelity to the Gospel!

-Pope John Paul II, July 7, 1999

Life in the monastery provides the setting for the monk's conversion and deepening union with the Blessed Trinity. The monk daily encounters this Trinitarian life through the Mass, the Liturgy of the Hours, and *Lectio Divina* (spiritual reading).

The monks of St. Benedict's Abbey serve God's people in a variety of Apostolates. This includes the educational work at *Benedictine College* and *Maur Hill Mount Academy*. It also includes pastoral work in parishes, chaplaincies and a mission in Brazil. The monks also help with the upkeep of the Abbey grounds, and the many daily tasks around the monastery.

Father Meinrad Miller, O.S.B.
St. Benedict's Abbey
1020 N. Second St.
Atchison, KS 66002
(913) 360-7885
mmiller@benedictine.edu
www.kansasmonks.org

Use the Benedictine Monks of St. Benedict's Abbey postcard to request further information.

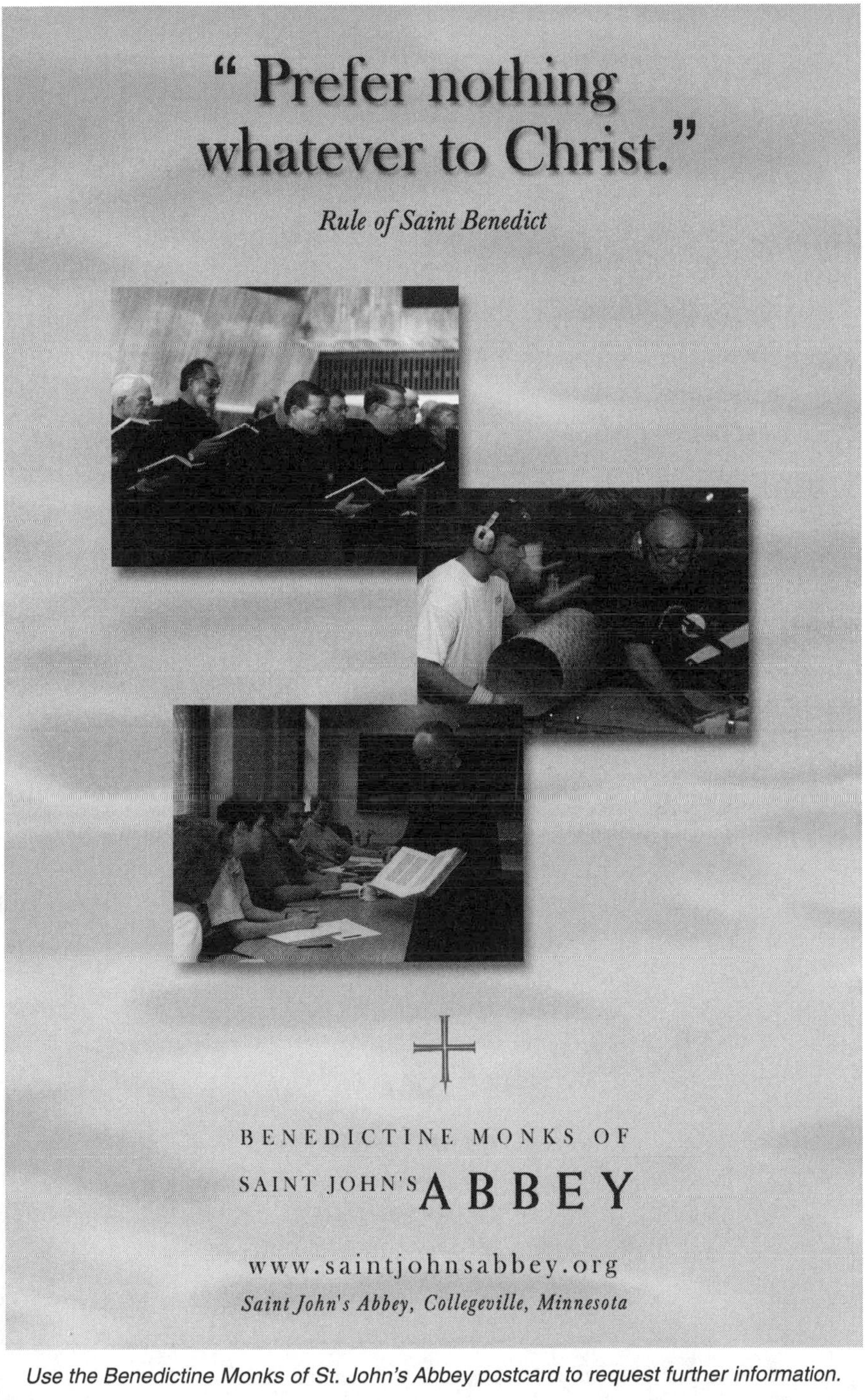

Use the Benedictine Monks of St. John's Abbey postcard to request further information.

SAINT LOUIS ABBEY

WHY A MONK AT SAINT LOUIS ABBEY?

A monk is one who has been smitten by the love of Christ – his love for us which awakens a corresponding love for him and a desire to be formed by him into his likeness. This formation takes place in the Spirit and through imperfect human beings who are also allowing themselves to be formed by him. The monk's goal is to surrender himself daily to the love of God until that love begins to become the animating principle of his whole being. He seeks a humble love, not a personal greatness or importance or even apostolic success. Through daily prayer and interaction with the word of God he learns to entrust his cares to the Lord, to await all from him, and to call for his help in the struggle against egoism and sin. At Saint Louis Abbey we try to live out our discipleship of Christ in spreading the good news of his love to others through the education of teenage boys, parish work based on the monastery and the ministry of hospitality. We believe that our regular monastic prayer is powerful because it is the prayer of Christ offered in the heart of the Church. It also gives witness, at the beginning of the new millennium, to the primacy of God in our lives.

Write for Information:

Father Ralph Wright, OSB • Saint Louis Abbey
500 South Mason Road • Saint Louis, MO 63141.
Tel: 1-800-638-1527 • E-mail: frralph@priory.org
WEB: www.stlouisabbey.org

Use the Benedictine Monks of St. Louis Abbey postcard to request further information.

Consider the monastic life as a Benedictine monk of St. Procopius Abbey

Do you truly seek God? If the answer is yes, then you have made the first step towards both the sincere practice of Christianity and, perhaps, the particular expression of the Christian life known as Benedictine monasticism.

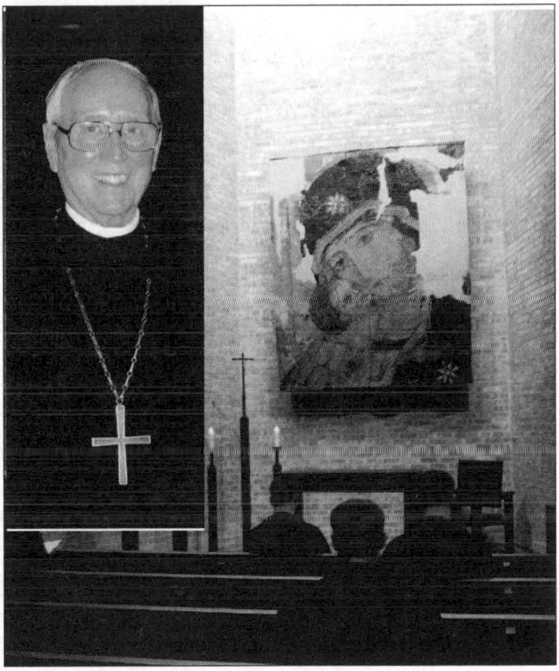

What is monasticism? It is a response, found in various religions under diverse forms, to the human need to stand apart from the frantic pace of the world and explore instead the ultimate meaning of existence. By clearing away the ephemeral clutter of life, the monk hopes to find God – or, rather, allows God to find him.

What is Benedictine monasticism? Those who follow the monastic way of life as set down in the sixth-century Rule of St. Benedict are called Benedictines. The Benedictine monk engages in the quest for God, under the guidance of an abbot, or spiritual father, in a community of like-minded individuals to whom he makes a permanent commitment and with whom he spends his life in prayer and work.

What is St. Procopius Abbey? We are a Benedictine monastic community, founded in 1885 and located in Lisle, Illinois, nearly thirty miles west of Chicago. Numbering about fifty men, we strive to come closer to God through our prayer and our service to the Church, especially our educational apostolates at Benedictine University and Benet Academy (a college-preparatory high school).

How does one know whether one has a monastic vocation? St. Benedict begins his Rule with the words, "Listen, my son, to the precepts of the Master; incline the ear of your heart." One discovers one's calling in life by opening oneself to God in prayer and listening for His response; often a priest or other spiritual adviser can be of assistance in discerning God's will. Not everyone has a vocation to the monastic life; if you do, God will offer you the means to recognize it.

If you think God is calling you to the monastic life of St. Procopius Abbey, you can explore the possibility by writing to us. We will be glad to help you in your search.

Please address your inquiries to:
Director of Vocations
St. Procopius Abbey
5601 College Road
Lisle, Illinois 60532
E-Mail guyrj@megsinet.net
www.procopius.org

Send one of the postcards in this book for more information.

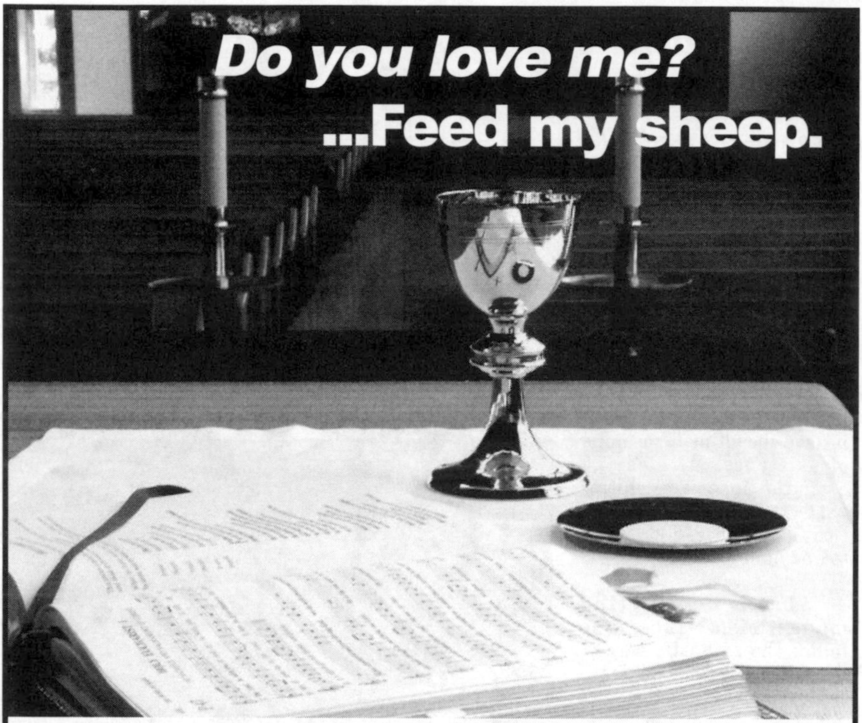

CONGREGATION OF THE BLESSED SACRAMENT

to make ***known*** *and* ***loved*** *every aspect of the* ***Eucharist***

Priests
Deacons
Brothers

Founded in 1856 by
St. Peter Julian Eymard

blessedsacrament.com

Use the Congregation of the Blessed Sacrament postcard to request further information.

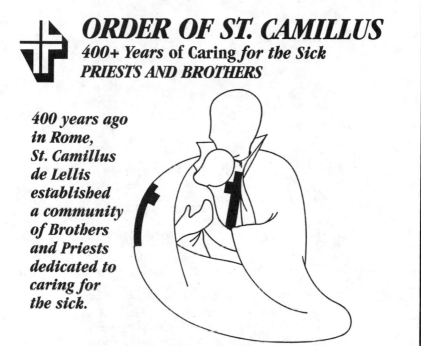

Why go to Carmelites?

As a Carmelite, you can be a pastor, teacher, spiritual director. But, we are also lawyers, authors, and prison chaplains. What holds us together is our 800-year tradition of prayer. As a community, Carmelite friars pray to experience God's love and to search for meaning. We pray for the freedom to respond to needs wherever we find them.

What's in it for you?

A lifelong relationship with God. A community to support and sustain you. The opportunity to join other ordinary people on an extraordinary journey – being a witness to God's love for every person.

Contact one of our vocation directors at the numbers listed below. Or, use the convenient Carmelites postcard found in the front of this book to request additional information.

Fr. William Wert, O. Carm.
8433 Bailey Road
Darien, IL 60561
Phone: (630) 969-4141, ext. 107
Fax: (630) 969-3376
Email: vocations@carmelnet.org
www.carmelites.net

Fr. Matthew Faulkner, O.Carm
P.O. Box 3079, Carmelite Drive
Middletown, NY 10940
Phone: (845) 344-2225
Fax: (845) 344-2210
Email: ocarmvoc@frontiernet.net
www.frontier.net/~ocarmvoc

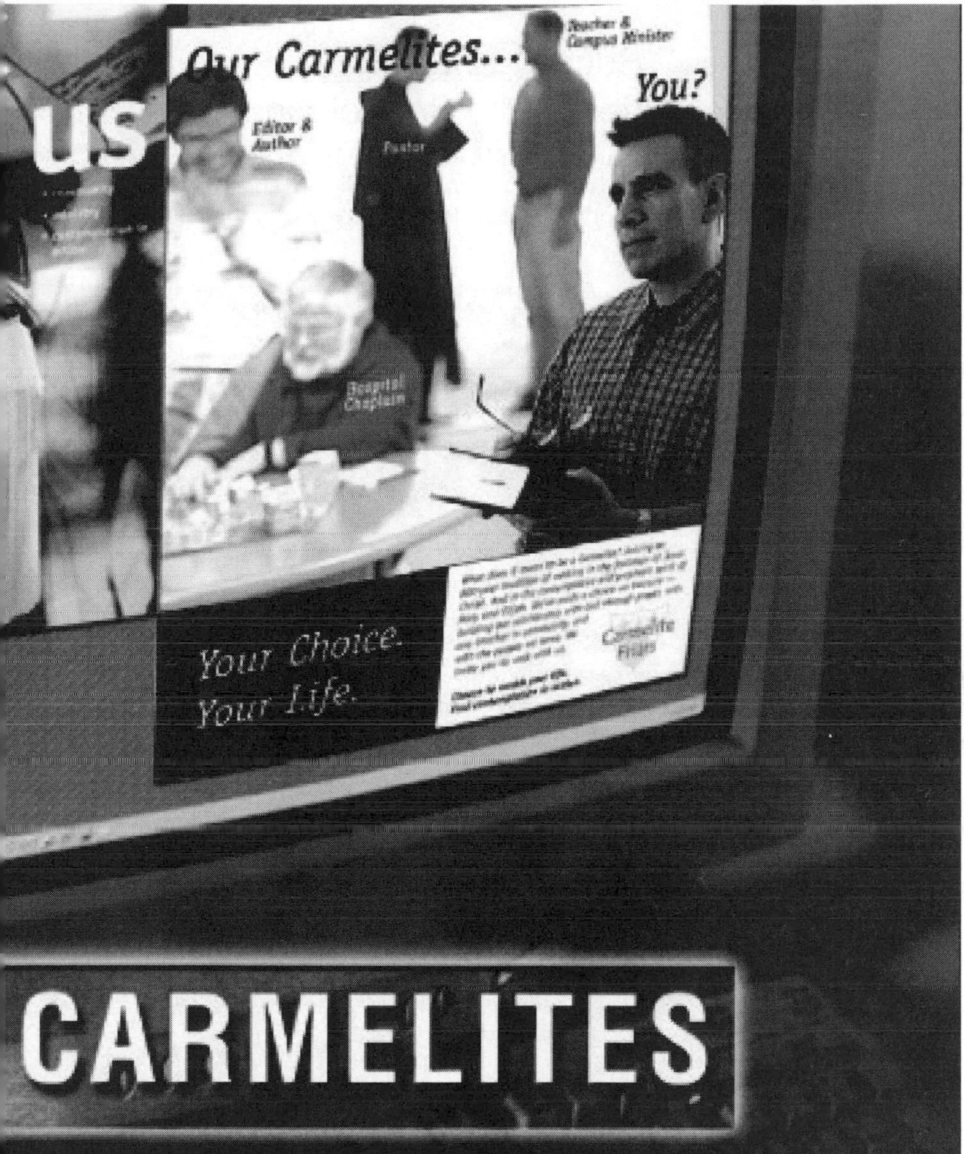
us
Our Carmelites...
Teacher & Campus Minister
You?
Editor & Author
Pastor
Hospital Chaplain
Your Choice.
Your Life.
Carmelite Friars
CARMELITES

Carmelite
Friars

Society of St. Paul
Pauline Priests and Brothers in Media

"Come join us and Communicate God's Word to the World through the Media"
The Society of St. Paul is an international religious congregation of both priests and brothers living the consecrated life in community.

From The Eucharist

Join us in meditation on the scriptures, daily Mass and Eucharistic adoration of Jesus, the Divine Master and become a modern apostle as a Pauline brother or priest. Like Paul, our patron, you are invited to become a light to the nations and under the guidance of Mary, Queen of Apostles, focus your entire life on Jesus the way, the truth and the life.

To The Media Mission

Your deepened knowledge and love of Christ's transforming power will motivate and challenge you to spread the Gospel through all forms of the media. You will become a part of a pontifical congregation in the Catholic Church that is working in 28 countries. You will be joining Pauline brothers and priests who work on book, magazine, radio, television, video and audio productions and utilize the latest technologies in their book centers and internet work. Your creativity will be fully utilized in the service of God's Kingdom.

Call or write:
Fr. Jeffrey Mickler or Br. Richard Brunner
SSP Vocation Office
Pauline Fathers and Brothers
P.O. Box 189
9531 Akron-Canfield Road
Canfield, OH 44406-0189
Telephone: (330) 702-0359
E-mail: spvocationoffice@aol.com

Send one of the postcards in this book for more information.

Brother (bruthər) *verb*. **1.** to live and pray in fraternal community. **2.** to live the vows of poverty, chastity and obedience. **3.** to be missioned by the Church for Christian education. **4.** to minister in the Spirit of Jesus and the traditions of Blessed Edmund Rice.

✝ The Congregation Of Christian Brothers ✝

Brothers serving others as...

*** Teacher**

*** Counselor**

*** Youth Minister**

*** Coach**

*** Campus Minister**

*** Administrator**

*** Moderator**

*** Retreat Director**

*** Social Worker**

*** Minister to Migrants**

*** Parish Administrator**

*** Missionary**

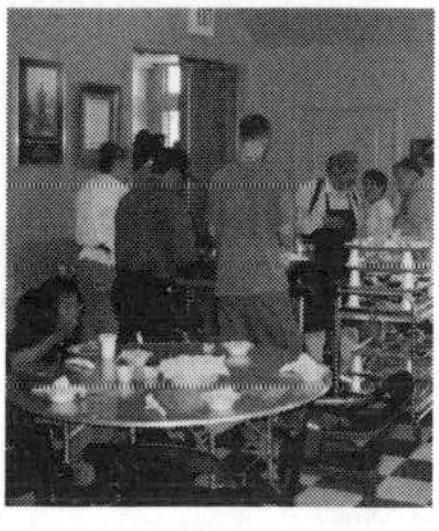

For more information contact:
Brother J. R. McDonald, C.F.C.
Christian Brothers
802 Terry Avenue
Seattle, WA 98104
(206) 622-6596, 2639
e-mail: brmac@odea.org

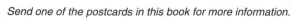

Send one of the postcards in this book for more information.

Brothers of Christian Instruction FIC

1200 Brothers in 25 Countries

"To spread the knowledge of Jesus Christ and His Gospel"

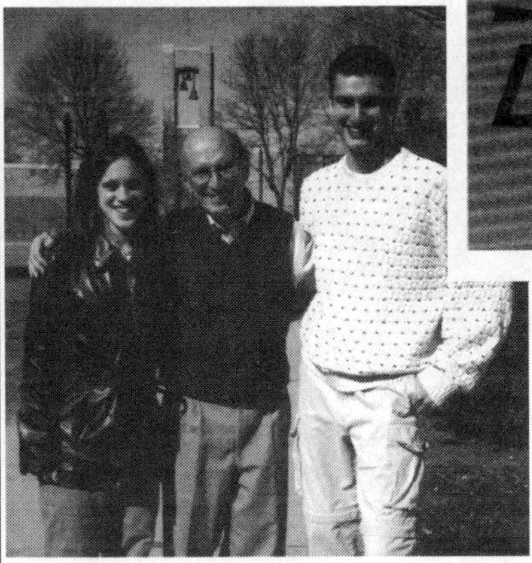

Ministries

- Schools on all levels
- Retreat Center
- Parish Ministry
- Services to the elderly, the poor, the homeless
- Foreign missions

Contact: Br. Daniel Caron, FIC
555 Eastern Avenue
Fall River, MA 02723
E-mail: djcaron43@yahoo.com
Web site: www.ficbrothers.org

100 Years in the United States

Send one of the postcards in this book for more information.

In circles that matter
you could be an insider

In mission villages and on inner city streets, Claretian Missionaries—priests and brothers—step forward to serve the poor and oppressed. In 63 nations, the Claretians foster justice and peace in the tradition of our founder, St. Anthony Claret.

We minister often under difficult circumstances to bring the love of Jesus to those in need. Working together, living together, and praying together as a community, we balance our work with a commitment to deepening our own spirituality.

If joining our circle might appeal to you, contact:

U.S. East Contact:
Father Carl Quebedeaux, C.M.F.
205 West Monroe Street
Chicago, IL 60606
800-328-6515
frcarl2307@claret.org
www.claretianvocations.org

U.S. West Contact:
Father Art Gramaje, C.M.F.
1119 Westchester Place
Los Angeles, CA 90019
323-733-7712
cmffvoc@earthlink.net

THE CLARETIANS
On Fire with God's Love

Use the Claretians postcard to request further information.

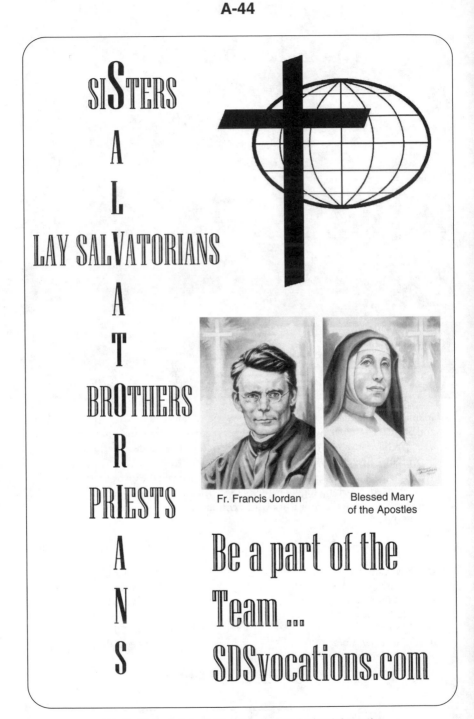

DÒNG TRUYỀN GIÁO NGÔI LỜI

Dòng Truyền Giáo Ngôi Lời là một tập thể Công Giáo gồm 5,700 thành viên thuộc nhiều sắc tộc trên thế giới. Các thành viên của Dòng hiện đang hăng say phục vụ tại 59 quốc gia, trong nhiều lãnh vực khác nhau như giáo dục, xứ đạo, kỹ nghệ, y tế, canh nông... Riêng tại Hoa Kỳ, Dòng có 4 trung tâm cho các chương trình tìm hiểu và giáo dục trong việc đào tạo linh mục và tu sĩ cho cánh đồng truyền giáo:

Divine Word College Seminary tại Epworth, Iowa, là một đại chủng viện với chương trình 4 năm khởi đầu cho việc huấn luyện các chủng sinh trở thành những nhà truyền giáo.
Associate Program là chương trình 1 năm dành cho những thỉnh sinh đã tốt nghiệp đại học, tới tìm hiểu Dòng.
Wendelin House tại Washington, D.C., là một học viện huấn luyện chủng sinh trở thành tu sĩ. Chủng sinh theo học các đại học trong vùng.
Divine Word Theologate tại Chicago, Illinois, là một thần học viện dành cho những đại chủng sinh theo học để trở thành linh mục.

Để biết rõ hơn về các chương trình của Dòng Truyền Giáo Ngôi Lời, bạn hãy liên lạc với:
Lm. Binh Nguyen, SVD
P.O. Box 380
Epworth, IA 52045-0380
1-800-553-3321
www.svd.org

Use the Divine Word Missionaries postcard to request further information.

DOMINICAN FATHERS AND BROTHERS

ORDER OF PREACHERS

IDENTITY

The Order of Preachers was founded in 1216 by St. Dominic de Guzman in response to a then desperate need for informed preaching - a need that could not be met by the existing resources within the Church. Against a heresy which denied the dignity of our humanity, St. Dominic trained a group of preachers who would serve the Church in its affirmation of the world as the place where Christ was discovered. He adapted the structure of monasticism so that his friars, vowed to poverty, chastity, and obedience, were nevertheless free to move wherever their preaching was needed. He replaced the tradition of manual labor with the sustained reflection on the mystery of Christ. And he began a tradition of spirituality that is rooted in community life, liturgical and choral prayer, and meditation – a spirituality which was meant to bear the fruit of an active apostolate.

SERVICE

We Dominicans continue to draw on our origins and the charism of St. Dominic in order to serve our calling as preachers of the Gospel. While the preaching apostolate remains the chief commitment of the Order, that task is supplemented by numerous other ministries. From the beginning, the Friars sought association with centers of learning and teaching. Presently, a variety of campus ministries continue to be a vital mission for us. Our interests and activities include retreat centers, research, hospitals, preaching teams, numerous parishes, universities, liturgy, art, communications and media, as well as ministries in the area of social justice. Our work extends from the U.S. to our missions in Latin America and Africa.

A call to ordination is not a necessary dimension for a Dominican vocation. A man may feel called to join our preaching community as a cooperator brother. Such men, with a background or interest in the arts, trades and the professional and academic world may find their calling to Christian ministry fulfilled in the Order of Preachers.

INVITATION

Dominic envisioned a family of priests, brothers and sisters proclaiming the message of Jesus. The time of spiritual, academic, pastoral and professional formation seeks to bring to fruition the personal charisms of each friar as he responds to God's call within the Dominican community.

If you are interested in living with the Word of God in a life dedicated to preaching, please contact:

CENTRAL PROVINCE
Promoter of Vocations
7200 W. Division
River Forest, IL 60305-1294
(708) 771-7254

SOUTHERN PROVINCE
Promoter of Vocations
4640 Canal St
New Orleans, LA 70119
Voice: (504) 488-2652 x221
E-mail: hgrooverop@aol.com

EASTERN PROVINCE
Promoter of Vocations
487 Michigan Ave., NE
Washington, DC 20017
(800) 529-1205

WESTERN PROVINCE
Promoter of Vocations
5877 Birch Court
Oakland, CA 94618-1626
(510) 658-8722

Send one of the postcards in this book for more information.

A-47

The Franciscans (OFM)

A religious community of men founded by St. Francis of Assisi with a passion for the Gospel of Jesus Christ, living a simple lifestyle in Prayer, Fraternity and Ministry.

Assumption BVM Province
503 South Browns Lake Dr.
Burlington, WI 53105
877-OFM-FRIAR

St. John the Baptist Province
5000 Colerain Ave
Cincinnati, OH 45223
800-827-1082

Holy Name of Jesus Province
135 W 31st Street
New York, NY 10001
800-677-7788

Province of Santa Barbara
1112 26th Street
Sacramento, CA 95816
877-573-5558

Immaculate Conception Province
459 River Road
Andover, MA 01810
800-521-5442

Vice-Province of the Holy Family
(Croation)
2864 E 96th Street
Chicago, IL 60617
773-768-1423

Our Lady of Guadalupe Province
318 Oblate Drive
San Antonio, TX 78216
210-366-5053

Vice-Province of St. Casimir
(Lithuanian)
PO Box 980
Kennebunkport, ME 04046
207-967-2011

Sacred Heart of Jesus Province
4860 West 29th Street
Cicero, IL 60804
800-933-4871

Our national toll free number **1 - 800 - 234 - FRIAR**

and web site: **http://ofm-usa.com**

Send one of the postcards in this book for more information.

Do you desire to serve God in our Middle East Mission as a brother or priest?

Faithful to the mission handed on by our founder, St. Francis of Assisi, in 1217, we imitate the life of Jesus Christ through religious, educational and social services to bring Christ to the native and pilgrim peoples, and preserve those shrines which embrace the Life, Death, and Resurrection of Our Lord Jesus Christ.

PREACH PENANCE AND PEACE TO ALL THE NATIONS

Beginning from Jerusalem

Vocation Director
Holy Land Franciscans
1400 Quincy Street, NE
Washington, DC 20017
Phone (202) 526-6800
www.myfranciscan.com

Name ____________________
Address ____________________
City ____________________ State ________
Zip ____________________ Age ________
Education ____________________
Phone ____________________

C

GRM-2004

Use the Holy Land Franciscans postcard to request further information.

Journey *with* Us

God's call to St. Francis nearly 800 years ago to "rebuild my Church" reverberates in our hearts today. We go forth as Franciscan priests and brothers, bringing Christ's message of mercy and love to a modern—yet hurting world. Our many works are focused not on simply maintaining buildings but on transforming lives into deeper relationship with Jesus Christ.

We find renewal for this important work by living in vibrant communities, with prayer and the ongoing conversion of our own hearts at the center of our communal life.

"Come Journey with Us" as a Franciscan Friar, Third Order Regular priest or brother.

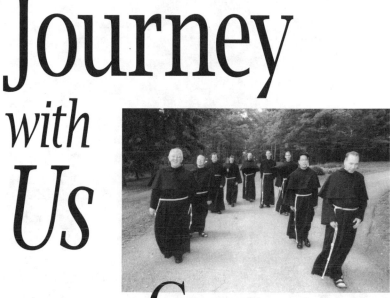

The TOR Friars are proud to serve at Franciscan University of Steubenville and St. Francis University, Loretto, PA.

Province of the Most Sacred Heart of Jesus—Loretto, PA

Franciscan Friars, T.O.R., Vocation Office
PO Box 104, Loretto, PA 15940 Phone: 814-472-9527
E-mail: davistor@uov.net Web: www.franciscanstor.org

2004 GRM

Send one of the postcards in this book for more information.

Looking for work that matters?
Take a look at Glenmary priesthood or brotherhood.
Please feel free to contact Glenmary's vocation director at 800.935.0975 or vocation@glenmary.org
GLENMARY
HOME MISSIONERS
www.glenmary.org

Use the Glenmary Home Missioners postcard to request further information.

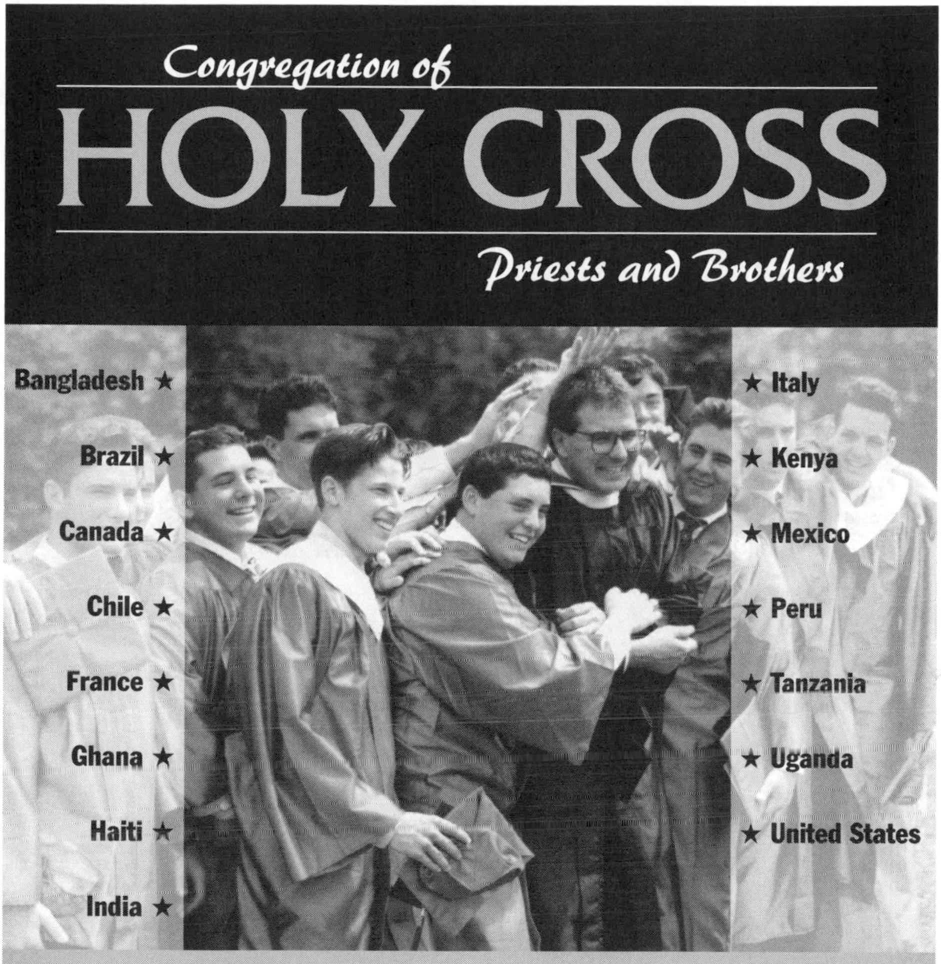

Congregation of
HOLY CROSS
Priests and Brothers
Bangladesh ★
Brazil ★
Canada ★
Chile ★
France ★
Ghana ★
Haiti ★
India ★
★ Italy
★ Kenya
★ Mexico
★ Peru
★ Tanzania
★ Uganda
★ United States
In fifteen countries, from the University of Notre Dame to the slums of Dhaka, HOLY CROSS is educating apostles to evangelize the world.
www.nd.edu/~vocation (priests)
www.holycrossbrothers.org (brothers)

Send one of the postcards in this book for more information.

Where are you heading?

Do you ever think God has a plan for you
that you haven't quite connected with?
Could you imagine being called to spread the gospel?

Spiritans do just that!

as preachers, teachers, and missionaries
here and abroad.
If your thoughts lean towards
spirituality and service, give us a call.
We'll help you sort it out.

SPIRITANS
ONE HEART, ONE SPIRIT

Please give THE SPIRITANS a call at 412.765.0733

Vocation Office   Laval House   Duquesne University   Pittsburgh, PA 15282

fax: 412.765.1983   e: hickey@duq.edu   www.spiritans.org

Use the Spiritans postcard to request further information.

PROVIDING
COMPASSION
and LOVE to
THOSE IN NEED

The Brothers of St. John of God

For the Brothers of St. John of God, their vocation means helping those who are disabled, sick or in need of compassion. It means devoting their lives to hospitality. It means experiencing community living with the opportunity to share their faith, ministry and daily lives with other men who have chosen the same vocation.

To learn more about how you can offer your unique gifts to the ministry of hospitality, contact:

Brother Thomas Osorio, O.H.
Hospitaller Brothers of St. John of God
1145 Delsea Drive
Westville Grove, NJ 08093
(856) 848-4700, ext. 163
e-mail: sjogvocationsnj@aol.com
website: www.brothersofstjohnofgod.org

Use the Brothers of St. John of God postcard to request further information.

What's in your heart?

Teacher Scholar Doctor Lawyer Actor Pastor Artist

Retreat Director Counselor Spiritual Director

As a high school teacher, **Chris Devron, SJ** recognizes that children come to school with all their needs. He has coordinated an inner-city volunteer teacher corps and set up an outreach program for low-income students. "The more children express their struggles and challenges, the more I want to serve as a companion of Jesus, whose love and grace are sufficient for all of us."

Sometimes our hearts desire more than a job.

Sometimes our hearts desire companions on the spiritual journey. Are you thinking about becoming a priest or brother? If so, The Jesuits offer many joyful opportunities for service. We would be honored to hear what you feel in your heart.

The Jesuits
Society of Jesus

www.jesuit.org

Director of Vocations • 1616 P Street, NW, Suite 300
Washington, DC 20036-1420 • (202) 462-0400 • usjc@jesuit.org

Send one of the postcards in this book for more information.

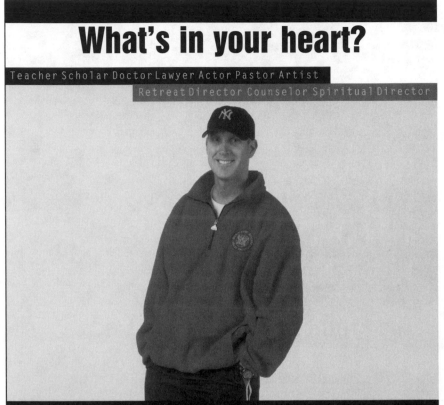

Take that leap of faith.
"Yet in all this we are more than conquerors because of Him who loves us."
Romans 8:37
The Josephites:
Serving the African-American community since 1871. We are an interracial society of brothers and priests.
Consider it.
A Vocation with the Josephites
Call toll free: 1.800.897.1827 fax: 410.727.1006 email: vocationsssj@aol.com www.josephite.com

Use the Josephites postcard to request further information.

Little Brothers Of The Good Shepherd

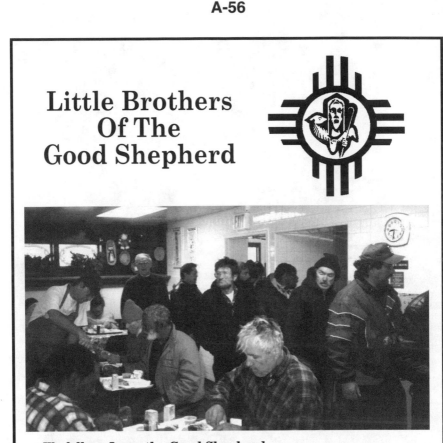

We follow Jesus the Good Shepherd

We claim His Gospel as our First Rule

WE WORK IN MANY FIELDS: Homeless shelters, mentally & physically disabled, the elderly, troubled youth, abused women & children, the terminally ill, persons with AIDS, priests retreats.

THE U.S., CANADA, ENGLAND AND IRELAND

CONTACT: **VOCATION DIRECTOR**
VILLA MATHIAS
PO BOX 389
ALBUQUERQUE, NEW MEXICO 87103
PHONE: 505-243-4238
WEB SITE: www.lbgs.org

Send one of the postcards in this book for more information.

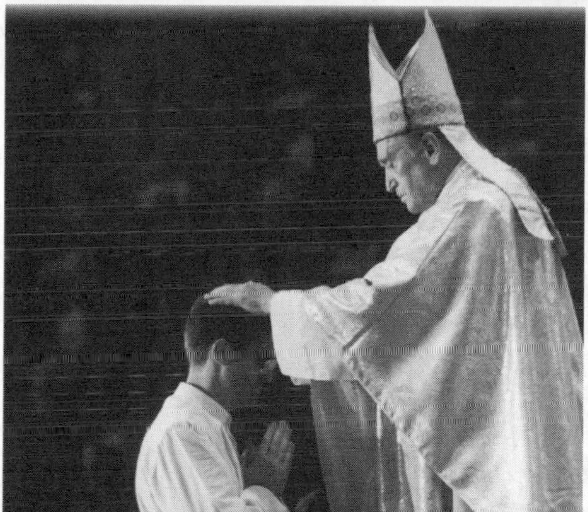

The Marianists

Who are The Marianists?

The Society of Mary (Marianists) is an international religious order of priests and brothers, with more than 600 serving in the Province of the United States, including Korea, India, Eastern Africa and Mexico.

Founded by Blessed William Joseph Chaminade in 1817, the order is closely aligned with the Marianist Sisters and lay Marianists in what is known as the Marianist Family. The Marianists uphold the idea of a "discipleship of equals," where brothers, priests, sisters and lay Marianists work with each other in the work of the Gospel. The Marianist charism – gifts of the spirit -- is centered on developing small faith communities in which the spirit of Mary, faith, equality and hospitality are honored.

How do Marianists make a difference?

Marianist brothers or priests are engaged in many apostolic ministries: education, including middle schools, high schools and universities; parish work; retreat houses; counseling centers; inner-city neighborhood ministries; adult education; the trades; the arts, as well as business, law and medicine. The Marianists are involved in the fight against poverty and injustice in many areas of the world. They take an active stand on issues such as the environment, racism, sweatshops and the death penalty.

What's the next step?

The Marianists hold discernment retreats for men who are interested in getting acquainted with the Society of Mary. To talk with the vocations director and learn more, call 1-877-820-6494 or visit our website at *www.buildingcommunity.org*.

The Marianists

PROVINCE OF THE UNITED STATES

Use the Marianists postcard to request further information.

Some Careers Promise The World...
The Marianists Promise You'll Change It.

If you want to make a difference with your life, talk with the Marianists. Whether you're interested in education, science, business, art, the trades, as a Marianist your talents will help us create communities of service and change. As a Brother or Priest, Marianists serve in the U.S. and foreign countries. With the Marianists, you'll be part of a community that serves the world — and makes a world of difference. For more information, call 1-877-820-6494.

The Marianists
PROVINCE OF THE UNITED STATES
www.buildingcommunity.org

THE MISSIONARIES OF MARIANNHILL

The Congregation of Mariannhill Missionaries was founded in South Africa out of a need, seen by our founder Abbot Francis Pfanner, for missionary work. We now have houses of formation for missionary priests and brothers in Germany, Austria, Holland, Poland, Spain, Switzerland, the United States and the province of Quebec in Canada. We also have missions and houses of formation in South Africa, Papua New Guinea, Zambia, Zimbabwe, Mozambique and Kenya. Our generalate is in Rome, Italy.

In the United States, our vocation/formation center for priest and brother candidates is in Dearborn Heights, Michigan. These candidates would come to our formation center to begin a period of postulancy (pre-novitiate), after which they would enter the novitiate for a period of at least one year. The novitiate is a time away from academic studies and concentrates mainly on living the religious life and learning about the congregations history, spirituality, founder, prayer, etc. At the end of the novitiate the candidates apply to make a temporary profession of the evangelical vows of chastity, obedience and poverty.

The newly professed religious priest candidates would then attend either the seminary college program or major seminary theology program, depending on what education they have by this time . The brother candidates would further their theological studies as well as complete some degree or technical trade program. After a period of at least three years in temporary vows, but not more than six years, these candidates would apply for permanent profession of their vows.

Those men, who feel called to follow the life and example of our Lord Jesus Christ, working with His people around the world as missionary priests and brothers, are invited to inquiry to our vocation office for more information and assistance in discerning their vocation. Bring your gifts and talents and make them a part of ours!

For more information, write to: **Mariannhill Vocation Office**
23715 Ann Arbor Trail
Dearborn Heights, Michigan 48127
E-mail: vheier@juno.com

Use the Marianhill Missionaries postcard to request further information.

PRO CHRISTO ET ECCLESIA

Marians of the Immaculate Conception

"*Our Call* to *Serve Christ* and His Church, out of love for *Mary Immaculate*, the Mother of God, impel us to be prophetic bearers of God's *Merciful Love*, especially to *People in Greatest Need*."

Our Work & Ministries

•The Divine Mercy Message •
•Immaculate Conception • Souls in Purgatory •
• Community Life & Prayer • Publishing •
• Parish Ministry •

Fr. Anthony Gramlich, MIC
Vocations Director

Email: vocations@marian.org
Phone: 740-282-5058

For more information, please go to www.marian.org

Use the Marians of the Immaculate Conception postcard for more information.

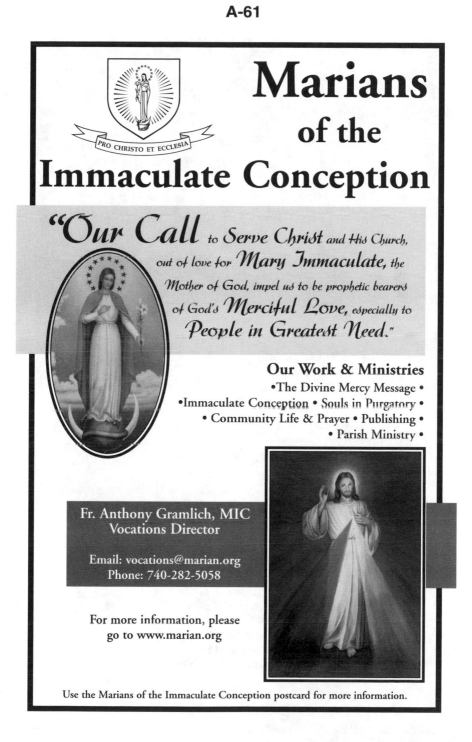

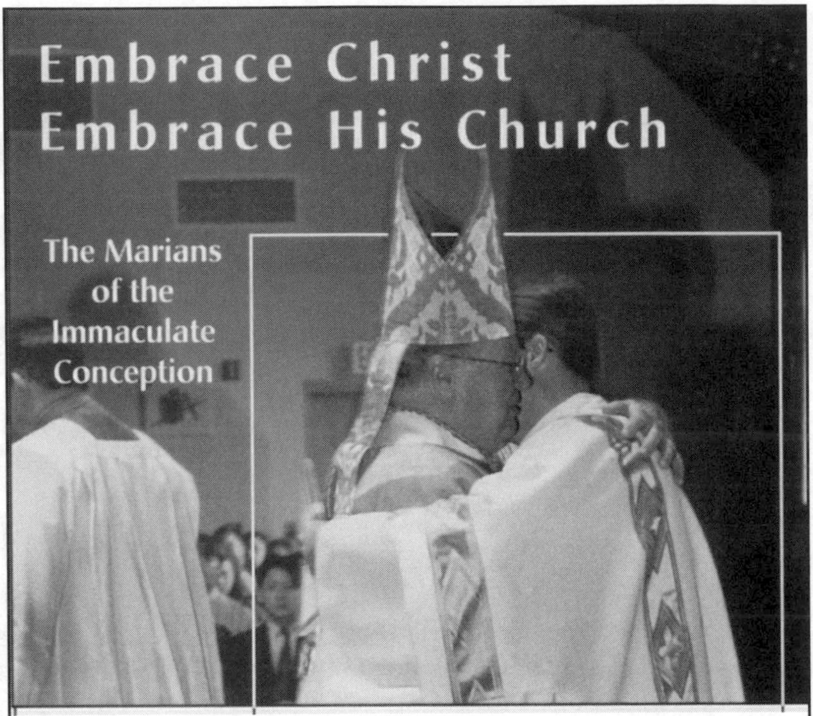
Embrace Christ
Embrace His Church
The Marians
of the
Immaculate
Conception

The Marians embrace Christ through prayer and a common lifestyle that includes:
Parish Ministry ● Educating Youth ● Printing ● Mission Work

For over 300 years, throughout the world, the Marians have appealed to men from diverse backgrounds and ages for the unique purpose of becoming the special instruments He intended them to be.

To learn more about the Marians
Write or Call:
Father Dan Cambra, M.I.C.
Marian Vocation Office
701 Plainfield Road
Darien, Illinois 60561
630-323-4333 ext. 14
email: yippy605@yahoo.com

Use the Marians of the Immaculate Conception postcard to request further information.

The Society of Mary

THE MARIST FATHERS & BROTHERS

An International Religious Community

LIVING THE SPIRIT OF MARY

As Marists we bear the name of Mary. Because of this Marists strive to be extensions of Mary – to be her hands and arms and bring her spirit of mercy and compassion into the Church and world.

We are an active apostolic congregation with a variety of ministries. We teach in high schools and colleges and serve in parishes. We conduct retreat houses and provide chaplains for hospitals, universities and prisons. We also bring Christ's message to far-off mission lands; to Africa and South America, the Philippines, as well as the far-flung islands of the Pacific.

In our **life of prayer, in our community living, and in our choice of ministries,** Marists strive, as our founder urged, "to think as Mary, judge as Mary, feel and act as Mary". Like her we are willing to give up all show and vanity as long as the LORD is proclaimed.

Come and join us! Help us make the mystery of Christ come alive in today's Church through Mary's loving approach of mercy and compassion.

FOR THE GLORY OF GOD AND THE HONOR OF MARY!

For more information about the Society of Mary (Marists), write to:

Fr. Albert DiIanni, s.m.
Marist Vocation Office
27 Isabella Street
Boston MA 02116-5216
(617) 426-4448
E-mail: rlajoie@aol.com

Use the Marists postcard to request further information.

Sister
Priest
Brother
There's Space for You to Spread the Word of God as a Maryknoll Missioner!
For more information about becoming a Maryknoll Sister contact:
Sister Loretta Harriman
Maryknoll Sisters
P.O. Box 311
Maryknoll, NY 10545
e-mail: vocation@mksisters.org
or call: (914) 941-7575
For more information about becoming a Maryknoll Priest or Brother contact:
Rev. Mike Snyder, M.M.
PO Box 302
Maryknoll, NY 10545-0302
e-mail: vocation@maryknoll.org
or call: (914) 941-7636, ext. 2416
or toll free: 1-888-627-9566
We are bound by a singular purpose—to live and proclaim the Gospel of Jesus Christ to all nations, and to build a world where all peoples enjoy the blessings of God's creation.
Visit our website: www.maryknoll.org

Use the Maryknoll postcard to request further information.

Missionaries of the Holy Family

"Servants of God — Builders of Family"

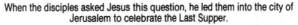

Where do you wish us to go
to prepare the supper for you?

When the disciples asked Jesus this question, he led them into the city of Jerusalem to celebrate the Last Supper.

When we ask Jesus this question, he leads us to prepare for his Supper in many places throughout the world.

We serve in mission areas, promote a Christian spirit in families, and encourage others to become missionary priests and brothers.

You can help prepare for his Supper as part of our community. We invite you to learn more about our life and mission.

History/Charism

The congregation of the Missionaries of the Holy Family was founded in 1895 at Grave, Holland by Fr. John Berthier. Fr. Berthier dedicated the community to the Holy Family which is "the perfect model of every religious community and of every Christian family." Fr. Berthier taught us to seek out and encourage vocations, particularly among mature adults, the poor, and to form community by living as a family. Our community strives to live a missionary spirit by bringing the Gospel message to areas and places where others were not present or would not go.

Ministry/Service

As Missionaries of the Holy Family, we involve ourselves in a large variety of apostolates, always in an attempt to serve the Church's current needs. Throughout the world we promote and serve the needs of Church, local community, family and congregation.

Here in the North American Province (Canada, United States, Mexico) we are involved in many types of pastoral service. As priests and brothers we work in parishes, schools, hospitals, and homes for the aged. Our work reflects the concern and respect we have for family life.

In the U.S.A. & Canda
MSF Vocation Office
306 South Salinas Blvd.
Donna, TX 78537
(956) 464-3331

Send one of the postcards in this book for more information.

May the Sacred Heart of Jesus Be Loved Everywhere

Missionaries of the Sacred Heart
(MSC)

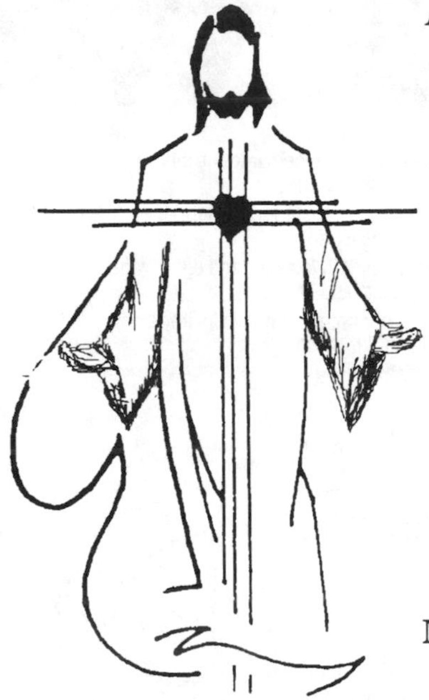

A men's religious community, bringing the compassion of Christ to people around the world.

Be salt of the earth,
light of the world,
be an MSC priest or Brother.

Contact:
Mr. Mario Delgado
Vocation Promoter
Missionaries of the Sacred Heart
P.O. Box 270
Aurora, IL 60507-0270
(630) 892-2371

http://www.misacor-usa.org

Send one of the postcards in this book for more information.

Missionaries of the Sacred Hearts of Jesus and Mary

We are committed to offering our lives and talents in service of God's Family on Earth wherever the Holy Spirit leads us...

- † Pastoral Apostolates
- † Spiritual guidance of the young and aged
- † Supporting the needs of the abandoned of society
- † Active promotion of devotion to the Sacred Hearts of Jesus and Mary

"Let Us Kindle The Love Of The Sacred Hearts Of Jesus And Mary In The Hearts Of All People."

Blessed Gaetano Errico, M.SS.CC.
(1791-1860)
Founder

As Priests and Brothers dedicated to the Sacred Hearts of Jesus and Mary, the words of our Founder are a vital heritage that sustain and inspire our apostolates around the world...in the United States, Italy, India, Argentina and Slovakia.

You are invited to deepen the love of the Sacred Hearts within your own heart and discern if you, too, are called to share that love with those who are searching for a closer relationship with Jesus and Mary.

We welcome you to call or write to us for more information

MISSIONARIES OF THE SACRED HEARTS
Vocation Director, 2249 Shore Road, Linwood, NJ 08221
609-927-5600 Fax: 609-927-5262
E-mail: msscusa@aol.com
Please visit our website: www.missionofsacredhearts.org

Use the Missionaries of the Sacred Hearts of Jesus and Mary postcard to request further information.

Missionary Benedictine
Priests, Brothers & Sisters

Seek God in...

Community Life

We value our life in community. In love and mutual obedience we strengthen one another on our journey to love and serve the Lord.

Prayer

The Eucharistic Celebration, Liturgy of the Hours, spiritual reading and interior prayer are essential to our daily life.

and Missionary Service

In the United States and in foreign lands, we are sent to proclaim the Good News. We seek to lead people to faith in Jesus Christ.

North America	Africa
South America	Europe
Australia	Asia

For more information

Missionary Benedictine Priests and Brothers
Bro. Tobias Dammert OSB
Christ the King Priory
Schuyler, NE 68661
(402) 352-2177
E-mail: tobias.bmh@dtnspeed.net
www.megavision.net/benedict

Missionary Benedictine Sisters
Sr. Rosann Ocken, OSB
Immaculata Monastery
300 N. 18th St.
Norfolk, NE 68701
(402) 371-3438
E-mail: vocations@norfolkosb.org
www.norfolkosb.org

...To speak the mystery of Christ. Col. 4:3

Send one of the postcards in this book for more information.

MISSIONARY OBLATES of MARY IMMACULATE

We are an international congregation of 4700 priests and brothers working in 68 countries:

"TO PREACH THE GOOD NEWS TO THE POOR"

is our mission.

We invite you to share with us the mission of Jesus Christ in an apostolic community.

Here is YOUR chance:

Phone: 800.358.4394 – English & Español
Email: vocations@omiusa.org Web: www.omiusa.org

Send one of the postcards in this book for more information.

Send one of the postcards in this book for more information.

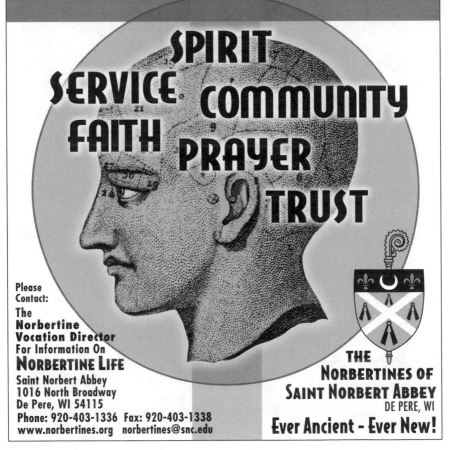

Send one of the postcards in this book for more information.

MEN COME FROM AROUND THE WORLD TO BECOME OBLATES OF THE VIRGIN MARY.

Then we send them back out again.

From our seminary in Boston to our many houses around the world, we're on a mission to bring spiritual guidance and direction to everyone seeking the peace of Christ in their life. As an Oblate of the Virgin Mary, you will find a community that emphasizes the authentic teachings of the Catholic Church, and expresses itself to the world through active ministry and reflective retreats. For more information, call Fr. Peter Grover at (617) 266-5999 ext. 202 or email vocation@oblatesofthevirginmary.org. No matter where you're from, we think you'll like where you end up.

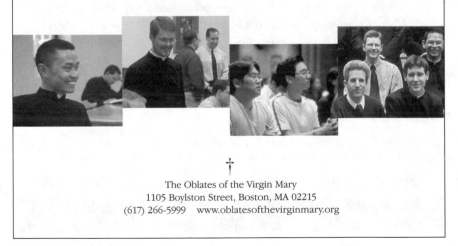

†

The Oblates of the Virgin Mary
1105 Boylston Street, Boston, MA 02215
(617) 266-5999 www.oblatesofthevirginmary.org

Use the Oblates of the Virgin Mary postcard to request further information.

LISTEN TO YOUR MOTHER!

"Do whatever Jesus tells you." (See Jn 2:5)

Our Lord May Be Calling YOU to the

Order of the B.V.M. of Mercy

Mercedarian Friars

- **Ancient Order of Friars**
  - Founded in 1218
  - Habit of Mary
- **Spirituality**
  - Marian
  - Eucharistic
  - Community Life based on the *Rule of St. Augustine*
- **Diversity of Education**
- **Loyal to Magisterium**
- **Variety of Ministries**
  - Education
  - Parish
  - Chaplaincies
  - Missions

REDEMPTIONEM MISIT POPULO SUO

For more information contact us at

Mercedarian Friars
6398 Drexel Road
Philadelphia, PA 19151-2596
1.877.O.L.MERCY
www.orderofmercy.org
vocations@orderofmercy.org

Use the Mercedarian Friars postcard to request further information.

This could be the best move you've ever made!

Come see what the Pallottines have to offer you.

Our founder, St. Vincent Pallotti, believed that ALL people, both young and older men and women, can be apostles. Through using your gifts and talents, whatever they may be, you can help to further the growth and deepening of faith. We Pallottines do that each day through our work with others in schools, parishes, hospitals, retreats, adult education, and liturgical celebrations. We invite you to use your gifts and talents with us for God's Kingdom. This could be the best move you ever made!

For more information about the Pallottine lifestyle, write:

Bro. Jim Scarpace, SAC
Pallottine Vocation Office
5424 W. Bluemound Rd.
Milwaukee, WI 53208-3097
Website: pallotti.net
E-mail: vocsacmil@juno.com

Send one of the postcards in this book for more information.

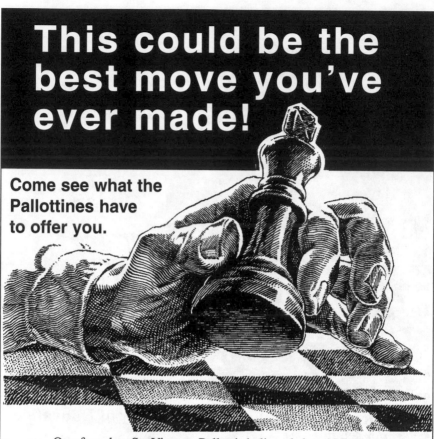

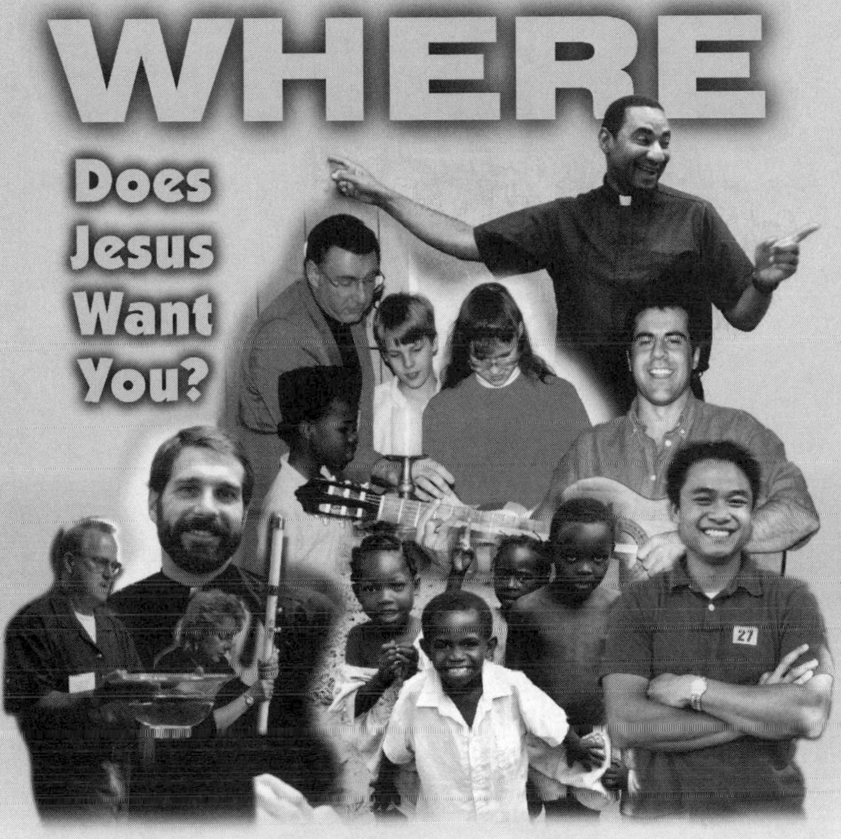
WHERE
Does Jesus Want You?
27

Community... Prayer... Service... if these inspire you, we invite you to discover the Priests of the Sacred Heart. We are an apostolic community of brothers and priests bringing the message of God's love and mercy to people around the world. We live, pray and serve Christ together in a variety of ministries, especially with the poor and neglected.

Wherever Jesus calls us, we bring the story of salvation, strengthening the local church, and work to promote human dignity — all within the context of community and supported by our personal and communal prayer. If Jesus wants you to serve others while living and praying in community, the Priests of the Sacred Heart may be your answer.

For more information about the Priests of the Sacred Heart contact:

Vocation Director
SCJ Vocation Office
P.O. Box 206
Hales Corners, WI 53130-0206

Voice: 414-529-4255
Fax: 414-529-3377
E-mail: vocationcentral@wi.rr.com
Website:www.scjvocation.org

Use the Priests of the Sacred Heart postcard to request further information.

SALESIANS OF DON BOSCO

"Salesians for the third millennium! May you be enthusiastic teachers & guides, saints, & formers of saints, as was Don Bosco." – John Paul II

Salesian brothers and priests have been accompanying young people on the journey of faith for over one hundred and fifty years. Along the way they have provided homes that welcome, schools that prepare for life, parishes that evangelize, and playgrounds where friends can meet and enjoy one another's company – all under the guidance and protection of the Blessed Virgin Mary.

If you would like to learn more about serving Jesus Christ in the young and the poor please contact:

FR. STEVE RYAN, SDB
SALESIAN VOCATION OFFICE
315 SELF PLACE SOUTH ORANGE, NJ 07079
(973)761-0201 SALVOC@AOL.COM

FR. CHRIS WOEIZ, SDB
SALESIAN VOCATION OFFICE
PO BOX 1639 ROSEMEAD, CA 91770
(626)280-1742 VOCATION@AOL.COM

Send one of the postcards in this book for more information.

in all things love

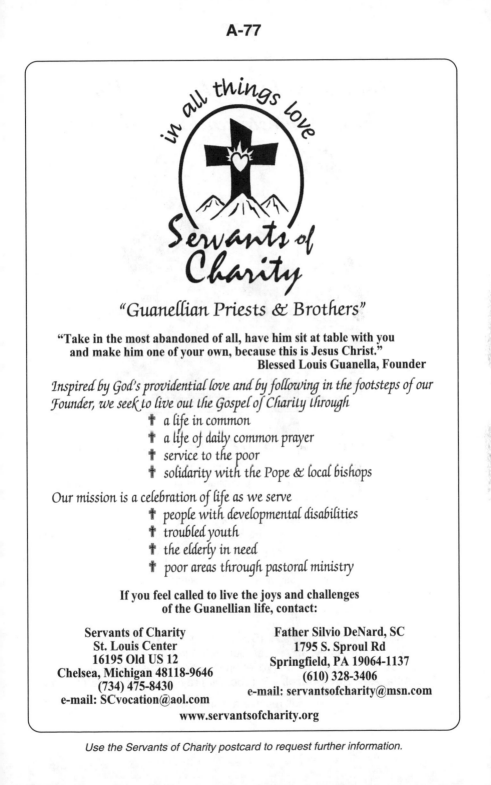

Servants of Charity

"Guanellian Priests & Brothers"

"Take in the most abandoned of all, have him sit at table with you and make him one of your own, because this is Jesus Christ."
Blessed Louis Guanella, Founder

Inspired by God's providential love and by following in the footsteps of our Founder, we seek to live out the Gospel of Charity through

- ✝ a life in common
- ✝ a life of daily common prayer
- ✝ service to the poor
- ✝ solidarity with the Pope & local bishops

Our mission is a celebration of life as we serve

- ✝ people with developmental disabilities
- ✝ troubled youth
- ✝ the elderly in need
- ✝ poor areas through pastoral ministry

If you feel called to live the joys and challenges of the Guanellian life, contact:

Servants of Charity
St. Louis Center
16195 Old US 12
Chelsea, Michigan 48118-9646
(734) 475-8430
e-mail: SCvocation@aol.com

Father Silvio DeNard, SC
1795 S. Sproul Rd
Springfield, PA 19064-1137
(610) 328-3406
e-mail: servantsofcharity@msn.com

www.servantsofcharity.org

Use the Servants of Charity postcard to request further information.

EVERYWHERE
we are Friars & Sisters
Servants of Mary
Friars serving in parish ministry, schools, foreign missions, counseling, chaplaincies, clerical and administrative work
Sisters serving in education, parish ministry, social work, nursing, prison ministry, counseling, retreat work and senior care
USA Friars - www.servite.org
Sisters -
Blue Island/Plainfield, IL - www.mantellatesistersmsm.com
Ladysmith, WI - www.servitesisters.org
Omaha, NE - www.osms.org

Send one of the postcards in this book for more information.

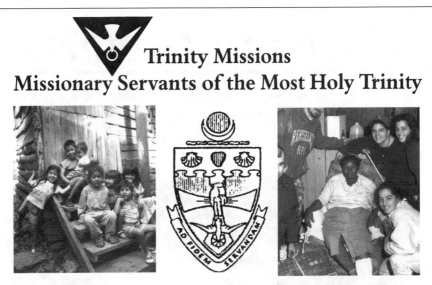

Trinity Missions
Missionary Servants of the Most Holy Trinity

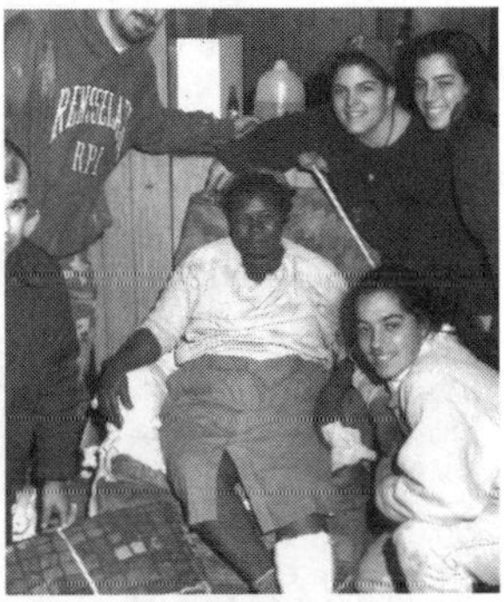

We Invite You To Minister With The Poor And Abandoned

- Join our family of missionaries as we work for justice throughout the Americas.
- Our missionary family is made up of Lay Missionaries, Religious Sisters, Priests and Brothers.
- We bring the light and hope of Jesus Christ to the forgotten people of the United States, Mexico, Puerto Rico, Costa Rica, and Colombia.
- Join us for a week, a month, a year, or a lifetime to help us spread the Good News of the Gospel.

CONTACT US:

Vocation: 800-298-5602 / mccann@trinitymissions.org
Volunteer: 800-272-8850 / trinityctr@aol.com

Visit our website: www.tmc3.org

Trinity Missions Vocation Department
9001 New Hampshire Ave.
Silver Spring, MD 20903

Use the Trinity Missions postcard to request further information.

Use the Xaverian Missionaries postcard to request further information.

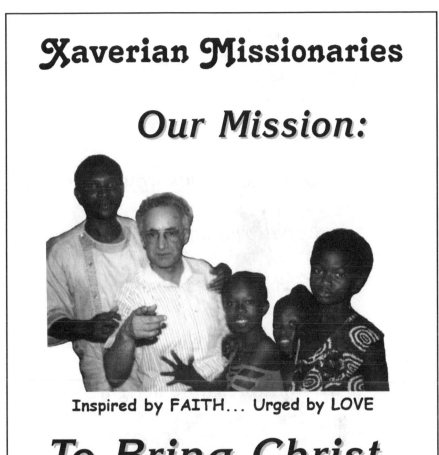

As we progress in this way of life...

we shall run on the path

of God's commandments,

our hearts overflowing

with inexpressible delight

of LOVE

St. Benedict

Catholic Colleges in the United States

Alabama

SPRING HILL COLLEGE
4000 Daupin Street
Mobile, AL 36608
251-380-4000
www.shc.edu

California

NOTRE DAME DE NAMUR UNIVERSITY
1500 Ralston Ave.
Belmont, CA 94002
650-593-1601
www.ndnu.edu

DOMINICAN UNIVERSITY OF CALIFORNIA
50 Acacia Ave.
San Rafael, CA 94901
415-482-3580
www.dominican.edu

DON BOSCO TECHNICAL INSTITUTE
1151 San Gabriel Boulevard
Rosemead, CA 91770-4299
626-940-2000
www.boscotech.tec.ca.us

HOLY NAMES COLLEGE
3500 Mountain Boulevard
Oakland, CA 94619-9989
510-436-1000
www.hnc.edu

LOYOLA MARYMOUNT UNIVERSITY
One LMU Drive
Los Angeles, CA 90045
310-338-2700
www.lmu.edu

MARYMOUNT COLLEGE
30800 Palos Verdes Drive East
Rancho Palos Verdes, CA 90275
310-377-5501
www.marymountpv.edu

MOUNT ST. MARY'S COLLEGE
Chalon Campus
12001 Chalon Road
Los Angeles, CA 90049
310-954-4000
www.msmc.la.edu

QUEEN OF THE HOLY ROSARY COLLEGE
43326 Mission Blvd.
Mission San Jose, CA 94539
510-657-2468
www.msjdominicans.org/college.html

ST. MARY'S COLLEGE OF CALIFORNIA
P.O. Box 4800
Moraga, CA 94575
925-631-4224
www.stmarys-ca.edu

SANTA CLARA UNIVERSITY
500 El Camino
Santa Clara, CA 95053
408 -554-4700
www.scu.edu/ugadm/

THOMAS AQUINAS COLLEGE
10000 No. Ojai Road
Santa Paula, CA 93060
805-525-4417
www.thomasaquinas.edu

UNIVERSITY OF SAN DIEGO
5998 Alcala Park
San Diego, CA 92110
619-260-4506
www.sandiego.edu

UNIVERSITY OF SAN FRANCISCO
2130 Fulton St.
San Francisco, CA 94117
415-422-5555
www.usfca.edu

Colorado

REGIS UNIVERSITY
3333 Regis Blvd.
Denver, CO 80221
303-458-4100
www.regis.edu

Connecticut

ALBERTUS MAGNUS COLLEGE
700 Prospect Street
New Haven, CT 06511
203-773-8550
www.albertus.edu

FAIRFIELD UNIVERSITY
1073 North Benson Road
Fairfield, CT 06824
203-254-4000
www.fairfield.edu

SACRED HEART UNIVERSITY
5151 Park Ave.
Fairfield, CT 06432-1000
203-371-7999
www.sacredheart.edu

SAINT JOSEPH COLLEGE
1678 Asylum Avenue
West Hartford, CT 06117
860-232-4571
www.sjc.edu

ST. VINCENT'S COLLEGE
2800 Main Street
Bridgeport, CT 06606
203-576-5235
www.stvincentscollege.edu

District of Columbia

THE CATHOLIC UNIVERSITY OF AMERICA
620 Michigan Avenue, NE
Washington, DC 20064
202-319-5000
www.cua.edu

GEORGETOWN UNIVERSITY
37th & O Streets, N.W.
Washington, DC 20057
202-687-0100
www.georgetown.edu

TRINITY COLLEGE
125 Michigan Ave., N.E.
Washington, DC 20017
202-884-9000
www.trinitydc.edu

Florida

AVE MARIA UNIVERSITY
1025 Commons Circle
Naples, FL 34119
877-283-8648
www.naples.avemaria.edu

BARRY UNIVERSITY
11300 N.E. Second Avenue
Miami Shores, FL 33161
305-899-3000
www.barry.edu

SAINT LEO UNIVERSITY
P.O. Box 6665 MC 2008
St. Leo, FL 33574
904-588-8283
www.saintleo.edu

ST. THOMAS UNIVERSITY
16400 N.W. 32nd Avenue
Miami, FL 33054
305-628-6546
www.stu.edu

Hawaii

CHAMINADE UNIVERSITY OF HONOLULU
3140 Waialae Avenue
Honolulu, HI 96816-1578
808-735-4711
www.chaminade.edu

Illinois

BARAT COLLEGE OF DePAUL
Barat Campus
700 East Westleigh Rd.
Lake Forest, IL 60045
847-234-3000
www.barat.depaul.edu

BENEDICTINE UNIVERSITY
5700 College Road
Lisle, IL 60532
630-829-6300
www.ben.edu

DE PAUL UNIVERSITY
25 E. Jackson Boulevard
Chicago, IL 60604-2287
312-362-8000
www.depaul.edu

DOMINICAN UNIVERSITY
7900 W. Division Street
River Forest, IL 60305
708-524-6800
www.dom.edu

LEWIS UNIVERSITY
1 University Parkway
Romeoville, IL 60446
815-836-5250
www.lewisu.edu

LOYOLA UNIVERSITY OF CHICAGO
6525 N. Sheridan Road
Chicago, IL 60626
312-915-6500
www.luc.edu

QUINCY COLLEGE
1800 College Avenue
Quincy, IL 62301
217-228-5210
www.quincy.edu

JESUIT COMMUNITY AT LOYOLA UNIVERSITY OF CHICAGO
6551 N. Sheridan Road
Chicago, IL 60626
773-508-8800
www.luc.edu

SAINT XAVIER UNIVERSITY
3700 W. 103rd Street
Chicago, IL 60655
773-298-3062
www.sxu.edu

SPRINGFIELD COLLEGE
1500 N. 5th Street
Springfield, IL 62702
217-525-1420
www.sci.edu

UNIVERSITY OF ST. FRANCIS
500 N. Wilcox Street
Joliet, IL 60435
815-740-3360
www.stfrancis.edu

Indiana

ANCILLA COLLEGE
P.O. Box 1, 9601 Union Road
Donaldson, IN 46513
574-936-8898
www.ancilla.edu

CALUMET COLLEGE OF SAINT JOSEPH
2400 New York Avenue
Whiting, IN 46394
219-473-7770
www.ccsj.edu

HOLY CROSS COLLEGE
P.O. Box 308
Notre Dame, IN 46556
574-239-8400
www.hcc-nd.edu

MARIAN COLLEGE
3200 Cold Spring Road
Indianapolis, IN 46222
317-955-6000
www.marian.edu

UNIVERSITY OF SAINT FRANCIS
2701 Spring Street
Fort Wayne, IN 46808
260-434-3100
www.sf.edu

ST. JOSEPH'S COLLEGE
P.O. Box 909
Rensselaer, IN 47978
219-866-6000
www.saintjoe.edu

SAINT MARY-OF-THE-WOODS COLLEGE
St. Mary-of-the-Woods, IN 47876
812-535-5151
woods.smwc.edu

SAINT MARY'S COLLEGE
Notre Dame, IN 46556
574-284-4556
www.saintmarys.edu

UNIVERSITY OF NOTRE DAME
Notre Dame, IN 46556
574-631-5000
www.nd.edu

Iowa

BRIAR CLIFF UNIVERSITY
P.O. Box 2100
Sioux City, IA 51104
712-279-5321
www.briarcliff.edu

CLARKE COLLEGE
1550 Clarke Drive
Dubuque, IA 52001
563-588-6300
www.clarke.edu

THE FRANCISCAN UNIVERSITY
400 North Bluff Boulevard
Clinton, IA 52732
563-242-4023
www.clare.edu

LORAS COLLEGE
1450 Alta Vista
Dubuque, IA 52004
563-588-7100
www.loras.edu

MERCY COLLEGE OF HEALTH SCIENCES
928 6th Avenue
Des Moines, IA 50309-1239
515-643-3180
www.mchs.edu

MOUNT MERCY COLLEGE
1330 Elmhurst Drive, N.E.
Cedar Rapids, IA 52402
319-363-8213
www.mtmercy.edu

ST. AMBROSE UNIVERSITY
518 W. Locust Street
Davenport, IA 52803
563-333-6000
www.sau.edu

Kansas

BENEDICTINE COLLEGE
1020 N. 2nd St.
Atchison, KS 66002
913-367-5340
www.benedictine.edu

DONNELLY COLLEGE
608 North 18th Street
Kansas City, KS 66102
913-621-6070
www.donnelly.edu

NEWMAN UNIVERSITY
3100 McCormick Avenue
Wichita, KS 67213
316-942-4291
www.newmanu.edu

UNIVERSITY OF SAINT MARY
4100 S. 4th Street Trafficway
Leavenworth, KS 66048
913-682-5151
www.stmary.edu

Kentucky

BELLARMINE COLLEGE
Newburg Road
Louisville, KY 40205
502-452-8000
www.bellarmine.edu

BRESCIA UNIVERSITY
717 Frederica Street
Owensboro, KY 42301
270-685-3131
www.brescia.edu

ST. CATHARINE COLLEGE
2735 Bardstown Road
St. Catharine, KY 40061
606-336-5082
www.sccky.edu

SPALDING UNIVERSITY
851 S. Fourth Street
Louisville, KY 40203
502-585-9911
www.spalding.edu

THOMAS MORE COLLEGE
333 Thomas More Parkway
Crestview Hills, KY 41017
859-341-5800
www.thomasmore.edu/welcome.html

Louisiana

LOYOLA UNIVERSITY
6363 St. Charles Avenue
New Orleans, LA 70118
504-865-2011
www.loyno.edu

OUR LADY OF HOLY CROSS COLLEGE
4123 Woodland Drive
New Orleans, LA 70131
504-394-7744
www.olhcc.edu

OUR LADY OF THE LAKE COLLEGE
7434 Perkins Road
Baton Rouge, LA 70808
225-768-1700
www.ololcollege.edu

XAVIER UNIVERSITY OF LOUISIANA
One Drexel Drive
New Orleans, LA 70125
504-486-7411
www.xula.edu

Maine

SAINT JOSEPH'S COLLEGE
278 White's Bridge Rd.
Standish, ME 04084
207-892-6766
www.sjcme.edu

Maryland

COLLEGE OF NOTRE DAME OF MARYLAND
4701 North Charles Street
Baltimore, MD 21210
410-435-0100
www.ndm.edu

LOYOLA COLLEGE
4501 No. Charles Street
Baltimore, MD 21210
410-617-2000
www.loyola.edu

MOUNT ST. MARY'S COLLEGE AND SEMINARY
Emmitsburg, MD 21727
301-447-6122
www.msmary.edu

Massachusetts

ANNA MARIA COLLEGE
50 Sunset Lane
Paxton, MA 01612
508-849-3300
www.annamaria.edu

ASSUMPTION COLLEGE
500 Salisbury Street
Worcester, MA 01615-0005
508-767-7000
www.assumption.edu

BOSTON COLLEGE
140 Commonwealth Ave.
Chestnut Hill, MA 02467
617-552-8000
www.bc.edu

COLLEGE OF THE HOLY CROSS
Worcester, MA 01610
508-793-2011
www.holycross.edu

ELMS COLLEGE
291 Springfield Street
Chicopee, MA 01013-2839
413-594-2761
www.elms.edu

EMMANUEL COLLEGE
400 The Fenway
Boston, MA 02115
617-277-9340
www.emmanuel.edu

MERRIMACK COLLEGE
315 Turnpike St.
North Andover, MA 01845
978-837-5000
www.merrimack.edu

REGIS COLLEGE
235 Wellesley St.
Weston, MA 02193
781-768-7000
www.regiscollege.edu

STONEHILL COLLEGE
320 Washington Street
North Easton, MA 02357
508-565-1000
www.stonehill.edu

Michigan

AQUINAS COLLEGE
1607 Robinson Road, SE
Grand Rapids, MI 49506
616-459-8281
www.aquinas.edu

AVE MARIA UNIVERSITY
300 West Forest Ave.
Ypsilanti, MI 48197
734-337-4100
www.avemaria.edu

MADONNA UNIVERSITY
36600 Schoolcraft Rd.
Livonia, MI 48150
734-432-5300
www.madonna.edu

MARYGROVE COLLEGE
8425 W. McNichols Rd.
Detroit, MI 48221
313-927-1200
www.marygrove.edu

ST. MARY'S COLLEGE OF AVE MARIA UNIVERSITY
Commerce & Orchard Lake Roads
Orchard Lake, MI 48324
248-682-1885
www.stmarys.avemaria.edu

SIENA HEIGHTS UNIVERSITY
1247 Siena Heights Drive
Adrian, MI 49221
517-263-0731
www.sienahts.edu

UNIVERSITY OF DETROIT MERCY
4001 W. McNichols Road, Box 19900
Detroit, MI 48219-0900
313-993-1000
www.udmercy.edu

COLLEGE OF ST. BENEDICT
37 S. College Ave.
St. Joseph, MN 56374
320-363-5011
www.csbsju.edu

COLLEGE OF ST. CATHERINE
2004 Randolph Avenue
St. Paul, MN 55105
612-690-6000
www.stkate.edu

COLLEGE OF ST. SCHOLASTICA
1200 Kenwood Ave.
Duluth, MN 55811
218-723-6000
www.css.edu

ST. JOHN'S UNIVERSITY
Box 2000
Collegeville, MN 56321
320-363-2011
www.csbsju.edu

ST. MARY'S UNIVERSITY OF MINNESOTA
700 Terrace Heights
Winona, MN 55987
507-452-4430
www.smumn.edu

UNIVERSITY OF ST. THOMAS
2115 Summit Ave.
St. Paul, MN 55105
651-962-5000
www.stthomas.edu

Missouri

AVILA COLLEGE
11901 Wornall Road
Kansas City, MO 64145
816-942-8400
www.avila.edu

FONTBONNE COLLEGE
6800 Wydown Boulevard
St. Louis, MO 63105
314-862-3456
www.fontbonne.edu

ROCKHURST COLLEGE
1100 Rockhurst Rd.
Kansas City, MO 64110
816-501-4000
www.rockhurst.edu

ST. LOUIS UNIVERSITY
221 N. Grand Boulevard
St. Louis, MO 63103
314-977-2500
www.imagine.slu.edu

Montana

CARROLL COLLEGE
1601 N. Benton Avenue
Helena, MT 59625
406-447-4300
www.carroll.edu

UNIVERSITY OF GREAT FALLS
1301 20th Street S.
Great Falls, MT 59405
406-761-8210
www.ugf.edu

Nebraska

COLLEGE OF SAINT MARY
1901 So. 72nd Street
Omaha, NE 68124
402-399-2400
www.csm.edu

CREIGHTON UNIVERSITY
2500 California Plaza
Omaha, NE 68178
402-280-2700
www.creighton.edu

New Hampshire

MAGDALEN COLLEGE
511 Kearsarge Mountain Road
Warner, NH 03278-9206
603-456-2656
www.magdalen.edu

RIVIER COLLEGE
429 Main St.
Nashua, NH 03060
603-888-1311
www.rivier.edu

SAINT ANSELM COLLEGE
100 Saint Anselms Drive
Manchester, NH 03102
603-641-7000
www.anselm.edu

THE THOMAS MORE COLLEGE OF LIBERAL ARTS
6 Manchester Street
Merrimack, NH 03054
603-880-8308
www.thomasmorecollege.edu

New Jersey

CALDWELL COLLEGE
9 Ryerson Avenue
Caldwell, NJ 07006
973-618-3000
www.caldwell.edu

COLLEGE OF SAINT ELIZABETH
2 Convent Road
Morristown, NJ 07960
973-290-4000
www.cse.edu

FELICIAN COLLEGE
262 S. Main Street
Lodi, NJ 07644
201-559-6000
www.felician.edu

GEORGIAN COURT COLLEGE
900 Lakewood Avenue
Lakewood, NJ 08701
732-364-2200
www.georgian.edu

SAINT PETER'S COLLEGE
2641 Kennedy Boulevard
Jersey City, NJ 07306
201-915-9000
www.spc.edu

SETON HALL UNIVERSITY
400 South Orange Avenue
South Orange, NJ 07079
973-761-9000
www.shu.edu

New Mexico

COLLEGE OF SANTA FE
1600 St. Michael's Drive
Santa Fe, NM 87505-7634
505-473-6011
www.csf.edu

New York

CANISIUS COLLEGE
2001 Main Street
Buffalo, NY 14208
716-883-7000
www.canisius.edu

COLLEGE OF MOUNT SAINT VINCENT
6301 Riverdale Avenue
Riverdale, NY 10471-1093
718-405-3200
www.mountsaintvincent.edu

THE COLLEGE OF NEW ROCHELLE
29 Castle Place
New Rochelle, NY 10805
914-654-5000
www.cnr.edu

COLLEGE OF SAINT ROSE
432 Western Avenue
Albany, NY 12203
518-454-5111
www.strose.edu

DOMINICAN COLLEGE OF BLAUVELT
470 Western Highway
Orangeburg, NY 10962
845-359-7800
www.dc.edu

D'YOUVILLE COLLEGE
320 Porter Avenue
Buffalo, NY 14201
716-881-3200
www.dyc.edu

FORDHAM UNIVERSITY
E. Fordham Road
Bronx, NY 10458
718-817-1000
Lincoln Center:
New York, NY 10023
212-636-6710
Tarrytown Center:
Tarrytown, NY 10591
914-332-6000
www.fordham.edu

HILBERT COLLEGE
5200 South Park Avenue
Hamburg, NY 14075
716-649-7900
www.hilbert.edu

IONA COLLEGE
715 North Avenue
New Rochelle, NY 10801
914-633-2000
www.iona.edu

LE MOYNE COLLEGE
1419 Salt Springs Road
Syracuse, NY 13214-1399
315-445-4100
www.lemoyne.edu

MANHATTAN COLLEGE
Manhattan College Parkway
Bronx, NY 10471
718-862-8000
www.mancol.edu

MARIA COLLEGE OF ALBANY
700 New Scotland Avenue
Albany, NY 12208
518-438-3111
www.mariacollege.edu

MARYMOUNT COLLEGE
(See Fordham Listing)

MARYMOUNT MANHATTAN COLLEGE
221 East 71st Street
New York, NY 10021
212-517-0400
marymount.mmm.edu

MOLLOY COLLEGE
1000 Hempstead Avenue
Rockville Centre, NY11571
516-678-5000
www.molloy.edu

MOUNT SAINT MARY COLLEGE
Newburgh, NY 12550-3498
845-561-0800
www.msmc.edu

NIAGARA UNIVERSITY
Niagara University, NY 14109
716-285-1212
www.niagara.edu

ST. BONAVENTURE UNIVERSITY
St. Bonaventure, NY 14778
716-375-2000
www.sbu.edu

ST. FRANCIS COLLEGE
180 Remsen Street
Brooklyn Heights, NY 11201
718-522-2300
www.stfranciscollege.edu

ST. JOHN'S UNIVERSITY
8000 Utopia Parkway
Jamaica, NY 11439
718-990-6161
www.stjohns.edu

ST. JOSEPH'S COLLEGE
245 Clinton Avenue
Brooklyn, NY 11205
718-636-6800
www.sjcny.edu

ST. THOMAS AQUINAS COLLEGE
125 Route 340
Sparkill, NY 10976
845-398-4000
www.stac.edu

SIENA COLLEGE
515 Loudon Road
Loudonville, NY 12211
518-783-2300
www.siena.edu

TROCAIRE COLLEGE
360 Choate Avenue
Buffalo, NY 14220
716-826-1200
www.trocaire.edu

VILLA MARIA OF BUFFALO
240 Pine Ridge Road
Buffalo, NY 14225
716-896-0700
www.villa.edu

North Carolina

BELMONT ABBEY COLLEGE
100 Belmont Mount Holly Road
Belmont, NC 28012
704-825-6700
www.bac.edu

North Dakota

UNIVERSITY OF MARY
7500 University Drive
Bismarck, ND 58504
701-255-7500
www.umary.edu

Ohio

CHATFIELD COLLEGE
20918 State Street Rte. 251
St. Martin, OH 45118
513-875-3344
www.chatfield.edu

COLLEGE OF MOUNT ST. JOSEPH
5701 Delhi Road
Cincinnati, OH 45233
513-244-4200
www.msj.edu

FRANCISCAN UNIVERSITY OF STEUBENVILLE
1235 University Boulevard
Steubenville, OH 43952
740-283-3771
www.franuniv.edu

JOHN CARROLL UNIVERSITY
20700 North Park Boulevard
Cleveland, OH 44118
216-397-1886
www.jcu.edu

LOURDES COLLEGE
6832 Convent Boulevard
Sylvania, OH 43560
419-885-3211
www.lourdes.edu

NOTRE DAME COLLEGE OF OHIO
4545 College Road
South Euclid, OH 44121
216-381-1680
www.notredamecollege.edu

OHIO DOMINICAN UNIVERSITY
1216 Sunbury Road
Columbus, OH 43219
614-253-2741
www.ohiodominican.edu

UNIVERSITY OF DAYTON
300 College Park
Dayton, OH 45469
937-229-1000
www.udayton.edu

URSULINE COLLEGE
2550 Lander Road
Cleveland, OH 44124
440-449-4200
www.ursuline.edu

WALSH UNIVERSITY
2020 Easton Street, N.W.
Canton, OH 44720
330-499-7090
www.walsh.edu

XAVIER UNIVERSITY
3800 Victory Parkway
Cincinnati, OH 45207-5311
513-745-3000
www.xu.edu

Oklahoma

ST. GREGORY'S COLLEGE
1900 W. MacArthur
Shawnee, OK 74804
405-878-5100
www.sgc.edu

Oregon

MARYLHURST COLLEGE
P.O. Box 261, 17600 Pacific Hwy.
Marylhurst, OR 97036
503-636-8141
www.marylhurst.edu

UNIVERSITY OF PORTLAND
5000 N. Willamette Boulevard
Portland, OR 97203
503-943-7911
www.uofport.edu

Pennsylvania

ALVERNIA COLLEGE
400 Saint Bernardine Street
Reading, PA 19607
610-796-8220
www.alvernia.edu

CABRINI COLLEGE
610 King of Prussia Road
Radnor, PA 19087-3698
610-902-8100
www.cabrini.edu

CARLOW COLLEGE
3333 Fifth Avenue
Pittsburgh, PA 15213
412-578-6000
www.carlow.edu

CHESTNUT HILL COLLEGE
9601 Germantown Avenue
Philadelphia, PA 19118-2693
215-248-7000
www.chc.edu

COLLEGE MISERICORDIA
301 Lake Street
Dallas, PA 18612
570-674-6400
www.misericordia.edu

DE SALES UNIVERSITY
2755 Station Avenue
Center Valley, PA 18034
610-282-1100
www.desales.edu

DUQUESNE UNIVERSITY
600 Forbes Avenue
Pittsburgh, PA 15282
412-396-6000
www.duq.edu

GANNON UNIVERSITY
University Square
Erie, PA 16541
814-871-7000
www.gannon.edu

GWYNEDD-MERCY COLLEGE
Sumneytown Pike, P.O. Box 901
Gwynedd Valley, PA 19437
215-646-7300
www.gmc.edu

HOLY FAMILY COLLEGE
Grant & Frankford Avenues
Philadelphia, PA 19114
215-637-7700
www.hfc.edu

IMMACULATA UNIVERSITY
1145 King Road
Immaculata, PA 19345
610-647-4400
www.immaculata.edu

KING'S COLLEGE
133 North River Street
Wilkes Barre, PA 18711
570-208-5900
www.kings.edu

LA ROCHE COLLEGE
9000 Babcock Boulevard
Pittsburgh, PA 15237
412-367-9300
www.laroche.edu

LA SALLE UNIVERSITY
1900 W. Olney Avenue
Philadelphia, PA 19141
215-951-1000
www.lasalle.edu

MANOR COLLEGE
700 Fox Chase Road
Jenkinton, PA 19046
215-885-2360
www.manor.edu

MARYWOOD COLLEGE
2300 Adams Avenue
Scranton, PA 18509
570-348-6211
www.marywood.edu

MERCYHURST COLLEGE
501 E. 38th Street
Erie, PA 16546
814-824-2000
www.mercyhurst.edu

MOUNT ALOYSIUS COLLEGE
7373 Admiral Peary Highway
Cresson, PA 16630
814-886-4131
www.mtaloy.edu

NEUMANN COLLEGE
One Neumann Drive
Aston, PA 19014
610-459-0905
www.neumann.edu

ROSEMONT COLLEGE
1400 Montgomery Avenue
Rosemont, PA 19010
610-527-0200
www.rosemont.edu

ST. FRANCIS UNIVERSITY
P.O. Box 600
Loretto, PA 15940
814-472-3000
www.francis.edu

SAINT JOSEPH'S UNIVERSITY
5600 City Avenue
Philadelphia, PA 19131
610-660-1100
www.sju.edu

ST. VINCENT COLLEGE
300 Fraser Purchase Road
Latrobe, PA 15650
724-539-9761
www.stvincent.edu

SETON HILL UNIVERSITY
Greensburg, PA 15601
724-834-2200
www.setonhill.edu

UNIVERSITY OF SCRANTON
Scranton, PA 18510
570-941-7400
www.scranton.edu

VILLANOVA UNIVERSITY
800 Lancaster Avenue
Villanova, PA 19085
610-519-4500
www.villanova.edu

Rhode Island

PROVIDENCE COLLEGE
River Avenue & Eaton Street
Providence, RI 02918
401-865-1000
www.providence.edu

SALVE REGINA UNIVERSITY
100 Ochre Point Avenue
Newport, RI 02840
401-847-6650
www.salve.edu

South Dakota

MOUNT MARTY COLLEGE
1105 West 8th St.
Yankton, SD 57078
605-668-1514
www.mtmc.edu

PRESENTATION COLLEGE
1500 North Main Street
Aberdeen, SD 57401
605-225-1634
www.presentation.edu

AQUINAS COLLEGE
4210 Harding Road
Nashville, TN 37205
615-297-7545
www.aquinas-tn.edu

CHRISTIAN BROTHERS UNIV.
650 E. Parkway S.
Memphis, TN 38104
901-321-3000
www.cbu.edu

Texas

OBLATE SCHOOL OF THEOLOGY
285 Oblate Drive
San Antonio, TX 78216-6693
210 341 1366
www.ost.edu

OUR LADY OF THE LAKE UNIVERSITY
411 S.W. 24th Street
San Antonio, TX 78207
210-434-6711
www.ollusa.edu

ST. EDWARD'S UNIVERSITY
3001 S. Congress Ave.
Austin, TX 78704
512-448-8400
www.stedwards.edu

ST. MARY'S UNIVERSITY OF SAN ANTONIO
One Camino Santa Maria
San Antonio, TX 78228
210-436-3011
www.stmarytx.edu

UNIVERSITY OF DALLAS
1845 E. Northgate Drive
Irving, TX 75062
972-721-5000
www.udallas.edu

UNIVERSITY OF THE INCARNATE WORD
4301 Broadway
San Antonio, TX 78209
210-829-6000
www.uiw.edu

UNIVERSITY OF ST. THOMAS
3800 Montrose Boulevard
Houston, TX 77006
713-522-7911
www.stthom.edu

Vermont

COLLEGE OF ST. JOSEPH
71 Clement Road
Rutland, VT 05701
802-773-5900
www.csj.edu

SAINT MICHAEL'S COLLEGE
One Winooski Park
Colchester, VT 05439
802-654-2000
www.smcvt.edu

Virginia

CHRISTENDOM COLLEGE
134 Christendom Dr.
Front Royal, VA 22630
540-636-2900
www.christendom.edu

MARYMOUNT UNIVERSITY
2807 North Glebe Road
Arlington, VA 22207-4299
703-522-5600
www.marymount.edu

GONZAGA UNIVERSITY
502 E. Boone Avenue
Spokane, WA 99258
509-328-4220
www.gonzaga.edu

SAINT MARTIN'S COLLEGE
5300 Pacific Ave. SE
Lacey, WA 98503
360-491-4700
www.stmartin.edu

SEATTLE UNIVERSITY
900 Broadway
Seattle, WA 98122
206-296-6000
www.seattleu.edu

West Virginia

WHEELING JESUIT UNIVERSITY
316 Washington Avenue
Wheeling, WV 26003
304-243-2000
www.wju.edu

Wisconsin

ALVERNO COLLEGE
3400 S. 43rd Street
Milwaukee, WI 53234-3922
414-382-6000
www.alverno.edu

CARDINAL STRITCH UNIVERSITY
6801 N. Yates Road
Milwaukee, WI 53217
414-410-4000
www.stritch.edu

EDGEWOOD COLLEGE
1000 Edgewood College Dr.
Madison, WI 53711
608-663-4861
www.edgewood.edu

MARIAN COLLEGE OF FOND DU LAC
45 South National Avenue
Fond du Lac, WI 54935
920-923-7600
www.mariancollege.edu

MARQUETTE UNIVERSITY
Milwaukee, WI 53201
414-288-7700
www.mu.edu

MOUNT MARY COLLEGE
2900 N. Menomonee River Parkway
Milwaukee, WI 53222
414-258-4810
www.mtmary.edu

ST. NORBERT COLLEGE
100 Grant Street
DePere, WI 54115
920-403-3181
www.snc.edu

SILVER LAKE COLLEGE OF THE HOLY FAMILY
2406 So. Alverno Road
Manitowoc, WI 54220
920-684-6691
www.sl.edu

VITERBO UNIVERSITY
815 South 9th Street
La Crosse, WI 54601
608-796-3000
www.viterbo.edu

Web Sites for Discerning a Religious Vocation

www.religiousministries.com

A comprehensive database of more than 3,000 Catholic organizations nationwide. The site contains in-depth information about men's and women's communities active in the United States plus many part time opportunities. Visitors to the Online Guide can search for Men's Communities, Women's Communities, Diocesan Vocation Directors, Secular Institutes, Lay Ministry Organizations , Retreat Centers and Religious Study Opportunities.

www.nccv-vocations.org

This site, maintained by NCCV (National Coalition for Church Vocations), provides resources for vocation ministry, awareness, education and discernment and includes an extensive glossary of vocation-related terms.

www.visionguide.org

This is the site for "Vision", an annual publication for vocation discernment produced by the National Religious Vocation Conference through Claretian Publications. This site includes articles on vocations as well as links to other vocation resources, including vocation discernment sites of numerous archdiocesan/diocesan vocation offices.

www.vocations.com

This site, from Fr. John Regan, Vocation Director, Diocese of Joliet (Illinois) Vocation Office, contains links to "Vocation Frequently Asked Questions", a list of other sites pertinent to vocations, a link to discovering your talents and discerning a religious vocation, as well as a link to resources for vocation directors.

www.geocities.com/Wellesley/1114/index.html

SisterSite - of interest to women religious and those interested in religious vocations - contains links to vocations; a listing of periodicals, publishers, best-sellers and services, etc. of interest to sisters; and a link to history/research of religious life, theology, scripture studies and religious studies.

members.aol.com/decide2b/home.html

"Who 2 Be" will help you discern your vocation in life, and whether that vocation is to the religious life. Links are given to "Making Choices", "Decisions, Decisions, Decisions", "Frequently Asked Questions About Vocations" and "Frequently Asked Questions About Older Priestly Vocations" as well as general vocation discernment, including "The Enneagram Inventory" and the "Myers-Briggs Personality Inventory."

www.vocations.com/priest/faqolder.html

This site, by the faculty of Sacred Heart of Theology (Hales Corner, WI) answers the following questions about becoming a priest later on in one's life: Does my age make a difference?, Will I be accepted simply because I want to be a priest?, Will I be treated like a "20 something" in the seminary?, What kind of education is needed?, What if I have been married?, What if I have made mistakes in my life?, Who will pay for the seminary education?, Do I have to sell my house?, How important is my work background?, What options in priesthood are available?, What options outside of priesthood are available?, What's the next step?

www.sistersholyredeemer.org/regform.html

Weekly chat room to meet other woman discerning a call to religious life.

www.chicagopriest.org

This site from the Archdiocese of Chicago discusses discernment questions on the calling, education and training of priests such as: Why be a priest?, Is it easy to become a priest?, What qualities does the Church look for in a candidate?, Am I holy enough to be a priest? and If I decide to go to seminary, am I committed for life?

www.vocationsplacement.org

This site can help turn your concept of religious life into an experience by arranging for you to attend a free "Live-in Experience" retreat at a community that interests you most.

www.religiouslife.com/mpd01.phtml

Take the *Ministry Potential Discerner (MPD) Self-Assessment Survey*. The *MPD* is a comprehensive spiritual evaluation tool consisting of 39 simple questions designed to measure one's vocational potential in serving the Lord and His Church as a priest, religious or consecrated person. It points out many areas of strengths, insight and Catholic values when taken honestly and conscientiously.

All are Called

"All the faithful of Christ - of whatever rank or status - are called to the fullness of the Christian life and to the perfection of charity."

(Vatican II, *On the Church,* #40)

There are many ways in which the faithful of Christ follow the call to fullness of life - and the contemplative religious life is one way. It is a unique way, with a long and treasured history in the Church. Members of contemplative communities give themselves to God alone in solitude, silence and through continual prayer and self-denial. The entire atmosphere of a monastery - the place, the schedule, and the people - all are directed toward making it possible to experience God and His love.

By choosing contemplative life, members decide to direct all their energies to deepening the "God Life" within their hearts: by an attentive listening to the Spirit, an awareness of the Divine presence and activity in the world, and an ever deepening communion with God. The study of Scripture and other important writings of the Church helps to further develop spiritual understanding and values. Private and liturgical prayer, spiritual reading, and Lectio Divina nourish and deepen this goal.

Contemplative communities experience a number of essential elements:

- community life fully shared
- prayer and solitude
- Eucharist and Liturgy of the Hours
- sacred reading
- public vows
- work in the monastic setting
- meals in common

Also fundamental are interior discipline, silence, simplicity of life, hospitality and a readiness to pray with, and for, others. Community works, within the monastery setting, may include: spiritual direction, retreats, catechetics, publications, counseling the marginalized, baking and distributing altar breads, and making liturgical vestments.

By daily labor, members support the Community, develop their gifts and unite with their sisters and brothers all over the world who must also work.

Monastic contemplative life is centered around the communal celebration of the Liturgy of the Hours and the Eucharistic Liturgy, which gives primary meaning to the life of each member. All contemplative communities have a rhythm of prayer, work and leisure within their monastery. Throughout the centuries, the Church has promoted various expressions of the contemplative life. Individual communities reflect and share the charism and spirit of their founders in a particular way. "Come and See!"

A typical day might consist of

- Early rising with morning prayers and meditation
- Mass
- Work time (e.g., vestments, altar breads, clerical work)
- Midday prayers followed by dinner
- Afternoon work time with some free time
- Evening prayers and evening meditation
- Evening meal
- Recreation
- Free time before retiring
- Night prayers

Eucharistic Missionaries of St. Dominic

Is God calling you to service with a special edge?

- *Our world struggles with violence!*
  Families feel conflict!
  God's people hunger and hurt!

Are you called...
to seek justice,
to bring peace,
to provide the healing of God's Love,
to help others find God's Joy?

If you are stirred
to do something special,
let's talk . . .

Sister Kathy Broussard and
Sister Rachel Sena have
chosen this life.

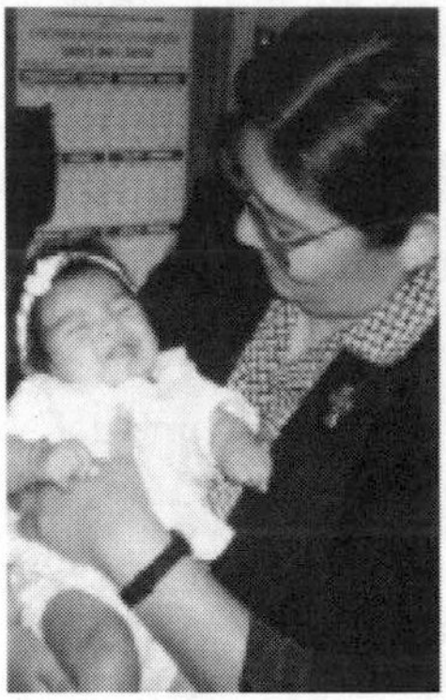

Not sure where your gifts might fit. **Let's talk...**

Vocation Office
Eucharistic Missionaries of St. Dominic
3801 Canal Street, Suite 400
New Orleans, LA 70119
504-486-0098 866-484-5451
Fax: 504-486-6547
www.emdsisters.org EMDOffice@aol.com

A GUIDE TO
RELIGIOUS
MINISTRIES
For Catholic Men and Women

Community Profiles

Women

The following pages contain profiles of women's communities that are sponsors of the 2004 edition of A Guide to Religious Ministries for Catholic Men and Women. These orders have made a special effort to describe their life's work. Review these pages to determine which of these women's orders perform the sort of ministry that may be of interest to you.

If you would like information about becoming a member of a religious order but are unsure of which ones to consider, complete the card below and you will receive literature from several communities.

Sending in this postcard does not obligate you to anything, but it may be the first step towards your life's work.

You may also visit our website, **www.religiousministries.com** to obtain more information about any of these orders.

Request for Information - Women's Communities

I am interested in a life of religious ministry. Please forward information about different religious communities. I am interested in becoming a:

☐ Sister ☐ Lay Minister

My particular interest for ministry in a religious life is in:

☐ Parish Work ☐ Education
☐ Missions ☐ Health Care
☐ Undecided ☐ Social Service
☐ Other: ____________________

Type of Community:
Refer to front of A section for a description of each
☐ Apostolic/Active
☐ Contemplative/Cloistered
☐ Monastic

Ms.____

Address ____

City/State/Zip ___________________________________

Telephone (Optional) ______________________________

E-mail Address (Optional)___________________________

Last Grade Completed ____________________Age__________

Comments ______________________________________

A Guide to Religious Ministries
Index to Women's Profiles

A-100

Benedictine Nuns of Corpus Christi Monastery

About a tenth of a mile off Earhart Road lies Corpus christi Monastery. Here is where we, a group of Benedictine Nuns, have a humble abode. With a Wooded background, the area is very conducive to meditation and prayer.

Today

If you hear His voice—

We are clothed in the traditional garb, sing the Divine Office in Gregorian Chant in English, have daily Eucharistic Adoration, are loyal to the Magisterium of the Church, and live a family-like community life, according to the Rule of St. Benedict.

We are engaged in various apostolates. Regardless of age, talents, education, or background, there is a place for each and everyone who fells God is calling her.

If you are interested in our Community, have any further questions, would like to visit us, or wish to remain in communication with us while discerning your vocation, please write to:

Vocation Director
Corpus Christi Monastery
4485 Earhart Road
Ann Arbor, MI 48105-9710

Send one of the postcards in this book for more information.

What do a musician, an accountant, a dentist and a teacher have in common?

They're all Sisters of Saint Benedict!

If you think that God may be calling you to a life of service and prayer, contact

Vocation Director
Mount Saint Benedict Monastery
620 Summit Ave.
Crookston, MN 56716-2799
Phone: 218-281-3441
Fax: 218-281-6966
Email: vocation@msb.net

That in all things God may be glorified.

Use the Sisters of Saint Benedict postcard to request further information.

If You're Worried about Your Wardrobe Going out of Style . . .

OUR "habits" are always up-to-date. They include prayer, ministry, and an active, engaged community of religious women. Contact:

Sr. Margarita Walters, OSB
Benedictine Sisters of Chicago
7430 North Ridge Boulevard
Chicago IL 60645/773-764-2413, ext 267
Email: srmwalters@aol.com

Send one of the postcards in this book for more information.

One thing
I ask of the Lord,
this I seek,
to live in the
house of the Lord
all the days of my life
Psalm 27

The Benedictine Sisters of Perpetual Adoration...

- *Lectio divina*
- *Community Life*
- *Eucharist*
- *Mindfulness*
- *Liturgy of the Hours*
- *Hospitality*
- *Adoration*
- *Contemplative Prayer*

Contemplative Life for the Sake of the World

To learn more please contact

Sister Colleen Maura McGrane, OSB
vocation@benedictinesisters.org
Call toll free: 1-877-632-6665
Benedictine Sisters of Perpetual Adoration
31970 State Highway P, Clyde, MO 64432
www.benedictinesisters.org

Send one of the postcards in this book for more information.

Just a quick note to say, "Hey!"

Life here on the hill is great! Today started out quietly with morning prayer, but boy did it get crazy at work. Couldn't wait to get home. Prayed and had dinner with everyone, then went for a walk around the lake. Guess I didn't know how close I was to the edge... sneakers in the dryer.

You'd love it here. Come visit. Call me!

Sarah

SISTERS OF ST. BENEDICT

Monastery Immaculate Conception
802 E. 10th Street • Ferdinand, Indiana 47532-9239

For more information, please contact:
Sister Anita Louise Lowe or Sister Tess Dueñas • 1-800-738-9999
vocation@thedome.org • www.thedome.org/vocations

Use the Sisters of St. Benedict postcard to request further information.

Inquirers often say they feel *different* from other people. They don't always fit in.

God may be calling you.

We invite you to visit us on your vocation journey. Take time to stroll through our wooded grounds and reflect on God's call to you. Sit by the lake and know peace. Come to prayers and meals. Talk and laugh with us. "Listen with the ear of your heart." You may feel one step closer to home.

How can you know?

Benedictine Sisters at St. Mary Monastery

2200 88th Avenue West, Rock Island, IL 61201

For more information, or to arrange a visit, please contact us.

309 283-2300 • 800 650-1257 • vocation@stmarymonastery.org

Send one of the postcards in this book for more information.

Monastery of St. Scholastica

SEEK GOD?

Saint Scholastica

So have the Sisters of St. Scholastica Monastery! We have been a Benedictine tradition in Arkansas for 125 years!

We seek God every day by embracing a Spirit of Prayerful Hospitality, through Simplicity, Communal Living, Ministry and Service, and a balanced life of Work, and Leisure!

STILL SEEK GOD?

For more information Contact:
Sister Kimberly Rose Prohaska, OSB
St. Scholastica Monastery
PO Box 3489
Fort Smith, Arkansas 72913
1-479-783-4147
vocationdirector@scholasticafortsmith.org
www.scholaticafortsmith.org

Send one of the postcards in this book for more information.

Send one of the postcards in this book for more information.

Send one of the postcards in this book for more information.

Small enough to offer you a true sense of community and faith sharing

...large enough to make a difference to the many people we serve.

***We invite you to... Live** with us in community...*
***Pray** with us deepening your relationship with God...*
***Serve** with us in our healing ministries...*
***Join** us in creating the future...*

Sr. Pat Dowling, CBS, Vocation Director
1525 Marriottsville Road
Marriottsville, Maryland 21104
410-442-0267 or 1-877-742-0277 (toll free)
pat_dowling@bshsi.com
www.bonsecours.org/vocations

BON SECOURS

SISTERS OF BON SECOURS, USA
HERMANAS del BUEN SOCORRO

Founded in 1824 to provide compassion, healing, and liberation to the poor, the sick and the dying.

Send one of the postcards in this book for more information.

Canossian Sisters

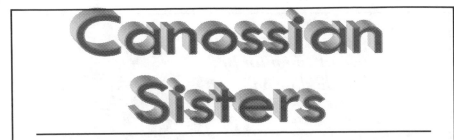

Daughters of Charity, Servants of the Poor

We are women,
fascinated by the Greatest
Love of the Crucified One,
sharing life and prayer with
one another as we journey,
in all humility and love
with our crucified brothers
and sisters in the spirit of
Magdalene of Canossa.

- ✓ *contemplatives in action*
- ✓ *serving in diverse ministries*
- ✓ *living a common life*
- ✓ *worldwide missionary*

Canossian Sisters
5625 Isleta Blvd. SW
Albuquerque, NM 87105
Vocation Director,
505-877-6383
Vocationsfdcc@aol.com

There is no greater *Act of Love* than that of making Jesus known. (St. Magdalene of Canossa)

Send one of the postcards in this book for more information.

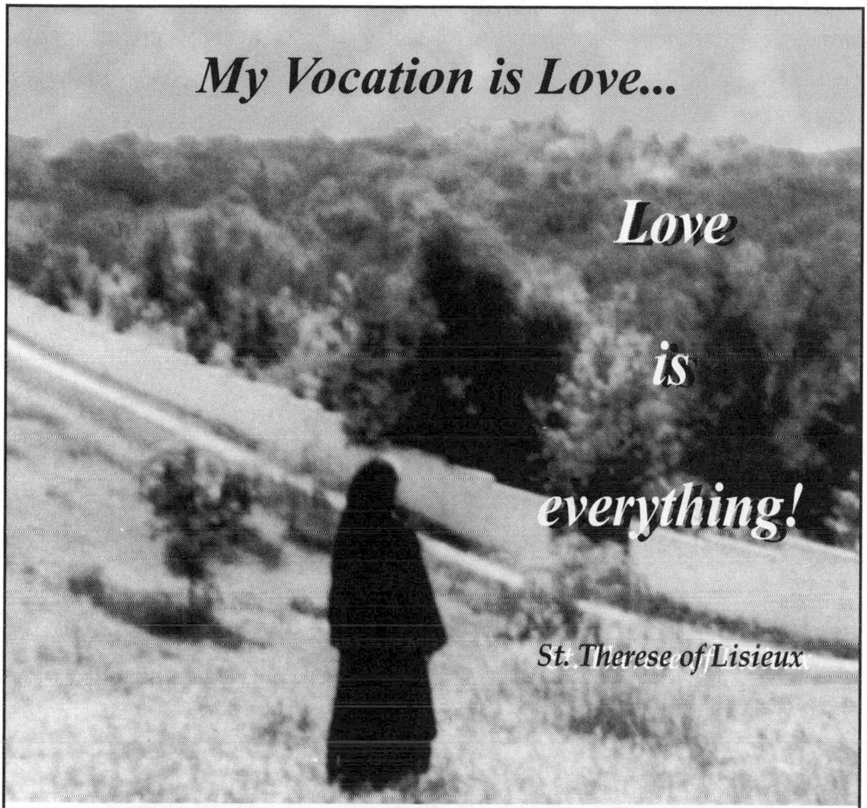

Discalced Carmelite Nuns

A life of love and hidden prayer...
...praising God and pleading for His people...
...in simplicity, silence, solitude, sacrifice and sharing...
...St. Therese's contemplative apostolate...
...apart from the world...yet at the heart of the world and the Church today!

Contact: Vocation Directress
DISCALCED CARMELITE NUNS
2901 S. CECELIA ST.
SIOUX CITY, IA 51106-3299
(712) 276-1680 E-mail: carmelitesiouxc@aol.com

Send one of the postcards in this book for more information.

SISTERS OF CHARITY OF ST. JOAN ANTIDA

A reputation for prayer, community, serving the poor...

...and welcoming new members!

Experience our welcome by contacting:

Sister Elizabeth Weber
8560 North 76th Place
Milwaukee, WI 53223-2699
414-354-9233

elizabeth@scsja.org
www.scsja.org

TOGETHER WITH THE POOR FOR A NEW WORLD

ST. JOAN ANTIDA
SISTERS OF CHARITY

Send one of the postcards in this book for more information.

Daughters of St. Mary of Providence

The Guanellian Sisters Mission:

- ✝ *Listen to the voice of God - become a mother and sister to every person to whom they minister*
- ✝ *Lovingly share with all, accepting and providing for even the unexpressed needs.*
- ✝ *Bring joy and inspire faith*
- ✝ *Provide quality of life–for children, youth, senior citizens, the sick, and the mentally and physically disabled.*

As a sign of their total consecration to Christ, the Sisters wear a simple, uniform habit with veil and a crucifix.

Prayer has a central role in the lives of the Daughters of St. Mary of Providence. Each day begins with the community praying the Liturgy of the Hours Morning Prayer, followed by personal meditation, and the Eucharistic Liturgy. Other parts of the Divine Office, rosary, spiritual reading, personal prayer, are interspersed throughout the day. A time for recreation and relaxation is shared by all.

If you feel called to commit yourself
to a Guanellian life lived for others, please contact:

Vocation Directress
Daughters of St. Mary of Providence
4200 North Austin Avenue
Chicago, IL 60634
(773) 545-8300

Daughters of St. Mary of Providence

Use the Daughters of St. Mary of Providence postcard to request further information.

A-114

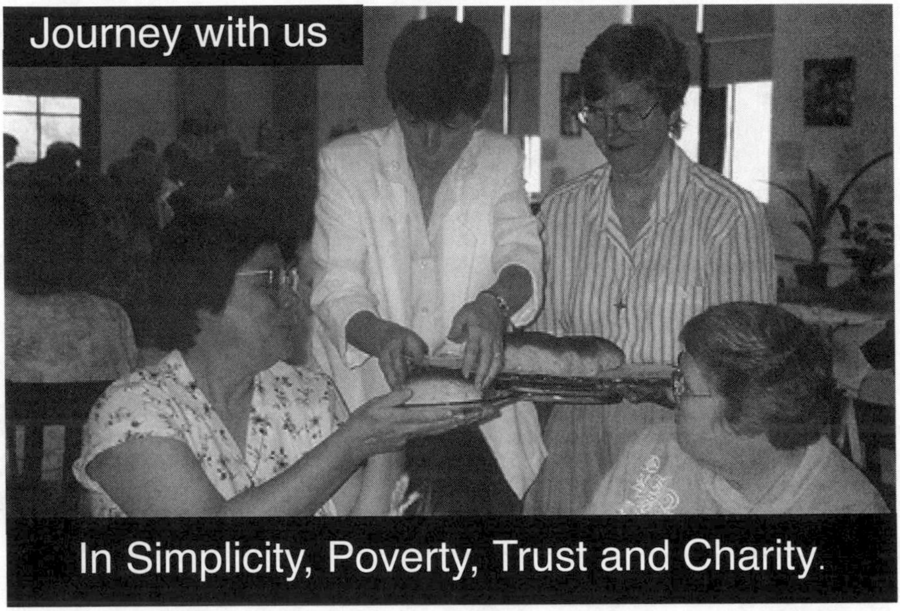
Journey with us
In Simplicity, Poverty, Trust and Charity.

At the heart of our life is the contemplation of Jesus in whose life and death we know God's providential love. Confident of this love we are impelled to reach out to others through works of mercy.

Whatever form our ministry takes, we speak the message of God by the way we live. We become signs of hope, living expressions of the tender love of God.

Sisters of Divine Providence

Melbourne, Kentucky

For more information contact:
Sister Fidelis Tracy, CDP
1000 St. Anne Drive
Melbourne, KY 41059
(859) 441-0700 Ext. 324
www.cdpkentucky.org
vocation@cdpkentucky.org

Send one of the postcards in this book for more information.

SISTERS
A
L
LAY SALVATORIANS
A
T
BROTHERS
R
PRIESTS
A
N
S

Fr. Francis Jordan

Blessed Mary
of the Apostles

Be a part of the
Team ...
SDSvocations.com

Use the Salvatorians postcard to request further information.

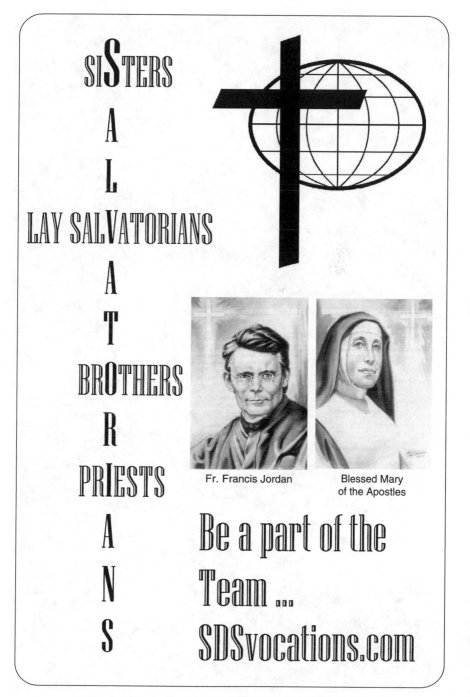

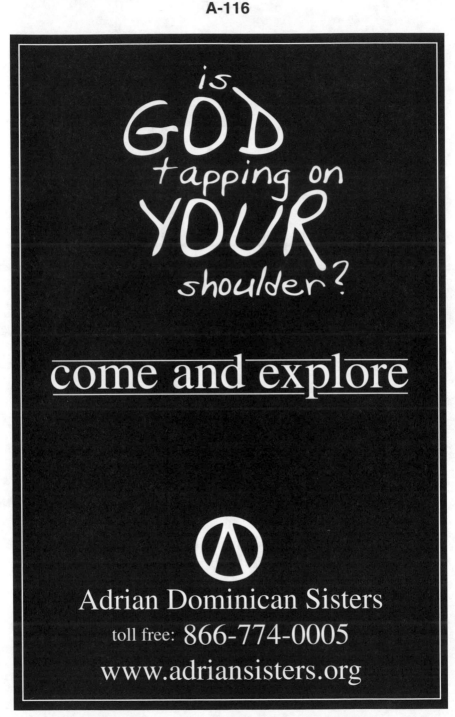

THE DOMINICAN SISTERS OF HAWTHORNE

TO KNOW, LOVE, AND SERVE GOD

Through daily Mass, Liturgy of the Hours, reading of Scripture, personal and communal prayer, we seek to perfect our love of God. Devotion to Our Blessed Mother Mary, Mother of God, and to her Rosary is important to us as well.

In attempting to be true daughters of St. Dominic, we strive to share with each other and with those we serve the fruits of our prayer and love of God. We also strive to be faithful to the Holy Father and to the Church's teaching.

Our apostolate is singular and unique, that of caring for incurable cancer patients. Our Sisters come from varied backgrounds. Not all are registered nurses, but all help in the care of the patients.

While the work is naturally rewarding, prayer, the living out of our vows and community life must be the center of our existence.

Prayerfulness, compassion, cheerfulness, and generosity are qualities highly prized by our community.

To enter, you must be in good health and have at least a high school diploma. Age is decided on an individual basis.

Interested women are invited to visit throughout the year to discern the presence of their vocation.

For more information write or call:

Sr. Teresa Marie Barnaby, O.P.
Vocation Director

THE DOMINICAN SISTERS OF HAWTHORNE
600 Linda Avenue, Hawthorne, NY 10532
TEL: 914-769-4794 or 914-769-0114

E-MAIL ADDRESS: SrTeresaM@aol.com

VISIT OUR WEB SITE: www.hawthorne-dominicans.org

Use the Dominican Sisters of Hawthorne postcard to request further information.

DOMINICANS OF ST. CATHARINE KENTUCKY
Sisters and Associates in Mission
Sometimes it just hits you. The answer to whatever you've been searching for. Enlightenment can come in many forms. For some, truth slowly reveals itself over time. For others, it's those "aha!" moments that may only come once in a lifetime.
The calling to enter religious life is a precious call to action. No matter how far your search has led you, let us light your path. Your quest to serve others is what brought the Dominican Family to the green hills of Kentucky in 1822. Let us help you explore religious life. It may be just the spark your imagination is looking for.
Dominicans of St. Catharine, Kentucky
For more information contact: Sister Christine Connolly, OP
5345 South Hyde Park Boulevard
Chicago, IL 60615-5722
(773) 684-1595
e-mail: chrisctu@juno.com
website: www.opkentucky.org

Send one of the postcards in this book for more information.

Consider Us in Your Future Plan...

At this time in your life,
you are searching
for answers to life's
tough questions
about your future.

It's important that you
consider **all** of the
options.

**RELIGIOUS LIFE...
WORTH EXPLORING**

For more information, contact:

**Sr. Elyse Marie Ramirez, OP,
Vocation Director**

**DOMINICAN SISTERS
OF SPRINGFIELD**

Phone 217.787.0481
e-mail: SEMRamirez@spdom.org
1237 West Monroe
Springfield, IL 62704

website:
www.springfieldop.org

Send one of the postcards in this book for more information.

A-120

Joliet Franciscans...
Women of living faith

and loving service.

Sisters of St. Francis of Mary Immaculate
Sr. Margaret Kelly, OSF, Director of New Membership
801 N. Larkin Ste. 101 ~ Joliet, IL 60435 www.jolietfranciscans.org
309-829-0455 or 815-725-8735 e-mail: osfj520@mtco.com

Use the Joliet Franciscans postcard to request further information.

Send one of the postcards in this book for more information.

We are a community of Christ-centered women living the Gospel in today's world.

Risking all...
Serving all...
At home with all people...

Together in community and prayer, in the footsteps of Francis and Clare.

Franciscan Sisters of Allegany, NY

Sr. Mary McNally, OSF
Vocation Director
(813) 870-6314
fsavoc@aol.com
www.franciscansister.com

Send one of the postcards in this book for more information.

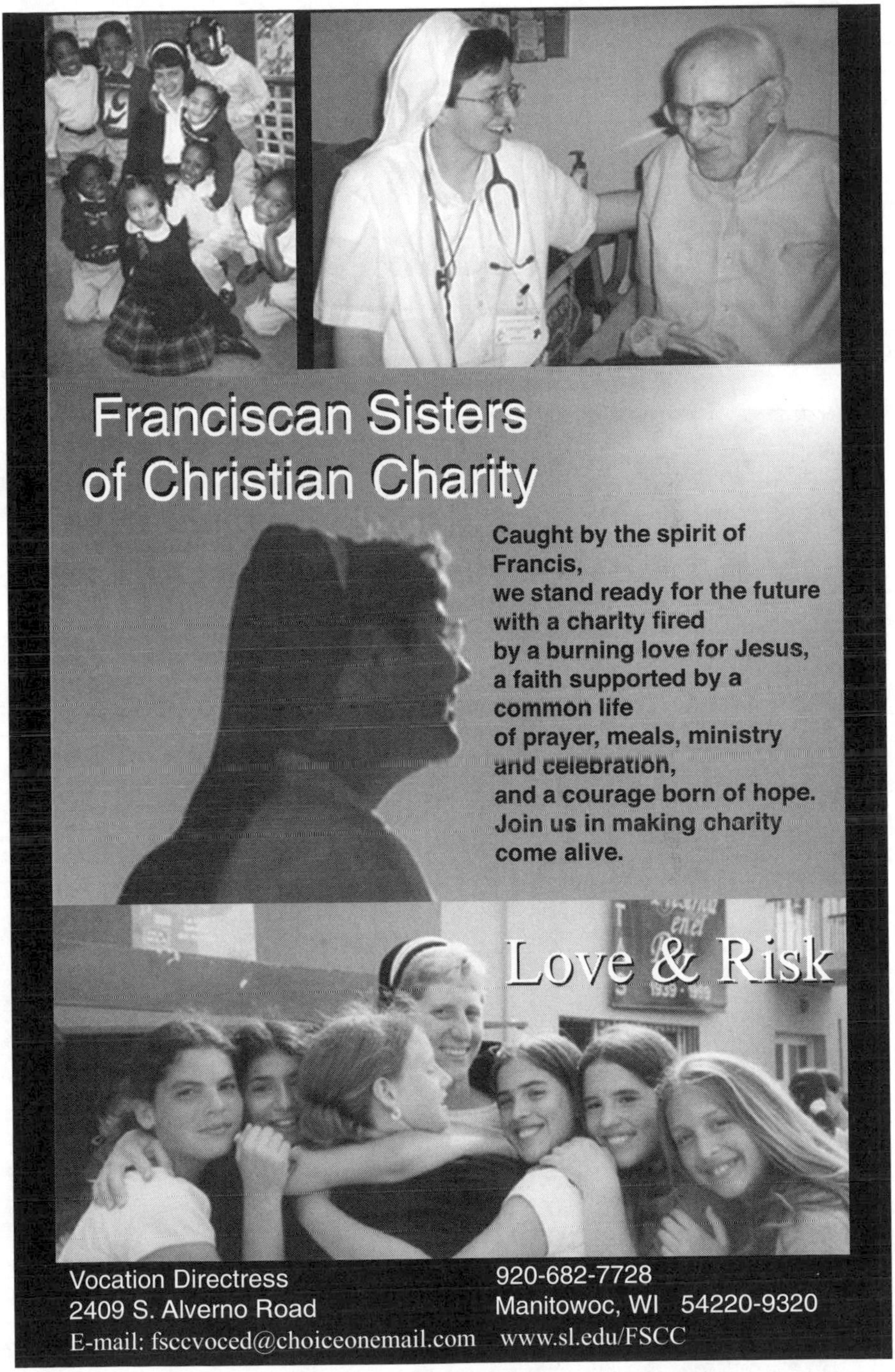
Franciscan Sisters
of Christian Charity
Caught by the spirit of
Francis,
we stand ready for the future
with a charity fired
by a burning love for Jesus,
a faith supported by a
common life
of prayer, meals, ministry
and celebration,
and a courage born of hope.
Join us in making charity
come alive.
Love & Risk
Vocation Directress
2409 S. Alverno Road
E-mail: fsccvoced@choiceonemail.com
920-682-7728
Manitowoc, WI 54220-9320
www.sl.edu/FSCC

Send one of the postcards in this book for more information.

Live Peace!

The Wheaton Franciscans!

Join us!

www.wheatonfranciscan.org

PO Box 667 Wheaton, IL 60189-0667 630.462.4722

Send one of the postcards in this book for more information.

Use the Franciscan Sisters of Little Falls postcard to request further information.

SfP

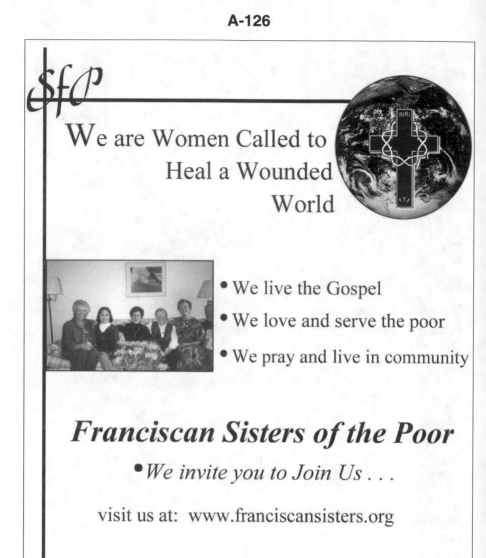

We are Women Called to
Heal a Wounded
World

- We live the Gospel
- We love and serve the poor
- We pray and live in community

Franciscan Sisters of the Poor

- *We invite you to Join Us . . .*

visit us at: www.franciscansisters.org

Vocation Minister

Sr. Arlene McGowan, SFP
513-761-9040 x 112 • OHIO
arlenemcgowan@msn.com

Use the Franciscan Sisters of the Poor postcard to request further information.

I have done what is mine to do, may Christ teach you what is yours.
Francis of Assisi
...What is Yours?
Rochester Franciscan Community
(Sisters & Cojourners)
1001 14th Street NW
Rochester, MN 55901-2511
Central Minister – Franciscan Life Team
1-888-277-4741
www.rfvocation.org

Send one of the postcards in this book for more information.

What Do These Women Have in Common?

We are <u>simply</u> Franciscan Sisters of the Sacred Heart!

We are women who have chosen to live a simple life-style in the spirit of St. Francis and spread the Gospel message of hope and peace in today's world. Through our vows and sisterly love, we share together in community, ministry, and prayer. We serve the needs of the church through our "works of neighborly love". We are located in Indiana, Illinois, California, and Brazil. We invite you to contact us if you are interested in more information:

Sr. Deborah Suddarth OSF
St. Francis Convent
9201 W. St. Francis Rd
Frankfort, IL 60423

Telephone: (815) 464-3873 • E-mail: sdeborah@aol.com • Website: www.fssh.net

Send one of the postcards in this book for more information.

Franciscan Sisters of St. Elizabeth

Our Congregation honors the
Traditional Values of Religious Life:
Community Living, Life of Intense Prayer,
Religious Habit, Common Apostolate

We give ourselves in loving service
to God's people on four continents.

Vocation Office
Franciscan Sisters
of St. Elizabeth
499 Park Road
Parsippany, NJ 07054-1736
(973) 539-3797
e-mail: sr_cathylynn@yahoo.com
web site: www.franciscansisters.com

Send one of the postcards in this book for more information.

Yes you can!

Challenge yourself. Get involved. Be a peacemaker.

We offer our life and energy to carry on God's mission. With lives of prayer and service, supporting and challenging one another, we are inspired to ***be and do together*** what we cannot be or do alone.

We respond to the needs of our times--working to uphold the human dignity of every person, pursuing peace in our own hearts and in the world, and promoting Gospel Justice. Today we do this as parish leaders, educators, health caregivers, youth ministers, minority and environmental advocates, artists, social workers, literacy counselors, retreat directors, missionaries and administrators.

Do you feel called to serve those in need? Do you feel called to do MORE, to be involved more, to give more? Are you willing to give your life to God?

Share God's love.

Sisters of St. Francis of the Holy Cross

Get to know us. We invite you to call or write to learn more:
Sister Laura Zelten • 3025 Bay Settlement Road, Green Bay, WI 54311
www.gbfranciscans.org • 920-468-4737
Vocations@gbfranciscans.org

Send one of the postcards in this book for more information.

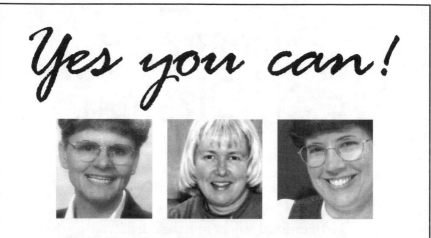

The Sisters of The Third Order of St. Francis

We, the Sisters of the Third Order of St. Francis of East Peoria, Illinois are a Religious Community whose mission it is to serve the people of God, especially the sick and the poor, in the spirit of the Gospel and St. Francis of Assisi.

Because Christ is the center of our lives, a deep prayer life is fostered and is the foundation from which all our apostolic works flow. Our Sisters serve mainly in the apostolates of healthcare and education. We have medical centers, colleges of nursing, nursing homes and clinics in Illinois and Michigan. Our Sisters serve in accounting, administration, education, food service, pharmacy, physical therapy, management information services, nursing, pastoral care and social service.

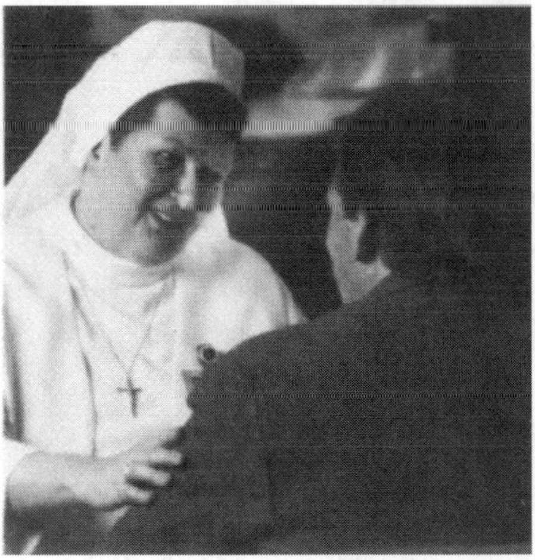

For further information, contact:
Vocation Director
The Sisters of the Third Order of Saint Francis
1175 St. Francis Lane, East Peoria, IL 61611-1299
(309) 699-9313 Fax: (309) 699-7225
e-mail: vocation.info@osfhealthcare.org
Website: http//www.osfhealthcare.org

Use the Sisters of the Third Order of St. Francis postcard to request further information.

We call each other **Sister**

Franciscan life is about building **relationships**

One cannot be a **sister** alone

The Sisters of St. Francis of Assisi

3221 S. Lake Dr.

Milwaukee, WI 53235

414.744.1160
vocdir@lakeosfs.org
www.lakeosfs.org

Send one of the postcards in this book for more information.

Sisters of St. Francis of Perpetual Adoration

Immaculate Heart of Mary Province
Mishawaka, Indiana

"...we strive in community to combine the contemplative life with the active through perpetual adoration...

...and the works of mercy in education, healthcare, and other ecclesial ministries." (Constitution)

Sister Lois DeLee, OSF
Vocation Director
PO Box 766
Mishawaka, IN 46546-0766

e-mail: Srlois@yahoo.com
phone: (574) 259-5427
website: www.ssfpa.org

Send one of the postcards in this book for more information.

Where is God's road taking you?
The back roads of the rural south and Appalachia are well traveled by the Glenmary Sisters as we find God by serving others in the home missions. Our small community and unique charism may be what God has in His plans for you.
Vocation or volunteer opportunities are available. Call us today for discernment assistance.
The Glenmary Sisters
Owensboro, Kentucky
1-800-301-2689
www.glenmarysisters.org

Send one of the postcards in this book for more information.

Compassion has a human face.

The Sisters of the Good Shepherd approach each person with the same care of Jesus the Good Shepherd. We are guided by the principle that *"One person is of more value than a world."*

Through Action and Contemplation our mission of *reconciliation* impels us to promote justice and peace. Our vow of *zeal*, the heart of the Good Shepherd vocation, leads us to search out the wounded and those left behind by the world. We minister in all areas of human service, with a particular focus on the needs of women and children.

There are two ways that a Sister of the Good Shepherd can express her zeal for God's people—*apostolic* and *contemplative*.

Is God calling you to love with the heart of a shepherd?

CONTACT: Sister Jean Marie Fernandez at 314-381-3400, or e-mail her at *jmfernandez@goodshepherdsisters.org*

www.goodshepherdsisters.org

Send one of the postcards in this book for more information.

Have you heard Jesus ask you to take up your cross and follow him?

In 1856 our founder said, "I need sisters who understand the Cross. With them I can accomplish anything."

Now, 150 years later, more than 4,450 Holy Cross Sisters are alleviating human suffering on 5 continents. Our U.S. community serves the poor, sick, elderly, abused, and otherwise forgotten in 7 states.

Jesus made the Cross holy.

In all we do, his Cross is our model, our consolation, and our strength.

It teaches us every day that life triumphs over death.

Holy Cross Sisters

USA PROVINCE

And what is it that we do?

The Holy Cross Sisters have always enjoyed a special freedom in ministry. As society changes, so do people's needs. We seek to identify the particular needs of *our* time and then to do whatever it takes to transform those challenges into hope.

As a community of sisters and associates, we are united in our love for the Cross, but we are diverse in the ways that we respond to it. We want each one to follow God's particular call to share with others the life-giving power of the Cross.

If your heart burns with this same desire, please give us a call.

Sister Linda Songy, 501 S. Center Avenue, Merrill, WI 54452
Tel: 504-888-4329 Email: lsongyscsc@msn.com

Use the Holy Cross Sisters postcard to request further information.

Holy Spirit Missionary Sisters

WE ARE an international community of 4,000 women called together to witness to the presence and power of the Holy Spirit through our life and prayer in the community and through our service in the Church.

WE CONTINUE the saving mission of Jesus in forty countries throughout the world: Angola, Antigua (West Indies), Argentina, Australia, Austria, Bolivia, Botswana, Brazil, Chile, China, Cuba, Czech Republic, England, Ethiopia, Germany, Ghana, India, Indonesia, Ireland, Italy, Japan, Korea, Mexico, Mozambique, Netherlands, Papua New Guinea, Paraguay, Philippines, Poland, Portugal, Romania, Russia, Slovakia, Spain, Switzerland, Taiwan, Togo, Ukraine, United States and Vietnam.

WE ARE INVOLVED in the ministries of education, health care, business, parish and social services, fine arts, domestic arts, retreat work, spiritual direction or whatever occupation is needed to be of service to others. "Wherever the work of the Church calls us, our service and our love should lead people to Christ."

WE WELCOME young women between the ages of 20 and 40 who:

- feel called by God to a religious / missionary lifestyle;
- enjoy good physical and mental health;
- have the ability to help others and who are open to personal and professional growth;
- want to share their lives and faith with other women who have similar goals.

For more information, write or phone:

Vocation Minister
Holy Spirit Missionary Sisters
Office of Vocation Ministry

P.O. Box 6026, Techny, Illinois 60082-6026 (847) 441-0126
Residential address: 319 Waukegan Rd., Northfield, IL 60093

Send one of the postcards in this book for more information.

We want to be what we want the world to be: ONE FAMILY

Building simple, friendly, mutual relationships, we touch the larger world by touching the smaller worlds of home, heart and neighborhood.

At the heart of the Little Sisters' mission is the belief that God is discovered and proclaimed in the concrete realities of everyday life. We commit ourselves to living and working among the most poor so that they can take their lives in hand, grow in humanity and discover their dignity as children of God.

In the spirit of Mary's Assumption, the Little Sisters work to renew the whole person by developing communities that Lift Each Other Up.

We want to be ONE FAMILY. What do you want?

For more information on:

Our International Religious Community
Our Family Lifeline Volunteer Program

Little Sisters of the Assumption
475 East 115 Street
New York, NY 10029
212-369-4406
800-482-4376

info@littlesisters.org   www.littlesisters.org

Send one of the postcards in this book for more information.

Use the Little Company of Mary Sisters postcard to request further information.

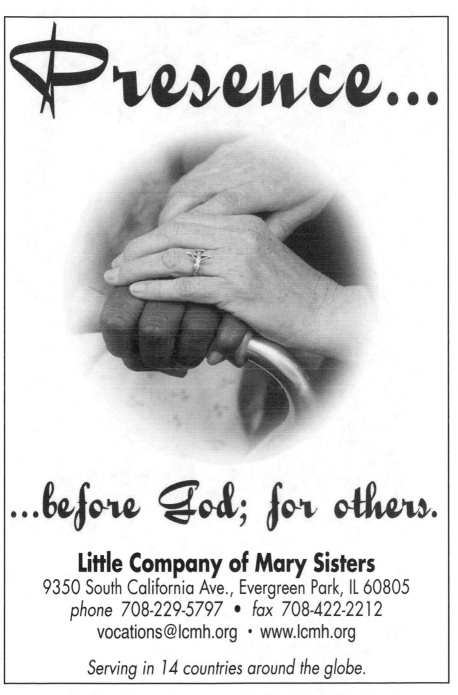

Little Sisters of the Poor–

living in joy as we deepen our love for God, the elderly and each other!

Founded in France in 1839 by Blessed Jeanne Jugan, we serve the elderly poor in 215 homes in 31 countries.

If you would like to learn more about us and our life, please contact:

Sr. Marguerite, l.s.p.
Little Sisters of the Poor
601 Maiden Choice Lane
Baltimore, MD 21228
(410) 744-9367

Send one of the postcards in this book for more information.

Take Your Passion To A Higher Level

with the Sisters of the Living Word, an emerging heart and voice for today's oppressed.

"We joyfully offer our lives as bearers of the Word"

- *founded in 1975 in the spirit of renewal*
- *serving in the Midwest and South*
- *creatively using our gifts and talents in responding to the needs of today*
- *ministering in education, pastoral ministry, care of the elderly, counseling, spiritual direction, creative arts and more.*

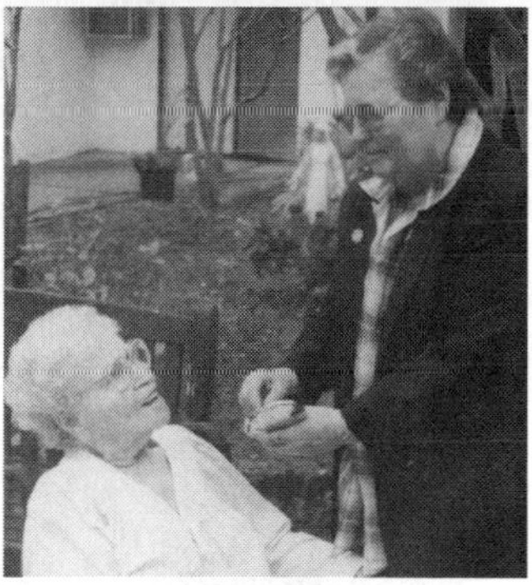

Learn more about our life and mission by visiting our web site – www.slw.org

Living Word Center
800 N. Fernandez – B
Arlington Heights, IL 60004
847-577-5972

Sister Sharon Glumb, SLW
Director of New Membership
P.O. Box 726
Holly Springs, MS 38635
662-252-9801
glumbs@aol.com

our name is our mission
Sisters of the Living Word

Send one of the postcards in this book for more information.

Marist Missionary Sisters

Do you want to make a difference in this world?
Let us tell you how Marist Missionary Sisters try to do it.

We are inspired by Mary to live among and minister to the world's poor and neglected, especially women and children.

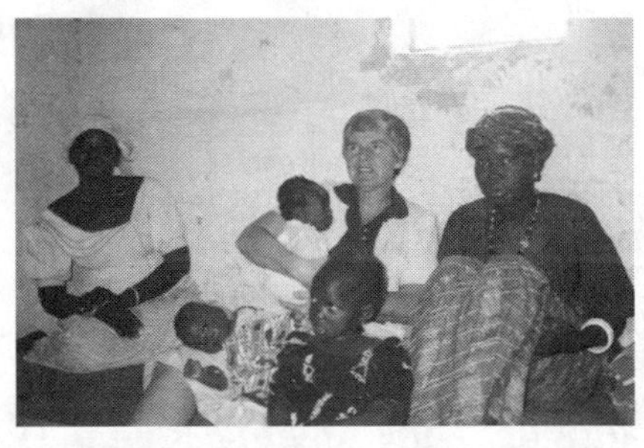

Our lives are based on the gospel values of prayer and shared living experiences.

We are an international community of women who come from all over the world and minister in dozens of different countries.

1515 Boxwood Ave., San Leandro, CA 94579

For more information, email: smsmvoc@aol.com
Or, visit our website: www.maristmissionarysmsm.org

Phone/Fax 510-357-7876

Send one of the postcards in this book for more information.

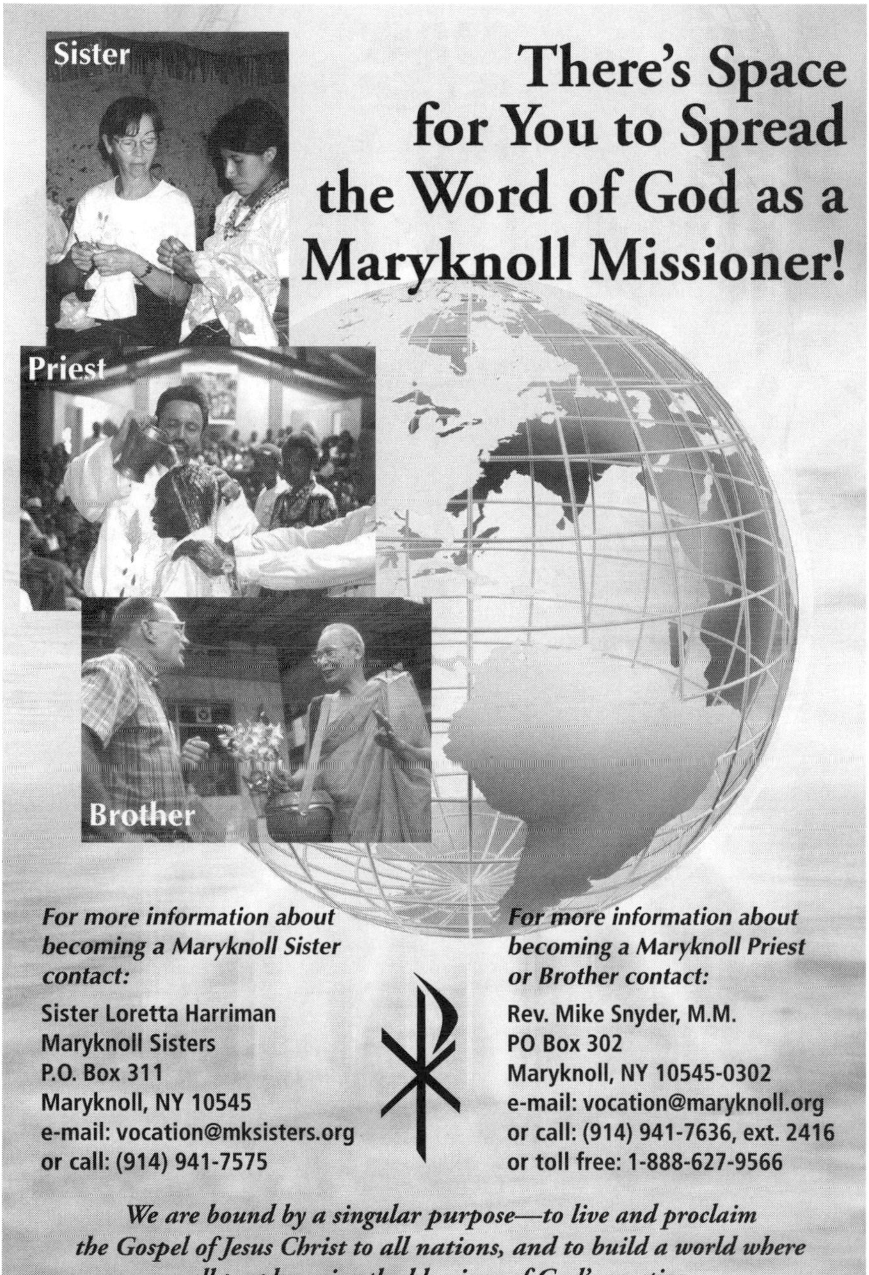

Use the Maryknoll postcard to request further information.

Missionary Benedictine
Priests, Brothers & Sisters

Seek God in...

Prayer

The Eucharistic Celebration, Liturgy of the Hours, spiritual reading and interior prayer are essential to our daily life.

Community Life

We value our life in community. In love and mutual obedience we strengthen one another on our journey to love and serve the Lord.

and Missionary Service

In the United States and in foreign lands, we are sent to proclaim the Good News. We seek to lead people to faith in Jesus Christ.

North America	Africa
South America	Europe
Australia	Asia

For more information

Missionary Benedictine Priests and Brothers
Bro. Tobias Dammert OSB
Christ the King Priory
Schuyler, NE 68661
(402) 352-2177
E-mail: tobias.bmh@dtnspeed.net
www.megavision.net/benedict

Missionary Benedictine Sisters
Sr. Rosann Ocken, OSB
Immaculata Monastery
300 N. 18th St.
Norfolk, NE 68701
(402) 371-3438
E-mail: vocations@norfolkosb.org
www.norfolkosb.org

...To speak the mystery of Christ. Col. 4:3

Send one of the postcards in this book for more information.

Sisters of the Most Holy Trinity

"Radiating the Love of the Three Divine Persons of the Most Holy Trinity"

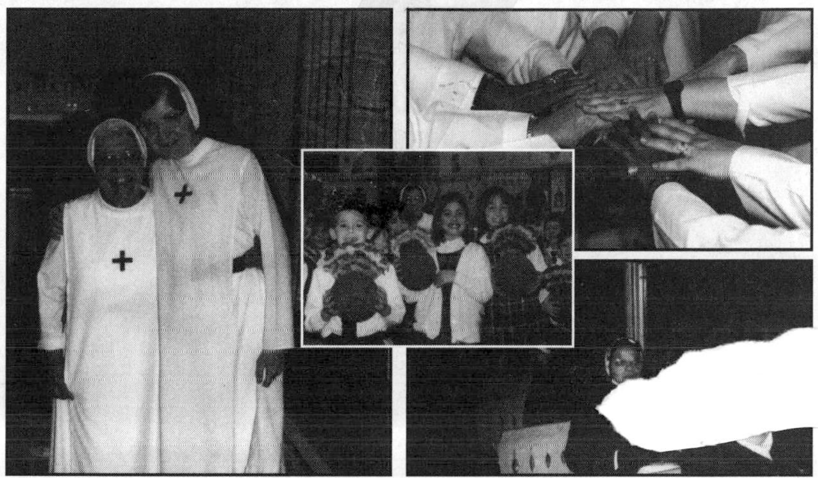

- In 1198 St. John of Matha was inspired to found a community dedicated to spread the love of the Trinity through redemptive charity. On September 8, 1762 Teresa Cucchiari followed her call of the Trinity by beginning a female branch of the Trinitarian Order established to be of service to the poor, the women and children found in the small towns of the hills of Avezzano, Italy.
- Today Trinitarians still teach those who otherwise would not have access to an education. We teach in inner city schools and maintain a haven of prayer at Our Lady of Lourdes Shrine, our motherhouse in Euclid, Ohio.
- We live a community life, praying in common, promoting devotion to the Most Holy Trinity

What are you waiting for? Come join us!

For more information, call or write to:
Vocation Directress
Sisters of the Most Holy Trinity
21281 Chardon Rd.
Euclid, Ohio 44117
(216) 481-8232
www.srstrinity.com

Send one of the postcards in this book for more information.

Answer Christ's Call as a Sister of Nazareth

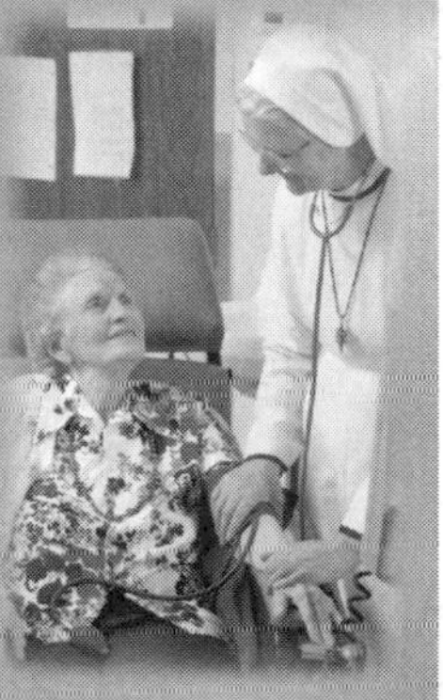

A Prayerful, Dynamic Community of Sisters Dedicated to Jesus and the Loving Care of People in Need

CHARISM OF THE SISTERS OF NAZARETH

Mother St. Basil founded the Sisters of Nazareth in London in 1851 to bring love, respect and dignity to those in need by providing a home built on the example of the Holy Family of Nazareth. Loving care and support is given by the sisters to all who struggle in a world filled with many challenges, especially children and those elderly too frail to look after themselves. The Sisters of Nazareth center their lives on the Gospel message, "Come to Me all you who are burdened and I will give you rest."
Matthew 11:v 28

Today, the Sisters of Nazareth serve God's people through 50 Nazareth Houses located throughout the world.

If you feel called to dedicate your life to the service of others, do consider a vocation as a Sister of Nazareth.

Nazareth House
3333 Manning Avenue
Los Angeles CA 90064

Please contact the vocations director.
E-mail: vocations@nazarethhousela.org or call 310.839.2361
www.nazarethhouse.org

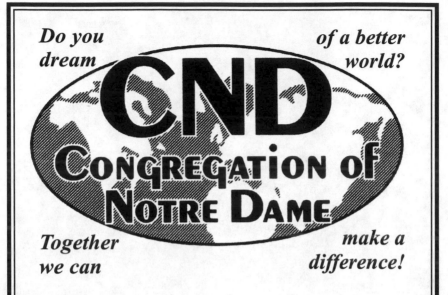

Do you dream of a better world?

CND

CONGREGATION OF NOTRE DAME

Together we can make a difference!

We CNDs see ourselves called by God, as Mary was, to be united intimately with the life and mission of Jesus. We are women who value prayer, who love each other as Sisters, and who cherish our life together in community. We desire to be in solidarity with the poor, the oppressed, the excluded.

www.cnd-m.com
or Sr. Rose Mary Sullivan, **1-718-447-0291**
rmbsully@aol.com

Sr. Rose Mary Sullivan, CND
Notre Dame Academy Convent
76 Howard Avenue
Staten Island, New York 10301

Send one of the postcards in this book for more information.

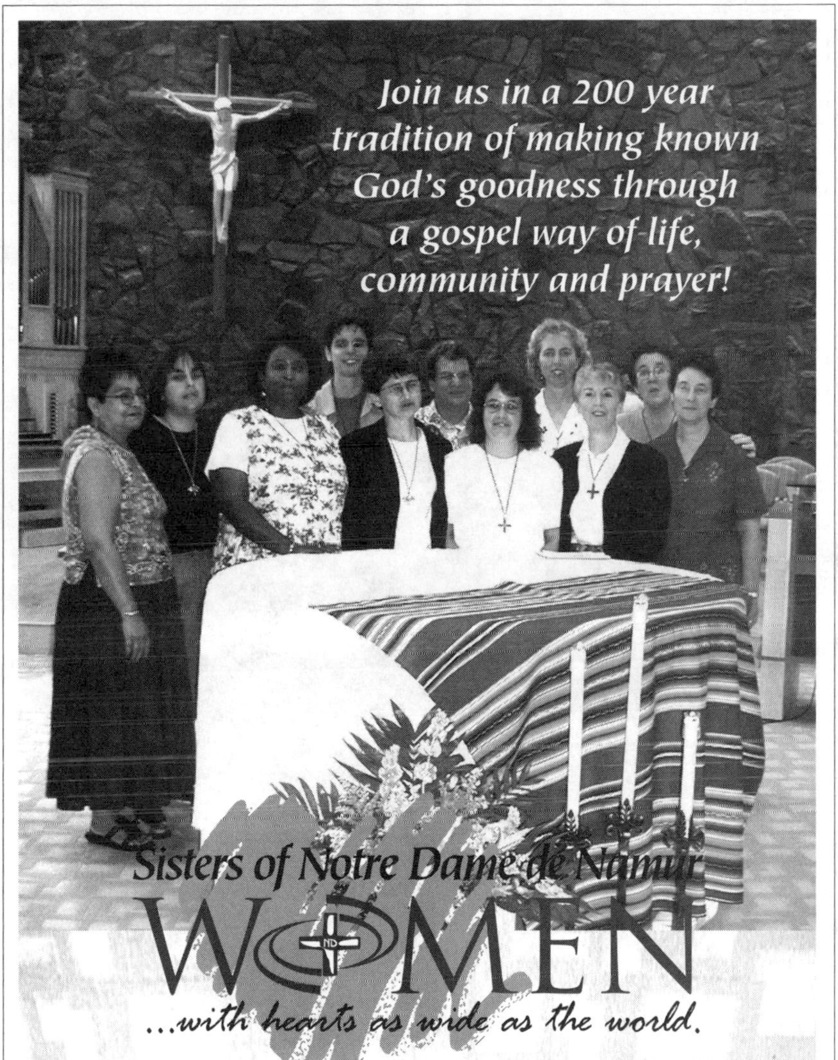

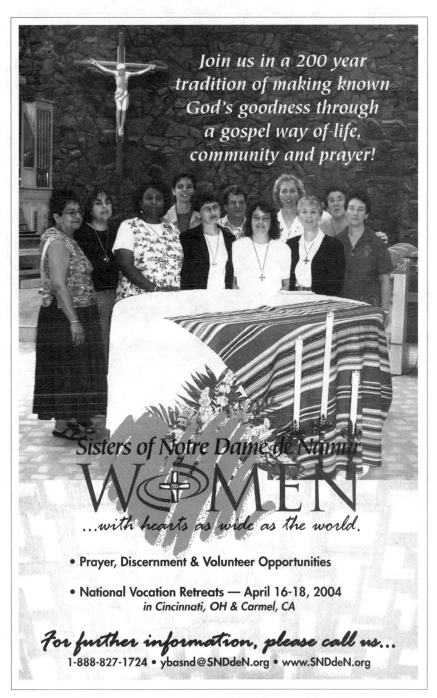

Send one of the postcards in this book for more information.

Sisters of the Holy Cross

participate in the mission of Jesus to reveal God's love for all people, to proclaim the Good News to the poor, freedom to the oppressed, and healing to the afflicted.

Compassion ❖ Faith ❖ Prayer ❖ Community

A member of the family of sisters, brothers and priests of Holy Cross

Sisters of the Holy Cross
পবিত্র ক্রুশ ভগিনীগণ
Irmãs da Santa Cruz
Hermanas de la Santa Cruz

Saint Mary's ❖ Notre Dame, IN 46556
(574) 284-5560 ❖ vocations@cscsisters.org
www.cscsisters.org

Use the Mercedarians postcard to request further information.

Send one of the postcards in this book for more information.

Parish Visitors of Mary Immaculate

Contemplative–Missionaries: Evangelizers and Catechists

Joyful apostles, we do the work of the Good Shepherd, seeking the strayed and the neglected to bring them back to the Church.

"The apostolate of the family (is) one of the priority tasks rendered even more urgent by the present state of the world"
Pope John Paul II

Holy Mass, Holy Hour, Meditation, the Rosary, Divine Office, Retreats, Spiritual Reading... provide the graces to *help families in parishes* through door-to-door evangelizing and teaching *the Faith* to adults and children.

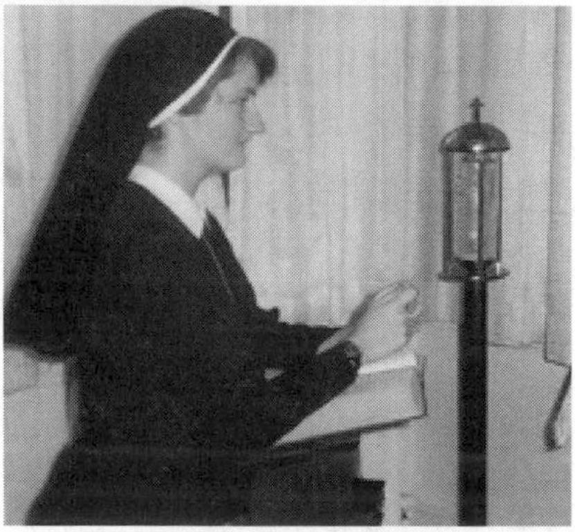

Dedicated to Jesus: poor, chaste and obedient, and living a life of prayer.

Please write:
Vocation Director
Parish Visitors of
Mary Immaculate
Box 658
Monroe, NY 10950
Phone: (845) 783-2251

Send one of the postcards in this book for more information.

Passionist Nuns

Monastic, Contemplative, Cloistered

Throughout the history of the Church there have always been people who were called to leave all and live a life of prayer and solitude in union with Jesus Christ. That call continues in affluent America, in small communities such as the Passionist Nuns. Here young women seek a life of prayer and contemplative knowledge of Jesus for the glory of the Father and the good of others.

Consecrating themselves totally to the mystery of the Passion and Death of Jesus, the Passionist Nuns proclaim God's redemptive love for the world by their life of prayer, penance and community. Their message is one of hope–that the Cross of Christ is a testimony of love in a world of suffering.

Passionist Nuns
1151 Donaldson Highway
Erlanger, Kentucky 41018
859-371-8568

Send one of the postcards in this book for more information.

"Come with Me by yourselves to a quiet place."

Is our Lord speaking these words to you?

We are a community of

Poor Clare Colettine Nuns,

followers of Saint Francis and Saint Clare, living a cloistered contemplative life. We have dedicated ourselves to the Gospel call of poverty, simplicity, charity; living a humble, hidden life of prayer, penance and work for the praise and glory of God and the salvation of souls.

We recite the entire Liturgy of the Hours daily, rising at midnight for the hour of Matins. Eucharistic adoration is an important part of our daily schedule. Except for one hour of sharing together at recreation, we keep silence in order to be attentive to the voice of the Lord Who speaks to our hearts.

We are loyal daughters of our holy Mother the Church and our holy Father the Pope, the Vicar of Christ.

If you think that God may be calling you to this joyful way of life, please contact:

MOTHER MARY REGINA, P.C.C.
CORPUS CHRISTI MONASTERY
2111 S MAIN ST
ROCKFORD IL 61102
815-963-7343
http://poorclare.org/rockford

Send one of the postcards in this book for more information.

POOR CLARE COLETTINE

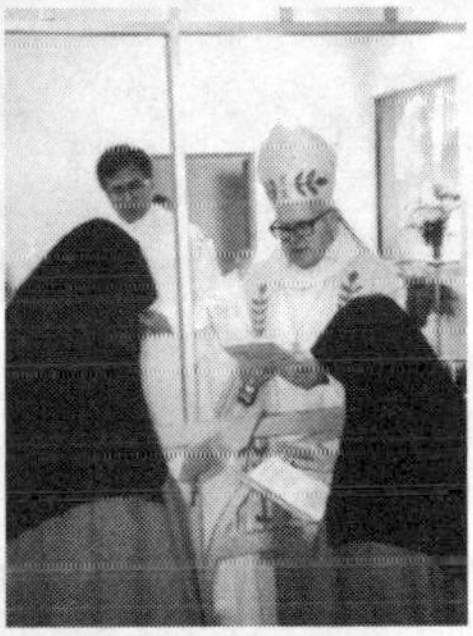

As enclosed, contemplative nuns we cherish the spirit of our Father St. Francis of Assisi who taught us to follow the Poor and Humble Christ and His Most Holy Mother through our Holy Mother St. Clare. Through her whose very name means light, we catch the fire of loving gratitude to God. She wrote in her Testament: "Among the other favors we have received and daily continue to receive from the Giver of all good gifts and for which we should render all the more thanks, great is the grace of our vocation."

A renewal of this Gospel way of living was given to us by our second mother, Saint Colette, who reformed our order in the fifteenth century. Love marked her entire existence as she strove generously to find practical expression for it within the enclosure.

We also seek to enflesh this rich heritage as we devote ourselves to creating and maintaining an atmosphere of quiet prayer and ready penance. Our prayer is focused on the Holy Mass, Exposition of the Blessed Sacrament and the Liturgy of the Hours. The Hour of Matins, chanted at midnight, is symbolic of the eschatological thrust of our life: an ardent thirst for the coming of the Lord Jesus as we hold precious every soul purchased by His Sacred Blood. Our penance is comprised of our fasting and abstinence, our manual labor and by our going barefoot. Our work consists in supplying First Communion veils, spiritual remembrance cards and the care of our monastery and garden.

Our prayer is intensified and our penance lightened by sharing it with our sisters. Within the walls of the monastery we form a true and close family and experience together what it means to be a church in miniature, for we are at the heart of the Church for the needs of the Body of Christ.

To learn more about life in our Monastery please write Mother Mary Dorothy at the address below, or call (815) 467-0032

Annunciation Monastery
6200 E. Minooka Rd. Minooka, Il. 60447

Send one of the postcards in this book for more information.

Send one of the postcards in this book for more information.

A-158

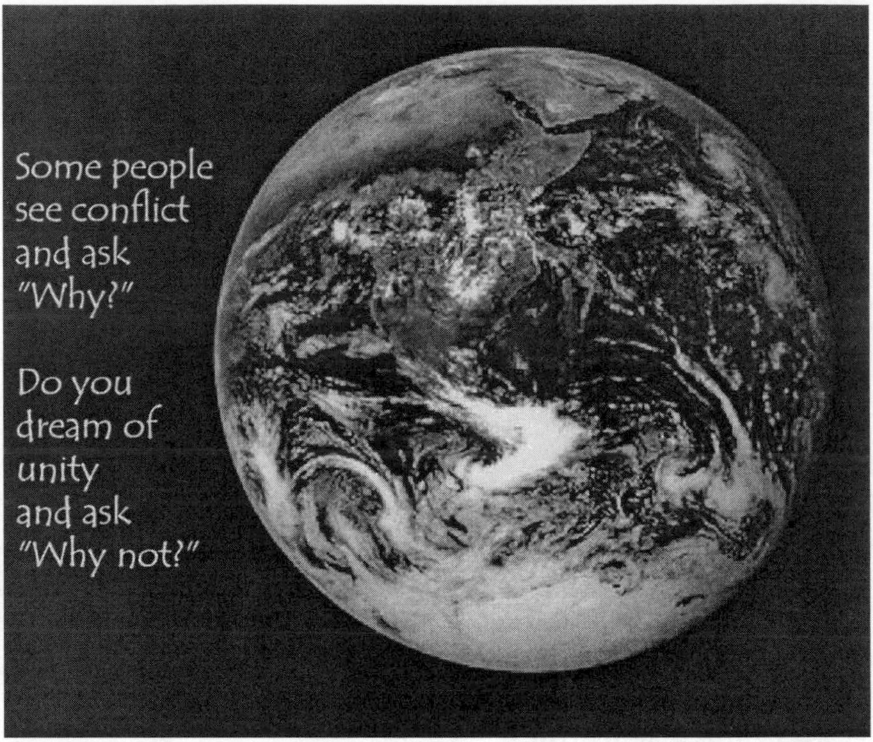

Some people
see conflict
and ask

Why Not?

Make your life a witness to the teachings of Jesus
Do all you can to eliminate the causes of poverty
Work for peace and justice
Help in the struggle for stewardship of the Earth
Put your faith in unconditional Peace and Reconciliation

We do.

Call our Vocation Director
Sue Torgersen, CSJ (507) 359-1674
or Chris March, CSJ (708) 482-5084
Also, visit our web site:
www.csjlagrange.org
E-mail: vocations@csjlagrange.org

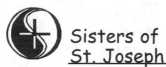

Sisters of
St. Joseph of LaGrange

Do you
dream of
unity
and ask

Send one of the postcards in this book for more information.

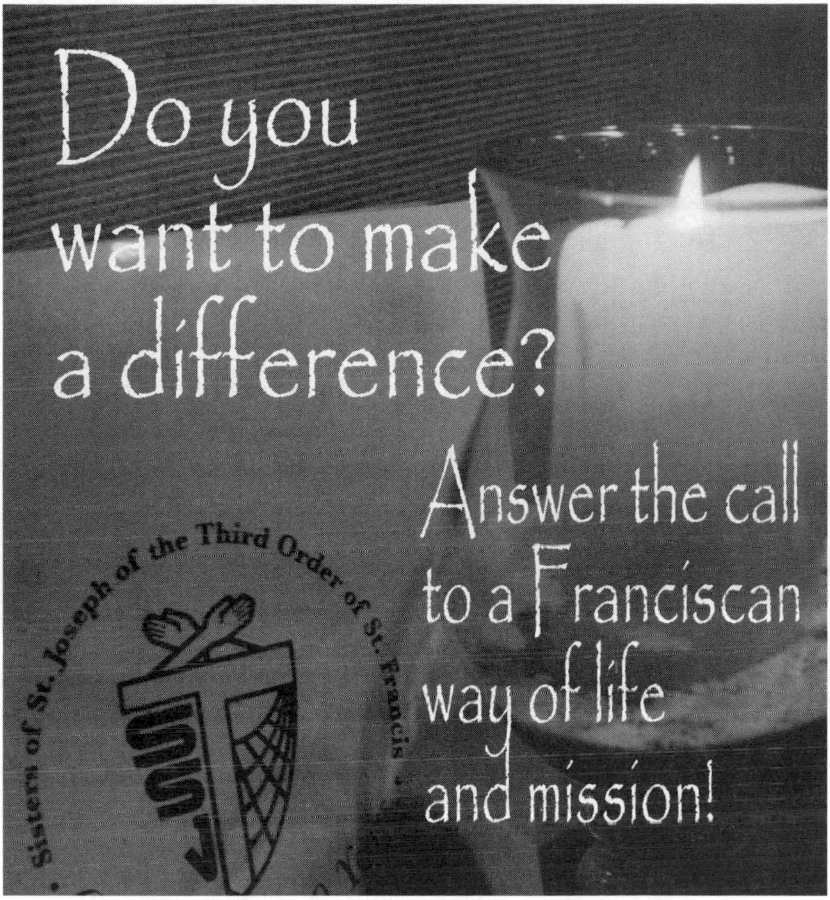

Sisters of St. Joseph

of the Third Order of St. Francis

P.O. Box 305
Stevens Point, WI 54481-0305

Phone: (715) 341-8457 **Fax: (715) 341-8830**

E-mail: vocation@ssj-tosf.org

www.ssj-tosf.org

Use the Sisters of St. Joseph of the Third Order of St. Francis postcard to request further information.

Salesian Sisters of St. John Bosco

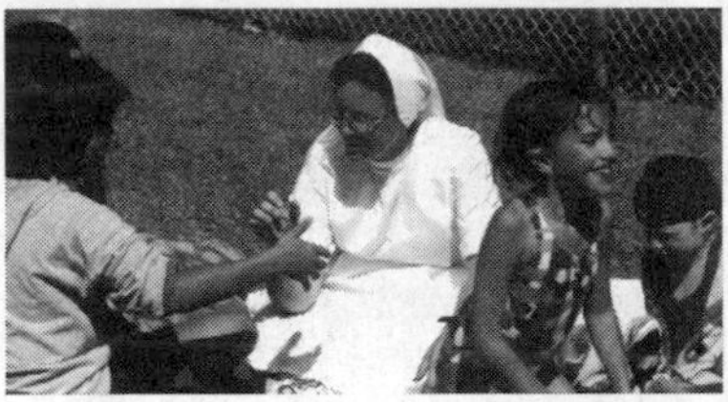

Walking with the young...

infusing courage...

reawakening energy...

developing gifts...

the ***Salesian Sisters***

challenge and are

challenged by the young!

Salesian Sisters

serving, teaching, inspiring, laughing and working with youth

For more information contact the Sister nearest you:

Sr. Antoinette Cedrone, FMA – NJ
973.790.4408
fmavoc@aol.com

Sr. Maria Colombo, FMA – LA
504-347-8044
fmavoc@aol.com

Sr. Carmen Botello, FMA – CA
562-866-0675
fmasuovoc@aol.com

Sr. Kathy Keane – TX
210-432-1919
Skkfma@aol.com

Visit our website

www.salesiansisters.org
Eastern Province

www.salesiansisterswest.org
Western Province

Send one of the postcards in this book for more information.

We commit ourselves:

To develop nonviolent, healing processes and mechanisms to achieve mutuality, reconciliation and justice among ourselves, in our ministries, in the Church and in broader society.

SSSF U.S. Province Direction for 2003–2007

SCHOOL SISTERS OF ST. FRANCIS

www.sssf.org

Sister Christine Myskow
Co-Director of New Membership
(414) 385-5253
cmyskow@sssf.org

Send one of the postcards in this book for more information.

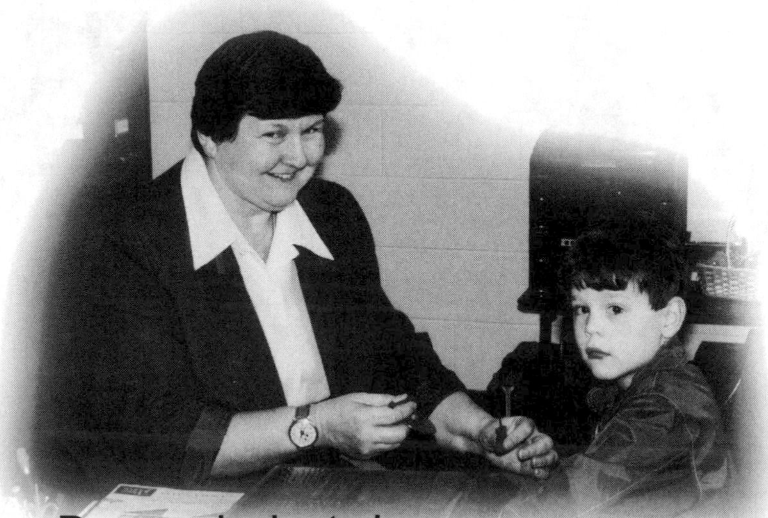

Do you desire to be a presence…

of Faith?

of Family Love?

of Self Giving?

SERVANTS OF THE HOLY HEART OF MARY

For more information, contact:

Sr. Myra Lambert, SSCM
Servants of the Holy Heart of Mary
717 North Batavia Avenue
Batavia, Illinois 60510
630-879-1296
e-mail: lam-bert@inil.com

Use the Servants of the Holy Heart of Mary postcard to request further information.

Send one of the postcards in this book for more information.

Send one of the postcards in this book for more information.

Trinity Missions
Missionary Servants of the Most Holy Trinity

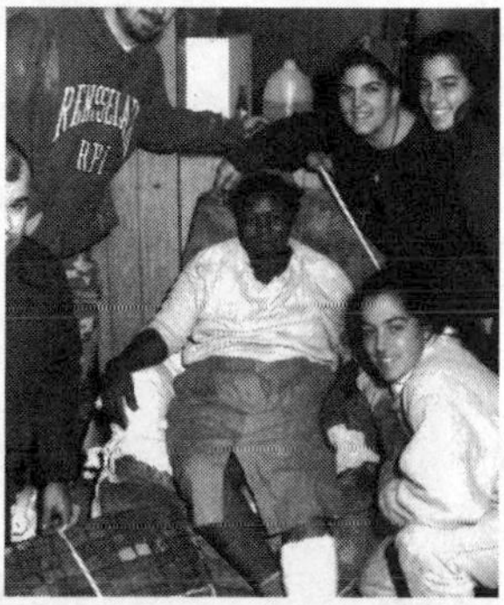

We Invite You To Minister With The Poor And Abandoned

- Join our family of missionaries as we work for justice throughout the Americas.
- Our missionary family is made up of Lay Missionaries, Religious Sisters, Priests and Brothers.
- We bring the light and hope of Jesus Christ to the forgotten people of the United States, Mexico, Puerto Rico, Costa Rica, and Colombia.
- Join us for a week, a month, a year, or a lifetime to help us spread the Good News of the Gospel.

CONTACT US:

Vocation: 800-298-5602 / mccann@trinitymissions.org
Volunteer: 800-272-8850 / trinityctr@aol.com

Visit our website: www.tmc3.org

Trinity Missions Vocation Department
9001 New Hampshire Ave.
Silver Spring, MD 20903

Use the Trinity Missions postcard to request further information.

Who said a leap of faith has to be such a big jump?

Finding the right path to follow can seem like a daunting task. The Ursuline Sisters believe that choosing a way of life can make a difference.

The **Ursuline Sisters of Louisville** believe that service and love are a way of life and can change a life forever. We see this happen every day. We hope you will come see it as well.

Talk to Sister Merry Marcotte
(502) 896-3948
mmarcotte@ursulineslou.org
or, in South Carolina,
Sister Julienne Guy
(803) 738-1294
julie.guyosu@juno.com

URSULINE SISTERS
OF LOUISVILLE

3105 Lexington Road
Louisville, KY 40206
www.ursulineslou.org

Mission: Teaching Christian living by assisting others in living more fully and developing a personal relationship with God.

Send one of the postcards in this book for more information.

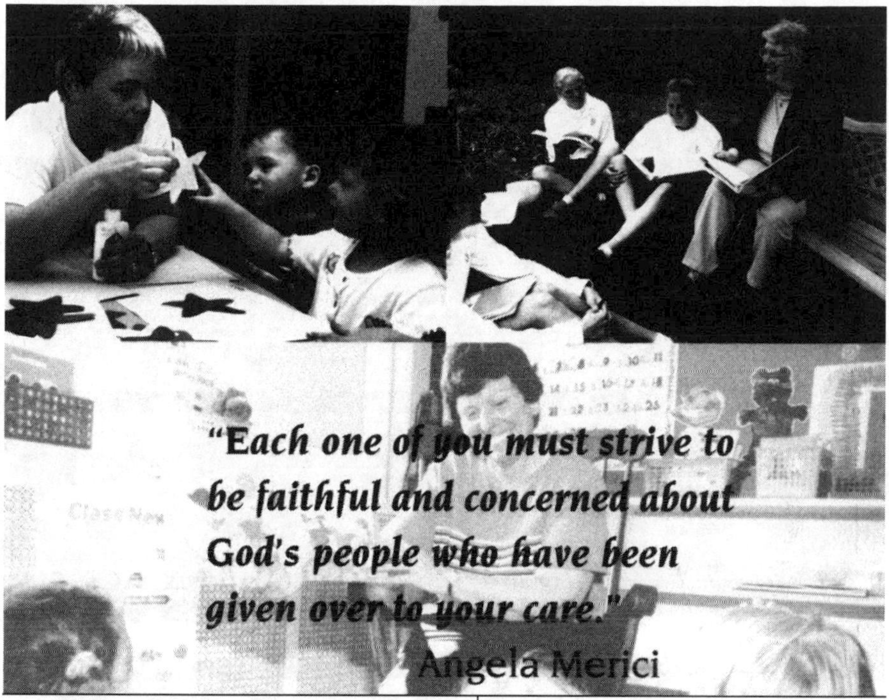
"Each one of you must strive to
be faithful and concerned about
God's people who have been
given over to your care."
Angela Merici

WE ARE THE Ursuline Sisters OF CLEVELAND

VOCATION OFFICE
2600 Lander Road
Cleveland, Ohio 44124

Tel 440-449-1200, EXT 138

Fax 440-449-3588

E-mail rgoebel@ursulinesisters.org

Web www.ursulinesisters.org

Our Foundress, Saint Angela Merici, freed women for new roles in the Church. Ursulines brought her ministry of education to Cleveland in 1850 and continue to empower women and children around the corner and around the world – from Cleveland to El Salvador to Bolivia. We are a community of women with diverse backgrounds united in spirit by contemplation, and committed to the mission of justice and compassion.

Use the Ursuline Sisters of Cleveland postcard to request further information.

Religious Ministries Online

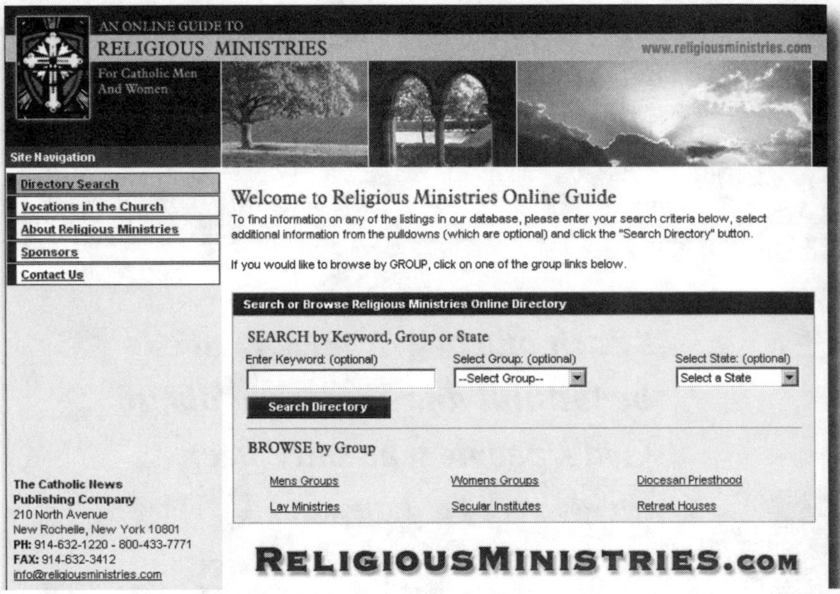

www.religiousministries.com

A comprehensive database of more than 3,000 Catholic organizations nationwide. Visit the site for in-depth information about men's and women's communities active in the United States plus many part time opportunities. Use the Online Guide to search for religious communities that offer your desired ministry.

Search by Category:

Men's Communities Women's Communities Diocesan Priesthood
Secular Institutes Lay Ministry Organizations
Retreat Centers Religious Study Opportunities

Search by Apostolic Work: (for example)

Education Parish Work Health Care Communications
Child Care Elderly Care

Diocesan Vocation Offices

ALABAMA

Diocese of Birmingham
Very Rev. Robert J. Sullivan, V.V.,
Vicar of Vocations
Sacred Heart of Jesus
PO Box 5010, 3005 Woodbridge Dr.
Anniston, AL 36205
(256) 237-3011, ext. 106
E-mail: father@sacredheart anniston.org
Dr. Stephen Smith,
Coordinator for Vocations
PO Box 12047
Birmingham, AL 35202-2047
(205) 838-2184
E-mail: ssmith@bhmdiocese.org

Archdiocese of Mobile
Rev. Alejandro E. Valladares,
Vocation Director
6051 Old Shell Rd.
Mobile, AL 36608
(251) 343-3662
Fax: (251) 460-4687
E-mail: sacredhrtfralex@ bellsouth.net
Web: rcamobile.org/keyindex/ vocatio1.html

ALASKA

Archdiocese of Anchorage
Bro. Craig Bonham, O.M.I.,
Vocation Office
225 Cordova St.
Anchorage, AK 99501
(907) 297-7774
Fax: (907) 279-3885
E-mail: craig.bonham@caa-ak.org
Web: www.archdioceseof anchorage.org/

Diocese of Fairbanks
Fr. John Hinsvark,
Vocation Director
St. Joseph Parish
PO Box 1010, 100 King Place
Nome, AK 99762-1010
(907) 474-0753
Fax: (907) 474-8009
Web: www.cbna.info

Diocese of Juneau
Rev. Michael W. Warfel,
Vocation Director
415 6th St.
Juneau, AK 99801
(907) 586-2227, ext. 25
E-mail: bishopmike@gci.net
Web: www.dioceseofjuneau.org/

ARIZONA

Diocese of Phoenix
Rev. Don Kline, Director,
Office for Diocesan Priesthood
400 E. Monroe St.
Phoenix, AZ 85004
(602) 354-2004
Fax: (602) 258-3425
E-mail: frkline@diocesephoenix.org
Web: www.diocesephoenix.org/ vocations

Diocese of Tucson
Rev. Remigio "Miguel" Mariano, Jr.,
Director of Vocations
PO Box 31
Tucson, AZ 85702-0031
(520) 792-3410
Fax: (520) 792-0291
E-mail: vocations@diocese tucson.org
Web: www.diocesetucson.org

ARKANSAS

Diocese of Little Rock
Fr. Les Farley,
Vocation Director
2500 N. Tyler St.
PO Box 7565
Little Rock, AR 72207
(501) 664-0340
Fax: (501) 664-9075
E-mail: farleysaintles@aol.com

CALIFORNIA

Diocese of Fresno
Rev. Msgr. Anthony Janelli,
Vocation Director
1550 N. Fresno St.
Fresno, CA 93703-3788
(559) 488-7478
Fax: (559) 488-7475
E-mail: vocations@dioceseo ffresno.org
Web: www.dioceseoffresno.org

Archdiocese of Los Angeles
Fr. James Forsen,
Sr. Kathy Bryant, RSC,
Fr. Bob Juarez,
Fr. Truc Nguyen,
Vocation Team
Office for Vocations
3424 Wilshire Blvd.
Los Angeles, CA 90010-2241
(213) 637-7248
Fax: (213) 637-6248
E-mail: FrJRForsen@ la–archdiocese .org (Fr. Forsen)
kbryt@aol.com (Sr. Bryant)
Taticbob@aol.com (Fr. Juarez)
nqtruc@yahoo.com (Fr. Nguyen)
Web: http://vocations. la–archdiocese.org

Diocese of Monterey
Sr. Molly Neville, SNJM,
Director, Vocation Office
405 Palma Dr.
Salinas, CA 93901-1822
(831) 796-0136
Fax: (831) 796-0138
E-mail: vocations@dioceseof monterey.org
Web: www.dioceseofmonterey.org
Fr. Antonio Sanchez,
Assistant Vocation Director
Our Lady of the Assumption Church
100 Salinas Rd.
Watsonville, CA 95076
(831) 722-1104
Fr. Michael Volk,
Assistant Vocation Director
St. Theodore's Church
PO Drawer B
Gonzales, CA 93926
(831) 675-3648

Diocese of Oakland
Fr. Larry D'Anjou,
Director of Vocations
Office of Vocations
2900 Lakeshore Ave.
Oakland, CA 94610
(510) 267-8356
E-mail: ldanjou@oakdiocese.org
Web: www.oakdiocese.org

Diocese of Orange
Rev. Msgr. Wilbur Davis,
Vocation Director
(714) 282-3033
E-mail: msgr.wdavis@rcbo.org
Sister Eymard Flood, OSC,
Women's Vocations
(714) 282-3120
E-mail: sr.eflood@rcbo.org
2811 E. Villa Real Dr.
Orange, CA 92863-1595
Web: www.rcbo.org

Diocese of Sacramento
Rev. Mark R. Richards, J.C.L.,
Rev. Humberto Gomez,
Co-Directors of Vocations
Sr. Maria Campos, RSM,
Associate Vocation Director
Pastoral Center
2110 Broadway
Sacramento, CA 95818
(916) 733-0258
Fax: (916) 733-0224
E-mail: callserve@aol.com, mrichard@diocese-sacramento.org, hgomez@diocese-sacramento.org, mcampos@diocese-sacramento.org
Web: www.diocese-sacramento.org

Diocese of San Bernardino
Sr. Sarah Shrewsbury, O.S.C.,
Vocations Director
Rev. Paul Granillo,
Associate Vocations Director
1201 East Highland Ave.
San Bernardino, CA 92404-4607
(909) 475-5470 (Sr. Shrewsbury)
(909) 475-5344 (Fr. Granillo)
Fax: (909) 475-5457
E-mail: vocations@sbdiocese.org
Web: www.sbdiocese.org

Diocese of San Diego
Deacon Ray Arnold,
Director, Office for Vocations
Sr. Nancy Kane,
Director, Office for Women Religious
P.O. Box 85728
San Diego, CA 92186-5728
(858) 490-8351, 8289
E-mail: rarnold@dioces-sdiego.org
Web: diocese-sdiego.org

Archdiocese of San Francisco
Rev. Craig Forner,
Director of Vocations
445 Church St.
San Francisco, CA 94114
(415) 565-3618
Fax: (415) 565-3648
E-mail: craigfsf@aol.com
Web: hometown.aol.com/craigfsf

Diocese of San Jose
Rev. Mark Catalana,
Vocation Director
Melissa Bosé
900 Lafayette St., Suite 301
Santa Clara, CA 95050-4966
(408) 983-0255, 0155
Fax: (408) 983-0257
E-mail: frmark@dsj.org (Fr. Mark), bose@dsj.org (Melissa Bosé)
Web: www.dsj.org/vocations/dsjvocations.htm

Diocese of Santa Rosa
Rev. Loren Allen,
Director of Vocations
St. Bernard Church
PO Box 169
Eureka, CA 95502
(707) 442-6466
E-mail: sbchurch@humboldt1.com
Web: www.santarosacatholic.org

Diocese of Stockton
Sr. Wanda M. Billion, MSC
Director of Vocations
1125 N. Lincoln St.
Stockton, CA 95203-2410
(209) 466-0636, ext. 619
Fax: (209) 463-5937
E-mail: wbillion@stocktondiocese.org

COLORADO

Diocese of Colorado Springs
Vocation Office
29 West Kiowa St.
Colorado Springs, CO 80903
(719) 636-2345
Fax: (719) 636-1216
E-mail: info@diocs.org
Web: www.diocesecs.org

Archdiocese of Denver
Rev. Kent F. Drotar,
Director of Vocations
Rev. Jeff Wilborn,
Associate Director of Vocations
1300 S. Steele St.
Denver, CO 80210
(303) 282-3429
E-mail: vocation@archden.org
Web: www.archden.org/vocations

Diocese of Pueblo
Vocation Director
1001 N. Grand Ave.
Pueblo, CO 81003
(719) 544-9861, ext.116
Web: www.dioceseofpueblo.com

CONNECTICUT

Diocese of Bridgeport
Rev. Chris J. Walsh,
Vocation Director
Saint John Fisher Seminary Residence
894 Newfield Ave.
Stamford, CT 06905
(203) 322-5331
Fax: (203) 461-9876
E-mail: fatherwalsh@saintjohnfisher.org
Web: www.saintjohnfisher.org

Archdiocese of Hartford
Fr. Alphonso Fontana,
Vocation Director
467 Bloomfield Ave.
Bloomfield, CT 06002
(860) 286-7670
Fax: (860) 242-9701
E-mail: fralfontana@aol.com
Web: www.archdiocese-hartford.org

Diocese of Norwich
Rev. Msgr. Thomas R. Bride, P.A., K.H.S., V.G.,
Vocation Director
Rev. Mark O'Donnell,
Director of Vocation Promotion/Development
Rev. Michael Phillippino,
Assistant Director of Vocations
201 Broadway
Norwich, CT 06360-4328
(860) 887-9294
E-mail: vocations@norwichdiocese.org
Web: www.God-calls.org

DELAWARE

Catholic Diocese of Wilmington
Rev. James Nash,
Vocation Director
1925 Delaware Ave.
PO Box 2030
Wilmington, DE 19899
(302) 573-3113
E-mail: vocdir1@aol.com
Web: www.priests2be.org

DISTRICT OF COLUMBIA

Archdiocese of Washington/ Suburban Maryland
Rev. Robert J. Panke,
Director, Office of Priestly Vocations
Archdiocese of Washington
PO Box 29260
Washington, DC 20017-0260
(301) 853-4580
E-mail: Vocations@adw.org
Web: www.dcvocations.org

FLORIDA

Archdiocese of Miami
Father Pedro M. Corces,
Director of Vocations
9401 Biscayne Blvd.
Miami Shores, FL 33138
(305) 762-1137
E-mail: vocations@miamiarch.org

Diocese of Orlando
Rev. Thomas Barrett,
Vocation Director
PO Box 1800
Orlando, FL 32802
(407) 246-4875
E-mail: frtomdvd@aol.com

Diocese of Palm Beach
Rev. Gavin Badway,
Director of Vocations
Sr. Helen Kilijanski, ASCJ,
Coordinator for Religious Vocation Directors
P.O. Box 109650
9995 North Military Trail
Palm Beach Gardens, FL 33410-9650
(561) 775-9552
E-mail: vocations@diocesepb.org
Web: www.diocesepb.org

Diocese of Pensacola-Tallahassee
Rev. Msgr. C. Slade Crawford,
Director of Vocations
P.O. Drawer 17329
Pensacola, FL 32522-7329
(850) 432-1515
Fax: (850) 436-6424
E-mail: crawfordc@ptdiocese.org
Web: ptdiocese.org

Diocese of St. Augustine
Rev. H. John Tetlow,
Director of Vocations
Catholic Center
P.O. Box 24000
Jacksonville, FL 32241-4000
(904) 262-3200, ext. 101
Fax: (904) 262-0698
E-mail: jtetlow@dosafl.com
padrehjt@earthlink.net
Web: www.dosafl.com

Diocese of St. Petersburg
Rev. Leonard J.M. Plazewski,
Director of Vocations
PO Box 40200
6363 9th Ave. N.
St. Petersburg, FL 33710
(727) 345-3452
E-mail: spvocation@aol.com
Web: www.spvocation.org

Diocese of Venice
Fr. Bob Kantor,
Associate Vocations Director
P.O. Box 2006
Venice, FL 34284-2006
E-mail: Kantor@dioceseofvenice.org
Web: www.dioceseofvenice.org

GEORGIA

Archdiocese of Atlanta
Rev. Brian J. Higgins,
Vocations Director
680 West Peachtree St., N.W.
Atlanta, GA 30308-1984
(404) 888-7844
E-mail: bhiggins@archatl.com
Web: www.archatl.com

Diocese of Savannah
Rev. Brett A. Brannen,
Vocation Director
St. Peter Claver Church
131 Ward St.
Macon, GA 31204
(478) 743-1454
Fax: (478) 743-9868
E-mail: Frbrett@savannahpriest.com
Web: www.savannahpriest.com

HAWAII

Diocese of Honolulu
Rev. Gary Secor,
Director of Vocations
1184 Bishop St.
Honolulu, HI 96813
(808) 585-3343
Fax: (808) 585-3384
E-mail: gsecor@rcchawaii.org
Web: www.pono.net

IDAHO

Diocese of Boise
Fr. Jairo Restrepo,
Vocations Director
804 N. 9th St.
Boise, ID 83702
(208) 342-1328
Fax: (208) 324-4082
E-mail: jrestrepo@rcdb.org
Web: catholicidaho.org

ILLINOIS

Diocese of Belleville
Rev. Eugene H. Wojcik,
Vocation Director
Diocesan Pastoral Center
2620 Lebanon Ave.
Belleville, IL 62221-3299
(618) 235-9601, ext. 148
Fax: (618) 235-7416
E-mail: gwojcik@diobelle.org

Archdiocese of Chicago
Sister Peter Mary Hettling, C.S.J.,
Vocation Director
Vocation Office
155 E. Superior St.
Chicago, IL 60611-2911
(312) 751-5245
E-mail: phettling@archchicago.org
Web: www.archchicago.org/departments/vocation/vocation.shtm

Diocese of Joliet
Rev. John Regan,
Vocation Director
St. Charles Pastoral Center
402 S. Independence Blvd.
Romeoville, IL 60446-2264
(815) 834-4004
E-mail: frjohnr@aol.com
Web: www.vocations.com

Diocese of Peoria
Rev. Brian K. Brownsey,
Vocation Director
613 N. E. Jefferson St.
Peoria, IL 61603
(309) 671-1569
E-mail: frbrownsey@cdop.org

Diocese of Rockford
Rev. Aaron Brodeski,
Vocation Office
1204 N. Church St.
Rockford, IL 61103
(815) 963-1009
Fax: (815) 963-1030
E-Mail: mail@RockVoc.org
Web: www.rockvoc.org

Diocese of Springfield in Illinois
Rev. John M. Titus,
Director of Vocations
1615 W. Washington St.
PO Box 3187
Springfield, IL 62708-3187
(217) 698-9500, ext. 182
Fax: (217) 698-8602
E-mail: jtitus@dio.org
Web: www.getalifeinChrist.org

INDIANA

Diocese of Evansville
Father Bernard Etienne,
Vocation Director
Sr. Jenny Schmitt, OSB,
Vocations Team
PO Box 4169
4200 N. Kentucky Ave.
Evansville, IN 47724-0169
(812) 424-5536
E-mail: betienne@evansville-diocese.net;
jschmitt@thedome.org
Web: www.evansville-diocese.org/vocations/vocation.htm

Diocese of Fort Wayne-South Bend
Rev. Bernard J. Galic,
Vocation Director
114 W. Wayne St.
South Bend, IN 46601
(574) 234-0687
Fax: (574) 232-8483
E-mail: bjgalic@earthlink.net
Web: diocesefwsb.org

Diocese of Gary
Rev. Kevin Huber,
Vocation Director
Diocese of Gary Pastoral Center
9292 Broadway
Merrillville, IN 46410
(219) 769-9292
E-mail: vocations@garyvocation.org
Web: garyvocation.org

Archdiocese of Indianapolis
Rev. Joseph B. Moriarty,
Vocation Director
1400 Meredion St.
Indianapolis, IN 46202
(317) 236-1496
E-mail: jmoriarty@archindy.org
Web: vocations@archindy.org

Diocese of Lafayette-in-Indiana
Rev. Brian M. Doerr,
Office of Vocations
St. Mary Cathedral
1212 South St.
Lafayette, IN 47901-1576
(765) 742-4440
E-mail: revbdoerr@priestforever.org
Web: www.priestforever.org

IOWA

Diocese of Davenport
Rev. Charles A. Adam,
Vocation Director
St. Ambrose University
518 W. Locust St.
Davenport, IA 52803
(563) 333-6151
E-mail: AdamCharlesA@ambrose.sau.edu
Web: www.davenportdiocese.org

Diocese of Des Moines
Rev. John W. Acrea,
Vocation Director
601 Grand Ave.
Des Moines, IA 50309
(515) 237-5050
E-mail: jacrea@dmdiocese.org
Web: www.vocationsonline.com

Archdiocese of Dubuque
Rev. Phillip Gibbs,
Director of Vocation Awareness
Archdiocesan Center
1229 Mt. Loretta Ave., PO Box 479
Dubuque, IA 52004-0479
(563) 556-2580, ext. 281
Fax: (563) 556-5464
E-mail: dbqcvo@arch.pvt.k12.ia.us

Diocese of Sioux City
Rev. Brian C. Hughes,
Vocation Director
1821 Jackson St.
Sioux City, IA 51105
(712) 233-7933
Fax: (712) 233-7598
E-mail: hughes@scdiocese.org
Web: www.scdiocese.org

KANSAS

Diocese of Dodge City
Rev. Pascal L. Klein,
Vocation Director
St. John the Evangelist
122 East Fifth St.
Hoisington, KS 67544
(620) 653-2963
Fax: (620) 653-2934
E-mail: pklein@dcdiocese.org,
vocations@dcdiocese.org
Web: www.dcdiocese.org

Archdiocese of Kansas City
Rev. Brian Schieber,
Vocation Director
Catholic Church Offices
12615 Parallel Parkway
Kansas City, KS 66109
(913) 721-1570, ext. 146
Fax: (913) 721-1577
E-mail: vocation@archkck.org

Diocese of Salina
Father David Metz,
Vocation Director
Immaculate Heart of Mary Parish
1805 Vine St.
Hays, KS 67601
(785) 625-7339
E-mail: salinavocations@hotmail.com
Web: salinadiocese.org

Diocese of Wichita
Rev. Matthew C. McGinness,
Vocation Director
1810 N. Roosevelt
Wichita, KS 67208
(316) 684-6896
Rev. Joseph C. Tatro
Assistant Vocation Director
St. Patrick Church
638 Ave. D West
Kingman, KS 67068
(620) 532-5440
Rev. Hien Paul Nguyen,
Assistant Vocation Director
3600 East Harry
Wichita, KS 67218
(316) 689-5050
Web: www.cdowk.com

KENTUCKY

Diocese of Covington
Rev. John R. Sterling,
Vocation Director
PO Box 18548
947 Donaldson Rd.
Covington, KY 41018-0548
(859) 283-6300
Fax: (859) 283-6334
E-mail: jsterling@covingtondiocese.org
Web: www.covingtondiocese.org

Diocese of Lexington
Rev. Mark D. Dreves,
Director of Vocations
1310 W. Main St.
Lexington, KY 40508-2048
(859) 253-1993, ext. 249
E-mail: mdreves@cdlex.org
Web: www.cdlex.org

Archdiocese of Louisville
Rev. J. Ronald Knott,
Vocation Director
Maloney Center
1200 So. Shelby St.
Louisville, KY 40203-2600
(502) 636-0296
Fax: (502) 636-2379
E-mail: vocation@archlou.org
Web: www.archlou.org

Diocese of Owensboro
Father Brad Whistle,
Precious Blood Church
3306 Fenmore St.
Owensboro, KY 42301
(270) 684-6888

LOUISIANA

Diocese of Alexandria
Fr. Jason Gootee,
Director of Vocations
2618 Vandenburg Dr.
PO Box 7417
Alexandria, LA 71306-0417
(318) 445-2401
Fax: (318) 448-6121
E-Mail: vocations@diocesealex.org
Web: www.diocesealex.org

Diocese of Baton Rouge
Rev. M. Jeffery Bayhi,
Director of Vocations
Sister Dianne Heinrich, CDP,
Associate Director of Seminarians
1800 South Acadian Thruway
Baton Rouge, LA 70808-1998
Mailing address: PO Box 2028
Baton Rouge, LA 70821-2028
(225) 336-8778, 387-0561
Fax: (225) 242-0342
E-mail: vocations@diobr.org
Web: www.diobr.org

Diocese of Houma Thibodaux
Fr. Jim Morrison,
Vocation Director
PO Box 505
Schriever, LA 70395
(985) 850-3138, 446-6201
Fax: (985) 850-3215
E-mail: ht_vocations@hotmail.com,
jmorrison@htdiocese.org
Web: www.htdiocese.org/vocations

Diocese of Lafayette
Fr. Aaron Melançon,
Vocation Director
Our Lady of Victory Church
PO Box 365
Loreauville, LA 70552
(337) 229-4254
Web: www.dol-louisiana.org

Diocese of Lake Charles
Fr. Tim Goodly,
Director of Vocations
411 Iris St.
Lake Charles, LA 70601
(337) 439-7426, ext. 17
Fax: (337) 439-7428
E-mail: lcdiocese@laol.net
Web: http://lcdiocese.org

Archdiocese of New Orleans
Rev. Msgr. Henry J. Bugler,
Director of Vocations
Rev. Joseph Palermo,
Associate Director of Vocations
7887 Walmsley Ave.
New Orleans, LA 70125-3496
(504) 861-6298
Fax: (504) 866-2906
E-mail: vocations@archdiocese-no.org
Web: www.vocationoffice-no.org

Diocese of Shreveport
Fr. Mark Watson,
Vocation Director
3500 Fairfield Ave.
Shreveport, LA 71104
(318) 868-4441; (800) 256-1542
Fax: (318) 868-4605
E-mail: mwatson@dioshpt.org
Web: www.dioshpt.org

MAINE

Diocese of Portland
Rev. Frank Murray,
Vocation Director
St. Dominic High School
121 Gracelawn Rd.
Auburn, ME 04210
(207) 782-6911, ext. 3109
E-mail: vocations@portland diocese.net
Web: www.portlanddiocese. net

MARYLAND

Archdiocese of Baltimore
Rev. Gerard Francik,
Director of Vocations
Rev. J. Kevin Farmer,
Associate Director
320 Cathedral St.
Baltimore, MD 21201 4415
(410) 547-5426
Fax: (410) 234-2953
E-mail: vocations@archbalt.org
Web: www.archbalt.org/vocations

MASSACHUSETTS

Archdiocese of Boston
Fr. Oscar J. Pratt, II,
Vocation Director
Vocation Office
127 Lake St.
Brighton, MA 02135
(617) 746-5435
Fax: (617) 746-5468
E-mail: info@bostonpriesthood.org
Web: www.bostonpriesthood.org

Diocese of Fall River
Rev. Craig A. Pregana,
Vocation Office
PO Box 2577
Fall River, MA 02722-2577
(508) 675-1311
Fax: (508) 679-9220
E-mail: vocations@dioc-fr.org
Web: www.fallrivervocations.org

Diocese of Springfield
Rev. Daniel S. Pacholec,
Vocation Director
PO Box 1730
Springfield, MA 01101-1730
(413) 732-3175
E-mail: vocations@ diospringfield.org
Web: www.diospringfield.org

Diocese of Worcester
Rev. Msgr. Thomas Sullivan,
Vocation Director
49 Elm St.
Worcester, MA 01609
(508) 929-4350
Fax: (508) 754-2768
E-mail: vocdir@aol.com
Web: www.worcesterdiocese.org

MICHIGAN

Archdiocese of Detroit
Rev. James D. Bilot,
Vocation Director
Sr. Angela Cerna-Plata, IHM,
Associate Vocation Director
305 Michigan Ave.
Detroit, MI 48226-2605
(313) 237-5875
Fax: (313) 237-6070
E-mail: vocations@aol.com
Web: www.vocationsdetroit.org

Diocese of Gaylord
Rev. Joseph Blasko,
Director of Vocations
611 North St.
Gaylord, MI 49735
(989) 732-5147
Fax: (989) 705-3589
E-mail: jblasko@dioceseof gaylord.org
Web: dioceseofgaylord.org

Diocese of Grand Rapids
Rev. Paul A. Milanowski,
Director of Vocations
St. Joseph Center
600 Burton St. S.E.
Grand Rapids, MI 49507-3290
(616) 243 0401, ext. 530
E-mail: pmilan@dioceseof grandrapids.org
Web: www.dioceseof grandrapids.org

Diocese of Kalamazoo
Rev. Robert F. Creagan,
Director, Office of Vocations
215 N. Westnedge Ave.
Kalamazoo, MI 49007-3760
(616) 349-8714, ext. 242
E-mail: Creaganfr@aol.com,
vocation@dioceseofkalamazoo.org
Web: www.dioceseofkalamazoo.org

Diocese of Lansing
Carla Moeggenborg, O.P.,
Director of Vocation Services
300 W. Ottawa St.
Lansing, MI 48933
(517) 342-2506
Fax: (517) 342-2515
E-mail: cmoeggenborg@diocese oflansing.org
Web: www.2beapriest4Christ.com

Diocese of Marquette
Rev. James Ziminski,
Director of Vocations
444 S. Fourth, P.O. Box 550
Marquette, MI 49855-0550
(906) 228-0229
E-mail: vocations@priesthood possibilities.org
Web: www.priesthood possibilities.org

Diocese of Saginaw
Rev. Thomas Moore, O.S.F.S.,
Director of Seminarians
5800 Weiss St.
Saginaw, MI 48603
(989) 797-6661
E-mail: tomm@dioceseof saginaw.org
Web: dioceseofsaginaw.org

MINNESOTA

Diocese of Crookston
Fr. Vincent Miller,
Vocation Director
Box 610
Crookston, MN 56716
(218) 281-4533
Ray Hollcraft
Associate Vocation Director
PO Box 610
Crookston, MN 56716
(218) 281-4533
Mitch Walski,
Associate Vocation Director
PO Box A
Greenbush, MN 56726
(218) 782-2467
E-mail: rhollcraft@crookston.org
Web: www.crookston.org

Diocese of Duluth
Deacon Michael Knuth,
Office of Vocations
2830 East 4th St.
Duluth, MN 55812
(218) 724-9111
E-mail: mknuth@dioceseduluth.org
Web: www.dioceseduluth.org

Diocese of New Ulm
Fr. Todd Petersen,
Coordinator of Priesthood Candidates
Japanese Martyrs
30881 Co. Rd. 24
Sleepy Eye, MN 56085
(507) 794-6974
E-mail: frtoddpetersen@ hotmail.com
Sr. Sue Torgersen, CSJ,
Coordinator, Office of Vocations
Catholic Pastoral Center
1400 6th St. N.
New Ulm, MN 56073-2099
(507) 359-2966
Fax: (507) 354-3667
E-mail: storgersen@dnu.org
Web: www.dnu.org/admin/ vocations.html

Diocese of St. Cloud
Rev. Gregory Mastey,
Director, Office of Vocations
305 7th Ave. N., Suite 102B
St. Cloud, MN 56303-3633
(320) 251-5001
E-mail: gmastey@gw.stcdio.org

Archdiocese of St. Paul & Minneapolis
Fr. Tom Wilson,
Vocation Director
Sr. Dianne Perry, SSND,
Religious Life Liasion
2260 Summit Ave.
St. Paul, MN 55105-1094
(651) 962-6890, 6891
Fax: (651) 962-5790
E-mail: twwilson@stthomas.edu,
dperry@stthomas.edu
Web: www.10000vocations.org

Diocese of Winona
Fr. Thomas Melvin,
Director of Vocations
Box 588
Winona, MN 55987
(507) 454-4643
Fax: (507) 454-8106
E-mail: tmelvin@dow.org
Web: www.dow.org

MISSISSIPPI

Diocese of Biloxi
Rev. Dennis J. Carver,
Director of Vocations
St. Paul Church
140 East Beach Blvd., PO Box 548
Pass Christian, MS 39571
(228) 255-7453
E-mail: fathercarver@stpaulcs.com
Web: www.biloxidiocese.org
Bragg Moore,
Associate Director
(228) 702-2142
Rev. Tommy Conway,
Vocations Director for Irish Seminarians
(601) 736-3136

Diocese of Jackson
Fr. Joseph Tonos,
Director of Vocations
237 East Amite St.
PO Box 2248
Jackson, MS 39225-2248
(601) 949-6934
Fax: (601) 949-6933
E-mail: joe.tonos@jacksondiocese.org
Web: www.jacksondiocese.org

MISSOURI

Diocese of Jefferson City
Rev. Robert A. Kurwicki,
Vocations Committee Coordinator
PO Box 417, 605 Clark Ave.
Jefferson City, MO 65102
(573) 635-9127, ext. 211
Fax: (573) 635-2286
E-mail: vocations@diojeffcity.org
Web: www.diojeffcity.org/vocation.htm

Diocese of Kansas City-St. Joseph
Rev. Robert Stewart,
Vocation Director
Rev. Stephen Cook,
Associate Vocation Director
PO Box 419037
Kansas City, MO 64141-6037
(816) 756-1850
E-mail: vocations@diocesekcsj.org
Web: www.diocese-kcsj.org/vocation

Archdiocese of St. Louis
Rev. Michael Butler,
Vocation Director
5200 Glennon Dr.
St. Louis, MO 63119
(314) 792-6460
Fax: (314) 792-6502
E-mail: michaelb@archstl.org
Web: www.stlvocations.org

Diocese of Springfield-Cape Girardeau
Rev. David F. Hulshof,
Vocation Director
Rev. Thomas P. Kiefer,
Associate Vocation Director
601 South Jefferson
Springfield, MO 65806-3143
(417) 866-0841
Fax: (417) 866-1140
E-mail: dhulshof@diocspfdcape.org
Web: www.diocspfdcape.org

MONTANA

Diocese of Great Falls-Billings
Rev. Dale Yurkovic,
Vocation Director
St. Mary's Church
P.O. Box 646
Livingston, MT 59047-0646
(406) 222-1393
Fax: (406) 222-1405
E-mail: ddaled@mcn.net
Web: www.dioceseofgfb.org/priestly_vocations.htm

Diocese of Helena
Rev. Thomas O'Donnell,
Vocation Director
SS. Cyril and Methodius Parish
120 West Riggs St., PO Box 1110
East Helena, MT 59635
(406) 227-5334
Fax: (406) 227-5891
E-mail: cyrilmethodius@juno.com

NEBRASKA

Diocese of Grand Island
Rev. Bryan Ernest,
Vocation Director
Holy Rosary Church
1104 Cheyenne
Alliance, NE 69301
(308) 762-2009
Fax: (308) 762-7474
E-mail: bryanvoc@premaonline.com

Diocese of Lincoln
Rev. Robert A. Matya,
Vocation Director
St. Thomas Aquinas Church/
Newman Center
320 N. 16th St.
Lincoln, NE 68508
(402) 474-7914
Fax: (402) 476-2620
E-mail: frmatya@usa.net
Web: www.dioceseoflincoln.org

Archdiocese of Omaha
Rev. Ralph O'Donnell,
Director of Vocations
E-mail: beapadre@cs.com
Web: www.omahapriests.org
Sr. Jackie Thorn, OSM,
Director of Office for Consecrated Life
E-mail: consecratedlife@archomaha.org
Web: marian.creighton.edu/~conlife
100 North 62nd St.
Omaha, NE 68132
(402) 558-3100
Fax: (402) 558-3026

NEVADA

Diocese of Las Vegas
Fr. Anthony Vercellone,
Vocation Director
P.O. Box 18316
Las Vegas, NV 89114-8316
(702) 696-1668
E-mail: lvpriest@aol.com

Diocese of Reno
Fr. Chuck T. Durante,
Vocation Director
290 South Arlington Ave., Ste. 200
Reno, NV 89501
(775) 326-9425
Fax: (775) 348-8619
E-mail: Vocations@catholicreno.org
Web: www.vocationsreno.com

NEW HAMPSHIRE

Diocese of Manchester
Rev. Marc F. Guillemette,
Rev. Marc Montminy,
Co-Directors of Vocations
153 Ash St., PO Box 310
Manchester, NH 03104-0310
Office (603) 669-3100, ext. 116
E-mail: mguillemette@rcbm.org
Web: www.catholicchurchnh.org

NEW JERSEY

Diocese of Camden
Rev. Cadmus D. Mazzarella,
Director of Vocations
Sr. Dorothy Aloisio, FMIHM,
Associate Director of Vocations
Nazareth House
300 Cuthbert Rd.
Cherry Hill, NJ 08002
(856) 910-4930, 4900
Fax: (856) 662-8917
E-mail: sreed@camdendiocese.org
Web: www.beapriest.org

Diocese of Metuchen
Rev. Robert W. Medley,
Director of Vocations
P.O. Box 191
Metuchen, NJ 08840
(732) 562-1990
E-mail: vocations@diometuchen.org
Web: www.diomethuchen.org/vocations

Archdiocese of Newark
Fr. Brian Plate,
Director of Vocations
Sr. Marilyn Minter, C.S.S.F.,
Associate Vocation Director
171 Clifton Ave., PO Box 9500
Newark, NJ 07104-0500
(973) 497-4365
Fax: (973) 497-4369
E-mail: platebri@rcan.org
Web: www.rcan.org/vocation/contactus.htm

Diocese of Paterson
Rev. Paul S. Manning,
Director of Vocations
Rev. Hernan A. Arias,
Assistant Director of Vocations
707 Valley Rd.
Clifton, NJ 07013
(973) 777-2955
Fax: (973) 777-4597
E-mail: vocationdirector@patersondiocese.org
Web: www.patersondiocese.org

Diocese of Trenton
Rev. Mick Lambeth,
Director of Vocations
Sacred Heart
343 South Broad St.
Trenton, NJ 08608
(609) 393-2801
E-mail: vocations@dioceseoftrenton.org
Web: www.Godiscallingyou.com

NEW MEXICO

Diocese of Gallup
Fr. Timothy Farrell,
Vocation Director
414 N. Allen
Farmington, NM 87401
(505) 325-9743
Fax: (505) 325-8860
E-mail: fathertim@sacredheartfarmington.org
Web: dioceseofgallup.org

Diocese of Las Cruces
Fr. Enrique Lopez,
Vocation Director
1280 Med Park Dr.
Las Cruces, NM 88005
(505) 523-7577
Fax: (505) 524-3874
E-mail: elopez@dioceseoflascruces.org;
pastoralcenter@dioceseoflascruces.org
Web: www.dioceseoflascruces.org

Archdiocese of Santa Fe
Fr. Scott Mansfield,
Vocation Director
Catholic Center
4000 Saint Joseph's Pl., N.W.
Albuquerque, NM 87120
(505) 831-8143
E-mail: FrMansfield@aol.com
Web: www.vocations@archdiocesesantafe.org

NEW YORK

Diocese of Albany
Sr. Katherine Hanley, csj,
Rev. Thomas Konopka,
Rev. James Walsh,
Vocation Office
40 N. Main Ave.
Albany, NY 12203
(518) 453-6670
E-mail: kitty.hanley@rcda.org (Sr. Hanley),
tkonopka@nycap.rr.com (Fr. Konopka)
jjwalshie@aol.com (Fr. Walsh)
Web: www.rcda.org

Diocese of Brooklyn
Rev. James Fitzpatrick,
Director of Vocations
Sr. Regina Wilson, I.H.M.,
Associate Director of Vocations
PO Box C
75 Greene Ave.
Brooklyn, NY 11202
(718) 399-5900, ext. 5505, 5525
Fax: (718) 399-5992
E-mail: bklynvoc@aol.com
Web: www.bklynvoc.org

Diocese of Buffalo
Rev. Leon J. Biernat,
Vocations Director
Catholic Center
795 Main St.
Buffalo, NY 14203-1215
(716) 847-5535
E-mail: vocations@buffalodiocese.org
Web: www.buffalodiocese.org/voca/1.html

Archdiocese of New York
Rev. Joseph P. Tierney,
Vocation Director
St. Joseph's Seminary
201 Seminary Ave.
Yonkers, NY 10704
(914) 968-1340
Fax: (914) 968-6671
E-mail: vocations@archny.org
Web: www.ny-archdiocese.org/pastoral/seminary.cfm
Sr. Deanna Sabetta, CND,
Director-Women's Vocations
1011 First Ave., 18th Fl.
New York, NY 10022
(212) 371-1011, ext. 2803
E-mail: sr.deanna.sabetta@archny.org
Web: www.ny-archdiocese.org/education/Vocation_Office.cfm

Diocese of Ogdensburg
Rev. Douglas J. Lucia,
Vocation Director
PO Box 369
Ogdensburg, NY 13669
(315) 393-2920
E-mail: dlucia@dioogdensburg.org
Web: www.myvocation.net

Diocese of Rochester
Rev. John De Socio,
Assistant to the Bishop for Vocations
314 Gregory St., Becket Hall
Rochester, NY 14607
(716) 461-2890
E-mail: beckethall@juno.com
Patricia Finnerty,
Director, Vocations Awareness
1150 Buffalo Rd.
Rochester, NY 14624
(716) 328-3228, ext. 229
Web: www.dor.org/vocations/staff.html

Diocese of Rockville Centre
Rev. Thomas Coogan,
Vocation Director
440 West Neck Rd.
Huntington, NY 11743
(631) 424-9888
Fax: (631) 424-9889
E-mail: vocations@drvc.org
Web: drvc.org

Diocese of Syracuse
Fr. John Donovan,
Director, Office of Vocation Promotion
240 E. Onondaga St.
PO Box 511
Syracuse, NY 13201-0511
(800) 471-1468; (315) 470-1468
Fax: (315) 478-4619
Web: www.syracusediocese.org

NORTH CAROLINA

Diocese of Charlotte
Rev. John Allen,
Director of Vocations
Pastoral Center
1123 S. Church St.
Charlotte, NC 28203-4003
(704) 370-3353
Fax: (704) 370-3291

Diocese of Raleigh
Rev. Michael G. Clay,
Vocation Director
Fr. Price House of Formation
740 Gimghoul Rd.
Chapel Hill, NC 27514-3811
(919) 967-2205
Fax: (919) 967-3048
E-mail: clay@raldioc.org
Rev. Dan Oschwald,
Assistant Vocation Director
The Catholic Center
715 Nazareth St.
Raleigh, NC 27606-2187
(919) 821-8159
E-mail: oschwald@raldioc.org
Web: www.raldioc.org

NORTH DAKOTA

Diocese of Bismarck
Rev. Thomas R. Richter,
Vocation Director
PO Box C
New Salem, ND 58563
(701) 843-7061
(701) 391-8005 (cell phone)
E-mail: frrichter@bismarck diocese.com
Web: http://bismarckdiocese.com

Diocese of Fargo
Vocation Director
Diocesan Vocation Office
100 35th Ave. N.E.
Fargo, ND 58102-1299
(701) 271-1205
E-mail: vocations@fargo diocese.org
Web: www.fargodiocese.org/ vocation.html

OHIO

Archdiocese of Cincinnati
Rev. Mark T. Watkins,
Vocation Director
100 E. Eighth St.
Cincinnati, OH 45202
(513) 421-3131
Fax: (513) 421-6225
E-mail: vocations@Catholic Cincinnati.org
Web: www.catholiccincinnati.org/ admin/vocations.htm

Diocese of Cleveland
Rev. Bob Stec,
Co-Director,
Diocesan Vocation Office
1031 Superior Ave., #721
Cleveland, OH 44114-2519
(216) 696-6525, ext. 3490
E-mail: fatherbob@church vocations.com
Web: www.churchvocations.com

Diocese of Columbus
Fr. Matt Hoover,
Director of Vocations
197 E. Gay St.
Columbus, OH 43215
(614) 221-5565
Fax: (614) 241-2572
E-mail: vocmailbox@colsdioc.org
Web: www.colsdioc.org

Diocese of Steubenville
Rev. Msgr. Kurt H. Kemo,
Vocation Director
PO Box 969
Steubenville, OH 43952
Fr. Daniel Heusel,
Fr. Jason Prati,
Assistant Directors of Vocations
(740) 282-3631, 472-0187
Fax: (740) 282-3327
E-mail: kkemo@diosteub.org (Msgr. Kemo),
dheusel@diosteub.org (Fr. Heusel)
frprati@catholic.org (Fr. Prati)
Web: www.diosteub.org

Diocese of Toledo
Rev. David W. Nuss,
Director of Vocations
E-mail: dnuss@toledodiocese.org
Sister Marilyn Marie Ellerbrock, SND,
Associate Director of Vocations
E-mail: mellerbrock@toledodiocese.org
Office of Vocations
1933 Spielbusch Ave.
P.O. Box 985
Toledo, OH 43697-0985
(419) 244-6711
Fax: (419) 244-4791
Web: www.toledodiocese.org or
www.toledovocations.com

Diocese of Youngstown
Rev. Leo J. Wehrlin,
Vocation Director
144 W. Wood St.
Youngstown, OH 44503
(330) 744-8451
E-mail: lwehrlin@youngstown diocese.org

OKLAHOMA

Archdiocese of Oklahoma City
Rev. Lowell Stieferman,
Vocations Director
7501 NW Expressway
Oklahoma City, OK 73132
(405) 721-5651, 9351
E-mail: jmulligan@catharch dioceseokc.org

Diocese of Tulsa
Fr. Jack A. Gleason,
Vocations Director
Theresa Witcher,
Assistant
Wayne Rziha,
Recruitment & Promotion
Church of the Madalene
3188 East 22nd St. South
Tulsa, OK 74114-1822
(918) 744-0023
Fax: (918) 744-0024
E-mail: tulvoc@aol.com
Web: www.dioceseoftulsa.org

OREGON

Diocese of Baker
Rev. Rick Fischer,
Vocation Director
4880 Bristol Ave.
Klamath Falls, OR 97603
(541) 884-4242
Web: www.dioceseofbaker.org

Archdiocese of Portland
Rev. Kelly Vandehey,
Vocation Director
2838 E. Burnside St.
Portland, OR 97214
(503) 233-8368
Fax: (503) 230-1477
E-mail: kvandehey@archdpdx.org

PENNSYLVANIA

Diocese of Allentown
Rev. Francis A. Nave,
Director of Vocations
P.O. Box F
Allentown, PA 18105-1538
(610) 437-0755
Fax: (610) 433-7822
E-mail: fnave@allentown diocese.org
Web: www.beapriest.com

Diocese of Altoona-Johnstown
Fr. John D. Byrnes, JCL,
Director of Vocations
Prince Gallitzin Chapel House
357 St. Mary St., PO Box 99
Loretto, PA 15940-0099
(814) 472-5441
Fax: (814) 472-5446
E-mail: jbyrnes@dioceseaj.org
Web: diocesealtjtn.org

Diocese of Erie
Rev. Edward M. Lohse,
Vocation Director
St. Mark Catholic Center
429 East Gradnview Blvd.
PO Box 10397
Erie, PA 16514-0397
(800) 374-3723, (814) 824-1200
Fax: (814) 824-1181
E-mail: fatherhoffman@eriercd.org
Web: www.erievocations.org

Diocese of Greensburg
Rev. Larry J. Kulick,
Consultant, Priestly Vocations
Office for Ministry Development
723 E. Pittsburgh St.
Greensburg, PA 15601
(724) 837-0901
Fax: (724) 837-0857
E-mail: ljk@westol.com
Web: www.dioceseofgreensburg.org

Diocese of Harrisburg
Rev. Michael Messner,
Director of Seminarian Formation
Sister Deborah Marie Borneman, SSCM,
Coordinator of Vocation Awareness
4800 Union Deposit Rd.
PO Box 2161
Harrisburg, PA 17105-2161
(717) 657-4804
Fax: (717) 657-4042
E-mail: vocations@hbgdiocese.org
Web: www.hbgdiocese.org/vocations

Archdiocese of Philadelphia
Rev. John F. Babowitch,
Vocation Director for Diocesan Priesthood
St. Charles Borromeo Seminary
100 East Wynnewood Rd.
Wynnewood, PA 19096-3028
(610) 667-5778
E-mail: frjbabo@adphila.org
Web: www.scs.edu/vocation/vocation.html

Diocese of Pittsburgh
Rev. James A. Wehner, S.T.D.,
Director of Vocations - Rector
Saint Paul Seminary
2900 Noblestown Rd.
Pittsburgh, PA 15205
(412) 921-5800, ext. 22
E-mail: vocations@diopitt.org
Web: www.diopitt.org

Diocese of Scranton
Rev. Jeffrey J. Walsh,
Director of Vocations
Diocesan Vocation Office
1000 Seminary Rd.
Dalton, PA 18414
(570) 563-8504
Fax: (570) 563-1584
E-mail: scrvoc3@aol.com
Web: www.dioceseofscranton.org

RHODE ISLAND

Diocese of Providence
Rev. Albert A. Kenney,
Vocation Director
Rev. Marcel L. Taillon,
Vocation Recruiter
485 Mt. Pleasant Ave.
Providence, RI 02908
(401) 831-8011
Web: www.catholicpriest.com

Sr. Jacqueline Dickey, S.S.Ch.,
Associate Director for Religious
One Cathedral Square
Providence, RI 02903
(401) 278-4633

SOUTH CAROLINA

Diocese of Charleston
Rev. Dennis B. Willey,
Director of Vocations
Rev. Mr. Joseph F. Cahill,
Assistant Director of Vocations
1662 Ingram Rd.
Charleston, SC 29407
(800) 660-4102
(843) 402-9115, ext. 22
Fax: (843) 402-9071
E-mail: vocdirsc@catholic-doc.org
Web: www.catholic-doc.org/vocations.html

SOUTH DAKOTA

Diocese of Rapid City
Rev. Brian P. Christensen,
Director of Vocations
PO Box 678
Rapid City, SD 57701
(605) 343-3541
E-mail: Godscall@diorc.org
Web: www.rapidcitydiocese.org

Diocese of Sioux Falls
Father James Mason,
Vocations Director
523 N. Duluth Ave.
Sioux Falls, SD 57104
(605) 988-3772
Fax: (605) 988-3795
E-mail: rtebbe@sfcatholic.org
Web: www.sfcatholic.org/vocations/index.html

TENNESSEE

Diocese of Knoxville
Rev. Michael Creson,
PO Box 1015
Soddy-Daisy, TN 37379
(423) 332-5300

Diocese of Memphis
Fr. Keith Stewart,
Diocesan Vocation Director
Cathedral of the Immaculate Conception
1695 Central Ave.
Memphis, TN 38104
(901)725-2700, ext. 5
E-mail: jks1993@midsouth.rr.com
Web: www.cdom.org

Diocese of Nashville
Rev. James E. Armour,
Vocation Promotion and Recruitment
Cathedral of the Incarnation
2015 West End Ave.
Nashville, TN 37203
(615) 327-2330
Fax: (615) 320-5650
E-mail: FrJim@NashvillePriest.com
Web: www.NashvillePriest.com

TEXAS

Diocese of Amarillo
Rev. Mike Colwell, JCL,
Director of Vocations
PO Box 5644
Amarillo, TX 79117-5644
(806) 383-2243, ext. 123
Fax: (806) 383-8452
E-mail: mcolwell@amarillodiocese.org
Web: www.amarillodiocese.org/index.htm

Diocese of Austin
Rev. David Konderla,
Vocation Director
PO Box 13327
Austin, TX 78711
(512) 476-4888
Fax: (512) 469-9537
E-mail: fr-david-konderla@austindiocese.org
Web: www.austindiocese.org

Diocese of Beaumont
Rev. Andy Moore,
Director, Vocations Office
Rev. John Hughes,
Director of Seminarians
1010 E. Virginia
P.O. Box 10095, LUS
Beaumont, TX 77710
(409) 835-5037
Fax: (409) 832-4129
E-mail: amoore@dioceseofbmt.org
Web: www.dioceseofbmt.org/vocations

Diocese of Brownsville
Rev. Juan Victor Heredia,
Director for Vocations
Rev. Carlos A. Villarreal,
Assistant Director for Vocations
1910 E. Elizabeth St.
Brownsville, TX 78520-4998
PO Box 2279
Brownsville, TX 78522-2279
(956) 542-2501
Fax: (956) 782-1728
E-mail: cvillarreal@cdob.org
Web: www.cdob.org

Diocese of Corpus Christi
Rev. Paul A. Hesse,
Vocations Director
PO Box 2620 (620 Lipan)
Corpus Christi, TX 78403
(361) 882-6191, ext. 550
Fax: (361) 882-1018
E-mail: phesse@DioceseCC.org;
vocations@DioceseCC.org
Web: www.goccn.org/diocese/depts/vocations

Diocese of Dallas
Rev. Josef Vollmer-König,
Director of Vocations
Juanita Ramirez,
Administrative Assistant
3725 Blackburn St.
PO Box 190507
Dallas, TX 75219
(214) 528-2360, ext. 228, 227
Fax: (214) 521-5674
E-mail: jvkonig@cathdal.org
E-mail: jramirez@cathdal.org
Sister M. Margaret Langsett, CSFN,
Associate Director of Vocations
1814 Egyptian Way
PO Box 530959
Grand Prairie, TX 75050
(972) 641-4496
E-mail: mlangset@cathdal.org
Web: www.cathdal.org/vocation.htm

Diocese of El Paso
Fr. Joe Molina,
Facilitator, Vocations Office
499 St. Matthews St.
El Paso, TX 79907
(915) 872-8400
Web: www.elpasodiocese.org/directory.htm

Diocese of Fort Worth
Rev. Anh Tran,
Vocation Director
800 W. Loop 820 South
Fort Worth, TX 76108-2919
(817) 560-3300, ext. 106
E-mail: atran@fwdioc.org
Web: www.fwdioc.org

Diocese of Galveston-Houston
Rev. Clint Ressler, STL,
Sr. Rosalie Karstedt, CDP,
Vocation Directors
1700 San Jacinto St.
Houston, TX 77002
(713) 659-5461, ext. 237
E-mail: cressler@diogh.org or karstedt@diogh.org

Diocese of Lubbock
Father David Cruz,
Vocation Director
Dora Fierro,
Secretary, Vocations Committee
Catholic Center
PO Box 98700
Lubbock, TX 79499
(806) 792-3943
E-mail: dfierro@catholiclubbock.org
Web: www.catholiclubbock.org/vocations.htm

Diocese of San Angelo
Rev. Tom Barley, J.C.L.
Director of Vocations and Seminarians
PO Box 1829
San Angelo,TX 76902-1829
(325) 651-7500
Fax: (325) 651-6688
Web: www.san-angelo-diocese.org

Archdiocese of San Antonio
Rev. Jose Arturo Cepeda,
Vocation Director
Sister Mary Fagan, SHSp,
Associate Vocation Director
2600 W. Woodlawn, PO Box 28240
San Antonio, TX 78228
(210) 735-0553
Fax: (210) 734-2324
E-mail: maryshsp@satx.rr.com
Web: www.savocations.org

Diocese of Tyler
Diocesan Vocation Director
1015 ESE Loop 323
Tyler, TX 75701-9663
(903) 534-1077, ext. 145
Fax: (903) 534-1370
E-mail: vocations@dioceseoftyler.org
Web: www.dioceseoftyler.org

Diocese of Victoria
Rev. Matthew Huehlefeld,
Vocation Director
PO Box 4070
Victoria, TX 77903
(361) 573-0828
Fax: (361) 573-5725
Web: www.victoriadiocese.org

UTAH

Diocese of Salt Lake City
Fr. Bill Wheaton,
Vocation Director
St. Francis Xavier Church
PO Box 18631
Kearns, UT 84118-0631
(801) 968-2123
Fax: (801) 966-1639
E-mail: frbill92@hotmail.com
Web: www.dioslc.org

VERMONT

Diocese of Burlington
Rev. Michael W. DeForge,
Vocation Director
The Catholic Center at UVM
Redstone Campus
390 South Prospect St.
Burlington, VT 05401-3534
(802) 862-8403
E-mail: Myhalyk@aol.com
Web: www.vermontcatholic.org

VIRGINIA

Diocese of Arlington
Rev. Robert E. Avella,
Director, Office of Vocations
Rev. Brian G. Bashista,
Promoter of Vocations
200 N. Glebe Rd., Ste. 600
Arlington, VA 22203
(703) 841-2514
Fax: (703) 841-4786
Rev. Ovidio Pecharromán,
Spanish Speaking Vocations Coordinator
80 N. Glebe Road
Arlington, VA 22203
(703) 524-2122
Fax: (703) 524-4261
E-mail: vocations@arlingtondiocese.org
Web: www.arlingtondiocese.org

Diocese of Richmond
Rev. Michael A. Renninger,
Vicar for Priestly Vocations
Vincent VanderHeijden,
Associate Director of Vocations
811 Cathedral Place, Suite B
Richmond, VA 23220-4801
(804) 359-5661
E-mail: mrenninger@richmonddiocese.org; vvanderheijden@richmonddiocese.org
Web: www.richmonddiocese.org/vocations

WASHINGTON

Archdiocese of Seattle
Richard Shively,
Director, Office of Vocations
910 Marion St.
Seattle, WA 98104
(206) 382-4595
Fax: (206) 654-4654
E-mail: richs@seattlearch.org
Web: seattlearch.org

Diocese of Spokane
Rev. Darrin Connall,
Director of Vocations
Bishop White Seminary
429 E. Sharp Ave.
Spokane, WA 99202-1857
(509) 326-3761
Fax: (509) 326-3761
E-mail: bws@gonzaga.edu
Web: www.dioceseofspokane.org/clergy/Vocations.htm

Diocese of Yakima
Rev. Msgr. John A. Ecker,
Vocation Director
15 S. 12th Ave.
Yakima, WA 98902
(509) 575-3713
E-mail: stpaul@wolfenet.com

WEST VIRGINIA

Diocese of Wheeling-Charleston
Very Rev. John R. Gallagher, V.G.,
Director, Office of Vocations
1300 Bryon St., PO Box 230
Wheeling, WV 26003
(888) 4-DIOCESE
(304) 233-0880, ext. 242
Fax: (304) 233-4086
E-mail: jgallagher@dwc.org
Web: vocations.dwc.org

WISCONSIN

Diocese of Green Bay
Rev. Doug LeCaptain,
Vocation Director
PO Box 23825,
Green Bay, WI 54305-3825
(920) 437-7531, ext. 8293
E-mail: vocations@gbdioc.org
Web: www.gbdioc.org

Diocese of La Crosse
Fr. Joseph Hirsch,
Vocation Director
Box 4004
La Crosse, WI 54602-4004
(608) 788-7700
Fax: (608) 788-8413
Web: www.dioceseoflacrosse.com

Diocese of Madison
Most Rev. William H. Bullock, D.D., E.D.S.,
Vocations Coordinator
Mary Lestina,
Administrative Assistant
Bishop O'Connor Catholic Pastoral Center
3577 High Point Rd.
Madison, WI 53719-4999
(800) 833-8452,
(608) 821-3088
Fax: (608) 821-3090
E-mail: vocations@straphael.org
Web: www.madisondiocese.org

Archdiocese of Milwaukee
Rev. Robert Stiefvater,
Director, Vocation Office
Joan C. Sobczak,
Assistant Vocations Director
3257 S. Lake Dr.
St. Francis, WI 53235
(414) 747-6437
E-mail: vocations@sfs.edu
Web: thinkpriest.org or www.sfs.edu

Diocese of Superior
Fr. Andrew Ricci,
Director of Vocations
St. Francis deSales
409 Summit St.
Spooner, WI 54801
(715) 635-3105
Fax: (715) 635-7341
E-mail: pastapadre@centurytel.net
Sr. Bonnie Alho, OSM,
Associate Director
St. Joseph Church
111 W. Marshall St.
Rice Lake, WI 54868
(715) 234-2032
Fax: (715) 234-7757
E-mail: balho@discover-net.net
Web: www.catholicdos.org/vocations

WYOMING

Diocese of Cheyenne
Fr. Ray Rodriguez,
Vocation Director
1800 E. Grand Ave.
Laramie, WY 82070-4316
(307) 745-5461
Fax: (307) 742-0521
E-mail: rae@newmancenter.org
Web: www.dioceseofcheyenne.org/Vocations.htm

TERRITORIAL SEES

AMERICAN SAMOA

Diocese of Samoa-Pago Pago
Rev. Viane Etuale,
Director of Vocations
PO Box 596
Pago Pago, American Samoa 96799
011-(684) 699-1402
Fax: 011-(684) 699-1459
E-mail: QUINN@samoatelco.com
Web: www.relpac.org.fj/Samoa-pago.htm

CAROLINE MARSHALL ISLANDS

Diocese of the Caroline Islands
Rev. Julio Angkel,
Director, Vocation Promotion (Chuuk)
PO Box 202
Chuuk, Caroline Islands, FM 96942
011-(691) 330-2672
Fax: 011-(691) 330-4394
Web: www.diocesecarolines.org

GUAM

Archdiocese of Agana
Rev. James L.G. Benavente,
Rev. Adrian Cristobal
Co-Directors of Vocations
196-B Cuesta San Ramon
Agana, Guam 96910
011-(671) 472-6116
Fax: 011-(671) 477-3519
Web: www.guam.net/pub/archdiocese

MARIANA ISLANDS

Diocese of Chalan Kanoa
Fr. Roger P.T. Tenorio,
Diocesan Vocation Director
PO Box 500745
Saipan, MP 96950
01 (670) 234-3000, ext. 111
Fax: 01 (670) 235-3002
E-mail: chancellor@gtepacifica.net
Web: www.cnmicatholic.org

PUERTO RICO

Diocese of Arecibo
Rev. Antonio J. Vazquez,
Vocation Director
Seminary of Jesus the King
PO Box 2164
Arecibo, PR 00613
(787) 878-1528
Web: www.diocese.com/site/home/prarecibo

Diocese of Caguas
Rev. P. Jorge Cardona,
Pro-Vicar of Vocations
PO Box 8698
Caguas, PR 00726
(787) 869-0861
Fax: (787) 747-5616
E-mail: jcardona@prtc.net
Rev. P. Floyd Mercado Vidro,
Preseminariam Director
PO Box 302
Naranjito, PR
(787) 869-2840

Diocese of Mayaguez
Fr. Orlando Rosas,
Vocation Director
PO Box 2272
Mayaguez, PR 00681-2272
(787) 833-5411
E-mail: prodioma@caribe.net
Web: www.geocltles.com/Heartland/Meadows/1324/page2.html

Diocese of Ponce
Rev. Melvin Diaz Aponte,
Vocation Director/Seminary Administrator
Msgr. Jesus R. Diez,
Rector of Seminarians
PO Box 32110
Ponce, PR 00732-2110
Tel., Fax: (787) 848-4380
E-mail: regcleri@caribe.net

Archdiocese of San Juan
Rev. P. Ivan L. Huertas,
Vocations Vicar
Arquidiocesis de San Juan
P.O. Box 11714
San Juan, PR 00922-1714
(787) 706-9455
E-mail: vocaciones@arqsj.org
Web: www.diocese.com/site/home/prsanjuan

VIRGIN ISLANDS

Diocese of St. Thomas in the Virgin Islands
Rev. Cecil Corneille,
Director of Vocations
PO Box 2150
Kingshill, St. Croix, VI 00851-2150
(340) 692-2005
Fax: (340) 692-2748
E-mail: stjoschurch@islands.vi
Web: www.islands.vi/~stjoschurch/

EASTERN RITE DIOCESES

Byzantine Catholic Eparchy of Van Nuys
Rev. Robert M. Pipta,
Eparchial Director of Vocations
2250 East Maule Ave.
Las Vegas, NV 89119-4607
(702) 361-2431
E-mail: rmp.byzcath@juno.com
Web: www.archangelgabriel.org

Eparchy of Newton (Melkite-Greek Catholic)
Rt. Rev. Philip Raczka,
Director of Vocations
600 W. Exchange St.
Akron, OH 44302
(330) 535-7364
E-mail: stjoemelk@acorn.net

Eparchy of Stamford
Rev. Bohdan J. Danylo,
Vocation Director
14 Peveril Rd.
Stamford, CT 06902-3019
(203) 324-7698
E-mail: vocstamford@netscape.net or Ukrcathsem@aol.com
Web: www.stbasilcollegesem.net

Diocese of St. Nicholas in Chicago for Ukrainians
Most Rev. Richard Seminack, D.D.,
Office of Vocations
2245 W. Rice St.
Chicago, IL 60622-4858
(773) 276-5080
Fax: (773) 276-6799
E-mail: sneparchy@iols.com

Byzantine Catholic Diocese of Passaic
Very Rev. Edward G. Cimbala,
Vocation Director
St. Mary Church
1900 Brooks Blvd.
Hillsborough, NJ 08876
(908) 725-0615
E-mail: ecim@aol.com

Byzantine Catholic Eparchy of Parma
Rev. Dennis M. Hrubiak,
Vocation Director
1900 Carlton Rd.
Parma, OH 44134
(216) 741-8773 (W)
(440) 884-8452 (H)
Fax: (216) 741-9356 (W)
Fax: (440) 884-8453 (H)
E-mail: frdennis@megsinet.net
Rev. Fr. Deacon Joseph Marquis,
Assistant Vocation Director
3471 Bishop Rd.
Detroit, MI 48224
(313) 369-5781
Fax: (313) 369-5775
E-mail: josephmarquis@ameritech.net

Ukrainian Catholic Eparchy of St. Josaphat in Parma, Ohio
Rev. Steven M. Paliwoda,
Director of Vocations
St. Andrew
7700 Hoertz Rd.
Parma, OH 44134-6404
(440) 843-9149
Fax: (440) 845-2586
E-mail: pastor@standrewucc.org

Archeparchy of Pittsburgh (Byzantine-Ruthenian Rite)
Rev. Dennis Bogda,
Vocation Director
St. John the Baptist
105 Kohler Ave.
Lyndora, PA 16045
(724) 287-5000

Metropolitan Archdiocese of Philadelphia-Ukrainian
Rev. Robert Hitchens,
Director of Vocations
Vocation Office
827 N. Franklin St.
Philadelphia, PA 19123-2097
(215) 627-0143, ext. 26
Fax: (215) 627-0377
E-mail: ukrmet@catholic.org

Eparchy of Our Lady of Lebanon of Los Angeles
Fr. Sharbel G. Maroun,
Director of Vocations
Eparchy of Our Lady of Lebanon
600 University Ave. NE
Minneapolis, MN 55413
(612) 379-2758
Fax: (612) 379-7647
E-mail: abouna@stmaron.com

Eparchy of St. Maron of Brooklyn
Rev. James A. Root,
Director of Vocations
Our Lady of Victory Church
1000 Lindsay Rd.
Carnegie, PA 15106
(412) 278-0841
Fax: (412) 278-0846

Archdiocese for the Military Services

The Archdiocese for the Military Services, found wherever military personnel or diplomatic personnel are serving, is located in the Arctic Circle in Greenland and Alaska, at Antarctica, in Asia, Europe, Africa, the Far East, the Mideast, South America, and in almost every state; it serves Catholics in the Army, Navy, Air Force, Marine Corps, Coast Guard, Veterans Administration and Government Service Overseas. Its priests are loaned to the Archdiocese from almost every American diocese and from many religious institutes. For more information on serving as a priest in the military, write or call:

Most Reverend John J. Kaising, Vocations Office,
Archdiocese for the Military Services,
United States of America,
P.O. Box 4469, Washington, DC 20017-0469,
(202) 269-9100, Fax: (202) 269-9022,
E-mail: info@milarch.org, Web: www.milarch.org.

Religious Communities for Men

ADORNO FATHERS (CRM)
(Clerics Regular Minor)
St. Michael's Seminary, 575 Darlington Ave., Ramsey, NJ 07446. (201) 327-7375. E-mail: amrgcrm@optonline.net; Web: members.tripod.com/~adornofathers
Conduct: 2 parishes, 1 house of studies.
Apostolic Work: Parish work, retreats, teaching, missions and chaplaincies.
Represented in the Archdiocese of Newark and in the Diocese of Charleston. Also in Italy, Germany, Congo (Africa), India and the Philippines.
Vocation Director: Fr. Michael Marotta, CRM

SOCIETY OF AFRICAN MISSIONS (S.M.A.)
An international community of priests and lay missionaries in service of the peoples of Africa and those of African origin.
American Provincialate: 23 Bliss Ave., Tenafly, NJ 07670-3038. (201) 567-0150. E-mail: smausa w@smafathers.org; Web: smafathers.org
Conduct: Pastoral work, education, health care, formation of local clergy and lay leaders, social and agricultural development, Justice & Peace ministry, care for refugees, AIDS ministry and education, ministry among street children and handicapped people.
Represented in the (Arch)dioceses of Boston, Newark and Washington, DC. Missions in Angola, Benin, Central African Republic, Cote D'Ivoire, Democratic Republic of Congo, Egypt, Ghana, Kenya, Liberia, Morocco, Niger, Nigeria, Republic of the Congo, South Africa, Tanzania, Togo and Zambia.
Vocation Directors: Deacon Keith McKnight, SMA Society of African Missions, 23 Bliss Ave., Tenafly, NJ 07670-3038. (201) 567-0277. Fax: (201) 567-7156; Ms. Theresa Hicks, Director/Lay Missionaries, Society of African Missions, 256 North Manor Circle, Takoma Park, MD 20912. (301) 891-2037. Fax: (301) 270-6370

ALEXIAN BROTHERS (C.F.A.)
(Immaculate Conception Province)
600 Alexian Way, Elk Grove Village, IL 60007. (800) 556-0332. E-mail: vocations@alexian.net; Web: www.alexianbrothers.org
45 Brothers
Conduct: 2 medical centers, 2 life care centers, 1 behavioral health hospital, 2 nursing homes, 1 rehabilitation hospital, 2 PACE programs, 2 AIDS ministries, 2 novitiates.
Apostolic Work: Housing and all aspects of the health care field.
Represented in the Archdioceses of Chicago, St. Louis and Milwaukee and in the Dioceses of Knoxville, Davao, Philippines and Gyor, Hungary.
Vocation Contacts: Patrick Gaughan, Vocation Director; Bro. Theodore Loucks, C.F.A., Assistant Vocation Director

THE APOSTLES OF JESUS (A.J.)
829 Main St., Northampton, PA 18067-1838. (610) 502-1732. Fax: (610) 502-1733. E-mail: worldaj@email.com; Web: www.apostlesofJesus.net
Apostolic Work: New evangelization of Africa and the world; the service of the spiritual, pastoral and social welfare of all people with preference to the poor, in the spirit of Christ who came "to serve and not be served." (Mt. 20:28)
Represented in the Archdiocese of New York and in the Diocese of Allentown. In Europe and in Africa (Ethiopia, Kenya, South Africa, Sudan, Tanzania and Uganda)

ASSUMPTIONISTS (A.A.)
(Augustinians of the Assumption)
US Provincial House: 330 Market St., Brighton, MA 02135. (617) 783-0400. Fax: (617) 783-8030. E-mail: Peterrp@juno.com; Web: www.vocationsaa.org
60 Priests, 15 Brothers
Conduct: 5 parishes, 3 shrines, 1 house of studies, 2 hospital chaplaincies, 2 missions, 3 formation centers, 1 university.
Apostolic Work: Teaching: college & high school, parishes, Hispanic apostolate, ecumenical work, foreign missions, retreats, chaplaincies, campus ministry, journalism, preaching, youth work and administration.
Represented in the Archdioceses of New York and Boston and in the Dioceses of Worcester and Knoxville. Also in Canada, Kenya, Mexico, Moscow, Jerusalem and Rome.
Vocation Director: Fr. Peter R. Precourt, A.A., 512 Salisbury St., Worcester, MA 01609. (508) 767-7520

ATONEMENT FRIARS (SA)
(Franciscan Friars of the Atonement)
Graymoor, PO Box 300, Garrison, NY 10524-0300. (845) 424-2126. Fax: (845) 424-2170. E-mail: vocdirsa@aol.com, sylvaindaniel@hot mail.co; Web: atonementfriars.org
85 Friar-Priests, 41 Friar-Brothers, 2 Friars in Formation, 1 Novice, 1 Tertiary
Conduct: 1 US and 0 Canadian parishes; 1 retreat and conference center; 1 shelter for homeless and needy men; 2 alcohol and drug rehabilitation centers; 1 library (Rome); 2 ecumenical centers (New York, Rome); 2 houses of formation; 1 novitiate.
Apostolic Work: Ecumenical ministry (annual Week of Prayer for Christian Unity; ecumenical centers in U.S. and Rome; ecumenical agency staffing: U.S., Rome and London; ecumenical publications); alcohol and drug rehabilitation; parishes at home and overseas (Japan and England); institutional chaplaincies (hospitals and prisons); AIDS ministries.
Represented in the Archdioceses of Boston, Los Angeles, New York, and Washington, DC, and in the Dioceses of Arlington (VA), Ogdensburg (NY), Raleigh (NC); and Sacramento (CA); and in Canada, Great Britain, Italy and Japan.
Vocation Ministers: Fr. Ken Cienik, SA, Fr. Daniel Sylvain, SA

AUGUSTINIAN FRIARS (O.S.A.)
(Order of St. Augustine)

(Province of St. Thomas of Villanova) St. Augustine Friary, 214 Ashwood Rd., PO Box 340, Villanova, PA 19085-0340. (610) 527-3330, ext. 284. Fax: (610) 520-0618. E-mail: vocations@augustinian.org; Web: www.augustinian.org

260 Friars

Conduct: 43 friaries, 18 parishes, 1 university, 1 college, 3 high schools, 2 foreign missions.

Apostolic Work: Friars work as active contemplatives in preaching and teaching, parish ministry and renewal, spiritual direction, counseling and liturgical arts, Hispanic ministry. In education: Theological research and the arts and sciences; secondary, college, graduate levels in teaching and administration. Foreign missions in Japan, Peru and South Africa; Formation–Pre-Novitiate: Washington, DC; Novitiate: Racine, WI; Theological Studies: Washington, DC.

Represented in the Archdioceses of Boston, New York, Milwaukee, Philadelphia, Washington, DC, Miami and Tokyo and Nagasaki, Japan; and in the Dioceses of Albany, Camden, Orlando, Venice, FL, Nagoya and Fukuoka, in Japan, and Piura, in Peru.

Vocation Director: Fr. James D. McBurney, O.S.A.

AUGUSTINIAN RECOLLECT FATHERS (OAR)

(Province of Saint Nicholas of Tolentine – USA Delegation) 2800 Schurz Ave., Bronx, NY 10465. (718) 823-0460

24 Priests

Conduct: 12 parishes, Hispanic center.

Represented in the Archdioceses of New York and Newark and in the Dioceses of El Paso and Las Cruces.

Vocation Director: Saint John Vianney Parish, 715 Castle Hill Ave., Bronx, NY 10473. (718) 863-4411. Fax: (718) 863-1673. Web: www.agustinosrecoletos.com

AUGUSTINIAN RECOLLECTS (O.A.R.)

(Province of St. Augustine) Provincial Residence: Monastery of St. Cloud, 29 Ridgeway Ave., West Orange, NJ 07052. (973) 731-0616

42 Priests, 9 Brothers, 13 Professed Students, 9 Postulants

Conduct: 1 pre-novitiate, 1 philosophy and a residence for theological students, 8 parishes, 1 Cursillo center.

Apostolic Work: Dedicated to working with the Hispanics in the US (main apostolate), pastoral ministry, retreats, charismatic renewal, Cursillos, hospital chaplaincies, neocatechumenate movement and working with youths.

Represented in the Archdioceses of New York, Newark, Los Angeles, Kansas City (KS), Omaha and Mexico City and in the Diocese of Orange.

Vocation Directors: Fr. Jose Luis Martinez, O.A.R., St. Augustine Priory, 400 Sherwood Way, Oxnard, CA 93033. (805) 486-9651; Fr. Marlon Beof, OAR, Tagaste Monastery, 220 Lafayette Ave., Suffern, NY 10901. (914) 357-0067. E-mail: jlmsueskun@yahoo.com

AUGUSTINIAN FRIARS (O.S.A.)
(Order of St. Augustine)

(Province of St. Augustine) 1605 28th St., San Diego, CA 92102. (619) 235-0247. E-mail: osacole@pacbell.net; Web: www.osa-west.org

29 Priests, 3 Brothers

Conduct: High schools, parishes, retreat house, housing ministry, chaplaincies to hospitals, charismatic renewal.

Represented in the Archdioceses of Los Angeles and Portland, OR and in the Dioceses of Oakland and San Diego.

Vocation Director: Fr. Thomas J.F. Whelan, OSA, 108 Cole St., San Francisco, CA 94117-1116. (415) 387-3626.

AUGUSTINIAN FRIARS (O.S.A.)
(Order of St. Augustine)

(Province of St. Joseph in North America) Motherhouse: The Augustinian Monastery at Marylake, PO Box 550, King City, Ontario, Canada. L7B 1A7. (905) 833-5368

16 Priests, 17 Brothers

Apostolate: Parish work, retreats.

Represented in the Archdioceses of Toronto and Vancouver and in the Diocese of Antigonish (Nova Scotia).

Vocation Director: Fr. Francis Galvan, O.S.A., St. Brigid's Rectory, 300 Wolverleigh Blvd., Toronto, Ontario M4C 1S6, Canada

AUGUSTINIAN FRIARS (O.S.A.)
(Order of St. Augustine)

(Province of Our Mother of Good Counsel) Tolentine Center, 20300 Governor's Hwy., Olympia Fields, IL 60461-1081. (708) 748-9500. Fax: (708) 481-2090. E-mail: vocations@midwestaugustinians.org; Web: www.midwestaugustinians.org/vocatform.html

110 Priests, 25 Brothers

Apostolic Work: Secondary education, parochial ministry, foreign missions, retreat work, adult education, hospital chaplaincies.

Represented in the Archdioceses of Chicago, Detroit, Milwaukee and St. Louis and in the Dioceses of Ft. Worth, Hamilton, Joliet, Kalamazoo and Tulsa, with missionaries in Japan and Peru.

Vocation Director: Rev. John Merkelis, OSA

BARNABITE FATHERS AND BROTHERS (C.R.S.P.)
(Clerics Regular of St. Paul)

(North American Province) 1023 Swann Rd., Youngstown, NY 14174. (716) 754-7489

16 Priests

Conduct: 1 novitiate, 1 house of studies, 4 parishes, a spiritual center, a Marian Shrine-Basilica, Our Lady of the Rosary of Fatima.

Apostolic Work: Working with youth and young adults, teaching, retreats, spiritual direction, parishes, hospital chaplaincies (including 1 state hospital), directing of Our Lady of Fatima National Shrine-Basilica, Youngstown, NY, publishing of "The North American Voice of Fatima". Also ministering in Albania, Argentina, Belgium, Brazil, Chile, France, Italy, Mexico, Philippines, Poland, Rwanda, Spain and Zaire.

Represented in the Dioceses of Allentown, Buffalo, San Diego and Hamilton, Ontario, Canada.

Vocation Directors: Rev. Peter M. Calabrese, CRSP, Barnabite Spiritual Center, RR1, Box 4301, Bethlehem, PA 18020-9801. (610) 691-8648. E-mail: gpatil@fast.net; Web: www.catholic.church.org/barnabites; Fr. Julio Ciavaglia, 1023 Swann Rd., Youngstown, NY 14174. (716) 754-7489

BASILIAN FATHERS (C.S.B.)
(Congregation of St. Basil)

Motherhouse: Cardinal Flahiff Basilian Centre, 95 St. Joseph St., Toronto, Ont. M5S 3C2 Canada. (416) 921-6674. E-mail: vocation@basilian.org; Web: www.basilian.org

Conduct: In the US: 1 college, 1 university, 4 campus ministries, 6 high schools, 10 parishes. In Canada: 3 colleges, 2 universities, 8 campus ministries, 5 high schools, 13 parishes. In Mexico: 1 novitiate, 4 mission parishes. In Colombia: 1 novitiate, 1 school, 1 mission parish. In St. Lucia: 1 parish.

Apostolates: The service of the Church in any priestly capacity but have centered their work on education and evangelization.

Represented in the US Dioceses of Rochester, Detroit, Gary, Galveston-Houston, Las Cruces, Santa Fe,

Phoenix and Oakland. In the Canadian Dioceses of Toronto, Hamilton, London, Sault Ste. Marie, Saskatoon, Edmonton, Calgary, Nelson and Vancouver.
Vocation Director: Rev. Dennis Kauffman, CSB, 1098 Military, Detroit, MI 48209

BASILIAN FATHERS OF MARIA POCH
See Eastern Catholic Religious Communities for Men

BASILIAN ORDER OF ST. JOSAPHAT
See Eastern Catholic Religious Communities for Men

BASILIAN SALVATORIAN FATHERS
See Eastern Catholic Religious Communities for Men

BENEDICTINE CONGREGATION OF OUR LADY OF MOUNTE OLIVETO (Benedictine Monastery of Hawaii)
PO Box 490, Waialua, Oahu, HI 96791. (808) 637-7887. Fax: (808) 637-8601. E-mail: benedicthi@aol.com, Web: www.catholichawaii.com/religious/benedictine
4 Monks
Apostolic Work: Retreats, spiritual direction, parish assistance.
Represented in the Diocese of Honolulu.
Vocation Contact: Vocation Director

BENEDICTINE MONKS (O.S.B.)
St. Bernard Abbey, Cullman, AL 35055. (256) 734-8291, ext. 256. E-mail: francisosb@yahoo.com; Web: www.stbernardabbey.com/becoming_a_monk.htm
28 Monks
Conduct: 5 parishes; co-ed prep school; ecumenical retreat house; parish weekend assistance.
Represented in the Dioceses of Birmingham and Mobile.
Vocation Director: Fr. Francis, OSB

BENEDICTINE MONKS (O.S.B.)
Subiaco Abbey, 405 N. Subiaco Ave., Subiaco, AR 72865-9798. (479) 934-1047
60 Priests & Brothers
Community life and prayer, apostolic works of pastoral ministry, teaching in boys academy, retreat work, hospitality, summer youth camps. Full complement of manual works including farming, vineyards and cattle ranching.
Represented in the Dioceses of Little Rock and Fort Worth.
Vocation Director: Br. Francis Kirchner, O.S.B., Subiaco Abbey, 405 N. Subiaco Ave., Subiaco, AR 72865-9798. (479) 934-1047. Fax: (479) 934-4328. E-mail: vocation@subi.org; Web: www.subi.org

BENEDICTINE MONKS (O.S.B.)
Prince of Peace Abbey, 650 Benet Hill Rd., Oceanside, CA 92054-1246. (760) 430-1305
9 Priests, 11 Brothers, 1 Oblate, 3 in Temporary Vows, 1 Novice, 4 Postulants
Conduct: Monastic life gives emphasis to Liturgy, community life in the cloister, manual labor, retreat house apostolate.
Represented in the Diocese of San Diego.
Vocation Director: Br. Mario V. Quizon, O.S.B., Prince of Peace Abbey, 650 Benet Hill Rd., Oceanside, CA 92054-1246. (760) 430-1305, ext. 244. E-mail: Bmarioosb@aol.com; Web: hometown.aol.com/princeabby/myhomepage/faith.html

BENEDICTINE MONKS (O.S.B.)
Woodside Priory, 302 Portola Rd., Portola Valley, CA 94028
4 Priests, 1 Brother
Conduct: 1 preparatory school (grades 6-12).
Apostolic Work: Education and related activities.
Represented in the Archdiocese of San Francisco.
Vocation Contact: Fr. Martin Mager, O.S.B., Superior, Woodside Priory, 302 Portola Rd., Portola Valley, CA 94028. (650) 851-6133. Fax: (650) 851-2839. E-mail: mmager@woodsidepriory.com; Web: www.woodsidepriory.com

BENEDICTINE MONKS (O.S.B.)
St. Anselm's Abbey, 4501 S. Dakota Ave. N.E. Washington, DC 20017
23 Monks, including Priests and Brothers
Conduct: Centers on prayer, both liturgical and private; on living together in fraternal community; and on work, especially in high-school and university-level education, spiritual guidance, and hospitality.
Vocation Director: Fr. John Farrelly, O.S.B., St. Anselm's Abbey, N.E. Washington, DC 20017. (202) 269-2300. E-mail: mjfarrelly@aol.com or dcabbey@erols.com; Web: www.stanselms.org

BENEDICTINE MONKS (O.S.B.)
Saint Leo Abbey, Saint Leo, FL 33574-2350
11 Priests, 18 Brothers
Conduct: 1 parish, 1 mission.
Apostolic Work: Retreat center.
Represented in North Carolina.
Vocations Director: Br. Mukasa Theodore, O.S.B., Saint Leo Abbey, P.O. Box 2040, Saint Leo, FL 33574-2350. English: (352) 588-8183, Español: (352) 588-5151. Fax: (352) 588-5217. (Respuestas correspondencia en Español). Web: monks vocations@saintleoabbey.org

BENEDICTINE MONKS (O.S.B.)
Marmion Abbey, 850 Butterfield Rd., Aurora, IL 60504
38 Priests, 11 Brothers
Conduct: Marmion Academy and San Jose Seminary (Primary work is teaching).
Represented in Rockford Diocese in IL and in Quetzaltenango Diocese in Guatemala.
Contact: Vocation Director, Marmion Abbey, 850 Butterfield Rd., Aurora, IL 60504. (630) 897-7215, ext. 334. E-mail: vbataille@marmion.org; Web: www.marmion.org

BENEDICTINE MONKS (O.S.B.)
Monastery of the Holy Cross, 3111 S. Aberdeen St., Chicago, IL 60608-6503.(1-888) 539-4261. E-mail: vocations@chicagomonk.org; Web: www.chicagomonk.org/vocations.html
Vocation Director: Brother Peter Funk, O.S.B.

BENEDICTINE MONKS (O.S.B.)
St. Procopius Abbey, 5601 College Rd., Lisle, IL 60532. (630) 969-6410
50 Monks
Conduct: Praising God through the Celebration of the Eucharist and the Liturgy of the Hours; serving the Church by teaching in Benedictine University and Benet Academy, by parish work, and foreign missions in Taiwan.
Vocation Director: Bro. Guy Jelinek, O.S.B., St. Procopius Abbey, 5601 College Rd., Lisle, IL 60532. (630) 969-6410. Fax: (630) 969-6426. E-mail: guyrj@megsinet.net; Web: www.procopius.org

BENEDICTINE MONKS (O.S.B.)
St. Bede Abbey, Route 6 West, Peru, IL 61354. (815) 223-3140
30 Priests, 5 Brothers, 1 Junior, 4 Postulants
Conduct: 6 parishes, 1 high school.
Represented in the Diocese of Peoria.
Vocation Director: Br. Mark Strassburger, OSB, St. Bede Abbey, Route 6 West, Peru, IL 61354. (815) 223-3140, ext. 208. Fax: (815) 223-

8580. E-mail: brmark@st-bede.com; Web: www.theramp.net/stbede

BENEDICTINE MONKS (O.S.B.)
Saint Meinrad Archabbey, St. Meinrad, IN 47577
1 Archbishop, 86 Priests, 25 Brothers, 5 Junior Monks, 3 Novices
Conduct: Interdiocesan/continuing education center, school of theology, various trades and crafts in a monastic context of recollection, spiritual reading and common prayer.
Vocation Director: Br. Kenan Kapina, OSB, Vocation Office, Saint Meinrad Archabbey, 100 Hill Dr., St. Meinrad, IN 47577-1010. (800) 581-6905, (812) 357-6716. Fax: (812) 357-6325. E-mail: kkapina@saintmeinrad.edu; Web: www.saintmeinrad.edu/abbey/vocations.htm

BENEDICTINE MONKS (O.S.B.)
St. Benedict's Abbey
38 Priests, 18 Brothers
Apostolic Work: Benedictine College, Maur Hill Mount Academy, parishes, mission in Brazil.
Represented in the Archdiocese of Kansas City (KS). Also in Brazil.
Vocation Director: Fr. Meinrad Miller, O.S.B., Benedictine College, 1020 N. Second St., Atchison, KS 66002. (913) 367-7853, ext. 2885. E-mail: mmiller@benedictine.edu; Web: http://www.kansasmonks.org

BENEDICTINE MONKS (O.S.B.)
St. Joseph Abbey, St. Benedict, LA 70457. (985) 892-1800. E-mail: augustine70457@yahoo.com; Web: stjosephabbey.org
50 Monks (Priests and Brothers)
Apostolate: College seminary, retreat house, summer camp for children, staffs several parishes, bake bread for poor.
Represented in the Archdiocese of New Orleans.
Vocation Director: Father Augustine Foley, O.S.B.

BENEDICTINE MONKS (O.S.B.)
Glastonbury Abbey, Order of St. Benedict, 16 Hull St., Hingham, MA 02043. (781) 749-2155
10 Monks (Priests and Brothers)
Conduct: Monastery and retreat center.
Represented in the Archdiocese of Boston.
Contact Person: Fr. Thomas, Glastonbury Abbey, Order of St. Benedict, 16 Hull St., Hingham, MA 02043. (781) 749-2155. E-mail: oconnort@glastonburyabbey.org; Web: www.glastonburyabbey.org

BENEDICTINE MONKS (O.S.B.)
St. Benedict Abbey, 252 Still River Rd., Box 67, Still River-Harvard, MA 01467
8 Priests, 12 Brothers, 1 Oblate
Apostolic Works: Monastic life, centered on contemplative prayer and the celebration of Mass and the Divine Office in Latin to Gregorian chant, and flowing over into the dissemination of Catholic doctrine through publishing and guest apostolates.
Represented in the Diocese of Worcester.
Vocation Director: Fr. Xavier, O.S.B., St. Benedict Abbey, 252 Still River Rd., Box 67, Still River-Harvard, MA 01467. (978) 456-3221. Fax: (978) 456-8181. E-mail: abbey@abbey.org

BENEDICTINE MONKS (O.S.B.)
Saint John's Abbey, Collegeville, MN 56321-2015
170 Monks
Apostolic Work: University, graduate school of theology, seminary and preparatory school education; parochial and hospital ministry; publishing house; campus ministry, carpentry, retreats, counseling, writing, gardening, forestry.
Represented in the Archdiocese of St. Paul/Minneapolis and in the Diocese of Saint Cloud. Dependent priories in the Bahamas and Japan.
Contact: Br. Paul-Vincent Niebauer, O.S.B., Saint John's Abbey, Box 2015, Collegeville, MN 56321-2015. (320) 363-2548. E-mail: vocations@osb.org; Web: www.saintjohnsabbey.org

BENEDICTINE MONKS (O.S.B.)
Conception Abbey, PO Box 501, 37174 State Hwy. VV, Conception, MO 64433-0501. (660) 944-2823
70 Monks (Priests & Brothers)
Apostolic Work: Public prayer is chanted six times daily; Conception Seminary College serves students from 28 dioceses and religious orders; Printery House publishes Christian cards, icons, and religious art; parochial and hospital ministry outside the monastery; Abbey Center for Prayer and Ministry conducts retreats for youth and adults; work in trades and crafts.
Represented in the (Arch)dioceses of Kansas City (KS), Kansas City-St. Joseph, Little Rock, Springfield-Cape Girardeau, Dodge City and Wichita.
Vocation Director: Fr. Albert J. Bruecken, OSB, Conception Abbey, PO Box 501, 37174 State Hwy. VV, Conception, MO 64433-0501. (660) 944-2857. Fax: (660) 944-2800. E-mail: monks@conception.edu; Web: www.conceptionabbey.org/Abbotletter.htm

BENEDICTINE MONKS (O.S.B.)
Saint Louis Abbey, 500 South Mason Rd., St. Louis, MO 63141-8500
13 Priests, 9 Brothers, 3 Novices
Apostolic Work: Own, operate and teach in boys' college prep school, grades 7-12; parish and retreat work and convent chaplaincies.
Vocation Director: Rev. Ralph Wright, O.S.B., Saint Louis Abbey, 500 South Mason Rd., St. Louis, MO 63141-8500. (800) 638-1527 or (314) 434-5774. Fax: (314) 434-4526. E-mail: fr_ralph@priory.org; Web: www.stlouisabbey.org

BENEDICTINE MONKS (O.S.B.)
Mount Michael Abbey, 22520 Mount Michael Rd., Elkhorn, NE 68022-3400
15 Priests, 10 Brothers
Apostolic Work: College preparatory high school, parish assistance, retreat work, counseling, monastic hospitality, liturgical art.
Represented in the Archdiocese of Omaha and in the Diocese of Pueblo.
Vocation Director: John Hagemann, OSB, Mount Michael Abbey, 22520 Mount Michael Rd., Elkhorn, NE 68022-3400. (402) 289-2541. E-mail: hagemann_john@hotmail.com; Web: www.mountmichael.org/vocation.htm

BENEDICTINE MONKS (OSB)
St. Anselm Abbey, 100 St. Anselm Dr., Manchester, NH 03102-1310. (603) 641-7000
40 Monks
Conduct: 1 parish, 1 college, 1 dependent house.
Apostolic Work: Education and related activities.
Represented in the Diocese of Manchester and in the Archdiocese of San Francisco.
Vocation Director: Rev. William Sullivan, OSB, St. Anselm Abbey, 100 St. Anselm Dr., Manchester, NH 03102-1310. (603) 641-7000. E-mail: vocations@anselm.edu; Web: www.anselm.edu

BENEDICTINE MONKS (O.S.B.)
St. Mary's Abbey, Delbarton, 230 Mendham Rd., Morristown, NJ 07960
50 Monks
Conduct: 1 preparatory school for boys, 1 summer sports camp, co-ed summer school, 1 retreat center, 2 parishes.

Apostolic Work: Secondary school teaching and administration, parish ministry, pastoral work at local parishes on weekends, college campus ministry and retreat ministry, hospital chaplaincies.
Represented in the Dioceses of Paterson and Trenton and in the Archdiocese of Newark.
Vocation Director: Fr. Edward Seton Fittin, O.S.B., (973) 538-3231, ext. 2036. Fax: (973) 538-7109. E-mail: osbmonks@delbarton.org; Web: www.osbmonks.org

BENEDICTINE MONKS (O.S.B.)
St. Paul's Abbey, Newton, NJ 07860. (973) 383-2470
(Part of Waegwan Abbey, Korea)
13 Monks (Korean, American, African)
Retreat house, gift shop, Christmas tree farm, foreign mission.
Represented in the Diocese of Paterson.
Vocation Director: Fr. Samuel Kim, O.S.B., St. Paul's Abbey, Newton, NJ 07860. (973) 383-2470, ext. 201. Fax: (973) 383-5782. Web: www.osbnewton.org

BENEDICTINE MONKS (O.S.B.)
Newark Abbey, 528 Dr. Martin Luther King Jr. Blvd., Newark, NJ 07102-1314
15 Priests, 8 Brothers
Conduct: 1 abbey, 1 parish, 1 preparatory high school.
Represented in the Archdiocese of Newark.
Vocation Director: Rev. Augustine Curley, O.S.B., Director of Vocations, Newark Abbey, 528 Dr. Martin Luther King Jr. Blvd., Newark, NJ 07102-1314. (973) 792-5800, ext. 1150. E-mail: vocations@sbp.org; Web: www.newarkabbey.org

BENEDICTINE MONKS (O.S.B.)
Mount Saviour Monastery (Elmira), 231 Monastery Rd., Pine City, NY 14871-9787. (607) 734-1688. Fax: (607) 734-1689. E-mail: info@msaviour.org; Web: www.msaviour.org
13 Monks
Represented in the Diocese of Rochester.
Vocation Director: Very Rev. Martin Boler, OSB, Prior

BENEDICTINE MONKS (O.S.B.)
Belmont Abbey, 100 Belmont Mount-Holly Rd., Belmont, NC 28012. (1-800) 743-6681
21 Monks
Apostolic Work: Teaching on the college level, liturgical and pastoral ministry, common prayer.
Represented in the Diocese of Charlotte.
Vocation Director: Br. Agostino Fernandez, O.S.B., Belmont Abbey, 100 Belmont Mount-Holly Rd., Belmont, NC 28012. (704) 825-6674. Fax: (704) 825-6680. E-mail: agostinofernandez@bac.edu; Web: www.belmontabbey.org

BENEDICTINE MONKS (O.S.B.)
Assumption Abbey, PO Box A, Richardton, ND 58652. (701) 974-3315
32 Priests, 25 Brothers
Apostolic Work: Farm, print shop, parish work, hospitality, teaching. Mission community and school in Bogota, Columbia, South America.
Represented in the Diocese of Bismarck.
Vocation Director: Thomas Wordekemper, OSB, Assumption Abbey, PO Box A, Richardton, ND 58652. (701) 974-3315. E-mail: frthomas@assumptionabbey.com; Web: www.assumptionabbey.com

BENEDICTINE MONKS (O.S.B.)
St. Andrew Svorad Abbey, 10510 Buckeye Rd., Cleveland, OH 44104. (216) 721-5300
39 Monks
Conduct: Apostolic communal life of liturgy, lectio and meditation; active works of hospitality, secondary education, parochial and pastoral services.
Represented in the Dioceses of Cleveland and Great Falls-Billings.
Vocation Director: Rev. Albert Marflak, O.S.B., St. Andrew Svorad Abbey, 10510 Buckeye Rd., Cleveland, OH 44104. (216) 721-5300, ext. 208. E-mail: albertmarflakosb@yahoo.com; Web: www.bocohio.org

BENEDICTINE MONKS (O.S.B.)
St. Gregory's Abbey, 1900 W. MacArthur Dr., Shawnee, OK 74804-2499
32 Monks
Apostolic Work: The monastic community maintains its daily prayer and common life, and the monks, both priests and brothers, serve principally in the following areas: St. Gregory's University, early child development, parishes in Oklahoma, weekend supply work, retreats and hospitality, and manual labor.
Represented in the Archdiocese of Oklahoma City and in the Diocese of Tulsa.
Contact: Rev. Lawrence Stasyszen, OSB, St. Gregory's Abbey, 1900 W. MacArthur Dr., Shawnee, OK 74804-2499. (405) 878-5491. Fax: (405) 878-5170. E-mail: vocations@stgregorys.edu; Web: www.monksok.org

BENEDICTINE MONKS (O.S.B.)
Mount Angel Abbey, One Abbey Dr., St. Benedict, OR 70 Monks
Conduct: 1 seminary, 1 retreat house, 3 parishes.
Represented in the Archdioceses of Portland, (OR) and Seattle and in the Diocese of Cuernavaca, Mexico.
Vocation Director: Fr. Joseph Nguyen, O.S.B., Mount Angel Abbey, One Abbey Dr., St. Benedict, OR 97373. (503) 845-3226. E-mail: frjoseph@mtangel.edu; Web: www.mtangel.edu

BENEDICTINE MONKS (O.S.B.)
Saint Vincent Archabbey, 300 Fraser Purchase Rd., Latrobe, PA 15650-2690. (724) 532-6600
180 Monks
Conduct: 1 archabbey, 3 dependent priories, 30 parishes, 5 chaplaincies, 1 seminary, 1 college, 1 high school.
Apostolic Work: Education, foreign missions, parochial ministry and chaplaincies.
Represented in the Archdiocese of Baltimore and in the Dioceses of Altoona-Johnstown, Erie, Greensburg, Harrisburg, Pittsburgh, Richmond and Savannah. Foreign missions in Taiwan and Brazil.
Vocation Director: Fr. Fred Byrne, OSB, Saint Vincent Archabbey, 300 Fraser Purchase Rd., Latrobe, PA 15650-2690. (724) 532-6655.
E-mail: vocations@stvincent.edu or fred.byrne@email.stvincent.edu; Web: http://benedictine.stvincent.edu/archabbey/

BENEDICTINE MONKS (O.S.B.)
Portsmouth Abbey, Cory's Ln., Portsmouth, RI 02871
17 Monks
Apostolate: Boarding secondary school for boys and girls (Portsmouth Abbey School).
Vocation Director: Fr. Ambrose, O.S.B., Portsmouth Abbey, Cory's Ln., Portsmouth, RI 02871. (401) 683-2000. E-mail: fatherambrose@portsmouthabbey.org; Web: www.cwsne.com/portsmouthabbey

BENEDICTINE MONKS (O.S.B.)
Blue Cloud Abbey, 46561 147th St., PO Box 98, Marvin, SD 57251-0098
23 Priests, 17 Brothers
Apostolic Work: Divine Office & common life; retreat work at Abbey; associate program (2 months); pastoral work in South Dakota and

Guatemala. The Abbey invites men to explore monastic life: 2 weeks to 2 months, or for a lifetime.
Represented in the Dioceses of Sioux Falls, SD and Coban, Guatemala.
Vocation & Associate Promoter: Fr. Denis Quinkert, O.S.B., Blue Cloud Abbey, 46561 147th St., PO Box 98, Marvin, SD 57251-0098. (605) 398-9208. Fax: (605) 398-9201. E-mail: vocation@bluecloud.org; Web: www.bluecloud.org/assoc-cand.html

BENEDICTINE MONKS (O.S.B.)
Weston Priory, 58 Priory Hill Rd., Weston, VT 05161-6400. (802) 824-5409. E-mail: brphilip@westonpriory.org; Web: www.westonpriory.org
15 Monks
Represented in the Diocese of Burlington.
Vocation Director: Brother Philip Fronckiewicz, O.S.B.

BENEDICTINE MONKS (O.S.B.)
Mary Mother of the Church Abbey, 12829 River Rd., Richmond, VA 23233-7206. (804) 784-3508, ext. 137. E-mail: frtheo@mmotcva.org or vocations@richmondmonks.org; Web: www.richmondmonks.org/Vocations.html
Apostolic Work: Celebration of the Eucharist and community prayer, teaching in high school, parochial and hospital ministry, chaplaincies and retreats.
Represented in the Diocese of Richmond.
Vocation Director: Fr. Theophile Brown, O.S.B.

BENEDICTINE MONKS (O.S.B.)
Saint Martin's Abbey, 5300 Pacific Ave. SE, Lacey, WA 98503-1297
37 Monks
Conduct: 1 college, 2 parishes, 5 chaplaincies
Apostolic Work: Daily prayer and common life; St. Martin's College, parishes and hospital chaplaincies.
Represented in the Archdioceses of Seattle and Portland and in the Dioceses of Yakima and Spokane.
Vocation Director: Fr. Benedict Auer, O.S.B., Saint Martin's Abbey, 5300 Pacific Ave. SE, Lacey, WA 98503-1297. (360) 491-4700. Fax: (360) 438-4441. E-mail: vocations@stmartin.edu, auer@stmartin.edu; Web: www.stmartin.edu

BENEDICTINE MONKS (O.S.B.)
St. Benedict's Abbey, 12605 224th Ave., Benet Lake, WI 53102
20 Monks
Conduct: Abbey and retreat center.
Represented in the Archdiocese of Milwaukee.
Vocation Director: Br. Michael O'Brien, OSB, St. Benedict's Abbey, 12605 224th Ave., Benet Lake, WI 53102. (262) 396-4311. Fax: (262) 396-4365. E-mail: vocations@benetlake.org; Web: www.benetlake.org

BENEDICTINE MONKS - Byzantine Rite (Holy Trinity Monastery)
See Eastern Catholic Religious Communities for Men

BENEDICTINE MONKS (O.S.B.) (Congregation of the Annunciation)
St. Andrew's Abbey, PO Box 40, Valyermo, CA 93563-0040
26 Monks
Apostolic Work: Retreat house, youth center, teaching, chaplaincies.
Represented in the Archdiocese of Los Angeles.
Vocation Director: Fr. Joseph Brennan, O.S.B., St. Andrew's Abbey, PO Box 40, Valyermo, CA 93563-0040. (661) 944-2178. Fax: (661) 944-1076. E-mail: joseph@valyermo.com; Web: www.valyermo.com

BENEDICTINE MONKS (O.S.B.) (Olivetan Benedictines)
Holy Trinity Monastery, P.O. Box 298, St. David, AZ 85630. (520) 720-4642
3 Priests, 7 Monks
Represented in the Diocese of Tucson.
Vocation Director: Fr. Henri Capdeville, O.S.B., Prior

BENEDICTINE MONKS (O.S.B.) (Olivetan Benedictines)
Our Lady of Guadalupe Abbey, PO Box 1080, Pecos, NM 87552-1080
9 Priests, 4 Brothers, 2 Postulants
Represented in the Archdiocese of Santa Fe.
Vocation Contact: Rev. Paul Meaden, OSB, Prior, Our Lady of Guadalupe Abbey, PO Box 1080, Pecos, NM 87552-1080. (505) 757-6415. Fax: (505) 757-2285. E-mail: guestmaster@pecos-nm.com; Web: www.pecosabbey.org

BENEDICTINE MONKS (O.S.B.) (Congregation of St. Ottilien for Foreign Missions)
Christ the King Priory-Benedictine Mission House, PO Box 528, Schuyler, NE 68661-0528
4 Priests, 4 Brothers
Conduct: U.S. headquarters for the financial support for the Benedictine missions in Africa, Asia, the Philippines and South America. Parish assistance and a retreat center.
Vocation Director: Brother Tobias Dammert, OSB, Christ the King Priory-Benedictine Mission House, PO Box 528, Schuyler, NE 68661-0528. (402) 352-2177, ext. 303. E-mail: tobias.bmh@dtnspeed.net; Web: www.megavision.net/benedict

BENEDICTINE MONKS (O.S.B.) (Benedictines, Subiaco Congregation)
Monastery of Christ in the Desert, P.O. Box 270, Abiquiu, NM 87510-0270
30 Monks
Represented in the Archdioceses of Santa Fe and Chicago. Also in Mexico.
Vocation Director: Br. Andre, O.S.B., Monastery of Christ in the Desert, P.O. Box 270, Abiquiu, NM 87510-0270. (801) 545-8567. E-mail: vocmcid@lycos.com; Web: www.Christdesert.org

BENEDICTINE MONKS (O.S.B.) (Sylvestrine Congregation O.S.B.)
St. Benedict Monastery, 2711 E. Drahner Rd., Oxford, MI 48370-2815
Community of Priests and Lay Brothers
Apostolic Work: Teaching, parish work and catechetical work in addition to monastic, community life and youth retreat ministry.
Represented in the Archdiocese of Detroit and in the Diocese of Paterson, NJ.
Vocation Director: Rev. Damien Gjonaj, OSB, St. Benedict Monastery, 2711 E. Drahner Rd., Oxford, MI 48370-2815. E-mail: saintben@core.com; Web: www.benedictinemonks.com

CONGREGATION OF THE BLESSED SACRAMENT (S.S.S.)
(United States Province of St. Ann)
Provincial Offices: 5384 Wilson Mills Rd., Highland Heights, OH 44143. (440) 442-7243
75 Priests, Deacons and Brothers
Conduct: novitiate, 7 parishes, specialized ministries.
Apostolic Work: Prayer and work focused specifically on the Eucharist. Active ministry includes: staffing selected parishes, Eucharistic retreats, seminars, writing, teaching, preaching, hospital chaplains, university chaplains, counseling, spiritual direction, prayer, adoration.
Represented in the Archdioceses of Chicago, New York, San Antonio and Santa Fe and in the Dioceses of Cleveland, Houston and St. Petersburg.

Vocation Office: 5384 Wilson Mills Rd., Cleveland, OH 44143-3092. (440) 442-7243. E-mail: sssvocations@sbcglobal.net; Web: www.blessedsacrament.com

BRIGITTINE MONKS (O.Ss.S.) (Order of the Most Holy Savior)

Priory of Our Lady of Consolation, 23300 Walker Ln., Amity, OR 97101. (503) 835-8080

9 Monks, 2 Novices

Apostolic Work: Contemplative.

Represented in the Archdiocese of Portland.

Contact: Bro. Steven Vargo, O.Ss.S., Prior, Priory of Our Lady of Consolation, 23300 Walker Ln., Amity, OR 97101. (503) 835-8080. Fax: (503) 835-9662. E-mail: monks@brigittine.org; Web: www.brigittine.org

BROTHERS OF THE ANNUNCIATION

See Eastern Catholic Religious Communities for Men

BROTHERS OF THE CHRISTIAN SCHOOLS

See De La Salle Christian Brothers

BROTHERS OF THE POOR OF ST. FRANCIS (C.F.P.)

See "F" - Franciscans - Brothers of the Poor of St. Francis

BROTHERS OF ST. JOHN OF GOD

See "H" - Hospitaller Brothers of St. John of God

CALASANZIAN FATHERS

See Piarists

CAMALDOLESE HERMITS OF MONTE CORONA

Holy Family Hermitage, 1501 Fairplay Road, Bloomingdale, OH 43910-7971

3 Priests

Contemplative, no exterior ministry.

Represented in Italy, Poland, Spain, Colombia and Venezuela.

CAMALDOLESE HERMITS (O.S.B.Cam.)

New Camaldoli Hermitage, 62475 Hwy. 1, Big Sur, CA 93920-9656. (831) 667-0244 (tel, fax). E-mail: vocations@contemplation.com; Web: www.contemplation.com

26 Monks in US

Contemplative monastic life combining community and solitude with emphasis on prayer.

Represented in the Dioceses of Monterey and Oakland and in Italy, Brazil and India.

Vocation Director: Brother Bede Healey, OSB Cam.

CAMILLIANS (O.S.Cam.) (Servants of the Sick)

Camillian Provincialate of North American Province: St. Camillus Community, 3661 S. Kinnickinnic Ave., St. Francis, WI 53235

10 Priests, 5 Brothers, 2 Temporary Professed

Conduct: 3 religious houses, health center, 1 retirement center, 1 home health agency, 2 parishes and are on staff at several public and private health care institutions.

Apostolic Work: Known throughout the world as Camillians, an Order founded by St. Camillus de Lellis in 1582 – caring for the sick as chaplains, counselors, nurses, doctors, psychologists, physical therapists, ethicists, health care administrators, and serving in all the fields of health care, medicine and rehabilitation.

Represented in the Archdiocese of Milwaukee and in the Dioceses of Madison and Worcester. Also in 32 other countries throughout the world.

Vocations Coordinator: Deacon Albert Schempp, O.S.Cam., 3661 S. Kinnickinnic Ave., St. Francis, WI 53235. (414) 259-6300, ext. 3478. E-mail: vocations@camillians.org; Web: www.camillians.org

CANONS REGULAR OF PRE-MONTRE

See Norbertines

CAPUCHIN FRANCISCAN FRIARS (O.F.M.Cap.)

(Our Lady of Angels-Western American Province) 1345 Cortez Ave., Burlingame, CA 94010. (415) 342-1489

67 Friars (Brothers and Priests)

Apostolic Works: Parish ministries, chaplaincies, high school and college education, retreat and renewal ministries, mission work, social justice and peace, and similar ministries of prayer and service.

Represented in the Archdioceses of Los Angeles and San Francisco and in the Dioceses of Baker, Fresno and Oakland. Also in Obregon, Chihuahua, Monterrey, Mexico.

Vocation Director: Fr. Jesús Vela, OFM. Cap., San Lorenzo Seminary, PO Box 247, 1802 Sky Dr., Santa Ynez, CA 93460-9500. (805) 688-5630. E-mail: jesusmitodo@hotmail.com; Web: www.ktb.net/~bjm/cap/index.html

CAPUCHIN FRANCISCAN FRIARS (O.F.M. Cap.)

(Capuchin Province of Mid-America) St. Francis of Assisi Friary, 3553 Wyandot St., Denver, CO 80211

60 Friars (Priests and Brothers)

Conduct: All types of service for the Church as parish pastors, hospital chaplains, teachers, counselors, preachers, with ministries in a homeless shelter, migrant labor camps, on college campuses and in prisons. Evangelization efforts in foreign missions.

Represented in the Archdioceses of Denver, Saint Louis and Kansas City (KS) and in the Dioceses of Colorado Springs and Salina. Also in Mendi (Papua New Guinea), Puerto Rico and Mexico.

Vocation Directors: Fr. John Lager, ofm. Cap., Fr. Michael Scully, ofm. Cap., St. Francis of Assisi Friary, 3553 Wyandot St., Denver, CO 80211. (303) 433-0296. E-mail: johnclager@aol.com; Web: www.midamcaps.org

CAPUCHIN FRANCISCAN FRIARS (ofm Cap)

(Province of St. Joseph) 1740 Mt. Elliott St., Detroit, MI 48207

200 members (Brothers and Priests)

Apostolic Work: Serving the poor (African-American and Hispanic inner city ministries, Native American missions, social justice issues), preaching and evangelization (retreat work, parish mission preaching, teaching), parish ministry. Foreign missions in Central America.

Represented in WI: Milwaukee, Green Bay, La Crosse, Madison, MI: Detroit, Saginaw, Marquette; IL: Chicago; IN: Fort Wayne/South Bend; MT: Great Falls, and in Central America: Nicaragua, Honduras, Costa Rica, Panama.

Vocation Directors: Michael Bertram, OFM Cap, Rob Roemer, OFM Cap, Capuchin Vocation Office, 301 Church St., Mt. Calvary, WI 53057. (888) 297-2702. Fax: (920) 753-7514. E-mail: vocation@capuchinfranciscans.org; Web: www.capuchinfranciscans.org

CAPUCHIN FRANCISCAN FRIARS (OFM Cap.)

(Province of the Stigmata of St. Francis – New Jersey and Eastern coast) Provincialate: Our Lady of Guadalupe Friary, PO 789, Union City, NJ 07087-0789

65 Friars

Apostolic Work: Parish ministries, hospital chaplaincies, preaching apostolate, social ministry with destitute men and women, Secular Franciscans, foreign missions, Hispanic ministry, AIDS ministry, street ministry, soup kitchens and shelters, spiritual direction.

Represented in the Archdioceses of Newark and New York and in the

Dioceses of Paterson, Wilmington, Charlotte, St. Petersburg and Zambia, Africa. Mission in Mexico.
Vocation Coordinator: Bro. Miguel Ramirez, ofm Cap., PO Box 789, Union City, NJ 07087-0789. (201) 863-3871. E-mail: capuchinlife@aol.com

CAPUCHIN FRANCISCAN FRIARS (O.F.M. Cap.)
(Province of St. Mary of New York and New England)
Provincialate: St. Conrad Friary, 30 Gedney Park Dr., White Plains, NY 10605. (914) 761-3008
200 Perpetually Professed Friars
Conduct: 21 friaries, 12 parishes, 1 parish high school, 5 parish grammar schools, 3 houses of formation, 1 youth and family ministries center.
Apostolic Work: Pastoral counselling, hospital, home for aged, military, prison chaplaincies, parish ministries, work with the disabled, work with the dying in a cancer hospital, preaching apostolate, marriage encounters, youth ministries; teaching in grammar school, high school, college and seminary; inner-city ministry with poor, college campus ministries.
Represented in the (Arch)dioceses of New York and Boston and in the Dioceses of Brooklyn, Rockville Centre, Rochester, Norwich and Bridgeport, Springfield, Manchester and Portland. Also in the Marianas Islands, Japan and Central America.
Vocation Ministry Coordinator: Brother Tim Jones, O.F.M. Cap., St. Joseph Friary, 34 South Chestnut St., New Paltz, NY 12561. (845) 255-5680. Fax: (845) 255-6125. E-mail: capuchins@franciscan vocation.org; Web: www.franciscan vocation.org

CAPUCHIN FRANCISCAN FRIARS (O.F.M. Cap.)
(Province of St. Augustine)
Provincialate: 220 - 37th St., Pittsburgh, PA 15201. (412) 682-6011
200 Friars (Brothers and Priests)
Conduct: 17 friaries, 30 parishes, 1 novitiate, 2 houses of study, hermitage, 2 foreign missions (Papua, New Guinea and Puerto Rico).
Apostolic Work: Parishes, chaplaincies, inner city ministry, work with the poor, Hispanic ministry, justice and peace ministry, Appalachian ministry, youth ministry, preaching, teaching, foreign missions.
Represented in the States of DC, IN, KY, MD, OH, PA, WV as well as in Puerto Rico and Papua, New Guinea.
Vocation Director: Brother Mike Joyce, OFM Cap., National Capuchin Vocation Office: 220 - 37th St., Box G, Pittsburgh, PA 15201. (412) 682-7974. Fax: (412) 682-0506. E-mail: come-and-see@capuchin.com; Web: www.capuchin.com

CAPUCHIN FRANCISCAN FRIARS (O.F.M. Cap.)
(Capuchin Viceprovince of Texas) 5605 Bernal Dr., Dallas, TX 75212-4499. (214) 631-1937
14 Priests, 1 Lay Brother
Apostolic Work: Parish, renewal movements, hospitals, schools, preaching.
Represented in the (Arch)dioceses of Dallas and Fort Worth.
Vocation Director: Fr. Ignacio Cizur, O.F.M. Cap., 5605 Bernal Dr., Dallas, TX 75212-4499. (214) 637-6673. E-mail: cubas@juno.com; Web: www.ktb.net/~bjm/cap/directors.html

CARMELITE FRIARS (O.Carm.)
(Province of St. Elias), PO Box 3079, Carmelite Dr., Middletown, NY 10940
89 Carmelites in the Province
Apostolic Ministry: 10 parishes, retreats and renewal work, lay Carmelites, social work, counseling, campus ministry, teaching (all levels: elementary, high school, college), hospital chaplaincy and other specialized ministries.
Represented by 13 Carmelite residences in the Archdiocese of New York and in the Dioceses of Albany, Rochester (NY), Greenburg (PA) and Palm Beach (FL). Also missions in Vietnam and Trinidad.
Vocation Director: Fr. Matthew Faulkner, O.Carm., Carmelite Vocation Office, PO Box 3079, Carmelite Dr., Middletown, NY 10940. (845) 344-2225. Fax: (845) 344-2210. E-mail: ocarmvoc@frontiernet.net; Web: www.frontiernet.net/~ocarmvoc

CARMELITES (O. Carm.)
(Province of the Most Pure Heart of Mary)
Provincial Office: 1313 Frontage Rd., Darien, IL 60561
248 Priests & Brothers
Seminaries: Pre-Novitiate House in Houston, TX. Novitiate in Middletown, NY, Theology at Washington Theological Union, with residence at Whitefriars Hall, Washington, DC.
Apostolates: Community, contemplative prayer and prophetic ministry are the Carmelite charism. Priests and brothers minister at 4 retreat houses, 35 parishes, 6 high schools and various ministries in 16 dioceses throughout the United States and Canada, with missions in Peru and Mexico.
Represented in the Archdioceses of Boston, Chicago, Kansas City, Lima (Peru), Louisville, Los Angeles, Newark, Toronto (Ontario, Canada), and Washington, DC and in the Dioceses of Galveston-Houston, Joliet, Phoenix, Sacramento, St. Catherines (Ontario, Canada), Sicuani (Peru), Torreon (Mexico), Tucson and Venice (FL).
Vocation Director: Fr. William Wert, O. Carm., Carmelite Vocation Office, 8433 Bailey Rd., Darien, IL 60561. (630) 969-4141, ext. 107. Fax: (630) 969-3376. E-mail: vocations@carmelnet.org; Web: www.carmelites.net

ORDER OF CARMELITES (O. Carm.)
Mt. Carmel Hermitage, 244 Baileys Rd., Bolivar, PA 15923. (724) 238-0423
2 Priests, 1 Brother
Contemplative, semi-eremitical life.
Represented in the Diocese of Greensburg.
Vocation Director: Fr. Bede Mulligan, O.Carm.

CARMELITES OF MARY IMMACULATE (C.M.I.)
North American Headquarters: Holy Family Church, 21 Nassau Ave., Brooklyn, NY 11222
Generalate: P.B. No. 1056 Ernakulam, Cochin 682 011, Kerala, India
76 Priests in US and Canada
Apostolic Work: Ministry to parishes, hospitals, universities, prisons, mission to Syro-Malabar Catholics.
Represented in the (Arch)dioceses of Alexandria, Beaumont, Boston, Brooklyn, Hartford, Joliet, Lafayette, Lake Charles, Nashville, New Ulm, New York, Philadelphia, Rockville Centre, St. Augustine, Tyler and Toledo. Also in Canada.
Vocation Director: Holy Family Church, 21 Nassau Ave., Brooklyn, NY 11222. (718) 388-5145, 4866. Fax: (718) 387-1877. E-mail: cmiusa@hotmail.com; Web: www.cmicongregation.org

CARMELITES (TERESIAN)
See "C" section - Community of Teresian Carmelites

ORDER OF CARTHUSIANS (Cart.)
Charterhouse of the Transfiguration, 1800 Beartown Rd., Arlington, VT

05250-9315. (802) 362-2550. Fax: (802) 362-3584. E-mail: carthusians _in_america@juno.com; Web: www.chartreux.org

5 Choir Religious, 7 Brothers

A purely contemplative semi-eremitic order, strictly cloistered.

Represented in the US in the Diocese of Burlington. There are 23 monasteries (of which 5 for nuns) in Argentina, Brazil, England, France, Italy, Korea, Portugal, Slovenia, Spain and Switzerland.

Vocation Contacts: Fr. M. Joseph Kim, Vocation Director; Fr. Lorenzo M. DeLaRosa, Prior

THE BROTHERS OF CHARITY (F.C.)

American Region: Brothers of Charity

Apostolic Work: Education, special education, social work and foreign missions.

Represented in the Archdiocese of Philadelphia and 23 other countries.

Vocation Director: Director of Vocations, 7720 Doe Lane, Laverock, PA 19038. (215) 887-6361. E-mail: mlonswayfc@aol.com; Web: www.fracarita.org

BROTHERS OF CHRISTIAN INSTRUCTION (FIC)

(Notre Dame Province) Alfred, ME 04002. (207) 324-0067

40 Members in US; 1,200 worldwide

Apostolic Work: Programs for academic and faith development in school, parish and retreat settings, foreign missions.

Represented in the Dioceses of Fall River, Ogdensburg, Portland (ME) and Youngstown. Foreign missions: Japan, Philippines, Tanzania, Uganda, Kenya, Ivory Coast, Congo, Rwanda, Burundi, Benin, Senegal, Togo, Haiti, Tahiti, Chile, Bolivia and Indonesia.

Vocation Counselor: Br. Daniel J. Caron, 555 Eastern Ave., Fall River, MA 02723. (508) 672-5763. E-mail: djcaron43@yahoo.com; Web: www.ficbrothers.org

CHRISTIAN BROTHERS (F.S.C.)

See De La Salle Christian Brothers

CONGREGATION OF CHRISTIAN BROTHERS (C.F.C.)

(Western American Province) Brother Rice Provincialate, 958 Western Ave., Joliet, IL 60435. (815) 723-5464

90 Brothers

Conduct: Secondary schools and volunteer community ministry.

Apostolic Work: Specialize in the education of young people. Special interest in education of poor and underprivileged.

Represented in the Archdioceses of Chicago, Detroit and Seattle and in the Dioceses of Honolulu, Joliet, Monterey, Owensboro and Phoenix. Also, missions in Peru.

Vocation Director: Br. J.R. McDonald, C.F.C., 802 Terry Ave., Seattle, WA 98104-1294. (206) 622-6596, 2639. E-mail: brmac@odea.org; Web: www.cfc-west.org

CONGREGATION OF CHRISTIAN BROTHERS (C.F.C.)

(Eastern American Province) 21 Pryer Terrace, New Rochelle, NY 10804. (914) 636-6194

185 Brothers

Conduct: 1 college, 15 high schools, 4 grammar schools, 1 St. Joseph's Care Center. Missions in Peru and Bonita Springs.

Apostolic Work: Specialize in the education of young people. Special interest in education of poor and underprivileged.

Represented in the Archdioceses of Boston, Miami, Newark and New York and in the Dioceses of Albany, Brownsville, Charleston, Jackson, Orlando, Owensboro, Providence, Rochester, Tampa and Venice (FL) as well as in the missionary areas of Peru.

Vocation Director: Br. James Harlow, CFC, 21 Pryer Terrace, New Rochelle, NY 10804. (914) 636-6194, ext. 26. E-mail: JLH@cbinstitute.org. Web: www.Iona.edu

CISTERCIAN FATHERS (O.C.)

Cistercian Monastery, 564 Walton Ave., Mt. Laurel, NJ 08054

3 Priests

Conduct: Teaching, missions, parish work.

Vocation Director: Superior of Monastery, Cistercian Monastery, 564 Walton Ave., Mt. Laurel, NJ 08054. (856) 235-1330

CISTERCIAN FATHERS (O. Cist.)

Cistercian Monastery of Our Lady of Dallas, One Cistercian Rd., Irving, TX 75039. (972) 438-2044

20 Priests, 3 Novices

Ministries: Teaching and pastoral work both in college and in secondary school, parish assistance.

Represented in the Dioceses of Dallas and Fort Worth.

Vocation Director: Rev. Paul McCormick, O. Cist., One Cistercian Rd., Irving, TX 75039. (972) 438-2044, ext. 258. E-mail: fr-paul@cistercian.org; Web: www.cistercian.org

CISTERCIAN ORDER (O. Cist.)

St. Mary's Cistercian Priory, 70 Schuylkill Rd., New Ringgold, PA 17960. (570) 943-2645

3 Priests

Conduct: A contemplative community, with intramural ecumenical activity.

Vocation Director: Rev. Hugh Montague, O. Cist., St. Mary's Cistercian Priory, 70 Schuylkill Rd., New Ringgold, PA 17960. (570) 943-2645

CISTERCIAN ORDER (O. Cist.)

Cistercian Abbey of Our Lady of Spring Bank

3 Priests, 1 in Temporary Vows, 1 Novice

Conduct: Contemplative monastic life.

Vocation Director: Rev. Robert Keffer, O. Cist., Cistercian Abbey, 17304 Havenwood Rd., Sparta, WI 54656. (608) 269-8138. Fax: (608) 269-2800. E-mail: frrobert@MonksOnline.org; Web: www.MonksOnline.org

THE CLARETIAN MISSIONARIES (C.M.F.) (Missionary Sons of the Immaculate Heart of Mary)

126 Fathers, 12 Brothers, 17 Students, 4 Novices

Conduct: 2 provinces, formation house, parishes, Hispanic ministry (Casa Claret), youth ministry, Claretian Publications ("U.S. Catholic", "Vision"), Claret Center for Resources in Spirituality, hospital ministry, prison ministry; work among the poor, elderly, hungry and marginated; campus ministry.

Apostolic Work: Men, women, and couples, vowed religious and laity seek to respond to the most urgent needs of evangelization, especially in favor of the poor. Claretian priests and brothers, lay Claretians and Claretian volunteers each seek to live out this call according to their own charism.

Represented in the Archdioceses of Atlanta, Chicago, Los Angeles and San Antonio and in the Dioceses of Baker, Fresno, Metuchen, Oakland, Phoenix, Santa Rosa and Springfield-Cape Girardeau. Also in Kingston, Jamaica and Juarez, Mexico.

Vocation Directors: Eastern Province: Father Carl Quebedeaux, C.M.F., 205 W. Monroe St., Room 2307, Chicago, IL 60606. (1-800) 328-6515, (312) 236-7846. E-mail: frcarl6h@claret.org; Western Province: Father Art Gramaje, C.M.F., 1119 Westchester Pl., Los Angeles, CA 90019. (323) 733-7712. E-mail: cmffvoc@earthlink.net; Web: www.claretianvocations.org

CLERICS OF ST. VIATOR (C.S.V.) (Viatorians)
(Chicago Province) 1212 E. Euclid St., Arlington Heights, IL 60004
94 Brothers and Priests
Apostolic Work: Education, parish ministry.
Represented in the Archdioceses of Chicago and Kansas City (KS) and in the Dioceses of Joliet, Springfield-in-Illinois, Rockford, Peoria, Las Vegas, Little Rock, San Diego, San Jose, Manchester, Monterey and Tucson. Missionary foundation in Bogota, Colombia (South America) and Belize (Central America).
Director of Vocation Ministry: Fr. Dan Nolan, C.S.V., 1212 E. Euclid St., Arlington Heights, IL 60004. (847) 398-0685. E-mail: DanNolan@viatorians.com; Web: www.viatorians.com

CLERICS REGULAR OF ST. PAUL
See Barnabite Fathers and Brothers

COLUMBAN FATHERS (S.S.C.) (St. Columban's Foreign Mission Society)
PO Box 10, St. Columbans, NE 68056
680 Priests engaged exclusively in foreign mission work
Conduct: 1 theologate, 1 pre-theology house, 1 spiritual year.
Apostolic Work: Advocates of prophetic justice working alongside the poor and most marginalized people in the world; ministers of the Word and sacraments; missionary priests working in 15 countries throughout the world; creative partners with others in evangelization, community and human development, mission education and justice issues (homeless, prisoners, workers, refugees, migrants, indigenous peoples); and men of prayer committed to the mission of Jesus and God's kingdom.
Represented in the (Arch)dioceses of Boston, Chicago, El Paso, Los Angeles, Omaha, Providence and San Bernardino.
Foreign Missions: Australia/New Zealand, Brazil, Britain, Chile, Fiji/Vanuatu, Ireland, Japan, Korea, Pakistan, Peru, Philippines and Taiwan.
Vocation Director: Fr. Arturo Aguilar, S.S.C., Columban Vocation Office, The Columban Fathers, PO Box 10, St. Columbans, NE 68056. (402) 291-1920. E-mail: vocations@columban.org; Web: www.columban.org

COMBONI MISSIONARIES (M.C.C.J.)
1318 Nagel Rd., Cincinnati, OH 45255-3120. (513) 474-4997. Fax: (513) 474-0382. E-mail: info@ComboniMissionaries.org; Web: www.combonimissionaries.org
An international order of Priests and Brothers, working for the most part in 22 countries of Africa and Latin America. They come from 15 different countries around the world.
Apostolic Work: Evangelization, social development and promotion of mission awareness. Work among the poorest and most disadvantaged people in the world. Involved in pastoral ministry among minority groups, and conduct formation programs for college-level and graduate candidates.
Represented in North America in the (Arch)dioceses of Newark, Cincinnati, Detroit, Chicago, Los Angeles and Hamilton (Ontario).
Vocation Director: Fr. José Luis Cuevas, M.C.C.J., Casa Comboni, 525 N. Pasadena Ave., Azusa, CA 91702-3052. (626) 812-0818. Fax: (626) 969-8681. E-mail: pepe44@sbcglobal.net

COMMUNITY OF TERESIAN CARMELITES (C.T.C.)
(A community of Consecrated Men, Women and Lay Associates) PO Box 826, Worcester, MA 01613-0826. (508) 752-5734
6 Consecrated Members, 2 Postulants for Consecrated Life, 9 Professed Lay Associates, 8 Lay Novices
Apostolic Work: Contemplative/active: telephone prayer-line, television ministry; soul, mind and body institute; Domus Mariae House of Prayer, missions and spiritual conferences, spiritual guidance, retreats, spiritual formation, lay associate meetings, parish religious education, spiritual periodical.
Represented in the Diocese of Worcester.
Vocation Directors: Brother Dennis Anthony Wyrzykowski, CTC, Sister Nancy-Marie Connors, CTC; Lay Director: Arlene Wyrzykowski, c.t.c.s., Community of Teresian Carmelites, Box 826, Worcester, MA 01613-0826. (508) 752-5734. E-mail: srnancymarie@yahoo.com or broden39@aol.com; Web: www.teresiancarmelites.org

CONGREGATION OF THE BLESSED SACRAMENT
See Blessed Sacrament, Congregation of

CONGREGATION OF CHRISTIAN BROTHERS
See Christian Brothers, Congregation of

CONGREGATION OF HOLY CROSS
See Holy Cross Priests & Brothers

CONGREGATION OF THE IMMACULATE HEART OF MARY
See Missionhurst Congregation of the Immaculate Heart of Mary

CONGREGATION OF JESUS AND MARY
See Eudist Fathers and Brothers

CONGREGATION OF THE MISSION
See Vincentians

CONGREGATION OF MISSIONARIES OF THE BLOOD OF CHRIST
See Society of the Precious Blood

CONGREGATION OF THE PASSION
See Passionists

CONGREGATION OF THE SACRED HEARTS OF JESUS AND MARY
See Sacred Hearts Community

CONGREGATION OF SACRED STIGMATA (C.S.S.) (Stigmatine Fathers and Brothers)
(Province of the Holy Spouses, Mary and Joseph)
Provincial Office: 554 Lexington St., Waltham, MA 02452-3097. (781) 209-3100
26 Priests, 1 Brother
Conduct: Retreat house, 6 parishes. Missions in Brazil and Italy.
Apostolic Work: Seminary formation, spiritual direction, counseling, retreats, campus/youth/parish ministry, voluntary foreign missions, parish missions.
Represented in the Archdioceses of Boston and New York and in the Dioceses of Springfield (MA) and Worcester.
Vocation Minister: Fr. Richard A. Scioli, C.S.S., 554 Lexington St., Waltham, MA 02452-3097. (781) 209-3102. E-mail: richards@stigmatines.com or vocations@stigmatines.com; Web: www.stigmatines.com

CONGREGATION OF ST. JOSEPH
See St. Joseph, Congregation of

CONSOLATA MISSIONARIES (I.M.C.)
2301 Rt. 27, PO Box 5550, Somerset, NJ 08875. (732) 297-9191. Fax: (732) 940-3121
1,000 Priests and Brothers; 37 in US

and Canada
Conduct: 6 mission centers, 1 formation program.
Apostolic Work: Foreign missions - and wherever the Gospel needs to be proclaimed and witnessed to, especially among the poor.
Present in Argentina, Bolivia, Brazil, Colombia, Equador, Venezuela, Ethiopia, Guinea Bissau, Ivory Coast, Kenya, Liberia, Libya, Mozambique, Republic of Congo, Somalia, Tanzania, South Africa and Uganda, Europe (Italy, Portugal, England, Spain, Switzerland), Canada, South Korea and in the United States.
Vocation Director: Fr. David Gikonyo, IMC, Consolata Missionaries, 1321 Otis St. NE, Washington, DC 20017. (202) 832-3582. Fax: (202) 832-3583. Web: www.consolata.org

CROSIER FATHERS AND BROTHERS (O.S.C.)
(Canons Regular of the Order of the Holy Cross)
3510 Vivian Ave., St. Paul, MN 55126-3852. 1-800-407-5875
The Crosiers are an international Order of Catholic priests and brothers. As canons regular, there are three pillars on which their life is built: 1) living in COMMUNITY; 2) praying the LITURGY of the Church together; and 3) serving the needs of the Church through their MINISTRY. As pastoral leaders they are involved in parish and campus ministry, missionary activity in Indonesia and Zaire, education, retreat work, Hispanic ministry and ministry with, and among, the poor.
Represented in the Archdioceses of St. Paul-Minneapolis, Chicago and Detroit and in the Dioceses of Duluth, Phoenix and St. Cloud. Also in Agats, Irian Jaya, Indonesia.
Vocation Director: Rev. Stephan Bauer, OSC, 3510 Vivian Ave., St. Paul, MN 55126-3852. 1-800-407-5875. E-mail: info@crosier.org; Web: www.crosier.org

DE LA SALLE CHRISTIAN BROTHERS (F.S.C.)
(Brothers of the Christian Schools) (Christian Brothers)
Regional Office for the United States and Toronto, Canada: Brother Jeffrey L. Calligan, FSC, Director of Vocations and Formation, 4351 Garden City Dr., Suite 200, Landover, MD 20785. (301) 459-9410
1,000 Brothers in the USA/Toronto Region: 7,800 Brothers worldwide, 6 Provinces, 1 Delegation in the USA/ Toronto Region
Apostolic Work: An International Institute of Brothers involved in all forms of EDUCATION on the elementary, secondary, collegiate, literacy and GED levels. The Brothers are teachers, social workers, religious educators, human service providers, counselors, spiritual directors, youth ministers, campus ministers, educational administrators and foreign missionaries.
Vocation Director: Brother Jeffrey Calligan, FSC, Office of Lasallian Formation, 4351 Garden City Dr., Suite 200, Landover, MD 20785. (301) 459-9410. Fax: (301) 459-8056. E-mail: jeffreycal@aol.com; Web: www.cbconf.org

DE LA SALLE CHRISTIAN BROTHERS (F.S.C.)
(Brothers of the Christian Schools) (Christian Brothers)
Baltimore Province: Provincialate, PO Box 29, Adamstown, MD 21710. (301) 874-5188. E-mail: brudered ward@hotmail.com; Web: www.cbconf.org
200 Brothers
Conduct: 1 house of studies, 9 high schools, 3 child care institutions for court adjudicated youth, La Salle University, 1 retreat center, 3 middle schools, campus ministry.
Represented in the (Arch)dioceses of Pittsburgh, Philadelphia, Baltimore, Camden, Washington, DC and Newark. Also in the Philippines, Kenya, Guatemala, Bolivia and Costa Rica.
Vocation Director: Brother Ed Hofmann, FSC

DE LA SALLE CHRISTIAN BROTHERS (F.S.C.)
(Brothers of the Christian Schools) (Christian Brothers)
Long Island-New England Province: Provincialate, 635 Ocean Rd., Narragansett, RI 02882-1314
95 Brothers
Conduct: 3 high schools, 1 boarding school, 1 urban parish school, 1 special inner-city middle school, 1 special education center and related group residence, 1 school for adjudicated youth and related residences, 1 at-risk youth and family counseling program, 11 mission educational centers, 10 community houses.
Represented in the (Arch)dioceses of Brooklyn, Providence and Rockville Centre. Also in Bethlehem, Kenya, Ethiopia and Eritrea.
Vocation Director: Brother Peter Iorlano, FSC, 15 Claver Pl., Brooklyn, NY 11238. (718) 398-0897. E-mail: linevoc@aol.com; Web: www.cbconf.org

DE LA SALLE CHRISTIAN BROTHERS (F.S.C.) (Brothers of the Christian Schools) (Christian Brothers)
Midwest Province: Provincialate, 7650 S. County Line Rd., Burr Ridge, IL 60521-6950. (630) 323-3725
229 Brothers
Conduct: Provincialate, 14 high schools, 3 middle schools, 3 retreat centers, Lewis University, Saint Mary's University of Minnesota, Christian Brothers University, 1 youth home for boys, 2 Catholic worker houses, 1 development office, 1 socially conscious investment service, 31 community houses, Saint Mary's Press.
Represented in the (Arch)dioceses of Chicago, Dubuque, Green Bay, Jackson, Jefferson City, Joliet, Kansas City-St. Joseph, Memphis, Omaha, St. Louis, St. Paul/Minneapolis, Santa Fe, Tulsa and Winona. Also in Bethlehem, Central America, Kenya, Pakistan, the Philippines, Ethiopia, Nigeria, Thailand and Italy.
Vocation Director: Brother Rob Veselski, FSC, 7650 S. County Line Rd., Burr Ridge, IL 60521-6950. (630) 323-3725. Fax: (630) 323-3779. E-mail: rob-veselski@cbmid west.org; Web: www.cbmidwest.org

DE LA SALLE CHRISTIAN BROTHERS (F.S.C.)
(Brothers of the Christian Schools) (Christian Brothers)
New Orleans-Santa Fe Province: Provincialate, 1522 Carmel Dr., Lafayette, LA 70501. (337) 234-1973
109 Brothers
Apostolic Work: Elementary, high school and college education, campus ministry, social work, foreign missions.
Conduct: 1 college, 6 high schools, 3 elementary schools, 13 community houses.
Represented in the (Arch)dioceses of Santa Fe, Lafayette, Denver, El Paso and New Orleans. Also in Africa and the Philippines.
Vocation Director: Bro. Jerry Vincent, FSC, De La Salle Christian Brothers, 1522 Carmel Dr., Lafayette, LA 70501. (337) 235-3576. E-mail: JerryVin@bellsouth.net; Web: www.cbconf.org

DE LA SALLE CHRISTIAN BROTHERS (F.S.C.)
(Brothers of the Christian Schools) (Christian Brothers)
New York Province: Provincialate, 800 Newman Springs Rd., Lincroft, NJ 07738. (732) 842-7420
190 Brothers
Conduct: 1 novitiate, 3 elementary schools, 5 middle schools, 10 urban

and suburban high schools, Manhattan College, 1 special education school for delinquent and neglected adolescents, 1 urban community-based adult education center, 1 day-care program, 1 hospital chaplaincy, 9 campus ministries, 17 community houses, 1 nursing and retirement community.

Represented in the (Arch)dioceses of New York, Newark, Trenton, Albany, Syracuse, Buffalo and Detroit. Also in Central America, Africa, West Indies, the Holy Land, the Philippines.

Vocation Directors: Brother Stephen Olert, FSC, 800 Newman Springs Rd., Lincroft, NJ 07738. (732) 842-7420. E-mail: bsofsc@delasallehall.com; Brother Michael Shubnel, FSC, 14600 Common Rd., Warren, MI 48088. (586) 773-8668. E-mail: BroMShub@aol.com; Web: www.cbconf.org

DE LA SALLE CHRISTIAN BROTHERS (F.S.C.) (Brothers of the Christian Schools) (Christian Brothers)

San Francisco Province: Provincialate, Box 3720, Napa, CA 94558-0372. (707) 252-0222

130 Brothers

Conduct: St. Mary's College, 9 high schools, 16 community houses, 1 house of studies, 1 novitiate, 1 educational group home, 1 inner city educational center, 1 elementary school, 1 educational center in Tijuana, Mexico.

Represented in the (Arch)dioceses of Oakland, Orange County, Sacramento, San Jose, Santa Rosa, Los Angeles, Portland, San Francisco and Yakima. Also in Tijuana, Mexico.

Vocation Directors: Brother James Joost, FSC, De La Salle Institute, 4401 Redwood Rd., Napa, CA 94558. (925) 381-8399. E-mail: BroJames@dlsi.org; Brother Kevin Slate, FSC, 1055 Ellis St., San Francisco, CA 94100. (415) 775-6626, ext. 609. E-mail: brokevin@shcp.edu; Web: www.delasalle.org

DE LA SALLE CHRISTIAN BROTHERS (F.S.C.) (Brothers of the Christian Schools) (Christian Brothers)

Toronto Delegation

46 Brothers

Conduct: 1 high school, 2 community houses, 3 summer places.

Represented in the (Arch)diocese of Toronto. Also in Nigeria and Kenya.

Vocation Director: Brother Dominic Viggiani, FSC, De La Salle "Oaklands", 131 Farnham Ave., Toronto, Ontario, Canada M4V 1H7. Web: www.cbconf.org

DISCALCED CARMELITE FATHERS (O.C.D.)

(Polish Province of the Holy Spirit) Our Lady of Mt. Carmel Monastery/ Shrine, 1628 Ridge Rd., Munster, IN 46321. (219) 838-7111. Fax: (219) 838-7214. E-mail: karmel@netnitco.net

11 Priests, 2 Brothers

Represented in the Diocese of Gary.

Vocation Director: Fr. Jack Palica, OCD

DISCALCED CARMELITE FATHERS AND BROTHERS (O.C.D.)

(Oklahoma Province of St. Therese of the Child Jesus)

Provincial House: 5151 Marylake Dr., Little Rock, AR 72206. (501) 888-3052

23 Priests, 2 Solemnly Professed Brothers, 5 Students in Vows, 1 Novice

Conduct: 1 contemplative monastery, 1 center of adult spirituality, 3 parishes, 1 student house.

Represented in the Archdioceses of New Orleans, San Antonio and Oklahoma City and in the Dioceses of Dallas and Little Rock.

Vocation Director: Fr. Francis Majors, OCD, Mt. Carmel Center, 4600 W. Davis St., Dallas, TX 75211. (214) 331-6224. E-mail: vocationdirectorocd@earthlink.net

DISCALCED CARMELITE FRIARS (O.C.D.)

(Province of St. Joseph of the Western US) Provincial House: PO Box 2178, Redlands, CA 92373. (909) 793-0424

30 Priests, 6 Brothers in Solemn Vows, 10 Brothers in Simple Vows, 3 Novices, 5 Postulants, 1 Secular Brother

Conduct: 4 parishes, 1 retreat house,1 institute of spirituality, 1 house of prayer, 1 novitiate, 1 house of studies, mission in Kyengeza (Africa).

Represented in the Archdioceses of Los Angeles and Seattle and in the Dioceses of Portland, San Bernardino, San Jose, Santa Rosa and Tucson. Mission in Africa.

Vocation Director: Fr. Jan Lundberg, OCD, Mt. St. Joseph, PO Box 3420, San Jose, CA 95156. (408) 251-1361. E-mail: Frjlund@familink.com

DISCALCED CARMELITE FRIARS (O.C.D.)

141 Carmelite Dr., Bunnell, FL 32110. (386) 437-2910. Fax: (386) 437-5125. E-mail: saintjoseph1988@aol.com

DISCALCED CARMELITE FRIARS (O.C.D.)

(Province of the Immaculate Heart of Mary) Discalced Carmelite Friars, 1233 So. 45th St., W. Milwaukee, WI 53214. (414) 672-7212

1 Bishop, 55 Priests, 13 Brothers, 15 Students, 5 Novices, 3 Postulants

Conduct: 1 Marian shrine, 1 retreat house, 2 parishes, 1 hermitage community, 3 formation communities, 1 international publication, 1 publishing house.

Apostolates: Retreats, spiritual direction, parishes, translation, publication, teaching, secular order, chaplaincies, in-house ministries: cook, tailor, maintenance, formation, administration. Overseas missions in the Philippines and Kenya.

Represented in the Archdioceses of Boston, Chicago, Milwaukee and Washington, DC and in the Diocese of Wheeling-Charleston.

Vocation Directors: Fr. Steven Payne, OCD, Discalced Carmelite Friars, 2131 Lincoln Rd., NE, Washington, DC 20002-1199. (202) 832-6622, Fax: (202) 832-5711. E-mail: payneocd@erols.com; Fr. Bonaventure Lussier, OCD, Edith Stein House of Studies, 5345 So. University Ave., Chicago, IL 60615. (773) 752-6943. Fax: (773) 752-6594. E-mail: lussierocd@hotmail.com; Web: www.ocdfriarsvocation.com

SONS OF DIVINE PROVIDENCE (FDP) (Don Orione Fathers)

Don Orione Home, 111 Orient Ave., East Boston, MA 02128

11 Priests in US

Conduct: 1 Marian Shrine, 1 nursing home, 1 home for retarded men, 1 vocation center, 2 parishes.

Apostolic Work: Multiple.

Represented in the Archdioceses of Boston and New York and in the Dioceses of Evansville.

Vocation Director: Rev. Mario Guarino, FDP, Don Orione Home, 111 Orient Ave., East Boston, MA 02128. (617) 569-2100

SOCIETY OF THE DIVINE SAVIOR (S.D.S.) (The Salvatorians)

alvatorian Provincial Residence, 1735 N. Hi-Mount Blvd., Milwaukee, WI 53208

93 Priests, 42 Brothers, 100 Lay Salvatorians

Apostolic Work: Founded to use "any means which the Love of Christ inspires" to bring the Gospel to the world. Involved in parishes, home and foreign missions, education, hospital and military chaplaincies, youth ministry, communications, counselling, campus ministry,

specialized ministries.
Represented in the Archdioceses of Baltimore, Louisville, Milwaukee, New York, San Francisco and Washington and in the Dioceses of Bismarck, Birmingham, Camden, Green Bay, Kalamazoo, Knoxville, La Crosse, Nashville, Oakland, Orlando, Phoenix, Sacramento, Santa Rosa, Savannah, Tucson and Wilmington. American Salvatorians are also serving in Tanzania, East Africa.
Vocation Director: Fr. Joseph P. Lubrano, S.D.S., 1735 N. Hi-Mount Blvd., Milwaukee, WI 53208-1720. (414) 258-1735. E-mail: FatherJoe@SDSvocations.com; Web: www.SDSvocations.com

DIVINE WORD MISSIONARIES (S.V.D.)
Divine Word Missionaries, Vocation Office, PO Box 380, Epworth, IA 52045-0380
Over 6,000 members worldwide; 350 priests and brothers in 3 US Provinces.
Apostolic Work: An international missionary community of Brothers and Priests working in over 60 countries. Also involved in African-American, Latino, Vietnamese, Appalachian and multicultural apostolates in the US
FORMATION PROGRAMS:
*Divine Word College Seminary, Epworth, IA: a four-year accredited college seminary with degrees in philosophy and cross-cultural studies, ESL Program.
*Wendelin House, Washington, DC: a community for Brother candidates pursuing studies at various colleges and universities in Washington.
*Divine Word Theologate, Chicago, IL: seminarians who have completed their undergraduate degree and who meet the admissions requirements at Catholic Theological Union in Chicago may begin pre-novitiate formation at Divine Word Theologate.
Vocation Director: Vocation Office, Divine Word Missionaries, PO Box 380, Epworth, IA 52045-0380. (800) 553-3321. E-mail: dwm@mwci.net; Web: www.svd.org

DOMINICANS (O.P.) (Order of Preachers)
(Central Province - Province of St. Albert the Great) 1909 S. Ashland Ave., Chicago, IL 60608-2994
200 Priests, 5 Novices, 22 Brothers, 12 Student Brothers
Apostolic Work: Preaching, teaching, research and writing, campus and parish ministry, social justice.
Represented in the (Arch)dioceses of Chicago, Colorado Springs, Des Moines, Denver, Detroit, Grand Rapids, Madison, Milwaukee, Pueblo, St. Cloud, St. Louis, St. Paul/Minneapolis, Santa Fe, Sioux Falls, Springfield, West Lafayette and Winona. Foreign missions in Bolivia and Nigeria.
Promoter of Vocations: Fr. Andrew-Carl Wisdom, O.P., 1909 S. Ashland Ave., Chicago, IL 60608-2994. (312) 829-0295. E-mail: vocations@dominicans.org; Web: www.op.org/domcentral

DOMINICANS (O.P.)
(Order of Preachers)
(Eastern Province) 141 E. 65 St., New York, NY 10021-6607. (212) 737-5757
234 Priests, 12 Cooperator Brothers, 8 Deacons, 20 Clerical Students, 11 Novices
Conduct: 15 parishes, 1 college, 1 house of studies, 1 novitiate, 1 foreign mission, 4 campus ministries, 1 retreat house.
Apostolic Work: Preaching, teaching, parishes, foreign missions, campus ministry, hospital chaplaincy, spiritual renewal center.
Represented in the Archdioceses of Boston, Cincinnati, Hartford, Louisville, Newark, New York and Washington and in the Dioceses of Albany, Buffalo, Camden, Columbus, Providence, Richmond, Springfield (MA) and Youngstown. Foreign mission in Kenya, Africa.
Director of Vocations: Fr. William P. Garrott, O.P., Dominican Vocation Office, 487 Michigan Ave., N.E., Washington, DC 20017-1585. (800) 529-1205 - toll-free, (202) 529-9003. Fax: (202) 636-1700. E-mail: vocations@dominicanfriars.org; Web: www.dominicanfriars.org

DOMINICANS (O.P.)
(Order of Preachers)
(Province of the Holy Name-Western Province) 5877 Birch Court, Oakland, CA 94618-1626
124 Priests, 6 Brothers, 32 Student Brothers, 8 Novices
Conduct: 12 parishes, 12 campus ministries, 1 house of study and 1 novitiate.
Represented in the Archdioceses of Anchorage, Los Angeles, Portland, San Francisco and Seattle. Also in the Dioceses of Oakland, Phoenix, Sacramento, Salt Lake City, San Bernardino and Tucson. Also represented in missions in Mexical (Baja, Mexico).
Promoter of Vocations: Fr. Mark C. Padrez, OP, Vocation Office, 5877 Birch Court, Oakland, CA 94618-1626. (510) 658-8722; Fax: (510) 658-1061. E-mail: padrezop@yahoo.com; Web: www.opwest.org

DOMINICANS (O.P.)
(Order of Preachers)
Southern Dominican Province (Province of St. Martin de Porres) 1421 N. Causeway Blvd., Ste. 200, Metairie, LA 70001-4144. (504) 837-2129, ext. 15
165 Friars (Priests and Brothers)
Apostolic Work: Preaching, teaching, chaplaincies, parish and campus ministry. Missionaries; Peru, Honduras, Cuba.
Province covers 11 southern states.
Promoter of Vocations: Fr. Henry Groover, O.P., Vocation Office,1421 N. Causeway Blvd., Ste. 200, New Orleans, LA 70001-4144. (504) 837-2129, ext. 15. E-mail: hgroover@opsouth.org; Web: www.opsouth.org

EDMUNDITES (S.S.E.)
(Society of St. Edmund)
Edmundite Generalate, 270 Winooski Park, Colchester, VT 05439-0270. (802) 654-3400
45 Priests & Brothers
Apostolic Work: Catholic higher education; retreats and renewal; African-American ministry; parochial ministry.
Represented in AL, VT, CT, LA, MI and Venezuela.
Vocation Director: Rev. Richard M. Myhalyk, S.S.E., Edmundite Generalate, 270 Winooski Park, Colchester, VT 05439-0270. (802) 654-3400. Fax: (802) 654-3409. E-mail: Myhalyk@aol.com; Web: www.sse.org

EUDISTS (C.J.M.)
(Congregation of Jesus and Mary)
744 Sonrisa St., Solana Beach, CA 92075. (858) 755-8394
101 Priests, Deacons and Laymen in North American Province
Apostolic Work: Parishes, young adult ministry, youth ministry, campus and Newman Center ministries, counseling, teaching, ministry formation.
Represented in the Dioceses of Buffalo and San Diego and also in Rome; France; Ivory Coast, Benin and Central Africa; Canada; Brazil, Chile, Colombia, Equador, Peru and Venezuela; Cuba, Dominican Republic and Mexico.
Vocation Director: Rev. Andres Arango, C.J.M., Eudist Vocation Center, 4544 El Cerrito Dr., San Diego, CA 92115. (619) 583-3020. E-mail: eud-form@packbell.net

FRANCISCAN BROTHERS (The Congregation of the Religious Brothers of the Third Order Regular of St. Francis)

Franciscan Brothers Generalate: St. Francis Monastery, 135 Remsen St., Brooklyn, NY 11201

Conduct: 5 high schools, 1 elementary school, 1 college, 1 summer camp, 1 novitiate, 1 pre-novitiate community and retreat center.

Apostolic Work: Education on all levels and in every aspect of its work (special education, elementary, secondary, and college levels, administration), parish Religious Education coordinators, Catholic Charities, health careers, campus ministry, youth ministry, prison ministry, counselling, parish ministry, retreat work.

Represented in the (Arch)dioceses of Brooklyn, New York, Raleigh, Rockville Centre, Paterson and Springfield-Cape Girardeau.

Vocation Director: St. Francis Monastery, 135 Remsen St., Brooklyn, NY 11201. (718) 858-8217. Web: www.franciscanbrothers.org

FRANCISCAN BROTHERS OF THE HOLY CROSS (F.F.S.C.)

2500 St. James Rd., Springfield, IL 62707

15 Brothers

Apostolic Work: Work with developmentally disabled adults, elementary education and pastoral ministry.

Represented in the Dioceses of Madison and Springfield (IL).

Vocation Director: 2500 St. James Rd., Springfield, IL 62707. (217) 747-5947. E-mail: brojohnfrancis@aol.com

FRANCISCANS – BROTHERS OF THE POOR OF ST. FRANCIS (C.F.P.)

Provincial Office: 324 Donham Ave., Cincinnati, OH 45226-2116

Conduct: 1 novitiate, 4 parochial schools, 1 nursing home ministry, 1 development office, 1 prison ministry, pastoral ministry, counseling.

Apostolic Work: Human services, especially the care and education of youth.

Represented in the Archdiocese of Cincinnati and in the Dioceses of Covington, Davenport, El Paso and Little Rock.

Vocational Minister: Bro. Julian Lane, CFP, 324 Donham Ave., Cincinnati, OH 45226-2116. (513) 896-5326. Fax: (513) 321-3777. E-mail: hibrothers@fuse.net or franciscanbrscfp@aol.com

FRANCISCAN BROTHERS OF THE SACRED HEART (O.S.F.)

3 Brothers

Apostolic Work: Education (administration and teaching), catechetics (religious education, CCD, RCIA, DRE), diocesan staff, liturgical music, youth ministry, nursing, pro-life, parish work.

Represented in the Diocese of Fargo.

Vocation Director: Bro. Anthony Keidl, O.S.F., 650 Baker St., Gallup, NM 87301-7026. E-mail: brothers@fargocity.com

FRANCISCAN FATHERS (BYZANTINE FRANCISCANS)

See Eastern Catholic Religious Communities for Men

FRANCISCAN FRIARS (O.F.M.)

(Province of the Assumption of the B.V.M.) Francis & Clare Friary, 9230 W. Highland Park Ave., Franklin, WI 53132

173 Priests, 89 Brothers, 8 Students in Formation

Conduct: 23 parishes, 19 friaries, 1 novitiate, 2 retreat houses, 1 diocesan high school, 1 printery, publishing house, 1 social justice center.

Apostolic Work: Parish work, social service, retreats, teaching, institutional chaplaincies, foreign missions, home missions, publication, world peace and justice, special education, inner city apostolate. Bi-ritual: Byzantine and Latin Rites.

Represented in the Archdioceses of Chicago, Milwaukee and Philadelphia and in the Dioceses of Fort Wayne-South Bend, Gary, Gaylord, Grand Rapids, Green Bay, Joliet, Natchez-Jackson, Pittsburgh, Rochester, Rockford, Saginaw and Toledo. Also in the Philippines, Africa, Papua New Guinea, Mexico and Thailand.

Vocation Director: Fr. Linus Kopczewski, OFM, Vocation Office, St. Francis Friary, 503 S. Brown's Lake Dr., Burlington, WI 53105. Toll-free: (1-877) 636-3742 or (262) 763-3600. Fax: (262) 763-4229. E-mail: vocationdirector@hotmail.com; Web: www.ofm-usa.com/AP

FRANCISCAN FRIARS (O.F.M.)

(Province of the Holy Gospel) Roger Bacon College, 2400 Marr St., El Paso, TX 79903. (915) 565-2921

3 Priests, 1 Brother

Represented in the Diocese of El Paso

FRANCISCAN FRIARS (O.F.M.)

(Province of the Immaculate Conception) 125 Thompson St., New York, NY 10012. (212) 674-4388

206 Friars

Conduct: 51 parishes, 1 novitiate, 4 retreat houses, 3 formation residences.

Apostolic Work: Teaching, colleges, high school, campus ministry, hospital and school chaplaincies, pastoral counseling, parishes, soup kitchens, ecumenical work, retreats, renewals, and Christian Formation, foreign and home missions, inner-city projects, tutorial programs, Spanish and Italian speaking apostolates, special services, pilgrimages, development programs, formation and vocation apostolates, experimental communities, medical and clerical work, CCD apostolates, teenage apostolates with prisoners, mentally retarded, addicts, alcoholics, caring for the aged, Secular Franciscan apostolates, summer camps, working with the poor, the Apostolate of Prayer.

Represented in the Archdioceses of Boston, Hartford, New York and Toronto (Canada) and in the Dioceses of Albany, Fall River, Brooklyn, Manchester, Metuchen, Pittsburgh, Portland, Trenton, Wheeling and Youngstown. Also in Honduras, Guatemala and El Salvador.

Vocation Director: Br. Charles Gingerich, ofm, Franciscan Friary, 459 River Rd., Andover, MA 01810-4213. (978) 863-0042, 0041, (800) 521-5442, (888) 521-5442. Fax: (508) 863-0172. E-mail: charles848@aol.com; Web: www.franciscanvoc.org

FRANCISCAN FRIARS (O.F.M.)

(Province of the Most Holy Name) Holy Name Provincialate, 158 W. 27th St., New York, NY 10001. (212) 924-1451

4 Friar Bishops, 334 Friar Priests, 92 Friar Brothers, 18 Friar Students, 8 Friar Novices, 6 Postulants

Conduct: 5 large service churches in city apostolates, 3 inner-city apostolates, 1 university, 1 college, 1 novitiate, member of Washington Theological Union, 35 parishes in East, 6 southern parishes, 4 publications, house of prayer.

Apostolic Work: Social work, counseling, teaching, parishes, home missions, foreign missions (Peru, Brazil, Bolivia, Japan, Africa), retreats, Newman Centers, inner-city, urban ministry centers.

Represented in Eastern Coastal States from Maine to Florida, South America, Asia and Africa.

Vocation Director: Fr. Francis DiSpigno, OFM, Franciscan Vocation Office, St. Francis Friary, 135 W.

31st St., New York, NY 10001. (212) 629-5868. (1-800) 677-7788. Fax: (212) 629-4060. E-mail: hnpvoc@aol.com; Web: www.hnp.org

FRANCISCAN FRIARS (O.F.M.)
(Province of Our Lady of Guadalupe) 1350 Lakeview Rd. SW, Albuquerque, NM 87105
87 Friars, 18 Brothers, 69 Priests
Conduct: Parishes and missions among the culturally rich American Indian, Hispanic, and Anglo Communities, retreats, social work, renewal preaching.
Represented in the Archdioceses of Santa Fe and San Antonio and in the Dioceses of Gallup and Las Cruces.
Vocation Director: Fr. Charlie Martinez, OFM, Franciscan Vocation Office, Our Lady of Guadalupe Province, 1350 Lakeview Rd., SW, Albuquerque, NM 87105. (505) 877-5425. E-mail: charlieofm@aol.com

FRANCISCAN FRIARS (O.F.M.)
(Sacred Heart Province)
Motherhouse: St. Anthony Friary, 3140 Meramec St., St. Louis, MO 63118. (314) 353-7470
300 Priests and Brothers
Apostolic Work: Work is determined by the talents and interests of the members. 70 parishes, 1 university, 2 high schools, foreign missions, and work with minorities (Mexicans, Blacks, Native Americans) at home. Many engaged in special ministries; nursing care, chaplains at a variety of institutions (hospitals, jails, etc.), teachers at other colleges and high schools, military chaplains, retreats, campus ministry, Social Justice issues, youth ministry, music ministry, etc.
Vocation Directors: Fr. Paul Paré, OFM, Br. Moises Gutierrez, OFM, 4860 W. 29th St., Cicero, IL 60804. (800) 933-4871, (708) 656-2520. E-mail: PPPare1@aol.com or brmoises@brotherfrancis.com; Web: www.brotherfrancis.com or www.thefriars.org

FRANCISCAN FRIARS (ofm)
(Province of St. Barbara) 1500 34th Ave., Oakland, CA 94601. (510) 536-3722
245 Friars
Ministries: "All honest work can be Franciscan Ministry." Parishes, retreat houses, Native American and foreign missions, education, social work, social justice, hospital chaplains, skilled trades, other professions.
Represented in the Archdioceses of Los Angeles, Portland (OR) and San Francisco and in the Dioceses of Fresno, Monterey, Oakland, Orange, Phoenix, Sacramento, San Diego, Spokane and Tucson. Province boundaries include WA, OR, CA, NV, AZ and NM. Also in foreign missions.
Vocation Coordinator: Fr. Chuck Talley, ofm, 1112 26th St., Sacramento, CA 95816. (916) 443-2714. E-mail: vocations@sbfranciscans.org; Web: www.sbfranciscans.org

FRANCISCAN FRIARS (O.F.M.)
(Viceprovince of St. Casimir) Franciscan Friary, PO Box 980, Kennebunkport, ME 04046
15 Priests in US and Canada
Apostolic Work: Parish work, retreats, missions, printed word apostolate.
Represented in Portland, ME; St. Petersburg, FL; Toronto and Hamilton (Ontario, Canada). Main work is in Lithuania: friary, novitiate, parish, seminarians' friary.
Vocation Director: (Note: candidates need to learn the Lithuanian language, as well as go to Lithuania for their formation) Fr. John Bacevicius, O.F.M., Franciscan Friary, PO Box 980, Kennebunkport, ME 04046. (207) 967-2011. E-mail: johnbac@adelphia.net; Web: www.framon.net

FRANCISCAN FRIARS (O.F.M.)
(Order of Friars Minor)
(Province of Saints Francis and James) Our Lady of Guadalupe, 504 E. Santa Clara St., Hebbronville, TX 78361. (361) 527-3865. Fax: (361) 527-5548
3 Priests, 2 Brothers
Apostolic Work: Missions in Peru, Mexico and Africa, poor parishes, schools.
Represented in the Diocese of Laredo. 12 dioceses in Mexico. Foreign missions in Africa (Uganda, Tanzania, Zimbabwe, Marruecos, Kenya); Peru and Israel.
Vocation Director: Belen 220, 44290 Guadalajara Jal, Mexico

FRANCISCAN FRIARS (O.F.M.)
(Province of St. John the Baptist) 1615 Vine St., Cincinnati, OH 45210. (513) 721-4700
224 Friars: 64 Brothers, 2 Deacons, 157 Priests; and 10 in Formation
Ministries: In the vision and the Rule of St. Francis of Assisi, one of the primary ministries of the friars is to live the Gospel life in a community of brothers.
Community itself is a ministry and a witness to the world of the Reign of God coming among us. From their community lives, the friars of St. John the Baptist Province serve the poor and the middle class, heritages, farmers, Appalachians, inner city folk, suburbanites and Secular Franciscans. They minister in homes and on the streets and in the friaries; in parishes, schools, retreats, hospitals and mission lands.
Represented in 11 states from Michigan to Texas and from Pennsylvania to Arizona. Also in Mexico, Japan, Jamaica, Kenya, Peru, South Africa, Germany, the Philippines and Switzerland.
Vocation Directors: Fr. Donald Miller, O.F.M., Fr. Bruce Kremp, O.F.M., 5000 Colerain Ave., Cincinnati, OH 45223. (800) 827-1082. (513) 542-1082. Fax: (513) 542-1083. E-mail: francis@eos.net; Web: www.franciscan.org

FRANCISCAN FRIARS (O.F.M.)
(Croatian Franciscan Custody of the Holy Family)
4851 S. Drexel Blvd., Chicago, IL 60615-1703. (773) 536-0552. Fax: (773) 536-2094
34 Friars
Conduct: 16 parishes, 1 friary, 1 printery.
Apostolic Work: Pastoral ministry among American Croatians and other entities in the US and Canada; Croatian Franciscan Press (Chicago).
Represented in the US (Arch)dioceses of Chicago, New York, Milwaukee, Detroit, St. Louis, Allentown, Erie and Canadian (Arch)dioceses of Montreal, London, Hamilton and Sault Ste. Marie.
Vocation Director: Fr. Stephen Bedenikovic, O.F.M., Sacred Heart Church, 2864 East 96th St., Chicago, IL 60617. (773) 768-1423. E-mail: Croatiancustody@aol.com

FRANCISCAN FRIARS (O.F.M.)
(Custody of the Holy Land)
US Foundation: 1400 Quincy St., N.E., Washington, DC 20017. (202) 526-6800
97 Priests, 44 Brothers, 55 Students in Formation, 7 Novices, 35 Candidates in US and Holy Land.
Apostolic Work: All areas of Church service in Washington, DC, in the Holy Land and Middle East.
Vocation Director: 1400 Quincy St. N.E., Washington, DC 20017. (202) 526-6800. Fax: (202) 529-9889. Web: www.myfranciscan.com

FRANCISCAN FRIARS OF THE ATONEMENT
See Atonement Friars

FRANCISCAN FRIARS OF THE IMMACULATE (F.I.)
Motherhouse and Novitiate: Marian House of Our Lady of Guadalupe, 199 Colonel Brown Rd., Griswold, CT 06351
25 Friars, 7 Novices, 3 Friaries in US, over 300 Friars worldwide
Apostolate: To make the Immaculate known and loved by every heart using preaching, the Sacraments, writing, music, mass media, computer, etc. The Friars live a community life of prayer, poverty and peace in the spirit of the vow of total consecration to the Immaculate, so that she may transform us, like St. Francis, into Jesus Crucified, and make us her instruments for the conquest of all souls for God in the spirit of St. Maximilian Kolbe. Daily, the Friars pray 5 hours in common, including Holy Mass, the Rosary, the Liturgy of the Hours, mental prayer, adoration and benediction.
Vocation Director: Fr. George Mary, F.I., Marian House, Our Lady Queen of the Seraphic Order, PO Box 3003, New Bedford, MA 02741-3003. (508) 996-8274. E-mail: ffi@marymediatrix.com; Web: www.marymediatrix.com

FRANCISCAN FRIARS OF THE RENEWAL (COMMUNITY OF) (CFR)
St. Crispin Friary, 420 E. 156th St., Bronx, NY 10455. (718) 665-2441
65 Friars, 14 Novices, 15 Postulants, 8 Friaries
Apostolate: Spiritual and corporal works of mercy extended toward the poor and homeless; evangelization in all forms.
Conduct: The Padre Pio Shelter and The Saint Anthony Residence - short and long-term housing for men in the South Bronx; the St. Francis Youth Center; La Casa de Juan Diego - a center for evangelization, education and hospitality in Yonkers; retreats, days/evenings of recollection, parish missions, conferences, street evangelization, youth prayer festivals.
Represented in the Archdiocese of New York. Foreign missions in Comayagua (Honduras) and London (England).
Vocation Director: Fr. Luke Fletcher, CFR, St. Joseph Friary, 523 W. 142nd St., New York, NY 10031. (212) 234-9089. Web: www.franciscanfriars.com

FRANCISCAN FRIARS
(O.F.M. Conv.)
(Order of Friars Minor Conventual)
(Immaculate Conception Province) Provincial Office: Immaculate Conception Friary, 517 Washington Ave., Box 629, Rennselaer, NY 12144. (518) 472-1000
122 Priests and Brothers, 4 Student Friars, 3 Novices, 4 Pre-Novitiate Students
Apostolate Work: Active-contemplative men involved in parish ministry, education (secondary, college, graduate level teaching and administration), campus ministry, youth ministry, hospital chaplaincies, counseling, retreats, Secular Franciscan Order, social work, health care, manual labor, service to the poor, special education, Spanish speaking apostolates and missions in Costa Rica and Brazil. Pre-novitiate house: Philadelphia; Novitiate: Mishwaka (IN); Major Theological Seminary, WTU.
Represented in the Archdiocese of New York and in the Dioceses of Albany, Syracuse, Trenton, Metuchen, Charlotte and Raleigh.
Vocation Directors: Friar Tom Purcell, OFM Conv., Vocation Office, 804 N. Salina St., Syracuse, NY 13208. (315) 423-0077. E-mail: tfpurcell@aol.com; Friar Michael Lorentsen, OFM Conv., Vocation Office, P.O. Box 1638, Pittsboro, NC 27312. (919) 545-2969. E-mail: ncfriars@aol.com; Web: www.franciscans.org

FRANCISCAN FRIARS
(O.F.M. Conv.)
(Order of Friars Minor Conventual)
(Province of Our Lady of Consolation) Mount Saint Francis, IN 47146
100 Priests, 25 Brothers, 10 Students
Apostolic Work: Parish, retreats, education, campus, youth, counseling, chaplaincies, teaching. Missions in Zambia, Africa; Central America and Denmark.
Represented in the Archdioceses of Minneapolis-Saint Paul, MN, Dubuque, IA, Washington, DC, Indianapolis, IN, Louisville, KY and San Antonio, TX and in the Dioceses of Cleveland and Toledo, OH, El Paso, TX, Grand Rapids and Lansing, MI, Fort Wayne, IN, Las Cruces, NM and Savannah, GA.
Vocation Directors: Fr. Jim Kent, OFM Conv., Conventual Franciscans, 6901 Dixie Hwy., Louisville, KY 40258. (502) 933-4439 or (1-800) 424-9955; Fr. John Stowe, OFM Conv., 131 S. Zaragosa Rd., El Paso, TX 79907. (1-800) 424-9955. E-mail: franvoc@aol.com; Web: www.franciscans.org

FRANCISCAN FRIARS
(O.F.M. Conv.)
(Order of Friars Minor Conventual)
(St. Anthony of Padua Province, USA) 12300 Folley Quarter Rd., Ellicott City, MD 21042-1419. (410) 531-9200. Fax: (410) 531-4881
152 Priests, 24 Brothers, 4 Temporary Vows, 1 Novice
Apostolic Work: Parish ministry, secondary education, campus ministry, counselling, foreign missions, retreats, nursing.
Represented in the Archdioceses of Atlanta, Baltimore, Boston and Hartford and in the Dioceses of Altoona-Johnstown, Bridgeport, Brooklyn, Buffalo, Erie, Fall River, Harrisburg, Birmingham, Norwich, Ogdensburg, Palm Beach, Paterson, Rochester, Savannah, Springfield and Trenton.
Vocation Director: Br. Michael Duffy, O.F.M. Conv., PO Box 43363, Philadelphia, PA 19129-3363. (215) 844-7913. Fax: (215) 844-3684. E-mail: duffym@ix.netcom.com; Web: www.stanthonyprovince.org/vocation.htm

FRANCISCAN FRIARS
(O.F.M. Conv.)
(Order of Friars Minor Conventual)
(St. Bonaventure Province) 6107 N. Kenmore Ave., Chicago, IL 60660. (773) 274-7681
50 Friars, 4 Simply Professed, 4 Candidates
Conduct: 8 friaries, 5 parishes, 3 residences.
Apostolic Work: Parish, education, counseling, catechectics, publications, nursing and health care, retreats, skilled trades, institutional chaplaincies, foreign missions, Marian and Eucharistic Apostolate.
Represented in the Archdioceses of Chicago, Detroit and Milwaukee and in the Dioceses of Rockford and Peoria.
Vocation Contact: Br. Joseph Wood, O.F.M. Conv., Marytown, 1600 W. Park Ave., Libertyville, IL 60048. (847) 367-7800, ext. 251. E-mail: chicagofranciscans@yahoo.com; Web: franciscancommunity.com

FRANCISCAN FRIARS
(O.F.M. Conv.)
(Order of Friars Minor Conventual)
(St. Joseph Cupertino Province) P.O. Box 820, Arroyo Grande, CA 93421-0820. (805) 489-1012
43 Priests, 14 Brothers, 12 Seminarians, 3 Novices, 3 Postulants
Conduct: 11 parishes, 1 high school, 5 hospital chaplains, 1 military chaplain, 12 friaries, 3 formation houses.
Represented in the Archdioceses of Los Angeles and San Francisco and in the Dioceses of Fresno, Monterey, Oakland, San Bernardino and Reno.
Vocation Director: Bro. Patrick Lytell, OFM Conv., 19697 Redwood Rd., Castro Valley, CA 94546-3456. (510)

582-7314, ext. 10. Fax: (510) 582-7455. E-mail: calfriars@aol.com; Web: www.franciscans.org

FRANCISCAN FRIARS, THIRD ORDER REGULAR (T.O.R.)
(Province of the Immaculate Conception) Provincialate: St. Bridget Church, 3811 Emerson Ave. N., Minneapolis, MN 55412
60 Friars in Province (Priests and Brothers)
Apostolic Work: Parish ministry, high school/college/graduate school teaching, social work, health care, spiritual development centers.
Represented in the Archdioceses of Minneapolis-St. Paul and Washington and in the Dioceses of Altoona-Johnstown, Davenport, Orlando and Wheeling-Charleston.
Vocation Director: Bro. David Liedl, TOR, St. Bridget Friary, 3811 Emerson Ave. N., Minneapolis, MN 55412. (800) 2200TOR (220-0867). E-mail: liedl02@yahoo.com; Web: www.franciscanfriarstor.com

FRANCISCANS, THIRD ORDER REGULAR (T.O.R.)
(Province of The Most Sacred Heart of Jesus) Loretto, PA 15940
110 Priests, 27 Brothers, 15 Friars in Formation
Apostolic Work: Parishes, high schools, houses of formation, Church renewal, campus ministries, social justice, hospital chaplaincies, home and foreign missions, 2 universities (St. Francis University and Franciscan University of Steubenville).
Represented in the Archdioceses of Baltimore, Philadelphia, Washington and Manaus (Brazil) and in the Dioceses of Altoona-Johnstown, Arlington, Borba (Brazil), Charlotte, Erie, Fort Worth, Pittsburgh, St. Augustine, St. Petersburg, Sioux Falls, Steubenville, Trenton, Venice and Wheeling-Charleston.
Vocation Director: Fr. Richard Davis, TOR, Vocation Office, St. Bonaventure Friary, PO Box 104, Loretto, PA 15940. (814) 472-9527. Fax: (814) 472-9546. E-mail: davistor@uov.net; Web: www.franciscanstor.org

FRANCISCAN FRIARS, THIRD ORDER REGULAR (T.O.R.)
Generalate: Mexico
35 Priests
Represented in the Archdiocese of San Antonio and in the Dioceses of Fort Worth and Austin. Also in Mexico.
Vocation Director: Fray Florencio Rodriguez, T.O.R., Saint Lawrence Parish, 236 E. Petaluma, San Antonio, TX 78221. (210) 924-4401. Fax: (210) 924-4075. E-mail: floren@stic.net

FRANCISCAN MISSIONARY BROTHERS OF THE SACRED HEART OF JESUS (O.S.F.)
Our Lady of the Angels Monastery, Eureka, MO 63025
12 Brothers
Apostolic Work: Nursing.
Vocation Director: Br. John Spila, O.S.F., Franciscan Missionary Brothers, Our Lady of the Angels Monastery, Eureka, MO 63025. (636) 938-5361. E-mail: shrine1olc@aol.com; Web: www.franciscancaring.org/becomingabrother.html

GLENMARY HOME MISSIONERS
Box 465618, Cincinnati, OH 45246-5618
54 Priests, 17 Brothers, 3 Men in Training
Apostolic Work: Mission work with the poor, unchurched, and Catholic minority in the US: Appalachia, South, and Southwest.
Conduct: Over 60 mission locations. Candidacy program and novitiate in Hartford, KY. Theology and advanced training at various schools/locations depending upon individual needs of priesthood/brotherhood candidates.
Represented in the (Arch)dioceses of Atlanta, GA; Birmingham, AL; Cincinnati, OH; Covington, KY; Jackson, MS; Lexington, KY; Little Rock, AR; Knoxville, TN; Nashville, TN; Owensboro, KY; Richmond, VA, Savannah, GA; Tulsa, OK and Wheeling-Charleston, WV.
Contact: Vocation Director, Glenmary Home Missioners, P.O. Box 465618, Cincinnati, OH 45246-5618. (800) 935-0975. Fax: (513) 874-1690. E-mail: vocation@glenmary.org; Web: www.glenmary.org

GUANELLIAN PRIESTS AND BROTHERS
See "S" Servants of Charity

HERMITS OF THE BLESSED VIRGIN MARY OF MOUNT CARMEL (O. Carm)
Mount Carmel Hermitage, P.O. Box 337, Christoval, TX 76935-0337
5 Hermits
Apostolic Work: Contemplative community of hermits-monks, following the Carmelite Rule in its eremitical form.
Represented in the Diocese of San Angelo.
Vocation Director: Fr. Fabian Maria of Jesus Crucified, O. Carm., Mount Carmel Hermitage, P.O. 337, Christoval, TX 76935-0337. (325) 896-2249 (tel, fax). E-mail: fatherfabian@carmelitehermits.org; Web: www.carmelitehermits.org

HERMITS OF THE MOST BLESSED VIRGIN MARY OF MOUNT CARMEL (O. Carm.)
Carmelite Hermitage of the Blessed Virgin Mary, 8249 de Montreville Trail, Lake Elmo, MN 55042. (651) 779-7351 (tel, fax). E-mail: carmelus@earthlink.net
6 Hermits
Apostolic Work: Contemplative life with focus on prayer, the celebration of the liturgy and spiritual direction.
Represented in the Archdiocese of St. Paul and Minneapolis.
Vocation Contact: Fr. John Burns, O. Carm.

HOLY APOSTLES, SOCIETY OF THE MISSIONARIES OF THE (M.S.A.)
See listing under "M" - Missionaries of the Holy Apostles (Society of the)

HOLY CROSS BROTHERS (C.S.C.)
(Eastern Province) Holy Cross Vocations Office, Stonehill College #1962, Easton, MA 02357
128 Brothers
Conduct: 4 high schools, 1 middle school, 1 social service agency, alternative education programs, 1 spiritual life center and missions in Kenya, Uganda and Tanzania.
Apostolic Works: Education, spiritual direction/retreats, parish and social ministry, health care, ministries to the chemically dependent, foreign missions, migrant ministry, outreach to the homeless, jail ministry.
Represented in the Archdioceses of Hartford, New York and Washington, DC and in the Dioceses of Albany, Brooklyn-Queens, Fall River, Scranton and Wilmington.
Vocation Director: Brother Lawrence Atkinson, CSC, Holy Cross Vocations Office, Stonehill College #1962, Easton, MA 02357. (508) 565-1746. Fax: (508) 565-1420. Web: www.holycrossbrothers.org

HOLY CROSS BROTHERS (C.S.C.)
(Midwest Province) Provincial House, Box 460, Notre Dame, IN 46556-0460. (574) 251-2221. Fax: (574) 289-0487
220 Brothers, 5 Novices
Apostolic Work: Brothers are engaged in education, campus and youth ministry, retreat ministry, parish and social work, health care, work with the poor and elderly, in

trades and other areas of service in the United States and overseas in Bangladesh, South America, Ghana and Liberia.

Represented in the Archdioceses of Anchorage, Chicago, Detroit, Louisville, Milwaukee, Los Angeles and Miami and in the Dioceses of Cleveland, Evansville, Venice, Portland, OR, Fort Wayne-South Bend and Gary. Also in Bangladesh, Ghana and Liberia.

Vocation Director: Brother Carlos Parrilla, C.S.C., Provincial House, 54515 State Rd. 933 N., PO Box 460, Notre Dame, IN 46556-0460. (574) 251-3254. E-mail: cparrilla@hcc-nd.edu; Web: www.hcc-nd.edu/mwp/

HOLY CROSS BROTHERS (C.S.C.)

(South-West Province) Province Center: St. Edward's University, 3001 S. Congress Ave. #1046, Austin, TX 78704-6489. (512) 442-7856

112 Brothers, 3 in Initial Formation

Apostolic Work: Holy Cross Brothers are "educators in the faith" in a variety of ministries; spreading the Good News of God's love and presence, not only in schools and universities, but also in many other works that respond to the needs of God's people: parish ministry, health and social services, campus ministry, counseling and spiritual direction, youth ministry, migrant ministry, maintenance work, legal services and mission work in the United States and in other countries.

Represented in the Archdioceses of Los Angeles, New Orleans and San Antonio and in the Dioceses of Austin, Beaumont, Cheyenne, Knoxville, Oakland, Portland, San Jose and Savannah. Also in Bangladesh, Brazil and Chile.

Vocation Director: Brother Donald Blauvelt, CSC, Brother Charles Anderson Residence, 320 Brahan Blvd., San Antonio, TX 78215-1020. (210) 410-9538. (210) 223-2081. E-mail: bhcsw2000@aol.com; Web: www.stedwards.edu/holycross, www.holycrossbrothers.org

HOLY CROSS FATHERS AND BROTHERS (C.S.C.)

(Southern Province) Provincial House: 2111 Brackenridge St., Austin, TX 78704

32 Fathers, 2 Brothers,12 Initial Formation

Apostolic Work: Parishes, ministry to Hispanics, youth work, campus ministry, retreats, renewals, and foreign missions (Africa, Asia, Central and South America). Southern Province includes the Gulf States and the row of states above the Gulf States.

Represented in the Archdioceses of New Orleans, St. Louis and San Antonio and in the Dioceses of Austin, Baton Rouge, Fort Wayne-South Bend, Lafayette (LA) and Las Cruces.

Vocation Director: Rev. Joseph Tomei, c.s.c., 2111 Brackenridge St., Austin, TX 78704. (512) 443-3886. Fax: (512) 416-1216; St. Ignatius Martyr Church, 2309 Euclid Ave., Austin, TX 78704. (512) 442-3602. E-mail: Vocation.Director@SouthernCSC.org or jtomei@st-ignatius.org; Web: southerncsc.org

HOLY CROSS PRIESTS (C.S.C.)

(Indiana Province) Provincial House: 1304 E. Jefferson Blvd., South Bend, IN 46617

284 Priests, 18 Brothers, 83 Seminarians

Apostolic work: University and secondary education, preaching, parishes, hospital chaplains, military chaplains, scholars, authors, publishers, social work, minorities, counseling, psychology, music, liturgy, inner-city, elderly, marriage encounter, catechetical, seminary formation, spiritual directors, youth ministry and administration. Foreign missionaries in Chile, South America; Kenya, Tanzania and Uganda, Africa; and Bangladesh.

Represented in Archdioceses of Austin, Boston, Cleveland, Chicago, Colorado Springs, Los Angeles, New Orleans, Portland (OR) and Washington and in the Dioceses of Fort Wayne-South Bend, Fresno, Kalamazoo, Oakland, Phoenix, San Diego, San Francisco, San Jose, San Bernardino, Santa Rosa and Tucson.

Contact: Fr. Jim King, C.S.C., Director of Vocations, PO Box 541, Moreau Seminary, Notre Dame, IN 46556. (574) 631-6385; E-mail: vocation.1@nd.edu; Web: www.nd.edu/~vocation

HOLY CROSS PRIESTS AND BROTHERS (C.S.C.)

(Eastern Province) Provincial House: 835 Clinton Ave., Bridgeport, CT 06604. (203) 367-7252

118 Priests, 12 Brothers, 23 Men in Formation, 4 Affiliates

Conduct: 2 colleges, retreat house, Holy Cross Family Ministries, Family Rosary and Family Theater, Pastoral Institute for the Family (US, Peru, Ireland), missionary district of Peru, 3 houses of formation (2 in Peru), administer or assist in 12 parishes.

Apostolic Work: University and secondary education, campus ministry, parishes, hospital chaplains, health care, prison ministry, retreat house, family ministries, foreign missions, social work, counseling, formation, chaplains to Holy Cross Associates.

Represented in the Archdioceses of Boston, Chicago, Hartford, Los Angeles and New York and in the Dioceses of Albany, Austin, Bridgeport, Burlington, Fall River, Fort Wayne-South Bend, Manchester, New Orleans, Norwich, Orlando, Portland (ME), Rochester, St. Petersburg and Scranton. Missionaries in Africa, Asia, Latin America and in 4 dioceses in Peru.

Formation: College and post-college programs, one-year candidacy program, affiliate programs.

Vocation Director: Fr. Jim Fenstermaker, C.S.C., Stonehill College # 1962, 320 Washington St., Easton, MA 02357. (508) 565-1746. Fax: (508) 565-1420. E-mail: csc-ep@stonehill.edu; Web: www.holycrosscsc.org

BROTHERS OF HOLY EUCHARIST (F.S.E.)

General Motherhouse: P.O. Box 25, Plaucheville, LA 71362. (318) 922-3630; 3401. Fax: (318) 922-3776

Conduct: 1 house, 1 high school, 1 elementary school, 1 novitiate.

Represented in the Diocese of Alexandria.

Vocation Director: Bro. Andre M. Lucia, F.S.E., Superior General

CONGREGATION OF THE MISSIONARIES OF THE HOLY FAMILY

See "M" - Missionaries of the Holy Family

SONS OF THE HOLY FAMILY (S.F.)

(North American Vice Province) 401 Randolph Rd., P.O. Box 4138, Silver Spring, MD 20904. (301) 622-1184

Generalate: Barcelona, Spain

North American Vice Province: 26 Priests, 4 Men in Formation

Apostolic Work: Teaching, social work, parishes, retreats, Hispanic ministry.

Represented in East and Southwest US, Spain, Italy, Argentina, Columbia, Brazil, Venezuela and Mexico.

Vocation Director: Fr. Ron Carrillo, S.F., Holy Cross, P.O. Box 1228, Santa Cruz, NM 87567. (505) 753-3345. Fax: (505) 753-3787. E-mail: rcarrillo@cybermesa.net

HOLY GHOST FATHERS OF IRELAND (C.S.Sp.)

48-49 37th St., Long Island City, NY 11101. (718) 729-5273

65 Fathers

Represented in the Archdioceses of Miami, New Orleans, New York and San Francisco and in the Dioceses of Brooklyn, Fargo, Metuchen, St. Augustine and West Palm Beach.

Vocation Director: Laval House, Duquesne University, Pittsburgh, PA 15282. (412) 396-1666. Web: spiritans.org

HOLY GHOST FATHERS

See The Spiritans - Congregation of the Holy Spirit

BROTHERS OF THE HOLY ROSARY (Congregation of Our Lady of the Rosary)

Motherhouse: 232 Sunnyside Dr., Reno, NV 89503-3510. (775) 747-4441

Apostolic Work: A small diocesan community serving the needs of the Diocese of Reno with emphasis on educational apostolate in elementary and secondary schools. Also work in the areas of CCD, adult education and parish ministry.

Represented in the Diocese of Reno.

Vocation Director: Bro. Philip Napolitano, F.S.R., 232 Sunnyside Dr., Reno, NV 89503-3510. (775) 747-4441. E-mail: bros-reno@moondog.net

HOSPITALLER BROTHERS OF ST. JOHN OF GOD (O.H.)

Immaculate Conception Province, 1145 Delsea Dr., Westville Grove, NJ 08093

4 Brothers, 1 Novice

Apostolic Work: School and vocational center for children and adults with special needs. Outreach program and pastoral counselling for the underprivileged. A worldwide order of Brothers founded by St. John of God at Granada, Spain in 1539. A Community of Brothers sharing love, hope and respect with those who need it most. Headquarters of the Order in Rome.

Represented in the Diocese of Camden.

Vocation Director: Bro. Thomas Osorio, OH, 1145 Delsea Dr., Westville Grove, NJ 08093. (856) 848-4700, ext. 163. Fax: (856) 848-2154. E-mail: sjogvocationsnj@aol.com; Web: www.brothersofstjohnofGod.org

HOSPITALLER BROTHERS OF ST. JOHN OF GOD (O.H.)

(Our Lady Queen of Angels Province) U.S. Provincial House: 2425 S. Western Ave., Los Angeles, CA 90018-2025

3 Priests, 28 Brothers

Conduct: 2 skilled nursing facilities, social model for alcohol rehabilitation service, 1 novitiate, 1 Christian community, co-ministry in acute care facility, 1 HIV transitional housing

Apostolic Work: Called daily to witness Christ's healing love through a community of prayer and service to God's suffering people.

Represented in the Archdiocese of Los Angeles and in the Diocese of San Bernadino, CA. International Headquarters of Order's 225 hospitals and schools at Tiber Island, Rome. Missions in Africa, South America, Korea, Japan, Vietnam, India, Philippines and the Holy Land.

Vocation Director: Fr. Thaddeus Bui, O.H., Brothers of St. John of God, 2425 S. Western Ave., Los Angeles, CA 90018-2025. (323) 734-0233. Fax: 323-731-5987. E-mail: vocations@sbcglobal.net; Web: www.hospitallers.org

IDENTE MISSIONARIES OF CHRIST CRUCIFIED (Association Id of Christ the Redeemer) (M.Id.)

2352 St. Raymond Ave., Bronx, NY 10462. (718) 828-2380

4 Priests, 7 Brothers, 3 Novices

Apostolic Work: Spiritual direction, parish ministry, campus ministry, youth ministry, retreat center, college/theology/pre-theology residence, house of formation, domestic and foreign missions.

Represented in New York. Also in Europe, Africa, Asia and in most countries of South America.

Vocation Director: Fr. Cristobal Martin, M.Id., Church of Santa Maria, 2352 St. Raymond Ave., Bronx, NY 10462. (718) 828-2380. E-mail: crismartin@mail.com; Web: www.frielo.com

BROTHERS OF THE IMMACULATE HEART OF MARY (I.H.M.)

609 N. 7th St., Steubenville, OH 43952

4 Brothers in Apostolic Works

Apostolic Work: Parishes, CCD teachers, master of ceremonies for the bishop, bishop's residence.

Represented in the Diocese of Steubenville.

Contact Vocation Director: Brother Patrick Geary, 609 N. 7th St., Steubenville, OH 43952. (740) 283-2462

INSTITUTE OF CHARITY (I.C.) (The Rosminian Priests and Brothers)

15 Priests: US; 450 Priests and Brothers: worldwide

Apostolic Work: Founded to accept ANY and ALL works of charity. At present, members are involved in teaching the handicapped, parish work, and missionary activity throughout the world.

Represented in the Dioceses of Peoria and St. Petersburg.

Vocation Director: Fr. Paul Stiene, I.C., 2327 W. Heading Ave., Peoria, IL 61604. (309) 676-6341

INSTITUTE OF THE INCARNATE WORD (I.V.E.)

Province of the Immaculate Conception, St. Paul's Church, 113 E. 117th St., New York, NY 10035-4469

Generalate: Rome

Represented in the Arch)dioceses of Brooklyn, Boston, New York and Philadelphia. Also in Canada and Guyana.

Vocation Director: Rev. Louis Baudry, I.V.E., St. Paul's Church, 113 E. 117th St., New York, NY 10035-4469. (212) 534-4422. Fax: (212) 534-5258. E-mail par.newyork@ive.org; Web: www.ive.org

JESUITS (S.J.) (Society of Jesus)

(Province of the Antilles) Correa y Cindron, 28, PO Box 76, Santo Domingo, Dominican Republic. (809) 532-5628

US Address: Villa Javier, Belen Jesuit Fathers, 13339 S.W. 9th Terrace, Miami, FL 33184

107 Fathers, 44 Scholastics, 17 Brothers

Conduct: 2 high schools, 3 houses of retreat, 2 residences, 4 parishes.

Represented in the Archdiocese of Miami. Majority of members in the Dominican Republic

Vocation Director: Rev. Eduardo Alvarez, S.J., Villa Javier, Belen Jesuit Fathers, 13339 S.W. 9th Terrace, Miami, FL 33184. (305) 559-9066. Fax: (305) 222-1256. E-mail: villajavier@att.net, belensj@aol.com

JESUITS (S.J.) (Society of Jesus)

(California Province) PO Box 519, Los Gatos, CA 95031. (408) 884-1600

376 Priests, 34 Brothers, 47 Scholastics

Conduct: 14 parishes, 3 universities, 5 high schools, 1 novitiate, 1 theologate, 1 retreat center.

Represented in the Archdioceses of Los Angeles and San Francisco and in the Dioceses of Fresno, Honolulu, Monterey, Oakland, Orange, Phoenix, Reno, Sacramento, Salt Lake, San Bernardino, San Diego, San Jose, Stockton and Tucson. Also in Mexico, Japan, Taiwan, Philippines, Honduras, Thailand, Brazil, Ecuador, Peru and Fiji.
Vocation Director: Rev. Wayne Negrete, S.J., PO Box 519, Los Gatos, CA 95031. (408) 884-1630. E-mail: vocations@calprov.org; Web: www.calprov.org

JESUITS (S.J.)
(Society of Jesus)
(Chicago Province) 2050 N. Clark St., Chicago, IL 60614. (773) 975-6363
190 Priests, 27 Scholastics, 14 Brothers
Conduct: 3 parishes, 2 universities, 5 high schools, 1 house of study, 2 retreat houses, 1 house of writers, 1 center for action/research, 1 publishing house.
Represented in the Archdioceses of Chicago, Cincinnati and Indianapolis and in the Dioceses of Gary, IN, Covington and Lexington, KY. Also in Nepal, Patna, India, Peru and East Africa.
Vocation Director: Rev. David Godleski, S.J., 2050 N. Clark St., Chicago, IL 60614. (773) 975-6882, 6363. E-mail: godleski@jesuits-chi.org; Web: www.jesuits-chi.org

JESUITS (S.J.)
(Society of Jesus)
(Detroit Province) 7303 W. Seven Mile Rd., Detroit, MI 48221-2198. (313) 861-7500
147 Fathers, 12 Scholastics, 16 Brothers
Conduct: 6 parishes, 2 universities, 5 high schools, 3 retreat houses, 1 novitiate.
Represented in MI: in the Archdiocese of Detroit and in the Dioceses of Gaylord, Grand Rapids, Kalamazoo, Lansing, Marquette and Saginaw. In OH: Cleveland, Columbus, Steubenville, Toledo and Youngstown. Also in India, Nepal, Nicaragua, Sudan, Tanzania, Uganda and Kenya.
Vocation Director: Br. Jim Boynton, S.J., Loyola House, 2599 Harvard Rd., Berkley, MI 48072-1596. (248) 399-8132. E-mail: boynton@jesuits.net

JESUITS (S.J.)
(Society of Jesus)
(Maryland Province) 5704 Roland Ave., Baltimore, MD 21210
412 Priests, 27 Brothers, 48 Men in Formation
Conduct: 4 universities, 1 college, 5 high schools, 12 parishes, 2 houses of retreat, 1 spiritual center, 1 novitiate, 9 residences.
Apostolic Work: Teaching higher and secondary education, parishes, retreats, chaplaincies, spiritual direction, social ministries, foreign missions.
Represented in the (Arch)dioceses of Allentown, Arlington, Baltimore, Camden, Charlotte, Erie, Harrisburg, Philadelphia, Raleigh, Richmond, Scranton, Trenton, Washington, Wheeling-Charleston and Wilmington. Also in Chile, England, El Salvador, Ghana, Honduras, Hong Kong, India, Italy, Japan, Kenya, Mexico, Micronesia, Nicaragua, Nigeria, Philippines, Russia, South Africa, Sudan, Thailand and Zimbabwe.
Vocation Director: Rev. Robert E. Reiser, S.J., 39 E. 83 St., New York, NY 10028. (212) 774-5500. E-mail: vocations@mdsj.org; Web: www.marprovjesuits.org

JESUITS (S.J.)
(Society of Jesus)
(Missouri Province) 4511 W. Pine Blvd., St. Louis, MO 63108-2191
199 Priests, 15 Scholastics (Men in Formation), 22 Brothers
Conduct: 3 universities, 1 junior college, 6 high schools, 1 house of study for Jesuit seminarians, 7 parishes, 3 retreat centers, the Sacred Heart radio program, 1 novitiate.
Apostolic Work: Teaching, parish work, retreats, hospital chaplaincy, campus ministry, publications, social service, arts and communications (writing, radio), domestic and foreign missions.
Represented principally in the states of Missouri, Colorado, Kansas and Oklahoma. Also in the Central American countries of Belize and the Republic of Honduras.
Assistant for Vocations: Fr. Chris P. Pinné, S.J., 4511 W. Pine Blvd., St. Louis, MO 63108-2191. (800) 325-9924, (314) 361-7765. Fax: (314) 758-7164. E-mail: vocation@jesuits-mis.org; Web: www.jesuits-mis.org/vocations.html

JESUITS (S.J.)
(Society of Jesus)
(New England Province) 85 School St., Watertown, MA 02472-4251. (617) 607-2800. Fax: (617) 536-8074. E-mail: hayessj@bc.edu; Web: www.nenjesuits.org
346 Priests, 17 Brothers, 24 Seminarians
Conduct: 3 parishes, 2 universities, 1 college, 3 high schools, 1 middle school, 2 houses for retreats, 1 seminary.
Apostolic Work: Teaching, parish work, hospital, prisons, military chaplaincies, administration, social service, retreats, writing, foreign missions.
Represented in the Arch(dioceses) of Allentown, Anchorage, Baltimore, Boston, Bridgeport, Buffalo, Burlington, Chicago, Gallup, Honolulu, Los Angeles, Manchester, Miami, Milwaukee, Nashville, New York, Norwich, Oakland, Philadelphia, Portland (ME), Rapid City, St. Augustine, St. Louis, St. Paul-Minneapolis, San Diego, San Francisco, Scranton, Seattle, Springfield (MA), Spokane, Syracuse, Tucson, Venice, Washington, Wheeling and Worcester. Also, in the international field: Bahamas, Brazil, Canada, Egypt, Ethiopia, Germany, Italy, Jamaica, Jordan, Lebanon, Nepal, Spain and Tanzania.
Vocation Director: Rev. James M. Hayes, S.J., PO Box 799, Back Bay Annex, Boston, MA 02117-0799

JESUITS (S.J.)
(Society of Jesus)
(New Orleans Province) 500 S. Jefferson Davis Pkwy., New Orleans, LA 70119-7128
260 Priests, 35 Scholastics, 16 Novices, 32 Brothers
Conduct: 13 parishes, 1 university, 1 college, 4 high schools, 1 novitiate, 5 houses of retreat.
Apostolic Work: Teaching higher and secondary education, parishes, retreats, chaplaincies, spiritual direction, campus ministry, prisons, social ministries, foreign missions in Brazil and Paraguay.
Represented in the Archdioceses of Atlanta, Miami, New Orleans, San Antonio and Santa Fe and in the Dioceses of Alexandria, Austin, Baton Rouge, Charleston, Corpus Christi, Dallas, El Paso, Fort Worth, Galveston-Houston, Lafayette, Las Cruces, Little Rock, Mobile, Natchez-Jackson, Orlando, Palm Beach and St. Petersburg.
Vocation Director: Fr. Marvin Kitten, S.J., 500 S. Jefferson Davis Pkwy., New Orleans, LA 70119-7128. (504) 821-0334. E-mail: mkitten@norprov.org; Web: www.norprov.org/vocations/

JESUITS (S.J.)
(Society of Jesus)
(New York Province) 39 E. 83 St., New York, NY 10028
519 Priests, 33 Brothers, 95 Men in Formation
Conduct: 1 university, 3 colleges, 7

high schools, 1 novitiate, 4 retreat houses, 8 parishes, publications, hospital chaplaincies, prison chaplaincy, Society for Blind, Shrine of North American Martyrs.

Apostolic Work: To be with Christ on mission, building and strengthening the Kingdom of God, serving faith through evangelization, collaboration with the laity, dialogue with culture, interreligious dialogue, foreign missions and the promotion of justice.

Represented in the Archdioceses of New York and Newark and in the Dioceses of Albany, Brooklyn, Buffalo, Paterson, Rochester, Rockville Centre and Syracuse. Also in Caroline-Marshall Islands, Central America, Ecuador, England, Ghana, Italy, Kenya, Nigeria, Philippines, Puerto Rico, South Germany and Zambia-Malawi (Zimbabwe).

Vocation Director: Rev. Robert E. Reiser, S.J., 39 E. 83 St., New York, NY 10028. (212) 774-5500. E-mail: vocations@nysj.org; Web: www.nysj.org

JESUITS (S.J.)
(Society of Jesus)

(Oregon Province) 3215 SE 45th Ave., Portland, OR 97206 (mailing address: PO Box 86010, Portland, OR 97286-0010)

220 Priests, 14 Brothers, 37 Scholastics

Conduct: 36 parishes (including 17 Alaskan and 8 Indian missions), 2 universities, 4 high schools, 1 novitiate.

Represented in the Archdioceses of Anchorage, Portland, OR and Seattle and in the Dioceses of Baker, Boise, Fairbanks, Helena, Spokane and Yakima. Also in Italy, Kenya, Malawi, Mozambique, Uganda and Zambia.

Vocation Director: Rev. Stephen Lantry, S.J., 710 S. 13th St., Tacoma, WA 98405. (253) 272-5136. E-mail: lantry@gonzaga.edu

JESUITS (S.J.)
(Society of Jesus)

(Wisconsin Province) PO Box 080288, 3400 W. Wisconsin, Milwaukee, WI 53208-0288. (414) 937-6949, ext. 231

350 Priests, Brothers and Scholastics

Conduct: 2 universities, 3 high schools, 8 urban parishes, 2 middle schools, 2 grade schools, 3 retreat centers, 3 Native American missions with 14 parishes, a radio station and 2 museums.

Apostolic Work: Teaching, retreats, spiritual direction, missions (Native American and overseas), parishes.

Represented in Wisconsin, Minnesota, Iowa, North and South Dakota, Nebraska and Wyoming, with missions in South Korea, India and Eastern Africa.

Vocation Director: Rev. Warren Sazama, S.J., Wisconsin Province Offices, PO Box 080288, 3400 W. Wisconsin Ave., Milwaukee, WI 53208-0288. (414) 937-6949, ext. 231. Fax: (414) 937-6950. E-mail: vocations@jesuitwisprov.org; Web: www.jesuitswisprov.org

JOSEPHITE FATHERS (C.J.)

180 Patterson Rd., Santa Maria, CA 93455. (805) 937-5378

Novitiate: 180 Patterson Rd., Santa Maria, CA 93455

14 Priests, 2 Scholastics

Conduct: 2 parishes, 2 high schools

Represented in the Archdiocese of Los Angeles, Belgium, England, Congo, Gabon, Camroon.

Vocation Director: 180 Patterson Rd., Santa Maria, CA 93455. (805) 937-5378. E-mail: jalbert@sjhsknights.com

JOSEPHITE FATHERS AND BROTHERS (S.S.J.) (St. Joseph's Society of the Sacred Heart)

105 Priests, 9 Brothers

Conduct: 59 city and rural parishes, hospital and prison chaplaincies, campus ministry, 1 high school, a college house of studies for seminarians, a major seminary for graduate theology and the Josephite Pastoral Center.

Apostolic Work: The Josephite Society is dedicated to a spiritual, educational and social ministry to the African-American community and has worked exclusively in the African-American community since 1871. The Josephite Society affords its members the mutual support of community life in an active ministry.

Represented in the Archdioceses of Los Angeles, Baltimore, Washington and New Orleans and in the Dioceses of Arlington, Baton Rouge, Beaumont, Biloxi, Birmingham, Fort Worth, Galveston-Houston, Jackson, Lafayette, Lake Charles and Mobile.

Vocation Director: Rev. Charles Moffatt, SSJ, 1130 N. Calvert St., Baltimore, MD 21202-3802. (410) 727-8482. E-mail: vocationsssj@aol.com; Web: www.josephite.com

LA SALETTE MISSIONARIES (M.S.)
(Missionaries of Our Lady of La Salette)

(Province of Mary, Mother of the Americas)

164 Priests, 41 Brothers

Conduct: In the US: 25 parishes, 3 shrines, 1 pre-novitiate, 1 novitiate, 1 post-novitiate house.

Apostolic Work: Inner-city and suburban parishes, retreats, shrines, preaching, seminary professor, military, institutional and high school chaplaincies, professional counseling, spiritual direction, parish missions, foreign missions.

Represented in the Archdioceses of Atlanta, Boston, Hartford, Milwaukee, New York, St. Louis, St. Paul-Minneapolis and Washington, DC and in the Dioceses of Albany, Alexandria, Beaumont, Galveston/Houston, Lake Charles, Manchester, Norwich, Orlando, Raleigh, Springfield (MA), Tyler and Worcester.

Vocation Director: Rev. Peter D. Kohler, MS, La Salette Vocation Office, 401 Medford St., Somerville, MA 02145. (617) 628-3335. E-mail: Mafybe2@juno.com or msvocation@aol.com; Web: www.lasalette.org

LEGIONARIES OF CHRIST (L.C.)

Territorial Directorate: Legionaries of Christ, 393 Derby Ave., Orange, CT 06477. (203) 795-2800

Membership: a Roman Catholic Congregation of priests which, since founded in 1941, has grown to 500 Priests and 2,500 Seminarians

Seminaries: High school in New Hampshire for boys interested in the priesthood. Novitiate and Humanities in Connecticut. Philosophy in New York and Rome. Theology in Rome.

Primary Apostolic Works: Combining a deep spiritual life with an urgent apostolate (get people building Christ's Kingdom in society), the Priests engage in extensive work with lay apostolate, youth, education, family, missions, the poor, media, catechetics, and run vocation retreats for high school and college-age men.

Represented in the Archdioceses of Hartford, New York, Washington, Detroit, Atlanta, Los Angeles, Chicago and Denver and in the Dioceses of Manchester, Providence, Madison, Lincoln, Dallas and Sacramento. Also in Canada, Ireland, Spain, France, Italy, Holland, Germany, Czechoslovakia, Poland, Brazil, Argentina, Chile, Colombia, Venezuela, Mexico and Australia.

Foreign Missions: Diocese of Chetumal, Quintana Roo, Mexico.

Vocation Director: Fr. Anthony Bannon, LC, Legionaries of Christ, 393 Derby Ave., Orange, CT 06477. (203) 795-2800. E-mail: vocation@legionaries.org; Web: www.legionofchrist.org

LITTLE BROTHERS OF THE GOOD SHEPHERD (B.G.S.)

Generalate: Good Shepherd Centre, 412 Queen St., East, Toronto, Ontario, Canada, M5A 1T3. (416) 869-3619

Conduct: 5 shelters serving the transient and destitute poor (men, women and children), 2 home facilities serving the elderly and infirm, 1 center for AIDS ministry, 1 hospice, 1 center for priests, 2 centers for youth, 2 centers for abused women and children and 1 center for formation.

Represented in the Archdioceses of Miami, Santa Fe, Los Angeles and Toronto and in the Dioceses of Joliet; Hamilton, Ontario (Canada); Ossory (Ireland) and Birmingham (England).

Vocation Directors: Br. Bill Osmanski, BGS, Villa Mathias, PO Box 389, Albuquerque, NM 87103. (505) 244-0895; Br. Sean McIsaac, BGS, 412 Queen St., East, Toronto, Ontario, CN M5A 1T3.(416) 869-3619. Web: www.lbgs.org

LITTLE BROTHERS OF JESUS

5870 Baker, Detroit, MI 48209. (313) 849-1531. E-mail: brosdet@msn.com

Apostolic Work: Contemplative life in imitation of the life of Jesus at Nazareth

LITTLE BROTHERS OF SAINT FRANCIS (L.B.S.F.)

General Fraternity: 785-789 Parker St., Mission Hill (Boston), MA 02120-3021. (617) 442-2556

3 Perpetually Professed, 4 Candidates in Formation

Apostolic Work: Combine contemplative life, Eucharistic Adoration and evangelical street ministry, living in radical poverty and prayerful solidarity with the poorest of Christ's poor in the ghettos, favelos or barrios of the world.

Vocations: Bro. Anthony J. Dusza, L.B.S.F.

MARIANISTS, SOCIETY OF MARY (SM)

(Province of the U.S.) 4425 W. Pine Blvd., St. Louis, MO 63108-2301. (1-877) 820-6494. Web: http://buildingcommunity.org

461 Brothers, 169 Priests

Apostolic Work: Education (universities, high schools, 1 middle school), retreat and renewal work, parish work, campus ministry, youth programs in camps, home for disadvantaged youth. International missions include Kenya, Korea, India, Ireland, Malawi, Mexico, and Zambia.

Represented in the US in the Archdioceses of Baltimore, Boston, Cincinnati, Los Angeles, Miami, Philadelphia, San Francisco and St. Louis and in the Dioceses of Brooklyn, Cleveland, Honolulu, Monterey, Pittsburgh, San Antonio and San Jose.

National Vocation Director: Bro. Charles Johnson, SM, 4425 W. Pine Blvd., St. Louis, MO 63108-2301. (1-877) 820-6494. E-mail: cjohnson@sm-usa.org; Web: http://buildingcommunity.org

Regional Vocation Directors: Fr. Joseph Tedesco, SM, Marianist Vocation Ministry, Alumni Hall, Room 225, University of Dayton, Dayton, OH 45469-0323. (937) 229-2741. Fax: (937) 229-2772. E-mail: mvm@udayton.edu; Bro. Mike Sullivan, SM, Marianist Vocation Ministry, St. Mary's University, One Camino Santa Maria, San Antonio, TX 78228-8556. (210) 431-2193. E-mail: mumike@stmarytx.edu; Fr. John McEnhill, SM, 22825 San Juan Rd., Cupertino, CA 95014-3934. (408) 252-4631. E-mail: frjohn@earthlink.net; Bro. Dennis Schmitz, SM, Center Marianist Community, 3140 Waialae Ave., Honolulu, HI 96816-1578. (808) 735-4081. E-mail: Baldschmitz@aol.com. Lay Members: Tony Garascia, Marianist Lay Network of North America, 1210 Fairview Ave., South Bend, IN 46614. (219) 287-0409. E-mail: agarascia@worldnet.att.net

MARIANISTS, SOCIETY OF MARY (S.M.)

(Province of Meribah) Provincial House: 240 Emory Rd., Mineola, NY 11501. (516) 742-5555

7 Priests, 35 Brothers

Conduct: 2 high schools, 2 retreat houses.

Vocation Director: Fr. James Williams, S.M., 240 Emory Rd., Mineola, NY 11501. (516) 742-5555. E-mail: frjames@chaminade-hs.org

MARIANNHILL MISSIONARIES (CMM)

(American-Canadian Province) 23715 Ann Arbor Trail, Dearborn Heights, MI 48127

16 Priests, 3 Brothers

Conduct: Community house, novitiate, vocation/formation center, parish assistance, youth retreat center.

Apostolic Work: Foreign missions, parish assistance, publications - "Leaves" magazine, youth retreat work and vocation/formation guidance.

Represented in the Archdiocese of Detroit and in the Dioceses of Austin, TX and Sherbrooke (Quebec, Canada). Houses in Germany, Austria, Holland, Poland, Spain, Switzerland and Rome, Italy. Foreign missions in South Africa, Zimbabwe, Zambia, Papua New Guinea, Kenya and Mozambique.

Vocation Director: Fr. Vergil Heier, CMM, 23715 Ann Arbor Trail, Dearborn Heights, MI 48127. (313) 561-7140. Fax: (313) 561-9486. E-mail: vheier@juno.com

MARIANS OF THE IMMACULATE CONCEPTION (M.I.C.)

(Province of St. Casimir) 6336 S. Kilbourn Ave., Chicago, IL 60629

25 Priests, 5 Brothers, 2 Novices, 3 Postulants, 4 Candidates; approximately 600 Priests & Brothers worldwide

Conduct: 5 parishes, 1 high school totalling 6 community houses.

Apostolic Work: Parishes with an emphasis on teaching and publishing. Some members working in Argentina.

Represented in the Archdioceses of Chicago and Milwaukee and in the Dioceses of Joliet, IL and Norwich, CT. Worldwide members in Argentina, Australia, Brazil, Byelorussia, England, Estonia, France, Germany, Italy, Kazakhastan, Latvia, Lithuania, Poland, Portugal, Rwanda, Ukraine and Wales.

Vocation Director: Fr. Dan Cambra, M.I.C., 701 Plainfield Rd., Darien, IL 60561. (630) 323-4333, ext. 14. Fax: (630) 323-4354. E-mail: yippy605@yahoo.com

MARIANS OF THE IMMACULATE CONCEPTION: PRIESTS AND BROTHERS (M.I.C.)

(St. Stanislaus Kostka Province) 515 Belleview Blvd., Steubenville, OH 43952. (1-877) 261-8806 (toll-free), (740) 282-5058. E-mail: vocations@marian.org; Web: www.Marian.org

43 Members total. 35 Perpetually Professed Members. 24 Priests, 7 Brothers, 6 Student Brothers, 3 Novices, 1 Postulant

Conduct: The National Shrine of the Divine Mercy, The Marian Helpers Center (publishing apostolate), 3 religious houses 2 formation houses of studies, 2 residences, 2 parishes.

Apostolic Work: The Divine Mercy message, The Blessed Virgin Mary, the Immaculate Conception, praying for the souls in purgatory, chaplains for two convents, daily masses, daily confessions, assisting pilgrims, conducting retreats, workshops, conferences, spiritual direction, counseling, pastoral assistance of diocesan clergy, parish administration, teaching, preaching, publishing, printing, writing articles and books, Divine Mercy Sunday, Alaska mission, military chaplaincy, African-American apostolate hospital chaplain, assisted living facility, Friends of the Needy, John Paul II Institute of Divine Mercy, Eucharistic Apostles of Divine Mercy, Mother of Mercy Messengers, Marian pilgrimages.

Represented in the (Arch)dioceses of Fairbanks (AK), Portland (ME), Springfield (MA), Steubenville (OH) and Washington (DC).

Formation: Undergraduate: Franciscan University of Steubenville, Steubenville, OH; Graduate: Dominican House of Studies, Washington, DC.

Vocation Director: Rev. Anthony Gramlich, MIC

MARIST BROTHERS OF THE SCHOOLS (F.M.S.)

(Province of the United States of America) 1241 Kennedy Blvd., Bayonne, NJ 07002

220 Brothers in the US: 4,800 Brothers in 76 countries worldwide

Apostolic Work: "Christian education of youth, particularly the most neglected" through youth ministry, all levels of education, counseling, catechetical work, retreats, summer camps, social ministry and foreign missions.

Represented in the Archdioceses of Boston, Chicago, Miami, Newark, New Orleans and New York and in the Dioceses of Brooklyn, Brownsville, Laredo, Manchester, Rockville Center, St. Augustine, St. Petersburg and Wheeling-Charleston. American Brothers also present in Australia, Japan, the Philippines, Rome and the US Virgin Islands

Vocation Director: Bro. Steve Milan, FMS, Marist Brothers, 1241 Kennedy Blvd., Bayonne, NJ 07002. (201) 823-1115. E-mail: smilanfms@aol.com: Web: www.maristbr.com

MARIST FATHERS AND BROTHERS (S.M.) (Society of Mary)

(Boston Province) 27 Isabella St., Boston, MA 02116-5216. (617) 426-5297

85 Fathers and Brothers

Conduct: 8 parishes, 2 high schools, foreign missions (in Peru, Venezuela, Brazil, Africa, the Philippines and the islands of the Pacific), 2 houses of studies for seminarians, 2 shrines in Boston, 4 hospital chaplaincies, 3 college chaplaincies, 2 retreat houses and specialized ministries (preaching parish missions, teaching on college level, military chaplaincy, special education, drug counseling, ministry to the elderly).

Apostolic Work: Parish work, teaching (college and high school levels), foreign missions, chaplaincies (in hospitals, schools, prisons and armed services), retreat work, home missions, charismatic renewal, houses of prayer, specialized ministries.

Represented in the Archdioceses of Boston, Detroit and New York City; in the Dioceses of Brooklyn, Burlington, Portland (ME), Providence, and Rochester; in the Western Pacific Dioceses of Fiji, New Caledonia, New Guinea, New Hebrides, New Zealand, Samoa, Solomon Islands and Tonga; Peru and Africa.

Vocation Director: Fr. Albert Dilanni, Marist Vocation Office, Our Lady of Victories Rectory, 27 Isabella St., Boston, MA 02116-5216. (617) 426-4448. E-mail: rlajoie@aol.com; Web: users.aol.com/rlajoie/marists.htm.

MARIST FATHERS AND BROTHERS (S.M.)

(Atlanta Province) PO Box 81144, Atlanta, GA 30366-1144. (770) 458-1435

92 Priests and Brothers

Conduct: 13 parishes, 1 high school, 2 houses of study and special ministries.

Apostolic Work: Parish work, teaching, chaplaincies, retreats, missions, Hispanic ministry, renewal, communications, foreign missions (Fiji, Solomon Islands, New Caledonia, Samoa, Tonga, Vanuatu, Wallis-Futuna, Brazil, Philippines, Japan, Peru, Venezuela).

Represented in the Archdioceses of Atlanta, New Orleans, Philadelphia, St. Paul, San Francisco and Washington, DC and and in the Dioceses of Cleveland, Brownsville, Baton Rouge, Honolulu, Monterey, St. Petersburg, Savannah and Wheeling-Charleston.

Vocation Director: Fr. Bill Rowland, SM, Director for Vocations, 2335 Warring St., Berkeley, CA 94704. (1-866) 853-0697. E-mail: wrowland@aol.com; Web: www.maristsociety.org

MARYKNOLL FATHERS & BROTHERS (The Catholic Foreign Mission Society of America)

Maryknoll, NY 10545-0302 (located in the Town of Ossining, NY)

580 Priests and Brothers

Conduct: Maryknoll Priests and Brothers work as missionaries in 32 countries around the world, in Latin America, Asia, Africa, Russia and the Middle East.

Foundation: Popularly known as Maryknoll, US bishops established in 1911 as a society of secular priests and lay brothers to be an overseas mission expression of the Catholic Church of the United States.

Charism/Spirit: Maryknollers are grounded in faith in Jesus Christ, particularly in the context of His mission: "Then he told them, 'Go out to the whole world and proclaim the Good News to all creation!' " (Mark 16:14-15); and "Seek first the Kingdom of God and His justice" (Matt. 6:33). It is this mission of Jesus that is the foundation of Maryknoll spirituality.

Mission Work: Maryknoll Fathers and Brothers engage in a variety of different ministries, depending on need, among people they serve, most of whom are poor people in Third World countries. Examples of such works are: parish ministries, teaching, setting up schools, social action and community development, health care, developing basic Christian communities, justice and peace, assisting refugees, etc. Oftentimes what Maryknollers do in witnessing to the Gospel is to respond to people's concrete needs.

Vocation Director: Fr. Michael J. Snyder, MM, Vocation Ministries, PO Box 302, Maryknoll, NY 10545-0302. (914) 941-7636, ext. 2416. E-mail: vocation@maryknoll.org; Web: www.maryknoll.org

MERCEDARIANS

See Order of the Blessed Virgin Mary of Mercy

BROTHERS OF MERCY (F.M.M.)

(American Province) 4520 Ransom Rd., Clarence, NY 14031

15 Brothers, 2 Candidates

Apostolic Work: Health care.

Represented in the Diocese of Buffalo.

Vocation Director: Br. Jude Holzfoerster, 4520 Ransom Rd., Clarence, NY 14031. (716) 759-8341. E-mail: Jude@BrothersofMercy.org; Web: www.brothersofmercy.org

FATHERS OF MERCY (C.P.M.) (Congregation of Priests of Mercy)

Generalate: 806 Shaker Museum Rd., Auburn, KY 42206. (270) 542-4146. Fax: (270) 542-4147. E-mail: vocations@fathersofmercy.com; Web: www.fathersofmercy.com

39 Members

Apostolic Work: The propagation of the Faith and the salvation of souls through the preaching of parish missions, retreats and the staffing of rural missions. Strong Eucharistic and Marian devotion; unwavering loyalty to the Magisterium of the Church.

Vocation Director: Fr. Wade L. J. Menezes, CPM

MILL HILL MISSIONARIES (M.H.M.) (St. Joseph's Missionary Society)

Regional Office and Superior: 222 W. Hartsdale Ave., Hartsdale, NY 10530-1667. (914) 682-0645. Fax: (914) 682-0862

17 Fathers, 2 Brothers, 1 Associate

Conduct: 21 mission territories in Africa, Asia and South America.

Apostolic Work: foreign missions.

Represented in the Archdioceses of New York and Los Angeles.

Vocation Directors: Rev. Brian Coffey, MHM, 222 W. Hartsdale Ave., Hartsdale, NY 10530-1667. (914) 682-0645, Fax: (914) 682-0862; Rev. Henk Riesthuis, MHM, 1841 Camino Palmero, Los Angeles, CA 90046. (213) 876-0505

MINIM FATHERS (O.M.)

General Motherhouse: Rome, Italy

US Delegation: All Saints Church, 3431 Portola Ave., Los Angeles, CA 90032. (323) 223-1101

3 Priests

Represented in the Archdiocese of Los Angeles.

Vocation Director: Fr. Gino Vanzillotta, 3431 Portola Ave., Los Angeles, CA 90032. E-mail: jvega@earthlink.net; Web: www.earthlink.net/~jvega/

MISSIONARIES OF CHARITY (M.C.)

(founded by Mother Teresa of Calcutta), 1316 S. Westlake Ave., Los Angeles, CA 90006. (213) 384-6116

7 Brothers in US, 450 Brothers worldwide

Apostolic Work: Giving wholehearted and free service to the poorest of the poor. In the US: work with homeless, youth, handicapped; minister to the imprisoned and to homeless immigrants.

Represented in the Archdiocese of Los Angeles.

Vocation Director: Bro. James Walker, MC, Missionaries of Charity, 1316 S. Westlake Ave., Los Angeles, CA 90006. (213) 380-5225 (w); (213) 384-6116 (evening)

SOCIETY OF THE MISSIONARIES OF THE HOLY APOSTLES (M.S.A.)

US Headquarters: 24 Prospect Hill Rd., Cromwell, CT 06416. (860) 632-3039. E-mail: infogen@msagen.org

Conduct: 6 formation houses, 3 seminaries, 2 homes for abandoned persons, 2 retreat centers, 1 high school and assist in many parishes worldwide.

Apostolic Work: Primarily the theological and spiritual preparation of adult men for the priesthood. Also involved in the education of laymen and women for positions of leadership in the Church. Concerned with the evangelization and humanization ministry in mission territories.

Represented in the Archdiocese of Washington (DC) and in the Dioceses of Norwich and Venice (FL). Also ministering in Africa, Brazil, Canada, Italy, Peru and Venezuela.

Vocation Director: Isaac Martinez, M.S.A., 8594, rue Berri, Montreal, Quebec H2P 2G4, Canada (514) 387-2222. Fax: (514) 387-0863. E-mail: infogen@msagen.org

MISSIONARIES OF THE HOLY FAMILY (M.S.F.)

"Servants of God - Builders of Family"

Provincial House: 3014 Oregon Ave., St. Louis, MO 63118-1498. (314) 577-6300. Fax: (314) 577-6301

29 Priests and Brothers

Apostolic Work: Involved in a large variety of apostolates, always in an attempt to serve the Church's current needs. Work in parishes, schools and homes for the aged, reflecting the order's concern and respect for family life. Staffs 1 house of study, 1 novitiate, 9 parishes, 1 nursing home chaplaincy.

Represented in the Archdioceses of Ottawa, Canada, St. Louis, MO and San Antonio, TX and in the Dioceses of Brownsville, TX, Corpus Christi, TX, Richmond, VA and Saltillo, Mexico.

Vocation Director: Rev. Philip Sosa, MSF, St Joseph Church, 306 S. Salinas Blvd., Donna, TX 78537. (956) 464-3331. Web: www.catholic-forum.com/msf

MISSIONARIES OF THE HOLY SPIRIT (M.Sp.S.)

Generalate: Avenida Universidad 0702-04010, Mexico D.F.

US Headquarters: Christ the Priest Province, 9792 Oma Pl., Garden Grove, CA 92841. (714) 534-5476. Fax: (714) 534-5184. E-mail: mspscpp@aol.com

260 Priests, 131 Brothers, 52 Novices, 29 Postulants

Primary Apostolic Work: Spreading the spirituality of the Cross, living the lifestyle of Christ, Priest and Victim, through spiritual direction for priests, religious men and women, and lay people; spirituality centers, seminaries and parish ministry.

Represented in the (Arch)dioceses of Los Angeles, Orange, Portland (OR) and Seattle. Presence in Chile, Colombia, Costa Rica, Italy, Mexico, and Spain.

Vocation Director: Fr. Jose Garcia, M.Sp.S., (714) 534-5725. E-mail: jgfmsps@yahoo.com

MISSIONARIES OF OUR LADY OF LA SALETTE

See La Salette Missionaries

MISSIONARIES OF THE PRECIOUS BLOOD

See "P" - Precious Blood

MISSIONARIES OF THE SACRED HEART (M.S.C.)

(US Province) Provincial House: 305 S. Lake St., PO Box 270, Aurora, IL 60507. (630) 892-2371

59 Fathers, 19 Brothers, 7 Students

Conduct: 13 parishes.

Apostolic Work: Christian evangelization in the US and in 50 countries around the world pursued through parishes, chaplaincies, retreat/renewal work and one Native American reservation.

Represented in the US in the Archdioceses of Philadelphia, Chicago and Washington, DC and in the Dioceses of Rockford, Allentown, Ogdensburg, Youngstown, San Bernardino and San Antonio.

Vocation Director: Mr. Mario Delgado, 305 S. Lake St., PO Box 270, Aurora, IL 60507. (630) 892-2371. E-mail: vocation@misacor-usa.org; Web: www.misacor-usa.org

MISSIONARIES OF THE SACRED HEARTS OF JESUS AND MARY (M.SS.CC.)

Motherhouse: Naples, Italy

American Headquarters: 2249 Shore Rd., Linwood, NJ 08221. (609) 927-5600

10 Priests, 1 Brother, 2 Brothers in Temporary Vows, 2 Novices in US; 70 Priests worldwide

Conduct: 2 parishes in the Diocese of Camden, NJ; 2 parishes in the Diocese of Harrisburg, 1 novitiate.

Apostolic Work: Inner city and suburban parishes, chaplaincies, retreats, active promotion of devotion to the Sacred Hearts of Jesus and Mary.

Represented in the Dioceses of Camden, NJ and Harrisburg, PA and in Italy, Argentina and India.

Vocation Contact: Director of Vocations, Missionaries of the Sacred Hearts, 2249 Shore Rd., Linwood, NJ 08221. (609) 927-5600. Fax: (609) 927-5262. E-mail: mssccusa@aol.com; Web: www.missionofsacredhearts.org

MISSIONARIES OF ST. CHARLES/SCALABRINIANS

See "S" - St. Charles

MISSIONARY BENEDICTINE MONKS OF ST. OTTILIEN

See "B" - Benedictine Monks

MISSIONARY OBLATES OF MARY IMMACULATE (O.M.I.)

(United States Province)

Our Congregation is committed to carrying the Gospel of Jesus Christ to others, with a special preference for the most abandoned in our society. We work in parishes, retreat centers, shrines, educational institutions, prisons and hospital chaplaincies; on reservations with Native peoples, and with minorities as well as in foreign missions.

500 Oblate Brothers and Priests in US Province; 4,700 worldwide in 68 countries

Central Oblate Vocation Office: 327 Oblate Dr., San Antonio, TX 78216-6602. (800) 358-4394, English and Spanish (y en español). E-mail: vocations@omiusa.org; Web: www.omiusa.org

Four regional Vocation Directors in Saint Paul (MN), Lowell (MA), San Antonio (TX) and San Fernando (CA)

MISSIONARY SERVANTS OF THE MOST HOLY TRINITY

See Trinity Missions

MISSIONARY SOCIETY OF ST. JAMES THE APOSTLE

24 Clark St., Boston, MA 02109

An association of 40 diocesan priest volunteers, sent by their bishops through the Society of St. James to work in mission parishes in South America, from 33 dioceses of the United States, Canada, England, Scotland, Ireland, Wales, Australia, and New Zealand serving in the Dioceses of Quito, Santo Domingo de Los Colorados and Guayaquil, Ecuador; Lima, Chimbote, Piura, Lurin, Carabayllo, Sicuani, Tacna-Moquegua, Peru; and Santa Cruz and Oruro, Bolivia.

Vocation Director: Rev. Robert Thomas. 24 Clark St., Boston, MA 02109. (617) 742-4715. E-mail: thomas@socstjames.com; Web: www.socstjames.com

MISSIONARY SOCIETY OF ST. PAUL THE APOSTLE

See Paulist Fathers

MISSIONARY SONS OF THE IMMACULATE HEART OF MARY

See Clarentian Fathers and Brothers

MISSIONHURST CONGREGATION OF THE IMMACULATE HEART of MARY (C.I.C.M.)

Motherhouse: Rome, Italy

US Province: Missionhurst, 4651 25th St. N., Arlington, VA 22207-3518. (703) 528-3800. Fax: (703) 528-5355

45 Fathers, 1 Brother, 5 Students

Apostolic Work: Parishes, hospitals, prison ministry.

Represented in the Archdioceses of Detroit, Hartford, New York, Philadelphia and San Antonio and in the Dioceses of Arlington and Brownsville.

Vocation Contact: Rev. Anselm Malonda, CICM, 1147-A Cupples Rd., San Antonio, TX 78226. (210) 432-2651. Fax: (210) 432-2621. E-mail: Malonda@aol.com; Web: www.missionhurst.org

THE MONKS OF ADORATION

See "T" - The Monks of Adoration

MONKS OF THE MOST HOLY TRINITY MONASTERY

See Eastern Catholic Religious Communities for Men

MONKS OF MT. TABOR (Holy Transfiguration Monastery)

See Eastern Catholic Religious Communities for Men

MONTFORT MISSIONARIES (S.M.M.)

101-18 104th St., Ozone Park, NY 11416. (718) 849-0071

35 Members

Conduct: 2 parishes, 5 community houses, 1 house of formation, 2 shrines, publications, 2 spirituality centers, 1 center for teenagers in crisis and human services center. Mission in Nicaragua.

Apostolic Work: Preaching, foreign missions, pastoral work, hospital chaplaincies, publications.

Represented in the Archdioceses of Hartford and St. Louis and in the Dioceses of Brooklyn and Rockville Centre. Also in Nicaragua. The Montfort Missionaries minister in 30 countries and 11 foreign missions.

Vocation Director: Fr. Roy E. Tvrdik, SMM, 101-18 104th St., Ozone Park, NY 11416. (718) 849-0071. E-mail: montfortRT@aol.com; Web: montfortmissionaries.com

BROTHERS OF OUR LADY, MOTHER OF MERCY (C.F.M.M.)

7140 Ramsgate Ave., Los Angeles, CA 90045. (310) 649-3370

3 Brothers

Conduct: 1 university

Represented in the Archdiocese of Los Angeles.

Vocation Director: Bro. Anthony P. Smulders, One LMU Dr., MS 8220, Los Angeles, CA 90045-2659. (310) 338-5954. E-mail: asmulder@lmu.edu; Web: www.cmmbrothers.nl/indexe.html#top

NORBERTINE FATHERS (O. PRAEM.) (Canons Regular of Premontre)

St. Michael's Abbey, 19292 El Toro Rd., Silverado, CA 92676-9710

43 Priests, 1 Solemnly Professed Cleric, 13 Clerics, 6 Novices, 1 Brother

Conduct: 1 dependent house, 1 novitiate, 1 seminary for college resident students, 1 prep high school, 1 summer camp, 1 pious association.

Represented in the Archdiocese of Los Angeles and in the Diocese of Orange.

Vocation Director: Rev. Justin S. Ramos, O. Praem., St. Michael's Abbey, 19292 El Toro Rd., Silverado, CA 92676-9710. (949) 858-0222, ext. 333. Fax: (949) 858-4583. E-mail: vocationdirector333@yahoo.com; Web: AbbeyNews.com

NORBERTINE FATHERS (O. Praem.) (Canons Regular of Premontre)

St. Norbert Abbey, 1016 North Broadway, De Pere, WI 54115-2697. (920) 337-4300

86 Priests, 4 Brothers, 5 Novices, 3 Simple Professed, 2 Transitional Deacons

Conduct: 1 dependent priory, 1 seminary, 1 house of studies, 1 novitiate, 1 college, 1 high school, 4 hospital chaplaincies, 14 parishes, 1 campus ministry center, 1 retreat/renewal center, 2 military chaplaincies.

Apostolic Work: Parish work, ecumenical work, chaplaincies, foreign missions, campus ministry work, retreats, teaching and educational administration.

Represented in the Archdioceses of Albuquerque/Santa Fe and Chicago and in the Dioceses of Green Bay, Jackson and Madison.

Vocation Coordinator: Fr. Jim Baraniak, St. Norbert Abbey, 1016 N. Broadway, De Pere, WI 54115-2697. (920) 403-1336. E-mail: norbertines@snc.edu; Web: www.norbertines.org

NORBERTINE FATHERS AND BROTHERS (O. Praem.)

Priory of St. Moses the Black, 653 Claiborne Ave., Jackson, MS 39209-6299. (601) 354-3287. Foundation House: St. Norbert Abbey, DePere, WI

5 Priests, 1 Professed Junior, 2 Novices

Apostolic Work : Ministry primarily among African-Americans; ministry

to the poor of any race; parishes, education, retreats, campus ministry, spiritual direction.
Represented in the (Arch)diocese of Jackson.
Vocation Director: Xavier G. Colavechio, O. Praem., Priory of St. Moses the Black, 653 Claiborne Ave., Jackson, MS 39209-6299. (601) 354-3287. Fax: (601) 944-1606. E-mail: xcprmmtb@juno.com; Web: www.snc.edu/norbertines

NORBERTINE FATHERS AND BROTHERS (O. Praem.)
(Canons Regular of Premontre)

Immaculate Conception Priory, 1269 Bayview Rd., Middletown, DE 19709

10 Priests

Conduct: 2 parishes

Apostolic Work: Common life, retreats, parish ministry.
Represented in the Archdiocese of Baltimore and in the Dioceses of Wilmington, Harrisburg and Green Bay.
Vocation Director: Father James D. Bagnato, O. Praem., Immaculate Conception Priory, 1269 Bayview Rd., Middletown, DE 19709. (302) 449-1840

NORBERTINES (O. PRAEM.)
(Canons Regular of Premontre)

Daylesford Abbey, 220 S. Valley Rd., Paoli, PA 19301. (610) 647-2530

29 Priests, 4 Brothers

Conduct: 4 parishes, spirituality center.
Apostolic Work: Daylesford Abbey exists to enrich the Church by our Norbertine Communio, nourished by contemplation on God's work, made visible in worship and service within the local Church.
Represented in the Archdiocese of Philadelphia. Also in Peru.
Vocation Director: Fr. Steven J. Albero, O. Praem., Daylesford Abbey, 220 S. Valley Rd., Paoli, PA 19301-1999. (610) 647-2530, ext. 21. Fax: (610) 651-0219. E-mail: salbero@daylesford.org; Web: www.Daylesford.org

OBLATES OF ST. FRANCIS DE SALES (OSFS)

(Wilmington-Philadelphia Province)

Provincial House: 2200 Kentmere Pkwy., Wilmington, DE 19804. (302) 656-8529

190 Priests, 20 Brothers, 1 Deacon, 4 Seminarians, 5 Postulants, 20 Associates

Conduct: 26 parishes, 1 scholasticate, 1 novitiate, 1 college, 1 retreat house, 5 high schools, 4 Newman Centers, 28 community houses.
Apostolic Work: High school teaching, parish work, college teaching, campus ministry, overseas missions, inner-city projects. Armed Forces chaplaincies, adult education, hospital ministry and chaplaincies, conduct retreats and parish missions.
Represented in the Archdioceses of Boston, Military Services, Philadelphia, Washington, DC and in the Dioceses of Allentown, Arlington, Camden, Charlotte, Harrisburg, Raleigh, Venice and Wilmington. Also in Benin, Brazil, Columbia, Equador, Haiti, India, Mexico, Namibia, Republic of South Africa and Uruguay.
Vocation Director: Fr. Kevin Nadolski, OSFS, 721 Lawrence St. N.E., Washington, DC 20017. (202) 526-5651. Fax: (202) 526-5653. E-mail: knadolski@oblates.org; Web: www.oblates.org

OBLATES OF ST. FRANCIS DE SALES (O.S.F.S.)

(Toledo-Detroit Province) 2056 Parkwood Ave., Toledo, OH 43620

94 Priests and Brothers

Minister in 25 parishes including colleges; 5 high schools and 1 grade school; 6 hospitals, elderly and handicapped chaplaincies; 1 military chaplain; missions; prison chaplaincy; ministry to the hearing impaired; 10 community houses, 2 formation houses and 1 summer camp.
Represented in the (Arch)dioceses of Buffalo, Detroit, Erie, Kalamazoo, Lansing, Miami, Military Services, Oakland, Saginaw, Salt Lake City, Stockton, Toledo and Toronto and mission regions in Brazil, Uruguay, Mexico, Namibia and S.W. Africa.
Vocation Director: Fr. Martin Lukas, osfs, 2056 Parkwood Ave., Toledo, OH 43620. (419) 243-5105. Fax: (419) 243-8827. E-mail: mlosfs@aol.com; Web: www.oblates.org

OBLATES OF ST. JOSEPH (O.S.J.)

(Western Province) 544 West Cliff Dr., Santa Cruz, CA 95060-0547. (831) 457-1868

15 Priests, 4 Brothers, 1 Temporary Professed, 2 Postulants, 2 Seminarians

Conduct: A religious family of priests and brothers who serve God in imitation of St. Joseph with total dedication to Jesus, special love for Mary, fidelity to the magisterial teaching of the Church, deep interior prayer life, hard work, and unshakeable trust in Divine Providence; 3 parishes; 2 houses of formation, 1 shrine.
Represented in the Archdiocese of Los Angeles and in the Dioceses of Fresno, Monterey and Sacramento. Also in Pennsylvania, Brazil, India, Italy, Mexico, Peru, Bolivia, Chile, Philippines, Poland, Nigeria and Romania.
Vocation Director: Fr. Brian Crawford, O.S.J., Mt. St. Joseph Novitiate and Seminary, P.O. Box 547, Loomis, CA 95650-0547. (916) 652-6336. Fax: (916) 652-0620. E-mail: vocations@osjoseph.org; Web: www.osjoseph.org

OBLATES OF ST. JOSEPH (O.S.J.)

(Our Lady of Sorrows Province) St. Joseph Oblate Seminary, 1880 Hwy. 315, Pittston, PA 18640-9618

11 Priests

Conduct: A religious community of brothers and priests, founded by St. Joseph Marello, and working to spread the Gospel in youth ministry, catechesis and parish ministry, under the inspiration of St. Joseph. 3 parishes, 1 house of study.

Represented in the Diocese of Scranton.

Vocation Director: Rev. Gregory Finn, O.S.J., St. Joseph Oblate Seminary, 1880 Hwy. 315, Pittston, PA 18640-9618. (570) 654-7758. Fax: (570) 654-8621. E-mail: finnosj@adelphia.net

OBLATES OF THE VIRGIN MARY

1105 Boylston St., Boston, MA 02215

Apostolic Work: Ignatian retreats, parish missions, formation of the clergy, defense of the Truth, formation of the laity, parishes, foreign missions, social communications.

Represented in the Archdiocese of Boston and Los Angeles and in the Dioceses of Springfield-in-Illinois, Metuchen, Montreal and Trois-Rivieres, Quebec, Canada. Foreign missions in Argentina, Austria, Brazil, France, Italy, Nigeria and the Philippines.

Vocation Director: Rev. Peter Grover, OMV, 1105 Boylston St., Boston, MA 02215. (617) 266-5999, ext. 202. Fax: (617) 247-7576. E-mail: vocation@oblatesofthevirginmary.org; Web: www.oblatesofthevirginmary.org

ORATORIANS (ORAT.)
(Congregation of the Oratory)

The Oratorian Community of Monterey, PO Box 1688, Monterey, CA 93942. (831) 373-0476

3 Priests

Represented in the Diocese of Monterey

Vocation Contact: Rev. Thomas A. Kieffer, Pro-Vicar, Oratorian Community, PO Box 1688, Monterey, CA 93942. (831) 373-0476

ORATORIANS (C.O.) (Congregation of the Oratory of St. Philip Neri)

4450 Bayard St., Pittsburgh, PA 15213. (412) 681-3181

5 Priests

Represented in the Diocese of Pittsburgh.

Vocation Director: Very Rev. David S. Abernethy, C.O., 4450 Bayard St., Pittsburgh, PA 15213. (412) 681-3181, ext. 222. E-mail: davida@andrew.cmu.edu; Web: www.cmu.edu/user/oratory

ORATORIANS (C.O.) (Congregation of the Oratory)

The Oratory of Rock Hill, P.O. Box 11586, 434 Charlotte Ave., Rock Hill, SC 29731. (803) 327-2097

6 Priests, 5 Brothers, 1 Deacon, 2 Novices

Apostolic Work: Parishes, retreats, campus ministry, lay ministry training, spiritual direction, nursing, Hispanic ministry, diocesan adult education.

Represented in the Diocese of Charleston.

Vocation Director: Fr. Ed McDevitt, C.O., P.O. Box 11586, 434 Charlotte Ave., Rock Hill, SC 29731. (803) 327-0106

ORATORIANS (C.O.) (Congregation of the Oratory)

The Oratory of Pharr, P.O. Box ii, Pharr, TX 78577-1235. (956) 843-8217

4 Priests, 1 Seminarian

Apostolic Work: Services to the poor, Mexican-American cultural services, parish work, health, bicultural Catholic elementary and secondary schools.

Represented in the Diocese of Brownsville. Also in Matanio, Tamiaulipas, Mexico

Vocation Director: Rev. Jose Encarnacion Losoya, C.O., St. Jude Thaddeus Rectory, 505 S. Ironwood, PO Drawer J, Pharr, TX 78577-1210. (956) 781-2489. Fax: (956) 783-4614. E-mail: pipponeri@aol.com

THE ORDER OF THE BLESSED VIRGIN MARY OF MERCY (O. de M.) (Mercedarian Friars)

One of the ancient Orders of the Catholic Church, the Mercedarian Friars were founded in 1218. The Friars honor Mary, as the foundress and mother of the work of mercy begun by Saint Peter Nolasco - the redemption of Christians in danger of losing their faith. This work of mercy is conducted in parishes, where faith is often attacked or broken due to influences and systems contrary to gospel and family values; in schools, where peer pressure and empty values threaten the faith of youth; in institutions of health care or detention, where despair and apostasy threaten one's faith in Christ; and in foreign missions, where human dignity and faith are robbed because of degrading social conditions.

Men, between the ages of 18-35, who desire to live a life centered in Mary and her Son, to pray the rosary daily in common, live in community with one's "brothers" based upon the Rule of St. Augustine (prayers, meals and recreation in common), have a deep love for the Magisterium and in preserving the Faith by catechesis, are invited to contact the Director of Vocations, 6398 Drexel Rd., Philadelphia, PA 19151-2596. Toll free: 1-877-OLMercy. E-mail: vocations@orderofmercy.org; Web: www.orderofmercy.org

ORDER OF FRIARS MINOR

See Franciscans

ORDER OF FRIARS MINOR CAPUCHIN

See Capuchins

ORDER OF FRIARS MINOR CONVENTUAL

See Franciscan Friars

ORDER OF THE HOLY CROSS

See Crosiers

ORDER OF THE MOST HOLY SAVIOR

See Brigittine Monks

ORDER OF THE MOST HOLY TRINITY

See Trinitarian Friars

ORDER OF PREACHERS

See Dominican Fathers and Brothers

ORDER OF ST. AUGUSTINE

See Augustinians

ORDER OF ST. BENEDICT

See Benedictines

ORDER OF ST. PAUL THE HERMIT

See Pauline Fathers and Brothers

PALLOTTINE FATHERS (S.A.C.) (Society of the Catholic Apostolate)

(Queen of the Apostles, Italian Province) 448 E. 116th St., New York, NY 10029. (212) 534-0681

8 Fathers, 1 Deacon

Conduct: Parishes, missionary work, diaconate director, schools.

Represented in the Archdiocese of New York and in the Dioceses of Albany and Pensacola-Tallahassee. Other houses, high schools and parishes in Italy and England.

Vocation Director: Rev. Peter J. Rofrano, S.A.C., Our Lady of Mt. Carmel, 448 E. 116th St., New York, NY 10029. (212) 534-0681. Fax: (212) 534-0629. Web: www.mtcarmelnyc.org

PALLOTTINES (S.A.C.) (Society of the Catholic Apostolate)

(Immaculate Conception Province) 5552 Rt. 70, Pennsauken, NJ 08109-4798

28 men in the Province including 7 in training; 2,349 men worldwide

Priests, Brothers, Lay Associates

Conduct: Lay formation programs, youth ministries, parishes, schools and foreign missions. Give: missions and retreats.

Information: Vocation Director: Brother James Beamesderfer, S.A.C., Pallottine Vocation Office, 5552 Rt. 70, Pennsauken, NJ 08109-4798. Dial: 1-800-APOSTLE; 1-856-486-0844; Fax: 1-856-486-0813. Web: www.sacapostles.org

PALLOTTINES (S.A.C.) (Society of the Catholic Apostolate)

Motherhouse: Poland

(Infant Jesus Delegature of the Annunciation Province) Mission House and Infant Jesus Shrine, 3452 Niagara Falls Blvd., PO Box 563, North Tonawanda, NY 14120-0563

13 Priests

Apostolic Work: Retreats, parish work, hospital chaplaincy, national shrine, pro-life ministry

Represented in the Dioceses of Brooklyn, Buffalo and Rockville Centre.

Vocation Info: Rev. Laslaw M. Gwarek S.A.C.

PALLOTTINES (Society of the Catholic Apostolate)

(Irish Province) 3352 Fourth Street, PO Box 249, Wyandotte, MI 48192

16 Priests, 1 Brother

Apostolic Work: Parishes, missions, hospital chaplaincy.

Represented in the Archdioceses of Detroit and Philadelphia and in the Dioceses of Fort Worth, Lubbock and Reno-Las Vegas.

Contact: Rev. Hubert Flanagan, S.A.C.

PALLOTTINES (S.A.C.)
(Society of the Catholic Apostolate)
(Mother of God Province) 5424 W. Bluemound Rd., Milwaukee, WI 53208-3097
13 Priests, 1 Brother, 2 Temporary Professed
Conduct: 3 parishes, 1 retreat house, 1 hospital chaplaincy, 1 health care chaplaincy, 1 high school
Represented in the Midwest, in the Archdiocese of Milwaukee, and in the Dioceses of Fargo and Superior. Also in the Diocese of Calgary (Alberta, Canada).
Vocation Coordinator: Bro. Jim Scarpace, SAC, 5424 W. Bluemound Rd., Milwaukee, WI 53208-3097. (414) 259-0653, ext. 155. E-mail: vocsacmil@juno.com; Web: www.dias.net/~pallotti/vocation.htm

PARIS FOREIGN MISSIONS SOCIETY (M.E.P)
Headquarters: Paris, France
US: 930 Ashbury St., San Francisco, CA 94117
2 Priests
Represented in the Archdiocese of San Francisco
Vocation Contact: Rev. Jacques Didier, M.E.P., 930 Ashbury St., San Francisco, CA 94117. (415) 664-6747

PASSIONISTS (C.P.) (Congregation of the Passion)
Holy Cross Province, 5700 N. Harlem Ave., Chicago, IL 60631-2342
94 Priests, 13 Brothers
Conduct: 4 retreat houses and 4 parishes; ministries include renewal preaching, spiritual guidance, chaplain ministry and parish assistance.
Represented in the Archdioceses of Chicago, Detroit, Los Angeles, Louisville and San Antonio and in the Dioceses of Galveston-Houston, Birmingham and Sacramento. Cross-cultural mission: India.
Vocation Directors: Fr. Clemente Barrón, C.P., Province Vocation Director, 700 Waverly, San Antonio, TX 78201. (210) 736-5228. Fax: (210) 737-6549. E-mail: cbarron@passionist.org; Web: www.passionist.org/vocations

PASSIONISTS (C.P.)
(Congregation of the Passion)
(Province of St. Paul of the Cross) Passionist Province Pastoral Center, 80 David St., South River, NJ 08882. (908) 257-7177
200 Priests, 31 Brothers
Conduct: 8 monasteries, 7 retreat houses, 10 parishes, 7 residences, 1 novitiate, 1 theologate, 1 college residence, 1 Newman Center, 1 volunteer program, missions in the West Indies and the Philippine Islands.
Represented in the Archdioceses of Atlanta, Baltimore, Boston, Hartford, Newark and New York, and in the Dioceses of Brooklyn, Metuchen, Pittsburgh, Raleigh, Rockville Centre, Scranton, Springfield, Palm Beach, Wheeling and Worcester. Also in Canada, Jamaica, W.I. and the Philippine Islands.
Vocation Director: Fr. Leo O'Boyle, C.P., Passionist Vocation Office, 86-45 Edgerton Blvd., Jamaica, NY 11432. (718) 739-4135. E-mail: voccp@aol.com; Web: www.cpvoca-stpaul.org

PAULINE FATHERS AND BROTHERS
(For Communications Ministry)
See St. Paul, Society of

PAULINE FATHERS AND BROTHERS (O.S.P.P.E.)
(Order of St. Paul the First Hermit)
Motherhouse: Czestochowa, Poland
US Headquarters: National Shrine of Our Lady of Czestochowa, Doylestown, PA 18901
Members in the US: 17 Priests, 5 Brothers
Apostolic Work: Contemplative order and apostolic work especially to foster devotion to the Blessed Virgin Mary.
Vocation Director: Pauline Fathers Monastery, Shrine of Our Lady of Czestochowa, P.O. Box 2049, Ferry Rd., Doylestown, PA 18901. (215) 345-0600

THE PAULIST FATHERS (C.S.P.)
(Missionary Society of St. Paul the Apostle)
The Paulists are the first community of priests founded in the US in 1858 by Isaac Hecker. An active missionary community serving North America.
Paulist Office: Jamaica Estates, NY
165 Priests, 12 Candidates in Theology
Apostolic Work: Parishes, university ministries, adult education, retreat and missionary preaching, Paulist Press, Paulist Media Works, Paulist Productions, ecumenical dialogue, reconciliation ministries, Paulist National Catholic Evangelization Association, Paulist Young Adult Ministry.
Represented in 25 cities throughout the United States and Canada.
Admissions: At least 2 years college; 35 years old maximum unless full-time ministry experience; 1 year novitiate followed by theological studies in Washington, DC including a pastoral year.
Vocation Director: Fr. Edward C. Nowak, C.S.P., 415 W. 59th St., New York, NY 10019. (800) 235-3456 or in New York (212) 757-4260. E-mail: vocations@paulist.org; Web: www.paulist.org

BROTHERS & FATHERS OF PENTECOST
1628 Walnut St., Cincinnati, OH 45202-6546
Apostolic Work: Pro-life; evangelization of youth, Hispanics, and Afro-Americans; building Christian community; Bible teaching.
Represented in the Archdiocese of Cincinnati.
Vocation Director: Bro. Dennis Michael Dooley, 1628 Walnut St., Cincinnati, OH 45202-6546. (513) 665-4333

PIARIST FATHERS (Sch.P)
(Californias' Vice-Province) Vice-Provincial Residence, 3940 Perry St., Los Angeles, CA 90063. (323) 261-1386. Fax: (323) 269-0883. E-mail: escolapios@catholic.org
21 Priests, 6 Novices, 7 Pre-Novices, 15 Seminarians
Conduct: 5 parishes, 2 grammar schools, 3 houses of formation.
Apostolic Work: Dedicated to the education of children and youth.
Represented in the Archdiocese of Los Angeles and in 34 countries around the world

PIARIST FATHERS AND BROTHERS (Sch.P.)
(Province of the United States of America) 1339 Monroe St., N.E., Washington, DC 20017. (202) 529-7734
21 Priests
Conduct: 1 novitiate, 1 house of studies for candidates to the priesthood and brotherhood, 2 college preparatory schools, 1 diocesan high school, 2 missions, 3 parishes, Hungarian ministry, Hispanic ministry.
Apostolic Work: The Piarists profess a fourth vow to educate youth. Education for the Piarists means the complete formation of the person. Thus the Piarists fulfill their vow by teaching on the elementary and secondary levels. In addition, they assist local parishes, conduct a summer mission in Macuspana, Mexico; and have an active outreach program in Eastern Kentucky, where they minister to the poor in Appalachia. Their founder, St. Joseph Calasanctius, is the Patron Saint of Christian Schools.

Represented in the Archdioceses of Miami, Philadelphia and Washington, DC and in the Dioceses of Lexington, Buffalo and Paterson.
Vocation Director: Very Rev. David B. Powers, Sch.P., 99 Martha's Vineyard, Prestonsburg, KY 41653. (610) 564-8893, (606) 285-3950; E-mail: dariff@hotmail.com; Web: www.calasanz.net

PIARISTS (Sch.P.)
(Calasanzian Fathers)
Vice Province: New York and Puerto Rico
25 Priests
Apostolic Work: Christian education, youth pastoral, C.C.D. programs, parish apostolate.
Vocation Contact: Fr. Felix Jimenez, Sch.P., Annunciation Church, 88 Convent Ave., New York, NY 10027. (212) 234-1919. Fax: (212) 281-7205

PIME MISSIONARIES
(Pontifical Institute for Foreign Missions)
US Regional Headquarters and Promotion Center: 17330 Quincy St., Detroit, MI 48221. (313) 342-4066
27 Priests, 1 Brother
Conduct: in the US: 1 parish, 4 mission centers.
Apostolic Work: PIME is a foreign mission society of international membership, engaged in evangelization, church-founding, human development, justice and peace, education, hospitals, orphanages, leprosy relief, dispensaries, homes for the aged, pastoral ministry, interreligious dialogue.
Represented in the Archdiocese of Detroit and in the Dioceses of Columbus, Palm Beach and Paterson. Also in Bangladesh, Brazil, Cambodia, Cameroon, Guinea-Bissau, Hong Kong, Italy, India, Ivory Coast, Japan, Mexico, Myanmar, Papua New Guinea, Philippines, Taiwan and Thailand.
Lay Volunteers: PIME offers young adults an opportunity to serve as lay mission volunteers in its foreign missions. For more information, contact: Fr. George Berendt, 17330 Quincy St., Detroit, MI 48221. (313) 342-4066. Fax: (313) 342-6816. E-mail: volunteers@pimeusa.org
Vocation Directors: For those interested in more information on becoming a PIME priest or brother, contact: Fr. Giancarlo Ghezzi, 34 Grandview Dr., Wayne, NJ 07470. (973) 694-1790. Fax: (973) 694-0444. E-mail: pimenj@optonline.net; Fr.Guy C. Snyder, 511 W. Forest St., Ypsilanti, MI 48197. (734) 637-1159. E-mail: frguy@htspemu.org; Web: www.beamissionary.org

BROTHERS OF THE POOR OF ST. FRANCIS (C.F.P.)
See "F" - Franciscans - Brothers of the Poor of St. Francis

MISSIONARIES OF THE PRECIOUS BLOOD (C.PP.S.)
19 Priests, 1 Brother
Mission: Founded by St. Gaspar del Bufalo to renew the Church through the ministry of the Word and the proclamation of the saving power of the Precious Blood of Jesus Christ.
Ministries: Parishes, education, preaching missions and retreats, foreign missions.
Represented in the Archdioceses of Toronto and Miami and in the Dioceses of Buffalo, Rochester and St. Catharines. Also in Morogoro (Tanzania, East Africa).
Vocation Director: Rev. Lui Santi, C.PP.S., 100 Pelmo Cres, Toronto, Ontario M9N 2Y1, Canada. (416) 531-4423. E-mail: preciousvocations@yahoo.com

MISSIONARIES OF THE PRECIOUS BLOOD (C.PP.S.)
(Cincinnati Province) Provincial House: 431 E. 2nd St., Dayton, OH 45402-1764. (937) 228-9263
160 Priests, 29 Brothers, 1 Deacon, 16 Candidates
Mission: Founded by St. Gaspar del Bufalo to renew the Church through the ministry of the Word and the proclamation of the saving power of the Precious Blood of Jesus Christ.
Ministries: Parishes, education, preaching missions and retreats, foreign missions, hospital, college and military chaplains
Represented in the Archdioceses of Chicago, Cincinnati, Detroit, Guatemala City, Lima (Peru), Louisville, Rome (Italy) and Santiago (Chile) and in the Dioceses of Cleveland, Coban (Guatemala), Columbus, Fort Wayne/South Bend, Gary, Huancayo (Peru), Lafayette-in-Indiana, Orlando, Osorno (Chile) and Toledo.
Vocation Director: Rev. Ken Schnipke, C.PP.S., 431 E. 2nd St., Dayton, OH 45402-1764. (937) 228-6224. E-mail: vocations@cpps-preciousblood.org; Web: www.cpps-preciousblood.org

MISSIONARIES OF THE PRECIOUS BLOOD (C.PP.S.)
(Kansas City Province) Provincial Office, PO Box 339, Liberty, MO 64069-0339. (816) 781-4344
1 Bishop, 64 Priests, 3 Brothers
Mission: Founded by St. Gasper del Bufalo to renew the Church through the ministry of the Word and the proclamation of the saving power of the Precious Blood of Jesus Christ.
Ministries: Parishes, education, preaching missions and retreats, chaplains, foreign missions.
Represented in the Archdioceses of Chicago, Cincinnati, Denver, Jefferson City, Kansas City in Kansas and Toronto, Canada and in the Dioceses of Davenport, Des Moines, Kansas City-St. Joseph, San Angelo and Toledo.
Vocation Directors: Rev. Al Ebach, C.PP.S., Marie Trout, PO Box 339, Liberty, MO 64069-0339. (816) 781-4344. E-mail: KCCPPSVocations@sbcglobal.net; Web: www.catholic-forum.com/cpps-kc

SOCIETY OF THE PRECIOUS BLOOD (C.PP.S.) (Congregation of Missionaries of the Blood of Christ)
(Pacific Province) 2337 134th West Ave., San Leandro, CA 94577-4132. (510) 357-4982. Fax: (510) 357-4036
18 Priests, 1 Brother, 1 Incorporated Seminarian, 50 Lay Associates (Companions)
Conduct: 7 parishes, 1 chaplaincy, 1 center house, 1 mission house, campus ministry, missions, retreats, spiritual direction.
Represented in the Archdioceses of Chicago, Los Angeles and San Francisco and in the Diocese of Oakland.
Vocation Contact: Fr. Gary Luiz, 2800 Milvia St., Berkeley, CA 94703-2209. (510) 848-1053. Fax: (510) 841-4051. E-mail: gluiz@oakdiocese.org

PRIESTLY FRATERNITY OF SAINT PETER (F.S.S.P.)
North American Headquarters: Griffin Rd., PO Box 196, Elmhurst, PA 18416. (570) 842-4000; Fax: (570) 842-4001. E-mail: info@fssp.com
48 Priests, 70 in Formation
Apostolic Work: Reconciliation of alienated Catholics to the Church, participating in the Church's endeavor to re-evangelize Western society by making use of traditional Roman Rites. Work in parishes, retreats, teaching at all levels of education, pastoral and educational support to home schoolers, all carried out in the spirituality of the ancient Roman Rite.
Represented in the (Arch)dioceses of Atlanta, Bismarck, Boise, Charleston, Colorado Springs, Corpus Christi, Dallas, Denver, Indianapolis, Kansas City, Lincoln, Little Rock,

Oklahoma City, Omaha, Paterson, Rapid City, Sacramento, Scranton, Tulsa and Youngstown. Also in Ottawa and St. Catherines (Ontario), Calgary (Alberta) and Vancouver (British Columbia) (Canada).
Contacts: The Priestly Fraternity of St. Peter, Vocations Office, Griffin Rd., PO Box 196, Elmhurst, PA 18416. (570) 842-4000, ext. 501. Fax: (570) 842-4001. E-mail: info@fssp.com or vocations@fssp.com; Fr. George Gabet, FSSP, District Superior, (570) 842-4000; Fr. James Jackson, FSSP, Rector, (402) 797-7700

PRESENTATION BROTHERS (F.P.M.)
Provincialate: 1602 Pettis Blvd., Kissimmee, FL 34741-3117
Apostolic Work: Christian formation, primarily of youth and in particular to the poor and disadvantaged: all forms of education, both elementary and high school, retreat work, social work, pastoral ministry, youth ministry and missionary involvement.
Represented in the Dioceses of Orlando, Knoxville and Toronto. Also in Ireland, England, Trinidad, St. Lucia, Grenada, Ghana and Peru.
Vocation Director: Brother Francis Schafer, F.P.M., 1602 Pettis Blvd., Kissimmee, FL 34741-3117. (407) 846-2033. Fax: (407) 846-7473. E-mail: fpm1802@juno.com; Web: www.PresentationBrothers.org

REDEMPTORISTS (C.Ss.R.)
(Baltimore Province)
234 Priests, 26 Brothers, 5 Novices, 25 Students
Conduct: 34 parishes, 4 retreat houses, college residence, theology residence.
Apostolic Work: Focused on preaching the Word of God, especially to the poor and most abandoned. Particular ministries include parish work, inner-city work, rural and suburban work, parish missions, foreign missions, youth ministries, AIDS ministry, and deaf ministry, as well as supplying military and hospital chaplains.
Represented in the Archdioceses of New York, Boston, Philadelphia, Hartford, Baltimore, and Washington as well as in the Dioceses of Albany, Brooklyn, Harrisburg, Toledo, Wilmington, Richmond, Atlanta, Charlotte, St. Augustine, Charleston, Orlando, and Venice. Also in St. Thomas, St. Lucia and Dominica.
Vocation Directors: Rev. Philip Dabney, C.Ss.R., St. Alphonsus Residence, 22-04 Parsons Blvd., Whitestone, NY 11357. (718) 321-1394; Rev. Al Bradley, C.Ss.R., Redemptorist Provincial Residence, 7509 Shore Rd., Brooklyn, NY 11209. (718) 833-1900. E-mail: p.a.dabney@worldnet.att.net Web: www.redemptorists-baltimore.org

REDEMPTORISTS (C.SS.R.)
(Denver Province) 3737 Washington Blvd., St. Louis, MO 63108. (314) 531-2777
220 Priests, 30 Brothers
Conduct: 2 retreat houses, 13 parishes, Liguori Publications, 3 formation communities.
Apostolic Work: Preaching the gospel by missions, retreats and publication ministries; ministry in African-American and Hispanic communities, youth ministry, deaf apostolate, parishes, and foreign missions in Brazil, Thailand and Nigeria.
Represented in the (Arch)dioceses of Grand Rapids, Chicago, Milwaukee, Minneapolis-St. Paul, Omaha, St. Louis, Kansas City, Wichita, Denver, Tucson, Seattle, Oakland and Los Angeles.
Contacts: Rev. Edward Vella, C.SS.R., Rev. Gary Lauenstein, C.SS.R., St. John Neumann House, 3737 Washington Blvd., St. Louis, MO 63108. (314) 531-2777, ext. 231. Fax: (314) 531-5726. E-mail: cssrinfo@catholic.org, frgarycssr@aol.com

REDEMPTORISTS (C.SS.R.)
(New Orleans Vice-Province) P.O. Box 53900, Baton Rouge, LA 70892-3900. (504) 355-2600
53 Priests, 7 Brothers, 6 Theologians, 5 Students
Apostolic Work: Dedicated to the evangelization of the poor and the most abandoned especially through neighborhood and parish mission preaching in the south-central and south-west United States.
Conduct: 6 parishes, 2 mission bands, college residence.
Represented in the Archdioceses of San Antonio and New Orleans and in the Dioceses of Galveston-Houston, Baton Rouge and Biloxi.
Vocation Director: Rev. Mark Scheffler, C.Ss.R., Liguori House, 1523 Iowa St., San Antonio, TX 78203. (210) 533-2406, 7001. E-mail: markscheffler@msn.com; Web: www.redemptoristvocation.org

REDEMPTORISTS (EASTERN RITE)
See Eastern Catholic Religious Communities for Men

RESURRECTIONISTS (CR)
(Congregation of the Resurrection)
(United States of America Province) 7050 N. Oakley Ave., Chicago, IL 60645-3426
62 Fathers, 6 Brothers
Conduct: 16 parishes, 1 high school, 1 retreat center, 3 chaplaincies, 1 mission, diocesan office in Hamilton, Bermuda.
Represented in the Archdioceses of Chicago, Louisville and St. Louis and in the Dioceses of Birmingham, Kalamazoo, Mobile, Pensacola-Tallahassee, Rockford and San Bernadino.
Vocation Director: Rev. Steven Bartczyszyn, C.R., 7050 N. Oakley Ave., Chicago, IL 60645-3426. (773) 465-8406. Fax: (773) 465-8314. E-mail: srbart@juno.com

RESURRECTIONISTS (C.R.)
(Congregation of the Resurrection)
(Ontario-Kentucky Province) Provincialate: Resurrection College, 265 Westmount Rd. North, Waterloo, Ontario N2L 3G7, Canada. (519) 885-3030. Fax: (519) 885-4951
64 Priests, 8 Brothers, 2 Permanent Deacons
Apostolic Work: Education of youth (high school and university as teachers and campus ministers), parish work and specialized apostolates.
Represented in the Archdioceses of Toronto (Ontario) and Louisville (KY) and in the Dioceses of Hamilton (Ontario) and Hamilton (Bermuda).
Vocation Director: Fr. Tim Uniac, C.R., c/o Resurrection College, 265 Westmount Rd. North, Waterloo, Ontario N2L 3G7, Canada. (519) 885-3030. Fax: (519) 885-4951

ROGATIONIST FATHERS AND BROTHERS (R.C.J.) (Rogationists of the Sacred Heart of Jesus)
US Delegation: 2688 S. Newmark Ave., Sanger, CA 93657. (559) 875-5808. Fax: (559) 875-1281
Conduct in the US: 2 parishes, 1 center for underprivileged people, 2 formation houses for candidates to the priesthood and brotherhood, 1 vocation center, 1 development office, 1 mission office, 1 publishing office, 1 magazine "Vocations and Prayer", 3 community houses. Also in Italy, Brazil, Albania, Argentina, Africa, Spain, Poland, Philippines and India.
Apostolic Work: Dedicated to heed and spread the command of Jesus: "Pray the Lord of the harvest to send laborers into His harvest." (Mt. 9:38). Both priests and brothers commit their lives to the education of youth, the social assistance of the underprivileged, especially children, orphans and the poor, vocation publications, parishes, missionary activities.
Represented in the Archdiocese of Los Angeles and in the Diocese of Fresno.
Vocation Director: Fr. Antonio

Carlucci, RCJ, 11049 Santa Rosa Rd., Camarillo, CA 93012. (805) 491-8995. Fax: (805) 491-8935. E-mail: RogVoc@aol.com; Web: www.rcj.org

ROSMINIAN PRIESTS AND BROTHERS

See Institute of Charity

BROTHERS OF THE SACRED HEART (SC)

(New England Province) Provincial House, 685 Steere Farm Rd., Pascoag, RI 02859-4601. (401) 568-3361. Fax: (401) 568-9810

85 Brothers

Apostolic Work: Christian education and related fields including teaching, counseling, social work, special education, CCD programs, religious education coordinators. Also direct and staff schools in three African countries.

Admission: Post high school, college and post college levels. Minimum four years college, 18-month novitiate. Stress on closely knit community participation and life-long spiritual and academic development.

Represented in the Dioceses of Manchester, Providence and Hartford and in England. Also in the southern African countries of Lesotho, Zambia and Zimbabwe.

Vocation Director: Br. Roland Ouellette, SC, St. John's Residence, 159 Earle St., Woonsocket, RI 02895. 800-633-2252, ext 375, (973) 966-5252. E-mail: brorol@aol.com; Web: www.Brothersofthesacred heart.org

BROTHERS OF THE SACRED HEART (S.C.)

(New Orleans Province) Provincial Office, 4540 Elysian Fields Ave., New Orleans, LA 70122. (504) 282-5693. Fax: (504) 288-9920

75 Brothers

Conduct: 3 community-owned high schools, 3 diocesan high schools, 11 community houses, 1 house of study, 1 novitiate.

Represented in the Archdioceses of Mobile and New Orleans and in the Dioceses of Baton Rouge, Biloxi, Gallup and Houma-Thibodaux. Mission in Uganda, Africa.

Vocation Director: Brother Ray Kuhn, S.C., 4540 Elysian Fields Ave., New Orleans, LA 70122. (1-800) 633-2252, ext 390, (504) 288-7456, Fax: (504) 288-9920. E-mail: broray01@aol.com; Web: www.brothers ofthesacredheart.org

BROTHERS OF THE SACRED HEART (S.C.)

(New York Province) Provincialate: 141-11 123rd Ave., S. Ozone Park, NY 11436. (718) 322-3309

45 Brothers

Conduct: 2 high schools, 2 elementary schools, 1 house of formation, retreat center, volunteer program.

Apostolic Work: Teaching, counseling, and administering in secondary and elementary schools, religious education, youth ministry.

Represented in the Dioceses of Brooklyn, Metuchen and Rockville Centre. Also in Kenya, East Africa.

Vocation Director: Brother Robert Ziobro, S.C., 1244 65th St., Brooklyn, NY 11219-5999. (718) 621-3164, (800) 633-2252, ext. 370. Fax: (718) 621-3165. E-mail: rcz@monmouth .com; Web: www.brothersofthe sacredheart.org

PRIESTS OF THE SACRED HEART (SCJ)

(United States Province)

PO Box 206/RM, Hales Corners, WI 53130-0206. (414) 529-4255. Fax: (414) 529-3377. E-mail: vocation central@wi.rr.com; Web: www.scj vocation.org

140 Priests and Brothers in the US; 2,500 in 35 countries worldwide

Apostolic Work: The SCJs are an apostolic congregation of brothers and priests who are inspired by the mystery of God's love, expressed in the heart of Christ. Fr. Leo John Dehon, the founder, was convinced that the best way to respond to our experience of God's love is by reaching out to those around us and helping them to experience that same love in their own lives. This often means addressing the unjust situations and circumstances that prevent people from reaching their full potential. Much of the work of the Priests of the Sacred Heart in the US and around the world is with the poor and working class. Foreign missions are available.

Represented in the Archdioceses of Chicago, Milwaukee and San Antonio and in the Dioceses of Green Bay, WI; Rapid City and Sioux Falls, SD; Jackson, MS; Galveston-Houston and Brownsville, TX; and St. Petersburg, FL. Foreign missions include South Africa, Congo, the Philippines, Indonesia and India.

Vocation Inquiries: Vocation Director

SACRED HEARTS COMMUNITY (SS.CC.) (Congregation of the Sacred Hearts of Jesus and Mary)

Eastern Province: Sacred Hearts Provincial House, 77 Adams St., P.O. Box 111, Fairhaven, MA 02719-0111. (508) 993-2442

63 Fathers, 5 Brothers

Conduct: 1 provincial house, 1 novitiate, 1 theologate, 1 house of formation, 1 center of the Enthronement of the Sacred Heart in the home, 1 retreat house, 8 parishes, 1 military chaplain, 3 hospital chaplains, 2 homes for the aged, 17 foreign mission parishes; also seminary and formation, vocation work, advanced studies, Cursillo, youth work, renewal, Catholic Charismatic prayer groups, parish retreats.

Apostolic Work: The Sacred Hearts Community is made up of priests, sisters, and brothers. Through a variety of ministries they attempt to proclaim the love of God in Jesus. By a communal life of prayer and service they strive to make real the Gospel imperative to love one another.

Represented in the Archdioceses of Boston and Washington, DC and in the Dioceses of Brownsville and Fall River. Also foreign missions in Japan, Bahamas, India and the Philippines.

Vocation Director: Fr. David Reid, SS.CC., Sacred Hearts Provincial House, 77 Adams St., P.O. Box 111, Fairhaven, MA 02719-0111. (508) 993-5010. E-mail: rforgit@sscc.org; Web: www.sscc.org

SACRED HEARTS COMMUNITY (SS.CC.) (Congregation of the Sacred Hearts of Jesus and Mary and of Perpetual Adoration of the Most Blessed Sacrament of the Altar)

(Hawaiian Province) Sacred Hearts Center, P.O. Box 797, Kaneohe, Oahu, HI 96744. (808) 247-5035. Fax: (808) 235-8849

36 Priests, 7 Brothers, 2 Novices, 3 Seminarians

Conduct: 11 churches, 4 chaplaincies, mission–Cook Islands

Vocation Contacts: Fr. Marisi Palepale, 6013 Inwood St., Cheverly, Landover, MD 20785. (301) 386-4840. Very Rev. Clyde Guerreiro, Provincial, Sacred Hearts Center, P.O. Box 797, Kaneohe, Oahu, HI 96744

SACRED HEARTS COMMUNITY (SS.CC.) (Congregation of the Sacred Hearts of Jesus and Mary)

(Western Province) Provinicial Office: 2150 Damien Ave., La Verne, CA 91750

21 Priests, 1 Brother

Conduct: 4 parishes, 2 high schools, 3 community houses, 1 novitiate for the five English speaking provinces, 1 house of studies for theology, retreats, centering prayer, marriage encounter, Choice, Kairos and Healing Light; young adult ministry, 3 chaplaincies.

Represented in the Archdiocese of Los Angeles and in the Dioceses of San Bernardino and Oakland.

Vocation Inquiries: Very Rev. Michael W. Barry, Provincial, 2150 Damien Ave., La Verne, CA 91750. (909) 593-5441. E-mail: ssccwest@cpl.net; Web: www.cpl.net/~ssccwest

MISSIONARIES OF ST. CHARLES BORROMEO (C.S.)
(Scalabrini Fathers and Brothers)

(Province of St. John the Baptist) 546 N. East Ave., Oak Park, IL 60302. (708) 386-4430

77 Fathers, 4 Brothers

Conduct: 15 parishes (US), 13 parishes, 1 mission (Canada), 2 homes for the aged, 3 centers, 5 houses of formation (US, Mexico)

Primary Work: Missionaries to immigrants and refugees in 29 countries.

Represented in the Archdioceses of Chicago, Cincinnati, Los Angeles and Vancouver and in the Dioceses of Kansas City, San Jose and Thunder Bay; in Mexico in Ciudad Juarez, Guadalajara, Zapopan, Purepero and Tijuana; in Guatemala in Guatemala City and Tecun-Uman.

Vocation Information: Rev. Gerardo Garcia, C.S., 5121 S. University Ave., Chicago, IL 60615. (773) 684-5230. Fax: (773) 684-5240. E-mail: gerardogarciap@hotmail.com

MISSIONARIES OF ST. CHARLES/ SCALABRINIANS (C.S.) (The Province of St. Charles Borromeo)

Provincial Residence, 27 Carmine St., New York, NY 10014-4423. (212) 675-3993. Fax: (212) 727-2866

Conduct: 3 college houses, 1 novitiate, 40 parishes, 3 homes for the aged, 3 centers for migration studies with publications, 3 vocation offices, 5 pastoral centers, 2 ethnic newspapers, 1 radio station, 4 radio programs, 1 magazine: "Scalabrinians".

Represented in the US in the (Arch) dioceses of New York, Brooklyn, Hartford, Providence, Boston, Newark, Syracuse, Buffalo, Washington, DC, Miami, Venice (FL) and Palm Beach; in Canada in the (Arch)dioceses of Montreal, Toronto, Hamilton; and with parishes and missions in Colombia, Venezuela, Dominican Republic and Haiti.

Vocation Contacts: Fr. Ives Touzin, C.S., Vocation Director, 25 Thomas St., Newark, NJ 07114. (973) 622-7712. E-mail: stcolumbarect@aol.com; Web: www.scalabrini.org. In Haiti: Fr. Mariano Cisco, c.s. In Bogota, Colombia: Fr. Jose Gabriel Forero, c.s., Fr. Carlos Villasano, c.s.

ST. COLUMBAN'S FOREIGN MISSION SOCIETY

See Columban Fathers

SOCIETY OF SAINT EDMUND

See Edmundites

ST. FRANCIS XAVIER FOREIGN MISSION SOCIETY

See Xaverian Missionary Fathers

ST. JOHN OF GOD BROTHERS

See "H" - Hospitaller Brothers

CONGREGATION OF ST. JOSEPH (C.S.J.)

US & Mexico Vice-Province: 4076 Case Rd., Avon, OH 44011. (440) 934-6270

26 Priests, 1 Scholastic, 650 Priests and Brothers worldwide

Conduct: Schools, youth & retreat centers, parishes, foreign mission.

Apostolic Work: Major interest is youth ministry in all its forms according to times, places and needs.

Represented in the (Arch)dioceses of Cleveland and Los Angeles. Also in Italy, Spain, Sierra Leone, Brazil, Colombia, Albania, Argentina, Chile, Equador, Ghana, Guinea Bissau, Mexico, Rumania and India.

Vocation Director: Fr. Giampietro Gasparin, C.S.J., 4076 Case Rd., Avon, OH 44011. (216) 934-6270. E-mail: avon@murialdo.org; Web: www.stleonard-yrc.org

ST. JOSEPH'S MISSION SOCIETY

See Mill Hill Missionaries

BROTHERS OF SAINT PATRICK (F.S.P.)

(California Province) Provincialate: St. Patrick's Novitiate, 7820 Bolsa Ave., Midway City, CA 92655

10 Brothers in US; 300 worldwide

Apostolic Work: Teaching, counseling, administration, CCD, youth work.

Represented in Ireland, Australia, India, Kenya and New Guinea, Thursday Island, the Archdiocese of Los Angeles and the Diocese of Orange.

Vocation Director: Brother Edwin Guidera, FSP, St. Patrick's Novitiate, 7820 Bolsa Ave., P.O. Box 116, Midway City, CA 92655. (714) 897-8181. Fax: (714) 898-9020. E-mail: brosstpatrick@aol.com; Web: www.iol.ie/~patbros/Global/global.html

ST. PATRICK FATHERS (SPS) (St. Patrick's Missionary Society)

American Headquarters: St. Patrick Fathers, 19536 Eric Dr., Saratoga, CA 95070-3354

360 Priests

Primary Apostolic Work: Foreign missions.

Represented in the Archdioceses of Newark and Chicago and in the Diocese of San Jose. Foreign Mission Areas: Nigeria, Kenya, Malawi, Zambia, Sudan, Zimbabwe, South Africa, Cameroon, Brazil, Grenada (West Indies).

Vocation Director: Fr. Steve Donohue, US Superior, 19536 Eric Dr., Saratoga, CA 95070-3354. (408) 253-3135. E-mail: spsca@spms.org; Web: stpatrickfathers.org

SOCIETY OF ST. PAUL (S.S.P.) (Pauline Priests and Brothers Communications Ministry)

Provincial Office: P.O. Box 139, Ellsworth, OH 44416-0139. (330) 533-7427 (phone, fax). E-mail: ssp_usprovince@msn.com

23 Brothers, 13 Priests in US; 1,100 Members worldwide

Conduct: 1 novitiate, 3 houses of formation, 7 book and communication centers, 3 houses of apostolate, book publishing, audio visuals, print projects, television, radio and video.

Apostolate Work: Paulines utilize the media of communications – press, tapes, cassettes, videos, CCD material and other telecommunications to spread the Gospel of Jesus. In the US, the major apostolic works are Alba House Publishing, Alba House Audio & Video, Pastoral Life Magazine and Alba House Book Centers.

Represented in the Archdioceses of New York and Detroit and in the Diocese of Youngstown. There are over 1,100 priests and brothers located in 28 countries involved in communications ministry.

Vocation Directors: Fr. Jeffrey Mickler, S.S.P., Br. Richard Brunner, S.S.P., SSP Vocation Office, Pauline Fathers and Brothers, PO Box 189, 9531 Akron-Canfield Rd., Canfield, OH 44406-0189. (330) 702-0359. Fax: (330) 702-0396. E-mail: spvocationoffice@aol.com; Web: www.albahouse.org

CLERICS OF ST. VIATOR (C.S.V.)

See Clerics of St. Viator

SALESIAN MONASTIC COMMUNITY (SMC)

Salesian Monastery, HC #1, Box 455, Frantz Rd., Brodheadsville, PA 18322-9630. (570) 992-3448 (abbot), (570) 992-0230

(monastery). E-mail: monk@epix .net; Web: www.gentlestrength.org
2 Solemnly Professed Monks, 1 Solemnly Professed Nun
Apostolic Work: Monastic life, Liturgy of the Hours, use of any gift/ talent compatible with monastic life, i.e., retreats, pastoral care, nursing and manual labor.
Represented in the Diocese of Scranton.
Abbot: Brother Bernard Seif, SMC

SALESIANS OF DON BOSCO (SDB)
(Eastern Province) Province of St. Philip the Apostle, 148 Main St., New Rochelle, NY 10802. (914) 636-4225
151 Priests, 51 Brothers
Conduct: 5 academic high schools, 1 junior high school, 2 Boys' and Girls' Club of America, 6 youth centers, 14 parishes, 3 home missions, 1 mission office, 2 retreat centers, 12 summer camps.
Apostolic Work: Salesians focus on youth ministry, becoming friends of Christ and friends of the young, in the family spirit of St. John Bosco. Their ministry expresses itself in schools, youth centers, parishes, retreat centers, summer camps, missions and wherever the young are found.
Represented in the Archdioceses of Boston, Chicago, Miami, Newark, New Orleans, New York and Washington (DC) in the Dioceses of Birmingham, Columbus, Palm Beach, Paterson and St. Petersburg and in the Eparchy of Passaic. Also active in 120 countries around the world, including mission areas throughout Latin America, Asia, and Africa.
Vocation Director: Fr. Steve Ryan, SDB, Salesian Vocation Ministry, 315 Self Place, South Orange, NJ 07079. (973) 761-0201. Fax: (973) 763-9330. E-mail: Salvoc@aol.com; Web: www.salesians.org

SALESIANS OF DON BOSCO (S.D.B.)
(Western Province) 1100 Franklin St., San Francisco, CA 94109. (415) 441-7144
86 Priests, 29 Brothers
Conduct: 7 parishes, 5 high schools, 1 seminary residence, 1 junior college, 2 retreat centers, 4 youth centers, 4 camps, 1 International House of Studies.
Apostolic Work: Youth ministry (youth centers, retreats, schools, parishes).
Represented in the Archdioceses of Los Angeles and San Francisco and in the Dioceses of Loredo, Monterey, Oakland and San Diego.
Vocation Directors: Fr. Chris Woeiz, SDB, Fr. Mel Trinidad, SDB, Office of Vocation Ministry, PO Box 1639, Rosemead, CA 91770. (626) 280-2574. Fax: (626) 280-1742. E-mail: Vocation@aol.com; Web: www.donboscowest.org, www.salesians.org

SALVATORIAN FATHERS AND BROTHERS
See Divine Savior, Society of the

SCALABRINIANS
See St. Charles Borromeo, Missionaries of

SERVANTS OF CHARITY (S.C.)
(Guanellian Priests and Brothers)
(US Vice Province) 1795 S. Sproul Rd., Springfield, PA 19064-1137. (610) 328-3406
10 Priests, 3 Brothers, 4 in Formation
Conduct: Residential facilities for people with mental retardation, homes for the aged, services for youth in need, and parishes/pastoral activity around the world.
Apostolic Work: Care for people with mental retardation; pastoral ministry in parishes and various pastoral situations; care for the elderly; Pious Union of St. Joseph, a prayer association and ministry for the dying.
Represented in the Archdiocese of Philadelphia and in the Dioceses of Lansing and Providence. Also in Italy, Switzerland, Spain, Chile, Brazil, Paraguay, Argentina, Colombia, Mexico, India, Israel, Nigeria, Mozambique, Guatemala, Ghana and the Congo.
Vocation Directors: Father Matthew Weber, SC, St. Louis Center, 16195 Old US 12, Chelsea, MI 48118-9646. (734) 475-8430. E-mail: frmatt@stlouiscenter.org; Father Silvio DeNard, SC, 1795 S. Sproul Rd., Springfield, PA 19064-1137. (610) 328-3406. E-mail: servantsofcharity@msn.com; Web: servantsofcharity.org/about.html

SERVANTS OF MARY
See Servite Fathers

SERVANTS OF THE PARACLETE (s.P.)
Servants of the Paraclete, PO Box 10, Jemez Springs, NM 87025-0010. (505) 829-3586, Fax: (505) 829-3706
27 Priests and Brothers, 1 Cleric
Apostolic Work: Ministry to priests and religious brothers: retreats, spiritual direction, residential treatment centers.
Represented in the Archdioceses of St. Louis and Santa Fe. Also in the United Kingdom.
Vocation Director: St. Michael's Center, 13270 Maple Dr., St. Louis, MO 63127. (314) 965-0860. Fax: (314) 965-7202. E-mail: philiptsp@aol.com; Web: www.theservants.org

SERVANTS OF THE SICK (O.S. Cam.)
See Camillians

SERVITE FRIARS (O.S.M.)
(Order of Friar Servants of Mary)
(United States of America Province) Provincial Center: 3121 W. Jackson Blvd., Chicago, IL 60612-2729
85 Priests, 13 Brothers
Conduct: 12 communities, 8 parishes, 2 high schools, 3 shrines.
Apostolic Work: Campus ministry (high school and university), hospital chaplains, prayer ministries, counseling and therapy programs, teaching, retreats and parish missions, parish ministry, Marian Center, National Shrine of Our Lady of Sorrows, National Shrine of Our Sorrowful Mother (the Grotto), National Shrine of St. Peregrine.
Represented in the Archdioceses of Chicago, Denver, Los Angeles, St. Louis and Portland and in the Dioceses of Oakland and Orange. Missions in South Africa and an Australian delegation.
Vocation Contact: Vocation Director, 3121 W. Jackson Blvd., Chicago, IL 60612-2729. (773) 533-0360; 1922 W. La Palma Ave., Anaheim, CA 92801-3595. E-mail: OSMVocations@aol.com; Web: www.servite.org

SMA FATHERS
See African Missions, Society of

SOCIETY OF AFRICAN MISSIONS
See African Missions, Society of

SOCIETY OF THE CATHOLIC APOSTOLATE
See Pallottines

SOCIETY OF CHRIST (S.Ch.)
(North American Province) 3000 18 Mile Rd., Sterling Heights, MI 48314-3808
55 Priests
Apostolic Work: Pastoral ministry to Polish Catholics worldwide.
Conduct: 13 parishes, 7 pastoral missions, 7 apostolates, ethnic radio programs, retreats.
Represented in the Archdioceses of Atlanta, Baltimore, Chicago, Detroit, Los Angeles, Miami, Portland, St. Louis, St. Paul-Minneapolis, San Francisco, Seattle and Washington (DC) and in the Dioceses of Dallas, Houston, Paterson, Phoenix, San

Diego, San Jose and Toledo. Also in Canada: Antigonish, Calgary, Halifax, Hamilton, London, Pembroke, Regina and Toronto.
Vocation Director: 3000 18 Mile Rd., Sterling Hts., MI 48314-3808. (586) 939-5022. E-mail: SChprov@aol.com

SOCIETY OF THE DIVINE WORD (S.V.P.)
See "D" - Divine Word Missionaries

SOCIETY OF JESUS
See Jesuits

SOCIETY OF MARY, MARIANISTS
See "M" - Marianists, Society of Mary

SOCIETY OF THE MISSIONARIES OF THE HOLY APOSTLES
See Missionaries of the Holy Apostles, Society of

SOCIETY OF OUR LADY OF THE MOST HOLY TRINITY (S.O.L.T.)
Casa San Jose, 109 W. Avenue F, Box 152, Robstown, TX 78380. (361) 387-2754.
120 Priests, 12 Deacons, 10 Novices, 90 Seminarians
Apostolic Work: Serving the neediest of the needy - taking them to the Trinity through Mary.
Represented in the US and in Mexico, Guatemala, Belize, Haiti, Papua New Guinea, England, Italy, Philippines, Russia, Macao and Thailand.
Vocation Director: Fr. Kevin Gillen, SOLT, Casa San Jose, 109 W. Avenue F, Box 152, Robstown, TX 78380. (361) 767-9567. E-mail: vocations@hotmail.com; Web: www.solt3.org

SOCIETY OF OUR MOTHER OF PEACE (SMP)
Mary the Font Solitude, 6150 Antire Rd., High Ridge, MO 63049-2135
1 Priest, 3 Brothers, 1 Novice (in US)
Apostolic Work: Contemplative-apostolic balance of life in the context of simplicity and poverty; emphasis on solitary prayer; apostolates of retreat work and spiritual direction; direct evangelization especially within the African-American community and among the poor.
Represented in the Archdiocese of St. Louis and in the Diocese of Springfield-Cape Girardeau. Also in the Philippines.
Vocation Director: Brother Andrew Peréz, SMP, Mary the Font Solitude, 6150 Antire Rd., High Ridge, MO 63049-2135. (636) 677-3235. Fax: (636) 677-0644

SOCIETY OF THE PRECIOUS BLOOD
See Precious Blood, Society of

SOCIETY OF ST. EDMUND
See Edmundites

SOCIETY OF ST. JOSEPH OF THE SACRED HEART
See Josephite Fathers and Brothers

SOCIETY OF ST. PAUL
See St. Paul, Society of

SOCIETY OF ST. SULPICE
See Sulpician Fathers, The

SOMASCAN FATHERS AND BROTHERS (C.R.S.)
Box 162, Allenstown, NH 03275. (603) 485-7141; 49 Winthrop St., Hartford, CT 06103. (860) 527-6459; Christ the King, 4419 N. Main St., Houston, TX 77009-5199. (713) 869-1449. Fax: (713) 869-1491
Apostolic Work: The Somascans carry on the legacy of their founder, St. Jerome Emiliani, the "Universal Patron of Orphans and Abandoned Youth", in the spiritual and material care of orphans, abandoned youth and the poor; in the education of youth and in pastoral ministry. In the US, the Somascans operate a treatment center for at-risk youth in New Hampshire and two bilingual (English/Spanish) parishes in Texas.
Vocation Director: Fr. Italo Dell'Oro, CRS, 4419 N. Main St., Houston, TX 77009-5199. (713) 869-1449, ext. 113. Fax: (713) 869-1491. E-mail: somascans@yahoo.com; Web: www.somascos.org

SONS OF MARY MISSIONARY SOCIETY (F.M.S.I.) (Sons of Mary, Health of the Sick)
567 Salem End Rd., Framingham, MA 01702-5599
Professed 13
Apostolic Work: Medical, social and catechetical in US and the Philippines.
Represented in the Archdioceses of Boston and Manila, Philippines.
Vocation Director: Br. John Murphy, FMSI, 567 Salem End Rd., Framingham, MA 01702. (508) 879-2541. E-mail: sonsofmary@prodigy.net; Web: www.sonsofmary.com

THE SPIRITANS - CONGREGATION OF THE HOLY SPIRIT (C.S.Sp.) (Holy Ghost Fathers and Brothers)
Priests, Brothers, Lay Associates
(Province of the United States East) 6230 Brush Run Rd., Bethel Park, PA 15102. (412) 831-0302
(Province of the United States West) 1700 W. Alabama St., Houston, TX 77098. (713) 522-2882
200 Priests and Brothers
Conduct: 1 university, 3 university chaplaincies, 2 novitiates, hospital chaplaincies, 2 renewal centers, 1 home for homeless boys, 1 high school, 37 parishes, foreign missions in the Archdiocese of Arecibo, Caguas and Ponce, Puerto Rico. Missions also in the Diocese of Cuidad Valles, Mexico, as well as Arusha and Moshi, Tanzania. Direct Pontifical Association of the Holy Childhood in the US and Puerto Rico. Algeria; Amazon Brazil and South Africa.
Apostolic Work: Foreign missions, education and parishes.
Represented in the Archdioceses of Chicago, Cincinnati, Detroit, New Orleans, New York, Philadelphia, San Antonio and Washington, DC and in the Dioceses of Alexandria, Arlington, Charleston, Charlotte, Erie, Little Rock, Houston, Pittsburgh, Providence and San Bernardino.
Vocation Directors: Spiritan Vocation Office, Duquesne University, Laval House Pittsburgh, PA 15282. (412) 765-0733. E-mail: skipcssp@juno.com; Spiritan Vocation Office, 1700 W. Alabama, Houston, TX 77098-2808. (713) 522-2882. E-mail: suazocssp@aol.com; Web: www.spiritans.org

STIGMATINE FATHERS AND BROTHERS (C.S.S.)
See "C" - Congregation of Sacred Stigmata

THE SULPICIAN FATHERS (S.S.) (Society of St. Sulpice)
US Province: 5408 Roland Ave., Baltimore, MD 21210
75 Priests
Apostolic Work: Educating diocesan seminarians and priests, developing vocations for a multi-cultural church and collaborating with seminary programs in mission countries.
Represented in the Archdioceses of Baltimore, San Antonio, San Francisco, Washington and Los Angeles and Lusaka, Zambia. Canadian Province: Canada, Brazil, Colombia and Japan. French Province: France, Vietnam, Benin, Cameroon.
Director of Vocations: Rev. Thomas R. Ulshafer, S.S., 5408 Roland Ave., Baltimore, MD 21210. (410) 323-5070. E-mail: tulshafer@sulpicians.org; Web: sulpicians.org

COMMUNITY OF TERESIAN CARMELITES (C.T.C)
See "C" section - Community of Teresian Carmelites

THE MONKS OF ADORATION
1227 Horizon Rd., Venice, FL 34293. (941) 492-6122

3 Monks
A completely contemplative monastic community dedicated to prayer. Rule of St. Augustine. Works include writing books and articles, publishing "The Tabernacle" (a small magazine); and maintaining an extensive Web site and Internet ministry, as well as cooking, gardening and maintaining bookstore. Faithful to the Holy Father, gray habit, Liturgy of the Hours and Rosary.
Vocation Contact: Brother Craig, The Monks of Adoration, 1227 Horizon Rd., Venice, FL 34293. (941) 492-6122. E-mail: monkadorer@comcast.net; Web: www.monksofadoration.org

THEATINE FATHERS (C.R.)
Provincial House: St. Andrew Seminary, 1050 S. Birch St., Denver, CO 80222. (303) 756-5522
19 Priests, 5 Clerics
Conduct: 9 parishes in four dioceses, primarily in Colorado.
Apostolic Work: Parish work, retreats, working with Spanish speaking, other special Hispanic ministries.
Represented in the Archdioceses of Pueblo, New York and Cuidad Juarez, Chiuhava (Mexico).
Vocation Director: Rev. Franco I. Plascencia, CR, Our Lady of Guadalupe Parish, 1209 W. 36th Ave., Denver, CO 80211. (303) 477-1402

TRAPPISTS (O.C.S.O.)
(Cistercians of the Strict Observance)
Abbey of New Clairvaux, Box 80, Vina, CA 96092-0080. (530) 839-2161. E-mail: pmschwan@juno.com; Web: www.maxinet.com/trappist
23 in Community, 6 Priests
Contact: Fr. Paul Mark Schwan

TRAPPISTS (O.C.S.O.)
(Cistercians of the Strict Observance)
St. Benedict's Monastery, 1012 Monastery Rd., Snowmass, CO 81654. (970) 927-3311. E-mail: mikamonk@rof.net; Web: www.snowmass.org
12 Monks, 1 Junior, 1 Novice
Vocation Director: Br. Micah

TRAPPISTS (O.C.S.O.)
(Cistercians of the Strict Observance)
Monastery of the Holy Spirit, 2625 Hwy. 212 S.W., Conyers, GA 30094-4044
54 Monks, 26 Priests, 6 Novices, 1 Observer, 5 Juniors
Represented in the Archdiocese of Atlanta.
Vocation Director: Bro. Elias, O.C.S.O., Monastery of the Holy Spirit, 2625 Hwy. 212 S.W. Conyers, GA 30094-4044. (770) 760-0959. E-mail: elias@trappist.net; Web: trappist.net

TRAPPISTS (O.C.S.O.)
(Cistercians of the Strict Observance)
New Melleray Abbey, Peosta, IA 52068. (563) 588-2319
Contemplative community of monks, brothers and priests.
Vocation Director: Fr. Stephen Verbest, New Melleray Abbey, 6632 Melleray Circle, Peosta, IA 52068. (563) 588-2319. E-mail: frsteve@newmelleray.org; Web: www.newmelleray.org

TRAPPISTS (O.C.S.O.)
(Cistercians of the Strict Observance)
Our Lady of Gethsemani Abbey, 3642 Monks Rd., Trappist, KY 40051-6152
17 Priests, 47 Brothers
Vocation Director: Fr. Carlos Rodriguez, Our Lady of Gethsemani Abbey, 3642 Monks Rd., Trappist, KY 40051-6152. (502) 549-4116. E-mail: gethvoc@juno.com; Web: www.monks.org

TRAPPISTS (O.C.S.O.)
(Cistercians of the Strict Observance)
Saint Joseph's Abbey, 167 North Spencer Rd., Spencer, MA 01562-1233
70 Monks (Brothers and Priests)
Contemplative community.
Vocation Director: Fr. James Palmigiano, O.C.S.O., Saint Joseph's Abbey. (508) 885-8700, ext. 518. E-mail: palmi@spencerabbey.org; Web: spencerabbey.org

TRAPPISTS (O.C.S.O.)
(Cistercians of the Strict Observance)
Assumption Abbey, Rt. 5, Box 1056, Ava, MO 65608. (417) 683-5110
6 Priests, 12 Monks
A Trappist-Cistercian community in the Ozark foothills of S.W. Missouri dedicated to the contemplative monastic life and supported by own manual labor.
Vocation Director: Fr. Cyprian Harrison, O.C.S.O., Assumption Abbey, Rt. 5, Box 1056, Ava, MO 65608. (417) 683-5110. E-mail: avavocations@usa.net; Web: www.assumptionabbey.org

TRAPPISTS (O.C.S.O.)
(Cistercians of the Strict Observance)
Abbey of the Genesee, Piffard, NY 14533
10 Priests
Contemplative order, solemn vows. Represented in the Diocese of Rochester.
Vocation Director: Br. Anthony Weber, O.C.S.O., (585) 243-0660. E-mail: Vocations@GeneseeAbbey.org; Web: www.geneseeabbey.org

TRAPPISTS (O.C.S.O.)
(Cistercians of the Strict Observance)
Our Lady of Guadalupe Abbey, 9200 NE Abbey Rd., Lafayette, OR 97127. (503) 852-7174; 0107. E-mail: timc@trappistabbey.org; Web: www.trappistabbey.org
12 Priests, 19 Brothers
Vocation Director: Br. Mark Filut, O.C.S.O.

TRAPPISTS (O.C.S.O.)
(Cistercians of the Strict Observance)
Mepkin Abbey,1098 Abbey Road, Moncks Corner, SC 29461
24 Monks (14 Brothers, 10 Priests)
Apostolic Work: Contemplative monastic community called to seek the face of God together in a life of liturgical prayer, simple manual labor and meditation.
Vocation Director: Fr. Aelred Hagan, o.c.s.o., Mepkin Abbey,1098 Abbey Road, Moncks Corner, SC 29461. (843) 761-8509. Fax: (843) 761-6719. E-mail: vocations@mepkinabbey.org; Web: www.mepkinabbey.org

TRAPPISTS (O.C.S.O.)
(Cistercians of the Strict Observance)
Holy Trinity Abbey, 1250 South 9500 East, Huntsville, UT 84317. (801) 745-3784. E-mail: hta@xmission.com; Web: www.xmission.com/~hta
22 Monks, Priests and Brothers
Contemplative monastic community
Vocation Director: Fr. Charles Cummings, ocso

TRAPPISTS (O.C.S.O.)
(Cistercians of the Strict Observance)
Abbey of Our Lady of the Holy Cross, 901 Cool Spring Lane, Berryville, VA 22611-2700
22 Solemnly Professed, 13 Priests, 1 Temporary Vows, 1 Novice
Contemplative monastic community.
Vocation Director: Fr. James Orthmann, Abbey of Our Lady of the Holy Cross, 901 Cool Spring Lane, Berryville, VA 22611-2700. (540) 955-1425. Fax: (540) 955-1356. Web: www.holycrossabbeybrryvlle.org/abbey/interest.htm

THE TRINITARIANS (O.SS.T.)
(Order of the Most Holy Trinity)
(Province of the Immaculate Heart of Mary)
Provincial Office: PO Box 5719, 8400 Park Heights Ave., Baltimore, MD 21282. (410) 484-2250

95 Priests and Brothers
Conduct: 11 parishes, 1 high school, 18 community houses, 1 retreat house.
Apostolic Work: Parish ministry, youth ministry, hospital chaplaincy, pastoral counseling, ministry to minorities, secondary, college and graduate level education, retreats, prison ministry, campus ministry, homeless men, promoting social justice, international release of Christian captives, missions.
Represented in the Archdioceses of Baltimore, New Orleans, New York, Philadelphia and Washington, DC and in the Dioceses of Corpus Christi, Trenton and Victoria. Internationally in Spain, Italy, Austria, France, Germany, Poland, Puerto Rico, Mexico, South America, Madagascar, Canada, India and the Congo.
Director of Vocations: Fr. Kurt Klismet, O.SS.T., PO Box 5719, Baltimore, MD 21282-0719. (800) 525-3554. E-mail: vocations@trinitarians.org; Web: www.trinitarians.org

TRINITY MISSIONS (S.T.) (Missionary Servants of the Most Holy Trinity)
9001 New Hampshire Ave., Silver Spring, MD 20903
112 Priests, 36 Brothers, 2 Deacons, 60 in Formation
Conduct: 40 parishes, 70 missions and stations, 2 theologates (major seminaries in U.S. and Mexico), 2 novitiates, 4 pre-novitiate formation communities in the United States, Mexico, Costa Rica and Colombia.
Apostolic Work: Members answer the pressing needs of the Church through lay apostolic and missionary development, inner-city parish and social service ministry, Appalachian and rural missions and retreat ministry. Ministry with Hispanics, Native Americans and African Americans. Ministry to the institutionalized and incarcerated; alcohol, drug and post-detention rehabilitation ministry, hospital chaplaincy, youth/young adult ministry.
Represented in the United States, Puerto Rico, Mexico, Costa Rica and Colombia.
Vocation Ministry: 9001 New Hampshire Ave., Silver Spring, MD 20903. (1-800) 298-5602. Fax: (301) 408-0721. E-mail: mccann@trinitymissions.org; Web: www.tmc3.org

VERONA FATHERS
See Comboni Missionaries

VIATORIANS
See Clerics of St. Viator

VINCENTIANS (C.M.) (Congregation of the Mission)
(American Spanish Branch) Holy Agony Church, 1834 3rd Ave., New York, NY 10029. (212) 289-5589. Fax: (212) 289-8321
6 Fathers
Conduct: 2 churches, 1 school.
Represented in the Archdioceses of Los Angeles and New York

VINCENTIANS (CM) (Congregation of the Mission)
(Eastern Province) 500 E. Chelten Ave., Philadelphia, PA 19144
175 Fathers, 7 Brothers
Conduct: 19 parishes, 2 universities, 2 seminaries.
Apostolic Work: Catholic education, priestly formation, parishes, missions in Panama, preaching, service to the poor.
Represented in the (Arch)dioceses of Baltimore, Birmingham, Brooklyn, Charleston, Charlotte, Metuchen, Mobile, New York Philadelphia and Rockville Center.
Vocation Director: Rev. John T. Maher, C.M., Vincentian Vocation Ministry, 75 Mapleton Rd., Princeton, NJ 08540-9614. (609) 520-9626. E-mail: jtm@cmeast.org; Web: www.vincentians.net

VINCENTIANS (C.M.) (Congregation of the Mission)
(Midwest Province) 13663 Rider Trail North, Earth City, MO 63045. (314) 344-1184
120 Priests, 16 Brothers
Conduct: 21 parishes, 1 university.
Apostolic Work: Clerical and lay formation, Catholic education, preaching parish missions, parishes, chaplaincies, foreign missions and service to the poor.
Represented in the (Arch)dioceses of Chicago, Colorado Springs, Pueblo, St. Louis and Springfield-Cape Girardeau as well as dioceses in Kenya.
Vocation Director: Fr. Ronald J. Hoye, C.M., 1010 Rosati Ct., Perryville, MO 63775. (1-800) DEPAUL-1 (337-2851). E-mail: RJHoye@attglobal.net; Web: www.explorethecall.org

VINCENTIANS (C.M.) (Congregation of the Mission)
(New England Province) 234 Keeney St., Manchester, CT 06040-7048
29 Priests, 1 Brothers
Conduct: 7 parishes.
Apostolic Work: Mission preaching, parochial apostolate.
Represented in the Archdiocese of Hartford and in the Dioceses of Brooklyn, Portland, ME, and Manchester, NH.
Vocation Director: Rev. A. Rafal Kopystynski, CM, St. Stanislaus Kostka, 607 Humboldt St., Brooklyn, NY 11222. (718) 388-0170. Fax: (718) 384-5290

VINCENTIANS (C.M.) (Congregation of the Mission)
(Southern Province) 3826 Gilbert Ave., Dallas, TX 75219. (214) 526-0234
25 Priests, 1 Brother
Conduct: Preaching missions in parishes, conducting continuing clergy education, parish work, home mission team, parishes in 8 cities, hospital chaplaincies in 2 cities.
Apostolic Work: A mobile community dedicated to instructing and ministering to the poor.
Represented in the Archdioceses of New Orleans and San Antonio and in the Dioceses of Dallas, Gallup and Little Rock.
Vocation Director: Rev. Mark Ford, C.M., Vincentian Vocation Office, 3826 Gilbert Ave., Dallas, TX 75219. (214) 526-0234. (800) DEPAUL-1 (337-2851). Fax: (214) 526-3477. E-mail: congmisssp@aol.com; Web: www.cmsouth.org

VINCENTIANS (C.M.) (Congregation of the Mission)
(Spanish Vincentian Fathers-Barcelona, Spain)
3 Priests
Conduct: Centro de Evangelizacion, "San Vicente de Paul", Cursillo Movement, Jornada Movement.
Represented in the Diocese of Brooklyn
Vocation Contact: 118 Congress St., Brooklyn, NY 11201-6045. (718) 624-5670. Fax: (718) 624-5806

VINCENTIANS (C.M.) (Congregation of the Mission)
(Province of the West) 420 Date St., Montebello, CA 90640
47 Priests, 3 Brothers, 1 Deacon, 5 Students in Formation
Conduct: Evangelization of the poor, priestly formation, home missions, parish ministry, foreign mission, hospital chaplaincies, retreat and evangelization centers.
Apostolic Work: Serving the needs of the Church in the spirit of St. Vincent de Paul.
Represented in the Archdiocese of Los Angeles and in the Dioceses of Phoenix, Stockton and Gallup.
Vocation Director: Fr. Bill Piletic, C.M., 420 Date St., Montebello, CA 90640. (323) 721-5486. Fax: (323)

721-5499. E-mail: vocations@vincentiansca.org; Web: www.vincentiansca.org

VOCATIONIST FATHERS (S.D.V.) (Society of the Divine Vocations)

St. Michael's, 172 Broadway, Newark, NJ 07104. (973) 484-7100

Apostolic Work: The Vocationist Fathers are a Community of Priests and Brothers who strive to search, recruit and guide vocations to both Religious life and Diocesan Priesthood. They pursue this goal through their work in parishes, missions and special vocation houses called Vocationaries.

Represented in numerous (Arch) dioceses in Italy, Brazil, Argentina, Nigeria, Philippines and India. In the US in the (Arch)dioceses of Newark and Paterson.

Vocation Director: Fr. James Buttz, S.D.V., 90 Brooklake Rd., Florham Park, NJ 07932. (973) 966-6262. E-mail: frjames07932@yahoo.com; Web: www.vocationist.org

WHITE FATHERS OF AFRICA

See Missionaries of Africa

XAVERIAN BROTHERS (C.F.X.)

(Xaverian Brothers Generalate) 4409 Frederick Ave., Baltimore, MD 21229. (410) 644-0034. Fax: (410) 644-2762

275 Brothers

Conduct: Schools in Belgium and the United States; missions and schools in Bolivia, Democratic Republic of Congo, Haiti, Kenya and Lithuania.

Apostolic Work: Education in elementary, high school and colleges, DRE and parish ministers, CCD, catechetical centers, counselors (alcoholic, career, personal), social ministry, educational specialists in prison ministry, hospital chaplaincy, centers for the homeless.

Represented in the Archdioceses of Baltimore, Boston, Chicago, Los Angeles, Louisville, Newark, New York and Washington and in the Dioceses of Arlington, Birmingham, Brooklyn, Charleston, Fairbanks, Memphis, Metuchen, Richmond, Rockville Center, Wilmington and Worcester and in the Dioceses of Aiquile, Bolivia, Hinche, Haiti, Lubumbashi, Republic of Congo, Bungoma, Lodwar, Nyeri, Kenya and Vilna, Lithuania.

Vocation Director: Bro. James Connolly, C.F.X., Xaverian Brothers, 43 Woodlawn Circle, Whitman, MA 02382. E-mail: xavbrosv@yahoo.com; Web: www.xaverianbrothers.org

XAVERIAN MISSIONARIES (s.x.)

US Provincial Office: 12 Helene Court, Wayne, NJ 07470-2813

Conduct: In the US: 4 vocation and mission education centers, and 1 international theology community.

Apostolic Work: Pastoral and community work, education, leadership training, social work and justice & peace work in poor, non-Christian and cross-cultural situations.

Represented in the Archdioceses of Boston, Chicago, Milwaukee and New York and in the Diocese of Paterson (NJ). Also in Asia: Bangladesh, Japan, Indonesia, Philippines and Taiwan. In Europe: Great Britain, Italy and Spain. In Latin America: Brazil, Columbia and Mexico. In Africa: Burundi, Cameroon, Chad, D.R. Congo, Sierra Leone and Mozambique.

Vocation Minister: Fr. Dario, s.x., 12 Helene Court, Wayne, NJ 07470. (973) 942-2975. Fax: (973) 942-5012. E-mail: askforinfo@xaviermissionaries.org; Web: www.XavierMissionaries.org

EASTERN CATHOLIC COMMUNITIES FOR MEN

BASILIAN FATHERS, BASILIAN ORDER OF ST. JOSAPHAT (O.S.B.M.) (Order of St. Basil the Great)

(Assumption of B.V.M. Province) 29 Peacock Lane, Locust Valley, NY 11560. In Canada: 737 Bannerman Ave., Winnipeg R2X 1J9, Canada

Conduct: 3 monasteries, 7 parishes, 4 parochial schools. The order works in the USA and throughout the world mainly among Ukrainians, Carpatho-Ukrainians/Ruthenians, Rumanians, Hungarians and Croatians.

Represented in the Archdioceses of Chicago, Detroit and New York and in the Dioceses of Passaic and Stamford.

Vocation Directors: Rev. Mauricio Popadiuk, O.S.B.M., 29 Peacock Lane, Locust Valley, NY 11560. (516) 609-3262. E-mail: mpopadiuk@aol.com. In Canada: Rev. Myron Chlmy, O.S.B.M., 737 Bannerman Ave., Winnipeg R2X 1J9, Canada. (204) 582-6695

BASILIAN FATHERS OF MARIA POCH (O.S.B.M.)

329 Monastery Lane, Matawan, NJ 07747-9703. (732) 566-8445

Apostolic Work: Retreat center, area social center, pilgrimage shrine.

Vocation Directors: Rev. Joseph Erdei, O.S.B.M., Rev. Basil Rakaczy, 329 Monastery Lane, Matawan, NJ 07747-9703. (732) 566-8445, Fax: (732) 566-8762

BASILIAN SALVATORIAN FATHERS (B.S.O.)

American Headquarters: St. Basil Seminary, 30 East St., Methuen, MA 01844

15 Priests in US

Conduct: 1 seminary, 1 novitiate, 1 center for ecumenical studies and retreats, 1 r & r house, 9 parishes.

Apostolic Work: Specialize in parishes, ecumenical activities, Cursillos, Teen Encounters, retreats, teaching, special ministries.

Represented in the (Arch)dioceses of Atlanta, Boston, Cleveland, Manchester, Norwich, Miami and in Canada, Mexico and South America.

Vocation Director: Rev. Larry Tumminelli, B.S.O., St. Basil Seminary, 30 East St., Methuen, MA 01844. (978) 683-2471. Fax: (978) 795-3452

CONGREGATION OF THE BROTHERS OF THE ANNUNCIATION OF MARY

Queen of Angels Convent, 245 N. Buckeye St., Wooster, OH 44691-3573

Apostolic Work: Traditional Roman Catholic priests and brothers. Divine Office in Latin, Tridentine mass, unchanged doctrine. Work among God's poor, especially the mentally challenged and multiply addicted.

Vocation Director: Father M. Raphael Guzzo, F.B.A., Queen of Angels Convent, 245 N. Buckeye St., Wooster, OH 44691-3573. (330) 262-6205. Fax: (330) 262-0327. E-mail: brothers@nvi.net; Web: www.nvi.net/brothers

HOLY TRINITY MONASTERY-BENEDICTINE MONKS - Byzantine Rite

P.O. Box 990, Butler, PA 16003-0990. (724) 287-4461. Fax: (724) 287-6160

5 Priests, 3 Brothers

Apostolic Works: Hospitality, private retreats, parochial work, and Eastern Christian religious articles.

Represented throughout the Byzantine Metropolitan Province of Pittsburgh.

Vocation Director: Fr. Leo R. Schlosser, O.S.B., Holy Trinity Monastery, P.O. Box 990, Butler, PA 16003-0990. (724) 287-4461

HOLY TRANSFIGURATION MONASTERY - MONKS OF MT. TABOR

17001 Tomki Rd., PO Box 217, Redwood Valley, CA 95470-0217

8 Monks

Apostolic Work: Contemplative; retreats, hospitality to all visitors, church unity, iconography, book writing.

Represented in the (Arch)diocese of St. Nicholas in Chicago.

Vocation Contact: Fr. Joachim, 17001 Tomki Rd., PO Box 217, Redwood Valley, CA 95470-0217. (707) 485-8959. Fax: (707) 485-1122. E-mail: mttabor@pacific.net; Web; www.byzantines.net/monastery/

HOLY TRANSFIGURATION SKETE

Ukrainian Catholic Monastery, Star Rte. 1, Box 226, Eagle Harbor, MI 49950

4 Monks

Apostolic Work: Contemplative.

Represented in the Diocese of St. Nicholas in Chicago.

Vocation Contact: Fr. Basil, Ukrainian Catholic Monastery, Star Rte. 1, Box 226, Eagle Harbor, MI 49950. (906) 289-4384, 4386. Fax: (906) 289-4388. E-mail: skete@society stjohn.com; Web: www.society stjohn.com

MARONITE MONKS OF MOST HOLY TRINITY MONASTERY (O. Mar.) (Eucharistic Adoration/Strictly Contemplative)

Motherhouse: Most Holy Trinity Motherhouse, 67 Dugway Rd., Petersham, MA 01366. (978) 724-3347

11 Priests, 7 Brothers

Represented in the Dioceses of St. Maron USA and St. Maron (Nova Scotia, Canada).

Vocation Director: Rev. Fr. William Driscoll, O. Mar., Abbot, 67 Dugway Rd., Petersham, MA 01366-0605. Tel., Fax: (978) 724-3347

UKRAINIAN REDEMPTORISTS

St. Joseph's Monastery, 250 Jefferson Ave., Winnipeg R2V 0M6 Canada. (204) 339-5737

Apostolic Work: Parish work, missions, retreats, teaching and formation work, inner-city ministry, martyr's shrine (Blessed Vasyl). Serve in US and Canada.

Vocation Ministry Director: St. Joseph's Monastery, 250 Jefferson Ave., Winnipeg R2V 0M6 Canada. (1-877) 582-6823. (204) 338-6823 (phone, fax). E-mail: ukryvm@mts .net; Web: www.yorktonredemptorists.com/vocation.htm

Religious Communities for Women

ADORERS OF THE BLOOD OF CHRIST (A.S.C.)
430 Sisters in United States Province. An international community of 9 provinces
(Columbia Province) 3950 Columbia Ave., Columbia, PA 17512. (717) 285-4536
Apostolic Work: Teaching on all levels, ministry to the elderly, health care, pastoral ministry, social services, ministry in diverse cultures, religious education and retreat ministry.
Represented in the Archdiocese of Chicago and in the Dioceses of Altoona-Johnstown, Harrisburg, Wilmington and Youngstown. Also in Guatemala.
Vocation Director: Sister Diana Rawlings, A.S.C., Vocation Director, United States Province, 1400 S. Sheridan, Wichita, KS 67213-1394. 1-877-ADORERS (1-877-236-7377). Fax: (877) 280-7732. E-mail: rawlingsd@adorers.org or ascvocations@adorers.org; Web: www.adorers.org

ADORERS OF THE BLOOD OF CHRIST (A.S.C.)
(Ruma Province) #2 Pioneer Lane-Ruma, Red Bud, IL 62278. (618) 282-3848
Apostolic Work: Health care, education (university, secondary, elementary), parish ministry, retreat work, social services, dietetics/domestic service, geriatrics, youth ministry, religious education, special outreach to women, the poor and the alienated in society and the Church.
Represented in the Archdiocese of St. Louis and in the Dioceses of Belleville, Gallup, Phoenix, Springfield (IL), Springfield-Cape Girardeau and Tucson. Foreign missions in Bolivia and in Guatemala.
Vocation Director: Sister Diana Rawlings, A.S.C., Vocation Director, United States Province, 1400 S. Sheridan, Wichita, KS 67213-1394. 1-877-ADORERS (1-877-236-7377). Fax: (877) 280-7732. E-mail: rawlingsd@adorers.org or ascvocations@adorers.org; Web: www.adorers.org

ADORERS OF THE BLOOD OF CHRIST (A.S.C.) (Wichita Province)
14000 S. Sheridan, Wichita, KS 67213. (316) 943-1203
Apostolic Work: Education (university, secondary, elementary), religious education, health care, parish ministry, care of the aging, social services, ministries targeting women and the poor.
Represented in the (Arch)dioceses of Dodge City, Kansas City and Wichita, KS; Oklahoma City, OK; Fort Worth, El Paso, San Angelo and San Antonio, TX; Springfield, IL; Lincoln, NE; Oakland, CA; Detroit, MI; Kansas City-St. Joseph, Jefferson City and St. Louis, MO; Gallup and Las Cruces, NM and Washington, DC. Foreign missions in Masan, Seoul and Pusan, Korea.
Vocation Director: Sister Diana Rawlings, A.S.C., Vocation Director, United States Province, 1400 S. Sheridan, Wichita, KS 67213-1394. 1-877-ADORERS (1-877-236-7377). Fax: (877) 280-7732. E-mail: rawlingsd@adorers.org or ascvocations@adorers.org; Web: www.adorers.org

SISTERS ADORERS OF THE PRECIOUS BLOOD (A.P.B.)
700 Bridge St., Manchester, NH 03104. (603) 623-4264, 669-2879
29 Professed Sisters
Apostolic Work: Cloistered, contemplative.
Represented in the Diocese of Manchester.
Contact: Directress of Novices

SISTERS ADORERS OF THE PRECIOUS BLOOD (A.P.B.)
1106 State St., Lafayette, IN 47905
Apostolic Work: Cloistered, contemplative.
Represented in the Diocese of Lafayette.
Contact: Vocation Directress, 1106 State St., Lafayette, IN 47905. (765) 742-8227. E-mail: smtherese@aol.com; Web: members.aol.com/saotproc/index.htm

SISTERS ADORERS OF THE PRECIOUS BLOOD (A.P.B.)
166 State St., Portland, ME 04101-3794. (207) 774-0861
Apostolic Work: Cloistered, contemplative.
Represented in the Diocese of Portland, ME.
Contact: Sr. Mary Aloysius, APB

SISTERS ADORERS OF THE PRECIOUS BLOOD (A.P.B.)
Precious Blood Monastery, 5400 Fort Hamilton Pkwy., Brooklyn, NY 11219. (718) 438-6371. Web: www.catholic.org/macc
12 Nuns
Apostolic Work: Cloistered, contemplative.
Represented in the Diocese of Brooklyn.
Vocation Contact: Sr. Eileen Bruton, APB

SISTERS ADORERS OF THE PRECIOUS BLOOD (A.P.B.)
Precious Blood Monastery, 400 Pratt St., Watertown, NY 13601-4299. (315) 788-1669. Fax: (315) 779-9046. E-mail: smarilyn@twcny.rr.com; Web: www.sisterspreciousblood.org
Apostolic Work: Cloistered, contemplative, intercessory prayer.
Represented in the Diocese of Ogdensburg.
Contact: Director of Novices

ANGELIC SISTERS OF ST. PAUL (A.S.S.P.)
St. Anthony Convent, 770 Washington St., Easton, PA 18042. (610) 258-7792
4 Sisters in US, 350 worldwide
Apostolic Work: Teaching, mission work, parish work, C.C.D. teaching, social work, youth group coordinator.
Represented in the Diocese of Allentown (PA).
Vocation Directress: Sister Maria Silva Ramos, A.S.S.P.

ANTONINE SISTERS (MARONITE)
See Eastern Catholic Religious Communities for Women

APOSTLES OF THE SACRED HEART OF JESUS (A.S.C.J.)
Provincial House: Mount Sacred Heart Provincialate, 265 Benham St., Hamden, CT 06514. (203) 288-2309, ext. 305. E-mail: ckileyascj@yahoo.com; Web: www.ascjusvocations.org
180 Sisters in US
Apostolic Work: Teaching in high schools, elementary schools, schools for children who are mentally handicapped or learning disabled, kindergartens and day nurseries, pastoral ministry, health care, legal services to the poor.
Represented in the (Arch)dioceses of Greensburg, Hartford, New York, Newark, Pensacola/Tallahassee, Pittsburgh, Providence, St. Louis and Palm Beach. Also in Africa, Albania, Argentina, Brazil, Chile, Italy, Uruguay, Mexico and Taiwan.
Vocation Director: Sr. Christine Kiley, A.S.C.J., Sacred Heart Vocation Office, 1651 Zerega Ave., Bronx, NY 10462. (718) 904-7989

RELIGIOUS OF THE ASSUMPTION (R.A.) Provincial House: 1001 47th St., Philadelphia, PA 19143. (215) 386-5016
22 Sisters in the US; 1,500 Sisters worldwide
Apostolic Work: Teaching, catechetics, campus ministry; retreats, ecumenical work, pastoral ministry, counseling, spiritual direction in Europe, USA, Africa, Central and South America, India, Japan and Philippines.
Represented in the Archdioceses of Philadelphia, PA; Worcester, MA and in 32 foreign countries.
Vocation Contact: Mary Joan Rice, R.A., 504 Crestview Rd., Lansdale, PA 19446. (215) 368-9733. Fax: (215) 368-4427. E-mail: smjrice@juno.com

SISTERS OF THE ASSUMPTION OF THE B.V. (S.A.S.V.)
Provincial House: Worcester, MA 01605
100 Sisters
Apostolic Work: Teaching, pastoral ministry, religious education, music instruction, campus ministry, spiritual renewal, foreign missionary work, nursing, adult literacy.
Represented in the (Arch)dioceses of Albany, Boston, Hartford, Manchester, Portland (ME) and Worcester. Also in Brazil, Ecuador, Haiti and Japan.
Vocation Team Director: Sister Sandra Dupre, S.A.S.V., 26 Sylvester St., Brockton, MA 02302. (508) 583-7420. E-mail: sandysasv@yahoo.com; Web: www.sasv.org

AUGUSTINIAN CONTEMPLATIVE NUNS (O.S.A.)
Augustinian Monastery, 440 Marley Rd., New Lenox, IL 60451. (815) 463-9662
Apostolate: Augustinian Nuns seek God and follow Jesus within a communal context which is wholly oriented to a contemplative life of prayer.
Contact: Sister Mary Grace, O.S.A., Prioress

AUGUSTINIAN RECOLLECT SISTERS (O.A.R.)
Motherhouse: Mexico
US: Immaculate Conception Convent, 121 Myrtle Ave., Irvington, NJ 07111. (973) 374-6397
Apostolic Work: Contemplative, centered around prayer and devotion/dedication to the worship of Christ in the Blessed Sacrament. Make vestments, art work, pottery, baking.
Represented in the Archdiocese of Newark.
Vocation Contact: Mother Ines M. Castillo, OAR, Prioress, Immaculate Conception Convent, 121 Myrtle Ave., Irvington, NJ 07111. (973) 374-6397. E-mail: agurecsisnj@aol.com

AUGUSTINIAN SISTERS (O.S.A.)
(Servants of Jesus and Mary)
St. John School, Brandenburg, KY 40108. (502) 422-2088. E-mail: sisters@stjohnonline.org; Web: www.stjohnonline.org
350 Sisters worldwide; 4 Sisters in US
Represented in the Archdiocese of Louisville

BASILIAN NUNS AND SISTERS
See Eastern Catholic Religious Communities for Women

BENEDICTINE CONGREGATION OF OUR LADY OF MOUNTE OLIVETO (Benedictine Monastery of Hawaii)
PO Box 490, Waialua, Oahu, HI 96791. (808) 637-7887. Fax: (808) 637-8601. E-mail: benedicthi@aol.com, Web: www.catholichawaii.com/religious.benedictine
3 Sisters
Apostolic Work: Retreats, spiritual direction, parish assistance.
Represented in the Diocese of Honolulu.
Vocation Contact: Vocation Director

BENEDICTINE NUNS (O.S.B.)
Abbey of St. Walburga, Virginia Dale, CO 80536-8942
24 Nuns
Apostolic Work: Full monastic office in English, Latin Gregorian Chant for Sunday mass, life of prayer interwoven with compatible work (guest house, farm and gardens, contract computer work, altar bread distribution).
Represented in the Archdiocese of Denver.
Vocations: Sr. Maria-Walburga Schortemeyer, O.S.B., Abbey of St. Walburga, Virginia Dale, CO 80536-8942. (970) 472-0612. E-mail: vocations@walburga.org; Web: www.walburga.org

BENEDICTINE NUNS (O.S.B.)
(Cloistered) St. Scholastica Priory, Box 606, 271 N. Main St., Petersham, MA 01366-0606. (978) 724-3213. Web: www.petershamosb.org
9 Nuns in Solemn Vows, 3 in Simple Vows, 1 Novice
Apostolic Work: Prayer.
Vocation Director: Sr. Mary Angela, O.S.B.

BENEDICTINE NUNS (O.S.B.)
Corpus Christi Monastery, 4485 Earhart Rd., Ann Arbor, MI 48105-9710. (734) 995-3876. Fax: (734) 930-9471. E-mail: benedictines@rc.net
4 Nuns, 10 Associates
Apostolic Work: Various works compatible with monastic schedule; sing Divine Office in Gregorian Chant in English, daily Eucharistic Adoration.
Represented in the Diocese of Lansing.
Vocation Director: Rev. Mother Regina Mary, O.S.B., Corpus Christi Monastery, 4485 Earhart Rd., Ann Arbor, MI 48105-9710. (734) 995-3876

BENEDICTINE NUNS (O.S.B.)
St. Emma Monastery, 1001 Harvey Ave., Greensburg, PA 15601-1494. (724) 834-3060
14 Sisters, 1 Temporarily Professed, 4 Novices
Apostolic Work: Monastic life.
Represented in the Diocese of Greensburg.
Vocations: Mother Mary Anne, O.S.B., St. Emma Monastery, 1001 Harvey Ave., Greensburg, PA 15601-1494. (724) 834-3060. Fax: (724) 834-5772. E-mail: benedictinenuns@stemma.org; Web: www.stemma.org

BENEDICTINE NUNS OF THE CONGREGATION OF SOLESMES (O.S.B.)
US Foundation: Monastery of the Immaculate Heart of Mary, 4103 VT Rte. 100, Westfield, VT 05874. (802) 744-6525. Web: www.solesmes.com
Cloistered Contemplative Nuns
13 Professed Nuns, 1 Temporary Professed, 1 Novice, 1 Postulant
Apostolic Work: Divine Office, in Latin with Gregorian Chant, according to the Rule of Saint Benedict and the Vatican II Constitution on the Liturgy.
Represented in the Diocese of Burlington. 22 monasteries of monks and 8 monasteries of nuns in 10 countries.
Vocation Contact: Mother Laurence A.M. Couture, O.S.B., Prioress

BENEDICTINE NUNS OF THE PRIMITIVE OBSERVANCE (O.S.B.)
Abbey of Regina Laudis, 273 Flanders Rd., Bethlehem, CT 06751. (203) 266-7727. Web: www.abbeyofreginalaudis.com
Cloistered. 1 Abbey
28 Professed Nuns, 5 in Temporary Vows, 6 Novices
Represented in the Archdioceses of Hartford and Seattle.
Vocation Contact: Rt. Rev. Mother David Serna, O.S.B., Abbess

BENEDICTINE SISTERS (O.S.B.)
Sacred Heart Monastery, 916 Convent Rd., Cullman, AL 35055
53 Sisters, 2 Postulants
Apostolic Work: Varies. As a monastic community, prayer and community are the primary "work". Beyond these, each Sister engages in a ministry which allows her to live this life of prayer and community.
Represented in the Archdiocese of Atlanta and in the Dioceses of Birmingham and Orlando.
Vocation Director: Sister Karen Ann Lortscher, O.S.B., PO Box 2040, Cullman, AL 35056. (256) 734-4622 or 2199. E-mail: osbcall@hiwaay.net; Web: www.shmon.org

BENEDICTINE SISTERS (OSB)
St. Scholastica Monastery, P.O. Box 3489, 1301 S. Albert Pike, Fort Smith, AR 72913. (479) 783-4147. E-mail: vocationdirector@scholasticafortsmith.org; Web: www.scholasticafortsmith.org
87 Sisters
Ministry: Essential ministry is to seek God in community and to praise God through a balanced life of prayer, work and leisure. Sisters are involved in teaching, retreat work, spiritual direction, pastoral care, parish work, youth ministry, social work, and service to one another in community.
Represented in the Diocese of Little Rock.
Vocation Director: Sister Kimberly Rose Prohaska, OSB

BENEDICTINE SISTERS (O.S.B.)
St. Lucy's Priory, 19045 E. Sierra Madre, Glendora, CA 91741
24 Sisters
Ministries: Education, pastoral ministry, ministry to disabled persons.
Represented in the Archdioceses of Los Angeles and San Diego
Vocation Director: Sr. Elizabeth Brown, O.S.B., Prioress, St. Lucy's Priory, 19045 E. Sierra Madre, Glendora, CA 91741. (818) 335-1682. Fax: (818) 335-4373

BENEDICTINE SISTERS (O.S.B.)
Holy Spirit Monastery, 22791 Pico St., Grand Terrace, CA 92313-2313. (909) 783-4446. Fax (909) 783-3525. E-mail: hsmonastery@prodigy.net; Web: www.rc.net/sanbernardino.hsmonastery
11 Sisters
Apostolic Work: Catholic education, early childhood/training, parish administration, counseling, retreats, spiritual direction, religious education and monastery works.
Represented in the Diocese of San Bernardino.
Vocation Contact: Sr. Mary Ann Schepers, OSB, Prioress

BENEDICTINE SISTERS (O.S.B.)
Benet Hill Monastery, 2555 N. Chelton Rd., Colorado Springs, CO 80909-1399. (719) 633-0655.
E-mail: benet@qwest.net;
Web: www.benethillmonastery.org/
42 Sisters
Apostolic Work: Seeking God in the monastic community, praise of God in liturgy and serving in the area of each Sister's giftedness and the needs of the People of God.
Represented in the Archdioceses of Denver and Santa Fe and in the Dioceses of Colorado Springs and Pueblo. Also in Jamaica.
Vocation Director: Sister Mary Jane Vigil, O.S.B.

BENEDICTINE SISTERS (O.S.B.)
Our Lady of Mount Caritas Monastery, 54 Seckar Rd., Ashford, CT 06278. (860) 429-7457
3 Sisters
Apostolic Works: Contemplative prayer.
Represented in the Diocese of Norwich.
Vocation Contact: Rev. Mother Mary Peter, O.S.B., Prioress, Our Lady of Mount Caritas Monastery, 54 Seckar Rd., Ashford, CT 06278. (860) 429-7457

BENEDICTINE SISTERS (OSB)
Monastery of St. Gertrude, HC 3 Box 121, Cottonwood, ID 83522-9408
67 Members
Ministry: The Sisters minister to the world through a monastic way of life, seeking God through prayer, community and service and in the ministries of education, health care, spirituality and more.
Represented in the (Arch)dioceses of Boise, Seattle and Spokane.
Vocation Director: Sr. Janet M. Barnard, OSB, Monastery of St. Gertrude, HC 3 Box 121, Cottonwood, ID 83522-9408. (208) 962-3224. E-mail: vocation@stgertrudes.org; Web: www.stgertrudes.org

BENEDICTINE SISTERS (O.S.B.)
St. Scholastica Monastery, 7430 N. Ridge Blvd., Chicago, IL 60645
69 Sisters
Apostolic Work: We are Benedictine women called to seek God in prayer and community, serving where there is need. We sponsor an academy for young women and serve the church and society in a variety of ways. We work in all areas of education, social service, pastoral ministry, spiritual development and health care. We minister to the elderly, homeless women, and the mentally ill, and underlying all we do is our desire to live the Gospel command to love God and neighbor. Women, 20-50, who wish to seek God in an active monastic community by living a balanced life of prayer, work and leisure are invited to contact us.
Represented in the Archdiocese of Chicago.
Vocation Director: Sr. Margarita Walters, OSB, St. Scholastica Monastery, 7430 N. Ridge Blvd., Chicago, IL 60645. (773) 764-2413, ext. 267. Fax: (773) 761-5131. E-mail: mwalters@osbchicago.org; Web: www.benedictine-sisters.org

BENEDICTINE SISTERS (O.S.B.)
Sacred Heart Monastery, 1910 Maple Ave., Lisle, IL 60532-2164
44 Sisters
Ministry: Living in a monastic life of seeking God in prayer and work, focusing on mission of hospitality.
Conduct: Senior citizen residence, education, pastoral ministry in parishes, administrators, counseling, nursing to elderly, ministry to

Hispanics, Taize prayer, Lectio Divina & centering prayer groups, transitional housing for the poor, distribution of food to the poor, community support services, secretaries and domestic services.

Represented in the Diocese of Joliet.

Vocation Contact: Sister Christine Kouba, O.S.B., Sacred Heart Monastery, 1910 Maple Ave., Lisle, IL 60532-2164. (630) 969-7040. Fax: (630) 969-4839. E-mail: ckouba2@aol.com; Web: www.shmlisle.org

BENEDICTINE SISTERS (O.S.B.)

St. Mary Monastery, 2200 88th Ave. W, Rock Island, IL 61201

64 Sisters

Ministries: Contemplative and active, we are called to prayer, community and work using our gifts. We serve in spiritual direction, retreats, parishes, pastoral care, campus ministry, education, social work, and outreach to the poor. We invite you to stroll through our wooded grounds and reflect on God's call to you. Come to prayers and meals. Talk and laugh with us. "Listen with the ear of your heart." You may feel one step closer to home.

Represented primarily in the Diocese of Peoria, IL.

Vocation Director: Sr. Phyllis McMurray, O.S.B., St. Mary Monastery, 2200 88th Ave. W, Rock Island, IL 61201. (800) 650-1257. E-mail: vocation@stmarymonastery.org; Web: www.stmarymonastery.org

BENEDICTINE SISTERS (OSB)

Monastery Immaculate Conception, 802 E. 10th St., Ferdinand, IN 47532-9239

217 Sisters, 21 in Formation

Apostolic Work: We are monastic women seeking God through the Benedictine tradition of community life, prayer, hospitality and service to others. By our life and work, we commit ourselves to be a presence of peace as we join our sisters and brothers in the common search for God. We minister in education, parish ministry, religious education, counseling, retreat work, spiritual direction, social services and health care. We do not identify with one specific ministry; rather we respect each individual's gifts as given by God.

We encourage women, ages 21-40, who earnestly seek God and want to live a balanced life of prayer and work to inquire about our monastic lifestyle. (A college education is helpful but not required.)

Represented in the Archdioceses of Louisville and Indianapolis and in the Dioceses of Evansville, Joliet, Lexington and Owensboro. Also in Guatemala, Peru and Rome.

Vocation Ministers: Sister Anita Louise Lowe, Sister Tess Dueñas, Monastery Immaculate Conception, 802 E. 10th St., Ferdinand, IN 47532-9239. (1-800) 738-9999. E-mail: vocation@thedome.org; Web: www.thedome.org/vocations

BENEDICTINE SISTERS (O.S.B.)

1128 - 1100th St., Harlan, IA 51537-4900

3 Sisters

Apostolic Work: Monastic way of life integrating community, prayer and work.

Represented in the Diocese of Des Moines.

Vocation Director: Sr. Linda Zahner, OSB, Covenant Monastery, 1128 - 1100th St., Harlan, IA 51537-4900. 712-755-2004. E-mail: benedictines@fmctc.com; web: www.mountosb.org/Covenant/vocation.html

BENEDICTINE SISTERS (O.S.B.)

Mount St. Scholastica, 801 S. 8th St., Atchison, KS 66002

187 Sisters, 3 Scholastics, 1 Novice, 1 Postulant

Ministry: A monastic community rooted in community life, prayer and ministry to God's people. The Sisters' ministries flow out of monastic living and focus on empowering women, particularly the young, the poor and those most in need. Some of these ministries include staffing the spirituality center at Mount St. Scholastica, education at all levels, women's centers in Atchison and Kansas City, pastoral ministry, counseling, health care and music conservatory.

Represented in the Archdiocese of Kansas City and in the Dioceses of Kansas City-St. Joseph and Des Moines. Also in Mineiros, Brazil.

Vocation Minister: Sister Patricia Seipel, OSB, Mount St. Scholastica, 801 S. 8th St., Atchison, KS 66002. (913) 360-6200 or 6219 (vocation office). Fax: (913) 360-6190. E-mail: vocation@mountosb.org; Web: www.mountosb.org

BENEDICTINE SISTERS (O.S.B.)

Mt. Tabor Benedictines, 150 Mt. Tabor Rd., Martin, KY 41649. (606) 886-9624

5 Sisters

Ministries: A monastic community of women challenged by the Gospel and the Benedictine tradition: to nurture the giftedness of each person, to serve the community through teaching, counseling, outreach to the poor, social work, agricultural work, care of the sick, parish and retreat work, liturgical prayer, ecumenism and sharing resources as well as other traditional and creative ministries.

Represented in the Diocese of Lexington.

Vocation Director: Sr. Carolyn Lambert, OSB, 150 Mt. Tabor Rd., Martin, KY 41649. (606) 886-9624. E-mail: mtabor150@hotmail.com; Web: www.geocities.com/athens/9871

BENEDICTINE SISTERS (O.S.B.)

St. Walburg Monastery, 2500 Amsterdam Rd., Covington, KY 41017

86 Sisters

Ministries: Vary according to the gifts and talents of each Sister and the needs of all God's people: the old and the young, the sick and the poor, the stranger and the guest. Sisters serve as pastoral ministers, spiritual and retreat directors, educators, social workers, counselors and healthcare ministers. The monastery provides opportunities for community for women who want to strengthen their faith and discern their call to holiness.

Represented in the Archdiocese of Cincinnati and in the Dioceses of Covington, Lexington and Pueblo.

Vocation Director: Sister Cathy Bauer, O.S.B., St. Walburg Monastery, 2500 Amsterdam Rd., Covington, KY 41017. (859) 331-6324. E-mail: bauerosb@yahoo.com; Web: www.stwalburg.org

BENEDICTINE SISTERS (O.S.B.)

Saint Gertrude Monastery, 14259 Benedictine Lane, Ridgely, MD 21660

30 Professed Sisters

Ministry: Prayer and community life. A sister with the prioress discerns a ministry of service. Presently sisters are involved in the Benedictine School for developmentally disabled children, Benedictine Job Training Center for developmentally disabled young adults, elementary and high school teaching, religious education, nursing, social work, pastoral ministry, ministry with the poor and social justice efforts.

Represented in the Diocese of Wilmington, DE.

Vocation Minister: Sr. Colleen Quinlivan, OSB, 113 Canterbury Dr., Wilmington, DE 19803. (302) 478-3754. Fax: (302) 478-9305. E-mail: scq99@aol; Web: www.ridgelybenedictines.org

BENEDICTINE SISTERS (O.S.B.)

Sisters of St. Benedict, Mount Saint Benedict Monastery, 620 Summit Ave., Crookston, MN 56716-2799

113 Sisters
Ministry: The primary work of the Benedictine is to seek God in community through prayer and service. The Sisters work in health care, education, pastoral care, parish ministry, retreat work, social work, domestic services, arts and crafts.
Represented primarily in the Dioceses of Crookston (MN) and Brownsville (TX).
Vocation Contact: Sister Lucille Marie Adelman, OSB, Mount Saint Benedict Monastery, 620 Summit Ave., Crookston, MN 56716-2799. (218) 281-3441. E-mail: vocation@msb.net; Web: msb.net

BENEDICTINE SISTERS (O.S.B.)
St. Scholastica Monastery, 1001 Kenwood Ave., Duluth, MN 55811-2300
144 Sisters
Apostolic Work: Ministries flowing from the twofold primary work of the Benedictine Sisters - the Work of God (prayer) and the Work of Building Community (common life) - include education, healthcare, pastoral care, parish ministry, retreat work, arts/crafts, and service to one another within community.
Represented in the Archdioceses of Chicago and St. Paul-Minneapolis and in the Dioceses of Duluth and Phoenix.
Vocation Ministers: Mary Rochefort, OSB, (218) 723-6505; Nancy Flaig, OSB, (218) 723-7059, St. Scholastica Monastery, 1001 Kenwood Ave., Duluth, MN 55811-2300. E-mail: mrochefo@css.edu, snancyosb@yahoo.com; Web: www.duluthbenedictines.org

BENEDICTINE SISTERS (O.S.B.)
Saint Benedict's Monastery, 104 Chapel Lane, St. Joseph, MN 56374-0220
380 Sisters
Benedictine Ministry: Seeking God especially in the context of Monastic Community, Liturgy of the Hours, and serving in whatever area the giftedness of the sisters and the needs of the people require.
Vocation Director: S. Mary Catherine Holicky, O.S.B., Saint Benedict's Monastery, 104 Chapel Lane, St. Joseph, MN 56374-0220. (320) 363-7180. E-mail: mholicky@csbsju.edu; Web: www.sbm.osb.org

BENEDICTINE SISTERS (OSB)
St. Paul's Monastery, 2675 Larpenteur Ave. E., St. Paul, MN 55109-5097. (651) 777-8181
73 Sisters
Ministries: Seeking God in monastic life, Liturgy of the Hours and contemplation; parish and liturgical ministry, education, spiritual direction, retreats, psychotherapy, pastoral care of the aged, child care, health care, food management, and other ministries needed by the people.
Represented in the (Arch)diocese of St. Paul/Minneapolis.
Vocation Contact: Sister Linda Soler, OSB, St. Paul's Monastery, 2675 Larpenteur Ave. E., St. Paul, MN 55109-5097. (651) 777-8181. Fax: (651) 777-4442. E-mail: lsoler@usinternet.com; Web: www.osb.org/spm

BENEDICTINE SISTERS (O.S.B.)
Our Lady of Peace Monastery, 3710 W. Broadway, Columbia, MO 65203-0116. (573) 446-2300
Apostolic Work: Wide variety of ministries flowing out of monastic prayer and presence: pastoral ministry, catechetics, care of sick, elderly, disabled, and those in crisis situations, counseling, prison ministry and legal services.
Represented in the (Arch)dioceses of Jefferson City and Springfield-Cape Girardeau.
Vocation Contact: Sister Rose Maria, O.S.B., Prioress, 3710 W. Broadway, Columbia, MO 65203-0116. (573) 446-2300. E-mail: rosemaria@benedictinesister.org; Web: benedictinesister.org

BENEDICTINE SISTERS (O.S.B.)
Epiphany Monastery, 3307 Hwy. 40 West, P.O. Box 8177, Columbia Falls, MT 59912. (406) 892-4670
3 Sisters
Apostolic Work: As a new community the Sisters seek God through communal and personal prayer, stewardship of the earth and service to one another in community. Varied ministries outside the community.
Represented in the Diocese of Helena.
Vocation Director: Sister Bernice Simon, OSB, 3307 Hwy. 40 West, P.O Box 8177, Columbia Falls, MT 59912. (406) 892-4670. E-mail: bgsosb@yahoo.com

BENEDICTINE SISTERS (O.S.B.)
Saint Walburga Monastery, 851 N. Broad St., Elizabeth, NJ 07208-2539
56 Sisters, 2 Scholastics
Apostolic Work: The Sisters are monastic women who seek God in community through Gospel values and the Rule of Saint Benedict. In active lives balanced with prayer, they witness to Jesus Christ through hospitality, community, and service in education, health care and spirituality.
Represented in the Archdioceses of New York and Newark and in the Diocese of Paterson.
Vocation Ministry: Sister Marita Funke, OSB, Saint Walburga Monastery, 851 N. Broad St., Elizabeth, NJ 07208-2539. (908) 352-4278, (908) 353-3028. E-mail: maritaosb@aol.com; Web: www.catholic-forum.com/bensisnj

BENEDICTINE SISTERS (O.S.B.)
Annunciation Monastery, 7520 University Dr., Bismarck, ND 58504
100 Sisters
Apostolic Work: The Sisters' commitment to seek God through prayer and community life overflows into ministries of education, health care, campus and parish ministry, social work and whatever best suits the talents of the Sister and the needs of the people of the area.
Vocation Coordinator: Sister Kathleen Atkinson, osb, Annunciation Monastery, 7520 University Dr., Bismarck, ND 58504. (701) 255-1520. E-mail: srkatkinson@bismarckdiocese.com; Web: www.annunciationmonastery.org

BENEDICTINE SISTERS (O.S.B.)
Sacred Heart Monastery, P.O. Box 364, Richardton, ND 58652. (701) 974-2121
31 Sisters
Ministries: Parish ministry, hospital chaplains, social work, spirituality center, monastery works, raising llamas.
Represented in the Diocese of Bismarck.
Vocation Director: Sr. Regina Murray, O.S.B., Sacred Heart Monastery, P.O. Box 364, Richardton, ND 58652. (701) 974-2121. E-mail: vocations@sacredheartmonastery.com; Web: www.sacredheartmonastery.com

BENEDICTINE SISTERS (O.S.B.)
Red Plains Monastery, 728 Richland Road, S.W., Piedmont, OK 73078-9324
11 Sisters
Apostolic Work: As a monastic community, the Sisters' first "work" is seeking God in community and prayer. Other works include spiritual direction, retreat ministry, hospice chaplaincy, religious education, arts and crafts and service to each other in community.
Represented in the Archdiocese of Oklahoma City.
Vocation Director: Sister Joanne

Yankauskis, OSB, 728 Richland Road, S.W., Piedmont, OK 73078-9324. (405) 373-4565. E-mail: benedictinevocation@ionet.net; Web: www.redplainsmonastery.org

BENEDICTINE SISTERS (O.S.B.)
St. Joseph Monastery, 2200 S. Lewis Ave., Tulsa, OK 74114
29 Sisters
Apostolic Work: Monastic community life and prayer, 1 private school grades pre-school through 8th grade coeducational. Other ministries: nursing, teaching, social services, pastoral ministry, catechetics, Benedictine Oblates.
Represented in the Archdiocese of Oklahoma City and in the Dioceses of Lincoln, Tulsa and Wichita.
Vocation Minister: Sr. Veronica Sokolosky, OSB, St. Gregory's University, 1900 W. MacArthur, Shawnee, OK 74804-2403. (405) 878-5379. E-mail: sisters@tulsaosb.org; Web: www.tulsaosb.org/vocation.htm

BENEDICTINE SISTERS (O.S.B.)
Queen of Angels Monastery, 840 S. Main St., Mt. Angel, OR 97362
49 Sisters
Apostolic Work: Seek God in a balanced life of prayer and work, simplicity, hospitality and service. Community ministries include a retreat and renewal center and a homeless shelter; individual ministries include teaching, pastoral care, health care, spiritual direction and parish work.
Represented primarily in rural Oregon.
Vocation Director: Sister Marietta Schindler, OSB, Queen of Angels Monastery, 840 S. Main St., Mt. Angel, OR 97362. (503) 845-6141. Fax: (503) 845-6585. E-mail: smarietta@juno.com; Web: www.benedictine-srs.org

BENEDICTINE SISTERS (O.S.B.)
Transfiguration Monastery, 526 Fairview St., Emmaus, PA 18049-3837
3 Sisters, 1 Affiliate
Ministries: A new foundation that seeks to be a sign of God's caring presence in the world, by monastic community life, prayer and Benedictine hospitality. Ministries vary according to the giftedness of each Sister and presently include pastoral ministry, education and spirituality.
Represented in the Diocese of Allentown.
Vocation Director: Sister Germaine Hartle, O.S.B., Transfiguration Monastery, 526 Fairview St., Emmaus, PA 18049-3837. (610) 965-6818. E-mail: monasteryosb@enter.net; Web: www.emmausosb.org

BENEDICTINE SISTERS (O.S.B.)
Mount St. Benedict Monastery, 6101 E. Lake Rd., Erie, PA 16511. (814) 899-0614
147 Sisters
Apostolic Work: Administration, education, food management, homemaking, liturgy, music, nursing, pastoral ministry, peace and justice, social work, technicians, hospitality/conference center, health care, inner-city ministries (neighborhood art house, soup kitchen, kid's cafe), spiritual direction and retreat ministry, ecology and stewardship programs, diocesean mission office, housing for elderly and handicapped, daycare, Head Start, Alliance for International Monasticism, prison ministry, sanctuary for refugees.
Represented in the (Arch)dioceses of Cleveland, Dodge City, Erie, Milwaukee, Orlando and Rochester. Also in Mexico and Columbia.
Vocation Director: Sr. Mary Ellen Plumb, OSB, Mount St. Benedict Monastery, 6101 E. Lake Rd., Erie, PA 16511. (814) 899-0614, ext. 511. E-mail: msbforma@erie.net

BENEDICTINE SISTERS (O.S.B.)
St. Joseph Monastery, 303 Church St., St. Marys, PA 15857
29 Sisters
Apostolic Work: Education, retreats, office work, tutoring, domestic services, crafts, music, recycling and health care.
Represented in the Diocese of Erie.
Vocation Directress: Sister Victoria Marconi, OSB, St. Joseph Monastery, 303 Church St., St. Marys, PA 15857. (814) 834-2267, ext. 212. E-mail: svallimont@alltel.net

BENEDICTINE SISTERS (OSB)
St. Martin Monastery, 2110-C St. Martin's Dr., Rapid City, SD 57702-9660
34 Members
Conduct: Retreat center, day care center. Also involved in religious education, tutoring, pastoral ministry, counseling, hospital chaplaincy, home health care, spiritual direction, directed retreats.
Represented in the (Arch)dioceses of Rapid City, Helena, Great Falls-Billings and Seattle. Dependent priory in Columbia Falls, MT.
Vocation Contact: Sister Margaret Hinker, OSB, St. Martin Monastery, 2110-C St. Martin's Dr., Rapid City, SD 57702-9660. (605) 343-8011. E-mail: FMartin620@aol.com; Web: www.blackhillsbenedictine.com

BENEDICTINE SISTERS (O.S.B.)
Mother of God Monastery, 110 28th Ave. SE, Watertown, SD 57201
69 Sisters
Apostolic Work: We are a community of monastic women rooted in the peaceful prairie land of rural South Dakota. We are called to seek God through our daily monastic prayer and in and through our ministry to others. Our ministry varies as the needs surface. Our Sisters are involved in teaching, nursing, pastoral care, ministry to Native American and Hispanic people, retreats and spiritual direction. We invite women who desire to seek God to journey with us.
Vocation Director: S. Emily Meisel, Mother of God Monastery, 110 28th Ave. SE, Watertown, SD 57201. (605) 882-6631. E-mail: sisteremily@hotmail.com; Web: www.watertownbenedictines.org

BENEDICTINE SISTERS (O.S.B.)
Sacred Heart Monastery, Yankton, SD 57078
145 Sisters
Apostolic Work: Prayer and the building of community are central to the Benedictine way of life and from this all other ministries flow. Individual and communal gifts and resources are used for the building of God's kingdom in a variety of ways. Ministry is characterized by a continual openness and response to the changing needs of the area and the times.
Represented primarily in rural areas in the Archdiocese of Omaha, NE and in the Dioceses of Sioux Falls, SD; and Lincoln, NE.
Vocation Director: Sr. Eileen O'Connor, Sacred Heart Monastery, 1005 West 8th, Yankton, SD 57078. (605) 668-6017. E-mail: eoconnor@mtmc.edu; Web: www.yanktonbenedictines.org

BENEDICTINE SISTERS (O.S.B.)
St. Scholastica Monastery, 416 W. Highland St., Boerne, TX 78006. (830) 249-2645
21 Sisters
Apostolic Work: Education, health care, pastoral outreach, community development, public policy, retreat.
Represented in the Dioceses of San Antonio and Laredo.
Vocation Director: Sr. Kathleen Higgins, O.S.B., St. Scholastica Monastery, 416 W. Highland St., Boerne, TX 78006. (830) 816-8504. E-mail: khiggins@boernebenedictines.com; Web: boernebenedictines.com

BENEDICTINE SISTERS (O.S.B.)
St. Benedict Monastery, 17825 South Western St., Canyon, TX 79015
2 Final Professed, 3 Temporary Professed, 1 Novice, 1 Postulant
Ministry: The primary ministry is to seek God through monastic life: community, Liturgy of the Hours, contemplation and work.
Vocation Contact: Sister Marcella Schmalz, OSB, St. Benedict Monastery, 17825 South Western St., Canyon, TX 79015. (806) 655-9317. E-mail: nuns@osbcanyontx.org; Web: www.osbcanyontx.org

BENEDICTINE SISTERS (O.S.B.)
Mount Benedict Monastery, 6000 South 1075 East, Ogden, UT 84405. (801) 479-6030
10 Sisters
Apostolic Work: Parish ministry, campus ministry, health care ministry, chaplaincy services, RCIA, retreat work, spiritual direction, liturgical music and the diocesan diaconate program.
Represented in the Diocese of Salt Lake City.
Vocation Director: S. Marilyn Mark, OSB, Mount Benedict Monastery, 6000 South 1075 East, Ogden, UT 84405. (801) 479-6030. Fax: (801) 479-4997. E-mail: mbmutah@hotmail.com; Web: www.mbmutah.org

BENEDICTINE SISTERS (O.S.B.)
St. Placid Priory, 500 College St., N.E., Lacey, WA 98516
20 Sisters
Apostolic Work: Ministries, within a rich Benedictine tradition, and chosen individually and in community, include spiritual direction, operating a retreat center and bookstore, massage, healing touch, teaching, study, liturgical preparation, and welcoming guests into St. Placid's.
Represented in the Archdiocese of Seattle.
New Membership Director: Monika Ellis, OSB, St. Placid Priory, 500 College St., N.E., Lacey, WA 98516. (360) 438-1771. E-mail: vocations@stplacid.org; Web: www.stplacid.org/vocations.html

BENEDICTINE SISTERS (O.S.B.)
St. Bede Monastery, PO Box 66, 1190 Priory Rd., Eau Claire, WI 54702-0066
40 Sisters
Ministries: Seeking God in monastic community life; serving guests in retreat/conference center; working in pastoral ministry, education, health care, parish administration, fund-raising and spiritual direction.
Represented in Wisconsin, Missouri, Texas and Jamaica.
Contact: Sister Ruth Feeney, O.S.B., St. Bede Monastery, PO Box 66, (1190 Priory Rd. - UPS zip 54701), Eau Claire, WI 54702-0066. (715) 834-3176. E-mail: vocation@saintbede.org; Web: www.saintbede.org

BENEDICTINE SISTERS (O.S.B.)
Monastery of Saint Benedict Center, Box 5070, Madison, WI 53705-0070
7 Members
Monastic Work: Ecumenical Benedictine women's monastic community offers a life of prayer, retreat hospitality, environmental restoration and global outreach to monastic women in developing countries.
Contact: Membership Coordinator, Monastery of Saint Benedict Center, Box 5070, Madison, WI 53705-0070. (608) 836-1631, ext. 158. E-mail: membership@sbcenter.org; Web: www.sbcenter.org

BENEDICTINE SISTERS OF BALTIMORE (O.S.B.)
Emmanuel Monastery, 2229 W. Joppa Rd., Lutherville, MD 21093. (410) 821-5792
15 Sisters
Apostolic Work: Committed to community through daily prayer; hospitality; and justice and peace. Ministries include teaching, pastoral associate, soup kitchen, spiritual/retreat directors, AIDS outreach, pastoral counseling.
Represented in the Archdioceses of Baltimore and Newark.
Vocation Directors: Sr. Marianne Yannarell, O.S.B., Sr. Eleanor Noll, O.S.B., Emmanuel Monastery, 2229 W. Joppa Rd., Lutherville, MD 21093. E-mail: myannarell@emmanuelosb.org

BENEDICTINE SISTERS OF FLORIDA (O.S.B)
Holy Name Monastery, PO Box 2450, St. Leo, FL 33574-2450
27 Sisters, 1 Scholastic, 3 Novices
Apostolic Work: Educational, pastoral and community services, alleviating the hungers of the human family.
Represented in the Diocese of St. Petersburg.
Vocation Director: Sister Lisa-Judene Erazmus, O.S.B., Holy Name Monastery, PO Box 2450, St. Leo, FL 33574-2450. (352) 588-8320. E-mail: lisa.judene.erazmus@saintleo.edu, vocation@saintleo.edu; Web: www.floridabenedictines.com

BENEDICTINE SISTERS OF PERPETUAL ADORATION (OSB)
31970 State Highway P, Clyde, MO 64432-8100; 800 N. Country Club Rd., Tucson, AZ 85716; Osage Monastery, 18701 W. Monastery Rd., Sand Springs, OK 74063; San Benito Monastery, Box 510, Dayton, WY 82836
114 Sisters
Apostolic Work: We are a contemplative monastic community with a special dedication to the Eucharist. Our life is guided by the tradition and wisdom of the Rule of Saint Benedict. We serve the Church through a ministry of prayer, support ourselves by work within the enclosure of the monastery and strive to witness to God's presence in the world through our prayer and community life and by offering a welcoming and peaceful space to those who visit.
If you're a woman between the ages of 18 and 40 and drawn to a life of prayer, we invite you to contact us.
Represented in the Dioceses of Kansas City-St. Joseph, Tucson, Tulsa and Casper.
Vocation Director: Sister Colleen Maura McGrane, O.S.B., Vocation Office, Benedictine Monastery, 31970 State Highway P, Clyde, MO 64432-8100. (660) 944-2221or (1-877) 632-6665 (toll-free). E-mail: vocation@benedictinesisters.org; Web: www.benedictinesisters.org

BENEDICTINE SISTERS OF PITTSBURGH (OSB)
4530 Perrysville Ave., Pittsburgh, PA 15229-2296
75 Sisters, 1 Temporary Professed, 1 Novice
Monastic community seeking God, uniting contemplation and action for the Church and the world. Community prayer, lectio divina, and shared life overflow into ministry.
Ministry: Education, CCD, parish ministry, Appalachia ministry, social justice, ministry to the homeless, adult services, social services, senior center, transitional housing for women with dependent children, visual arts, liturgy and music, administration, foster parenting, tutoring, counseling, spiritual direction, spirituality programs, private retreats.
Represented in the Dioceses of Greensburg, Lexington, Pittsburgh and Steubenville.
Vocation Director: Sister Judith Nero, OSB. (412) 931-2844, ext. 118. Fax: (412) 931-8970. E-mail: sjnero@osbpgh.org; Web: www.osbpgh.org

BENEDICTINE SISTERS OF VIRGINIA (O.S.B.)
9535 Linton Hall Rd., Bristow, VA 20136. (703) 361-0106
37 Sisters
Apostolic Work: Education, health care, parish ministry, retreats, administration, spirituality center.
Represented in the Dioceses of Richmond and Arlington.
Vocation Director: Sister Charlotte Lee, OSB, St. Benedict Monastery, 9535 Linton Hall Rd., Bristow, VA 20136-1217. (703) 361-0106. E-mail: benedictinevocations@hotmail.com

BENEDICTINE SISTERS OF THE BYZANTINE RITE
See Eastern Catholic Religious Communities for Women

BENEDICTINE SISTERS (O.S.B.) (Olivetan Benedictines)
Holy Trinity Monastery, PO Box 298, St. David, AZ 85630-0298. (520) 720-4642. Web: www.holytrinitymonastery.org
1 Sister, 1 Oblate Sister
Represented in the Diocese of Tucson, AZ

BENEDICTINE SISTERS (OSB) (Olivetan Benedictines)
Holy Angels Convent, Olivetan Benedictines, 1699 CR766 - PO Drawer 130, Jonesboro, AR 72403-0130
45 Sisters, 4 Novices, 5 Postulants
Apostolic Work: Teaching, hospital work, pastoral care, parish religious education, teaching music, day care center, Hispanic ministry.
Represented in the Dioceses of Little Rock and Fort Worth.
Vocation Director: Sister Judith Dalesandro, OSB, Holy Angels Convent, Olivetan Benedictines, 1699 CR766 - PO Drawer 130, Jonesboro, AR 72403-0130. (870) 935-5810. Fax: (870) 935-4210. E-mail: judithd@olivben.org; Web: www.olivben.org

BENEDICTINE SISTERS (O.S.B.) (Olivetan Benedictines)
Our Lady of Guadalupe Abbey, PO Box 1080, Pecos, NM 87552-1080
9 Sisters, 7 Novices, 2 Postulants
Apostolic Works: Retreat ministry, spiritual direction, school for charismatic spiritual directors.
Represented in the Archdiocese of Santa Fe.
Vocation Director: Sister Ann, OSB, Our Lady of Guadalupe Abbey, PO Box 1080, Pecos, NM 87552-1080. (505) 757-6415, 757-6600, ext. 225. Fax: (505) 757-2285. E-mail: guestmaster@pecos-nm.com; Web: www.pecosabbey.org

CONGREGATION OF THE BENEDICTINES OF JESUS CRUCIFIED (O.S.B.)
Monastery of the Glorious Cross, 61 Burban Dr., Branford, CT 06405-4003
130 Sisters in Congregation, 22 in US
Motherhouse: France
Other Locations: France, Japan.
Apostolic Work: A Benedictine contemplative monastic community open to women with certain physical limitations as well as those in good health. Good psychological and emotional balance is essential.
Vocation Director: Sr. M. Zita Wenker, OSB, Monastery of the Glorious Cross, 61 Burban Dr., Branford, CT 06405-4003. (203) 315-9964. Fax: (203) 481-4059. E-mail: monasterygc@juno.com; Web: www.catholic.org/macc

SISTERS OF ST. BENEDICT (OSB)
Our Lady of Grace Monastery, 1402 Southern Ave., Beech Grove, IN 46107-1197
84 Sisters
Apostolic Work: Teaching, administration, health care, directors of religious education, parish ministry, youth ministry, music ministry, retreat/education center.
Represented in the (Arch)dioceses of Cincinnati and Indianapolis.
Vocation Directress: Sr. Nicolette Etienne, OSB, Our Lady of Grace Monastery, 1402 Southern Ave., Beech Grove, IN 46107-1197. (317) 787-3287, ext. 3032. Fax: (317) 780-2368. E-mail: discernosb@aol.com; Web: www.benedictine.com

MISSIONARY BENEDICTINE SISTERS (O.S.B.)
See listing under M - Missionary Benedictine Sisters

TRANSFIGURATION HERMITAGE (O.S.B.)
548 Files Hill Rd., Thorndike, ME 04986-3122. (207) 568-3731. E-mail: srewagner@uninets.net
2 Sisters, 1 Postulant
Ministry: Contemplative (Benedictine).
Represented in the Diocese of Portland (ME).
Vocation Director: Sr. Elizabeth Wagner

BERNARDINE FRANCISCAN SISTERS (O.S.F.)
(United States Province) 460 St. Bernardine St., Reading, PA 19607-1737. (610) 777-2967
Over 500 Sisters, several hundred Associates (worldwide)
Apostolic Work: In 1894, Mother Veronica and four other women responded to the call to serve the immigrant Church in the US. Rooted in contemplative prayer and trusting in Divine Providence, Bernardine Franciscans strive to create communities of love and service wherever we are: early childhood, elementary, secondary and special education, religious education, colleges, parish and pastoral ministries, retreat centers, health care, and foreign missions as well as with, and on behalf of, the poor.
Represented across the US, Puerto Rico, Brazil, the Dominican Republic, Poland and Liberia. Several hundred Associates join us in prayer and faith.
Do you have a Franciscan heart? If so, contact us!
Vocation Director: S. Shaun Kathleen Wilson, OSF, Office of Vocations, 460 St. Bernardine St., Reading, PA 19607-1737. (610) 777-2967. E-mail: FollowFrancis@aol.com; Web: www.bfranciscan.org

SISTERS OF BETHANY (C.V.D.)
850 N. Hobart Blvd., Los Angeles, CA 90029. (323) 665-6937
14 Sisters in US
Conduct: Religious education, social service and 1 women's residence.
Represented in the Archdiocese of Los Angeles.
Vocation Director: Sr. Florelia Salazar, C.V.D., 850 N. Hobart Blvd., Los Angeles, CA 90029. (323) 665-6937. Fax: (323) 664-0754

BETHLEMITA DAUGHTERS OF THE SACRED HEART OF JESUS (BethL.)
St. Joseph Residence, 330 W. Pembroke Ave., Dallas, TX 75208. (214) 948-3597. E-mail: sisterab01@aol.com
7 Sisters in US
Apostolic Work: Teaching, mission work, social work, work with the elderly in Central and South America, Canary Islands, Italy, Africa, India and in the US in the Diocese of Dallas only.
Represented in the Diocese of Dallas.
Contact: Sister Adelaide Bocanegra

SERVANTS OF THE BLESSED SACRAMENT (S.S.S.)
American Provincial House: 311 E. Mesa, Pueblo, CO 81006. (719) 545-7729
17 Sisters in US
Apostolic Work: Eucharistic contemplative life – adoration of the Blessed Sacrament and sharing of prayer life with laity.

Represented in the Dioceses of Portland, ME and Pueblo, CO. Also in 9 foreign countries.
Vocation Directress: 101 Silver St., Waterville, ME 04901-5923. (207) 872-7072. E-mail: servantsinfo@blesacrament.org; Web: www.blessedsacrament.com/mission/servantsmission.html

SISTERS SERVANTS OF THE BLESSED SACRAMENT (S.J.S.)
US Vice Provincial: 3173 Winnetka Dr., Bonita, CA 91902
59 Sisters
Apostolic Work: Education.
Represented in the Archdiocese of Los Angeles and in the Dioceses of Fresno, Sacramento and San Diego.
Vocation Director: Sister Beatriz O. Gomez, SJS, 3173 Winnetka Dr., Bonita, CA 91902. (619) 267-0720. Fax: (619) 267-0920

SISTERS OF THE BLESSED SACRAMENT (SBS)
Motherhouse: 1663 Bristol Pike, Bensalem, PA 19020-8502
Members: about 210 (multi-racial, multi-cultural)
Apostolic Work: Share the Gospel message with the poor and oppressed, especially among Black and Native American peoples and challenge the deeply rooted injustice in the world today through a life of prayer, community and service. The SBS are involved in education, parish ministry, religious instruction, social and health services and spiritual ministries. They minister in the inner cities, rural areas, on Native American reservations, as well as in Haiti and Guatemala.
Represented in the Archdioceses of Atlanta, New York, Philadelphia, Boston, Chicago, Los Angeles, New Orleans, Santa Fe and Washington (DC) and in the Dioceses of Baton Rouge, Birmingham, Cincinnati, Dayton, Evansville, Lafayette, Lake Charles, Gallup, Tucson and Palm Beach. Also in Haiti and Guatemala.
Vocation Director: Sister Patricia Suchalski, 1663 Bristol Pike, Bensalem, PA 19020. (215) 244-9900, ext. 327. E-mail: sbsvocof@aol.com; Web: www.katharinedrexel.org

CONGREGATION OF BON SECOURS (C.B.S.) Provincial House and Novitiate: 1525 Marriottsville Rd., Marriottsville, MD 21104. (410) 442-1333
400 Sisters worldwide, 70 Associates, many Lay Ministry Volunteers and Coworkers
Apostolic Work: As an international congregation founded in 1824, our charisma of COMPASSION, HEALING and LIBERATION impels us to provide "good help to those in need" with a particular compassion for the poor, the sick and the dying. Nourished by prayer and community life, each Sister contributes through her unique gifts and talents to unity in faith and mission. We minister in health care, through 40 facilities in rural areas and cities; community-based outreach programs to the poor, ranging from housing to drop-in centers; and retreat ministry. In continuity with our foundress' innovative spirit, our vision brings compassionate healing and wholeness beyond the walls of tradition.
Represented in the (Arch)dioceses of Altoona-Johnstown, Baltimore, Charleston, Detroit, Lexington, Miami, New York, Newark, Philadelphia, Richmond St. Petersburg and Venice (FL). Provinces in France, Great Britain, Ireland and Peru.
Vocation Director: Sr. Pat Dowling, CBS, 1525 Marriottsville Rd., Marriottsville, MD 21104. Toll-free: (1-877) 742-0277; (410) 442-0267. E-mail: pat_dowling@bshsi.com; Web: www.bonsecours.org/vocations

BRIGITTINE SISTERS (O.SS.S.)
Convent of St. Birgitta, 4 Runkenhage Rd., Darien, CT 06820. (203) 655-1068. Fax: (203) 655-3496. E-mail: convent@birgittines-us.com; Web: www.birgittines-us.com
8 Sisters
Apostolic Work: Guest house, private retreats, active contemplative life.
Represented in the Diocese of Bridgeport. Houses in 16 foreign countries, missions in India (12 houses) and Mexico (4 houses).
Contact: Convent of St. Birgitta, 4 Runkenhage Rd., Darien, CT 06820.

BYZANTINE NUNS OF ST. CLARE
See Eastern Catholic Religious Communities for Women

CABRINI SISTERS
See Missionaries of the Sacred Heart of Jesus

CALIFORNIA INSTITUTE OF THE SISTERS OF THE MOST HOLY AND IMMACULATE HEART OF THE BLESSED VIRGIN MARY (I.H.M.)
3431 Waverly Dr., Los Angeles, CA 90027. (323) 664-1126
25 Sisters
Ministries: Conduct schools, serve as DRE's, engage in education at all levels from preschool to university, nursing, hospital ministry, retreat ministry.
Represented in the Archdiocese of Los Angeles.
Vocation Director: Sister Mary Teresa Parker, I.H.M., Holy Family Parish, 209 East Lomita Ave., Glendale, CA 91205-1689. (818) 240-6551, ext. 220. E-mail: rel-ed@hfglendale.org; Web: www.sistersihmla.org

CAMALDOLESE NUNS
Transfiguration Monastery, 701 N.Y. Rte. 79, Windsor, NY 13865-9230
Contemplative community.
Represented in the Diocese of Syracuse.
Vocation Director: Transfiguration Monastery, 701 N.Y. Rte. 79, Windsor, NY 13865-9230. (607) 655-2366. E-mail: bendon@dep.tds.net; Web: www.catholic.org/macc

CANOSSIAN DAUGHTERS OF CHARITY (FdCC) (Canossian Sisters)
Provincial House: 5625 Isleta Blvd., SW, Albuquerque, NM 87105. (505) 873-2854
4,000 Sisters worldwide
Apostolic Work: Discovering God's love in contemplation of Christ crucified, St. Magdalene of Canossa opened herself to the poorest. In Mary, at the foot of the Cross, she found the model of steadfast faith and ardent charity. Today's Canossian Sisters work as pastoral ministers in parishes, schools, retreat and youth centers; live in a community of faith and spiritual growth; mutually accept one another in love, sharing all; are part of the international family of 4,000 sisters, lay associates, oblates, and volunteers; serve the Church in 30 countries spanning 6 continents, including 7 communities in North America; and give special attention to education, evangelization, pastoral care of the sick, formation of the laity, and spiritual exercises.
Represented in the Archdioceses of Santa Fe and San Francisco and in the Diocese of Sacramento and in Canada, Mexico and 7 African countries, 3 South American countries, Australia, 10 Asian countries and 6 European countries.
Vocation Director: Canossian Sisters, 5625 Isleta Blvd., SW, Albuquerque, NM 87105. (505) 873-2059. E-mail: vocationsfdcc@aol.com

CAPUCHIN POOR CLARES
St. Veronica Giuliani Monastery, 816 Jefferson St., Wilmington, DE 19801-1432
12 Sisters
Apostolic Work: Cloistered, contemplative; cook meals for shelters for

the homeless, sew vestments, clerical work.

Represented in the (Arch)dioceses of Wilmington, DE and Denver, CO.

Vocation Director: Sr. Maria Elena Romero, St. Veronica Giuliani Monastery, 816 Jefferson St., Wilmington, DE 19801-1432. (302) 654-8727. Fax: (302) 652-3929

CARMELITE COMMUNITY OF THE WORD (C.C.W.)

Motherhouse of the Carmelite Community of the Word, Administration Center, 394 Bem Rd., Gallitzin, PA 16641. (814) 886-4098. Fax: (814) 886-7115

17 Sisters

Apostolic Work: Religious and academic education (all levels), pastoral ministry, family life ministry, ministry to the imprisoned, the homeless and the literal poor, evangelization, Catholic Charities, operate family soup kitchen.

Represented in the Diocese of Altoona-Johnstown.

Vocation Director: Sr. Martha Burbulla, C.C.W., Incarnation Center, 394 Bern Rd., Gallitzin, PA 16641. (814) 886-4098. E-mail: martccw@supernet.com

CARMELITE HERMIT OF THE TRINITY (C.H.T.)

Mount Carmel Hermitage, 4270 Cedar Creek Rd., Slinger, WI 53086-9795. E-mail: jmjose@catholic.org; Web: www.carmelitehermit.homestead.com, www.carmelitehermit.org

1 Hermit Sister, 1 Candidate, 1 Extern Secular Carmelite (OCDS)

Ministry: Prayer, facilities for private retreats, spiritual guidance, religious publications

Represented in the Archdiocese of Milwaukee.

Vocation Contact: Sister Joseph Marie, C.H.T., Prioress

CARMELITE MISSIONARIES OF ST. TERESA (C.M.S.T.)

Motherhouse: Mexico

Provincialate: 9548 Deer Trail Dr., Houston, TX 77038. (281) 445-5520

67 Sisters in US, 670 worldwide

Apostolic Work: Education, health care, pastoral ministry, spirituality, pastoral clinic, spirituality and missions.

Represented in the Archdioceses of St. Louis and Oklahoma City and in the Dioceses of Arkansas, Galveston-Houston, Corpus Christi and Little Rock. Also in Mexico, El Salvador, Guatemala, Honduras, Nicaragua, Costa Rica, Bolivia, Brazil and Peru (S.A.).

Vocation Director: Sister Gisela Rivera, C.M.S.T., 9548 Deer Trail Dr., Houston, TX 77038. (281) 445-5520

CARMELITE NUNS, DISCALCED (O.C.D.) Carmelite Monastery, 716 Dauphin Island Pkwy., Mobile, AL 36606

5 Nuns

Vocation Contact: Mother Marie Therese of Jesus, O.C.D., Prioress

CARMELITE NUNS, DISCALCED (O.C.D.) Monastery of St. Teresa of Jesus, 7201 W. 32nd St., Little Rock, AR 72204

15 Nuns

Vocation Director: Sr. Cecilia Chun, OCD, Monastery of St. Teresa of Jesus, 7201 W. 32nd St., Little Rock, AR 72204. (501) 565-5121. E-mail: lrcarmel@comcast.net; Web: www.aristotle.net/~carmelitenunslr

CARMELITE NUNS, DISCALCED (O.C.D.) Carmel of St. Teresa, 215 E. Alhambra Rd., Alhambra, CA 91801. (626) 282-2387. E-mail: teresacarm@aol.com; Web: www.carmelites.org/teresacarmel

15 Nuns

Vocation Director: Sister Maria, O.C.

CARMELITE NUNS, DISCALCED (O.C.D.) Monastery of Our Lady and St. Therese, 27601 Hwy. 1, Carmel, CA 93923. (831) 624-3043. Fax: (831) 624-5495. E-mail: olmediatrix-st@carmelite-nuns.org

Cloistered, contemplatives.

14 Nuns

Vocation Director: Mother Mercedes, O.C.D., Prioress

CARMELITE NUNS, DISCALCED (O.C.D.) Carmel of the Holy Family and St. Therese, 6981 Teresian Way, P.O. Box 1720, Georgetown, CA 95634. (530) 333-1617. Web: www.carmelitemonastery.com

15 Nuns

Vocation Director: Mother Christine, Prioress

CARMELITE NUNS, DISCALCED (O.C.D.) Carmelite Monastery of Christ, the Exiled King, 68 Rincon Rd., Kensington, CA 94707-1047

5 Nuns

Vocation Contact: Vocation Director

CARMELITE NUNS, DISCALCED (O.C.D.) Carmelite Monastery of the Trinity, 5158 Hawley Blvd., San Diego, CA 92116-1934. (619) 280-5424, ext. 111. E-mail: carmelsd@carmelsandiego.com; carmelsd@sbcglobal.net; Web: www.carmelsandiego.com

13 Nuns, 3 in Formation

Contemplative community.

Vocation Contact: Sister Ancilla Murray, O.C.D.

CARMELITE NUNS, DISCALCED (O.C.D.) Carmelite Monastery of Cristo Rey, 721 Parker Ave., San Francisco, CA 94118-4227. (415) 387-2640. Fax: (415) 751-5330

17 Nuns

Apostolic Work: Cloistered contemplatives.

Vocation Director: Mother Mary Joseph, O.C.D.

CARMELITE NUNS, DISCALCED (O.C.D.) Carmelite Monastery of the Mother of God, 530 Blackstone Dr., San Rafael, CA 94903. (415) 479-6872

4 Nuns, 1 Novice, 2 Postulants

Apostolic Work: Contemplative prayer for the Church; special emphasis to pray for the people of Russia.

Vocation Director: Mother Anna Marie of Jesus Crucified, O.C.D., Prioress

CARMELITE NUNS, DISCALCED (O.C.D.) Carmelite Monastery of the Infant Jesus, 1000 Lincoln St., Santa Clara, CA 95050. (408) 296-8412. E-mail: santaclaracarmel@aol.com; Web: www.members.aol.com/santaclaracarmel

18 Solemnly Professed, 1 Novice

Vocations: Sr. Roseanne of Jesus, O.C.D., Prioress

CARMELITE NUNS, DISCALCED (O.C.D.) Carmel of the Holy Spirit, 6138 S. Gallup St., Littleton, CO 80120-2702. (303) 798-4176

10 Nuns

Vocation Director: Mother Judith of the Immaculate Heart, Prioress

CARMELITE NUNS, DISCALCED (O.C.D.)

4 Nuns

Apostolic Work: Contemplative life of prayer.

Vocation Director: Sister Carmela Marolda, O.C.D., Carmelite Monastery, 11 W. Back St., Savannah, GA 31419. (912) 925-8505. E-mail: Carmelite@csam.net

CARMELITE NUNS, DISCALCED

1101 N. River Rd., Des Plaines, IL 60016. (847) 298-4241

16 Nuns

Vocation Contact: Mother Marie Andre of the Holy Spirit, Prioress

CARMELITE NUNS, DISCALCED (O.C.D.) 2500 Cold Springs Rd., Indianapolis, IN 46222-2323. (317) 926-5654. Fax: (317) 926-1492. E-mail: Joanne@praythenews.com; Web: www.praythenews.com
12 Nuns
Vocation Director: Sister Joanne Dewald, O.C.D., Prioress

CARMELITE NUNS, DISCALCED (O.C.D.) St. Joseph's Monastery, 59 Allendale, Terre Haute, IN 47802. (812) 299-1410. E-mail: vocations@heartsawake.org
11 Professed Nuns, 3 Novices
Apostolic Work: A purely contemplative apostolate, excluding all forms of active ministry. Member of a worldwide order composed of almost 800 monasteries, represented in over 60 dioceses in the US
Vocation Contact: Mother Anne Brackmann, O.C.D., Prioress

CARMELITE NUNS, DISCALCED (O.C.D.) Carmel of the Queen of Heaven, 17937 250th St., Eldridge, IA 52748. (563) 285-8387. Fax: (563) 285-7467. E-mail: solitude@netins.net
11 Nuns
Apostolic Work: Prayer.
Contact Person: Sister M. Carol, O.C.D.

CARMELITE NUNS, DISCALCED (O.C.D.) Monastery of the Discalced Carmelite Nuns, 2901 S. Cecelia St., Sioux City, IA 51106-3299. (712) 276-1680. E-mail: Carmelitesiouxc@aol.com; Web: www.siouxcitycarmel.com
10 Nuns
Vocation Contact: Vocation Directress

CARMELITE NUNS, DISCALCED (O.C.D.) Carmelite Monastery, 1740 Newburg Rd., Louisville, KY 40205. (502) 451-6796
10 Professed Nuns
Apostolic Work: Prayer and penance.
Vocation Director: Rev. Mother Prioress, Carmelite Monastery, 1740 Newburg Rd., Louisville, KY 40205. (502) 451-6796

CARMELITE NUNS, DISCALCED (O.C.D.) Monastery of St. Joseph and St. Teresa, 73530 River Rd., Covington, LA 70435-2206. (985) 898-0923. Fax: (985) 871-9333. E-mail: covingtoncarmel@aol.com; Web: www.ettinger.net/carmelcov
8 Nuns, 2 Junior Professed, 2 Novices
Vocation Contact: Sister Edith Turpin, OCD

CARMELITE NUNS, DISCALCED (O.C.D.) Monastery of Mary, Mother of Grace, 1250 Carmel Dr., Lafayette, LA 70501-5299. (337) 232-4651; Fax: (337) 232-3540
16 Nuns
Vocation Director: Sister Mary John Billeaud, OCD

CARMELITE NUNS, DISCALCED (O.C.D.) Carmelite Monastery, 1318 Dulaney Valley Rd., Baltimore, MD 21286-1399
14 Nuns, 2 Novices, 1 Postulant
Carmelite tradition centered in contemplation and community. Shared vibrant liturgical life.
Vocation Director: Sr. Colette Ackerman, Carmelite Monastery, 1318 Dulaney Valley Rd., Baltimore, MD 21286-1399. (410) 823-7415. E-mail: coletteackerman@baltimorecarmel.org; Web: www.geocities.com/baltimorecarmel

CARMELITE NUNS, DISCALCED (O.C.D.) Carmelite Monastery, 5678 Mt. Carmel Rd., La Plata, MD 20646. (301) 934-1654
15 Sisters
Cloistered, contemplative. Represented in the Archdiocese of Washington, DC.
Vocation Director: Mother Mary Joseph, OCD, 5678 Mt. Carmel Rd., La Plata, MD 20646. (301) 934-1654. E-mail: steresa@erols.com; Web: www.erols.com\carmel-of-port-tobacco

CARMELITE NUNS, DISCALCED (O.C.D.) 61 Mt. Pleasant Ave., Boston (Roxbury), MA 02119. (617) 442-1411. E-mail: bostoncarmel@juno.com; Web: carmelitesofboston.org
10 Nuns
Apostolic Work: Contemplative prayer.
Vocation Contact: Sr. Mary Clare, OCD, Vocation Director

CARMELITE NUNS, DISCALCED (O.C.D.) (Cloistered) 15 Mount Carmel Rd., Danvers, MA 01923-3796
14 Professed Nuns, 1 Novice, 1 Postulant
Prioress: Rev. Mother Anne of the Mother of God, O.C.D. (978) 774-3008

CARMELITE NUNS, DISCALCED Carmelite Monastery, 4300 Mt. Carmel Dr. N.E., Ada (Parnell), MI 49301-9784 (Grand Rapids)
15 Cloistered Nuns, 2 Externs

CARMELITE NUNS, DISCALCED (O.C.D.)
10 Nuns, 1 Extern Sister
Apostolic Work: A cloistered contemplative community, modeled on the life of Mary, Mother of the Church. Continual intercession for the needs of the Church, the sanctification of priests, and the salvation of souls.
Vocation Director: Rev. Mother Prioress, O.C.D., Monastery of St. Therese of the Child Jesus, 35750 Moravian Dr., Clinton Township, MI 48035-2138. (586) 790-7255. E-mail: CarmelClintonTwp@aol.com; Web: www.rc.net/detroit/carmelite

CARMELITE NUNS, DISCALCED (O.C.D.) Monastery of the Holy Cross, Hwy. U.S. 2, P.O. Box 397, Iron Mountain, MI 49801. (906) 774-0561
16 Cloistered Nuns, 2 Externs
Apostolic Work: Contemplative prayer for the Church.
Vocation Contact: Mother Maria of Jesus, O.C.D., Prioress, Monastery of the Holy Cross, Hwy. U.S. 2, P.O. Box 397, Iron Mountain, MI 49801

CARMELITE NUNS, DISCALCED (O.C.D.) Monastery of the Infant Jesus of Prague, 3501 Silver Lake Rd., Traverse City, MI 49684-8949. (231) 946-4960
9 Nuns
Vocation Director: Mother Celine of the Cross, O.C.D., Prioress

CARMELITE NUNS, DISCALCED (O.C.D.) Carmel of Our Lady of Divine Providence, 8251 De Montreville Trail N., Lake Elmo, MN 55042-9547. (651) 777-3882
11 Professed Nuns, 2 Novices, 2 Postulants
Vocation Director: Sister Rose of the Sacred Heart, O.C.D., Prioress

CARMELITE NUNS, DISCALCED (O.C.D.) 2155 Terry Rd., Jackson, MS 39204-5799. (601) 373-1460. E-mail: jm2155jt@aol.com
5 Nuns
Vocation Director: Sister Dona Marie, Prioress

CARMELITE NUNS, DISCALCED (O.C.D.) Monastery of the Sacred Heart and St. Joseph, 2201 W. Main St., Jefferson City, MO 65109. (573) 636-3364
14 Nuns
Vocation Contact: Mother Prioress

CARMELITE NUNS, DISCALCED (O.C.D.) Carmel of St. Joseph, 9150 Clayton Rd., (Ladue) St. Louis

County, MO 63124
8 Professed Nuns, 1 Professed Extern, 4 Temporary Professed
Apostolic Work: Prayer and penance, lived in a cloistered, contemplative community.
Vocation Director: Mother Stella Maris, O.C.D., Prioress, Carmel of St. Joseph, 9150 Clayton Rd., (Ladue) St. Louis County, MO 63124. (314) 993-4394. Fax: (314) 993-5039. E-mail: sr-maryjoseph@mindspring.com; Web: www.stormpages.com/mtcarmel

CARMELITE NUNS, DISCALCED (O.C.D.) Carmel of St. Anne, 424 E. Monastery St., Springfield, MO 65807. (417) 881-2115. E-mail: ozarkcarmel@juno.com
5 Nuns
Vocation Contact: Mother Mary Gemma, O.C.D., Prioress

CARMELITE NUNS, DISCALCED (O.C.D.) Carmel of Jesus, Mary and Joseph, 9300 Agnew Rd., Valparaiso, NE 68065
9 Professed Nuns, 4 Novices, 2 Postulants
Apostolic Work: Cloistered contemplatives.
Vocation Director: Mother Teresa of Jesus, O.C.D., Prioress

CARMELITE NUNS, DISCALCED (O.C.D.) Monastery of Our Lady of the Mountains, 1950 La Fond Dr., Reno, NV 89509-3099. (775) 323-3236. E-mail: clasachse@pyramid.net
16 Nuns
Vocation Director: Sr. Carol, O.C.D.

CARMELITE NUNS, DISCALCED (O.C.D.) 275 Pleasant St., Concord, NH 03301-2590
11 Nuns
Contemplative Community.
Represented in the Diocese of Manchester.
Contact Person: Sr. Theresa Horth, OCD, 275 Pleasant St., Concord, NH 03301-2590. (603) 225-5791. E-mail: vocationcarmel.concordnh@verizon.net

CARMELITE NUNS, DISCALCED (O.C.D.) The Carmelite Monastery of Mary Immaculate and St. Mary Magdalen, 26 Harmony School Rd., Flemington, NJ 08822
12 Nuns, 2 Novices, 2 Postulants
Cloistered contemplatives.
Vocations: Mother Anne, O.C.D., Prioress

CARMELITE NUNS, DISCALCED (O.C.D.) Monastery of the Most Blessed Virgin Mary of Mount Carmel, 189 Madison Ave., Morristown, NJ 07960-6101. (973) 539-0773. Fax: (973) 984-0509
8 Nuns
Vocation Director: Mother Therese, OCD, Prioress

CARMELITE NUNS, DISCALCED (O.C.D.) Discalced Carmelite Monastery, 49 Mount Carmel Rd., Santa Fe, NM 87505-0352. (505) 983-7232
11 Nuns
Contemplative community
Vocation Contact: Mother Rose Teresa, O.C.D., Prioress

CARMELITE NUNS, DISCALCED (O.C.D.) Carmel of the Incarnation, 89 Hiddenbrooke Dr., Beacon, NY 12508-3599. (845) 831-5572. E-mail: mhs@csnmail.net; Web: www.catholic.org/macc
25 Professed Nuns
Contemplative.
Vocation Contact: Vocation Director

CARMELITE NUNS, DISCALCED (O.C.D.) Monastery of Discalced Carmelites, 75 Carmel Rd., Buffalo, NY 14214. (716) 837-6499
18 Cloistered Nuns (Professed), 2 Extern Nuns (Professed), 2 Novices
Apostolic Work: Prayer.
Contact: Mother Miriam of Jesus, O.C.D.

CARMELITE NUNS, DISCALCED (O.C.D.) Our Lady/St. Joseph Monastery, 1931 W. Jefferson Rd., Pittsford, NY 14534
7 in Community
Apostolic Work: Contemplative prayer within enclosure.
Contact: Sr. John, O.C.D., Prioress, 1931 W. Jefferson Rd., Pittsford, NY 14534. (716) 427-7094

CARMELITE NUNS, DISCALCED (O.C.D.) St. Teresa of Jesus Monastery, 428 Duane Ave., Schenectady, NY 12304
12 Nuns
Apostolate of prayer and penance, lived in strict cloister.
Vocation Director: Mother John, OCD, Prioress

CARMELITE NUNS, DISCALCED (O.C.D.) Carmel of Holy Family, 3176 Fairmount Blvd., Cleveland Heights, OH 44118-4199. (216) 321-6568
15 Nuns

CARMELITE NUNS, DISCALCED (O.C.D.) Carmel of St. Joseph, 20000 N. County Line Rd., Piedmont, OK 73078
11 Nuns, 1 First Vows, 2 Novices
Cloistered, contemplative.
Vocation Director: Sister Donna Ross, OCD

CARMELITE NUNS, DISCALCED (O.C.D.) Carmel of Maria Regina, 87609 Green Hill Rd., Eugene, OR 97402. (541) 345-8649. Fax: (541) 345-4857. Web: http://home.attbi.com/~heartofmary1/
9 Nuns
Apostolic Work: Primary work is prayer. Community active in most countries of the world.
Vocation Director: Mother Teresa Mitchell, O.C.D., Prioress

CARMELITE NUNS, DISCALCED (O.C.D.) Carmelite Monastery, 70 Monastery Rd., Elysburg, PA 17824-9697
14 Nuns
Apostolate: Contemplative religious life.
Vocation Director: Sr. Patricia Boyd, O.C.D. (570) 672-2935. E-mail: elysburgcarmel@aol.com; Web: www.carmelelysburg.org

CARMELITE NUNS, DISCALCED (O.C.D.) Monastery of Holy Family, 510 E. Gore Rd., Erie, PA 16509. (814) 825-0846
Cloistered Contemplatives
Vocations: Mother Emmanuel, Prioress

CARMELITE NUNS, DISCALCED (OCD) Carmel of the Assumption, R.D. #6, Box 28, Center Dr., Latrobe, PA 15650-9008
13 Nuns
A cloistered contemplative community.
Vocation Contact: Sister Barbara Sitter, OCD, Prioress, Carmel of the Assumption, R.D. #6, Box 28, Center Dr., Latrobe, PA 15650-9008. (724) 539-1056. Fax: (724) 539-0752

CARMELITE NUNS, DISCALCED (O.C.D.) Carmel of St. Therese of Lisieux, P.O. Box 57, Loretto, PA 15940-0057. (814) 472-8620
9 Professed Nuns, 2 Novices, 1 Extern Sister
Contact: Mother Teresa of Jesus, O.C.D., Prioress

CARMELITE NUNS, DISCALCED (O.C.D.)
8 Nuns
Apostolic Work: A life of prayer and penance for the needs of the univer-

sal Church, especially for the sanctification of priests. Papal enclosure is maintained.
Vocation Director: Mother Prioress, Carmelite Monastery, 66 Ave. & Old York Rd., Philadelphia, PA 19126. (215) 424-6143

CARMELITE NUNS, DISCALCED (O.C.D.) Monastery of Our Lady of Mount Carmel and St. Therese of the Child Jesus, 25 Watson Ave., Barrington, RI 02806. (401) 245-3421, ext. 37. E-mail: mfdavin@juno.com
14 Nuns
Vocation Directors: Sister Mary Davin, O.C.D., Sister Vilma Seelaus, O.C.D.

CARMELITE NUNS, DISCALCED (O.C.D.) Monastery of the Most Holy Trinity, 5801 Mt. Carmel Dr., Arlington, TX 76017
9 Nuns, 2 Novices, 1 Postulant
Vocation Contact: Mother Anne Teresa of Jesus, O.C.D., Prioress, Monastery of the Most Holy Trinity, 5801 Mt. Carmel Dr., Arlington, TX 76017. (817) 468-1781. E-mail: arcarmel@ix.netcom.com; Web: www.carmelnuns.com

CARMELITE NUNS (O.Carm.)
Monastery of Our Lady of Grace, 6200 CR 339 Via Maria, Christoval, TX 76935-3023. (325) 853-1722. E-mail: desertcarmel@carmelnet.org; Web: http://carmelnet.org/christoval/christoval.htm
4 Professed, 1 Postulant
Apostolic Work: Joyful praise, adoration, intercession; charism: semi-eremitical community living in the presence of God with Mary; zeal inspired by the prophet Elijah. Desert setting similar to the Holy Land.

CARMELITE NUNS, DISCALCED (O.C.D.) Monastery of Discalced Carmelites, 600 Flowers Ave., Dallas, TX 75211
10 Nuns
Vocation Director: Mother Mary Regina of the Sacred Heart, O.C.D., Prioress

CARMELITE NUNS, DISCALCED (O.C.D.) Carmel of the Most Holy Trinity, 1100 Parthenon Pl., New Caney, TX 77357-3039. (281) 399-0270. E-mail: newcaneycarmel@icansurf.com; Web: www.icansurf.com/ocdnewcaney
9 Nuns
Vocation Director: Sr. Mary Ann, OCD, Novice Mistress

CARMELITE NUNS, DISCALCED (O.C.D.) Monastery of the Infant Jesus of Prague and Our Lady of Guadalupe, 6301 Culebra Ave. at St. Joseph's Way, San Antonio, TX 78238-4909. (210) 680-1834. E-mail: saocdnun@dcci.com; Web: www.carmelsanantonio.org
9 Nuns
Vocation Director: Mother Therese Leonard, O.C.D., Prioress

CARMELITE NUNS, DISCALCED (O.C.D.) Carmel of the Immaculate Heart of Mary, 5714 Holladay Blvd., Salt Lake City, UT 84121
10 Nuns
Apostolate Work: Contemplation.
Vocation Director: Mother Mary Ann, OCD, Carmel of the Immaculate Heart of Mary, 5714 Holladay Blvd., Salt Lake City, UT 84121. (801) 277-6075; Fax: (801) 277-4263. Web: carmelsl@xmission.com

CARMELITE NUNS, DISCALCED (O.C.D.) Carmelite Monastery, 2215 N.E. 147th St., Shoreline, WA 98155. E-mail: seattlecarmel@att.net
10 Nuns, 1 Postulant
Represented in the Archdiocese of Seattle.
Vocation Director: Sr. Michael Marie, ocd, Prioress

CARMELITE NUNS, DISCALCED (O.C.D.) Monastery of the Holy Name of Jesus, 6100 Pepper Rd., Denmark, WI 54208. (920) 863-5055. E-mail: carmel@catholicfamilies.net
8 Professed, 1 Novice, 2 Postulants

CARMELITE NUNS, DISCALCED (O.C.D.) Carmel of Mother of God, W267 N2517 Meadowbrook Rd., Pewaukee, WI 53072. (262) 691-0336. Fax: (262) 695-0143. E-mail: pewaukeecarmel@aol.com; Web: www.geocities.com/pewaukeecarmel
10 Nuns
Apostolate Work: Cloistered, contemplative nuns living a life of prayer for the Church and the world.
Vocation Contact: Sr. Mary Agnes, OCD, Prioress

CARMELITE NUNS (O. Carm.)
Carmel of the Sacred Heart, 430 Laurel Ave., Hudson, WI 54016-1688
6 Nuns
Apostolic Work: In a life of contemplative prayer centered on Jesus Christ and in union with Mary, the Carmelite listens in silence and responds in joyful service, supported by the warmth of a caring community.
Represented in the Diocese of Superior, WI.
Vocation Director: Sister Lucia La Montagne, O. Carm., 430 Laurel Ave., Hudson, WI 54016-1688. (715) 386-2156. E-mail: carmelit@pressenter.com; Web: www.pressenter.com/~carmelit/

CARMELITE NUNS OF THE ANCIENT OBSERVANCE (O. Carm.)
Carmel of Mary, 17765-78th St. SE, Wahpeton, ND 58075. (701) 642-2360. Web: www.massintransit.com/nd/carmelmary-nd-wahpeton
10 Solemn Professed, 1 Junior Professed
Apostolic Work: Contemplative prayer, Liturgy of the Hours in Gregorian Chant, Papal Enclosure, in the solitude of a rural setting.
Represented in the Diocese of Fargo

CARMELITE NUNS OF THE BYZANTINE RITE, DISCALCED
See Eastern Catholic Religious Communites for Women

CARMELITE NUNS-CALCED (O.Carm.) Carmelite Monastery of St. Therese, Saint Therese's Valley, 3551 Lanark Rd., Coopersburg, PA 18036-9324
Cloistered.
Apostolic Work: Contemplation, Perpetual Adoration of the Blessed Sacrament.
Represented in the Dioceses of Allentown, Fargo and Superior.
Contact: Mother Marie Charlotte, O. Carm., Superior

CORPUS CHRISTI CARMELITE SISTERS (O. Carm.)
Motherhouse: Tunapuna, Trinidad, WI; Regional House: 412 W. 18th St., Kearney, NE 68847. (308) 237-2287. Fax: (308) 236-9380
11 Nuns in US, 103 Nuns worldwide
Apostolic Work: Catechetics, care of the elderly, Christian unity, schools for mentally and physically challenged children.
Represented in the Dioceses of Grand Island and Providence. Also in England, South America and 6 Caribbean islands in the West Indies.
Vocation Contacts: Sister Emerentiana Pouliot, O.Carm., Novice Director, Sister Delphine Napoleoui, O.Carm., Regional Superior, 412 W. 18th St., Kearney, NE 68847. (308) 237-2287. Fax: (308) 236-9380. E-mail: brownun@yahoo.com; Web: www.corpuschristicarmelites.org

CARMELITE SISTERS FOR THE AGED AND INFIRM (O. Carm.)
Motherhouse: St. Teresa's Motherhouse, 600 Woods Rd., Germantown, NY 12526. (518) 537-5000
248 Sisters, 4 Temporary Vowed, 3 Novices
Conduct: 23 homes for the aged.
Represented in 6 Archdioceses and 13 Dioceses. Also in Ireland.
Vocation Director: Sr. Madeline Angeline, St. Teresa's Motherhouse, 600 Woods Rd., Germantown, NY 12526. (518) 537-5000. E-mail: carmsist@ix.netcom.com; Web: www.netcom.com/~carmsist/new.html

CARMELITE SISTERS, INSTITUTE OF THE SISTERS OF OUR LADY OF MT. CARMEL (O. Carm.)
Motherhouse: Rome, Italy
US Headquarters: Carmelite Sisters, 5 Wheatland St., Peabody, MA 01960
20 Nuns (in US)
Apostolic Work: Religious education, nursing, teaching.
Represented in the Archdioceses of Boston and Washington (DC) and in the Diocese of St. Augustine.
Vocation Directress: Sr. Kathleen Bettercourt, O.Carm, Carmelite Sisters, 5 Wheatland St., Peabody, MA 01960. (978) 531-4733. Fax: (978) 531-2468. E-mail: K63bet@aol.com

CARMELITE SISTERS OF CHARITY (C.C.V.) Formation House: 8138 15th Ave. #203, Hyattsville, MD 20783. (301) 431-3773
Apostolic Work: Ministry in health, education, parish, prison, immigration and social services.
Represented in the Archdiocese of Washington and in the Dioceses of Brooklyn and Wilmington.
Vocation Representative: Sr. Carmen M. Soto, C.C.V., 1222 Monroe St. NE, Washington, DC 20017-2507. (202) 265-1349, (202) 832-2114

CARMELITE SISTERS OF THE DIVINE HEART OF JESUS (Carmel D.C.J.)
Northern Province: 1230 Kavanaugh Pl., Milwaukee, WI 53213. (414) 453-4040. E-mail: carmelmilwaukee@aol.com; Web: www.carmelitedcjnorth.org
Central Province: 10341 Manchester Rd., St. Louis, MO 63122. (314) 965-7616. E-mail: vocations@carmelitedcj.org; Web: www.carmelitedcj.org
Southwestern Province: 8585 La Mesa Blvd., La Mesa, CA 91941. (619) 466-3116. E-mail: VocationDirectress@att.net; Web: www.carmeliteyouth200.homestead.com
94 Sisters in US; 527 worldwide
Conduct: 2 homes for youth, 10 homes for the aged, 4 day nurseries, mission work in Africa, Brazil, Iceland, Nicaragua and Venezuela .
Represented in the Archdioceses of Detroit, Milwaukee, St. Louis and San Antonio and in the Dioceses of Gary, Grand Rapids, Jefferson City, Owensboro and San Diego.
Vocation Directors: Sr. Mary Judith, Northern Province, (414) 453-4040; Sr. Mary Rose, Central Province, (314) 965-7616; Sr. Marie Elena, Southwestern Province, (619) 466-3116

CARMELITE SISTERS OF THE MOST SACRED HEART OF LOS ANGELES (O.C.D.)
Motherhouse: 920 East Alhambra Rd., Alhambra, CA 91801. (626) 289-1353
Loretto Convent, 1200 Fourteenth St., Douglas, AZ 85607. (520) 364-7571
Saint Theresa Convent, 1253 Anastasia Ave., Coral Gables, FL 33134. (305) 448-0662
Holy Name of Jesus Convent, 4040 Pierce St., Wheat Ridge, CO 80033. (303) 422-6419
St. Teresa Benedicta of the Cross Convent, 807 North St., Steubenville, OH 43952. (740) 282-3070
133 Professed Sisters, 8 Novices, 6 Postulants, 4 Candidates
Conduct: 7 grammar schools, 1 high school, 1 general hospital, 2 skilled nursing facilities for the care of the aged, 3 nursery schools with day care center and kindergarten, 2 retreat houses, 1 evangelization center.
Represented in the Archdioceses of Los Angeles, Denver and Miami and in the Dioceses of Steubenville and Tucson.
Vocation Directress: Sister Marina, O.C.D., 920 East Alhambra Rd., Alhambra, CA 91801. (626) 300-8938, 8810. E-mail: beautyofcarmel@earthlink.net; Web: carmelitevocation.homestead.com

CARMELITE SISTERS OF ST. THERESE OF THE INFANT JESUS (C.S.T.)
Villa Teresa Convent, 1300 Classen Dr., Oklahoma City, OK 73103-2447. (405) 232-7926
23 Final Professed
Apostolic Work: Education (early childhood: 2 1/2-year olds to 4th grade, high school, college), parish ministry, youth, social service.
Represented in the Archdiocese of Oklahoma City.
Vocation Contact: Sister Sylvia Negrete, C.S.T., Villa Teresa Convent, 1300 Classen Dr., Oklahoma City, OK 73103-2447. (405) 232-7926 (h), (405) 232-4286 (w). Fax: (405) 232-4286. E-mail: SrSylvia@OKSister.com; Web: www.oksister.com/vocations.htm

CARMELITES (TERESIAN)
See "C" section - The Community of Teresian Carmelites

CONGREGATION OF OUR LADY OF MT. CARMEL (O. Carm.)
Generalate: P.O. Box 476, Lacombe, LA 70445. (504) 882-7577
80 Professed Sisters in US; 20 in the Philippine Islands
Apostolic Work: Education, health care, social work, parish and campus ministry, day care, art, prison ministry, lay Carmelites, retreat and spiritual direction.
Represented in the Archdioceses of Chicago and New Orleans and in the Diocese of Lafayette. Also in the Philippine Islands.
Vocation Directress: Sr. Angele M. Sadlier, O.Carm, 4200 Courtland Dr., Metairie, LA 70002-3112. (504) 455-3107. E-mail: carmelitevoc@earthlink.net; Web: mountcarmel.home.mindspring.com

SISTERS OF THE CATHOLIC APOSTOLATE
See Pallottine Sisters

CENACLE SISTERS (r.c.) (Congregation of Our Lady of the Retreat in the Cenacle)
North America Province: The Cenacle, 513 Fullerton Parkway, Chicago, IL 60614
Apostolic Work: "Awakening and deepening faith – in the form of retreats, spiritual direction, education in the faith, or other spiritual ministries...to honor and be attentive to the Spirit's action in others as well as in ourselves. Ministry flows out of prayer and community life, and it necessarily leads back to prayer and community..."
Represented in several archdioceses and dioceses across the United States and in British Columbia.
Director of Vocations Sr. Janice Bemowski, r.c., Cenacle Formation Community, PO Box 797, Warrenville, IL 60555-0797. (630) 393-1085. Fax: (630) 393-1729. E-mail: sr.janice.m.bemowski@usa.net; Web: www.cenaclesisters.org

SISTERS OF CHARITY OF THE BLESSED VIRGIN MARY (B.V.M.)
Mount Carmel, Dubuque, IA 52003
740 Sisters

Apostolic Work: The Sisters choose their ministry in keeping with the BVM mission of being freed and helping others enjoy freedom in God's steadfast love. This mission finds expression in the traditional commitment to education and in ministries emerging from new needs in Church and society. The Sisters are called to live in any part of the world where there is promise of furthering the mission of Jesus through works of education, justice and peace.

Represented in 26 states, 53 dioceses throughout the US, in two countries in Central and South America and in Ghana, Africa.

Coordinator of Initial Membership: Theresa M. Gleeson, BVM, Mount Carmel, 1100 Carmel Dr., Dubuque, IA 52003. (563) 588-2351. E-mail: newmember@bvmcong.org; Web: www.bvmcong.org

SISTERS OF CHARITY OF CINCINNATI (S.C.)

Motherhouse: 5900 Delhi Rd., Mount St. Joseph, OH 45051

520+ Sisters

Apostolic Work: Ministering as teachers, religious educators, nurse practitioners and healthcare professionals of all types, social workers and counselors, environmentalists and consciousness-raisers; sponsoring institutions and programs that address education, healthcare and social service needs with particular concern for building a more just society through advocacy and providing direct service to poor populations.

Represented in the (Arch)dioceses of Brownsville, Chicago, Cincinnati, Cleveland, Colorado Springs, Columbus, Covington, Denver, Detroit, El Paso, Helena, Indianapolis, Kalamazoo, Lansing, Lexington, Little Rock, Louisville, Memphis, Miami, Newark, New York, Oakland, Orlando, Phoenix, Pueblo, Rapid City, Saginaw, St. Louis, St. Paul, St. Petersburg, San Francisco, Santa Fe, Savannah, Spokane, Toledo, Washington, DC and Wilmington. Also in Guatemala.

Contact: Sister Mary Kay Bush, S.C., 5900 Delhi Rd., Mount St. Joseph, OH 45051. (513) 347-5471. E-mail: smarykay.bush@srcharitycinti.org; Web: www.srcharitycinti.org

SISTERS OF CHARITY OF HALIFAX (S.C.H.) Motherhouse: Mount Saint Vincent, 150 Bedford Hwy., Halifax, Nova Scotia B3M 3J5 Canada. (800) 371-9613

Apostolic Work: All areas of education, pastoral ministry, social services, health care, earth ministry, social justice, community service/outreach.

Represented primarily in Massachusetts, New York and Nova Scotia. Also in other parts of US, Canada, Bermuda, Peru and the Dominican Republic.

Vocation Director: Sr. Susan Dean, SC, Sisters of Charity, St. Aidan Convent, 16 Pembroke St., Williston Park, NY 11596. (516) 741-0718. E-mail: SRDean2424@aol.com; Web: www.schalifax.ca

SISTERS OF CHARITY OF THE IMMACULATE CONCEPTION (S.C.I.C.) Motherhouse: Ivrea, Italy. Novitiate: Rome. US Foundations: Immaculate Virgin of Miracles, 268 Prittstown Rd., Mount Pleasant, PA 15666. (724) 887-6753; St. Mary Star of the Sea Convent, 28 Huntington St., New London, CT 06320. (860) 443-5870. Fax: (860) 443-8552

15 Sisters in US; 1,200 Sisters worldwide.

Apostolic Work: (in US): 1 Montessori school, 1 elementary school. Religious education, pastoral ministry, parish work.

Represented in the Arch(dioceses) of Greensburg (PA) and Norwich (CT). Also throughout Italy, Israel, Lebanon, Switzerland, Albania, Turkey, Libya, Kenya, Tanzania, Mexico and Argentina.

Vocation Contact: Sr. Letiza Garrubai, Regional Superior, Immaculate Virgin of Miracles Convent, 268 Prittstown Rd., Mount Pleasant, PA 15666. (724) 887-0220, 8810. Fax: (724) 887-2977

SISTERS OF CHARITY OF THE INCARNATE WORD (C.C.V.I.)

Incarnate Word Provincialate, 3200 McCullough, PO Box 15378, San Antonio, TX 78212-8578

Provinces: United States, Mexico, Region of Peru, Zambia

457 Sisters, 226 Associates, 7 Lay Missionaries

Apostolic Work: Serving the Christian community in Catholic schools, hospitals, children's centers, and as parish workers and in various other ministries in the United States, Mexico, Peru and Zambia (Africa).

Vocation Directors: Sr. Brigid Marie Clarke, CCVI, Sr. Lauren Moynahan, CCVI, 3200 McCullough, PO Box 15378, San Antonio, TX 78212-8578. (210) 734-8310. E-mail: clarke@universe.uiwtx.edu, moynahan@universe.uiwtx.edu, vocation@universe.uiwtx.edu; Web: www.incarnatewordsisters.org

SISTERS OF CHARITY OF THE INCARNATE WORD-HOUSTON (CCVI) Motherhouse: Villa de Matel, 6510 Lawndale Ave., P.O. Box 230969, Houston, TX 77223-0969. (713) 928-6053

200 Sisters

Apostolic Work: Serving the Christian community in clinics, hospitals, schools and parishes in Africa, El Salvador, Guatemala, Ireland and the United States.

Vocation Ministry: Sr. Pauline Troncale, CCVI, Vocation Office, 6510 Lawndale Ave., P.O. Box 230969, Houston, TX 77223-0969. (713) 928-6053. E-mail: ptroncale@ccvi-vdm.org; Web: www.sistersofcharity.org

SISTERS OF CHARITY OF LEAVENWORTH (SCL)

Motherhouse: 4200 S. 4th St., Leavenworth, KS 66048-5054. (913) 682-7500

400 Sisters

Apostolic Work: Health care: hospitals and clinics for the uninsured poor. Education: college, high school, elementary. Pastoral ministry: parish associates, administrators, religious education, spiritual direction, campus ministry, and youth ministry. Social services: Catholic Charities, AIDS ministry, social justice. Foreign missions: Peru.

Represented in the Archdioceses of Kansas City (KS), Los Angeles, Denver, Oklahoma City, Omaha and in the Dioceses of Kansas City, (MO), Helena, Great Falls-Billings, Pueblo and Cheyenne. Also in Peru.

Vocation Director: Sister Sharon Smith, SCL, 4200 S. 4th St., Leavenworth, KS 66048-5054. (913) 758-6522. E-mail: vocations@scls.org or ssmith@scls.org; Web: www.scls.org

SISTERS OF CHARITY OF MONTREAL (Grey Nuns) (S.G.M.)

Provincial House: 10 Pelham Rd., Lexington, MA 02173. (781) 862-4700

Apostolic Work: As an apostolic community, the Sisters serve those persons in need, especially the most forsaken, with compassionate love, through various ministries, as the care of the sick, the homeless and abandoned children; also, as pastoral ministers; handcrafting for the poor and by trying to alleviate the social injustices of our day.

Represented in Maine, Massachusetts, New Hampshire, Ohio, South America, and throughout Canada.

Vocation Director: Sister Marie Mansfield, S.G.M., 10 Pelham Rd., Lexington, MA 02173. (781) 862-4700. E-mail: hmsgmns@ncia.net

SISTERS OF CHARITY OF NAZARETH (SCN)
General Motherhouse: Nazareth, KY 40048.
798 Sisters worldwide
Apostolic Work: Through diverse ministries in education, health care, administration, law, pastoral ministry, communications, social service/ action and advocacy for the poor, abused, homeless and addicted, the Sisters care for the earth and work for justice in solidarity with oppressed peoples, especially the economically poor and women. Currently there are 68 in initial formation (8 in the US/Belize and 60 in India).
Represented in the Archdioceses of Boston, Chicago, Cincinnati, Louisville, Miami, Philadelphia and Washington, DC and in the Dioceses of Baton Rouge, Charleston, Columbus, Jackson, Jacksonville, Knoxville, Lexington, Little Rock, Memphis, Oakland, Owensboro, Providence, Richmond, San Jose, Steubenville and Worcester. Also in India, Nepal and Botswana, Africa; and Belize, Central America.
Vocation Directors: Sister Luke Boiarski, SCN, 208 Mound St., Tiltonsville, OH 43963. (1-800) 494-1433. E-mail: lukescn@lst.net; Sister Nancy Gerth, E-mail: ngsunshine@juno.com; Web: www.scnazarethky.org

SISTERS OF CHARITY OF OTTAWA (S.C.O.) (Grey Nuns of the Cross)
St. Joseph Province, 559 Fletcher St., Lowell, MA 01854-3434
35 Sisters in the US; 745 worldwide
Apostolic Work: Teaching, foreign missions: (South Africa, Japan, Central Africa, Brazil, Cameroon, Haiti, Papua New Guinea), nursing, care of the aged, parish work and social work.
Represented in the Archdioceses of Boston and Newark.
Vocation Director: Provincial Administration, 559 Fletcher St., Lowell, MA 01854-3434. (978) 453-4993

SISTERS OF CHARITY OF OUR LADY OF MERCY
Motherhouse: 424 Fort Johnson Rd., PO Box 12410, Charleston, SC 29422
25 Sisters
Apostolic Work: Parish ministry, education, social service, Hispanic ministry.
Represented in the Dioceses of Charleston and Baltimore.
Contact Person: Sr. Anne Francis Campbell, May Forest Motherhouse, 424 Fort Johnson Rd., PO Box 12410, Charleston, SC 29422. (843) 795-2866. Fax: (843) 795-6083

SISTERS OF CHARITY OF OUR LADY, MOTHER OF MERCY (S.C.M.M.) Provincial House: 520 Thompson Ave., East Haven, CT 06512. (203) 469-7872
20 Sisters in US; 1,375 worldwide
Apostolic Work: works of charity.
Represented in the Archdioceses of Hartford, St. Paul-Minneapolis and Detroit and in the Dioceses of Bridgeport and San Diego.
Vocation Director: 520 Thompson Ave., East Haven, CT 06512. (203) 469-7872

SISTERS OF CHARITY OF ST. AUGUSTINE (C.S.A.)
Motherhouse: Mt. Augustine, 5232 Broadview Rd., Richfield, OH 44286-9608
77 Sisters, 43 Associates
Apostolic Work: Education; pastoral ministry: parish associates, spiritual direction, directors of religious education; health care: hospitals, nursing home administration, AIDS ministry, pastoral care, social services, homeless, Catholic Worker houses, CSA Health System, foundations.
Represented in the Dioceses of Cleveland, Charleston, Lexington and Youngstown.
Director of Vocations: Sr. Catherine Walsh, CSA, Mt. Augustine, 5232 Broadview Rd., Richfield, OH 44286-9608. (330) 659-5100. E-mail: scw@srsofcharity.org; Web: www.srsofcharity.org

SISTERS OF CHARITY OF SAINT ELIZABETH (S.C.)
Convent of Saint Elizabeth, PO Box 476, Convent Station, NJ 07961-0476
550 Sisters
Apostolic Work: 1 college, 5 academies, 11 high schools, 40 elementary schools, 2 special education schools, 5 hospitals, 1 child care, 1 residence for women, 1 long term care nursing home, 3 homes for the aged, 2 adult literacy programs, 2 homes for aged and retired sisters, 1 novitiate,1 mission in the Virgin Islands, 1 mission in El Salvador, parish work.
Represented in the (Arch)dioceses of Boston, Santa Fe, Newark, New York, Omaha, Richmond, Washington, DC; Camden, Charlotte, El Paso, Fairbanks, Fall River, Hartford, Jackson, Metuchen, Palm Beach, Paterson, Pensacola-Tallahassee, Providence, Rochester, St. Petersburg, Syracuse, Trenton, Tucson, Venice, Wheeling-Charleston, Wilmington, St. Thomas, VI. Also in El Salvador.
Director of Vocation Promotion: Sr. Patricia Dotzauer, S.C., Convent of Saint Elizabeth, PO Box 476, Convent Station, NJ 07961-0476. (973) 290-5331. E-mail: MTracey611@aol.com; Web: scnj.org/member.html

SISTERS OF CHARITY OF ST. HYACINTHE (S.C.S.H.) (Grey Nuns)
Sisters of Charity, 1137 Washington Ave., Portland, ME 04103-3624. (207) 797-8607. (Bilingual - French and English)
10 Sisters in US
Apostolic Work: General hospital, nursing homes, home for the aged, child care center, pastoral care, CCD, pastoral ministry and missionary works in foreign country, education to the Indians, social services.
Represented in the Dioceses of Manchester (NH) and Portland (ME).
Vocation Director: Sr. Jacqueline Peloquin, 1137 Washington Ave., Portland, ME 04103-3624. (207) 797-8607. E-mail: jacquiep@juno.com

SISTERS OF CHARITY OF ST. JOAN ANTIDA (SCSJA)
Regina Mundi, 8560 N. 76th Pl., Milwaukee, WI 53223-2699
45 Sisters in the United States Province; approximately 3,800 Sisters in 7 European, 6 African, 4 Asian, 4 Middle East and 4 South American countries.
Apostolic Work: Teaching, nursing, pastoral work, parish work, social work, jail ministry and missionary work.
Represented in the Archdiocese of Milwaukee and in the Dioceses of Amarillo and Gallup in the US.
Director of Vocations: Sister Elizabeth Weber, Regina Mundi, 8560 N. 76th Pl., Milwaukee, WI 53223-2699. (414) 354-9233. E-mail: elizabeth@scsja.org; Web: www.scsja.org

SISTERS OF CHARITY OF ST. LOUIS (S.C.S.L.) Local Community: Our Lady of Victory Convent, 4907 So. Catherine St., Plattsburgh, NY 12901-3658
13 Sisters in US, 723 worldwide
Apostolic Work: Teaching: elementary, secondary, CCD; Nursing: in nursing homes for the aged and hospitals; retreat, parish and social work.
Represented in the Diocese of Ogdensburg.
Vocation Directress: Sister Louise Marceau, S.C.S.L., Our Lady of Victory Convent, 4907 So. Catherine St., Plattsburgh, NY 12901-3658. (518) 563-7410; Fax: (518) 563-0383

SISTERS OF CHARITY OF ST. VINCENT DE PAUL (S.V.Z.)
US Foundation; 171 Knox Ave., West Seneca, NY 14224
17 Sisters in the US
Apostolic Work: Nursery schools, elementary schools, CCD, parish services, hospital and health services.
Represented in the Diocese of Buffalo and in Oakville, Hamilton, Canada.
Vocation Director: 171 Knox Ave., West Seneca, NY 14224. (716) 825-5859. Fax: (716) 822-6841. E-mail: pozega@aol.com

SISTERS OF CHARITY OF NEW YORK (S.C.)
The Sisters of Charity of New York are a group of 480 religious women who seek to reveal God's love in their varied ministries with and for people who are poor.
Founded by St. Elizabeth Ann Seton in 1809 in Emmitsburg, MD, the community adopted a modified rule of St. Vincent de Paul. The congregation was established in New York City in 1817 in response to Bishop John Hughes' request for assistance in caring for the orphans. While the majority of the members still serve in the New York Archdiocese, the congregation is represented in 8 other localities as well.
The Sisters are engaged in traditional ministries of education, health care and social service as well as in a wide variety of other compassionate and effective responses to the signs of the times, including pastoral ministry and Guatemalan missions
Vocation Directors: Sr. Mary Lou McGrath, Sr. Mary McCormick, Box 1167, 6301 Riverdale Ave., Bronx, NY 10471. (718) 543-4898. E-mail: sistersofcharity@aol.com; Web: www.scny.org

SISTERS OF CHARITY OF SETON HILL (S.C.) De Paul Center, Mt. Thor Rd., Greensburg, PA 15601
503 Sisters
Apostolic Work: Prayer, service and life in community are the primary principles upon which the Sisters carry out their mission, which is to reveal the reality and beauty of God's love to people in need. The Sisters administer and staff educational institutions from preschools through universities; offer religious education and formation; chaplaincy, counseling, pastoral and social services.
Represented primarily in the dioceses of western Pennsylvania, West Virginia and Arizona. The Korean Province offers opportunities for foreign mission work.
Vocation Director: Mary Clark, SC, Seton House, 1343 Sheridan Ave., Pittsburgh, PA 15206. (412) 661-8545. E-mail: mclark17@juno.com; Web: www.scsh.org

SISTERS OF CHRISTIAN CHARITY (S.C.C.) (Daughters of the Blessed Virgin Mary of the Immaculate Conception) Eastern Province: Mallinckrodt Convent, 350 Bernardsville Rd., Mendham, NJ 07945
Western Province: 2041 Elmwood Ave., Wilmette, IL 60091-1533. (847) 920-9341
450 Sisters in US; 885 worldwide
Apostolic Work: Eastern Province: Teaching, retreat ministry, catechetics, nursing, health services, special care for the poor; Western Province: Academic education, care of abused and neglected children, religious education, parish ministry, social service and prayer ministry, and ministry to Native Americans.
Represented (Eastern Province) in the Archdioceses of Newark, New York and Philadelphia and in the Dioceses of Allentown, Camden, Harrisburg, Metuchen, Paterson and Scranton; (Western Province) in the Archdioceses of Chicago, New Orleans, St. Louis and Santa Fe and in the Dioceses of Jefferson City, Lansing and Tucson. Also provinces in Germany, Chile, Uruguay and Argentina with houses in Italy, Switzerland and the Philippines.
Vocation Contacts: Eastern Province: Sr. Bernadette Mc Cauley, S.C.C., Vocation Directress, Mallinckrodt Convent, 350 Bernardsville Rd., Mendham, NJ 07945. (973) 543-6528. E-mail: sccvocation@excite.com or sbernadette@hotmail.com; Western Province: Sr. Carol Bredenkamp, S.C.C., Our Lady of Guadalupe Convent, 1115 S. Florissant Rd., St. Louis, MO 63121-1102. (314) 521-5141. E-mail: sccvocationoffic@aol.com; Eastern/Western Provinces: Web: www.scceast.org

RELIGIOUS OF CHRISTIAN EDUCATION (RCE)
Motherhouse: France
35 Sisters
Apostolic Work: Religious education, education, teaching.
Represented in the Archdiocese of Boston.
Vocation Contact: Sr. Martha Brigham, RCE, Provincial Superior, 55 Parkwood Dr., Milton, MA 02186. (617) 696-7732. Fax: (617) 696-9405

CISTERCIAN NUNS (O.Cist)
Valley of Our Lady Monastery, E. 11096 Yanke Dr., Prairie du Sac, WI 53578-9737. (608) 643-3520. E-mail: volocist@chorus.net; Web: www.cistercianorder.org
10 Solemnly Professed Nuns, 2 Simple Professed, 1 Novice, 1 Postulant
Apostolic Work: As cloistered Nuns, the Sisters live the contemplative monastic life under the Rule of St. Benedict and are dedicated to the praise of God and intercession for the world through daily Mass, the Holy Eucharist, choir, sacred reading, personal prayer, study and work in silence within monastic enclosure. Choir prayer, the Divine Office, is sung in Cistercian Chant in sacred Latin.
Represented in the Diocese of Madison.
Vocation Directress: Sr. Marie Gabrielle Roux, O.Cist.

CISTERCIAN NUNS OF THE STRICT OBSERVANCE
See Trappistines

CLARETIAN MISSIONARY SISTERS (R.M.I.) (Religious of Mary Immaculate, Claretian Missionary Sisters)
18450 N.W. 12th Ave., Miami, FL 33169. (305) 652-4593; 7080 SW 99 Ave., Miami, FL 33173. (305) 274-6148; 7700 W. Lake Dr., West Palm Beach, FL 33406. (561) 433-4731. E-mail: vocations@claretiansisters.org; Web: www.claretiansisters.org
11 Sisters in US; 524 Sisters worldwide
Apostolic Work: Missions, education, youth, migrant, social and parish ministry. Theological formation in seminaries and institutes.
Represented in the Archdiocese of Miami and in the Diocese of Palm Beach. Also in Argentina, Belgium, Brazil, Cuba, Colombia, Dominican Republic, India, Korea, Panama, Venezuela, Honduras, Mexico, Philippines, Spain, Italy, Peru, Poland, Japan and Democratic Republic of Congo (Africa)

COLUMBAN SISTERS
See Missionary Sisters of St. Columban

COMBONI MISSIONARY SISTERS (C.M.S.) US Headquarters: 1307 Lakeside Ave., Richmond, VA 23228-4710. (804) 266-2975. E-mail: combonisrs@igc.org
1,780 Sisters
Apostolic Work: Foreign missions in

Africa, Latin America, and Middle East. Their charism is to share with the poorest of the poor God's love: to initiate and/or to collaborate in the building and strengthening of the local Christian community in union with the universal Church through their lives, words and works in schools, catechetical and pastoral centers, hospitals, dispensaries and leprosy centers; by fostering Christian family life and women's promotion and education; by collaborating in the formation of native clergy, sisters and laity; by working, living and dying for the realization of justice for the poor.

Represented in the Archdioceses of Philadelphia and Baltimore and in the Diocese of Richmond. The entire international community is represented in 33 different countries of the world.

Vocation Directress: Sr. Alzira Neres, CMS, 5405 Loch Raven Blvd., Baltimore, MD 21239. (410) 323-1469. E-mail: alziraneres@hotmail.com

COMMUNITY OF THE HOLY SPIRIT (C.H.S.) 6151 Rancho Mission Rd. #205, San Diego, CA 92108. (619) 584-0809

17 Sisters

Apostolic Work: Education, health care, social services.

Represented in the Dioceses of Oakland, Orange, Portland, Reno-Las Vegas, San Diego, San Jose and Wichita.

General Coordinator: Mary Jo Anderson, C.H.S., 2920 Union St., #103, San Diego, CA 92103. (619) 542-1448. E-mail: chsanderson@worldnet.att.net

COMMUNITY OF THE MOTHER OF GOD OF TENDERNESS

See Eastern Catholic Religious Communities for Women

COMMUNITY OF TERESIAN CARMELITES (C.T.C.)

(A community of Consecrated Men, Women and Lay Associates) Box 826, Worcester, MA 01613-0826. (508) 752-5734

6 Consecrated Members, 2 Postulants for Consecrated Life, 9 Professed Lay Associates, 8 Lay Novices

Apostolic Work: Contemplative/active: international telephone prayer-line, television ministry, Courage support group; soul, mind and body institute; Domus Mariae House of Prayer, missions and spiritual conferences, spiritual guidance, retreats, spiritual formation, lay associate meetings, parish religious education, newsletter, iconography.

Represented in the Diocese of Worcester.

Vocation Directors: Sister Nancy-Marie Connors, CTC, Brother Dennis Anthony Wyrzykowski, CTC; Lay Director: Arlene Wyrzykowski, c.t.c.s., Community of Teresian Carmelites, Box 826, Worcester, MA 01613-0826. (508) 752-5734. E-mail: srnancymarie@yahoo.com or broden39@aol.com; Web: www.teresiancarmelites.org

COMPANY OF MARY (O.D.N.)

Motherhouse: 16791 E. Main St., Tustin, CA 92780. (714) 541-3125

65 Sisters in US; 2,236 worldwide in 27 countries

Apostolic Work: Educators in the faith through: pre-schools to high school, free clinic, detention ministry, social service, retreat centers, parish ministry, residences for women, diocesan offices.

Represented in the Archdiocese of Los Angeles and in the Dioceses of Orange, San Bernardino and Tucson.

Vocation Minister: Sister Leticia Salazar, ODN, 16791 E. Main St., Tustin, CA 92780. (714) 282-3050. Fax: (714) 835-0648. E-mail: srlsalazar@rcbo.org; Web: www.Lestonnac.org

THE COMPANY OF THE SAVIOR (C.S.) 820 Clinton Ave., Bridgeport, CT 06604. (203) 368-1875

65 Sisters, 5 Novices, 5 Postulants

Represented in the Diocese of Bridgeport.

Vocation Director: Sr. Araceli Fernandez, 820 Clinton Ave., Bridgeport, CT 06604. (203) 368-1875

CONGREGATION OF THE CENACLE

See Cenacle, Congregation of the

CONGREGATION OF THE DIVINE SPIRIT (C.D.S.) Motherhouse: (Domus Caritas), 409 W. Sixth St., Erie, PA 16507

37 Sisters

Apostolic Work: Parish schools, CCD centers, home for senior citizens.

Represented in the Dioceses of Erie and Youngstown.

Vocation Directress: 409 W. Sixth St., Erie, PA 16507. (814) 455-3590

CONGREGATION OF THE INFANT JESUS

See Infant Jesus, Congregation of the

CONGREGATION OF NOTRE DAME (C.N.D.) (Blessed Sacrament Province)

Provincial House: 223 West Mountain Rd., Ridgefield, CT 06877. (203) 438-5282

170 Sisters, 1,700 worldwide

Apostolic Work: Teachers, social workers, school administrators, diocesan personnel, lawyers, counselors, parish ministers, retreat directors, campus ministers, college professors, chaplains and advocates for peace and nonviolence.

Represented in the (Arch)dioceses of Albany, Boston, Bridgeport, Brooklyn, Charlotte, Chicago, Hartford, Joliet, Newark, New York, Oklahoma City, Pensacola, Providence, Rapid City, Richmond, Scranton and Worcester. Also in Cameroon, Canada, El Salvador, France, Guatemala, Honduras, Japan and Paraguay.

Vocation Contact: Sr. Rose Mary Sullivan, CND, Notre Dame Academy Convent, 76 Howard Ave., Staten Island, NY 10301. (718) 447-0291. Fax: (718) 273-0462. E-mail: rmbsully@aol.com; Web: www.cnd-m.com

CONGREGATION OF THE RELIGIOUS MISSIONARIES OF ST. DOMINIC (O.P.)

Central House: 2237 Waldron St., Corpus Christi, TX 78418

Motherhouse: Rome, Italy

33 Sisters in US, 635 Sisters worldwide

Apostolic Works: Schools, religious education for Catholic students in public schools, day care centers, youth ministry, hospitals, residences for women college students.

Represented in the (Arch)dioceses of Corpus Christi and Los Angeles. Also in Italy, Spain, Portugal, Philippines, Taiwan, Thailand, Japan, Korea, Guam and Chile.

Vocation Contact: Vocation Promoter, 2237 Waldron Rd., Corpus Christi, TX 78418. (361) 939-8102. Fax: (361) 939-8203. E-mail: crmsdsis@swbell.net

CONGREGATION OF THE SISTERS OF JESUS CRUCIFIED

See Jesus Crucified, Congregation of the

CONGREGATION OF THE SISTERS OF OUR LADY OF MERCY

See "O" - Our Lady of Mercy, the Congregation of the Sisters of

CONSOLATA MISSIONARY SISTERS (MC) 6801 Belmont Ave., NE, P.O. Box 371, Belmont, MI 49306-9710. (616) 361-2072

Total members in Congregation: just

under 1,000, 24 Sisters in US
Apostolic Work: Primary work is evangelization among the poor which is carried out by ministries of teaching, nursing, social work, and pastoral ministry.
Represented in Michigan and Alabama, in 8 African countries, in 5 South American countries, and in 5 European countries.
Vocation Director: Sr. Zelia M. Cordeiro, MC, P.O. Box 97, Belmont, MI 49306-0097. (616) 361-9609. Fax: (616) 361-2049. E-mail: ghconsol@aol.com; Web: www.consolatasisters.org

CONTEMPLATIVE SISTERS OF THE GOOD SHEPHERD
See Sisters of the Good Shepherd

SISTERS OF THE CROSS OF THE SACRED HEART OF JESUS (R.C.S.C.J.) Motherhouse: Francisco Sosa 109, Delegacion Coyoacan, 04000 Mexico, D.F.
US Foundation: 1320 Maze Blvd., Modesto, CA 95351. (209) 526-3525
350 Sisters, 32 Novices, 12 Postulants
Apostolic Work: Contemplative Perpetual Adoration.
Represented in the Diocese of Stockton. Also in Rome, Guatemala, Costa Rica, Mexico, Spain and El Salvador.
Vocation Director: Sr. Adela Graciano, rcscj, 1320 Maze Blvd., Modesto, CA 95351. (209) 526-3525. E-mail: rcscjmodesto@hotmail.com

DAUGHTERS OF CHARITY OF THE MOST PRECIOUS BLOOD (D.C.P.B.)
500 Sisters
Apostolic Work: Education of the youth, care for the sick and the elderly. Apostolates in Italy, Brazil, Nigeria, India and the Philippines.
Conduct: 3 day nurseries, 1 rest home for elderly women.
Represented in the Dioceses of Albany, Bridgeport and Paterson
Vocation Directress: Sr. Maria Goretti Chaloux, D.C.P.B., 46 Preakness Ave., Paterson, NJ 07522. (973) 956-1921. E-mail: dcpbchalouxi@aol.com

DAUGHTERS OF THE CHARITY OF THE SACRED HEART OF JESUS (F.C.S.C.J.)
US Provincialate: Mount Sacred Heart, 226 Grove St., Littleton, NH 03561-4210. (603) 444-5346
Founded in France in 1823: Motherhouse in La Salle-de-Vihiers (Angers); Generalate in Montgeron (Paris)
60 Sisters (US); 1,200 in 10 countries.
Apostolic Work: Day care and education of children, youth and adults, health care, geriatric care, hospice, pastoral ministry, community service, retreat work, foreign missions.
Represented in the Archdiocese of Boston and in the Dioceses of Burlington, Fall River, Lafayette, Manchester, Ogdensburg and Portland (ME). Present in France, Canada, Lesotho, the Republic of South Africa, Togo, Benin, Madagascar, Brazil and Tahiti.
Vocation Director: Mount Sacred Heart, 226 Grove St., Littleton, NH 03561-4210. (603) 444-5346. Fax: (603) 444-5348. E-mail: wnddr.jed@verizon.net; Web: www.daughters-fcscj-charity-sacredheart.org

DAUGHTERS OF CHARITY OF ST. VINCENT DE PAUL (D.C.)
(Province of the West) 26000 Altamont Rd., Los Altos Hills, CA 94022-4317
140 Sisters; 23,000 worldwide
Ministries: High school, elementary schools, educational support services, health care, homes for children, home for unwed mothers, day care center, senior citizen apostolates, free dining room, transitional housing program, programs for babies prenatally-exposed to drugs, Catholic Charities, parish ministry, legal counseling, emergency assistance programs, ethnic minorities ministries, religious education, community outreach programs.
Represented in the Archdioceses of Los Angeles, San Francisco and Anchorage and in the Dioceses of Gallup, Monterey, Oakland, Phoenix, Salt Lake City and San Jose.
Vocation Director: Sr. Trang Truong, D.C., 26000 Altamont Rd., Los Altos Hills, CA 94022-4317. (650) 949-8890. E-mail: SrTrangTruong@dochs.org

DAUGHTERS OF CHARITY OF ST. VINCENT DE PAUL (D.C.)
(East Central Province) Mater Dei Provincialate, 9400 New Harmony Rd., Evansville, IN 47720-8912. (812) 963-7556. Fax: (812) 963-7526. E-mail: smb@doc-ecp.org; Web: www.doc-ecp.org
163 Sisters in Province, 24,000 Sisters worldwide
Apostolic Work: Sisters minister in elementary, high schools and universities, religious education, parish ministry, skilled nursing facilities, multi-hospital system, clinics, day care and neighborhood services, services and residences for the aged, social services and Catholic Charities offices, prison ministry, advocacy, homeless shelters, children's residence, home for retired Sisters, rural ministry and outreach services.
Represented in the Archdioceses of Chicago, Detroit, Indianapolis, Milwaukee and Mobile and in the Dioceses of Belleville, Birmingham, Evansville, Nashville, Jackson, Saginaw and Springfield (IL). Also in 90 countries worldwide.
Vocation Coordinator: Sister Mary Beth Kubera, D.C.

DAUGHTERS OF CHARITY OF ST. VINCENT DE PAUL (D.C.)
(Emmitsburg Province-Southeast)
Provincial House: Emmitsburg, MD 21727. (301) 447-3121
266 Sisters
Ministries: 3 high schools, 4 elementary schools, 5 hospitals, 4 ministry with the aged, 2 homes for unmarried mothers, 1 day care, 11 parish and social services, 3 Hispanic ministry, 2 soup kitchens, 3 diocesan work, 1 St. Elizabeth Seton Shrine and overseas missions.
Represented in the Archdioceses of Baltimore and Washington and in the Dioceses of Charleston, St. Augustine, Pensacola-Tallahassee, Raleigh, Richmond, Savannah and Wheeling-Charleston.
Vocation Directress: Sister Elizabeth Greim, D.C., 1201 Caton Ave., Baltimore, MD 21227-1092. (410) 646-2074. E-mail: dcvoc@atlantech.net; Web: www.daughtersofcharity-emmitsburg.org

DAUGHTERS OF CHARITY OF ST. VINCENT DE PAUL (D.C.)
(West Central Province) 4330 Olive St., St. Louis, MO 63108. (314) 533-4770
205 Sisters
Work in: parochial schools, high schools, hospitals, leprosarium, psychiatric hospitals, parish ministry, social service centers, day care centers, clinics, prison ministries, homes for aged, homes for children, shelter for women, neighborhood centers, Catholic Charities offices, refugee resettlement, senior citizens programs, higher education, diocesan offices, youth programs, HIV-AIDS ministry.
Represented in the Archdioceses of New Orleans, St. Louis and San Antonio and in the Dioceses of Austin, Baton Rouge, Brownsville, Dallas, El Paso, Kansas City, Little Rock, St. Joseph, San Angelo, Springfield-Cape Girardeau.

Vocation Contact: Sr. Loretto Gettemeier, D.C., Formation Councillor, 4330 Olive St., St. Louis, MO 63108. (314) 533-4770, ext. 223. E-mail: lgettemeier@dcwcp.org

DAUGHTERS OF CHARITY OF ST. VINCENT DE PAUL (D.C.)
(Northeast Province) Provincialate: De Paul Provincial House, 96 Menand Rd., Albany, NY 12204-1499. (518) 462-5593
199 Sisters
Apostolic Work: Campus ministries, child care centers, day care centers, elementary school, shelters, general hospitals and clinics, high schools, homes for special needs children, parish visiting, multi-service center, neighborhood centers, pastoral/parish ministries, social work with Catholic Charities, visiting home nursing, psychiatric care, geriatric care.
Represented in the Archdioceses of Boston, New York and Philadelphia and in the Dioceses of Albany, Allentown, Bridgeport, Brooklyn, Buffalo, Greensburg, Metuchen, Montreal, Ogdensburg, Syracuse and Wilmington. Also in over 50 foreign countries.
Vocation Director: Sr. Anne Marie Graham, D.C., Cathedral Residence, 420 Montgomery St., Syracuse, NY 13202-2920. (315) 471-6019. E-mail: amgrahamdc@yahoo.com; Web: www.dc-northeast.org

DAUGHTERS OF THE CROSS OF LIEGE (F.C.) Principal House: St. Bernard's Convent, 165 W. Eaton Ave., Tracy, CA 95376. (209) 835-7391. Also St. Joseph's Convent, 1168 S. Country Club, Stockton, CA 95204. (209) 944-9781. E-mail: fc1833@inreach.com
8 Sisters in the US
Apostolic Works: Serving the weak and poor in healthcare education and social ministries.
Represented in the Diocese of Stockton and in many countries worldwide.
Vocation Director: Sr. Marlene, F.C.

DAUGHTERS OF DIVINE CHARITY (F.D.C.) (Holy Trinity Province) St. Elizabeth's Briarbank, 39315 Woodward Ave., Bloomfield Hills, MI 48304-5024
23 Sisters
Conduct: 1 grammar school, 1 residence for women, 2 homes for the aged in the Midwest.
Represented in the Archdiocese of Detroit and in the Diocese of Ft. Wayne-So. Bend. Also on the East and West coasts of the US, Europe, No. and So. Brazil, Bolivia, Albania, Ukraine and Uganda (Africa).
Contact: Sister M. Innocentia, F.D.C., St. Elizabeth's Briarbank, 39315 Woodward Ave., Bloomfield Hills, MI 48304-5024. (248) 645-5318. Fax: (248) 644-1596

DAUGHTERS OF DIVINE CHARITY (F.D.C.) (St. Joseph Province) Provincial House: 205 Major Ave., Staten Island, NY 10305. (718) 720-4377
54 Sisters in US, 1,485 Sisters worldwide
Apostolic Work: Education (elementary and secondary), religious education, residence for young women in NYC, pastoral ministry.
Represented in the Archdiocese of New York and in the Dioceses of San Diego, Bridgeport and Metuchen.
Vocation Directors: Sister Marie Claire Weaver, Sister Denise Martin, St. Joseph Hill Convent, 850 Hylan Blvd., Staten Island, NY 10305. (718) 447-1374, ext. 103. Fax: (718) 447-3041. E-mail: srdenise1@hotmail.com

DAUGHTERS OF DIVINE CHARITY (F.D.C.) (St. Mary's Province) Provincial Motherhouse, 39 N. Portage Path, Akron, OH 44303-1183. (330) 867-4960
20 Sisters
Apostolic Work: Elementary education, home for young women, home for elderly senior men and women.
Represented in the Archdioceses of Milwaukee and Miami and in the Diocese of Cleveland.
Vocation Director: Leonora Hall Convent, 39 N. Portage Path, Akron, OH 44303-1183. (330) 867-4960. Fax: (330) 876-6334. E-mail: ddcakron@ameritech.net

DAUGHTERS OF THE HEART OF MARY (D.H.M.) Provincial House: 1339 Northampton St., Holyoke, MA 01040-1900. (413) 532-7406
US Province: 93; 1,800 professed members worldwide
Apostolic Work: Ministries are diversified according to gifts of individual women committed to Gospel values in the service of the Church.
Presently in US: Nardin Academy, Buffalo, NY; St. Joseph's School for the Deaf, Bronx, NY; Adelaides Place, Atlantic City, NJ. Serve on 5 continents in 30 countries.
Represented in the Archdioceses of New York, Boston, Philadelphia, Chicago, Newark, St. Paul, Detroit and St. Louis and in the Dioceses of Buffalo, Camden, Las Cruces, Ogdensburg, Springfield, Trenton and Venice.
Vocation Director: Anita Baird, D.H.M., Ephpheta Center, 140 N. Euclid Ave. #401, Oak Park, IL 60302. E-mail: anita1947@sbcglobal.net; Web: dhmna.org

DAUGHTERS OF THE HOLY SPIRIT (D.H.S.) Holy Spirit Provincial House, 72 Church St., Putnam, CT 06260
180 Sisters
Apostolic Work: Education: preschool through college; hospital and home nursing; pastoral work; migrant ministry; campus ministry; hospital chaplaincy; prison work; advocacy in the name of justice; home missions in the US; foreign missions in Chile, Peru, Nigeria, Cameroon, Burkina-Faso and Romania.
Serving in NY, New England, Alabama, California, Pennsylvania and Virginia.
Vocation Directress: Sr. Therese Vanasse, DHS, Holy Spirit Provincial House, 72 Church St., Putnam, CT 06260. (860) 928-0891. E-mail: srtherese@d-hs.org; Web: www.d-hs.org

DAUGHTERS OF THE HOLY SPIRIT (F.Sp.S.) 110 W. E Street, Lincoln, NE 68508
275 Sisters worldwide; 4 Sisters in US
Apostolic Work: Promotion of vocations to the priesthood; evangelization and youth ministry; in the US, acculturation of the Hispanic community.
Represented in the Diocese of Lincoln. Motherhouse (and most of the Sisters) in Mexico. Also in Rome, Bolivia and Chile.
Vocation Contact: Sr. Margarita Iturbide, F.Sp.S., 110 W. E Street, Lincoln, NE 68508. (402) 477-7646. E-mail: hijas2@alltel.net

DAUGHTERS OF MARY AND JOSEPH (D.M.J.) Provincialate: 5300 Crest Rd., Rancho Palos Verdes, CA 90275-5004. (310) 377-9968
Apostolic Work: Education, parish ministry, retreat ministry, counseling, Hispanic ministry.
Represented in the Archdioceses of Los Angeles and San Francisco and in the Dioceses of Monterey, Oakland, Orange, San Bernardino and San Diego.
Vocation Contact: Sr. Theresa Berry, DMJ, 10939 Rose Ave. #5, Los Angeles, CA 90034-5339. E-mail: tberrydmj@earthlink.net; Web: www.dmjca.org

DAUGHTERS OF MARY HELP OF CHRISTIANS (F.M.A.)
See "S" section - Salesian Sisters of St. John Bosco

CONGREGATION OF THE DAUGHTERS OF MARY IMMACULATE (Marianists) (F.M.I.)
See "M" - Marianist Sisters.

DAUGHTERS OF MARY OF THE IMMACULATE CONCEPTION (D.M.)
Motherhouse of the Immaculate Conception, 314 Osgood Ave., New Britain, CT 06053. (860) 225-9406
50 Sisters
Apostolic Work: 2 parochial schools, 1 home for the aged, 3 residences for women, 1 reading clinic, 2 skilled care facilities.
Represented in the Archdioceses of Boston, Hartford and New York and in the Diocese of Springfield.
Office of Vocations: Sister Mary Joseph Zimmerman, D.M., Vocation Director, St. Mary's Convent, 59 South St., Ware, MA 01082. (413) 967-5032. E-mail: dmvocdir@crossfire.org; Web: www.crossfire.org/daughtersofmary

DAUGHTERS OF OUR LADY OF THE HOLY ROSARY (F.M.S.R.)
1492 Moss St., New Orleans, LA 70119. (504) 486-0039
38 Sisters in US
Apostolic Work: Education of young people, especially the poorest. Parish ministry, nursing and counseling, and CCD. Ministry to both Vietnamese and American.
Represented in the Archdiocese of New Orleans. Also in Mississippi.
Vocation Director: Sr. Marie Francis Dang, F.M.S.R., 5122 N. Gates Ave., Long Beach, MS 39560. (228) 863-3045

DAUGHTERS OF OUR LADY OF MERCY (D.M.)
Provincial House & Novitiate: Villa Rossello, 1009 Main Rd., Newfield, NJ 08344-5348. (856) 697-2983
65 Sisters
Apostolic Work: Education, parish ministry, catechesis, counseling, child day care, ministry to elderly, missions.
Represented in the (Arch)dioceses of Camden, Harrisburg, Philadelphia and Scranton. Also in Italy, South America (Argentina, Bolivia, Brazil, Chile), England, Germany, Africa, India, Jamaica, Haiti and the Dominican Republic.
Vocation Directress: Villa Rossello, 1009 Main Rd., Newfield, NJ 08344-5348. (856) 697-2983. E:mail: dmnewfield@yahoo.com; Web: www.blessings-catalog.com/Special%20Orders/sp059.htmlfdmnet.org

DAUGHTERS OF OUR LADY OF THE SACRED HEART (F.D.N.S.C.)
St. Francis de Sales Convent, 424 E. Browning Rd., Bellmawr, NJ 08031
15 Sisters in US, 1,800 Sisters worldwide
Province: South Africa
Apostolic Work: Nursing, teaching (2 schools), pastoral ministry.
Represented in the (Arch)dioceses of Camden and Philadelphia.
Vocation Director: Sr. Mary Cradock, FDNSC, St. Francis de Sales Convent, 424 E. Browning Rd., Bellmawr, NJ 08031. (856) 931-8973. Web: www.religiouslife.com/w_dolshbellmawr.phtml

CONGREGATION OF THE DAUGHTERS OF ST. FRANCIS OF ASSISI (D.S.F.)
(American Province) 507 N. Prairie, Lacon, IL 61540
30 Sisters
Apostolic Work: Health care.
Represented in the Dioceses of Peoria and Springfield-Cape Girardeau. Also in Morelia, Mexico.
Vocation Director: Sister M. Donna Platte, DSF, 507 N. Prairie St., Lacon, IL 61540. (309) 246-2175

DAUGHTERS OF ST. JOSEPH (F.S.J.)
Provincial House: Mexico
US Foundation: 6677 Del Rosa Ave., San Bernardino, CA 92404
4 Sisters; 800 worldwide
Apostolic Work: Carrying the specific spirituality of Nazareth: work-prayer, especially with working women and laborers.
Represented in the Diocese of San Bernardino and in Mexico, Guatemala, Colombia, Argentina, Uruguay, Paraguay, Brazil, Africa, Spain, Portugal and Italy.
Vocation Director: Sr. Josephine Ornelas, F.S.J., 6677 Del Rosa Ave., San Bernardino, CA 92404. (909) 888-4877. Fax: (909) 888-4387

DAUGHTERS OF ST. MARY OF PROVIDENCE (D.S.M.P.) (The Guanellian Sisters)
Motherhouse: Daughters of St. Mary of Providence, 4200 N. Austin Ave., Chicago, IL 60634. (773) 205-1313
100 Sisters in US; 1,000 Sisters worldwide
Prayer Life: Divine Office, mass, rosary, meditation, holy hours, recollection days, yearly retreat for a week, spiritual reading, Stations of the Cross.
Apostolic Work: Residential facilities for developmentally disabled, parish work, nursing homes, retreat center, respite care.
Represented in the Archdioceses of Boston, Chicago and Philadelphia and in dioceses in Minnesota, South Dakota and Canada. Also in India, Italy, Mexico, the Philippines and South America.
Vocation Director: Sr. Barbara Moerman, D.S.M.P., 4200 N. Austin Ave., Chicago, IL 60634. (773) 545-8300. E-mail: dsmpnovchi@aol.com

DAUGHTERS OF ST. PAUL (F.S.P.)
US/Toronto Province: 50 Saint Pauls Ave., Boston, MA 02130-3491. (617) 522-8911. Fax: (617) 522-8648
Apostolic Work: Our mission of evangelization challenges us to bring the Gospel everywhere through our lives and all forms of media: books, music, radio, software, CD-ROM, audio and video tapes, Pauline Book & Media Centers, media education and catechetical workshops, Christian music seminars for youth and evangelization outreach in homes, schools and parishes. We are an international congregation of 2,600 women religious serving Christ and the Church in 49 nations.
Vocation Directors: Sr. Margaret Michael, FSP, 50 Saint Pauls Ave., Boston, MA 02130-3491. (617) 522-8911. Fax: (617) 541-9805. Sr. Helena Raphael, FSP, 3908 Sepulveda Blvd., Culver City, CA 90230. (310) 390-4699. Sr. Rebecca Marie, FSP, 4403 Veterans Blvd., New Orleans, LA 70006. (504) 887-0113. Sr. Linda James, FSP, 3022 Dufferin St., Toronto, Ontario, Canada M6B 3T5. (416) 781-9132. E-mail: vocations@pauline.org; Web: www.pauline.org

DAUGHTERS OF WISDOM (D.W.)
(US Province) Provincial House: 385 Ocean Ave., Islip, NY 11751-4600
International Congregation: Motherhouse: Vendee, France; Generalate: Rome, Italy
140 Sisters in US; 2,525 Sisters worldwide
Apostolic Work: Minister to a world broken by injustice and violence, especially to women, children and those displaced by war, oppression and poverty. Serving in rural communities and in the inner city to those lacking education, health care and basic human resources.
Represented in the Archdioceses of Chicago, Hartford, Mobile and

Washington (DC), and in the Dioceses of Arlington, Brooklyn, Burlington, Charleston, Portland (ME), Raleigh, Richmond, Rockville Centre, St. Augustine, St. Petersburg and Wheeling. Also in Africa, Asia, Canada, Europe, Haiti and South America.
Vocation Contact: Sr. Evelyn Eckhardt, D.W., Provincial Leader, Daughters of Wisdom, 385 Ocean Ave., Islip, NY 11751-4600. (631) 277-2660. E-mail: wisdomsisters@cs.com; Web: DaughtersofWisdom.org

SISTER DISCIPLES OF THE DIVINE MASTER (S.D.D.M.)
3700 North Cornelia Ave., Fresno, CA 93722. (559) 275-1656
48 Sisters in the US
Apostolic Work: Contemplative-active life style, Perpetual Adoration, collaboration with the priesthood, liturgical apostolate.
Represented in 27 nations throughout the world and in the Archdioceses of Boston, New York, Los Angeles, Fresno and San Jose.
Vocation Directress: Sr. Mary Peter Mendes, SDDM, 60 Sunset Ave., Staten Island, NY 10314. (718) 494-8597. E-mail: SrPeterM@aol.com; Web: www.pddm.us

SISTERS OF THE DIVINE COMPASSION (R.D.C.)
Motherhouse and Novitiate: Good Counsel Convent, 52 N. Broadway, White Plains, NY 10603. (914) 949-2950
120 Sisters
Apostolic Work: Education, health care, counseling, social service, parish ministry, migrant ministry, rural outreach, spiritual development.
Represented mostly in the Archdiocese of New York.
Vocation Director: Susan N. Becker, RDC, Good Counsel Convent, Office of Mission and Charism, 52 N. Broadway, White Plains, NY 10603. (914) 798-1109. E-mail: snbecker2000@yahoo.com; Web: www.divinecompassion.org

DIVINE MERCY (O.L.M.)
See "O" section - The Congregation of the Sisters of Our Lady of Mercy

COMMUNITY OF DIVINE PROVIDENCE (C.D.P.)
5 Cygnet Lane, Valley Cottage, NY 10989
Apostolic Work: House of prayer and hospitality, building Christian community through associate membership, retreats, spiritual direction, teaching, ministry to the sick.
Represented in the Archdiocese of New York.
Vocation Directors: Sister Catherine Reddy or Sister Gloria Jean Henchy, 5 Cygnet Lane, Valley Cottage, NY 10989. (914) 268-6314. E-mail: shenchy@aol.com

CONGREGATION OF DIVINE PROVIDENCE (CDP) SAN ANTONIO, TX Generalate: Our Lady of the Lake Convent, 515 S.W. 24th St., San Antonio, TX 78207-4619. (210) 434-1866
275 Sisters
Apostolic Work: Education: college, secondary and elementary; pastoral services, parish ministry, hospitals and clinics, hospice, social services, diocesan offices, retreats, counseling, spiritual direction, music.
Represented in the Archdioceses of Chicago, Denver, Mexico City, Milwaukee, New Orleans, Oklahoma City and San Antonio and in the Dioceses of Alexandria, Allentown, Austin, Baton Rouge, Brownsville, Corpus Christi, Dallas, El Paso, Fort Worth, Ft. Wayne-So. Bend, Fresno, Galveston-Houston, Lafayette, (LA), Lake Charles, Lexington, Oakland, San Angelo, St. Cloud, Springfield/Cape Girardeau, Tulsa and Victoria. Also in Mexico: Queretaro, Saltillo, San Cristobal, Tehuantepec.
Vocation Ministry Team: Sister Elsa Garcia, CDP, Sister Sharon Rohde, CDP, Our Lady of the Lake Convent, 515 S.W. 24th St., San Antonio, TX 78207-4619. (210) 434-1866, ext. 1130, 1132. E-mail: elsacdp@aol.com, srohde201@aol.com; Web: www.cdptexas.org

DAUGHTERS OF DIVINE PROVIDENCE (F.D.P.)
Motherhouse: Italy
US Delegation: 3100 Mumpfrey Rd., Chalmette, LA 70043-3735
About 300 Sisters worldwide; 6 in the US
Apostolic Work: Education, catechesis, parish ministry, ministry to the sick, elderly, poor and needy.
Represented in the Archdiocese of New Orleans and in the Diocese of Alexandria. Also in Italy, India, Chile, Spain and Mexico.
Vocation Director: 3100 Mumpfrey Rd., Chalmette, LA 70043-3735. (504) 279-4617. Fax: (504) 279-3002. E-mail: convent@bellsouth.net

SISTERS OF DIVINE PROVIDENCE (C.D.P.) St. Anne Convent, 1000 St. Anne Dr., Melbourne, KY 41059. (859) 441-0700
165 Professed Sisters
Apostolic Work: Education (Montessori, elementary, secondary, college), social services, religious education, pastoral ministry (parish, hospital), health care, foreign missions, peace and justice ministry, retreat ministry.
Represented in the (Arch)dioceses of Cincinnati, Covington, Duluth, Indianapolis, Jackson, Lexington, Louisville, Manchester, New York, Toledo and Washington (DC) and Wheeling-Charleston. Also in Latacunga, Ecuador and in Ghana, West Africa.
Vocation Director: Sister Fidelis Tracy, CDP, St. Anne Convent, 1000 St. Anne Dr., Melbourne, KY 41059. (859) 441-0700, ext. 324. E-mail: vocation@cdpkentucky.org; Web: www.cdpkentucky.org

SISTERS OF DIVINE PROVIDENCE (C.D.P.) (Province of Our Lady of Divine Providence)
Provincial House: 363 Bishops Hwy., Kingston, MA 02364
45 Sisters
Apostolic Work: Education at all school levels – pre-primary through high school, catechetical and spiritual leadership, counseling, pastoral ministry and nursing care.
Represented in the Archdiocese of Boston and in the Diocese of Richmond. Also in other US provinces in Germany, Puerto Rico, Peru and South Korea.
Vocation Directress: Sister Mary Francis Fletcher, 363 Bishops Hwy., Kingston, MA 02364. (781) 585-1745. E-mail: cdpfletcher@rcn.com

SISTERS OF DIVINE PROVIDENCE (C.D.P.) Marie de La Roche Province, Pittsburgh, PA 15101
Provincial Office: Providence Heights, 9000 Babcock Blvd., Allison Park, PA 15101. Web: www.divineprovidenceweb.org
320 Sisters, 180 Associates (Co-Members)
Apostolic Work: Higher education, high schools, elementary schools, religious education and special education, pastoral ministry, campus ministry, social service, hospital, clerical, pastoral care, House of Prayer, day care, ministry with the aging, social concerns, health care, foster care, retreat ministry, psychological counseling and therapy, advocacy, ministry with refugees, Hispanic ministry, ministry with the homeless; missionary work.
Represented in dioceses throughout the US. Also in Puerto Rico, Santo Domingo and Romania.

Vocation Directresses: Sr. Elena Almendarez, CDP, Vocation Discernment, 9000 Babcock Blvd., Allison Park, PA 15101. (412) 365-6309. Fax: (412) 635-5416. E-mail: elenacdp@juno.com; Sr. Linda Hylla, CDP, Vocation Discernment, Quest House, 1011 Alton Ave., Madison, IL 62060. (618) 451-9693. E-mail: srlindahylla@hotmail.com

SISTERS OF THE DIVINE REDEEMER (S.D.R.)

Divine Redeemer Motherhouse, 999 Rock Run Rd., Elizabeth, PA 15037. (412) 751-8600

45 Sisters

Apostolic Work: Witness to God's redeeming love through care of the sick, the poor, and the elderly; education, domestic service, parish ministry, retreat work and pastoral care.

Represented in the Diocese of Pittsburgh.

Vocation Director: Sister Joanne Tricsko, S.D.R. (412) 751-8600

SISTERS OF THE DIVINE SAVIOR

See "S" - Salvatorians

CLOISTERED DOMINICAN NUNS (O.P.) Monastery of the Infant Jesus, 1501 Lotus Ln., Lufkin, TX 75904-2600. (936) 634-4233. E-mail: spvernl@attglobal.net; Web: www.ewtn.com/infantjesus/

28 Sisters

Vocation Director: Sr. Mary William. (936) 634-4233

DOMINICAN CONTEMPLATIVE SISTERS, O.P. Monastery of the Heart of Jesus, 155 Church Street, Lockport, LA 70374. (985) 532-2411

5 Professed Sisters

Cloistered Contemplative Life.

Represented in the Diocese of Houma-Thibodaux.

Vocation Directress: Sr. Marie-Therese, O.P.

DOMINICAN NUNS (O.P.)

19 Sisters

Contemplative: Solemn liturgy, community life, solitude, study, work, adoration of the Blessed Sacrament.

Vocation Director: Sr. Mary of Nazareth, O.P., Corpus Christi Monastery, 215 Oak Grove Ave., Menlo Park, CA 94025-3272. (650) 322-1801, ext. 19. E-mail: mnazareth@juno.com; Web: www.op.org/nunsmenlo

DOMINICAN NUNS (O.P.)

Our Lady of Grace Monastery

38 Nuns, 2 in Formation

Apostolic Work: Monastic life constituted by the observances of the common life, the celebration of the liturgy and private prayer, solemn vows and the study of sacred truth. To fulfill these faithfully, the Sisters are helped by enclosure, silence, the habit, work and penitential practices. Monastery has perpetual adoration of the Blessed Sacrament.

Vocation Director: Sister Susan, O.P., Our Lady of Grace Monastery, 11 Race Hill Rd., North Guilford, CT 06437-1099. (203) 457-0599. E-mail: olgracevocations@juno.com; Web: www.op-stjoseph.org/nuns/olgrace/olgrace.htm

DOMINICAN NUNS (O.P.)

St. Dominic's Monastery, 4901 16th St. N.W., Washington, DC 20011-3839. (202) 726-2107

9 Solemnly Professed Sisters, 1 Novice, 1 Postulant

Cloistered contemplative life: Fidelity to the Holy Father, choral celebration of the Divine Office, daily exposition of the Blessed Sacrament. A life lived in community, balanced with lectio divina, private prayer, silence, study and work.

Vocation Directress: St. Dominic's Monastery, 4901 16th St. N.W., Washington, DC 20011-3839

DOMINICAN NUNS (O.P.)

(Province of St. Joseph) Mother of God Monastery, 1430 Riverdale St., West Springfield, MA 01089-4698

Apostolate Work: Monastic contemplative life with perpetual adoration of the Blessed Sacrament. 19 nuns daily celebrating the entire Liturgy of the Hours and having as the focal point of the day the solemn and joyful celebration of the Eucharistic Liturgy. Devotion to Mary, Mother of God, especially through praying the Rosary, is characteristic of the community.

Vocation Directress: Sister Mary of the Pure Heart, O.P., Mother of God Monastery, 1430 Riverdale St., West Springfield, MA 01089-4698. (413) 736-3639. Fax: (413) 736-0850. E-mail: monasteryws@aol.com; Web: www.op-stjoseph.org/nuns/ws

DOMINICAN NUNS (O.P.)

Monastery of the Blessed Sacrament, 29575 Middlebelt Rd., Farmington Hills, MI 48334

33 Sisters, 5 in Formation

Apostolic Work: Our monastic contemplative vocation balances a life of solitude with life in community. The whole of our life is aimed at the continual remembrance of God, especially through liturgical/personal prayer, study and work.

Vocation Directress: Sr. Mary Peter, O.P., Monastery of the Blessed Sacrament, 29575 Middlebelt Rd., Farmington Hills, MI 48334. (248) 626-8253. E-mail: vocdir1@qwest.net; Web: www.opnuns-fh.org

DOMINICAN NUNS (O.P.)

Monastery of Our Lady of the Rosary, 543 Springfield Ave., Summit, NJ 07901-4498

16 Solemnly Professed, 1 Novice, 1 Postulant

Apostolic Work: Monastic contemplative life. Consecrated to a life of prayer and praise, we share in the redemptive work of Christ in the heart of the Order of Preachers. In striving to live with one mind and heart in God, we seek to know and love God in the living of the traditional monastic observances of the daily Eucharist, chanted Divine Office, lectio divina, private prayer, study and work. We also have the privilege of Perpetual Adoration and Rosary, contemplating the mysteries of our salvation. The Dominican nun's life is one of hidden apostolic fruitfulness as she proclaims the Gospel of Christ by the witness of her life.

Represented in the Archdiocese of Newark.

Vocation Directress: Monastery of Our Lady of the Rosary, 543 Springfield Ave., Summit, NJ 07901-4498. (908) 273-1228. E-mail: vocations.summit@op.org; Web: www.op.org/nunsopsummit

DOMINICAN NUNS, CLOISTERED (O.P.) (Nuns of the Order of Preachers) (Corpus Christi Monastery) 1230 Lafayette Ave., Bronx, NY 10474-5399. (718) 328-6996. E-mail: maryofjesus@juno.com; Web: www.catholic.org/macc

Perpetual Adoration of the Most Blessed Sacrament, Contemplatives

17 Professed, 2 Novices

Prioress: Sr. Maria Pia of the Eucharist, O.P.

DOMINICAN NUNS (O.P.)

Monastery of Mary the Queen, 1310 W. Church St., Elmira, NY 14905

15 Nuns

Apostolic Work: We have dedicated ourselves to the following of Jesus Christ within the monastic, contemplative tradition given to us by St. Dominic. We do this principally through: Prayer offered both in a common liturgy, and in solitude which issues from an attentive listening to the Lord speaking in the Scriptures and the study of sacred truth; Community life marked by a freedom of spirit arising from our

poverty, chastity, and obedience, a common labor and a sisterly love; An Apostolic Spirit which finds expression in a joyful hospitality and a universal solidarity with all people in their needs.
Vocation Directress: Sister Joan, O.P., Monastery of Mary the Queen, 1310 W. Church St., Elmira, NY 14905. E-mail: elmiraop@local net.com; Web: www.op.org/mary queen/

DOMINICAN NUNS OF THE PERPETUAL ROSARY (O.P.)
Dominican Monastery of St. Jude, PO Box 170, Marbury, AL 36051
7 Sisters, 1 Postulant
Apostolic Work: Following the tradition established by St. Dominic in 1207, we live a life of contemplation in the monastic tradition. Our small community preaches the Gospel by the witness of our lives; we serve God by living out our vows of poverty, chastity and obedience and adoration of the Blessed Sacrament and devotion to Our Lady. Along with daily celebration of the Eucharist, we commit ourselves to praying the Liturgy of the Hours in English and Latin.
Vocation Directress: Mother Prioress, Dominican Monastery of St. Jude, PO Box 170, Marbury, AL 36051. (205) 755-1322. E-mail: stjudemonastery@juno.com; Web: www.archden.org/vocations/dominic annuns.htm

DOMINICAN NUNS OF PERPETUAL ADORATION (O.P.)
Monastery of the Angels, 1977 Carmen Ave., Los Angeles, CA 90068. (323) 466-2186. Web: www. op-stjoseph.org/nuns/angels
23 Sisters
Apostolic Work: A cloistered community observing norms of a full contemplative life.
Vocation Director: Sister Mary St. Peter, O.P.

DOMINICAN NUNS OF THE PERPETUAL ROSARY (O.P.)
Monastery of the Dominican Nuns of the Perpetual Rosary, 605 14th and West Sts., Union City, NJ 07087-3199. (201) 866-7004
8 Professed Sisters, 2 Aspirants
Cloistered
Prioress: Mother Mary Clare, O.P.

DOMINICAN NUNS OF THE PERPETUAL ROSARY (O.P.)
Monastery of the Perpetual Rosary, 1500 Haddon Ave., Camden, NJ 08103-3112
Contact: Mother Mary Anne, O.P., Prioress

DOMINICAN NUNS OF THE PERPETUAL ROSARY (O.P.)
Monastery of Our Lady of the Rosary, 335 Doat St., Buffalo, NY 14211-2199. (716) 892-0066
25 Nuns, 2 Extern Sisters, 3 Novices
Apostolic Work: Contemplative: Perpetual Adoration and Perpetual Rosary.
Vocation Director: Sr. Mary Gemma, O.P.

DOMINICAN NUNS OF THE PERPETUAL ROSARY (O.P.)
(Contemplative Community)
802 Court St., Syracuse, NY 13208-1766. (315) 471-6762
13 Sisters
Prioress: Sister Bernadette Marie, OP

DOMINICAN NUNS OF THE PERPETUAL ROSARY (O.P.)
Monastery of the Immaculate Heart of Mary, 1834 Lititz Pike, Lancaster, PA 17601-6585. (717) 569-2104
11 Nuns, 1 Aspirant
Apostolic Work: Contemplative monastic life.
Contact: Mother Prioress, Monastery of the Immaculate Heart of Mary, 1834 Lititz Pike, Lancaster, PA 17601-6585. (717) 569-2104. E-mail: monlanc@aol.com

DOMINICAN SISTERS OF ADRIAN (O.P.) Motherhouse: 1257 E. Siena Heights Dr., Adrian, MI 49221-1793. (517) 266-3400. Fax: (517) 266-3545
1,000+ Members
Apostolic Work: Education at all levels, pastoral work, health care, social work, direct social action, legal assistance, community development, theology, preaching and the fine arts.
Represented in 37 states, the Dominican Republic, Puerto Rico and South Africa.
Vocation Director: Sister Carleen Maly, OP, 1257 E. Siena Heights Dr., Adrian, MI 49221-1793. (1-866) 774-0005 toll-free; (517) 266-3537. Fax: (517) 266-3524. E-mail: voc@ adriansisters.org; Web: www.adrian sisters.org

DOMINICAN SISTERS OF AKRON (O.P.) Our Lady of the Elms Motherhouse, 1230 W. Market St., Akron, OH 44313-7108
89 Sisters
Apostolic Work: Education on all levels preschool through college including religious education and earth education; pastoral ministry in parishes, counseling, social work. Hospital ministry, ministry to elderly and shut-ins. Preaching, retreat work and spiritual direction. Library work, clerical, food service, administration, applied and fine arts, Guatemalan missions.
Represented in the Archdioceses of Anchorage, Portland (OR) and Seattle and in the Dioceses of Cleveland, Fort Wayne-South Bend, Lansing, Phoenix, Toledo, Venice and Youngstown.
Vocation Contact: Sister Bernadine Baltrinic, O.P., Our Lady of the Elms Motherhouse, 1230 W. Market St., Akron, OH 44313-7108. (330) 836-4908. E-mail: btbaltrinic@akronop .org; Web: www.akronop.org

DOMINICAN SISTERS OF AMITYVILLE (O.P.) Queen of the Rosary Motherhouse, 555 Albany Ave., Amityville, NY 11701
620 Sisters
Apostolic Work: Teaching, hospital ministry, parish ministry, communications and media, congregational service, counseling, religious education, campus ministry, social work, law, medicine, preaching teams and others.
Represented in five Archdioceses and 12 Dioceses. Also in Puerto Rico.
Vocation Director: Sr. Diane Capuano, O.P., Queen of the Rosary Motherhouse, 555 Albany Ave., Amityville, NY 11701. (631) 842-6000. Fax: (631) 841-3424. E-mail: sisdiop@aol.com; Web: www. amityvilleop.org

DOMINICAN SISTERS OF BLAUVELT (O.P.) Motherhouse: St. Dominic Convent, 496 Western Hwy., Blauvelt, NY 10913-2097. (845) 359-5600
Vowed, Associate Membership, Dominican Lay Volunteers
Apostolic Work: Education, college, high schools, elementary, child care, ministry with the blind, developmentally challenged, migrant children, pastoral, social and health care, preaching ministry, outreach to homeless and those with AIDS.
Represented in (Arch)dioceses in New York, New Jersey, Providence, RI, St. Petersburg, FL and Jamaica, W.I.
Vocation Minister: Sister Theresa Lardner, O.P., Convent of St. Dominic, 496 Western Hwy., Blauvelt, NY 10913-2097. (845) 359-0696. Fax: (845) 359-5773. E-mail: vocation@opblauvelt.org; Web: www.opblauvelt.org

DOMINICAN SISTERS, CABRA (O.P.) (Our Lady of the Rosary)
Regional House: 1930 Robert E. Lee Blvd., New Orleans, LA 70122.

(504) 288-1593
11 Sisters in US; 500 Sisters worldwide
Apostolic Work: A variety of educational ministries, pastoral work, spiritual direction, retreats, community organizing.
Represented in the Archdiocese of New Orleans, and in the Dioceses of Fort Worth and Houma-Thibodeaux.
Vocation Director: Sr. Mary Hilary Simpson, OP, 7300 St. Charles, New Orleans, LA 70118. (504) 861-2402. Fax: (504) 861-8184. E-mail: SrMHilary@dominican-sisters.net or archband@aol.com; Web: www.dominican-sisters.net/stmarys/joining.htm

DOMINICAN SISTERS OF CALDWELL, NEW JERSEY (O.P.)
Motherhouse: 1 Ryerson Ave., Caldwell, NJ 07006
190 Sisters
Apostolic Work: Education at all levels, pastoral ministry, health and human services, campus ministry, preaching and earth study (Genesis Farm).
Represented in the Archdiocese of Newark and in six other dioceses in the US. Also in the Dominican Republic.
Vocation Director: Sr. Kathleen Tuite, op, 1 Ryerson Ave., Caldwell, NJ 07006. (973) 228-2425. E-mail: ktuite@caldwellop.org; Web: www.caldwellop.org

DOMINICAN SISTERS OF CHARITY OF THE PRESENTATION OF THE BLESSED VIRGIN (O.P.)
3012 Elm St., Dighton, MA 02715
3,200 Sisters worldwide (in 37 countries)
Apostolic Work in US: 1 hospital, caring for the aged, rural health, pastoral care, education, parish ministry, 1 house of studies, home health care, social work, ministry to immigrants, ministry to Hispanics, mission in Korea.
Represented in the Archdiocese of Washington, DC and in the Dioceses of Brownsville, Fall River and Providence. Also in Puchon, Korea.
Vocation Directress: Sr. Faye Medina, O.P., 3012 Elm St., Dighton, MA 02715. (508) 669-5460. E-mail: srfaye@netscape.net; web: www.dominicansistersofthepresentation.org

DOMINICAN SISTERS OF GRAND RAPIDS (OP) Motherhouse: Marywood, 2025 E. Fulton St., Grand Rapids, MI 49503-3895
320 Sisters
Apostolic Work: Education at all levels, parish and campus ministry, health care, social service, liturgy, social justice ministries, retreat work, diocesan personnel.
Represented in 6 Michigan Dioceses, New Mexico and 17 other states. Foreign missions in Chimbote (Peru) and Honduras.
Vocation Director: Joellen Barkwell, O.P., Marywood, 2025 E. Fulton St., Grand Rapids, MI 49503-3895. (800) 253-7343, (616) 459-2910, ext. 144. Fax: (616) 454-6105. E-mail: jbarkwell@grdominicans.org; Web: www.GRDominicans.org

DOMINICAN SISTERS OF GREAT BEND (OP) 3600 Broadway, Great Bend, KS 67530-3692. (620) 792-1232
122 Sisters
Apostolic Work: Teaching, parish ministry, religious education, pastoral care, nursing, care of aging, home health, holistic health, social service, foreign missions, retreat and spirituality center, permaculture farming, presence with and housing for the poor.
Represented in the (Arch)dioceses of Denver, Dodge City, Phoenix, Pueblo, St. Louis, Salina, San Angelo and Wichita. Also in Nigeria, West Africa and Papua New Guinea.
Vocation Minister: Sister Teri Wall, OP, 3600 Broadway, Great Bend, KS 67530-3692. (620) 792-1232. Fax: (620) 792-1746. E-mail: teriop@ksdom.org; Web: www.ksdom.org

DOMINICAN SISTERS OF HAWTHORNE (O.P.) (Servants of Relief for Incurable Cancer)
Motherhouse and Novitiate: Rosary Hill Home, 600 Linda Ave., Hawthorne, NY 10532
Apostolic Work: Dedicated to the care of incurable cancer patients.
Represented in the Archdioceses of New York, Philadelphia and St. Paul and in the Dioceses of Cleveland and Atlanta.
Vocation Directress: Sister Teresa Marie Barnaby, O.P., Rosary Hill Home, 600 Linda Ave., Hawthorne, NY 10532. (914) 769-4794 or 0114. E-mail: SrTeresaM@aol.com; Web: www.hawthorne-dominicans.org

DOMINICAN SISTERS OF HOPE (O.P.) 299 N. Highland Ave., Ossining, NY 10562-2327
286 Sisters
Apostolic Work: Proclaiming HOPE for the new millennium, our Sisters minister wherever they have discerned a call to serve others. As followers of St. Dominic, we are called to embrace the values of prayer, study and common life for the sake of the mission. Our mission is to bring HOPE to the world by proclaiming and witnessing to the life-giving and healing Word of God.
Represented in 18 states and Puerto Rico.
Vocation Contact: Sr. Mary Headley, O.P., 299 N. Highland Ave., Ossining, NY 10562-2327. (914) 941-4420. Fax: (914) 941-1125. E-mail: mheadley@ophope.org; Web: www.ophope.org

DOMINICAN SISTERS OF HOUSTON (O.P.) Dominican Sisters, 6501 Almeda Road, Houston, TX 77021-2095. (713) 747-3310
124 Sisters Professed, 2 Temporarily Professed
Apostolic Work: Education at all levels, pastoral work, health care, social work, direct social action, theology, preaching and the fine arts, foreign mission.
Represented in Dioceses of Galveston-Houston, Austin, Beaumont, San Antonio, TX; Archdioceses of Los Angeles and San Francisco, CA; Dioceses of San Bernardino, CA; and Guatemala City, Guatemala, Central America.
Vocation Co-Directors: Sr. Julie Marie Greig, O.P., Sr. Lydia Delgado, O.P., 6505 Almeda Rd., Houston, TX 77021-2095. (713) 741-7076. E-mail: jgreig@domhou.org; Web: www.op.org/houstonop

DOMINICAN SISTERS (O.P.) (Congregation of the Immaculate Conception) Motherhouse: Poland; Provincial House, 9000 W. 81st St., Justice, IL 60458. (708) 458-3040
29 Sisters in US; approximately 400 worldwide
Apostolic Work: Teaching, ministry to the sick, parish work.
Represented in the (Arch)dioceses of Chicago, Milwaukee and Little Rock. Also in Calgary, Canada; Rome and Naples, Italy; Cameroon, Africa; Russia, Ukraine and Bielorussia.
Vocation Contact: Sister Koleta, O.P.

DOMINICAN SISTERS OF KENOSHA (O.P.) PO Box 1288, Kenosha, WI 53141-1288
20 Sisters
Apostolic Work: Education, healing ministry, care of the aged, social services, parish ministry, ministry to Hispanic peoples, foreign mission.
Represented in the Archdioceses of Milwaukee and San Francisco and in the Dioceses of Baker and Fresno.
Vocation Director: PO Box 1288, Kenosha, WI 53141-1288. (414) 694-2067. E-mail: kenoshaop@aol.com

DOMINICAN SISTERS OF MISSION SAN JOSE (O.P.) Motherhouse: PO Box 3908, Fremont, CA 94539

270 Sisters

Conduct: 1 junior college, 5 high schools, 19 elementary schools, 1 school of music.

Apostolic Work: Preachers of the Good News of Jesus Christ through the ministry of Christian education in elementary, high schools and colleges, campus ministry, parish ministry, pastoral ministry in hospitals, prisons, social justice and other ministries.

Represented in the Archdioceses of Los Angeles, Portland (OR) and San Francisco and in the Dioceses of Oakland, Orange, San Jose and Tucson. Also in Mexico and Germany.

Vocation Director: S. Helana Im, O.P., PO Box 3908, Fremont, CA 94539. (510) 657-2468. E-mail: msjhelena@yahoo.com; Web: www.msjdominicans.org

DOMINICAN SISTERS OF NASHVILLE (O.P.) General Motherhouse: St. Cecilia Convent, 801 Dominican Dr., Nashville, TN 37228-1909. (615) 256-5486

208 Sisters; 75 in Formation

Conduct: 1 college, 3 academies, 3 high schools, 20 elementary schools, 2 private elementary schools, 2 private kindergartens.

Represented in the Archdioceses of Baltimore, Chicago, Cincinnati, New Orleans, St. Paul/Minneapolis and Washington, DC and in the Dioceses of Arlington, Birmingham, Denver, Memphis, Knoxville, Nashville, Richmond and Rome, Italy.

Vocation Director: Sr. Catherine Marie, O.P., St. Cecilia Convent, 801 Dominican Dr., Nashville, TN 37228-1909. (615) 256-0147. E-mail: srcmarie@cs.com; Web: nashvilledominican.org

DOMINICAN SISTERS OF OAKFORD (O.P.) US Regional Center: 980 Woodland Ave., San Leandro, CA 94577. (510) 638-2822

21 Sisters

Conduct: 1 regional center, 1 novitiate. Serve in health care, home care, social work and parishes.

Represented in the Dioceses of Oakland, Phoenix, San Bernardino, San Jose and Tucson. Serve in South Africa, Germany and England.

Vocation Director: Sr. Lynn Allvin, OP, St. Timothy Catholic Community, 1730 W. Guadalupe Rd., Mesa, AZ 85202; 2754 S. Pennington, Mesa, AZ 85202. (480) 775-5215. E-mail: joy2allvin@juno.com

DOMINICAN SISTERS OF OXFORD
775 W. Drahner Rd. #250, Oxford, MI 48371-4866

42 Sisters

Apostolic Work: Education, health care, pastoral ministry, child care, retreats, preaching, spiritual direction, peace and justice.

Represented in the Archdiocese of Chicago and in the Dioceses of Detroit, Lansing and Saginaw, MI and East Chicago, IN. Summer ministry in Jamaica.

Vocation Director: Sr. Gene Poore, OP, 775 W. Drahner Rd. #250, Oxford, MI 48371-4866. (248) 628-2872. E-mail: gpoore@umich.edu; Web: www.op.org/oxford

DOMINICAN SISTERS OF THE PERPETUAL ROSARY (O.P.) (Cloistered, Contemplative)
217 N. 68th St., Milwaukee, WI 53213-3928. (414) 258-0579. E-mail: opvocdir@dsopr.org; Web: www.dsopr.org

12 Professed Sisters, 1 Novice, 1 Postulant

Vocation Director: Sr. M. Timothy Dominique, O.P.

DOMINICAN SISTERS OF RACINE (O.P.) Siena Center, 5635 Erie St., Racine, WI 53402-1900

212 Members

Apostolic Work: All levels of education, health care, pastoral ministry, retreats and spiritual direction, art and music, social services, counseling, prison ministry and social justice concerns.

Represented in 14 states.

Vocation Director: Sister Karen Vollmer, O.P., 5635 Erie St., Racine, WI 53402-1900. (262) 639-4100, ext. 1264. E-mail: racineop@execpc.com; Web: www.racinedominicans.org

DOMINICAN SISTERS OF THE ROMAN CONGREGATION (O.P.)
Provincial Residence: 123 Dumont Ave., Lewiston, ME 04240-6107. (207) 782-3535. Fax: (207) 782-0435. E-mail: moniqueb@megalink.net-e-mail

24 Sisters in US; 550 worldwide

Apostolic Work: Education at all levels, parish and pastoral ministries, mission work on the Navajo Reservation, health care.

Represented in the Archdioceses of New York and Chicago and in the Dioceses of Davenport, Gallup, Phoenix, Portland, ME and Portland, OR. In countries of US, Canada, Brazil, Belgium, Sweden, France, Italy, Switzerland, Benin, Japan, Spain.

Vocation Contacts: (Maine) Sr. Christine Plouffe, OP, Dominican Sisters, 61 Lisbon Rd., Sabattus, ME 04280. (New York) Sr. Francesca Cloutier, OP, Dominican Sisters, 61 Wellbrook Ave., Staten Island, NY 10314. (Mid-West) Sr. Jacqueline Provencher, OP, Dominican Sisters, 304 Oberlin St., Iowa City, IA 52245. (Southwest) Sr. Timothy McHatten, OP, Mount Angel Seminary, St. Benedict, OR 97373-0505

DOMINICAN SISTERS OF ST. CATHERINE DE' RICCI (OP)
750 Ashbourne Rd., Elkins Park, PA 19027-2596. (215) 635-6027

100 Sisters

Apostolic Work: Retreat ministry, religious education, parish ministry, pastoral counseling, ministry with the poor, social services.

Represented in the Archdioceses of Miami, Detroit, Albany, Philadelphia, Santa Fe and Baltimore and in 12 dioceses.

Vocation Director: Sr. Pat Moran, OP, 750 Ashbourne Rd., Elkins Park, PA 19027-2596. (215) 635-6027, ext. 12. Fax: (215) 635-5435. E-mail: spatmoranvoc@hotmail.com; Web: www.elkinsparkop.org/members.htm

DOMINICAN SISTERS OF ST. CATHARINE OF SIENA (O.P.)
St. Catharine Motherhouse, 2645 Bardstown Rd., St. Catharine, KY 40061. (859) 336-9303

230 Sisters

Apostolic Work: The Dominican charism of preaching the Word of God is lived by the Sisters in their ministries as educators, health-care providers, advocates for the homeless, pastoral ministers in parishes and retreat centers, counselors and through other ministries that address contemporary needs.

Represented in the Dioceses of Boston, Brooklyn, Chicago, Grand Island, Louisville, Memphis and Omaha; in about 17 other dioceses in lesser numbers.

Vocation Director: Sister Christine Connolly, O.P., 5345 S. Hyde Park Blvd. 3W, Chicago, IL 60615-5722. (773) 684-1595. E-mail: chrisctu@juno.com; Web: www.opkentucky.org

DOMINICAN SISTERS OF ST. MARY OF THE SPRINGS (O.P.)
2320 Airport Dr., Columbus, OH 43219-2098

305 Sisters

Conduct: 2 colleges, high schools, elementary schools, learning center,

parish ministry, senior citizens apartment building, involvement in many aspects of pastoral ministry. Foreign mission-Chimbote, Peru.
Apostolic Work: Diversified ministries which include education at all levels, parish ministries, health care, spirituality ministry, social work, foreign missions, etc.
Represented in (Arch)dioceses in Colorado, Connecticut, Florida, Indiana, Louisiana, Maryland, Massachusetts, Michigan, Missouri, New Mexico, New York, Ohio, Pennsylvania, Virginia, Washington State, West Virginia and Wisconsin. Also in Peru, South America, Honduras, and Italy.
Vocation Director: Sr. Margie Davis, OP, St. Mary of the Springs, 2320 Airport Dr., Columbus, OH 43219-2098. (614) 416-1056. E-mail: mdavis@columbusdominicans.org; Web: www.columbusdominicans.org

DOMINICAN SISTERS OF SAN RAFAEL (O.P.) Motherhouse: San Rafael, CA 94901. (415) 453-8303
145 Sisters
Apostolic Work: Education, health care, retreat ministry, parish ministry, social service and pastoral care.
Represented in the Archdioceses of Los Angeles and San Francisco and in the Dioceses of Oakland, Reno, Sacramento, San Jose, Santa Rosa and Stockton.
Vocation Director: Sister Patricia Farrell, O.P., Dominican Sisters of San Rafael, 1520 Grand Ave., San Rafael, CA 94901-2236. (415) 453-8303, (415) 257-4939. E-mail: pfarrellop@sanrafaelop.org; Web: www.sanrafaelop.org

DOMINICAN SISTERS OF SINSINAWA (O.P.) (Sinsinawa Dominican Congregation of the Most Holy Rosary)
Generalate: Dominican Motherhouse, 585 County Road Z, Sinsinawa, WI 53824-9700. (608) 748-4411
700 Sisters
Apostolic Work: A variety of educational, pastoral, health care and social service ministries.
Represented in 35 states, South and Central America and Trinidad.
Vocation Director: Membership Office, Dominican Motherhouse, 585 County Road Z, Sinsinawa, WI 53824-9700. (608) 748-4411, ext. 279. E-mail: member@sinsinawa.org; Web: www.sinsinawa.org

DOMINICAN SISTERS OF SPARKILL (O.P.) (Dominican Congregation of Our Lady of the Rosary)
175 Route 340, Sparkill, NY 10976-1047
408 Sisters
Apostolic Work: Elementary schools, high schools, college, child care, housing, foreign missions, nursing, religious education, pastoral ministry, secretarial, administration, campus ministry, health related, counseling, aging, art, communication, handicapped, Native American missions.
Represented largely in the US with a mission in Pakistan.
Vocation Contact: Sister Mary Carol Burke, O.P., Dominican Convent, 175 Route 340, Sparkill, NY 10976-1047. (845) 359-6400, ext. 272. Fax: (845) 359-6053. E-mail: mcburke3@juno.com; Web: www.sparkill.org

DOMINICAN SISTERS (O.P.) (St. Mary's New Orleans)
Motherhouse: 7300 St. Charles Ave., New Orleans, LA 70118. (504) 861-8183
60 Professed Sisters, 2 Candidates
Formation Orientation: House of discernment: Sept.-Jan. and/or Jan.-May. House of formation: New Orleans. National common novitiate: St. Louis. Affiliation possible (6 mo. to 2 yrs.)
Ministries: Education: all phases and levels; spiritual direction, sponsorship of two retreat centers and a private high school; presence to the elderly and those under hospice care; pastoral ministry; ministry to the deaf and to those mentally challenged.
Represented in the Archdiocese of New Orleans and in the Dioceses of Baton Rouge and Houma-Thibodaux.
Vocation Director: Sister Mary Hilary, O.P., 2833 Burdette St., New Orleans, LA 70125. (504) 861-2402 (tel, fax). E-mail: archband@aol.com; Web: www.dominican-sisters.net/stmarys/

DOMINICAN SISTERS OF SPRINGFIELD (O.P.) Sacred Heart Convent, 1237 W. Monroe St., Springfield, IL 62704
295 Professed Sisters, 2 in Formation
Apostolic Work: Preaching among the unserved and underserved through a variety of ministries: EDUCATION: literacy projects, elementary and secondary schools, colleges, hearing impaired, day care, communications, earth literacy and ecology; PARISHES: pastoral associates, directors of religious education, nursing, liturgist/musicians, visitors to elderly and shut-ins; HEALTH CARE: clinics, hospitals, retirement center, sisters' infirmary; ADMINISTRATIVE: parish administrators, diocesan offices, elementary and secondary school principals, hospital CEO; PASTORAL CARE: hospices, nursing homes, prisons, retreat and renewal centers, Native American and Peruvian missions, hospital chaplain, counseling; advocacy for persons poor and marginalized, mentally and physically handicapped; campus ministry, spiritual direction, social service.
Represented in 12 states and in Peru: in the Archdioceses of Chicago, Lima (Peru), St. Louis and St. Paul/Minneapolis and in the Dioceses of Baton Rouge, Belleville, Columbus, Dubuque, Duluth, Great Falls-Billings, Green Bay, Huancayo (Peru), Jackson, Joliet, Little Rock, Louisville, Peoria, Rockford and Springfield-in-Illinois.
Vocation Director: Sr. Elyse Marie Ramirez, O.P., Sacred Heart Convent, 1237 West Monroe St., Springfield, IL 62704. (217) 787-0481. E-mail: semramirez@spdom.org; Web: www.springfieldop.org

DOMINICAN SISTERS OF TACOMA (O.P.) Tacoma Dominican Center, 935 Fawcett Ave. S., Tacoma, WA 98402. (253) 272-9688. E-mail: marypmurphy@tacoma-op.org: Web: www.tacoma-op.org
76 Sisters, 23 Associates
Ministries: Education, parish ministry, pastoral care, counseling, contemplation; serving orphans, immigrants, Native Americans, elderly and poor people.
Represented in the Archdiocese of Seattle and in the Dioceses of Baker, Fresno, Jacksonville, Portland, San Diego, Sioux City, Spokane and Yakima. Also in Managua and Montreal.
Vocation Contact: Mary Pat Murphy, OP

EUCHARISTIC FRANCISCAN MISSIONARY SISTERS (E.F.M.S.)
Motherhouse: 943 S. Soto St., Los Angeles, CA 90023. (323) 264-6556
Novitiate: Nativity Convent, 1421 Cota Ave., Torrance, CA 90501. (310) 328-6725
Mission Centers: Blessed Sacrament Convent, 1205 N. San Joaquin St., Stockton, CA 95202. (209) 462-3906 and N. Sra de Guadalupe, 800 Crim Ave., Kilgore, TX 75662. (903) 986-3680
26 Sisters
Apostolic Work: Missionary work through Adoration of the Blessed Sacrament, catechetical ministry at all levels, parish ministry (social work), education, secretarial work, multi-cultural ministry, retreats, outreach programs and diocesan work.
Represented in the Archdiocese of

Los Angeles and in the Dioceses of Stockton and Tyler (TX).
Vocation Director: Motherhouse: 943 S. Soto St., Los Angeles, CA 90023. (323) 264-6556

EUCHARISTIC MISSIONARIES OF ST. DOMINIC (O.P.) Administrative Offices: 3801 Canal St., Ste. 400, New Orleans, LA 70119. (866) 484-5451 (toll free), (504) 486-0098. E-mail: squatman@aol.com; Web: www.emdsisters.org
45 Sisters
Apostolic Work: Health care, home visitation, religious education, spiritual direction, social work, parish administration, pastoral services, work with the terminally ill and the elderly, prison ministry, Maya ministry.
Represented in the Archdiocese of New Orleans and in the Dioceses of Beaumont, Biloxi, Houma-Thibodaux, Lafayette, Tucson and West Palm Beach.
Vocation Director: Sr. Jane Quatman, O.P.

FAITHFUL COMPANIONS OF JESUS (F.C.J.) (Society of the Sisters, Faithful Companions of Jesus)
Saint Philomena Convent, 324 Cory's Lane, Portsmouth, RI 02871. (401) 683-2222
Generalate in England; Provincialate in Toronto, Canada
19 Sisters in US; 325 Sisters worldwide
Apostolic Work: Companioning with Jesus and one another, the Sisters strive to answer the "I thirst" of Jesus in the world today. They are involved in various ministries including: education in all forms; retreat work; parish ministry; prison ministry; hospital chaplaincy; ministry to the elderly; and missionary work.
The Faithful Companions of Jesus are deeply rooted in Ignatian spirituality and are located throughout the world in 16 countries, including Romania, Indonesia, the Philippines, Argentina and Bolivia.
Represented in the (Arch)dioceses of Birmingham, Brooklyn, Fall River, Providence, Raleigh and San Francisco.
Vocation Contact: Sr. Ellen McCarthy, F.C.J., 4000 Linden Terrace, Durham, NC 27705. (919) 383-3844. E-mail: fcjel@aol.com; Web: www.fcjsisters.org

FELICIAN SISTERS (C.S.S.F.)
(Immaculate Conception Province)
Provincial House: Immaculate Conception Convent, 260 S. Main St., Lodi, NJ 07644-2196. (973) 473-7447. Fax: (973) 473-7126. E-mail: felicianslodi@hotmail.com
201 Sisters in the Province
Apostolic Work: Primary work: education on all levels: 10 elementary schools, 3 high schools, 1 college, 1 school for exceptional children, 2 religious education offices, a reading center and 2 child care centers. Also: 2 hospitals, 1 nursing home, 1 infirmary, 3 diocesan offices, 1 urban youth center, 1 retreat center, 1 home for children and 3 pastoral assistants/associates.
Represented in the Archdioceses of Newark and Philadelphia and in the Dioceses of Metuchen, Paterson and Wilmington.
Vocation Director: Sister Judith Marie Blizzard, C.S.S.F., Immaculate Conception Convent, 260 S. Main St., Lodi, NJ 07644-2196. (973) 473-5923. E-mail: cssf@inet.felician.edu; Web: www.feliciansisters.org

FELICIAN/FRANCISCAN SISTERS (C.S.S.F.) (Our Lady of the Angels Province)
Motherhouse and Novitiate: Our Lady of the Angels Convent, 1315 Enfield St., Enfield, CT 06082. (860) 745-7791, 4946. Fax: (860) 741-0819
109 Sisters in Province
Apostolic Work: Ministry in fields of health and education, adult day care, pastoral care. Also missionary work, e.g. Africa, Brazil.
Represented in the Archdioceses of Boston, Hartford and New York and in the Dioceses of Albany, Manchester, Norwich, Portland (ME), Providence and Springfield.
Director of Vocations: Sister Mary John Fryc, C.S.S.F., St. Adalbert Convent, 856 Atwells Ave., Providence, RI 02909. (401) 831-3336. Fax: (401) 351-9306. E-mail: stalprov@aol.com; Web: www.feliciansisters.org

FELICIAN SISTERS (C.S.S.F.)
(Immaculate Heart of Mary Province)
Provincial House and Novitiate: Villa Maria, 600 Doat St., Buffalo, NY 14211
248 Sisters in the Province
Apostolic Work: Institutions include a college, academy and institute of music. Felicians minister in education on the elementary, high school and college levels; also involved in religious education, pastoral ministry, retreat work, nursing, counseling, special education and prison ministry.
Represented in the Dioceses of Buffalo, Rochester and Syracuse.
Vocation Director: Sister M. Therese Chmura, CSSF, Villa Maria, 600 Doat St., Buffalo, NY 14211. (716) 892-4141, ext. 162. Fax: (716) 892-4177. E-mail: smtc@cssfbuffalo.org; Web: www.feliciansisters.org

FELICIAN SISTERS (C.S.S.F.)
(Our Lady of Sacred Heart Province)
Provincial House: 1500 Woodcrest Ave., Coraopolis, PA 15108-3099
110 Sisters in the Province, international Franciscan community of 12 provinces
Apostolic Work: Private high school, elementary schools, religious education centers, home for exceptional children, nursing home, assisted living facility. Engaged in adult education, youth ministry, health care, social ministry, retreats, parish ministry, tutoring, outreach to the poor, missionary work in Africa, home visiting and also other spiritual and corporal works of mercy.
Represented in the Dioceses of Altoona-Johnstown, Charleston, Cleveland, Greensburg, Harrisburg and Pittsburgh.
Vocation Director: Sister Louise Marie Olsofka, C.S.S.F., 155 South 15th St., Pittsburgh, PA 15203. (412) 431-1356 (w); (412) 264-2890 (h). Fax: (412) 264-7047. E-mail: slouisemo@hotmail.com; Web: www.felicianspa.org

FELICIAN SISTERS (Congregation of the Sisters of St. Felix) (C.S.S.F.)
(Presentation of the Blessed Virgin Mary Province)
Motherhouse and Novitiate: Presentation of the B.V.M. Convent, 36800 Schoolcraft Rd., Livonia, MI 48150. (734) 591-1730. E-mail: smdesales@felicians.org; Web: www.feliciansisters.org
219 Sisters in the Province
Apostolic Work: 1 university, 2 high schools, 15 elementary schools, 10 religious education centers, 1 Montessori center, 1 day care center, 2 nursing homes, 1 assisted living center, community out-reach programs, 1 hospice in-patient facility and home care program, 2 retreat centers, 3 child care centers, 1 prayer center, 5 parochial pastoral centers, foreign missions in Brazil and Kenya, 1 senior clergy residence, archival and secretarial services in seminary.
Represented in the Archdiocese of Detroit and in the Dioceses of Lansing, Toledo and Fort Wayne-South Bend. Also in Rome, Italy.
Vocation Director: Sister Mary De Sales Herman, CSSF

FELICIAN SISTERS (C.S.S.F.)
(Mother of Good Counsel Province)
Provincial and Novitiate: Mother of

Good Counsel Convent, 3800 W. Peterson Ave., Chicago, IL 60659-3116

207 Sisters in the Province

Apostolic Work: Instruction and administration in 16 elementary schools, 1 child development center, 2 hospitals, 2 senior living centers, 1 assisted-living facility for the elderly, 2 skilled-care facilities, 1 counseling program for high-risk children, teens and parents, social service especially among the poor, youth ministry, pastoral ministry, religious education, evangelization, diocesan work, domestic service, clerical work, foreign missions in Brazil and Kenya.

Represented in the Archdioceses of Chicago and Milwaukee and in the Dioceses of Green Bay, La Crosse, Belleville, Joliet and Rockford. Also in Rome, Brazil, Poland and 7 other North American provinces.

Vocation Director: Sister Mary Beth Bromer, C.S.S.F., 3800 W. Peterson Ave., Chicago, IL 60659-3116. (773) 463-3020 (w), (773) 767-2684, ext. 25 (h). E-mail: smarybeth@felicians.org; Web: www.feliciansisters.org

FELICIAN SISTERS (C.S.S.F.)

(Assumption of the B.V.M. Province) 4210 Meadowlark Ln. S.E., Rio Rancho, NM 87124

75 Sisters-Franciscans

Conduct: 1 high school, 11 grammar schools, 40 Christian Doctrine classes, 4 religious education centers, counseling, youth ministry, adult education, pastoral ministry, missionary ministry, domestic service, Eucharistic ministry, home visiting and other spiritual and corporal works of mercy.

Represented in the Archdioceses of Santa Fe, Los Angeles, San Antonio and San Bernardino and in the Dioceses of Austin and Saltillo, Coahuila, Mexico.

Vocation Director: Sister Carol Marie Wiatrek, 4210 Meadowlark Ln. S.E., Rio Rancho, NM 87124. (505) 892-8862. E-mail: cssfrrnm@nm.net

FILIPPINI SISTERS (M.P.F.)
(Religious Teachers Filippini)

St. Lucy Province - see listing under "R" - Religious Teachers Filippini

FILIPPINI SISTERS (M.P.F.)
(Religious Teachers Filippini)

(Queen of Apostles Province)

Provincial House: 474 East Rd., Bristol, CT 06010

30 Sisters

Conduct: 4 grammar schools, 1 mission, 4 religious education centers, 1 shrine.

Represented in the Archdiocese of Hartford and in the Dioceses of Bridgeport, Norwich, Orlando and Providence.

Vocation Directress: Sister Frances Stavalo, M.P.F., 474 East Rd., Bristol, CT 06010. (860) 584-2138. Fax: (860) 582-1119

FRANCISCAN HANDMAIDS OF THE MOST PURE HEART OF MARY (F.H.M.) 15 W. 124th St., New York, NY 10027. (212) 289-5655

25 Sisters

Conduct: 1 nursery, 1 summer camp, 1 house of prayer.

Apostolic Work: Teaching, pastoral work, social work, religious instruction, retreat work.

Represented in the Archdiocese of New York.

Vocation Directress: Sr. Vincent Marie, F.H.M., 444 Woodvale Ave., Pleasant Plains, Staten Island, NY 10309. (718) 984-1625

FRANCISCAN HOSPITAL SISTERS (O.S.F.) (Hospital Sisters of St. Francis)

St. Francis Convent, LaVerna Rd., Springfield, IL 62794-9431. (217) 522-3386

240 Sisters

Apostolic Work: All health-related ministries including nursing, social service, home health care, massage therapy, parish ministry, pastoral care and administration. Thirteen hospitals in Illinois and Wisconsin. Mission centers in Tanzania (Africa) and Haiti. International congregation with community members also in Germany, Poland, the Netherlands, Japan and India.

Vocation Directress: Sister Anna Phiri, O.S.F., St. Francis Convent, LaVerna Rd., Springfield, IL 62794-9431. (217) 522-3386. E-mail: vo@hsosf-usa.org; Web: www.springfieldfranciscans.org

FRANCISCAN HOSPITALLER SISTERS OF THE IMMACULATE CONCEPTION (F.H.I.C.)

St. Joseph Novitiate: 300 S. 17th St., San Jose, CA 95112-2245. (408) 998-2896. Fax: (408) 998-3407

20 Sisters

Apostolic Work: Schools, hospitals, social work, parish.

Represented in the Dioceses of Fresno, Monterey and San Jose. Also represented in Portugal, Brazil, India, Spain, Philippines, Italy, Angola, Mozambique, South Africa and Mexico.

Vocation Director: Sr. Rosa Maria Branco, Our Lady of Angels Convent, 6020 North Flora Ave., Fresno, CA 93710. (559) 261-1782. E-mail: rosamaria@stanthonyfresno.org or rosamaria@psnw.com

FRANCISCAN MISSIONARIES OF THE IMMACULATE HEART OF MARY (F.M.I.H.M.) Holy Saviour Convent, 30 Emerald Ave., Westmont, NJ 08108

St. Jude Convent, 420 S. Black Horse Pike, Blackwood, NJ 08012

8 Sisters in US, 800 worldwide

Apostolic Work: Teaching, foreign missions, parish work, nursing and social services.

Vocation Director: Sister M. Dorothy Aloisio, F.M.I.H.M., Holy Saviour Convent, 30 Emerald Ave., Westmont, NJ 08108. (856) 227-8658 or 858-2638. Fax: (856) 869-7972 or 374-2230. E-mail: fmihm@snip.net or hssbbr@snip.net; Web: fmihm.catholicweb.com

FRANCISCAN MISSIONARIES OF MARY (F.M.M.) Provincial House: Institute of Franciscan Missionaries of Mary, 3305 Wallace Ave., Bronx, NY 10467

Over 7,800 Sisters worldwide, 175 in US

Apostolic Work: Medical, educational, social, and pastoral, as well as special ministries among the poor and marginalized in 76 countries throughout Africa, Asia, Europe, Latin America, North America and Oceania.

Represented in the Archdioceses of Boston, New York, St. Louis and Chicago and in dioceses in Georgia, New Mexico, Rhode Island and Florida.

Vocation Contact: Vocation Office, Franciscan Missionaries of Mary, PO Box K, Millbrook, NY 12545. (845) 677-6739. E-mail: fmmvoc@aol.com; Web: www.fmmusa.org

FRANCISCAN MISSIONARIES OF OUR LADY (O.S.F.) 4200 Essen Ln., Baton Rouge, LA 70809. (225) 926-1627

26 Sisters in the US

Apostolic Work: Health care ministry, serving the poor in various ministries. Missionary work in Haiti.

Represented in 3 Louisiana dioceses and 12 other countries.

Vocation Director: 4200 Essen Ln., Baton Rouge, LA 70809. (225) 926-8161. Fax: (225) 925-5268

FRANCISCAN MISSIONARIES OF THE SACRED HEART

See Franciscan Sisters of Peekskill

FRANCISCAN MISSIONARY SISTERS FOR AFRICA (F.M.S.A.)

American Headquarters: 172 Foster St., PO Box 35095, Brighton, MA 02135

6 Sisters

Apostolic Work: An international and completely missionary Congregation working solely in Africa in education, refugee services, healthcare projects; ministry to patients with AIDS and their families; behavior change programs, adult literacy programs, vocational training of those in need, rehabilitation of handicapped children, and fostering vocations to the religious life.
Represented in the Archdiocese of Boston and in 8 foreign countries
Vocation Contact: Sr. Julia Connor, Mission Procurator, 172 Foster St., PO Box 35095, Brighton, MA 02135. (617) 254-4343. Fax: (617) 787-8007. E-mail: sisters172@aol.com

FRANCISCAN MISSIONARY SISTERS OF ASSISI (SFMA)
St. Francis Convent, 1039 Northampton St., Holyoke, MA 01040-1320
Apostolic Work: Pastoral work, teaching, nursing, social work, ministry of care, religious education, adult faith formation and domestic work.
Represented in the (Arch)dioceses of Springfield and New York. Also in missions in Brazil, China, Croatia, Italy, Japan, Kenya, Korea, the Philippines, Romania, Russia, United States and Zambia.
Vocation Directress: Sister Mary Veronica Zulu, SFMA, 1039 Northampton St., Holyoke, MA 01040-1320. (413) 532-8156. Fax: (413) 534-7741. E-mail: sistersofassisi@aol.com

FRANCISCAN MISSIONARY SISTERS OF THE DIVINE CHILD (FMDC)
Motherhouse: 6380 Main St., Williamsville, NY 14221. (716) 633-4011
25 Sisters
Apostolic Work: Ministries in city and rural areas alike through: catechetics, DRE, education (high schools, college, adult religious education), human services, parish religious surveys, pastoral ministry.
Represented in the (Arch)dioceses of Buffalo and Newark.
Vocation Director: Sister Concetta DeFelice, 6380 Main St., Williamsville, NY 14221. (716) 626-9499. E-mail: cdefelicefmdc@yahoo.com

FRANCISCAN MISSIONARY SISTERS OF THE IMMACULATE CONCEPTION (O.S.F.)
Provincial House: 13367 Borden Ave., Unit A, Sylmar, CA 91342-2804
113 Sisters
Conduct: Provincial home, 1 novitiate, 1 home for the aged, 2 grammar schools, 1 preschool, 2 hospitals, 1 retreat house, 2 houses in catechetical and pastoral ministries, 1 home for senior citizens.
Represented in the Archdioceses of Los Angeles and in the Dioceses of Orange and Gallup.
Vocation Contact: Sr. Angelica Tiscareno, OSF, Administrator, 11320 Laurel Canyon Blvd., San Fernando, CA 91340. (818) 898-1546

FRANCISCAN MISSIONARY SISTERS OF THE INFANT JESUS (F.M.I.J.)
Delegation (Regional) and Formation House: 1215 Kresson Rd., Cherry Hill, NJ 08003-2813. (856) 428-8834; Fax: (856) 428-7930
Motherhouse in Assisi (Italy) - Generalate in Rome.
Apostolic Work: Education, health care, pastoral assistance to elderly, youth; catechesis and other services to evangelization.
Represented on 5 continents and 12 countries.
Vocation Director: Sr. Vilma Butron, F.M.I.J., 1215 Kresson Rd., Cherry Hill, NJ 08003-2813. (856) 428-8834. Fax: (856) 428-7930. E-mail: fmijusdel@att.net; Web: www.cmswr.org/MemberCommunities/FMSIJ.htm

FRANCISCAN MISSIONARY SISTERS OF OUR LADY OF SORROWS (OSF)
3600 S.W. 170th Ave., Beaverton, OR 97006-5099. (503) 649-7127
50 Sisters
Conduct: 2 novitiates, 2 retreat houses, 3 foreign missions, 1 group home for Indian girls, parish ministry.
Represented in the Archdioceses of Portland, (OR), Vancouver (British Columbia) and of Taipei, Taiwan and in the Dioceses of Hong Kong, Monterey and Gallup.
Contact Person: Sister Anne Marie, OSF, 3600 S.W. 170th Ave., Beaverton, OR 97006-5099. (503) 649-7127. Fax: (503) 649-8382. E-mail: franmisisters@juno.com

FRANCISCAN SERVANTS (O.S.F.) (Holy Child Jesus) Regional Motherhouse and Novitiate: Villa Maria, 641 Somerset St., N. Plainfield, NJ 07060-4909. (908) 757-3050
23 Sisters
Apostolic Work: Health care, social services, education.
Represented in the Diocese of Metuchen and in the Archdioceses of Newark and Washington (DC).
Vocation Directress: Villa Maria, 641 Somerset St., N. Plainfield, NJ 07060-4909. (908) 753-8874

FRANCISCAN SISTERS OF ALLEGANY, NY (O.S.F.)
St. Elizabeth Motherhouse, Allegany, NY 14706
385 Sisters
Apostolic Work: We are a community of women living the Gospel in today's world. Our charism is that of St. Francis of Assisi: to live the Gospel life in the spirit of love, joy, simplicity, and hospitality. Supporting each other in community and prayer, together we use our varied gifts and talents to care for God's people. As Franciscan women, we commit ourselves to a Gospel stance of nonviolence focusing on actions which will transform unjust structures that affect the marginalized, the economically poor, and the environment. Our ministries include education, health care, social work, parish, retreat, spiritual and prison ministries, as well as care for the poor, the homeless, and the environment. Some of the ways we serve are as teachers, nurses, secretaries, social workers, directors of religious education, doctors, accountants, artists, pastoral ministers, office workers, administrators, lawyers, counselors, aides, liturgists, spiritual directors, computer technicians, principals, musicians, massage therapists, librarians, environmentalists, chaplains, and justice advocates.
Represented in the Archdioceses of New York, Boston, Hartford, Newark, Philadelphia, Miami and Wilmington and in the Dioceses of Buffalo, Syracuse, Albany, Rockville Centre, Paterson, Brooklyn, Metuchen, Trenton, Camden, Palm Beach, Venice, St. Petersburg, Columbus, Gallup and Spokane. Also in Jamaica, Brazil, Bolivia and the Philippines.
Vocation Minister: Sr. Mary McNally, OSF, 2924 W. Curtis St., Tampa, FL 33614. (813) 870-6314. Fax: (813) 350-9533. E-mail: fsavoc@aol.com; Web: www.franciscansister.com

FRANCISCAN SISTERS OF THE ATONEMENT (S.A.) 41 Old Highland Tpke., Graymoor, Garrison, NY 10524-9717
227 Sisters
Apostolic Work: Religious education at parish and diocesan levels, social services and community development programs, pastoral ministry and evangelization, adult social day care, home visitation, kindergartens and child care programs. Health care, youth ministry, justice and peace programs, retreat and hospitality. Ministries according to interest, background and experience.
Represented in the (Arch)dioceses of Boston, Bridgeport, Detroit, Monterey, Newark, New York and Washington, DC and in 15 other dioceses in the United States. Also in Brazil, Canada, Japan, Ireland and Italy.
Vocation Directresses: Sister René

Drolet, SA, Sister Rose Marita, SA, PO Box 55, Schuylerville, NY 12871. (518) 695-4854 (tel, fax). E-mail: vocationministry@graymoor.org; Web: www.graymoor.org

FRANCISCAN SISTERS OF CHICAGO (O.S.F.) 11500 Theresa Dr., Lemont, IL 60439

72 Professed Sisters

Apostolic Work: Ministry to the poor, the sick and elderly; religious education; pastoral ministry and evangelization; counseling and social services; liturgy and parish ministry.

Represented in the Archdiocese of Chicago and in the Dioceses of Cleveland, Gary, Lafayette, Louisville and San Antonio.

Vocation Director: Sr. Doloria Kosiek, O.S.F., 3115 N. Karlov, Chicago, IL 60641-5436. (773) 202-0310. E-mail: kdoloriaosf@cs.com; Web: chicagofranciscans.org

FRANCISCAN SISTERS OF CHRISTIAN CHARITY (O.S.F.) (Manitowoc Franciscans)

Holy Family Convent, 2409 South Alverno Road, Manitowoc, WI 54220-9320

430 Sisters

Apostolic Work: Catholic education, Catholic health care, and service to our sisters in community.

Represented in the (Arch)dioceses of Chicago, Columbus, Green Bay, Honolulu, Jackson, Marquette, Milwaukee, Omaha, Phoenix, Steubenville, Superior and Tucson.

Vocation Directress: Holy Family Convent, 2409 South Alverno Road, Manitowoc, WI 54220-9320. (920) 682-7728. E-mail: fccvoood@choiceonemail.com; Web: www.sl.edu/fscc

SCHOOL SISTERS OF ST. FRANCIS OF CHRIST THE KING (O.S.F.)

Mt. Assisi Convent, 13900 Main St., Lemont, IL 60439. (630) 257-7495

62 Sisters in America

Minister in: 1 academy, 5 grammar schools, 1 home for the aged, a house of prayer. Also serve as Directors of Religious Education, liturgy directors, nurses and in other pastoral capacities.

Represented in the Archdiocese of Chicago and in the Diocese of Joliet.

Vocation Director: Sr. Therese Ann, O.S.F., 13900 Main St., Lemont, IL 60439. (630) 257-7524. E-mail: ssfck@interaccess.com

FRANCISCAN SISTERS OF DUBUQUE, IA (O.S.F.)

3390 Windsor Ave., Dubuque, IA 52001-1311

394 Members, 70 Associates

Apostolic Work: Education (elementary, secondary, college), religious education, special education, health care, prayer and retreat ministry, social work, parish ministry, care of the elderly, counseling, justice and peace and other varied works depending on the gifts of the members and the needs of people.

Represented in more than 39 dioceses and in 24 states of the US. Also in El Salvador.

Vocation Minister: Sr. Nancy Miller, OSF, 3390 Windsor Ave., Dubuque, IA 52001-1311. (563) 583-9786. Fax: (563) 583-3250. E-mail: millern@osfdbq.org; Web: www.osfdbq.org

FRANCISCAN SISTERS OF THE EUCHARIST (F.S.E.) Motherhouse: 405 Allen Ave., Meriden, CT 06451

76 Sisters, 2 Novices, 2 Postulants

Ministries: Dedicated to the sacredness of human life, the Community's mission is carried out through programs of counseling, education, health care, music, land experience and service to families and the elderly.

Represented in the Archdioceses of Hartford, Portland, Seattle and Washington, DC and in the Dioceses of Boise, Duluth, Galveston-Houston and Grand Rapids. Also in Rome and Assisi, Italy, and Jerusalem.

Vocation Contact: Sister Barbara Johnson, F.S.E., 405 Allen Ave., Meriden, CT 06451. (203) 238-2243. E-mail: fseinfo@fsecommunity.org; Web: www.fsecommunity.org

SISTERS OF ST. FRANCIS OF THE IMMACULATE HEART OF MARY (O.S.F.) Motherhouse: St. Francis Convent, PO Box 447, Hankinson, ND 58041-0447. (701) 242-7105

55 Sisters

Apostolic Work: Health care, liturgical vestments, care for elderly and handicapped, retreats, education, pro-life work, parish work, social service and domestic work.

Represented in North Dakota and in Germany, Brazil, India, Spain, Switzerland and Albania.

Vocation Directresses: Sister M. Jean Louise Schafer, OSF, 301 Fourth St. SE, Rugby, ND 58368. (701) 776-6866 or Sister Donna Welder, St. Francis Provincial Motherhouse, 102 Sixth St. SE, PO Box 447, Hankinson, ND 58041-0447. (701) 242-7195. E-mail: osfhank@rrt.net; Web: www.fargodiocese.org/vocations/sfc

FRANCISCAN SISTERS OF HASTINGS-ON-HUDSON, NY (OSF)

Sisters of St. Francis Mission of the Immaculate Virgin, Immaculate Conception Motherhouse, 49 Jackson Ave., Hastings-on-Hudson, NY 10706-3217

76 Sisters

Apostolic Work: Child care, social work, education, health and hospitals, parish ministry, Franciscan Center for Retreats.

Represented in the Archdiocese of New York.

Vocation Director: Sister Veronica Wood, Immaculate Conception Motherhouse, 49 Jackson Ave., Hastings-on-Hudson, NY 10706-3217. (914) 478-3930. Fax: (914) 478-5470. E-mail: sveronwood@aol.com

SISTERS OF ST. FRANCIS OF THE HOLY CROSS 3025 Bay Settlement Rd., Green Bay, WI 54311-7301

83 Sisters, 2 in Formation, 31 Associates

Apostolic Work: We serve as parish leaders, educators (elementary, high school, college), health caregivers, youth ministers, minority and environmental advocates, social workers, literacy tutors, retreat directors, artists and in other ministries that promote understanding and peace.

Represented primarily in the Diocese of Green Bay (NE Wisconsin). Also in Nicaragua.

Director of Vocation Ministries: Sr. Laura Zelten, 3025 Bay Settlement Rd., Green Bay, WI 54311-7301. (920) 468-4737. E-mail: vocations@gbfranciscans.org; Web: www.gbfranciscans.org

FRANCISCAN SISTERS OF THE IMMACULATE (F.I.)

Convent of the Sacred Hearts of Jesus and Mary, 382 Main St., Fairhaven, MA 02719. (508) 992-0482. E-mail: fsi@marymediatrix.com; Web: www.marymediatrix.com

7 Sisters, 2 Postulants in US, over 300 Sisters worldwide

Apostolate: To make the Immaculate known and loved by every heart using music, children's catechesis, processions, mass media, computer, Rosary making, etc. The Sisters live a community life of prayer, poverty and penance in the spirit of the vow of total consecration to the Immaculate, so that she may transform us, like St. Francis, into Jesus Crucified, and make us her instruments for the conquest of all souls for God in the spirit of St. Maximilian Kolbe. Daily, the Sisters pray 5 hours in common, including Holy Mass, the Rosary, the Liturgy of the Hours, mental prayer, adoration and benediction.

Vocation Director: Mother Mary Francisca, F.I.

FRANCISCAN SISTERS OF THE IMMACULATE CONCEPTION (O.S.F.)
Motherhouse: Germany
Provincial House: 291 North St., Buffalo, NY 14201
7 Sisters
Apostolic Work: Care of the chronically ill – Nazareth Home, Buffalo, NY.
Represented in the Archdiocese of New York and in the Diocese of Buffalo. Also in Germany, Brazil, Argentina and Paraguay.
Vocation Contact: Sister M. Bernard, O.S.F., Provincial, 291 North St., Buffalo, NY 14201. Fax: (716) 881-1578

SISTERS OF ST. FRANCIS OF THE IMMACULATE CONCEPTION (O.S.F.)
Immaculate Conception Convent, 2408 W. Heading Ave., West Peoria, IL 61604
47 Sisters
Apostolic Work: Teaching, parish work, care of the elderly, religious education, social work, hospital chaplaincy, teen and adult retreat programs, spiritual direction. Ministries based in Midwest with a mission on an Indian reservation in South Dakota.
Vocation Director: Sister Jean Marie Ciuffini, OSF, Immaculate Conception Convent, 2408 W. Heading Ave., West Peoria, IL 61604. (309) 674-6168. Fax: (309) 674-2006. E-mail: sjciuffini@hotmail.com; Web: www.osfsisterswpeoria.org

FRANCISCAN SISTERS OF THE IMMACULATE CONCEPTION AND ST. JOSEPH FOR THE DYING (O.S.F.)
Motherhouse: Ave Maria Convent, 1249 Josselyn Canyon Rd., P.O. Box 1977, Monterey, CA 93942. (831) 375-8680
5 Sisters
Conduct: 1 convalescent hospital, home visiting.
Represented in the Diocese of Monterey.
Vocation Director: Sr. Rosanna, O.S.F., Ave Maria Convent, 1249 Josselyn Canyon Rd., P.O. Box 1977, Monterey, CA 93942. (831) 375-8680

FRANCISCAN SISTERS OF LITTLE FALLS, MINNESOTA (OSF)
St. Francis Convent, 116 8th Ave. SE, Little Falls, MN 56345-3597. (320) 632-2981
219 Sisters
Evangelical Ministry: Following the spirit of Saints Francis and Clare of Assisi, living the Gospel life in continual conversion through faithful prayer, simple living, caring community, reverencing and preserving all of God's creation and by seeking solidarity with persons who are poor.
Represented in 20 states. Also in Ecuador, Mexico and Tanzania.
Vocation Minister: Sister Grace Skwira, OSF, St. Francis Convent, 116 8th Ave. SE, Little Falls, MN 56345-3597. (320) 632-0652. Fax: (320) 632-1714. E-mail: vocations@fslf.org; Web: www.fslf.org

FRANCISCAN SISTERS OF THE MARTYR ST. GEORGE (F.S.G.M.)
Province: St. Elizabeth, St. Francis Convent, 2120 Central Ave., PO Box 9020, Alton, IL 62002-9020
151 Professed Sisters, 14 Novices, 5 Postulants
Apostolic Work: Teaching, nursing, social work, day care for children, parish work, youth ministry, missions in Brazil, secretarial and domestic work, adoration of the Blessed Sacrament.
Vocation Director: Sister M. Beata Ziegler, FSGM, 2120 Central Ave., PO Box 9020, Alton, IL 62002-9020. (618) 463-2756. Fax: (618) 465-5064. E-mail: altonfranciscans@piasanet.com; Web: www.sahc.org/sisters

FRANCISCAN SISTERS OF MARY (F.S.M.) 1100 Bellevue Ave., St. Louis, MO 63117-1883
158 members
Apostolic Works: Increasingly varied but emphasizing compassionate presence, healing, health promotion, restoration and health education. Focus is on wholeness of relationships and life, including communal and congregational life. Members serve in hospitals, clinics, birthing centers, parishes, chaplaincies, hospices, homes, women's drop-in centers of hospitality, counselling situations, group dynamics, organizational development, etc. Emphasis is given to the care of women and children.
Represented in the Archdioceses of Chicago, Cincinnati, Milwaukee, Oklahoma City and St. Louis and in the Dioceses of Brownsville, Charleston, Jefferson City, Kansas City-St. Joseph, Madison, Springfield-Cape Girardeau and Tucson. Cross-cultural mission in Brazil.
Vocation Contact: Sr. Sherri Coleman, FSM, Congregational Leadership, 1100 Bellevue Ave., St. Louis, MO 63117-1883. (314) 768-1826. E-mail: scoleman@fsmonline.org; Web: www.fsmonline.org

SISTERS OF ST. FRANCIS OF MARY IMMACULATE (OSF)
801 N. Larkin Ave., Ste. 101, Joliet, IL 60435
271 Professed Sisters
Apostolic Work: All levels of education, pre-school through adult, music and art specialists, parish ministry, social services, health care, religious education, care of elderly, holistic health.
Represented in 8 Archdioceses, 23 Dioceses of US, Brazil.
Director of New Membership: Sr. Margaret Kelly, OSF, 921 W. Wood St., Bloomington, IL 61701. (815) 725-8735. E-mail: osfj520@mtco.com; Web: www.jolietfranciscans.org

FRANCISCAN SISTERS OF MARY IMMACULATE (F.M.I.)
St. Francis Convent and Provincial House, 4301 N.E. 18th Ave., Amarillo, TX 79107-7220
37 Sisters, 2 Novices, 1 Postulant
Conduct: Education in primary, elementary and junior/senior high schools; nursing, catechetics, missions.
Represented in the Archdioceses of Los Angeles and Santa Fe and in the Dioceses of Amarillo and Monterrey (Mexico). Other communities in Central and South America (Colombia, Equador, Peru). Also in Switzerland, Romania, Cuba, Africa and Liechtenstein.
Vocation Directresses: Sr. Protasia Hofstetter, F.M.I., Sr. Hilda Rodriguez, F.M.I., St. Francis Convent and Provincial House, 4301 N.E. 18th Ave., Amarillo, TX 79107-7220. (806) 383-5769. Fax: (806) 383-6545. E-mail: francpro@worldnet.att.net

SISTERS OF ST. FRANCIS OF MILLVALE, PA (O.S.F.)
See "M" - Millvale Franciscans

FRANCISCAN SISTERS OF OLDENBURG (O.S.F.)
Motherhouse and Novitiate: Sisters of St. Francis, PO Box 100, Oldenburg, IN 47036-0100. (812) 934-2475. Fax: (812) 933-6403. E-mail: osf@oldenburgosf.com
320 Sisters, 6 in Formation, 252 Associates
Apostolic Work: Elementary, secondary, college, and religious education and administration; campus ministry, pastoral and hospital ministry; daycare; spiritual direction and retreat ministry; counseling; social work; nursing; library science; House of Prayer; clerical and supportive services; African-American, Native American, Hispanic and Appalachian ministries, and wherever the gifts of the Sisters are needed.
Represented in the (Arch)dioceses of Albuquerque, Billings, Chicago,

Cincinnati, Cleveland, Columbus, Covington, Detroit, El Paso, Evansville, Gallup, Indianapolis, Lexington, New York, San Francisco, St. Louis, St. Petersburg and Wheeling. Foreign missions in Papua New Guinea.

Vocation Director: Evelyn Forthofer, OSF, Sisters of St. Francis, PO Box 100, Oldenburg, IN 47036-0100. (812) 934-6417. E-mail: efort@oldenburgosf.com; Web: http://oldenburgfranciscans.org

FRANCISCAN SISTERS OF OUR LADY OF PERPETUAL HELP (O.S.F.)

335 South Kirkwood Rd., St. Louis, MO 63122-6117

134 Sisters

Ministries: Education, health care, pastoral ministry, social service, contemporary needs of the Church.

Represented in the (Arch)dioceses of Austin, Belleville, Cheyenne, Chicago, Dallas, El Paso, Kansas City, Las Cruces, New Ulm, New York, Omaha, Phoenix, Portland (OR), Pueblo, St. Louis, St. Petersburg, Santa Fe, Shreveport, Springfield (IL), Toledo, Wheeling-Charleston, Wichita.

Contact: Marcy Romine, OSF, 335 South Kirkwood Rd., St. Louis, MO 63122-6117. (314) 965-3700, ext. 3054. Fax: (314) 965-3710. E-mail: srmarcy@fsolph.org; Web: www.franciscansisters-olph.org

FRANCISCAN SISTERS OF PEACE (F.S.P.) 20 Ridge St., Haverstraw, NY 10927-1198. (845) 942-2527

87 Sisters; co-founded in 1986

Ministries: Education (pre-school through college), pastoral and campus ministry, prison ministry, religious education, spiritual direction, counselling, health care, day care, working with the poor and homeless.

Represented in the (Arch)dioceses of Albany, Chicago, New York, Newark, Paterson, Rockville Centre, San Francisco and Tucson.

Vocation Office: Ann Smith, FSP, Franciscan Sisters of Peace, 20 Ridge St., Haverstraw, NY 10927-1198. (845) 942-2527, ext. 100. Web: fspnet.org

FRANCISCAN SISTERS OF PEEKSKILL (F.M.S.C.) (Franciscan Missionaries of the Sacred Heart)

250 South St., Peekskill, NY 10566-4419

810 worldwide

Apostolic Work: Education, religious education, parish ministry, nursing, prison ministry and community service.

Represented in the Archdioceses of New York and Newark, NJ and in the Diocese of Brooklyn, NY. Also in 21 countries in Europe, Africa, South America and Asia.

Vocation Directress: Sister Anna Maria Not, F.M.S.C., Mount St. Francis, 250 South St., Peekskill, NY 10566-4419. (914) 737-3373. Fax: (914) 736-9614. E-mail: Vocations@CMSWR.org; Web: www.cmswr.org/MemberCommunities/FMSH.htm

FRANCISCAN SISTERS, T.O.R. OF PENANCE OF THE SORROWFUL MOTHER Motherhouse: Our Lady of Sorrows Monastery, 369 Little Church Rd., Toronto, OH 43964

20 Professed Sisters, 1 Novice

Apostolic Work: Contemplative/active; emphasis on prayer and Eucharistic adoration, with works of mercy which include care for the poor, catechetical, retreat work and parish missions.

Vocation Contact: Sr. Thérèse Marie, TOR, Our Lady of Sorrows Monastery, 369 Little Church Rd., Toronto, OH 43964. (740) 544-5542. Fax: (740) 544-5543. E-mail: torsisters vocations@juno.com; Web: www.torsisters.com

FRANCISCAN SISTERS OF PERPETUAL ADORATION (F.S.P.A.)

St. Rose Convent, 912 Market St., La Crosse, WI 54601-8800

410 Sisters, 200 Lay Affiliates

Apostolic Work: Perpetual Adoration of the Blessed Sacrament since 1878. Members synthesize prayer and action through work in diversified ministries including education, health care, social services and pastoral ministry. The Community operates four spirituality centers; two have a strong emphasis on ecology. Members work with people of various needs in prisons, immigrant services and intercultural awareness programs – wherever their talents and the world's needs meet.

Represented in 40 dioceses in the US and in Africa, Canada, El Salvador, Guam and Mexico.

Office of Membership: Sister Dorothy Dunbar, 912 Market St., La Crosse, WI 54601-8800. (888) 683-FSPA (3772). E-mail: membership@fspa.org; Web: www.fspa.org

SISTERS OF ST. FRANCIS OF PERPETUAL ADORATION (O.S.F.)

Mt. Saint Francis, 7665 Assisi Heights, Colorado Springs, CO 80919

90 Sisters (Colorado Springs Province)

Apostolic Work: Perpetual adoration of the Blessed Sacrament, ministry to the sick, the elderly, the poor; education of multicultural youth; parish ministry; hospital chaplaincy; facilitation of individual and family wellness; and justice and peace work. In all ministry, special emphasis on working with women and children.

Represented primarily in the Archdioceses of Denver, Omaha and Sante Fe and in the Dioceses of Colorado Springs, Grand Island and Lincoln.

Vocation Team: Sister Frances Sedlacek, osf, Vocation Minister, 3480 Upham St., Wheat Ridge, CO 80033. (303) 274-4001. Fax: (303) 202-6147. E-mail: sisfrances07@aol.com; Web: www.stfrancis.org

SISTERS OF ST. FRANCIS OF PERPETUAL ADORATION (O.S.F.)

St. Francis Convent, P.O. Box 766, 1515 Dragoon Trail, Mishawaka, IN 46546-0766. (574) 259-5427

140 Sisters (in Province)

Apostolic Work: Perpetual adoration of the Blessed Sacrament, healthcare, education and other ecclesial ministries.

Represented in the (Arch)dioceses of Fort Wayne-South Bend, Lafayette in Indiana, Gary, Indianapolis and Chicago.

Vocation Director: Sr. Lois DeLee, O.S.F., St. Francis Convent, P.O. Box 766, 1515 Dragoon Trail, Mishawaka, IN 46546-0766. (574) 259-5427. E-mail: srlois@yahoo.com; Web: www.ssfpa.org

SISTERS OF ST. FRANCIS OF PHILADELPHIA (O.S.F.) (Glen Riddle Franciscans)

Our Lady of Angels Convent, 609 S. Convent Rd., Aston, PA 19014. (610) 459-4125

750 Sisters

Conduct: Prayer ministry, health care, education (all levels), parish and diocesan ministry, spiritual and pastoral care; ministry with the homeless, the poor, persons with AIDS, immigrants and refugees; counseling, advocacy, leadership in national religious organizations, services to the elderly.

Mission: Committed to the needs of others, especially those who are economically poor, marginal and oppressed. Willing to take necessary risks to be a healing, compassionate presence.

Represented in 25 states and in Africa, Ireland, Nicaragua and Puerto Rico.

Vocation Director: Sr. Deborah Krist, OSF, Our Lady of Angels Convent,

609 S. Convent Rd., Aston, PA 19014. (610) 558-6789. E-mail: dkrist@osfphila.org; Web: www.osfphila.org

SISTERS OF ST. FRANCIS OF THE PROVIDENCE OF GOD, PITTSBURGH (O.S.F.) 3603 McRoberts Rd., Pittsburgh, PA 15234-2398

160 Sisters worldwide, 99 Sisters in US

Apostolic Work: Education, child care, health care, social services, pastoral ministry, prison ministry, catechetical work, campus ministry, retreat and spiritual direction ministry.

Represented in 8 dioceses in U.S. Also in Brazil, Bolivia and Lithuania.

Contact: Life Futuring Minister, 3603 McRoberts Rd., Pittsburgh, PA 15234-2398. (412) 885-7407. E-mail: FutureOSF@aol.com; Web: www.datablueprints.com/st.francis/html/vowed_membership.html

FRANCISCAN SISTERS OF THE POOR (S.F.P.) US Region: US Regional Office, 60 Compton Rd., Cincinnati, OH 45215-5199. (513) 761-9040, ext. 101. Fax: (513) 761-6703. E-mail: theusregionsfp@fuse.net; Web: www.franciscansisters.org

180 Sisters

Ministry: Ministries directed to care for the poor and neglected through social service centers, health-care settings, soup kitchens and centers for the abused, the addicted and those suffering with AIDS.

Represented in the Archdioceses of New York, Newark, Detroit and Cincinnati and in four dioceses in the US. Present also in Brazil, Italy and Senegal.

Vocation Ministers: Sr. Arlene McGowan, SFP, 60 Compton Rd., Cincinnati, OH 45215-5199. (513) 761-9040, ext. 112. E-mail: arlenemcgowan@msn.com; Sr. Marilyn Fischer, SFP, 222 E. 19th St., New York, NY 10003. (646) 654-0371. E-mail: fischersrm@aol.com

FRANCISCAN SISTERS OF THE RENEWAL (C.F.R.)

Our Lady of Guadalupe Convent, 3537 Bainbridge Ave., Bronx, NY 10467. (718) 547-9840. Web: www.franciscansisterscfr.com/

Apostolic Work: Evangelization and work with the very poor.

Represented in the Archdiocese of New York.

Contact: Sr. Clare Marie Matthiass, C.F.R., Vocation Director

FRANCISCAN SISTERS OF ROCHESTER, MN (O.S.F.)

1001 14th St. NW, Suite 100, Rochester, MN 55901-2525. (507) 282-7441

335 members, 117 Cojourners

Ministry choices are guided by societal need, the call to justice by education and through actions, care of creation, empowerment of women and the worth and dignity of every person. Some of the Sisters' ministries include health care, education, social work, counseling, advocacy and law, spiritual and pastoral care and integrative health and healing.

Represented in the (Arch)dioceses of Baltimore, Brownsville, Charleston, Charlotte, Chicago, Colorado Springs, Columbus, Covington, Denver, Dubuque, Duluth, El Paso, Fargo, Great Falls, Helena, Indianapolis, Joliet, La Crosse, Lafayette, Lexington, Madison, Metuchen, Milwaukee, New Ulm, Oakland, Orange, Owensboro, Pueblo, St. Cloud, St. Paul/Minneapolis, San Bernardino, San Diego, Santa Fe, Savannah, Seattle, Sioux Falls, Spokane, Springfield-Cape Girardeau, Springfield, Superior, Washington and Winona. Also in Colombia.

Contact: Central Minister, Rochester Franciscan Life Teams, 1001 14th St. NW, Suite 100, Rochester, MN 55901-2525. (507) 282-7441. E-mail: rfvocations@aol.com; Web: www.rfvocations.org

FRANCISCAN SISTERS OF THE SACRED HEART (O.S.F.)

Motherhouse: St. Francis Woods, 9201 W. St. Francis Rd., Frankfort, IL 60423-8335. (815) 464-3873

130 Sisters

Apostolic Work: Education, health care, parish ministry, retreat ministry, social services and missions.

Represented in Indiana, Illinois and California. Also in Brazil.

Vocation Director: Sr. Deborah Suddarth, OSF, St. Francis Woods, 9201 W. St. Francis Rd., Frankfort, IL 60423-8335. (815) 464-3873. E-mail: sdeborah@aol.com; Web: www.fssh.com

FRANCISCAN SISTERS OF SAINT ELIZABETH (F.S.S.E.)

Motherhouse: Rome; Delegate House and Novitiate, 499 Park Rd., Parsippany, NJ 07054-1736. (973) 539-3797. E-mail: sr_cathylynn@yahoo.com; Web: www.franciscansisters.com

53 Sisters in US

Apostolic Work: (in US) 1 novitiate, 1 elementary school, 4 pre-schools, 1 Montessori school, 4 mission houses and 1 infirmary.

Represented in the Archdiocese of Newark and in the Dioceses of Paterson and St. Petersburg. Also, throughout Italy, Panama, India, Philippines and Ethiopia.

Vocation Directress: Vocation Office, Franciscan Sisters of Saint Elizabeth

FRANCISCAN SISTERS OF ST. JOSEPH US Foundation: St. Paul College, 3015 4th St., N.E., Washington, DC 20017. (202) 832-6262

5 Sisters

Apostolic Work: Ministry in domestic areas.

Represented in the Archdiocese of Washington.

Vocation Contact: Mother Maria, Superior, St. Paul College, 3015 4th St., N.E., Washington, DC 20017. (202) 269-2515

FRANCISCAN SISTERS OF ST. JOSEPH (F.S.S.J.)

Immaculate Conception Convent, 5286 S. Park Ave., Hamburg, NY 14075. (716) 649-1205

155 Sisters

Apostolic Work: Education on elementary, secondary and college levels, health care service, pastoral ministry, social services and diversified ministries.

Represented in the Archdioceses of Baltimore, Detroit and Milwaukee and in 7 dioceses.

Vocation Director: Franciscan Sisters of St. Joseph, 5286 S. Park Ave., Hamburg, NY 14075. (716) 649-1205. E-mail: srmarciaann@yahoo.com

FRANCISCAN SISTERS OF ST. PAUL, MN (O.S.F.)

Franciscan Regional Center, 1388 Prior Ave. S., St. Paul, MN 55116-2659. (651) 690-1501. Fax: (651) 690-2509

International Congregation

500 worldwide; 13 Sisters in US

Apostolic Work: The Sisters live the Gospel simply and plainly among the people by serving the poor and new Americans in health related care, education and social work.

Represented in the Archdiocese of Minneapolis/St. Paul. Also in Germany, the Netherlands, Brazil and Portugal.

Vocation Directress: Sr. Mary Lucy Scheffler, O.S.F., 1388 Prior Ave. S., St. Paul, MN 55116-2659. (651) 690-1501. Fax: (651) 690-2509. E-mail: spfranci@cpinternet.com; Web: www.askmotherrose.org

SISTERS OF ST. FRANCIS OF SAVANNAH, MO (O.S.F.)
Provincial House, LaVerna Heights, P.O. Box 488, 104 East Park, Savannah, MO 64485. (816) 324-3179
20 Professed Sisters
Apostolic Work: Education, nursing, CCD ministry, pastoral care, nursing home care, AIDS ministry, supportive ministries, justice advocacy, prison ministry.
Represented in the Diocese of Kansas City-St. Joseph.
Vocation Director: S. Christine Martin, P.O. Box 488, 104 East Park, Savannah, MO 64485. (816) 324-3179. E-mail: osf@ccp.com; Web: sistersofstfrancis.org

FRANCISCAN SISTERS OF SYRACUSE (O.S.F.) (Sisters of the Third Franciscan Order-Syracuse, NY)
800 N. Salina St., Syracuse, NY, 13208. (315) 473-0952. E-mail: yesGodislove@juno.com; Web: www.osfsyr.org
325 Sisters
Real women seeking the human face of God
We are a creative, enthusiastic community looking for young women with a vision of what our world could be, who are willing to take risks to make it happen. Our vibrant prayer life is rooted in faith which springs from the initiative of God and is the foundation of our spiritual life. Primary to our religious life is our way of living together in community for it is in community that our prayer and ministry are supported and nurtured. Our Franciscan charism is the gift we give to the Church. In keeping with Saints Francis and Clare, we embrace varied ministries according to our gifts.
Represented in 12 states (including Hawaii) in the US and in Peru.
Vocation Directress: Jeanne Karp, OSF

FRANCISCAN SISTERS, DAUGHTERS OF THE SACRED HEARTS OF JESUS AND MARY, (Wheaton Franciscans) (O.S.F.)
Our Lady of the Angels Motherhouse, PO Box 667, Wheaton, IL 60189-0667
Apostolic Work: The Sisters respond to the needs of our times, ministering in mutuality and partnership, and collaborating with other religious communities and lay partners in health, shelter and other human service ministries. Individual ministries are as diverse as the gifts that each Sister brings to community life.
Represented in the Archdioceses of Chicago, Denver, Dubuque, Milwaukee and St. Louis and in the Dioceses of Gary, Green Bay, Joliet, La Crosse, Rockford and Springfield-Cape Girardeau. Also in Brazil, Rome, France, Germany, Holland, Indonesia and Romania.
Vocation Director: Sr. Sheila Kinsey, OSF, PO Box 667, Wheaton, IL 60189-0667. (630) 462-7422. E-mail: skinsey@wheatonfranciscan.org; Web: www.wheatonfranciscan.org

SISTERS OF ST. FRANCIS OF ASSISI (O.S.F.) Motherhouse: St. Francis Convent, 3221 South Lake Dr., Milwaukee, WI 53235-3799
350 Sisters and 85 Associates
Apostolic Ministry: Our Franciscan congregation is committed to bringing the teaching, healing, reconciling and liberating power of Jesus to every life we touch. We stand in solidarity with women, and those who are poor, oppressed and disenfranchised, promoting social justice and working for the preservation of the earth, harmony and world peace while seeking to deepen our Franciscan identity.
Diverse ministries include: administrators; teachers; health care providers; social workers and counselors; campus, prison and parish ministers; childcare workers; artists and musicians.
Represented in dioceses across the US and Taiwan.
Vocation Director: St. Francis Convent, 3221 South Lake Dr., Milwaukee, WI 53235-3799. (414) 744-1160. E-mail: vocdir@lakeosfs.org; Web: www.lakeosfs.org

SCHOOL SISTERS OF THE THIRD ORDER OF ST. FRANCIS (Bethlehem) (O.S.F.)
Provincial House: 395 Bridle Path Rd., Bethlehem, PA 18017. (610) 866-2597
55 Sisters Bethlehem Province, 500 Sisters worldwide
Apostolic Work: Parish schools, retreat ministry, CCD centers, day care, high schools, social ministry.
Represented in the Archdioceses of Newark and Philadelphia and in the Dioceses of Allentown, Paterson and Springfield. Also in Chile, South Africa, India, Czech Republic, Slovak Republic, Central Asia and Italy.
Vocation Contacts: Sr. Maria, OSF, Sr. Electa, OSF, Sr. Patricia Brennan, OSF, Vocation Office, 395 Bridle Path Rd., Bethlehem, PA 18017. (610) 866-2597. E-mail: stfrancis395@rcn.com

SCHOOL SISTERS OF THE THIRD ORDER OF ST. FRANCIS (Pittsburgh) (O.S.F.) Motherhouse: Mount Assisi Convent, 934 Forest Ave., Pittsburgh, PA 15202. (412) 761-6004
78 Sisters
Apostolic Work: Pastoral ministry, teaching (early childhood, elementary, secondary, adult education), prayer and retreat ministry, nursing, youth ministry, religious education, parish social services, home for the aged, counseling, clerical work, missionary work, ministry to Hispanics and Native Americans in Southwest, other works corresponding to the gifts of the members.
Represented in the Archdiocese of San Antonio and in the Dioceses of Erie, Greensburg, Pittsburgh, Phoenix and San Angelo. Also missions in South America and South Africa.
Vocation Minister: Sister Lorita Kristufek, OSF, 1905 Watch Hill Dr., Ambridge, PA 15003. (724) 266-0939. E-mail: lorikris@forcomm.net; Web: www.franciscansisters-pa.org

SCHOOL SISTERS OF THE THIRD ORDER OF ST. FRANCIS (Panhandle) (O.S.F.) North American Region: Sancta Maria Convent, PO Box 906, Panhandle, TX 79068
24 Sisters
Conduct: 3 grammar schools, 5 confraternity centers, 1 home for the aged.
Represented in the Dioceses of Amarillo and Victoria. Also in Austria, Europe and in Argentina, South America
Vocation Director: M. Bernadette Black, O.S.F., Sancta Maria Convent, PO Box 906, Panhandle, TX 79068. (806) 537-3182. E-mail: schsrs@amaonline.com; Web: members.amaonline.com/schsrspanhandle

SCHOOL SISTERS OF ST. FRANCIS (OSF) An international community of Franciscan sisters in service to the people of God.
US Province: 1515 S. Layton Blvd., Milwaukee, WI 53215. (414) 384-1515
800 Sisters (US Province)
Apostolic Work: Education, health care, pastoral ministry, social service, the arts, sponsorship of institutions.
Represented in dioceses throughout the United States, Latin America, Europe and India.
US Province Vocation Contact: Sister Christine Myskow, Co-Director of New Membership,1515 S. Layton Blvd., Milwaukee, WI 53215. (414) 385-5253. Fax: (414) 384-1950. E-mail: cmyskow@sssf.org; Web: www.sssf.org

SISTERS OF ST. FRANCIS (O.S.F.)
6832 Convent Blvd., Sylvania, OH 43560. (419) 824-3602
240 Professed Sisters

Apostolic Work: Religious and academic education at all levels (preschool through college), health care, parish ministries, retreat work, social services.
Represented in the Archdioceses of Detroit, New Orleans, St. Paul-Minneapolis and Santa Fe and in the Dioceses of Austin, Biloxi, Cleveland, Columbus, Dallas, Jackson, Lansing, Raleigh, Richmond, St. Cloud, Shreveport, Springfield, Steubenville, Toledo and Wheeling.
Contact Person: Sr. Pam Nosbusch, 6832 Convent Blvd., Sylvania, OH 43560. (419) 882-2016. E-mail: francenter@aol.com

SISTERS OF ST. FRANCIS OF THE HOLY EUCHARIST (O.S.F.)
2100 N. Noland, Independence, MO 64050. (816) 252-1673
18 Sisters
Apostolic Work: Teaching in grade school, high school, college, health care, domestic work, retreat center, parish ministry, material and financial support to a Brazilian mission and other Central and South American countries.
Represented in the Dioceses of Kansas City, MO and Kansas City, KS.
Vocation Director: Sister Andrea Kantner, O.S.F., 2100 N. Noland Rd., Independence, MO 64050. (816) 252-1673. E-mail: stfran2100 @aol.com

SISTERS OF ST. FRANCIS OF PENANCE AND CHRISTIAN CHARITY (OSF) 4421 Lower River Rd., Stella Niagara, NY 14144-1001. (716) 754-4312
192 Sisters, 61 Associates
Apostolic Work: Education (all levels), health care, foreign/home missions, parish ministry, retreat work, social work, homeless ministry, Hispanic ministry, small Christian communities, lay ministry formation, rural ministry, L'Arche community, refugee ministry.
Represented in the (Arch)dioceses of Buffalo, Chicago, Cincinnati, Columbus, Louisville, Miami, Orlando, Paterson, St. Petersburg, Sante Fe, Trenton and Wheeling-Charleston. Also in Chiapas (Mexico) and Tanzania.
Vocation Contact: Sister Ann McDermott, osf, 2615 Roosevelt St., Hollywood, FL 33020. E-mail: annmcd@miamiarch.org; Web: www.franciscans-stella-niagara.org

SISTERS OF ST. FRANCIS OF PENANCE AND CHRISTIAN CHARITY (O.S.F.)
(Sacred Heart Province) 2851 W. 52nd Ave., Denver, CO 80221
68 Sisters
Conduct: 2 assisted living facilities: 1 for the elderly and 1 for younger persons with physical disabilities and/or AIDS; food, clothing, job referral service; 1 home for homeless mothers with small children; Hispanic community center.
Apostolic Work: Work among Native Americans on 3 reservations, social ministries with very young, the aging and prisoners; campus ministry.
Represented in the Archdioceses of Denver, Omaha and Kansas City and in the Dioceses of Grand Island, Rapid City, Reno and Las Vegas. Also in Chiapas and Hidalgo, Mexico and Tanzania.
Vocation Contact: Sister Judy Leal, O.S.F., 2851 W. 52nd Ave., Denver, CO 80221. (303) 458-6270. E-mail: judyleal@aol.com

SISTERS OF ST. FRANCIS OF PENANCE AND CHRISTIAN CHARITY Redwood City Franciscans, PO Box 1028, 3910 Bret Harte Dr., Redwood City, CA 94064. (650) 369-1725. E-mail: gracielamar @earthlink.net
105 Sisters
Apostolic Work: Elementary and secondary education, pastoral ministry in parishes, administration, Catholic social services, day care center, residence for retired women and men, marriage tribunal ministry, religious education, retreat center; Reiki, massage, Qigong and Shiatsu practitioners; bilingual education, Hispanic ministry, psychological counseling, peace and justice ministry, refugee ministry, health care ministry, teaching English as a Second Language (ESL), work with indigenous women.
Represented in the Archdioceses of Los Angeles, Portland, San Francisco and Seattle and in the Dioceses of Oakland, Phoenix, Reno-Las Vegas and Sacramento. Also in Chiapas (Mexico) and Tanzania.
Vocation Director: Sr. Graciela Martinez, OSF

SISTERS OF ST. FRANCIS, TIFFIN (O.S.F.) 200 St. Francis Ave., Tiffin, OH 44883-3458. (419) 447-0435
131 Sisters
Apostolic Works: Education, health care, pastoral work, parish ministry, child care, care of elderly, social work, earth literacy, retreat and renewal programs, diocesan offices, minister to the people of Appalachia and to Hispanics, care for people with AIDS.
Represented in the (Arch)dioceses of Charlotte, Cleveland, Columbus, Evansville, Lansing, Lexington, Milwaukee, Owensboro, Rockford, Santa Fe, Toledo, Wheeling-Charleston and in Chiapas, Mexico.
Director of Vocation Ministry: Sister Leanne Kerschner, St. Francis Convent, 200 St. Francis Ave., Tiffin, OH 44883-3458. (419) 447-0435. E-mail: lkerschner@tiffinfranciscans .org; Web: www.tiffinfranciscans.org

SISTERS OF ST. FRANCIS OF WILLIAMSVILLE (Williamsville Franciscans) (O.S.F.) 201 Reist St., PO Box 275, Williamsville, NY 14231-0275
140 Sisters
Ministry: Choices are made in response to the needs of the Church and one's talents and skills. Present involvements include: health care, care for the elderly, teaching at all levels; justice and peace work; service to the poor; pastoral ministry in hospitals, parishes and among the elderly; missionary work.
Represented in the Archdioceses of Chicago, Newark and Washington, DC and in the Dioceses of Buffalo, Charleston, Ogdensburg, Pittsburgh, Rochester and Syracuse. Also in Meru (Kenya, Africa).
Vocation Directors: Sr. Mary of the Angels, Sr. Peggy Wetzel, 201 Reist St., PO Box 275, Williamsville, NY 14231-0275. (716) 632-2155, ext. 593. E-mail: pwetzel@osfwmsv.org; Web: www.wmsvlfranciscans.org

SISTERS OF THE THIRD ORDER OF ST. FRANCIS (O.S.F.)
1175 St. Francis Ln., E. Peoria, IL 61611-1299
Apostolic Work: Health care and education.
Represented in the Dioceses of Peoria and Rockford, IL and Marquette, MI.
Vocation Director: Sister Dorothy Lampe, O.S.F., 1175 St. Francis Ln., E. Peoria, IL 61611-1299. (309) 699-9313. Fax: (309) 699-7225. E-mail: vocation.info@osfhealthcare.org; Web: www.osfhealthcare.org

THE LITTLE PORTION FRANCISCAN SISTERS (O.S.F.) 645 Assisi Way, Republic, MO 65738. (417) 732-6684
3 Sisters
Apostolic Work: Being a presence of God's healing love to the needy through spiritual ministry, shelter, food kitchen, low-income residency for elderly, ABE programs, free walk-in clinic, transitional housing units, retreat ministry at Little Portion Retreat Center.
Represented in the Diocese of Springfield-Cape Girardeau.
Vocation Director: Little Portion

Franciscan Sisters, 645 Assisi Way, Republic, MO 65738. (417) 732-6684. E-mail: lportion@juno.com; Web: www.littleportionretreat.org

GLENMARY SISTERS (G.H.M.S.)

The Glenmary Center: 405 W. Parrish Ave., Owensboro, KY 42304-2264. (1-800) 301-2689, (270) 686-8401

Apostolic Work: The Glenmary Sisters work in the rural areas of Appalachia and the deep South. They are radically involved with the issue of injustice, spiritual and material poverty and the rights of the downtrodden. The Sisters let the people know that they and their Catholic Christian communities do care.

Represented in the Dioceses of Owensboro, Lexington and Savannah.

Vocation Director: Sr. Sharon Miller, G.H.M.S., PO Box 22264, Owensboro, KY 42304-2264. (270) 686-8401. E-mail: membershipteam@glenmarysisters.org; Web: www.glenmarysisters.org

SISTERS OF THE GOOD SHEPHERD

We, the Good Shepherd Sisters, are an international apostolic and contemplative congregation, numbering around 5,000, with communities in 67 countries throughout the world. Our mission is one of reconciliation. We believe that, "One person is of more value than a world." Through our prayer and ministry, we strive to model our lives after the heart of Jesus, the Good Shepherd, who left the 99 to respond to the one in special need. Our apostolic work includes a variety of human services, primarily social work and social justice advocacy, with a particular focus on women and children. Our contemplative prayer strives to bring the liberating love of Jesus, the Good Shepherd, to all of God's people.

Represented throughout numerous states and provinces in the United States and Canada, as well as located on 5 continents in 67 countries.

Vocation Contacts:

Sr. Adrienne F. Baker, 5100 Hodgson Rd., St, Paul, MN 55126. (1-800) 880-5805. E-mail: abake@hgsmn.net

Sr. Patricia Marie Barnette, 4802 North Flagler Dr., Apt. 1, West Palm Beach, FL 33407. (561) 848-6770. E-mail: SrPatriciaRgs@juno.com

Sr. Rose Behrend, 88 Bank St., Harwichport, MA 02646. (508) 432-5582. E-mail: RoseBehrend@goodshepherdsisters.org

Sr. Debbie Drago, 160 Conover Rd., Wickatunk, NJ 07765. (732) 946-0515. E-mail: srdebbie@optonline.net

Sr. Jean Marie Fernandez, 7654 Natural Bridge Rd., St. Louis, MO 63121. (314) 381-3400. E-mail: JMFernandez@goodshepherdsisters.org

Sr. Gilda Fernando, 204 Boulevard Gouin Ouest, Montreal, QC, H3L 1J6, Canada. (514) 337 2111. E-mail: gildags@attglobal.net

Sr. Mary Joanna Le, 1114 W. Grace St., Chicago, IL 60613. (773) 935-3434. E-mail: rgs@enteract.com

Sr. Therese Mott, 725 S. Twelfth St., Springfield, IL 62703. (217) 544-4613. E-mail: MaryTherseMott@goodshepherdsisters.org

Sr. Yen Loc Tran, 2711 Mullanphy Lane, Florissant, MO 63031. (314) 837-1719. E-mail: yenloc@yahoo.com

Visit the Website: www.goodshepherdsisters.org

GREY NUNS OF MONTREAL

See Charity, Sisters of

GREY NUNS OF THE SACRED HEART (G.N.S.H.) Motherhouse: 1750 Quarry Rd., Yardley, PA 19067-3990. (215) 968-4236

160 Vowed Members, 1 Temporary Professed

Apostolic Work: Education, health care, social work, pastoral ministry, retreat ministry, religious education, service on behalf of the poor.

Represented in the Archdioceses of Anchorage, Atlanta, Baltimore, New York, Philadelphia and Washington, DC and in the Dioceses of Allentown, Brooklyn, Buffalo, Camden, Erie, Metuchen, Newark, Ogdensburg, Richmond, Rockville Center, Trenton and Toronto, Canada.

Vocation Director: Sr. Eileen Spanier, GNSH, Holy Angels Academy, 24 Shoshone St., Buffalo, NY 14214. (716) 515-0629. E-mail: espangnsh@aol.com; Web: www.greynun.org

GUANELLIAN SISTERS

See "D" - Daughters of St. Mary of Providence

SISTERS OF THE GUARDIAN ANGEL (S.A.C.) Motherhouse: Madrid, Spain.

US Foundation: 4529 New York St., Los Angeles, CA 90022. (323) 266-4431

600 Sisters worldwide

Apostolic Works: Social/pastoral work, helping the sick and elderly, education and the missions.

Represented in the Archdiocese of Los Angeles. Also in Bolivia, Colombia, Ecuador, El Salvador, France, Germany, Guinea, Italy, Ivory Coast, Japan, Mali, Mexico, Nicaragua, the Philippines, Spain and Venezuela.

Vocation Contact: Sister Hilda Alfaro, S.A.C. E-mail: hilfrance@hotmail.com; Web: www.planalfa.es/confer

HANDMAIDS OF MARY IMMACULATE (A.M.I.) Holy House Convent, 674 Mountain View Rd., Asbury, NJ 08802. (908) 689-7330

9 Sisters, 1 Novice

Apostolic Work: Pray and work for the spread of the Gospel in light of the message of Fatima, through the Blue Army, the Shrine of the Immaculate Heart of Mary and related works.

Represented in the Diocese of Metuchen.

Vocation Director: Sister Mary Brigid, A.M.I., Holy House Convent, 674 Mountain View Rd., Asbury, NJ 08802. (908) 689-7330. E-mail: smami1@juno.com

HANDMAIDS OF THE PRECIOUS BLOOD (HPB) Motherhouse: Cor Jesu Monastery, P.O. Box 90, Jemez Springs, NM 87025. (505) 829-3906

23 Professed Sisters, 5 First Professed, 1 Postulant

Apostolic Work: Contemplative life of Perpetual Eucharistic Adoration for the sanctification of priests and needs of the entire world.

Represented in the Archdioceses of Santa Fe and Chicago. Also in Rome, Italy.

Vocation Director: Mother John Paul, HPB, Rev. Mother Prioress

HANDMAIDS OF REPARATION OF THE SACRED HEART OF JESUS (A.R) Sacred Heart Villa, 36 Villa Dr., Steubenville, OH 43953

5 Sisters in US, 230 worldwide

Apostolic Work: Education - all levels, parish and diocesan ministry, CCD, orphanages and missionary work in Africa, Brazil, Poland and Ukraine.

Represented in the Dioceses of Steubenville and Arlington. Also in Italy, Brazil, Africa, Poland and Ukraine.

Contacts: Vocation Director, Sacred Heart Villa, 36 Villa Dr., Steubenville, OH 43953. (740) 282-3801; Handmaids of Reparation, 6300 Capella Rd., Burke, VA 22015. (703) 455-4180

HANDMAIDS OF THE SACRED HEART OF JESUS (a.c.j.)

(US Province) 2976 Galahad Dr. NE, Atlanta, GA 30345

1,400 Sisters worldwide; 50 Sisters US

Apostolic Work: Adoration of the Blessed Sacrament, education,

social and pastoral ministries and retreat centers.
Represented in the (Arch)dioceses of Philadelphia, Atlanta, Miami and Beaumont as well as Latin America, Africa, Asia, India, Ireland, Great Britain, Europe and the Philippines.
Contact Person: Sr. Margarita Martin, acj, Pine Wood Estates North, 1465 Hwy. 29N, Lot G-21, Athens, GA 30601. (706) 714-6624. E-mail: acjvocationsatlanta@juno.com; Web: www.acjusa.org

HERMANAS CATEQUISTAS GUADALUPANAS (H.C.G.)
Motherhouse: Saltillo, Coahuila, Mexico
American Foundation: 4110 S. Flores St., San Antonio, TX 78214
17 Sisters in US
Apostolic Work: Missions, evangelization, catechesis. Pastoral work in parishes, rural areas, schools.
Represented in the Archdioceses of Oklahoma City and San Antonio and in the Diocese of Fort Worth.
Vocation Director: Sister Margarita Vasquez, HCG, 4110 S. Flores St., San Antonio, TX 78214. (210) 532-9344

HERMANAS JOSEFINAS (H.J.)
Motherhouse: Mexico
US Foundation: Assumption Seminary, 2600 W. Woodlawn Ave., PO Box 28240, San Antonio, TX 78284. (210) 734-0039
8 Sisters
Represented in the Archdioceses of Chicago, Denver, Los Angeles and San Antonio and in the Diocese of El Paso

HERMITAGE OF THE ADVENT
215 Highland St., Marshfield, MA 02050. (781) 319-6688. E-mail: hermitageoftheadvent@earthlink.net; Web: www.hermitage-oftheadvent.org
Apostolic Works: Contemplative monastic community in formation.

SOCIETY OF THE HOLY CHILD JESUS (S.H.C.J.) (American Province) Provincial House: 460 Shadeland Ave., Drexel Hill, PA 19026. (610) 626-1400
216 Sisters
Apostolic Work: The Society is an international congregation of women ministering through a variety of educational, pastoral, healthcare, spiritual, and sociopolitical apostolates. SHCJ sponsor one college and a number of secondary and elementary schools throughout the United States, as well as a lay ministry program entitled, "Response-Ability" which sends volunteers to teach in inner city Los Angeles, Philadelphia, New York, Washington (DC), Chile, and the Dominican Republic.
Represented in Europe, South America, the Dominican Republic, and the United States, specifically: California, Colorado, Connecticut, District of Columbia, Florida, Illinois, Louisiana, Maryland, Massachusetts, Missouri, New Jersey, New York, North Carolina, Oregon, Pennsylvania, and Wisconsin.
Vocation Coordinators: East: Jeanne Marie Hatch, SHCJ, 460 Shadeland Ave., Drexel Hill, PA 19026-2312. (610) 626-1400, ext. 304. E-mail: jhatch@shcj.org. West: Sheila McNiff, SHCJ, 1833 E. Orange Grove Blvd., Pasadena, CA 91104. (626) 345-1633. E-mail: smcniff@shcj.org; Web: www.shcj.org

HOLY CROSS SISTERS
501 S. Center Ave., Merrill, WI 54452
44 Sisters, 29 Associates (US); over 4,400 worldwide
Apostolic Work: All the Works of Mercy inspired by the motto: "The need of the times is the will of God."
Represented in the Archdioceses of Atlanta, Cincinnati, Detroit, Milwaukee, Minneapolis-St. Paul, New Orleans and Sioux Falls and in the Dioceses of Baton Rouge, Belleville, Gaylord, Green Bay, La Crosse, Lansing, Steubenville and Superior. Also in Switzerland.
Contact Person: Sister Linda Songy, 501 S. Center Ave., Merrill, WI 54452. (715) 539-5000. E-mail: info@holycrosssisters.com; Web: www.holycrosssisters.org

SISTERS OF THE HOLY CROSS (CSC)
Generalate: Saint Mary's, Notre Dame, IN 46556
559 Sisters
Represented in the United States, Mexico, Brazil, Peru, Ghana, Uganda, Bangladesh and India.
Apostolic Work: Education, health care, parish, retreats, social service, work for justice.
Vocation Director: Sister Pam Welch, CSC, St. Mary's, Notre Dame, IN 46556. (574) 284-5560 or 273-9598. E-mail: pwelch@cscsisters.org; Web: www.cscsisters.org

SISTERS OF HOLY CROSS (C.S.C.)
An international congregation
US Regional Office: 377 Island Pond Rd., Manchester, NH 03109-4811
160 Sisters in US; 843 worldwide
Educators for Liberation: teachers, principals, librarians, pastoral ministry, directors of religious education, hospital ministry; prison ministry, AIDS ministry, private adoption agency and more.
Represented in the Dioceses of Manchester, Burlington, Fall River and St. Petersburg. Also in Canada, Bangladesh, Chile, Mali, Peru and Haiti.
Director of Vocation Ministry: Anne D. Hoffler, CSC, 971 Chestnut St., Manchester, NH 03104-2313. (603) 622-5847. Fax: (603) 622-9782. E-mail: ahoffcsc@comcast.net; Web: www.sistersofholycross.org

CONGREGATION OF THE SISTERS OF THE HOLY FAITH (C.H.F.)
US Region: 12322 Paramount Blvd., Downey, CA 90242. (562) 869-6092
40 Sisters
Conduct: 9 grammar schools, 2 high schools, religious education directors, pastoral associates, social work, R.C.I.A. directors, ministry directors, parish sisters, spiritual directors, counselors.
Represented in the Archdioceses of Los Angeles, New Orleans and San Francisco and in the Diocese of Sacramento. Also in Ireland, Trinidad, New Zealand, Australia and Peru.
Vocation Director: Sr. Joan Hogan, Seasons Apt. 814, 23750 Highland Valley Rd., Diamond Bar, CA 91765. (909) 860-5700. E-mail: joganchf@yahoo.com

SISTERS OF THE HOLY FAMILY OF NAZARETH (C.S.F.N.) (Immaculate Heart of Mary Province) Marian Heights, 1428 Monroe Tnpk., Monroe, CT 06468-1400. (203) 268-7646
87 Sisters
Apostolic Work: 1 child-caring institution, 7 elementary schools, 17 Christian Doctrine centers, 1 foster home care center, 1 clinical dispensary, retreats, social services and prison ministry, pastoral care, chaplain ministry.
Represented in the (Arch)dioceses of Bridgeport, Brooklyn, Hartford, Rockville Centre, Syracuse and Worcester.
Vocation Coordinator: Marian Heights, 1428 Monroe Tnpk., Monroe, CT 06468-1400. (203) 268-7646. Web: www.csfn.org

SISTERS OF THE HOLY FAMILY OF NAZARETH (C.S.F.N.) (Immaculate Conception Province) 4001 Grant Ave., Philadelphia, PA 19114-2999
151 Sisters
Apostolic Work: Ministry to families in all levels of education, healthcare, child care, retirement and nursing homes, parish ministry, religious education, retreat work, inner-city ministries.

Represented in the Archdiocese of Philadelphia and in the Dioceses of Allentown and San Juan.

Vocation Director: Sister Virginia Rozich, CSFN, 2723 Holme Ave., Philadelphia, PA 19152-2015. (215) 335-6380. Fax: (215) 335-3764. E-mail: voc4naz@aol.com; Web: phila-csfn.org

SISTERS OF THE HOLY FAMILY OF NAZARETH (C.S.F.N.) (Sacred Heart Province) 310 N. River Rd., Des Plaines, IL 60016-1211

Apostolic Work: Ministry to families in education, nursing, retirement homes, parish ministry, religious education and retreat work.

Represented in the Archdiocese of Chicago.

Vocation Director: Sister Carmen Marie, C.S.F.N., 310 N. River Rd., Des Plaines, IL 60016-1211. (847) 298-6760, ext. 144. E-mail: CSFN carmen@netscape.net; Web: www.c sfn.org

SISTERS OF THE HOLY FAMILY OF NAZARETH (C.S.F.N.) (St. Joseph Province) Mt. Nazareth Center, Inc., 285 Bellevue Rd., Pittsburgh, PA 15229-2195. (412) 931-4778

111 Professed Sisters

Apostolic Work: Family ministry, education, healthcare, social services, parish ministry, religious education, elder care, child care, day care, housing.

Represented in the (Arch)diocese of Altoona-Johnstown, Cleveland, Detroit, Pittsburgh and Steubenville.

Membership Director: Sr. Rose Mary Modzelewski, CSFN, 285 Bellevue Rd., Pittsburgh, PA 15229-2195. (412) 931-4778, ext. 2281. E-mail: innazareth@aol.com; Web: www.geocities.com/csfn_pgh

SISTERS OF THE HOLY FAMILY OF NAZARETH (C.S.F.N.) (Blessed Frances Siedliska Province) 1814 Egyptian Way, P.O. Box 530959, Grand Prairie, TX 75053-0959. (972) 641-4496

43 Sisters

Apostolic Work: 2 elementary schools, 1 community college, 2 hospitals, parish ministry, religious education, social services.

Represented in the Dioceses of Dallas, Fort Worth and Tyler.

Vocation Director: Sr. M. Margaret Langsett, 1814 Egyptian Way, P.O. Box 530959, Grand Prairie, TX 75053-0959. (972) 641-4496. E-mail: srlangsett@yahoo.com; Web: www.tx-csfn.org

CONGREGATION OF THE SISTERS OF THE HOLY FAMILY (S.S.F.)

6901 Chef Menteur Hwy., New Orleans, LA 70126-5290. (504) 242-8315. Fax: (504) 241-5489

170 Sisters

Conduct: Education at elementary and secondary levels, 1 nursing home, 2 apartments for the elderly and 2 day care centers, pastoral and social service.

Represented in the Archdioceses of Los Angeles, New Orleans and Washington, DC and in the Dioceses of Alexandria, Houston and Lafayette and in the Diocese of Belize in Central America.

Vocation Director: Sr. Sienna Marie Braxton, SSF, 3219 Gibson St., New Orleans, LA 70119. (504) 949-9077. Fax: (504) 947-4372. Web: www.sistersoftheholyfamily.org

SISTERS OF THE HOLY FAMILY (S.H.F.) PO Box 3248, Fremont, CA 94539. (510) 624-4511

117 Sisters

Apostolic Work: Religious ed classes, teacher training for laity, parish home visiting, parent education, family programs, youth ministry programs, pastoral care (hospital chaplains, bereaved and infirmed, AIDS), parish pastoral administrators, social service/social workers, nurses and home health care, child and family counselors, director of worship, librarian, public school teachers, religious education classes for developmentally disabled children, diocesan religious education directors and coordinators, day care for pre-school children, associate pastors.

Represented in the Archdioceses of Anchorage, Los Angeles and San Francisco and in the Dioceses of Honolulu, Fresno, Monterey, Oakland, Reno, Sacramento, Salt Lake City, San Antonio, San Diego, San Jose, Seattle, Stockton and in Kentucky, South Dakota and California.

Vocation Director: Sr. Kathy Littrell, S.H.F., PO Box 3248, Fremont, CA 94539. (510) 624-4511. E-mail: shfmem@aol.com; Web: www.holyfamilysisters.com

SISTERS OF THE HOLY NAMES OF JESUS AND MARY (S.N.J.M.)

(New York Province) 1061 New Scotland Ave., Albany, NY 12208-1098. (518) 489-5469. Fax: (518) 489-5804. E-mail: bpavlic@snjmny.org; Web: www.snjm.org

96 Sisters

Ministries: Elementary, high school, college teachers, religious education directors, involved in parish ministry to elderly, pastoral work, counseling, health care, migrant ministry, advocacy work, missionary work in Africa, Haiti, South America.

Represented in the (Arch)dioceses of Albany, Baltimore, Jackson, New York, Orlando, Palm Beach, Roanoke, St. Paul/Minneapolis, St. Petersburg, Venice, Washington.

Vocation Contact: Sister Barbara Pavlic, SNJM

SISTERS OF THE HOLY NAMES OF JESUS AND MARY (S.N.J.M.)

(Province of Oregon) P.O. Box 25, Marylhurst, OR 97036

212 Sisters

Ministries: Elementary, high school, college teachers, religious education directors, parish ministry to elderly, retreat ministry, pastoral associates, pastoral care in hospitals, family education and counseling, various ministries to the disadvantaged.

Represented in the Archdiocese of Portland, OR, in the Diocese of Baker and in many other places throughout the US, Canada, Africa, Haiti and Brazil.

Vocation Director: Sister Janet Ryan, S.N.J.M., Box 25, Marylhurst, OR 97036. (503) 635-3621. E-mail: janetmryan@msn.com; Web: www.snjm.org/west/Locations/oregon_ province.htm

SISTERS OF THE HOLY NAMES OF JESUS AND MARY (S.N.J.M.)

(Province of California) PO Box 907, Los Gatos, CA 95031

241 Sisters, 116 Associates

Ministries: Educators at the preschool, elementary, high school and college levels, pastoral ministers, retreat guides, social workers, campus ministers, health care providers, community organizers; associate and volunteer opportunities for men and women.

Represented in the Archdioceses of Los Angeles and San Francisco and in the Dioceses of Oakland, Orange, Monterey, San Jose and San Bernardino. Also in Central and South America, Canada, Lesotho and Haiti.

Vocation Director: Rosemary Everett, snjm, 10364 B. Vista Dr., Cupertino, CA 95014-2039. (408) 873-7858. E-mail: everettsnjm@earthlink.net; Web: www.holynames.net

SISTERS OF THE HOLY NAMES OF JESUS AND MARY (S.N.J.M.)

(Province of Washington) 2911 West Fort Wright Dr., Spokane, WA 99224

175 Sisters; 88 Associates

Ministries: International teaching community: preschool through college; artists, musicians, social justice/advocacy, chaplains, spiritual directors and volunteer programs for low-

income and marginalized persons.
Represented in the (Arch)diocese of Seattle, Spokane and Yakima. Also in Brazil, Canada, Haiti, Lesotho and Peru.
Vocation Team Coordinator: Sr. Cathy Beckley, S.N.J.M., 2911 West Fort Wright Dr., Spokane, WA 99224. (509) 328-7470, ext. 123. Fax: (509) 328-9824. E-mail: membership@snjmwa.org; Web: www.snjm.org

SISTERS OF THE HOLY REDEEMER (CSR) Provincialate: 521 Moredon Rd., Huntingdon Valley, PA 19006
31 Sisters in US, 600 worldwide
Over 150 years ago, Mother Alphonse Maria desired to bring the healing presence and compassion of the Redeemer to all who suffer in body, mind and spirit. Today, her vision has become 600 sisters, ministering in Europe, Tanzania and in the US. Sponsors of the Holy Redeemer Health System, the Sisters serve Jesus in the person of the poor, the sick, the elderly and homeless women and their children through health care, social services and pastoral care. Discernment opportunities include the Long Distance Contact Program for women living at a distance and unable to visit regularly and the Affiliate Program which provides a deeper connection with community and an experience of religious spirituality for women continuing the discernment process.
Vocation Contact: Vocation Ministry Office, 521 Moredon Rd., Huntingdon Valley, PA 19006. (215) 914-4114. Fax: (215) 914-4111. E-mail: vocations@SistersHolyRedeemer.org; Web: www.SistersHolyRedeemer.org

SISTERS OF THE MOST HOLY SACRAMENT (M.H.S.)
See "M" section - Most Holy Sacrament

HOLY SPIRIT ADORATION SISTERS (Sister Servants of the Holy Spirit of Perpetual Adoration)
Mt. Grace Convent, 1438 E. Warne Ave., St. Louis, MO 63107. (314) 381-2654. Web: www.mountgraceconvent.org
70 Sisters in US
Apostolic Work: Perpetual Adoration of the Most Blessed Sacrament exposed in the monstrance day and night. Contemplative life.
Represented in the Archdiocese of Philadelphia and in the Dioceses of Corpus Christi and Lincoln. Also, in the Philippine Islands, Argentina, Germany, Holland, India, Brazil, Poland, Togo and Indonesia.
Vocation Director: Sr. Mary Leticia

HOLY SPIRIT MISSIONARY SISTERS (S.Sp.S.) Provincial House: Convent of the Holy Spirit, PO Box 6026, Techny, IL 60082-6026
120 Sisters in the US
An international community of 4,000 women called to witness to the presence and power of the Holy Spirit, and to continue the saving mission of Jesus Christ.
Apostolic Work: In schools from preschool through university; in technical and professional schools; in hospitals as administrators, physicians, nurses, technicians, dietitians, and chaplains; involved with the elderly and the marginalized; in parishes in religious education and youth ministry; in spiritual direction, retreat work, counseling and social work.
Represented in 38 countries: Angola, Antigua (West Indies), Argentina, Australia, Austria, Bolivia, Botswana, Brazil, Chile, China, Cuba, Czech Republic, England, Germany, Ghana, India, Indonesia, Ireland, Italy, Japan, Korea, Mexico, Mozambique (Africa), Netherlands, Papua New Guinea, Paraguay, Philippines, Poland, Portugal, Romania, Russia, Slovakia, Spain, Switzerland, Taiwan, Togo, Ukraine and in the United States.
Vocation Ministers: Sister Rosemartin Glenn, S.Sp.S., Sister Dolores Marie Kuhl, S.Sp.S., Office of Vocation Ministry, PO Box 6026, Techny, IL 60082-6026, (847) 441-0126 (w), 319 Waukegan Rd., Northfield, IL 60093 (h). Web: www.ssps-usa.org

MISSION SISTERS OF THE HOLY SPIRIT (M.S.Sp.) Motherhouse: 1030 N. River Road, Saginaw, MI 48609
11 Professed Sisters
Apostolic Work: Religious education, social work, pastoral ministry, pastoral administrators.
Vocation Director: Sister Joan Maher, M.S.Sp., 1030 N. River Rd., Saginaw, MI 48609. (517) 781-0934 or 7159 Main St., Box 118, Port Sanilac, MI 48469

SISTERS OF THE HOLY SPIRIT (S.H.S.) 5246 Clarwin Ave., Pittsburgh, PA 15229
50 Sisters
Apostolic Work: Teaching, retreat ministry, home for the elderly, nursing and nursing education, administration, business, social services, pastoral ministry, formation ministry, youth ministry, ministry to the poor, the arts. Open to emerging needs.
Represented in the Dioceses of Pittsburgh and Greensburg.
Vocation Director: Sister Marita Juras, SHS, 4736 Friendship Ave., Pittsburgh, PA 15224. (412) 683-2044. E-mail: mjuras2003@libcom.com

SISTERS OF THE HOLY SPIRIT (C.S.Sp.) 10102 Granger Rd., Garfield Heights, OH 44125
9 Sisters
Apostolic Work: Elementary and secondary education; nursing, nursing home administration, dietary supervision, medical records, physical therapy, occupational therapy, related health care services, other service areas according to the needs of the Church and the particular talents of the community.
Represented in the Diocese of Cleveland.
Superior General: Sr. Mary Assumpta, C.S.Sp., 10102 Granger Rd., Garfield Heights, OH 44125

SISTERS OF THE HOLY SPIRIT AND MARY IMMACULATE (S.H.Sp.)
Motherhouse: Holy Spirit Convent, 301 Yucca St., San Antonio, TX 78203. (210) 533-5149
98 Sisters
Apostolic Work: Minister with the poor and marginated in schools, catechetical centers, social services, parish ministry, health care, home for the aged.
Represented in the (Arch)dioceses of San Antonio, Dallas, Fort Worth, Brownsville, Beaumont, Galveston-Houston, New Orleans, Houma-Thibodaux, Lafayette, Biloxi, Jackson and Shreveport. Also in Nayarit and Oaxaca (Mexico) and Zambia (Africa).
Vocation Director: Sr. Mary Fagan, S.H.Sp., Holy Spirit Convent, 301 Yucca St., San Antonio, TX 78203. (210) 533-5140. Fax: (210) 533-3434. E-mail: maryshsp@satx.rr.com; Web: www.shsp.org

HOLY UNION SISTERS (SUSC) (US PROVINCE) US Province: P.O. Box 410, Milton, MA 02186-0006. (617) 696-8765. Fax: (617) 696-8571
153 Sisters
Apostolic Work: Education, pastoral ministry, social services, spiritual development, health care.
Represented in Florida, Kentucky, Maryland, Massachusetts, New York and Rhode Island. Also in Argentina, Belgium, Cameroon, Chile, England, France, Haiti, Ireland, Italy, Scotland, Tanzania and Wales.
Vocation Director: Sister Joan Guertin, susc, 14 Main St., Groton, MA 01450. (978) 448-5731. E-mail: huvocations@juno.com; Web: www. holyunionsisters.org

HOME VISITORS OF MARY (H.V.M.)
121 E. Boston Blvd., Detroit, MI 48202-1318. (313) 869-2160. E-mail: homevisitors@myexcel.net
15 Sisters
Apostolic Work: A small religious community founded in 1949, dedicated to the mission of serving Christ among people in the heart of the city. Pastoral ministry, evangelization, lay leadership development, retreat work, small Christian community development, human relations seminars, African American spirituality center.
Represented in the Archdiocese of Detroit. Also in Nigeria, West Africa.
Vocation Contact: Sr. Laura Marie Kendrick, HVM

CONGREGATION OF THE HUMILITY OF MARY (C.H.M.) 820 W. Central Park, Davenport, IA 52804-1900
160 Sisters, 75 Associates
Apostolic Work: Education: teaching and administration; pastoral ministry/religious education; social services: homeless and abused persons, substance abuse rehabilitation; other individual ministries: law, communications, artist, health services, ministry to the elderly, retreat and prayer ministry.
Vocation Contact: Sister Ramona Kaalberg, C.H.M., Coordinator of Formation, 820 W. Central Park, Davenport, IA 52804-1900. (515) 282-3521. E-mail: ramonak1@juno.com; Web: www.chmiowa.org

SISTERS OF THE HUMILITY OF MARY (H.M.) Motherhouse: Villa Maria Community Center, Villa Maria, PA 16155. (724) 964-8861
212 Sisters, 1 Novice, 67 Associates
Apostolic Work: Diversified ministries, including education, health care, parish ministry, evangelization, social services, work for justice and peace, and prayer.
Represented in Ohio and western Pennsylvania, but represented in smaller numbers in 10 other states. Also in Haiti.
Membership Office: Sr. Mary Ann Spangler, HM, 20015 Detroit Rd., Rocky River, OH 44116-2418. (440) 356-6560. E-mail: maspangler@hmministry.org; Web: www.humilityofmary.org

I.C.M. MISSIONARY SISTERS (I.C.M.) (Missionary Sisters of the Immaculate Heart of Mary) 238 E. 15th St., Apt. 5, New York, NY 10003-3901. (212) 677-2959
30 Sisters in US, 954 worldwide
Apostolic Work: Sisters involved in various forms of educational, pastoral, social, health care ministries and ecology. Similar ministries in foreign missions.
Represented in 11 mission posts in the US Archdioceses of Los Angeles and New York and in the Dioceses of Albany and Brownsville, 135 communities overseas in 14 different countries of Africa, Asia, Europe and Latin America.
Vocation Counselor: Sr. Annie Claes, icm, 238 E. 15th St., Apt. 5, New York, NY 10003-3901. (212) 677-2959. E-mail: icmusdist@juno.com

SISTERS OF THE IMMACULATE CONCEPTION (R.C.M.)
Delegation House: 2230 Franklin St., San Francisco, CA 94109
12 Sisters in US (550 around the world)
Conduct: Education-parochial schools, missionary work, social & parish work, catechesis, orphanages, youth ministry.
Represented in the Archdiocese of San Francisco and in the Diocese of Fresno. Also in Spain, Italy, Brazil, Venezuela, Cameroon, Dominican Republic, Japan, Zaire, Equatorial Guinea, S. Korea, Philippines and Mexico.
Vocation Director: Sr. Gloria Gil, 2230 Franklin St., San Francisco, CA 94109. (415) 474-0159. E-mail: delesf@yahoo.com; Web: www.rc.net/conception

SISTERS OF THE IMMACULATE CONCEPTION OF THE BLESSED VIRGIN MARY (Lithuanian)
Immaculate Conception Convent and Novitiate, 600 Liberty Hwy., Putnam, CT 06260-2503
110 Sisters worldwide
Apostolic Work: Committed to Christ through a life of dedicated service and prayer: Catechetics and religious instruction, spiritual renewal programs, education, camping, health care ministry of the sick and elderly, social service, social work with abused children, pastoral and parish ministries, communications and hospitality.
Represented in the Archdiocese of Chicago and in the Dioceses of Norwich, CT and Burlington, VT. Also in Toronto, Canada. Generalate and 5 dioceses in Lithuania.
Vocation Director: Sr. M. Bernadette Matukas, MVS, Immaculate Conception Convent and Novitiate, 600 Liberty Hwy., Putnam, CT 06260-2503. (860) 928-7955

SISTERS OF THE IMMACULATE HEART OF MARY (I.H.M.)
(US Province) 4100 Sabino Canyon Rd., Tucson, AZ 85750
28 Sisters in US
Conduct: 1 novitiate, 1 elementary school, 1 middle school, 1 high school, religious education programs in parishes.
Represented in the Archdiocese of Miami and in the Diocese of Tucson. Also in Spain, France, Italy, Cuba, Chile, Brazil and the US
Vocation Director: Sister Alice Martinez, I.H.M., 4100 N. Sabino Canyon Rd., Tucson, AZ 85750-6503. (520) 886-4273. E-mail: abmartinez theriver.com

SISTERS OF THE IMMACULATE HEART OF MARY OF WICHITA (I.H.M.)
605 North Woodchuck, Wichita, KS 67212
19 Sisters
Apostolic Work: Education and retreat work.
Represented in the Diocese of Wichita.
Vocation Director: Sr. Marie Therese Callea, I.H.M., 605 North Woodchuck, Wichita, KS 67212. (316) 722-9316. E-mail: vocations@sistersihmofwichita.org; Web: www.sistersihmofwichita.org

IDENTE MISSIONARIES OF CHRIST CRUCIFIED (Association ID of Christ the Redeemer) (M.Id.)
143-48 84th Dr., Briarwood, NY 11435-2232. (718) 526-3595
250 Sisters
Apostolic Work: Spiritual direction, campus ministry, catechesis, parish work, youth ministry.
Represented in New York. Also in Europe, the Far East, Cameroon, Chad and in most South American countries.
Vocation Director: Sr. Elaine Schenk, M.Id., 143-48 84th Dr., Briarwood, NY 11435-2232. (718) 526-3595. Fax: (718) 526-9632. E-mail: elaine.schenk@verizon.net

SISTERS OF THE INCARNATE WORD AND BLESSED SACRAMENT (S.I.W.)
Motherhouse & House of Formation: 6618 Pearl Rd., Parma Heights, OH 44130-3808
36 Vowed Members, 57 Associate Members
Apostolic Work: Education, pastoral care, hospital chaplaincy, social work, ministry with developmentally challenged and disadvantaged youth, retreats and spiritual direction, diocesan office.
Promoter of the Charism: Sister Mary Rose Kocab, SIW, 6618 Pearl Rd., Parma Heights, OH 44130-3808. (440) 886-6440. E-mail: smrksiw@yahoo.com

CONGREGATION OF THE INCARNATE WORD AND BLESSED SACRAMENT (C.V.I.) Motherhouse and Novitiate: 3400 Bradford Pl., Houston, TX 77025-3668. (713) 668-0423

60 Sisters, 5 Sisters in Formation

Apostolic Works: 5 elementary schools, 1 high school, religious education, department for aging, diocesan office, social services, retreat/renewal, hospital chaplaincy, Hispanic/community services, pastoral ministry, nursing.

Represented in the Dioceses of Beaumont and Galveston-Houston.

Vocation Contact: Sister Carmel O'Malley, C.V.I., Incarnate Word Convent, 3400 Bradford St., Houston, TX 77025-3668. (713) 668-0423. E-mail: comalley@incarnateword.org; Web: www.incarnateword.org/cvi

CONGREGATION OF THE INCARNATE WORD AND BLESSED SACRAMENT (IWBS) Motherhouse and Novitiate: Incarnate Word Convent, 1101 N.E. Water St., Victoria, TX 77901

110 Sisters, 3 in Formation

Apostolic Works: 11 parochial grade schools, 2 parochial high schools, 1 private high school, 2 religious education centers, 8 hospital/ hospice/ chaplaincy/health care, 1 academy (day care through pre-K, K through grade 8), 1 academy multi-level learning center (day care, pre-school through K, alternative high school, adult education). Special Assignments: administration, parish ministry, RCIA, retreats, spiritual directors, counseling, diocesan director of ministries, clerical and domestic work, religious goods shop, spiritual and corporal works of mercy.

Represented in the Archdiocese of San Antonio and in the Dioceses of Beaumont, Dallas, Galveston-Houston and Victoria. Also in France and Kenya, Africa.

Vocation Directresses: Sister Mildred Truchard, IWBS, Sister M. Jacinta Benavidez, IWBS, 1101 N.E. Water St., Victoria, TX 77901. (361) 575-7111, 771-3325. Fax: (361) 575-2165. E-mail: iwbsvoc@yahoo.com; Web: www.catholic-forum.com/iwbsvictoria or www.rsbp.org

CONGREGATION OF THE INCARNATE WORD AND BLESSED SACRAMENT (I.W.B.S.) (Sisters of the Incarnate Word and Blessed Sacrament of Corpus Christi) Motherhouse and Novitiate: 2930 S. Alameda St., Corpus Christi, TX 78404-2798. (361) 882-5413. Fax: (361) 880-4152

66 Sisters

Conduct: 1 private high school, 2 private middle schools, 2 private grade schools, 2 kindergartens, 1 Montessori, 3 parochial grade schools, 1 language school, 6 parish ministry, 4 diocesan offices, 3 health care.

Represented in the Dioceses of Beaumont, Brownsville, Corpus Christi and Houston.

Vocations: Sister Rose Miriam Gansle, IWBS, 2930 S. Alameda St., Corpus Christi, TX 78404-2798. (361) 882-5413. Fax: (361) 880-4152. E-mail: srmgansle@juno.com

CONGREGATION OF THE INFANT JESUS (C.I.J.) (Nursing Sisters of the Sick Poor) Motherhouse: Villa St. Joseph, 984 North Village Ave., Rockville Centre, NY 11570

62 Sisters

Apostolic Work: Healing ministry. Engaged in nursing, administration, social services, physical therapy, services to the handicapped and disabled, pastoral care, parish outreach, home health care and hospice care and other works related to health services.

Represented in the Dioceses of Brooklyn, Rockville Centre, Portland (ME) and Lexington.

Membership Team: Villa St. Joseph, 984 North Village Ave., Rockville Centre, NY 11570

INSTITUTE OF THE BLESSED VIRGIN MARY (I.B.V.M.) (Loretto Sisters) North American Branch

Loretto Convent, P.O. Box 508, Wheaton, IL 60189-0508. (630) 653-4740; 1600 Somerset Lane, Wheaton, IL 60187

IBVM New Membership Office: 70 St. Mary St., Toronto, Ontario, Canada M5S IJ3

209 Vowed Sisters, 88 in the US

Apostolic Work: Education in its broadest sense; spiritual, pastoral and social ministry.

Represented in the (Arch)dioceses of Marquette, Chicago, Phoenix, Joliet, Rockford, Sacramento; the Canadian Provinces of Ontario and Saskatchewan.

Vocation Director: Jeanine Glute, IBVM, 70 St. Mary St., Toronto, Ontario, Canada M5S IJ3. (416) 928-9044. E-mail: ibvmjg@aol.com; Web: www.ibvm.org

INSTITUTE OF THE BLESSED VIRGIN MARY (I.B.V.M.) (also known as Loretto Sisters)

Mary Ward House, 2521 W. Maryland Ave., Phoenix, AZ 85017. (602) 433-0658. E-mail: opncrlsh@northlink.com

20 Sisters

Apostolic Work: Teaching, religious instruction, hospital chaplaincy, parish ministry.

Represented in the Diocese of Phoenix; other Provinces in Peru, Kenya, S. Africa, Mauritius, India, Australia, Spain, England, Ireland.

Directress of Formation: Sr. Anne Fitzsimons, IBVM

INSTITUTE OF DIVINE MERCY (I.D.M.) 9306 Forest Hills Blvd., Dallas, TX 75218. (214) 324-2607

Apostolic Work: Monastic, contemplative, cloistered, fulfilling St. Maria Faustina's mission to pray for God's Divine Mercy on the whole world.

Represented in the Diocese of Dallas.

Vocation Contact: Sister Maria Goretti of Jesus Crucified, IDM, Prioress/Vocation Director, 8351 San Fernando Way, Dallas, TX 75218. (214) 324-2607. Fax: (214) 319-9996. E-mail: divmercy@onramp.net; Web: www.divinemercy.org

CONGREGATION OF THE BENEDICTINES OF JESUS CRUCIFIED (O.S.B.)

See "B" - Benedictine Sisters

POOR SISTERS OF JESUS CRUCIFIED AND THE SORROWFUL MOTHER (C.J.C.) Our Lady of Sorrows Convent, 261 Thatcher St., Brockton, MA 02302. (508) 588-5070

43 Sisters

Apostolic Work: Nursing homes, parochial schools.

Represented in the (Arch)dioceses of Boston and Scranton.

Vocation Director: Sister Geraldine Nevaras, CJC, 261 Thatcher St., Brockton, MA 02302. (508) 588-5070, ext.37. Fax: (508) 580-6770. E-mail: sgfn@sistersCJCbrocktonMA.org; Web: SistersCJCBrocktonMA.org

SISTERS IN JESUS THE LORD (C.J.D.) Motherhouse: Russia

Mary Mother of God Mission Society, 1854 Jefferson Ave., St. Paul, MN 55105-1662. (651) 291-7777. E-mail: info@cjd.cc; Web: www.cjd.cc

1 Sister, 3 Associates

Apostolic Works: A new private association initially focusing on the Christianization of far-Eastern Russia. Dedicated to evangelizing though the media, nursing, care of elderly, disabled and orphans, etc.

Represented in the Archdiocese of St. Paul/Minneapolis.

Vocation Director: Sr. Julia Mary

SISTERS OF THE LAMB OF GOD (A.D.) 2063 Wyandotte, Owensboro, KY 42301. (270) 926-8656. E-mail: sisterlambaudrey@aol.com

100 Sisters in Congregation; 11 in the US

Motherhouse in Brest, France

Apostolic Work: Offers to the healthy as well as to those with physical disabilities the opportunity to fulfill their vocation, witnessing to the love of God and serving in diverse apostolates, according to their interests and abilities.

Represented in the Diocese of Owensboro.

Vocation Directress: Sr. Audrey, A.D.

SISTERS OF LIFE (Sorores Vitae) (S.V.) St. Frances de Chantal Convent, House of Formation, 198 Hollywood Ave., Bronx, NY 10465

31 Professed Sisters, 12 Novices

Apostolic Work: Contemplative-apostolic. The Community's charism is the protection and enhancement of the sacredness of every human life.

Represented in the Archdiocese of New York.

Vocation Director: Sr. Mary Loretta, S.V., St. Frances de Chantal Convent, House of Formation, 198 Hollywood Ave., Bronx, NY 10465. (718) 863-2264. Fax: (718) 792-9645. Web: sistersoflife.org/vocations-fr.html

LITTLE COMPANY OF MARY SISTERS (L.C.M.) American Provincial House: 9350 S. California Ave., Evergreen Park, IL 60805. (708) 229-5797. Fax: (708) 422-2212. E-mail: vocations@lcmh.org; Web: www.lcmh.org

28 Sisters in US; 400 worldwide

Apostolic Work: Compassionate presence in health care ministries in hospitals and extended care facilities; parishes (pastoral ministry) and outreach programs.

Represented in the Archdioceses of Chicago and Los Angeles and in the Dioceses of Toledo, Orange and Evansville. Also in 13 foreign countries: England, Ireland, Scotland, Wales, Italy, Albania, Tunisia, South Africa, Zimbabwe, Korea, Australia, New Zealand and Tonga.

Vocations Coordinator: Suzanne Petrouski, (708) 229-5095

LITTLE FRANCISCANS OF MARY (P.F.M.) Regional House: 55 Moore Ave., Worcester, MA 01602

Total membership 250

Apostolic Work: Nursing, teaching, pastoral work, care of the aged, catechetical work, foreign mission in Madagascar.

Represented in the Dioceses of Portland and Worcester. Also in Quebec Province. Foreign Missions.

Coordinator of Vocations: Sister Rena Mae Gagnon, pfm, 55 Moore Ave., Worcester, MA 01602. (508) 755-0878. E-mail: rmgpfm@yahoo.com

LITTLE SERVANT SISTERS OF THE IMMACULATE CONCEPTION (L.S.I.C.)

Motherhouse: Poland

Immaculate Conception Convent, Provincialate/Novitiate, 1000 Cropwell Rd., Cherry Hill, NJ 08003. (856) 424-1962. Fax: (856) 424-5333

78 Sisters, 1 Novice; 1,455 Sisters worldwide

Apostolic Work: 1 provincialate, 1 novitiate, 2 retreat houses, 2 nursery schools, 2 elementary schools, 1 home nursing service, 1 senior day center, 3 residences for the aged, 2 nursing homes, religious education, prayer cenacles, hospital, prison pastoral care, social services, youth ministry.

Represented in the Archdioceses of Newark and Philadelphia and in the Dioceses of Camden and Metuchen. Motherhouse: Poland. Also represented in Italy, Austria, England, Germany, Moldova, Ukraine, Russia (including Eastern Siberia), South Africa and Zambia.

Vocation Contact: Sister M. Philomena, Little Servant Sisters, 1000 Cropwell Rd., Cherry Hill, NJ 08003. (856) 424-1962. Fax: (856) 424-5333. E-mail: lsicprov@aol.com

LITTLE SISTERS OF THE ASSUMPTION (L.S.A.)

US Provincialate: 100 Gladstone Ave., Walden, NY 12586.

Motherhouse in Paris, France

44 Sisters

Apostolic Work: Live and work among the poor. Seeking to build, in the Spirit of Jesus Christ, the wholeness of families faced with extreme health, social, and economic problems.

Represented in the Archdioceses of Boston, New York and Philadelphia and in the Diocese of Worcester, MA. Also in 28 countries.

Vocation Director: Little Sisters of the Assumption, 475 E. 115th St., New York, NY 10029. (1-800) 482-4376. Web: www.littlesisters.org

LITTLE SISTERS OF THE GOSPEL OF CHARLES DE FOUCAULD

PO Box 305, Mott Haven Station, Bronx, NY 10454

3 Sisters in the US; 70 Sisters worldwide

Apostolic Work: Fostering the growth of Christian community among the poor. Apostolate springs from a deep contemplative spirit, prayer and community life.

Represented in the Archdiocese of New York and in Europe, Africa, Central and South America and the Caribbean.

Vocation Director: Sister Rita Claus

LITTLE SISTERS OF JESUS

Regional House, 400 N. Streeper St., Baltimore, MD 21224-1230. (410) 327-7863. E-mail: littlesrs.chg@juno.com; Web: www.rc.net/org/littlesisters

1,300 Sisters worldwide; 24 Sisters in US

Apostolic Work: Contemplative life in the midst of the world, sharing the life and work of those who are poor and marginalized; a ministry of presence and friendship.

Represented in the Archdioceses of Anchorage, Baltimore, Chicago and Washington and in the Dioceses of Fairbanks, Altoona and in over 120 dioceses worldwide.

Vocations: Sister Anne-Marie Boucher

LITTLE SISTERS OF JESUS AND MARY (L.S.J.M.) Joseph House, P.O. Box 1755, Salisbury, MD 21802. (410) 543-1645. E-mail: lsjm@ezy.net; Web: www.thejosephhouse.org

6 Sisters, 2 Postulants

Apostolic Work: Active contemplatives called to cry the Gospel with their lives, particularly in the midst of the poor. Prime purpose is to help stabilize family life. Through crisis centers in poverty-ridden areas, provide direct service to the poor by addressing their social, spiritual and economic problems. Also conduct a religious art and book store.

Represented in the Diocese of Wilmington.

Vocations: Sr. Mary Elizabeth Gintling

LITTLE SISTERS OF THE POOR (l.s.p.) (Brooklyn Province) Provincialate: Queen of Peace Residence, 110-30 221st St., Queens Village, NY 11429

(Baltimore Province) Provincialate: Saint Martin's Home, 601 Maiden Choice Ln., Baltimore, MD 21228-3698

(Chicago Province) Provincialate: 80 W. Northwest Hwy., Palatine, IL 60067-3580

3,000 Sisters in 31 countries

Apostolic Work: Welcoming the needy aged to 32 homes in the United States and Canada. Also present in France, Belgium, Spain, Portugal, Malta, Italy, Algeria, Benin, Congo,

Nigeria, Kenya, Turkey, England, Ireland, Scotland, Jersey (Channel Islands), the Philippines, Colombia, Chile, Argentina, India, Sri Lanka, South Korea, Hong Kong, Malaysia, Taiwan, Western Samoa, New Zealand, Australia and New Caledonia.

Represented in the Archdioceses of New York, Boston, Hartford, Philadelphia, Baltimore, Cincinnati, Louisville, Indianapolis, New Orleans, Washington, Chicago, Los Angeles, Mobile, San Francisco, Denver, Saint Paul and Saint Louis, and in 14 other dioceses in the US.

Vocation Inquiries: Sr. Marguerite, l.s.p., Little Sisters of the Poor, 601 Maiden Choice Lane, Baltimore, MD 21228. (410) 744-9367. E-mail: serenitylsp@netscape.net

LITTLE WORKERS OF THE SACRED HEARTS (P.O.S.C.)

General Motherhouse: Rome, Italy; Regional House: 645 Glenbrook Rd., Stamford, CT 06906-1409. (203) 348-5531

23 Sisters in the US; 400 Sisters worldwide

Apostolic Work: Ministry in the fields of academic and religious education especially catechesis, parish ministry, social work, and care of aged and infirm.

Represented in the Dioceses of Bridgeport and in the Archdioceses of Philadelphia and Washington, DC.; also in Italy, Argentina, India and Albania.

Vocational Directress: Sister Gesuina Gencarelli, P.O.S.C., 645 Glenbrook Rd., Stamford, CT 06906-1409. (203) 964-0319. E-mail: littleworkerposc@aol.com

SISTERS OF THE LIVING WORD (SLW) Living Word Center, 800 N. Fernandez Ave.-B, Arlington Heights, IL 60004. (847) 577-5972. Fax: (847) 577-5980

75 Sisters

Apostolic Work: Education, pastoral ministries, social services, advocacy, spiritual direction, health care, creative arts.

Represented in 8 states in the Archdioceses of Chicago, Detroit, New Orleans and St. Paul/Minneapolis and in the Dioceses of Cleveland, Jackson, Lansing, Rockford, Sioux City and Sioux Falls.

Director of New Membership: Sister Sharon Glumb, SLW, PO Box 726, Holly Springs, MS 38635. (662) 252-9801. E-mail: glumbs@aol.com; Web: www.slw.org

SISTERS OF LORETTO (S.L.) (Sisters of Loretto at the Foot of the Cross) LORETTO COMMUNITY

Loretto Motherhouse, 515 Nerinx Rd., Nerinx, KY 40049-9999. (270) 865-5811

371 Sisters, 203 Co-Members (an ecumenical partnership of women and men who share community and ministry) located in 32 states and 6 foreign countries

Apostolic Work: A community of faith and service, working for justice and acting for peace. Ministries are determined by needs and personal talents and include education, advocacy on behalf of women and other minorities, efforts to change unjust systems, health care and social work. Sister communities in Africa and Guatemala. Beginning a foundation in Pakistan. The volunteer program welcomes others to mission.

Contact: Anna Koop, SL, 300 E. Hampden #400, Englewood, CO 80110. (877) LORETTO (toll-free, outside Colorado); (303) 783-0450 (Colorado). Fax: (303) 783-0611. E-mail: annakoop@lorettocommunity.org; Web: www.lorettocommunity.org

SISTERS OF LORETTO (I.B.V.M.)

See Institute of the Blessed Virgin Mary

LOVERS OF THE HOLY CROSS SISTERS (LHC) Holy Cross Convent, 14700 S. Van Ness Ave., Gardena, CA 90249. (310) 768-1906; (310) 516-0271

50 Sisters in US

Apostolic Work: Parish ministry, teaching, nursing and social work.

Represented in the Archdiocese of Los Angeles and in the Diocese of Orange and San Bernardino.

Contacts: Sr. Grace Duc T. Le, Vocation Director, 1401 S. Sycamore St., Santa Ana, CA 92707. (714) 973-1961; Sr. Anne Lanh Tran, Superior General, Holy Cross Convent, 14700 S. Van Ness Ave., Gardena, CA 90249. (310) 768-1906 or (310) 516-0271. E-mail: graceducle@aol.com or lhcmh@aol.com

MANTELLATE SISTERS

See "S" - Servants of Mary

MARIAN SISTERS (M.S.)

Motherhouse: Marycrest Motherhouse, 6765 N. 112th St., Waverly, NE 68462. (402) 786-2750. Fax: (402) 786-7256. E-mail: adivis@inetnebr.com

37 Sisters, 2 Postulants

Apostolic Work: Home-school for exceptional children, high schools, grade schools, home for the aged, catechetics, hospice work, parish nurse.

Represented in the Diocese of Lincoln.

Vocation Director: Sister Michelle Mohr, M.S.

MARIANIST SISTERS (F.M.I.)

US Foundation: 251 W. Ligustrum Dr., San Antonio, TX 78228. (210) 433-5501

19 Sisters in US Province

Apostolic Work: Faith community formation, campus ministry, educational, social and pastoral ministry. Novitiate in Dayton, OH.

Represented in the Archdioceses of Cincinnati and San Antonio.

Vocation Contact: Sr. Eileen Cehyra, FMI, 251 W. Ligustrum Dr., San Antonio, TX 78228. (1-877) 820-6494, (210) 433-5501. E-mail: cehyrafmi.@aol.com; Web: www.marianistsisters.org

MARIANITES OF HOLY CROSS (MSC)

(North American Continent) 1011 Gallier St., New Orleans, LA 70117. (504) 945-1620

200 Sisters

Apostolic Work: Education-primary through adult, pastoral ministry in parishes and hospitals, campus ministry, health care, social ministries, counseling, foreign missions.

Represented in the Archdioceses of New Orleans and New York and in the Dioceses of Alexandria, Austin, Baton Rouge, Biloxi, Camden, Dallas, Houma-Thibodaux, Houston, Jackson, Lafayette, Lake Charles, Manchester, Paterson and Trenton. Also in the Dioceses of Mt. Laurier and Sherbrooke in Canada. Foreign missions in Bangladesh and Haiti.

Vocation Director: Sr. Renee Daigle, MSC, 4123 Woodland Dr., New Orleans, LA 70131. (504) 394-8500, ext. 205. Fax: (504) 391-7206. E-mail: reneemsc@marianites.org; Web: www.marianites.org

MARIST MISSIONARY SISTERS (S.M.S.M.) Provincialate: 349 Grove St., Waltham, MA 02453-6018. (781) 893-0149. Fax: (781) 899-6838

600 Sisters worldwide

Apostolic Work: To proclaim Jesus to the world, SMSMs participate in pastoral ministries, education, health, social services, administration, etc. In respect and dialogue, SMSMs try to be bonds of communion between peoples, races and cultures and witnesses to God's universal love.

Represented in the (Arch)dioceses of Boston, Brownsville, Fairbanks, Memphis, Oakland, St. Petersburg and Venice (FL) and in dozens of countries in Asia, Africa, Caribbean, Europe, Pacific and Latin America. Director of SMSM Vocation Ministries: Sr. Avelina Raiwaleta, smsm, 1515 Boxwood Ave., San Leandro, CA 94579-1303. Tel./Fax: (510) 357-7876. E-mail: smsmvoc@aol.com; Web: www.maristmissionarysmsm.org

MARIST SISTERS (S.M.)
(US Province) 9312 S. Kolmar, Oak Lawn, IL 60453. (708) 636-0259
17 Sisters in US, 500 worldwide
Apostolic Work: Marist Sisters are missionaries, teachers, nurses, social workers, counsellors, pastoral ministers, retreat directors in 17 countries: US, Mexico, Brazil, Gambia, Senegal, New Zealand, Australia, Fiji, Italy, France, Scotland, England, Ireland, Canada, Philippines, Venezuela, Germany.
Represented in the Archdioceses of Chicago and Detroit and in the Dioceses of Laredo and Wheeling-Charleston.
Vocation Team Director: Sister Linda Sevcik, S.M., 1000 E. Maple, Mundelein, IL 60060. (847) 970-4851. E-mail: lsevcik@usml.edu; Web: www.marists.org

SISTERS OF MARY IMMACULATE (S.M.I.) US Foundation: RD 5, Box 1231, Leechburg, PA 15656-8811. (724) 845-2828. E-mail: smi@kiski.net
6 Sisters in the US

SISTERS OF MARY OF THE PRESENTATION (S.M.P.)
Maryvale Novitiato: 11550 River Rd., Valley City, ND 58072. (701) 845-2864
53 Sisters
Conduct: 2 elementary schools, 4 hospitals, parish ministry, home health agency, spirituality center.
Represented in the Dioceses of Crookston, Fargo and Peoria.
Vocation Director: Sister Dorothy Bunce, SMP, Maryvale, 11550 River Rd., Valley City, ND 58072. (701) 845-2864. E-mail: srdorothy@fargodiocese.org

SISTERS OF MARY REPARATRIX (S.M.R.) (Society of Mary Reparatrix, American Province) 17320 Grange Rd., Riverview, MI 48192
30 Sisters
Apostolic Work: Retreats, spiritual direction, religious education, parish ministry, eco-spirituality ministries, pastoral care for the hospitalized and elderly, programs for the poor and needy.
Represented in the Archdioceses of Detroit and New York and in the Diocese of Brooklyn. Foreign Missions: Africa, South America, Panama.
Vocation Contact: Sister Joan Pricoli, S.M.R., 17320 Grange Rd., Riverview, MI 48192. (734) 285-4510. E-mail: joanpricoli@glblnet.com; Web: www.smr.org

MARYKNOLL CONTEMPLATIVE COMMUNITY PO Box 311, Maryknoll, NY 10545-0311
Contemplative (for Maryknoll members only).
Vocation Director: PO Box 311, Maryknoll, NY 10545-0311. (914) 941-7575. E-mail: mkcontemplativecom@juno.com; Web: www.catholic.org/macc

MARYKNOLL SISTERS OF ST. DOMINIC (M.M.)
The charism of the Maryknoll Sisters is to participate in the Church's universal mission. Thus, ministry in a cross-cultural context is the life form that enriches and enlivens them. Living in the mystery of God's inclusive love, they find God's presence outside of their own cultural, economic and social boundaries. Living in multicultural communities, they walk with the poor, the oppressed and the abandoned peoples of many lands. Their way of life is in harmony with the people among whom they live and the focus of their ministries is the empowerment of those whom they serve. Appreciation of diversity and finding God present in diversity is the spirituality that unites and nourishes them. Multicultural membership.
606 Sisters
Represented in Africa, Asia, Pacific Islands, Central and South Americas and the US.
Contact: Sr. Loretta Harriman, M.M., Maryknoll Sisters, PO Box 311, Maryknoll, NY 10545. (914) 941-7575. E-mail: vocation@mksisters.org; Web: www.maryknoll.org

MARYVALE SISTERS (CLHC) (Congregation of Our Lady Help of the Clergy) Motherhouse: Maryvale Motherhouse, 2522 June Bug Rd., Vale, NC 28168
5 Sisters
Apostolic Work: Faith formation on all levels. Home visitation to the sick, elderly, shut-ins, hospital visitations, pastoral assistance in areas of counseling, youth ministry, day care, evangelization ministry, spiritual direction and retreat ministry; retreat residence available for private or directed individual/group retreats.
Represented in the Diocese of Charlotte.
Vocation Director: Sister Mary Norman, C.L.H.C. (704) 276-2626

MEDICAL MISSION SISTERS (MMS)
(North America) Headquarters: 8400 Pine Rd., Philadelphia, PA 19111
680 Sisters
Apostolic Work: At the heart of their common call to mission is the deep belief that they are called to be an active presence of Christ, the Healer. Together with the poor, the oppressed, the broken, the Sisters seek to struggle for wholeness, forgiveness, justice, healing and peace. Their ministry encompasses a wide variety of healing activities in Africa, Asia, South America, North America and Europe.
Vocation Contact: Sister Edna Villafuerte, M.M.S., Membership Advisor, 8400 Pine Rd., Philadelphia, PA 19111. (215) 742-6100. E-mail: ednavmms@juno.com; Web: www.medicalmissionsisters.org

MEDICAL MISSIONARIES OF MARY (M.M.M.) Motherhouse: Ireland
400 Sisters worldwide
Apostolic Work: An international congregation of religious women, with a lifelong commitment to prayer, and to a participation in the healing mission of Jesus. Ministry centers on healing of the whole person. Thus, work is varied: nurses, doctors, social workers, community development and pastoral ministry, to name a few. Strive to reach out to the very poor and those most in need: in 9 African countries, Brazil, Honduras and Appalachia (VA).
Represented in the Archdioceses of Boston, Chicago and New York and in the Dioceses of Richmond and San Diego.
Vocation Director: Sister Mary Donato, MMM, 179 Highland Ave., Somerville, MA 02143-1515. (617) 666-3223. E-mail: mkdonato@cs.com; Web: www.mmmusa.org, www.medical-missionaries.org

MEDICAL SISTERS OF ST. JOSEPH (MSJ) Motherhouse: India
US Foundation: 3435 E. Funston, Wichita, KS 67218. (316) 686-4746. E-mail: msjkansas@aol.com
700 Sisters (worldwide)
Apostolic Work: Health care.
Represented in the Diocese of Wichita and 10 dioceses in India

MERCEDARIAN MISSIONARIES OF BERRIZ (M.M.B.) Motherhouse: Berriz, Spain; Generalate: Rome, Italy
Our Lady of Mercy Country Home, 2205 Hughes Rd. #101B, Liberty, MO 64068-7985
17 Sisters in US, 600 Sisters worldwide
Apostolic Work: International mis-

sionary congregation; teachers, social workers, nurses, catechists, co-pastors, youth leaders.

Represented in the Diocese of Kansas City-St. Joseph. Foreign Missions: Micronesia: Mariana and Caroline Islands; Mexico; Guam; Guatemala; Nicaragua; Peru; Equador; Japan; Taiwan; Philippines; Zaire, Africa.

Vocation Office: Sister Betty Preston, MMB, Our Lady of Mercy Country Home, 2205 Hughes Rd. #101B, Liberty, MO 64068-7985. (816) 781-8202, 5711. Fax: (816) 781-7276. E-mail: mmbus@earthlink.net; Web: www.ourladyofmercy.net/ourstory.html

MERCEDARIAN SISTERS OF THE BLESSED SACRAMENT (HMSS)

Motherhouse: Mexico City; Regional House: 222 W. Cevallos St., San Antonio, TX 78204. (210) 222-1354. Fax: (210) 222-0275

32 Sisters in the US; over 800 worldwide

Apostolic Work: Education: preschools, elementary, secondary and junior college; parish and diocesan ministry to Hispanics; sick and aged and imprisoned.

Represented in the (Arch)dioceses of San Antonio, Cleveland, Corpus Christi and San Diego. Also in Mexico, Italy, Spain, Colombia, El Salvador, Chile, Venezuela, Guatemala and Costa Rica.

Regional Vocation Director: Sister Teresita Paz, HMSS, 222 W. Cevallos St., San Antonio, TX 78204. (210) 223-5013. Fax: (210) 444-0779. E-mail: hermanas@prodigy.net.mx

MERCEDARIANS

See "O" section - Sisters of Our Lady of Mercy

SISTERS OF MERCY OF THE AMERICAS (R.S.M.) (Regional Community of Albany)

Mercy Administrative Center, 310 South Manning Blvd., Albany, NY 12208-1793

183 Sisters

Apostolic Work: Education, health services, pastoral ministry, social services.

Represented in the Archdioceses of Anchorage and New York and in the Dioceses of Albany, Springfield, Syracuse and Washington, DC.

Vocation Minister: Sister M. Helen Dillon, R.S.M., Mercy Administrative Center, 310 South Manning Blvd., Albany, NY 12208-1793. (518) 437-3000. E-mail: HDillion@stpeters healthcare.org; Web: www.mercy albany.org/vocations.asp

SISTERS OF MERCY OF THE AMERICAS (R.S.M.) (Regional Community of Auburn)

Our Lady of Mercy Convent, 535 Sacramento St., Auburn, CA 95603-5699. (530) 887-2000

81 Sisters, 1 Novice

Apostolic Ministry: Schools, hospitals, parish ministry, Hispanic ministry, outreach clinics, ministry to homeless and aged, retreat and spirituality ministry, hospice and AIDS ministry.

Represented in the Diocese of Sacramento.

Vocation Minister: Sr. Michelle Gorman, RSM, 535 Sacramento St., Auburn, CA 95603-5699. (530) 887-2020. E-mail: mgormanrsm@aol.com; Web: www.mercysisters.org

SISTERS OF MERCY OF THE AMERICAS (R.S.M.) (Regional Community of Baltimore)

1322 E. Northern Pkwy., Baltimore, MD 21239. (410) 435-4400

197 Sisters, 1 Temporary Vows, 3 Novices

Apostolic Work: The spirit of the community is compassion for those in need: the poor, the sick, the uneducated and all those in any way wounded by contemporary society. Works include: education, health care, social services, especially to women and children, parish ministries, care of the elderly, hospice, AIDS services and housing ministry.

Serving in Maryland, Georgia, Alabama, Florida and Washington, DC

Vocation Minister: Sr. Regina Ann Hatton, RSM, 101 Wimbledon Dr. W., Mobile, AL 36608. (251) 342-4477. Web: www.mercybaltimore.org

SISTERS OF MERCY OF THE AMERICAS (R.S.M.) (Regional Community of Brooklyn)

273 Willoughby Ave., Brooklyn, NY 11205. (718) 622-5840

260 Sisters, 1 Novice, 1 Candidate

Apostolic Work: Elementary schools, high schools, catechetical centers, child-caring institutions, missions in Panama, social work, nursing, mission work, counseling, soup kitchen, women's shelter, parish ministry.

Represented in the Dioceses of Brooklyn and Rockville Centre. Also in Panama.

Director of Vocations and New Membership: Kathleen Hennessy, RSM, Our Lady of Mercy Convent, 815 Convent Rd., Syosset, NY 11791-3895. (1-877) 50 MERCY, (516) 921-5245 (w), (516) 921-3680 (h). E-mail: Kathleen@trymercy.org, KathRSM@aol.com; Web: www.trymercy.org

SISTERS OF MERCY OF THE AMERICAS (R.S.M.) (Regional Community of Buffalo)

Mercy Center, 625 Abbott Rd., Buffalo, NY 14220. (716) 825-5531

200 Sisters, 90 Associates

Apostolic Work: Junior colleges, academy, high schools, elementary schools, health system, parish ministry, social service, domestic service, pastoral ministry, speech therapy, religious education coordination, inner city services.

Represented in the Diocese of Buffalo. Also in the Philippines.

Contact Person: Sister Patricia Gilbert, R.S.M., Vocation Minister, 625 Abbott Rd., Buffalo, NY 14220. (716) 825-5531, ext. 424. E-mail: patg@bflorsm.com

SISTERS OF MERCY OF THE AMERICAS (R.S.M.) (Regional Community of Burlingame)

Motherhouse: 2300 Adeline Dr., Burlingame, CA 94010-5599. (650) 340-7400

180 Sisters

Conduct: Spirituality and conference center, missionary work in Latin America, elementary, secondary and higher education, pastoral religious education, peace and justice ministry, health care, social services (e.g. low-income housing, psychological counseling, legal services, child care, etc.).

Represented in the Archdioceses of Los Angeles and San Francisco and in the Dioceses of Fresno, Oakland, Orange, Phoenix, San Diego and San Jose.

Vocation Minister: Sister M. Lenore Greene, RSM, Sisters of Mercy of the Americas, 2300 Adeline Dr., Burlingame, CA 94010-5599. (1-877) 50-MERCY or (650) 340-7434, ext. 2. E-mail: lenorersm@aol.com; Web: www.sistersofmercy.org

SISTERS OF MERCY OF THE AMERICAS (R.S.M.) (Regional Community of Cedar Rapids)

1125 Prairie Dr., N.E., Cedar Rapids, IA 52402-2828. (319) 364-5196

93 Sisters

Conduct: 1 college, 1 hospital, 1 center for women (education, homeless, single homeless without children), co-sponsor of Mercy Housing.

Represented in the Archdioceses of Cincinnati, Dubuque, Milwaukee, New York, St. Louis and Washington (DC) and in the Dioceses of Des Moines, Davenport and Helena. Also in Puno (Peru).

Vocation Minister: Joan Margret Schwager, RSM, 1424 J St. SW, Cedar Rapids, IA 52404-2828. (319) 362-8379. E-mail: jmarg@ccr.net

SISTERS OF MERCY OF THE AMERICAS (R.S.M.) (Regional Community of Chicago)
10024 S. Central Pk. Ave., Chicago, IL 60655-3132
270 Sisters
Apostolic Work: Education, health care, parish and retreat ministry, housing, artists and musicians, elder care and social services.
Represented in the Archdioceses of Chicago, IL; Milwaukee, WI; and Madison, WI and in the Dioceses of Davenport, IA, Peoria, IL, Rockford, IL, and Joliet, IL. Also in Honduras.
Vocation Minister: Sister Bernadette Hart, RSM, 10024 S. Central Pk. Ave., Chicago, IL 60655-3132. (773) 779-6011, ext. 12. E-mail: clwnhart5@aol.com; Web: www.sistersofmercy.org

SISTERS OF MERCY OF THE AMERICAS (R.S.M.) (Regional Community of Cincinnati)
Administrative Offices, 2335 Grandview Ave., Cincinnati, OH 45206
330 Sisters
Conduct: 6 high schools, 1 college, 5 elementary schools, 2 child care homes, 14 hospitals, 5 nursing homes, 1 nursing college, 3 apartment complexes for the elderly, 2 special education schools, 3 Montessori schools, 1 retreat and renewal center; also serve in colleges and campus ministry, social service programs, parish ministry, parish schools and prison ministry.
Represented in the Archdioceses of Chicago, Cincinnati, Detroit, Louisville, Washington and Kingston, Jamaica and in the Dioceses of Charlotte, Cleveland, Covington, Memphis, Nashville, Owensboro, Richmond, Toledo and Montego Bay, Jamaica.
Vocation Minister: Sr. Mary Ellen Matts, RSM, 2335 Grandview Ave., Cincinnati, OH 45206. (513) 221-1800. E-mail: memattsrsm@aol.com; Web: www.mercycincinnati.org

SISTERS OF MERCY OF THE AMERICAS (R.S.M.) (Regional Community of Connecticut)
Administrative Office, 249 Steele Rd., West Hartford, CT 06117
219 Sisters
Apostolic Work: Education from pre-school through college, adult education, religious education, health services, social services, prison ministry, pastoral ministry, parish ministry, diocesan service, housing ministry, care of the elderly, retreat and spiritual direction ministry, counseling, peace and justice ministry.
Represented in the Archdioceses of Hartford and in the Dioceses of Bridgeport and Norwich. Also in Guatemala, Haiti and Belize.
Vocation Contact: Sister Beth Fischer, RSM, 249 Steele Rd., West Hartford, CT 06117. (860) 232-8602, ext. 317. E-mail: bfischer@sjc.edu; Web: www.sistersofmercy.org/connections/becoming.html

SISTERS OF MERCY OF THE AMERICAS (R.S.M.) (Regional Community of Dallas, PA)
Box 369, Dallas, PA 18612-0369
300 Sisters
Apostolic Work: Education, health care, social services, parish ministry, retreat work, communications, artistic services.
Represented in the Dioceses of Altoona-Johnstown, Brooklyn, Harrisburg, Rockville Centre, Scranon and Georgetown, Guyana, South America.
Vocation Director: Marina Culp, R.S.M., Box 369, Dallas, PA 18612. (570) 675-2048. E-mail: srmarina@somdallasreg.org; Web: sistersofmercy.org

SISTERS OF MERCY OF THE AMERICAS (R.S.M.) (Regional Community of Detroit)
29000 Eleven Mile Rd., Farmington Hills, MI 48336. (248) 476-8000
262 Sisters
Apostolic Work: Health care in hospitals, clinics, schools of nursing and public health organizations as nurses, physicans, administrators and chaplains; education from pre-school through college, religious education, special education and campus ministry; social work: prison ministry, care of the elderly and handicapped; Other ministries: retreat work, communications, pastoral ministry and diocesan administration; housing and a variety of direct ministries to the poor.
Represented primarily in the Archdioceses of Detroit and Dubuque and in the Dioceses of Davenport, Gary, Gaylord, Grand Rapids, Kalamazoo, Lansing, Saginaw, Sioux City. Also in Argentina.
Vocation Minister: Mary Ellen Matts, RSM, 29000 Eleven Mile Rd., Farmington Hills, MI 48336-1405. (248) 476-8000. E-mail: memattsrsm@aol.com; Web: www.sistersofmercy.org

SISTERS OF MERCY OF THE AMERICAS (R.S.M.) (Regional Community of Erie)
444 E. Grandview Blvd., Erie, PA 16504-6504. (814) 824-2516
70 Sisters
Apostolic Work: College, high school, diocesan elementary education office, elementary education, pre-school education, music education, catechetical work, parish ministry, service to civic community, houses of prayer, pastoral ministry, pastoral ministry in health care, inner city ministry, tutoring, advocacy/shelter for women and their children in need, provider of social services to senior citizens, senior citizen housing, prison ministry.
Represented in the (Arch)dioceses of Erie, Savannah and Washington (DC).
Vocation Directors: Sr. Maria Lucia B. Serrano, RSM, Sr. Patricia Tyler, RSM, 444 E. Grandview Blvd., Erie, PA 16504-6504. (814) 824-2509, (814) 453-5399. E-mail: rsmvocation444@yahoo.com; Web: www.sistersofmercy.org/connections/becoming.html

SISTERS OF MERCY OF THE AMERICAS (R.S.M.) (Regional Community of Merion)
Motherhouse: 515 Montgomery Ave., Merion, PA 19066. (610) 664-6650
400 Sisters
Apostolic Work: All levels of education, healthcare, social service and parish ministry.
Represented in the Archdioceses of Anchorage, Atlanta and Philadelphia and in the Dioceses of Allentown, Camden, Gallup, Orlando, Pensacola-Tallahassee, Richmond, St. Petersburg and Wilmington. Also in Peru.
Vocation Director: Carol Tropiano, RSM, 515 Montgomery Ave., Merion, PA 19066. (610) 664-6650. E-mail: sctrsmmer@aol.com; Web: www.sistersofmercy.org

SISTERS OF MERCY OF THE AMERICAS (R.S.M.) (Regional Community of New Hampshire)
Motherhouse: 21 Searles Rd., Windham, NH 03087-1297
172 Sisters
Apostolic Work: Teaching, parish ministry, health services, social service.
Represented primarily in the Diocese of Manchester and the Archdiocese of Boston.
Vocation Director: Sister Ellen Kurtz, RSM, 605 Stevens Ave., Portland, ME 04103-2691. (207) 797-7299. E-mail: emkrsm@aol.com; Web: www.sistersofmercy.org/connections/becoming.html

SISTERS OF MERCY OF THE AMERICAS (RSM) (Regional Community of New Jersey)
Mount Saint Mary, 1645 Hwy. 22 W., Watchung, NJ 07069-6587
300 Sisters
Apostolic Work: Education (all levels), parish and pastoral ministries, social

services, health care, catechetics. Service to the People of God where and how needed. Involved with those who are: economically poor, especially women and children; women seeking fullness of life and equality in Church and society; the elderly, distressed and handicapped.

Represented throughout New Jersey and in parts of California, Florida, Maryland, New York, North Carolina and Pennsylvania.

Vocation Minister: Patricia Donlin, RSM, Mount Saint Mary, 1645 Hwy. 22 W., Watchung, NJ 07069-6587. (1-877) 50-MERCY, (908) 756-0994, ext. 4037. E-mail: Patricia@trymercy.org, PatDRSM@aol.com; Web: www.trymercy.org

SISTERS OF MERCY OF THE AMERICAS (R.S.M.) (Regional Community of New York)

Administrative Offices: 150 Ridge Rd., Hartsdale, NY 10530

193 Sisters

Apostolic Work: All levels of education, health care, social services, pastoral ministry, hospital chaplaincy, religious education, retreat work.

Represented in the Archdiocese of New York and in the Dioceses of Ogdensburg and Worcester.

Vocational Contact: Patricia Donlin, RSM, 150 Ridge Rd., Hartsdale, NY 10530. (877) 50-MERCY. E-mail: Patricia@trymercy.org, PatDRSM@aol.com; Web: www.trymercy.org

SISTERS OF MERCY OF THE AMERICAS (R.S.M.) (Regional Community of North Carolina)

101 Mercy Drive, Belmont, NC 28012. (704) 829-5260

119 Sisters, 90 Associates

Apostolic Work: Teaching, nursing, social services (homeless shelter for women and children, home for persons with HIV/AIDS, home for special-needs children), pastoral care, campus ministry, religious education, youth ministry, spiritual retreat, counseling, diocesan pastoral planning.

Represented in the (Arch)dioceses of Charlotte, Miami, St. Louis and West Virginia. Also in Agana (Guam) and the Caroline Islands.

Vocation Directors: Sister Mary Cabrini Taitano, RSM, 101 Mercy Dr., Belmont, NC 28012. (704) 829-5260. E-mail: cabrini@mercync.org; Web: www.mercync.org; Sister Mary Mark Martinez, RSM, Tai Mercy Convent, PO Box 22865 GMF, Barrigada, Guam 96921. (671) 734-3312

SISTERS OF MERCY OF THE AMERICAS (R.S.M.) (Regional Community of Omaha)

Sisters of Mercy Regional Office, 1801 S. 72nd St., Omaha, NE 68124. (402) 393-8225

255 Sisters

Apostolic Work: Education, health services, parish ministry, social work, housing ministry, peace and justice ministry, retreat ministry and spiritual direction.

Represented in AZ, CA, CO, FL, IL, ID, IA, KS, MO, NE, NM, ND, OR, WA and WY.

Vocation Minister: Sister Maria Campos, RSM, 7262 Mercy Rd., Omaha, NE 68124. (402) 558-8873, 393-8145. E-mail: srmcamprsm@aol.com

SISTERS OF MERCY OF THE AMERICAS (R.S.M.) (Regional Community of Pittsburgh)

3333 Fifth Ave., Pittsburgh, PA 15213. (412) 578-6344

196 Sisters

Conduct: 1 college, grammar schools, 1 school of nursing, 2 hospitals.

Apostolic Work: A variety of health programs, home and foreign missions, parish services and a variety of individual ministries serving the people of God throughout the United States and the world.

Represented predominantly in the Dioceses of Pittsburgh, Greensburg, Miami, Fort Lauderdale, San Juan in Puerto Rico, Chimbote in Peru, Guatemala and in other areas throughout the United States and the world.

Vocation Minister: (Serving the Buffalo, Erie, Pittsburgh & Rochester Regional Communities of the Sisters of Mercy): Sister Beth A. Yoest, RSM, 3333 5th Ave., Pittsburgh, PA 15213. (412) 578-6344. E-mail: byoest@aol.com

SISTERS OF MERCY OF THE AMERICAS (R.S.M.) (Regional Community of Portland)

Motherhouse: 605 Stevens Ave., Portland, ME 04103

124 Sisters

Apostolic Work: Teaching: elementary – college; health care, parish work (religious education and social work), transitional housing for the homeless, ministry to Native Americans, spiritual direction.

Represented in the Diocese of Portland, Maine. Also in Andros Island (Bahama) and Peru.

Vocation Director: Sister Patricia Mooney, RSM, Sisters of Mercy, 605 Stevens Ave., Portland, ME 04103. (207) 797-7299. E-mail: joyinmercy@hotmail.com; Web: www.sistersofmercy.org/connections/becoming.html

DIOCESAN SISTERS OF MERCY OF PORTLAND (R.S.M.) Our Lady of Mercy Convent, 265 Cottage Rd., South Portland, ME 04106. (207) 767-5804

9 Sisters

Apostolic Work: Education, social work, pastoral ministry.

Represented in the Diocese of Portland (ME).

Vocation Director: Sr. Karen Hopkins, RSM

SISTERS OF MERCY OF THE AMERICAS (R.S.M.) (Regional Community of Providence)

Administration Office: 15 Highland View Rd., Cumberland, RI 02864-1124

360 Sisters

Apostolic Work: Education at all levels (preschool through college) uniquely developed literacy programs, social services, pastoral care in hospitals, prisons and parishes, ministry with homeless, religious education.

Represented in the Dioceses of Fall River and Providence and in the countries of Belize and Honduras, Central America.

Vocation Director: Sister Christina Costigan, RSM, 15 Highland View Rd., Cumberland, RI 02864-1124. (401) 333-6333. E-mail: ccostigan@mercyri.org; Web: www.sistersofmercy.org/connections/becoming.html

SISTERS OF MERCY OF THE AMERICAS (R.S.M.) (Regional Community of Rochester)

Motherhouse: 1437 Blossom Rd., Rochester, NY 14610

198 Sisters

Apostolic Work: Continually expanding to serve the poor, the sick, and the uneducated in today's world. Presently involved in all levels of education, administration, healthcare, pastoral ministry, and social ministry, including a foster home for children and missions in Chile.

Represented in the Dioceses of Rochester, NY; Jackson, MS; Atlanta, GA. Also in Santiago, Chile.

Vocation Director: Sister Kathleen Wayne, RSM, 1437 Blossom Rd., Rochester, NY 14610. (585) 288-2710, ext. 109. E-mail: kawmercyroch@yahoo.com

SISTERS OF MERCY OF THE AMERICAS (R.S.M.) (Regional Community of St. Louis)

2039 N. Geyer Rd., St. Louis, MO 63131-3332

295 Sisters

Apostolic Work: Education, health

care, pastoral and social work, religious education.
Represented primarily in the states of Arkansas, Kansas, Louisiana, Mississippi, Missouri, Oklahoma and Texas.
Vocation Minister: Sister Priscilla Moreno, RSM, Mercy Center, 2039 N. Geyer Rd., St. Louis, MO 63131-3332. (1-877) 50-MERCY, (314) 909-4647. Fax: (314) 909-4600. E-mail: prismore@aol.com or vocations@try mercy.org

SISTERS OF MERCY OF THE AMERICAS (R.S.M.) (Regional Community of Vermont)
Motherhouse: Mt. St. Mary, 100 Mansfield Ave., Burlington, VT 05401
73 Sisters
Apostolic Work: 1 private elementary school, 1 diocesan high school, 1 diocesan elementary school, religious education/parish ministry. Involvement in social work, spirituality, health care, prison ministry and housing ministry.
Represented in the Diocese of Burlington.
Vocation Contact Person: Sister Mary Crosby, RSM, Vocation and Formation Team, Mt. St. Mary, 100 Mansfield Ave., Burlington, VT 05401. (802) 863-6835. E-mail: mcrsm@hotmail.com; Web: www.sistersofmercy.org

MERCY SISTERS (R.S.M.)
Generalate: Dublin, Ireland
US Province: Sisters of Mercy,1075 Bermuda Dr., Redlands, CA 92374. (909) 798-4747
130 Sisters
Apostolic Work: Pastoral and health care, education, social work, ministry to women, the poor and the immigrant.
Represented in 12 Dioceses in the US.
Vocations: Sister Susan DeGuide, RSM, 1075 Bermuda Dr., Redlands, CA 92374. (909) 798-4747. Fax: (909) 798-5300. E-mail: sdeguide_sm@sbdiocese.org

MERCY SISTERS (R.S.M.)
St. Joan of Arc, 500 S.W. 4th Ave., Boca Raton, FL 33432. (561) 368-6655
4 Sisters
Represented in the Diocese of Palm Beach

(IRISH) SISTERS OF MERCY US PROVINCE Holy Infant Convent, 239 Nancy Pl., Ballwin, MO 63021. (636) 391-1528
3 Sisters
Apostolic Work: Education, pastoral ministries.
Represented in the Archdiocese of St. Louis.
Facilitator: Sister Laurentia Cusack, Holy Infant Convent, 239 Nancy Pl., Ballwin, MO 63021

MERCY SISTERS OF IRELAND (R.S.M.) (US Province)
4 Sisters in US
Apostolic Work: Teaching, social service and pastoral work.
Represented in the Diocese of Orlando.
Vocation Director: Sr. Joan Grace, RSM, St. Mary's Convent, 1136 Seminole Dr., Rockledge, FL 32955. (321) 636-1341

SISTERS OF MERCY-Elphin Community (S.M.) Sisters of Mercy, St. John's Convent, 2960 Mendoza Dr., Costa Mesa, CA 92626. (714) 545-2116. E-mail: sjb@surfside.net
2 Sisters
Represented in the Dioceses of Orange, San Bernardino and San Diego

(IRISH) SISTERS OF MERCY US PROVINCE (S.M.) Sacred Heart Convent, 6240 105th St., Jacksonville, FL 32244
5 Sisters
Represented in the Diocese of St. Augustine
Vocation Contact: Sister Patricia O'Hea, S.M., Sacred Heart Convent, 6240 105th St., Jacksonville, FL 32244. (904) 771-3858. Web: www.sacredjax.co

MERCY SISTERS (Galway) (R.S.M.)
Provincialate: Sisters of Mercy, 1075 Bermuda Dr., Redlands, CA 92374. Divine Mercy Convent, 1930 N. Courtenay, Merritt Island, FL 32953
2 Sisters
Primary Apostolic Work: Education (works of mercy).
Represented in the Diocese of Orlando
Vocation Contact: Mary Divilly, RSM, Divine Mercy Convent, 1930 N. Courtenay Pkwy., Merritt Island, FL 32953. (321) 452-1279/5955

MERCY SISTERS (R.S.M.)
St. Joseph Convent, 1402 Miller St., Palm Bay, FL 32905. (407) 723-5375; St. Joseph Church, (407) 727-1565
2 Sisters
Represented in the Diocese of Orlando

SISTERS OF MERCY OF THE BLESSED SACRAMENT (H.M.S.S.)
See "M" - Mercedarian Sisters of the Blessed Sacrament

MILL HILL SISTERS (F.M.S.J.) (Franciscan Missionaries of St. Joseph) Franciscan House, 1006 Madison Ave., Albany, NY 12208. (518) 482-1991
6 Sisters in US; 200 worldwide
Apostolic Work: Parish ministry, foreign missions, social work, teaching, nursing.
Represented in the Dioceses of Albany, Norwich and Syracuse. Also in Kenya, East Africa, Ecuador, South America.
Vocation Director: Sister Joan Kerley, Franciscan House, 1006 Madison Ave., Albany, NY 12208. (518) 482-1991. E-mail: kerleyjl@lemoyne.edu

MILLVALE FRANCISCANS (O.S.F.)
146 Hawthorne Rd., Pittsburgh, PA 15209
147 Sisters
Evangelical Work: Elementary education, secondary education, college education, campus ministry, Montessori, day care, hospitals, healthcare, healthcare education, senior adult housing, family home care, parish ministry, religious education, evangelization, social service, pastoral care, counseling services, diocesan offices.
Represented in the (Arch)dioceses of Pittsburgh, Altoona-Johnstown, Baltimore, Buffalo, Chicago, Erie, Greensburg, Indianapolis, La Crosse, Los Angeles, Lubbock, Miami, Newark, Philadelphia, Santa Fe, Steubenville, Youngstown and Washington. Also in Cayey and San Juan, PR, Benin City, Nigeria and Toronto.
Pre-Entrance Coordinator: Sister Kathy Adamski, OSF, Office of New Membership, 146 Hawthorne Rd., Pittsburgh, PA 15209. (800) 689-8237, (412) 215-7708. E-mail: guidance@nauticom.net; Web: www.millvalefranciscans.org

MINIM DAUGHTERS OF MARY IMMACULATE (C.F.M.M.)
General Motherhouse: Mexico; US: Regional/Retirement House, Our Lady of Lourdes Elementary/High School, P.O. Box 1865, Nogales, AZ 85628-1865. (520) 287-3377
23 Sisters in the US; 395 worldwide
Apostolic Work: Elementary/high school.
Represented in the Diocese of Tucson
Vocation Contact: Sr. Luise Marie Valdez, CFMM, 555 Patagonia Hwy., Nogales, AZ 85628-1865. (520) 287-3377. E-mail: lmvaldez@yahoo.com

SISTERS MINOR OF MARY IMMACULATE (S.M.M.I.)
St. Francis Villa, 138 Brushy Hill Rd., Danbury, CT 06810. (203) 744-8041
74 Sisters
Apostolic Work:
Contemplative/active order engaged in a variety of apostolic works and following St. Maximilian Kolbe and St. Therese; living out a fourth vow of total consecration to Our Lady. (Accepting candidates ages 17-35.)
Represented in the Arch(dioceses) of Bridgeport and Hartford. Also in foreign missions.
Vocation Director: Sr. Mary Elizabeth Lariviere, S.M.M.I., 656 Congress Ave., Waterbury, CT 06708. (203) 753-1408

MISERICORDIA SISTERS (S.M.)
Generalate: 12435 Ave. de la Misericorde, Montreal, Canada H4J 2G3. (514) 332-0550
3 Sisters in US
Apostolic Work: 1 maternity home for unwed mothers.
Represented in 3 Canadian Provinces and the Archdiocese of New York. Also in Ecuador.
Vocation Director: Sister Ellen Hunt, S.M., 225 Carol Ave., Pelham, NY 10803. (914) 738-1723. E-mail: rosaliehal@aol.com

MISSION HELPERS OF THE SACRED HEART (M.H.S.H.)
1001 W. Joppa Rd., Towson, MD 21204
94 Sisters, 1 Lay Minister in US, 3 in Venezuela
Apostolic Work: Visiting poor families in their homes to inquire about their needs, advocates for the handicapped and hearing impaired, feeding the homeless in cities, reaching out to the Hispanic community in the US, Puerto Rico and Venezuela, counseling and challenging young people, comforting families of the terminally ill, including those with AIDS, counseling families dealing with social, economic or psychological pressures, and proclaiming the Gospel through spirituality programs and formal religious education. Becoming aware of an existing need, a Mission Helper responds.
Represented in 14 states, Puerto Rico and Venezuela, South America, (States: Arizona, California, Connecticut, Delaware, District of Columbia, Florida, Indiana, Maryland, Massachusetts, Michigan, New York, North Carolina, Ohio, Pennsylvania).
Vocation Director: Sr. Loretta Cornell, M.H.S.H., 1001 W. Joppa Rd., Towson, MD 21204. (410) 823-8585, ext. 246. Fax: (410) 296-4050. E-mail: lcornell@missionhelpers.org; Web: www.missionhelpers.org

MISSIONARIES OF CHARITY (M.C.)
(North America Province)
4,000 Sisters in the whole congregation
Apostolic Work: Giving wholehearted and free service to the poorest of the poor.
Represented in the (Arch)dioceses of Atlanta, Baltimore, Baton Rouge, Boston, Bridgeport, Charlotte, Chicago, Dallas, Denver, Detroit, Gallup, Gary, Houston, Indianapolis, Jenkins, Lafayette, Little Rock, Los Angeles, Memphis, Miami, Newark, New Bedford, New York, Peoria, Philadelphia, Phoenix, St. Louis, San Francisco, Trenton and Washington (DC). Foreign missions in Albania, Argentina, Australia, Austria, Bangladesh, Belgium, Benin, Bolivia, Brazil, Burundi, Cameroon, Canada, Chile, Columbia, Costa Rica, Cuba, Czechoslovakia, Denmark, Dominican Republic, El Salvador, Ethiopia, Egypt, Equador, France, Germany, Ghana, Greece, Grenada, Guatemala, Guinea, Guyana, Haiti, Holland, Honduras, Hong Kong, Hungary, Iceland, India, Ireland, Italy, Ivory Coast, Japan, Jordan, Kenya, Lebanon, Liberia, Libya, Macau, Madagascar, Malta, Mauritius, Mexico, Mongolia, Nepal, Nicaragua, Nigeria, Pakistan, Panama, Papua New Guinea, Peru, Philippines, Poland, Portugal, Puerto Rico, Romania, Russia, Rwanda, Senegal, Seychelles, Sierra Leone, Singapore, South Korea, Spain, Sri Lanka, Sudan, Syria, Tanzania, Trinidad, United Kingdom, Uruguay, Venezuela, Yemen, Yugoslavia, Zaire.
Vocation Director: Sr. M. Dominga, MC, Regional Superior, 335 E. 145th St., Bronx, NY 10451. (718) 292-0019. Web: www.geocities.com/Athens/2960/mothert.htm

MISSIONARIES OF THE SACRED HEART OF JESUS (M.S.C.) (Cabrini Sisters) The Cabrini Family: MSC Vowed Religious Sisters; Lay Missionaries; Volunteers; Collaborators
Province Office: 222 E. 19th St., Apt. 5B, New York, NY 10003. (212) 995-6876. Cabrini Mission Corps (CMC): 610 King of Prussia Rd., Founders Hall-Basement, Radnor, PA 19087. (610) 971-0821. E-mail: cmcorps@aol.com
Way of Life: "To be Bearers of the Love of Christ in the world" through our missionary outreach, community, prayer, and works which include: evangelization; health care and education; youth and family ministry; pastoral outreach through parishes, in shrines, retreat houses and prisons; advocacy and work for justice on behalf of immigrants, refugees, women and children and those marginalized by society.
Represented in New York, Pennsylvania, New Orleans, Chicago, Denver and Seattle. Also in the Philippines, Swaziland, Ethiopia, Australia, Europe, Central America, Argentina, Brazil and Russia.
Vocation Contact: Sr. Diane Olmstead, MSC, (se habla Español), 139 Henry St., New York, NY 10002. (212) 393-1171. E-mail: mscvoc@aol.com; Web: www.cabrinivocation.org (vowed life and lay missionaries)

MISSIONARY BENEDICTINE SISTERS (O.S.B.) (Congregation of Missionary Benedictine Sisters)
Immaculata Monastery, 300 N. 18th St., Norfolk, NE 68701-3687. (402) 371-3438. Fax: (403) 379-2877. E-mail: vocations@norfolkosb.org; Web: www.norfolkosb.org
45 Sisters, 1 in Formation
Apostolic Work: Education, health care, catechetics, domestic and pastoral ministry, special apostolates among Hispanics and Native Americans.
Represented in the Dioceses of New Ulm and Omaha. Also in Angola, Argentina, Australia, Brazil, Bulgaria, China, Germany, India, Italy, Kenya, Namibia, the Philippines, Portugal, South Korea, Spain, Switzerland, Tanzania and Uganda.
Vocation Director: Sister Rosann Ocken, OSB

MISSIONARY CATECHISTS OF DIVINE PROVIDENCE (M.C.D.P.)
MCDP Vocation Office, 2318 Castroville Rd., San Antonio, TX 78237-3520
52 Sisters
Apostolic Work: Working with children, youth, young adults, adults in religious education within a parish setting. Also counselors, teachers, social work, consultants at the diocesan, state and local level. Special emphasis in Hispanic ministry.
Represented in Omaha, Alaska and Texas.
Vocation Committee: Sister Maria Guadalupe Castaneda, mcdp, Sister Joan Elise Rodriquez, mcdp, Sister Elvira Mata, mcdp, MCDP Vocation Office, 2318 Castroville Rd., San Antonio, TX 78237-3520. (210) 431-3217. E-mail: lupvoc@aol.com; Web: mcdp.org

MISSIONARY CATECHISTS OF THE SACRED HEARTS OF JESUS AND MARY (M.C.S.H.) Provincial Office, 805 S. Liberty St., Victoria, TX

77901. (361) 578-9302. Fax: (361) 580-2181
(Central Headquarters: Mexico City)
200 Sisters; 40 in US
Apostolic Work: Pastoral assistants, family orientation and formation, religious education ministry (C.C.D.), evangelization and catechesis in ministries, home visiting ministry, pastoral and liturgical activities at parish and diocesan levels.
Represented in the Dioceses of Victoria, Galveston-Houston, Ft. Worth, Lubbock and Metuchen. Also in Mexico, Africa, Spain and Bolivia.
Vocation Contacts: Sister Silvia Gomez, Vocation Ministry, 209 W. Murray, Victoria, TX 77901. (361) 575-7654; Sister Miriam Perez, Provincial Superior, 805 S. Liberty St., Victoria, TX 77901. (361) 578-9302. Fax: (361) 580-2181

MISSIONARY DAUGHTERS OF THE MOST PURE VIRGIN MARY (M.D.P.V.M.)
919 N. 9th St., Kingsville, TX 78363. (361) 595-1087
35 Sisters in US; 500 Sisters worldwide
Apostolic Work: Education, social work, missions (in Mexico), pastoral work, novitiate in Mexico.
Represented in the Dioceses of Brownsville, Corpus Christi, Yakima and Camden.
Vocation Director: 919 N. 9th St., Kingsville, TX 78363. (361) 595-1087

MISSIONARY FRANCISCAN SISTERS OF THE IMMACULATE CONCEPTION (MFIC)
Provincial House: 790 Centre St., Newton, MA 02458. (617) 527-1004. Fax: (617) 527-2528. E-mail: usaprov@aol.com
250 Sisters in US, 370 Sisters worldwide
Ministries: Varied, include education, pastoral care (especially among the poor), health care, social services, foreign missions.
Represented in 12 dioceses in the US (East Coast) and in 9 countries worldwide including Australia, Boliva, Canada, Egypt, England, Ireland, Italy, Papua New Guinea, Peru.
Vocation Minister: Sr. Mary Therese Brown, MFIC, MFIC Vocation Office, 20 Manet Rd., Chestnut Hill, MA 02467-1018. (617) 332-1907. E-mail: mficvocation@aol.com; Web: www.mficusa.org

MISSIONARY SERVANTS OF THE MOST BLESSED TRINITY (M.S.B.T.)
3501 Solly Ave., Philadelphia, PA 19136. (215) 335-7550
200 Sisters, 5 in Formation
Apostolic Work: Social services, pastoral ministry, religious education, health services, campus ministry, education and retreat ministry.
Represented in dioceses throughout the US, Puerto Rico and Mexico.
Vocation Ministers: Sr. Deborah Wilson, M.S.B.T., Sr. Barbara McIntyre, M.S.B.T., 3501 Solly Ave., Philadelphia, PA 19136. (215) 335-7534. E-mail: msbt@juno.com; Web: www.msbt.org

MISSIONARY SERVANTS OF ST. ANTHONY (M.S.S.A.)
100 Peter Baque Rd., San Antonio, TX 78209
5 Sisters
Apostolic Work: Ministering to children in learning centers, caring for retired priests.
Represented in the Archdiocese of San Antonio.
Vocation Contact: Sr. Mary Ann Domagalski, M.S.S.A., 100 Peter Baque Rd., San Antonio, TX 78209. (210) 824-4553. Fax: (210) 824-4554. Web: www.rsbp.org/mssa.html

MISSIONARY SISTERS OF THE BLESSED SACRAMENT AND MARY IMMACULATE (M.SS.MI.)
Convent of Mary Immaculate, 1111 Wordin Ave., Bridgeport, CT 06605. (203) 334-5681. Fax: (203) 333-1590. E-mail: misami1896@aol.com
Represented in the Archdioceses of Boston and Newark and in the Dioceses of Bridgeport and Oakland.
Vocation Director: Sr. Nexaida Soto, M.SS.MI., 1111 Wordin Ave., Bridgeport, CT 06605

MISSIONARY SISTERS OF THE HOLY ROSARY (M.S.H.R.)
741 Polo Rd., Bryn Mawr, PA 19010
385 Sisters
Apostolic Work: Teaching, medical work, pastoral work, social work, counseling, community building, organizing, refugee work, AIDS ministry.
Represented in the Archdiocese of Philadelphia. Also in Nigeria, Sierra Leone, Cameroon, Ghana, Kenya, Zambia, Ethiopia, South Africa, Brazil, Mexico, Ireland, England and Scotland.
Vocation Contact: Sr. Terry Shields, M.S.H.R., 741 Polo Rd., Bryn Mawr, PA 19010. (610) 520-1974. Fax: (610) 520-2002. E-mail: 75741@hotmail.com; Web: www.mshr.org

MISSIONARY SISTERS OF THE IMMACULATE CONCEPTION OF THE MOTHER OF GOD (S.M.I.C.)
Franciscan Sisters, 779 Broadway, Paterson, NJ 07509. (973) 279-3790
Generalate: (973) 279-1484
44 Sisters in US; 475 worldwide
Apostolic Work: Health care, education, social services, parish, retreats and art (any talent is utilized).
Represented in the Archdioceses of Newark and San Antonio and in the Dioceses of Paterson, Portland, Austin, Galveston-Houston, Gallup, San Bernadino and El Paso. Also in Brazil, Germany, Taiwan, Africa and Manila, Philippines.
Vocation Director: Vocation Ministry Office, c/o Sr. Andrea Westkamp, PO Box 3026, 779 Broadway, Paterson, NJ 07509. (973) 279-3790. E-mail: vocationteam@aol.com; Web: www.smic-missionarysisters.com

MISSIONARY SISTERS OF THE IMMACULATE HEART OF MARY
See ICM Missionary Sisters

MISSIONARY SISTERS OF JESUS, MARY AND JOSEPH (M.J.M.J.)
Motherhouse: Spain
US Formation House: 12940 Leopard St., Corpus Christi, TX 78410. (361) 241-1955
25 Sisters
Apostolic Work: Among Hispanic poor, social work, day care with children of working mothers, pastoral ministry, delinquency prevention program, religious education.
Represented in the Dioceses of Corpus Christi, El Paso and San Antonio. Also in Spain, Chile, Africa and Reynosa and Morelia (Mexico).
Vocation Director: Sister Rachel Vallarta, M.J.M.J., St. Joseph's Convent, 7681 Barton Dr., El Paso, TX 79915. (915) 779-6943

MISSIONARY SISTERS OF THE MOST SACRED HEART OF JESUS (M.S.C.)
U.S.A. US Province Center: 2811 Moyers Lane, Reading, PA 19605. (610) 929-0695. E-mail: mscvocdir@aol.com; Web: www.hometown.aol.com/mscvocdir/usa.html
950 Missionary Sisters worldwide
Ministries: Making God's love present to everyone through evangelization, social work, health care, education, pastoral ministries, counseling, parish ministry, religious education and foreign missions.
Represented in 8 dioceses in the US and in 17 other countries.
Vocation Office: Sr. Barbara Daniels, MSC

MISSIONARY SISTERS OF MOTHER OF GOD
See Eastern Catholic Religious Communities for Women

MISSIONARY SISTERS OF OUR LADY OF AFRICA (M.S.O.L.A.)
47 West Spring St., Winooski, VT 05404. (802) 655-4003
14 Sisters in US, 1,039 Sisters worldwide, 153 Communities
Apostolic Work: Working in 16 African countries for the development of a local African Church: primary evangelization, parish leadership training, social development of women, youth retreats, media, primary health care and other forms of medical work, programs for AIDS victims and their children, teaching, counseling, development projects together with the local people, formation of small Christian communities and local Sisterhoods.
Represented in the Archdiocese of Washington, DC and in the Dioceses of Burlington and Springfield (MA).
Vocation Director: Sr. Dolores Fortier, 3715 Williams Lane, Chevy Chase, MD 20815. (301) 654-2047. E-mail: msolachevch@aol.com; Web: http://www.smnda.org/ and http://soeurs-blanches.cef.fr/bis.htm

MISSIONARY SISTERS OF OUR LADY OF MERCY (M.O.M.)
Rainbow K, 388 Franklin St., Buffalo, NY 14202. (716) 854-5198
3 Professed Sisters
Represented in the Diocese of Buffalo
Vocation Contact: Sr. M. Neves, M.O.M., Superior

CONGREGATION OF MISSIONARY SISTERS OF OUR LADY OF PERPETUAL HELP (M.P.S.)
Regional House in US: 427 Rigsby St., San Antonio, TX 78210. (210) 532-3546 (tel, fax)
14 Sisters in US; 350 Sisters worldwide
Apostolic Work: Proclaiming the evangelical message of salvation by catechetical instruction of children, youth and adults, permanent and itinerant missions, home visitation, giving communion to the sick, parish work, campus ministry, prison ministry, orphanages.
Represented in the Diocese of San Antonio. Foreign missions: Mexico, Guatemala, Honduras, El Salvador, Venezuela, Argentina, Philippines, Macao China and India.
Vocation Directress: Sister Eva C. Coper, MPS, 259 W. Wildwood Dr., San Antonio, TX 78212. (210) 832-8985, 532-3546. E-mail: vocationmps@sbcglobal.net

MISSIONARY SISTERS OF THE PRECIOUS BLOOD (C.P.S.)
Regional House and Novitiate: Precious Blood Convent, PO Box 97, Reading, PA 19607-0097. (610) 777-1624
45 Sisters in North American Province, 1,000 worldwide
Apostolic Work: AIDS ministry, art/crafts, care for the aged, catechetics, education at all levels, Hispanic apostolate, liturgical ministry, medical work, pastoral ministry, ministry to persons who are physically or mentally handicapped, retreat ministry, social work, youth ministry.
Represented in the Dioceses of Allentown and Lexington. Also in Austria, Denmark, Germany, Italy, Kenya, Mozambique, Netherlands, Ontario (Canada), Papua New Guinea, Portugal, Romania, South Africa, South Korea, Tanzania, Zambia and Zimbabwe.
Vocation Director: Precious Blood Convent, PO Box 97, Reading, PA 19607-0097. (610) 777-1624. E-mail: vocationscps@hotmail.com; Web: www.cpsmissionarysisters.com

MISSIONARY SISTERS OF ST. CHARLES BORROMEO-SCALABRINIANS (MSCS)
Provincial House: 1414 N. 37th Ave., Melrose Park, IL 60160
820 Sisters in 21 countries
Apostolic Work: Evangelical and missionary service to immigrants, migrants and refugees. Realized through catechesis, Christian education, pastoral care of the sick and social services.
Represented in the (Arch)dioceses of Boston, Chicago, New York, Springfield, Washington, DC; Toronto (Canada); Manila, Philippines; Tijuana, Guadalajara and Mexico, D.F. Also in Albania, Angola, Argentina, Brazil, Colombia, Dominican Republic, Ecuador, France, Germany, Honduras, Italy, Mozambique, Paraguay, Poland, Portugal, South Africa and Switzerland.
Vocation Promotion Coordinator: Sister Noemia Silva, MSCS, 1414 N. 37th Ave., Melrose Park, IL 60160. (301) 459-4700. E-mail: noemiasilva@hotmail.com; Web: www.cmswr.org/MemberCommunities/MSSCBS.htm

MISSIONARY SISTERS OF ST. COLUMBAN (S.S.C.)
250 Sisters
Apostolic Work: Pastoral, chaplaincy, indigenous people, elderly, education, medical, migrant workers, developmentally disabled, ecumenism, organic farming, hospice, people with AIDS.
Represented in the Archdioceses of Boston and Los Angeles and in the Diocese of Buffalo. Also in Hong Kong, China, Myanmar, Korea, the Philippines, Chile, Peru, Pakistan, England, Scotland and Ireland.
Vocation Directress: Sr. Grace De Leon, 2500 S. Fremont Ave., Unit # E, Alhambra, CA 91803-4300. (626) 458-1869. Fax: (626) 570-6101. E-mail: gracedel@netsync.net; Web: columban.org/missioned/

MISSIONARY SISTERS OF ST. PETER CLAVER (S.S.P.C.)
667 Woods Mill Rd. S., PO Box 6067, Chesterfield, MO 63006-6067. (314) 434-8084
Contemplative in action and active in contemplation at the service of the Universal Church.
17 Sisters
Represented in the Archdioceses of St. Louis, St. Paul and Chicago.
Vocation Director: Sr. M. Irene, SSPC

MONASTIC FAMILY OF BETHLEHEM AND OF THE ASSUMPTION OF THE VIRGIN Our Lady of Lourdes Camp, Livingston Manor, NY 12758. (845) 439-4300
15 Nuns in US; 500 total
Apostolic Work: A life of contemplative prayer.
Represented in the Archdiocese of New York and in France, Austria, Belgium, Spain, Israel, Italy, Germany, Argentina, Canada, Lithuania and Chile.
Vocation Director: Sister Amena, Prioress

SISTERS OF THE MOST HOLY SACRAMENT (M.H.S.)
Administration Office: PO Box 90037, Lafayette, LA 70509-0037. (318) 981-8475
37 Sisters
Apostolic Work: Teaching, CCD, pastoral work, social work, health care, home missions and parish ministry.
Represented in the Archdiocese of New Orleans and in the Dioceses of Baton Rouge, Lafayette and San Antonio.
Vocation Director: Sr. Hilda Mallet, M.H.S., PO Box 90037, Lafayette, LA 70509-0037. (337) 989-9817 or (337) 289-2246. E-mail: 105241.1405@compuserv.com

SISTERS OF THE MOST HOLY SOUL OF CHRIST (S.S.C.H.)
1200 E. 10th St., Stuart, FL 34996. (772) 781-0350
Motherhouse: Poland
700 Sisters, 12 Novices, 10 Postulants (worldwide)

Apostolic Work: Active contemplative: teaching, healthcare, catechesis, parish ministry, propagating devotion to the Most Holy Soul of Christ and the sanctification of humanity.

Represented in the Diocese of Palm Beach. Also in Poland and Africa.

Vocation Director: Sister Anita, SSCH. (561) 287-2727

SISTERS OF THE MOST HOLY TRINITY (O.SS.T.)

21281 Chardon Rd., Euclid, OH 44117. (216) 481-8232

25 Sisters

Apostolic Work: Teaching, volunteer hospital ministry, National Shrine of Our Lady of Lourdes.

Represented in the Archdiocese of Philadelphia and in the Diocese of Cleveland, OH. Foreign mission in Madagascar. Generalate house in Rome, with about 20 houses spread throughout Italy.

Vocation Directress: Sisters of the Most Holy Trinity, 21281 Chardon Rd., Euclid, OH 44117-1591. (216) 481-8232. E-mail: Trinitarian@srstrinity.com; Web: www.srstrinity.com

SISTERS OF THE MOST PRECIOUS BLOOD (C.PP.S.) 204 N. Main St., O'Fallon, MO 63366-2299

240 Sisters

Mission: The Sisters, an apostolic community, are rooted in the Eucharist and personal prayer, and strive to be and experience Christ's redeeming presence as they affirm and empower one another and those they serve, especially the poor.

Apostolic Work: Education, parish ministry, geriatrics, special education, foreign missions, ecclesiastical art (the making of vestments), residential care, nursing, hospital ministry, health care services and social work.

Represented in 12 states in the US. Foreign missions in Bolivia, Finland, Italy, Peru and Estonia.

Vocation Team: Sr. Ellen Orf, C.PP.S., 204 N. Main St., O'Fallon, MO 63366-2299. (314) 808-1875. E-mail: elleno@cpps-ofallon.org; Web: www.cpps-ofallon.org

MOTHERS OF THE HELPLESS (M.D.)

Motherhouse: Spain

US: Sacred Heart Residence, 432 W. 20th St., New York, NY 10011

9 Sisters

Apostolic Work: in New York: 1 day nursery and 1 residence for young women. Worldwide: Houses in Spain (Motherhouse); Puerto Rico; Mexico; Chile; Argentina and Rome, Italy; Novitiates in Spain and Colombia. Foreign missions in Guatemala and Colombia. Home for the aged and orphaned children; schools, retreat house, residence and day care centers.

Represented in the Archdiocese of New York and 8 foreign countries.

Vocation Contact: Mother Rocio Campaña, Sacred Heart Residence, 432 W. 20th St., New York, NY 10011. (212) 929-5790, 0839

SISTERS OF NAZARETH (C.S.N.)

Regional House and Novitiate: Nazareth House, 3333 Manning Ave., Los Angeles, CA 90064. (310) 839-2361

Apostolic Work: The Sisters of Nazareth are a dynamic, prayerful community of consecrated religious serving the Lord through loving care given to seniors and the needy elderly at Nazareth House residential and skilled-nursing facilities throughout the globe, and to all children through quality religious and academic education offered at the Nazareth Schools.

Represented: Six US Nazareth Houses located in the California Archdioceses of Los Angeles and San Francisco, the Dioceses of San Diego and Fresno, and also Madison (WI) and Pago Pago (American Samoa) plus 50 locations worldwide.

Vocation Coordinator: Sr. Fintan, CSN, Nazareth House, 3333 Manning Ave., Los Angeles, CA 90064. (310) 839-2361. Fax: (310) 839-0648. E-mail: vocations@nazarethhouse.org; Web: www.nazarethhouse.org

SISTERS OF THE NEW COVENANT (S.N.C.) Motherhouse: Covenant House, 10620 Livingston Dr., Northglenn, CO 80234. (303) 451-8677

Mission: Following Jesus in the style of St. Francis. Evangelization, spreading the Good News of Jesus Christ.

Represented in the Archdiocese of Denver.

Contact: Sister Brigid Meierotto, S.N.C., Covenant House, 10620 Livingston Dr., Northglenn, CO 80234. (303) 451-8677. Web: www.catholicevangelizationweb.org

CONGREGATION OF NOTRE DAME (C.N.D.)

See "C" - Congregation of Notre Dame

NOTRE DAME de SION (N.D.S.) (Sisters of Sion) 3501 Decarie Blvd., Montreal, Quebec H4A 3J4 Canada

7 Sisters in US; 800 Sisters worldwide

Apostolic Work: Called to witness to God's faithful love for the Jewish people and to God's fidelity to the promises of justice, peace and love, which were revealed by the prophets of Israel for all humanity.

Represented in 23 countries. In the US: in the Archdiocese of Chicago and in the Dioceses of Brooklyn and Kansas City.

Vocation Contact: Sister Maria Vigna, NDS, 549 Elgin Ave., Winnipeg, Manitoba R3A 0L2 Canada. (204) 722-1538. E-mail: mariavigna@aol.com

NOTRE DAME SISTERS (ND)

Provincial Motherhouse: 3501 State St., Omaha, NE 68112

61 Sisters

Apostolic Work: Teaching, pastoral ministry, religious education, counseling, nursing, nursing home care, social work, day care work, hospital chaplaincy, campus ministry, mission work in Honduras.

Represented in the Archdioceses of Omaha, Denver, Dubuque and Kansas City and in the Dioceses of Lincoln and Pueblo.

Director of Vocation Ministry: Sr. Dorothy Rolf, ND, 3501 State St., Omaha, NE 68112. (402) 455-2994. Fax: (402) 455-3974. E-mail: nd.voc@juno.com; Web: www.notredamesisters.org

SISTERS OF NOTRE DAME (S.N.D.)

US Provinces: Ohio, Kentucky and California

2,600 Sisters and Associates worldwide

Apostolic Work: As a teacher in Germany shared her sandwich with little Agnes who had no lunch, a dream was born - and the Sisters of Notre Dame began. Today, the Sisters continue to share not only sandwiches, but bread for the soul: the Good News. Through schools, parish work, health care, social services, missionary and other ministries, they feed those hungering for love, hope and justice. Sharing their experiences of God's goodness and provident care, they in turn are enriched by others' sharing. On five continents, the Sisters strive to bring Christ to the world like Mary.

Represented in the Arch(dioceses) in Arlington, Cincinnati, Cleveland, Covington, Detroit, Fort Wayne, Joliet, Lafayette, Lexington, Los Angeles, Orlando, Raleigh, St. Augustine, St. Petersburg, Toledo, Venice (FL), Washington, DC and Youngstown. Also in Rome, Italy. Missions in the Philippines, India,

Indonesia, New Guinea, Tanzania and Uganda.

Cleveland Province: 13000 Auburn Rd., Chardon, OH 44024. (440) 286-7101. Vocation Director: Sr. Kathleen Hine, SND, 1635 Alameda Ave., Lakewood, OH 44107. (216) 221-3164. E-mail: khine@ndec.org

Covington Province: St. Joseph Heights, 1601 Dixie Hwy., Covington, KY 41011. (859) 291-2040. Vocation Director: Sr. Jean Marie Hoffman, SND, 132 Louise Dr., Ft. Mitchell, KY 41017. (859) 344-6258, 291-2040. E-mail: vocations@sndky.org

Toledo Province: 3837 Secor Rd., Toledo, OH 43623. Vocation Director: Sr. Patricia Dorobek, SND, 3837 Secor Rd., Toledo, OH 43623. (419) 474-5485. E-mail: pdorobek@yahoo.com

Los Angeles Province: 1776 Hendrix Ave., Thousand Oaks, CA 91360. (805) 496-3243, ext. 728. Web: www.sndca.org. Vocation Director: Sr. Mary Judeen Julier, SND, Notre Dame Center, 1776 Hendrix Ave., Thousand Oaks, CA 91360. (562) 301-7373. E-mail: smjudeen@hotmail.com

International Web: www.snd1.org

SISTERS OF NOTRE DAME DE NAMUR (SNDdeN)

Sisters of Notre Dame, women with hearts as wide as the world, make known God's goodness and love of the poor through a Gospel way of life, community and prayer. Julie Billiart and Françoise Blin de Bourdon began the congregation in France in 1804 in the midst of the religious, social and political upheaval of the French Revolution. Because of their friendship, and mutual vision, the mission "to the poor in the most abandoned places" endures today. This global vision has been realized as we strive to serve the good God on five continents: Africa (Congo, Kenya, Nigeria, South Africa and Zimbabwe), Europe (Belgium, France, Great Britain, and Italy), Japan, Latin America (Brazil, Mexico, Nicaragua, and Peru) and North America (United States).

The Sisters of Notre Dame de Namur serve in 12 Archdioceses and 38 Dioceses within the United States: (AZ) Phoenix; (CA) Los Angeles, San Francisco, Monterey, Oakland, Sacramento, San Jose, Stockton; (CT) Hartford, Bridgeport, Norwich; (DC) Washington; (DE) Wilmington; (FL) Jacksonville, Miami, Orlando, Palm Beach; (HI) Honolulu; (IL) Chicago, Joliet; (IN) Lafayette; (KY) Covington, Lexington, Louisville; (MA) Boston, Springfield, Worcester; (MD) Baltimore; (ME) Portland; (MI) Saginaw; (NC) Charlotte, Raleigh; (NY) New York, Brooklyn, Buffalo, Rockville Center; (OH) Cincinnati, Columbus; (OR) Baker; (PA) Philadelphia, Harrisburg; (RI) Providence; (SC) Charleston; (SD) Sioux Falls; (TX) Austin; (VT) Burlington; (VA) Arlington, Richmond; (WA) Seattle; and (WV) Wheeling-Charleston.

Apostolic Work: Religious education, formal education at all levels, health ministries, hospital chaplaincies, pastoral ministry, youth ministries, retreats and spiritual direction, ministry of prayer, social services, counseling, community development, legal services, service to immigrants and refugees, peace and justice work, prison ministry, missionary work and other developing ministries which respond to the needs in today's Church and world.

Internationally we are over 1,850 professed Sisters with 52 novices/affiliates and 498 Associates. In the United States we number over 1,150 with 6 novices and affiliates.

For information, call the vocation contact in your area or call toll free: (1-888) 827-1724. E-mail: ybasnd@SNDdeN.org; Web: www.SNDdeN.org

Sister Gerry Bolzan, SNDdeN, 3058 N. Mango Ave., Chicago, IL 60634-5216. (1-800) 293-3453 or (773) 237-6367. E-mail: bolzan@SNDdeN.org

Sister Marie Annette Burkart, SNDdeN, 1520 Ralston Ave., Belmont, CA 94002. (650) 593-2045, ext. 253. E-mail: burkartma@SNDdeN.org

Sister Josita Colbert, SNDdeN, 197 South Pine Creek Rd., Fairfield, CT 06430-5671. (203) 255-6309. E-mail: matjcsnd@aol.com

Sister Marlene Cunningham, SNDdeN, 3037 Fourth St., NE, Washington, DC 20017-1102. (202) 832-8770. E-mail: sndbcunit@aol.com

Sister Angele Lewis, SNDdeN, 30 Jeffreys Neck Rd., Ipswich, MA 01938. (978) 356-4381. E-mail: lewis@SNDdeN.org

Sister Kim Dalgarn, SNDdeN, 701 E. Columbia Ave., Cincinnati, OH 45215. (1-800) 662-7768 or (513) 761-7636. E-mail: dalgarn@SNDdeN.org

Sister Dottie Deger, SNDdeN, 6635 S. 14th Way, Phoenix, AZ 85042-4459. (602) 243-9929. E-mail: deger@SNDdeN.org

Sister Pat McSharry, SNDdeN, 18 Radnor Rd., Brighton, MA 02135-5110. (617) 787-0612. E-mail: mcsharry@SNDdeN.org

Sister Regina Pellegrini, SNDdeN, 1531 Greenspring Valley Rd., Stevenson, MD 21153. (410) 486-0524, ext. 412. E-mail: sndden@aol.com

Sister Carol Symons, SNDdeN, 112 N. Funk St., Strasburg, VA 22657. (540) 465-9368. E-mail: symons@SNDdeN.org

SCHOOL SISTERS OF NOTRE DAME (SSND)

The School Sisters of Notre Dame, an international congregation, are committed to serving God and God's people in order to bring Jesus' message of love and unity to our world. As women religious, they value prayer, faith sharing, and a community life that calls them to be of "one mind and one heart." Today 4,400 School Sisters of Notre Dame serve in 30 countries on five continents. They believe that their international network gives them a unique global perspective as they address, through various ministries, the urgent needs of our times, particularly the needs of women, youth and persons who are poor. You are invited to share this joy-filled life with them.

Apostolic Works: Education in colleges, high schools, elementary schools, preschools, day care, religious education, adult education, missionary work (domestic and oversees), social services, justice ministry and direct service to the poor, health and legal professions, parish and diocesan administration, pastoral ministry, prison ministry, retreat work and spiritual direction.

Serving in 40 states and in 36 countries: Argentina, Austria, Belarus, Bolivia, Brazil, Canada, Chile, Czech Republic, El Salvador, England, Germany, Ghana, Guam, Guatemala, Honduras, Hungary, Italy, Japan, Kenya, Korea, Marshall Islands, Micronesia, Nepal, Nigeria, Paraguay, Peru, Poland, Puerto Rico, Romania, Serbia, Sierra Leone, Slovenia, Sweden, The Gambia, USA.

SSND vocation ministers are located in eight regions throughout North America. Contact Sister Mary at 1-800-344-SSND (7763) for the vocation director nearest you or e-mail Sister Kathy at ssndsisters@juno.com. Visit their web site www.ssnd.org.

Northeastern Province: Wilton, CT
Vocation Director: Maria Iannuccillo, SSND, 345 Belden Hill Rd., Wilton, CT 06897. (203) 375-5070. E-mail: srmaria@ssndwilton.org

Eastern Province: Baltimore, MD
Vocation Director: Kathy Jager, SSND, 6401 N. Charles St., Baltimore, MD 21212-1099. (410) 377-5179. Fax: (410) 377-5363. E-mail: k-jager@juno.com

Chicago Province: Berwyn, IL
Vocation Director: Carolyn Jost, SSND, 1431 Euclid Ave., Berwyn, IL 60402-1216. (708) 749-1380, ext. 22. Fax: (708) 749-9446. E-mail: scarjost@aol.com

Milwaukee Province: Milwaukee, WI
Vocation Director: Marcie Solms, SSND, 13105 Watertown Plank Rd., Elm Grove, WI 53122-2291. (262) 782-9850, ext. 718. Fax: (262) 782-5725. E-mail: msolms@ssnd-milw.org

Mankato Province: Mankato, MN
Vocation Director: Joyce Kolbet, SSND, 1850 Mississippi Blvd., St. Paul, MN 55116. (612) 699-3387. E-mail: jkolbet@juno.com

St. Louis Province: St. Louis, MO
Vocation Director: Nancy Becker, SSND, 320 East Ripa St., St. Louis, MO 63125-2897. (314) 544-0455 (Tel., Fax). E-mail: snancybecker@ssnd-sl.org

Dallas Province: Dallas, TX
Vocation Director: Christine Garcia, SSND, 11106 Whisper Hollow, San Antonio, TX 78230. (210) 479-1734. E-mail: christinegarciassnd@yahoo.com

Canadian Province: Waterdown, Ontario
Vocation Director: Martha Fauteux, SSND, 1921 Snake Rd., Waterdown, Ontario, Canada L0R 2H0. (905) 689-6344, ext. 609. Fax: (905) 689-9418. E-mail: mjfauteux@yahoo.ca

NUNS OF THE PERPETUAL ADORATION OF THE BLESSED SACRAMENT (A.P.) (San Francisco Province) Monastery of Perpetual Adoration, 771 Ashbury St., San Francisco, CA 94117. (415) 566-2743
18 Sisters
Represented in the Archdiocese of San Francisco. Also in Mexico, Spain, Chile and Africa.
Contact: Mother Rosalba Vargas, A.P., Superior

NUNS OF THE PERPETUAL ADORATION OF THE BLESSED SACRAMENT (A.P.) (Autonomous Monasteries) Monastery of Perpetual Adoration, 145 N. Cotton Ave., El Paso, TX 79901. (915) 533-5323
20 Sisters
Spanish speaking community
Represented in the Archdioceses of Anchorage and San Francisco and in the Diocese of El Paso

NUNS OF SAINT BASIL THE GREAT
See Eastern Catholic Religious Communities for Women

SISTERS OBLATES TO THE BLESSED TRINITY (O.B.T.)
St. Clare's Convent, 1925 Hone Ave., Bronx, NY 10461. (718) 792-9267; St. Aloysius Gonzaga Novitiate, Beekman Rd., P.O. Box 98, Hopewell Junction, NY 12533. (845) 226-5671
Apostolic Work: Teaching in parish schools, catechetics and retreats.
Represented in the Archdiocese of New York and in the Dioceses of Madison, WI, San Juan and Ponce, Puerto Rico.
Superior General: Mother Gloria Castro, Beekman Rd., P.O. Box 98, Hopewell Junction, NY 12533. (845) 226-5671. E-mail: jstab35097@aol.com; Web: www.Staloysius-NY.org

OBLATE SISTERS OF JESUS THE PRIEST (O.J.S.) General Motherhouse: Mexico
28 Sisters in US, 135 Sisters in Mexico
Represented in the Archdioceses of Chicago, New York and San Francisco.
Vocation Directors: Sister Maria Esther Pinto, St. Paul the Apostle Church, 415 W. 59th St., New York, NY 10019. (212) 265-3209. E-mail: pinto551@yahoo.com; Sister Guadalupe Lopez, Saint Patrick's Seminary, 320 Middlefield Rd., Menlo Park, CA 94025. (650) 322-4111. Fax: (650) 325-1966; Sister Doris Monter, University of St. Mary of the Lake, 1000 E. Maple Ave., Mundelein, IL 60060-1174. (847) 949-9113, 970-7048, ext. 4827. Fax: (847) 970-4832

OBLATE SISTERS OF THE BLESSED SACRAMENT (O.S.B.S.)
Motherhouse: St. Sylvester Motherhouse, Marty, SD 57361-0217
American Indian Apostolate
7 Sisters
Represented in the Dioceses of Rapid City and Sioux Falls.
Vocation Director: St. Sylvester Motherhouse, PO Box 217, Marty, SD 57361-0217. (605) 384-3305. Fax: (605) 384-3575. E-mail: osbs@charles-mix.com

OBLATES OF THE MOST HOLY REDEEMER (O.SS.R.)
Motherhouse:Spain
US Foundation: Our Lady of the Way Residence, 60-80 Pond St., Jamaica Plain, MA. (617) 524-1640
3 Sisters in US, 800 Sisters worldwide
Apostolic Work: Primary apostolic work of the order is to every woman in need: drug addicts, prostitutes, unwed mothers, abandoned women and immigrants adjusting to a new culture.
Represented in the (Arch)dioceses of Boston and NY. Also in Spain, Italy, Puerto Rico, Argentina, Uruguay, Venezuela, Colombia, Mexico, Brazil, Philippines, Portugal, Dominican Republic, Guatemala and Angola.
Vocation Contact: Sr. Teresita, Mother of Good Counsel House, 290 Babylon Turnpike, Roosevelt, Long Island, NY 11575. (516) 223-1013

OBLATE SISTERS OF PROVIDENCE (O.S.P.) Motherhouse and Novitiate: 701 Gun Rd., Baltimore, MD 21227-3899. (410) 242-8500
99 Sisters (multi-racial, multi-cultural), 2 in Formation, Lay Associate Membership
Apostolic Work: 1 high school, 2 elementary schools, 1 reading center, 1 child development center, Spanish apostolate, outreach ministries, parish ministries.
Represented in the Archdioceses of Baltimore and Washington, DC, in the Diocese of Buffalo and in dioceses in Florida. Also in two vicariates in Costa Rica.
Vocation Contact: Sr. M. Stephen Beauford, OSP, 701 Gun Rd., Baltimore, MD 21227-3899. (410) 242-8500, ext. 136. Fax: (410) 242-4963. E-mail: stephenosp@aol.com; Web: members.aol.com/aliceosp/index.html

OBLATE SISTERS OF THE SACRED HEART OF JESUS (O.S.H.J.)
Villa Maria Teresa, 50 Warner Rd., Hubbard, OH 44425
22 Sisters
Apostolic Work: Minister with, and to, diocesan priests as Directors of Religious Education, care for elderly priests, pastoral ministry, primary and elementary education, mission work.
For information write: Sister Teresina Rosa, Villa Maria Teresa, 50 Warner Rd., Hubbard, OH 44425. (330) 759-9329 or (330) 759-8468. E-mail: JCOBLATE@aol.com; Web: www.oblatesister.org

OBLATE SISTERS OF ST. FRANCIS de SALES (O.S.F.S.)
399 Childs Rd., Childs, MD 21916. (410) 398-3699
17 Sisters
Apostolic Work: Teaching and social work.
Represented in the Archdiocese of Philadelphia and in the Dioceses of Arlington and Wilmington.
Vocation Director: Sr. Anne Elizabeth, 399 Childs Rd., Childs, MD 21916. (410) 398-3699. E-mail: oblatesisters@mountaviat.org; Web: www.oblatesisters.org

ORDER OF THE MOST HOLY REDEEMER
See Redemptoristine Nuns

SISTERS OF OUR LADY OF CHARITY (O.L.C.) (North American Union of the Sisters of Our Lady of Charity) General Administration Center: Sister Deana Kohlman, Superior General, PO Box 340, Carrollton, OH 44615-0340
126 Sisters
Primary Work: "girls and women", day care for children, social work, teaching in schools, working with people with AIDS, Spanish and English speaking parishes, CCD programs, retreats, nursing.
Represented in the (Arch)dioceses of New York, Buffalo/Rochester, NY; Erie/Pittsburgh, PA; El Paso/San Antonio, TX; Steubenville, OH; Green Bay, WI; Wheeling, WV; San Diego, CA and Venice, FL. Also in Canada and Mexico.
Vocation Director: General Administration Center, PO Box 340, Carrollton, OH 44615-0340. (330) 627-1641. Fax: (330) 627-1935

SISTERS OF OUR LADY OF CHARITY (O.L.C.) Mt. St. Michael Convent, 4500 W. Davis St., Dallas, TX 75211. 214-331-1754. Fax: 214-333-1659. E-mail: mmc4500@airmail.net

SISTERS OF OUR LADY OF CHRISTIAN DOCTRINE (R.C.D.)
Visitation House, 629 N. Midland Ave., Nyack, NY 10960-1032. (917) 495-7493
32 Sisters
Apostolic Work: Religious education, nursing, counseling, spiritual direction and retreat work, pastoral ministry, social work.
Represented in New Hampshire and New York.
Vocation Directress: Sr. Veronica Mendez, RCD, 240 E. 93rd St., Apt. 3E, New York, NY 10128. (212) 427-9278. E-mail: veroicon@aol.com; Web: www.sistersrcd.org

SISTERS OF OUR LADY OF THE GARDEN (O.L.G.)
67 Round Hill Rd., Middletown, CT 06457
12 Sisters in US; 1,050 Sisters worldwide
Apostolic Work: Teaching, nursing, social work, foreign missions, parish work.
Represented in the Archdiocese of Hartford and the Diocese of Norwich. Also in Italy, South America, Spain, Palestine, India and Africa.
Vocation Directress: Sr. Donna Beauregard, O.L.G., 67 Round Hill Rd., Middletown, CT 06457. (860) 346-5765

THE CONGREGATION OF THE SISTERS OF OUR LADY OF MERCY (O.L.M.) (Divine Mercy) General Motherhouse: Warsaw, Poland.
US: 241 Neponset Ave., Dorchester, MA 02122. (617) 288-1202. Fax: (617) 265-9405. E-mail: vocation@sisterfaustina.org; Web: www.sisterfaustina.org
9 Sisters in US; about 400 Professed Sisters, 35 Novices, 16 Postulants worldwide
Apostolic Work: Saint Faustina Kowalska belonged to this active-contemplative congregation. The Sisters cooperate with the infinite mercy of God by proclaiming the message of Divine Mercy to the men and women of our time and by imploring God's mercy for the world through prayer and sacrifice. They faithfully seek to fulfill its mission in the Church which Pope John Paul II confirmed when visiting the Congregation's shrine in Cracow: "Choosing from among you Sister Faustina, Christ...has called you to a particular apostolate, that of His Mercy...The people of today need your proclamation of mercy; they need your works of mercy and they need your prayer to obtain mercy." If you feel called to make the merciful Jesus known and loved, contact us.
Represented in the Archdiocese of Boston. Also in Rome, Jerusalem, Poland, Czech Republic, Belarus and Kazakhstan.
Vocation Director: Sr. M. Caterina Esselen, O.L.M.

SISTERS OF OUR LADY OF THE HOLY ROSARY (R.S.R.)
Motherhouse: Rimouski, P.Q., Canada G5L 3E3
Regional House: 25 Portland Ave., Old Orchard Beach, ME 04064. (207) 934-0592
8 Sisters in US; 503 Sisters worldwide
Apostolic Work: Christian education.
Represented in the Diocese of Portland, ME; in the Provinces of Quebec and New Brunswick in Canada and also in Honduras, Guatemala and Peru.
Vocation Contact: Sr. Juliette Michaud, R.S.R., 20 Thomas St., Portland, ME 04102-3638. (207) 774-3756. E-mail: rsr@maine.rr.com

SISTERS OF OUR LADY OF SORROWS (O.L.S.)
Motherhouse: Italy
US Headquarters: 9894 Norris Ferry Rd., Shreveport, LA 71106
31 Sisters in US; 371 worldwide
Conduct: 2 grammar schools, 2 residential facilities and 3 community homes for individuals with mental disabilities, 1 day care center, apostolic work in the parishes and education-art center for needy families.
Represented in the Dioceses of Alexandria and Shreveport, LA.
Also in Brazil, Albania, Italy, Mexico, Bangladesh and Zimbabwe.
Vocation Information: Our Lady of Sorrows Convent, 9894 Norris Ferry Rd., Shreveport, LA 71106. (318) 797-0213. Fax: (318) 797-7003. E-mail: vocations@ols.org; Web: ols.org

OUR LADY OF VICTORY MISSIONARY SISTERS (OLVM) Victory Noll, PO Box 109, Huntington, IN 46750-0109
161 Sisters in 17 states and Bolivia
Apostolic Work: Pastoral ministry, religious education, social services and health care. Prophetic ministry, promoting justice for the poor and oppressed, with emphasis on women.
Vocation Ministers: Srs. Ginger Downey and Margarita Moreno, OLVM, Victory Noll, PO Box 109, Huntington, IN 46750-0109. (260) 356-0628. Fax: (260) 358-1504. E-mail: voc@olvm.org; Web: www.olvm.org

PALLOTTINE SISTERS (C.S.A.C.) (Sisters of the Catholic Apostolate)
(Immaculate Conception Province)
Provincialate: St. Patrick's Villa, Harriman Heights, P.O. Box 118, Harriman, NY 10926. (845) 783-9007
57 Sisters; 700 worldwide
Apostolic Work: Parochial schools, private schools, day nursery, parish/astoral work, formation and education of lay groups, collaboration in communication, youth work.
Represented in the Archdioceses of Newark and New York and in the Diocese of Brooklyn. Also in Europe, South America, India and Mozambique.

Vocation Director: Sister Carmel Therese Favazzo, St. Patrick Villa, P.O. Box 118, Harriman, NY 10926. (845) 774-7585. Fax: (845) 783-4243. E-mail: csacvoc@frontiernet.net; Web: www.pallottinesisters.org or www.pallotti.org/vocations/csac.html or www.apostle-csac.org

PALLOTTINE SISTERS (S.A.C.) (Society of the Catholic Apostolate)

15270 Old Halls Ferry Rd., Florissant, MO 63034-1661

56 Sisters in US

Ministries: To increase faith and love using any and all means and to empower the laity in their call to be apostles.

Represented in Archdioceses of St. Louis, MO and Washington, DC and in the Diocese of Wheeling-Charleston, WV.

Vocation Director: Sr. Gail Borgmeyer, S.A.C., 15270 Old Halls Ferry Rd., Florissant, MO 63034-1661. (314) 837-1355. E-mail: vocsac@juno.com; Web: pallotti.org

PARISH VISITORS OF MARY IMMACULATE (P.V.M.I.)

Marycrest Convent, Box 658, Monroe, NY 10950-0658. (845) 783 2251

62 Sisters (including Postulants)

Apostolic Work: Contemplative-missionary community serving the Church in visitation/evangelization, through person-to-person contact by visiting families, individuals or groups; religious education for the total parish; spiritual counseling; social service; in all of this seeking out the spiritually, morally or materially impoverished, the rejected and neglected.

Represented in the Archdiocese of New York and in the Dioceses of Brooklyn, Syracuse and Scranton. Also in the Diocese of Okigwe, Nigeria.

Vocation Director: Sister Dolores Marie, P.V.M.I., Marycrest Convent, Box 658, Monroe, NY 10950-0658. (845) 783-2251. Web: http://oldserver.catholicity.com/cathedral/parishvisitors/

PASSIONIST NUNS (C.P.) (The Nuns of The Most Holy Cross and Passion of Our Lord Jesus Christ)

Apostolic Work: Contemplation.

Represented in five independent monasteries in the US: Our Lady of Sorrows Monastery of the Passionist Nuns, 2715 Churchview Ave., Pittsburgh, PA 15227. (412) 881-1155

7 Nuns, 1 Novice

St. Gabriel's Monastery, 631 Griffin Pond Rd., Clarks Summit, PA 18411. (570) 586-2791

9 Nuns

St. Joseph's Monastery, 8564 Crisp Rd., Whitesville, KY 42378-9729. (270) 233-4571

18 Nuns

Monastery of the Sacred Passion, 1151 Donaldson Hwy., Erlanger, KY 41018. (859) 371-8568

8 Nuns

Immaculate Conception Monastery, 1032 Clayton Rd., Ellisville, MO 63011. (636) 227-3550

13 Nuns, 1 Novice

Vocations: Passionist Nuns, 1151 Donaldson Hwy., Erlanger, KY 41018-1000. (859) 371-8568; Sr. Paul Colette, C.P., St. Gabriel's Monastery, 631 Griffin Pond Rd., Clarks Summit, PA 18411-8899. (570) 586-2791. Web: www.catholic.org/macc

PASSIONIST SISTERS (C.P.) (Sisters of the Cross and Passion)

Holy Family Convent, 1 Wright Ln., North Kingstown, RI 02852

303 Sisters

Apostolic Work: Education, retreats, pastoral care, social work, catechetics, foreign missions.

Represented in the Archdiocese of Hartford and in the Dioceses of Memphis, Providence and Rockville Centre. Also in Jamaica, West Indies and five foreign countries.

Vocation Director: Sr. Theresina Scully, CP, Vocation Office, 130 Legris Ave., West Warwick, RI 02893. (401) 822-2875. E-mail: vocations@snet.net

SISTERS OF PERPETUAL ADORATION (A.P.G.)

US Foundation: 2403 West Travis, San Antonio, TX 78207. (210) 227-5546

7 Sisters

Contact: Sr. Maria del Carmen Sanchez Obregon, Superior

SISTERS OF THE PIOUS SCHOOLS (Sch.P.) (Madres Escolapias)

US Headquarters: 17601 Nordhoff St., Northridge, CA 91325. Motherhouse in Rome

20 Sisters, 2 Junior Professed, 2 Postulants

Conduct: Schools, religious education.

Represented in the Archdiocese of Los Angeles. Also missions in Mexico, Latin America, India, Japan, Africa, Philippines, Spain, Poland and Italy.

Vocation Director: Sr. Guadalupe Gonzalez, Sch.P., 17601 Nordhoff St., Northridge, CA 91325. (818) 885-6265. Fax: (818) 718-6752. E-mail: camexschp@earthlink.net

POOR CLARE COLETTINE NUNS (P.C.C.) Corpus Christi Monastery, 2111 S. Main St., Rockford, IL 61102

21 Sisters, 1 Novice, 3 Postulants

Vocation Contact: Mother Mary Regina, P.C.C., Abbess, Corpus Christi Monastery, 2111 S. Main St., Rockford, IL 61102. (815) 963-7343. Web: http://poorclare.org/rockford

POOR CLARE MISSIONARY SISTERS (M.C.) Regional House and Novitiate: 1019 N. Newhope, Santa Ana, CA 92703

45 Sisters; approx. 600 worldwide

Apostolic Works: Education, nursing, catechesis, retreat houses, pastoral work.

Represented in the Archdiocese of Los Angeles and in the Diocese of Orange. Also in Mexico, Costa Rica, Japan, Indonesia, Ireland, Spain, Italy, India, Russia, Sierra Leone, Nigeria, Korea and Germany.

Vocation Contact: Sr. Celia Martinez, M.C., 1019 N. Newhope, Santa Ana, CA 92703. (714) 554-8850. Fax: (714) 554-5886. E-mail: clarisas@netzero.net

POOR CLARE NUNS (O.S.C.) or (P.C.C.)

The Poor Clare Nuns are a contemplative Order of over 1,000 independent monasteries worldwide. The nuns do not engage in any direct apostolate outside of their monasteries

POOR CLARE NUNS

St. Joseph's Monastery, 1671 Pleasant Valley Rd., P.O. Box 160, Aptos, CA 95001-0160. (831) 761-9659

13 Solemn Vows, 2 Professed Externs

Vocation Contact: Mother M. Clare, P.C.C., Abbess, Poor Clare Colettines

POOR CLARE NUNS

Immaculate Heart Monastery, 28210 Natoma Rd., Los Altos Hills, CA 94022. (650) 948-2947

16 Sisters

POOR CLARE NUNS (P.C.C.)

Monastery of Poor Clares, 215 E. Los Olivos St., Santa Barbara, CA 93105-3605. (805) 682-7670

13 Professed, 2 in Formation

Vocation Contact: Mother M. Clare, PCC, Abbess

POOR CLARE NUNS (O.S.C.)

Christ the King Monastery, 3900 Sherwood Blvd., Delray Beach, FL 33445-5699

10 Sisters
Franciscan Contemplative Nuns.
Contact: Sr. Frances Vass, O.S.C., Christ the King Monastery, 3900 Sherwood Blvd., Delray Beach, FL 33445-5699. (561) 498-3294. E-mail: ctkmdelray@aol.com

POOR CLARE COLETTINE NUNS (P.C.C.) Annunciation Monastery, 6200 East Minooka Rd., Minooka, IL 60447
9 Sisters, 2 Postulants
Represented in the Diocese of Joliet.
Vocation Director: Mother Dorothy, P.C.C., Annunciation Monastery, 6200 East Minooka Rd., Minooka, IL 60447. (815) 467-0032. E-mail: paxbonum@aol.com

POOR CLARE NUNS (O.S.C.)
Monastery of St. Clare, 6825 Nurrenbern Rd., Evansville, IN 47712-8518. (812) 425-4396. E-mail: smmartha@juno.com; Web: poorclare.org/evansville
13 Sisters
Contact Person: Sr. Jane Marie De Land, o.s.c., Abbess

POOR CLARE NUNS (P.C.C.)
Maria Regina Mater Monastery, 1175 N. 300 W, Kokomo, IN 46901. (765) 457-5743. Web: www.thepoorclares.org
9 Sisters, 2 Junior Sisters
Apostolic Work: Prayer and penance
Vocation Contact: Mother Miriam, P.C.C., Abbess

POOR CLARE NUNS (O.S.C.)
Order of St. Clare, St. Clare Monastery, 720 Henry Clay Ave., New Orleans, LA 70118
9 Solemnly Professed
Apostolic Work: Gospel-living women in the Franciscan tradition, devoted to the contemplative life, the liturgical life of the Church and the Church's mission in the world.
Vocation Director: Sister Rita Marie Hickey, OSC, St. Clare Monastery, 720 Henry Clay Ave., New Orleans, LA 70118. (504) 895-2019. E-mail: srrmh@juno.com; Web: poorclarenuns.com

POOR CLARE NUNS (O.S.C.)
Monastery of St. Clare, 445 River Rd., Andover, MA 01810-4213. (978) 683-7599
15 Sisters
Contact: Sr. Emily Marie Silveira, osc, Formation Director

POOR CLARE NUNS (O.S.C.)
Franciscan Monastery of St. Clare, 920 Centre St., Jamaica Plain, MA 02130. (617) 524-1760/7866. E-mail: bostonpoorclares@worldnet.att.net; Web: www.st.anthonyshrine.org/poorclares
20 Final Professed, 2 in Formation
Strictly contemplative cloistered order.
Represented in the Archdiocese of Boston.
Contact: Sr. Teresa Dericks, OSC, Abbess

POOR CLARE NUNS (O.S.C.) (Sisters of St. Clare)
4875 Shattuck Rd., Saginaw, MI 48603-2962
4 Sisters
Contemplative life style in community.
Represented in the Diocese of Saginaw.
Vocation Contact: Sr. Dianne Doughty, O.S.C., Abbess, 4875 Shattuck Rd., Saginaw, MI 48603-2962. (989) 797-0593. E-mail: srsclare@saginaw.org; Web: www.rc.net/saginaw/srsclare

POOR CLARE NUNS (O.S.C.)
St. Clare Monastery, 8650 Russell Ave. S., Minneapolis, MN 55431-1998
11 Sisters
Franciscan contemplative community.
Apostolic Works: Prayer and welcoming others to pray with us.
Vocation Director: Sister Jo M. Casey, osc, 8650 Russell Ave. S., Minneapolis, MN 55431-1998. (952) 881-4766. E-mail: mplsclares@juno.com

POOR CLARE NUNS (O.S.C.)
St. Clare's Monastery, 421 South 4th St., Sauk Rapids, MN 56379-1898. (320) 251-3556
21 Members: 15 Perpetually Professed, 1 Junior Professed, 1 Novice, 1 Postulant, 3 Extern Sisters
Contemplatives with Papal Enclosure

POOR CLARE NUNS (O.S.C.)
Monastery of St. Clare, 200 Marycrest Dr., St. Louis, MO 63129-4813
10 Nuns in Solemn Vows
Cloistered contemplatives

POOR CLARE NUNS (O.S.C.)
416 2nd Ave SW, Great Falls, MT 59404-2904. (406) 453-7891. Fax: 406-453-8689. E-mail: sisters@poorclaresmt.org: Web: www.poorclaresmt.org
4 Sisters
Apostolic Works: Enclosed contemplative community established in 1999 living the Form of Life written by St. Clare of Assisi. Members of the Holy Name Federation of Poor Clare Nuns.
Contact: Sister Judith Ann Crosby, OSC, Abbess

POOR CLARE NUNS (O.S.C.)
Monastery of St. Clare, 3626 N. 65th Ave., Omaha, NE 68104-3299. (402) 558-4916. Web: www.omahapoorclare.org
8 Sisters, 1 Novice, 1 Postulant
Contact: Sister Mary Clare Brown, OSC, Abbess

POOR CLARE NUNS (Cloistered)
Monastery of St. Clare, 150 White Pine Rd., Chesterfield Township, Columbus, NJ 08022
15 Sisters
Contemplative Community
Vocation Contact: Sr. Claire André, OSC, Abbess, Monastery of St. Clare, 150 White Pine Rd., Chesterfield Township, Columbus, NJ 08022. (609) 324-2638. E-mail: clandreosc@aol.com

POOR CLARE NUNS (P.C.C.)
Monastery of Our Lady of Guadalupe, 809 E. 19th St., Roswell, NM 88201-7599. (505) 622-0868. Fax: (505) 627-2184
31 Sisters
Cloistered contemplative community
Contact: Mother Mary Francis, P.C.C., Abbess

POOR CLARE NUNS (O.S.C.)
Monastery of St. Clare, 86 Mayflower Ave., New Rochelle, NY 10801-1615. (914) 632-5227. E-mail: maryckeyserosc@juno.com; Web: www.catholic.org/macc
12 Sisters
Vocation Director: Sister Mary C. Keyser, OSC

POOR CLARE NUNS
Sisters of the Passion and Cross, PO Box 3904, Boardman, OH 44513-3904. E-mail: JesuMaria@aol.com; Web: www.rc.net/spc/
Apostolic Work: Contemplation

POOR CLARE NUNS (O.S.C.)
Monastery of St. Clare, 1505 Miles Rd., Cincinnati, OH 45231-2427. (513) 825-7177. Fax: (513) 825-4071. E-mail: dianneshort@juno.com; Web: www.poorclare.org
9 Sisters
Apostolic Work: Contemplative.
Represented in the Archdiocese of Cincinnati.
Vocation Director: Sr. Dianne Short, O.S.C.

POOR CLARE NUNS (P.C.C.)
Monastery of the Blessed Sacrament, 3501 Rocky River Dr., Cleveland, OH 44111-2998. (216) 941-2820
19 Solemnly Professed Nuns, 3

Extern Sisters, 1 Junior Professed, 1 Novice

Apostolic Work: Dedicated to contemplative prayer and the Divine Office, living in joyous penance, poverty and simplicity and in Papal Enclosure. Perpetual Adoration of the Blessed Sacrament.

Contact Person: Reverend Mother Mary Jude, P.C.C., Abbess

POOR CLARE NUNS (O.S.C.) (Contemplative Life Style)

Monastery of Saint Clare, 1271 Langhorne-Newtown Rd., Langhorne, PA 19047-1297. E-mail: stclare@voicenet.com; Web: www.voicenet.com/~stclare

14 Sisters

Vocation Director: Sr. Evelyn, O.S.C. (215) 968-5775

POOR CLARE NUNS (O.S.C.)

Monastery of St. Clare, 1916 N. Pleasantburg Dr., Greenville, SC 29609-4080

16 Sisters

Contemplative.

Vocation Director: Sr. Nancy Shively, osc, Monastery of St. Clare, 1916 N. Pleasantburg Dr., Greenville, SC 29609-4080. (864) 244-4514. Fax: (864) 268-9379. E-mail: oscgreenville@juno.com; Web: pages.prodigy.net/abrgreenville

POOR CLARE NUNS (O.S.C.)

St. Clare Monastery, 1310 Dellwood Ave., Memphis, TN 38127. (901) 357-6662. Fax: (901) 353-3783. E-mail: stclare@mem.net; Web: www.poorclare.com/memphis

8 Sisters

Contemplative community.

Contact: Sr. Mary John, osc

POOR CLARE SISTERS (O.S.C.)

107 N. Depot St., Victoria, TX 77901-6826

2 Solemnly Professed Sisters.

Franciscan contemplative nuns. Ministry: prayer, giftshop and bakery.

Vocation Directress: Sr. Katherine, O.S.C. (361) 576-6347. E-mail: poorclares@cox-internet.com; Web: poorclaresvictoria.org

POOR CLARE NUNS (P.C.C.)

Monastery of Poor Clares Collettine P.C.C., 5500 Holly Fork Rd., Barhamsville, VA 23011

15 Nuns

Vocation Director: Mother Mary Colette, P.C.C., Monastery of Poor Clares Collettine P.C.C., 5500 Holly Fork Rd., Barhamsville, VA 23011. (757) 596-5942. E-mail: poorclares@megasurf.net

POOR CLARE NUNS (O.S.C.)

Monastery of St. Clare, 4419 N. Hawthorne St., Spokane, WA 99205-1399. (509) 327-4479. Fax: (509) 327-5171. E-mail: stclare@poorclare.org; Web: www.calledbyjoy.com and www.poorclare.org/spokane

7 Solemnly Professed Sisters

Apostolic Work: Contemplative prayer.

Vocation Directress: Sr. Marcia Kay LaCour, O.S.C.

POOR CLARES NUNS OF PERPETUAL ADORATION (P.C.P.A.)

Sancta Clara Monastery, 4200 N. Market Ave., Canton, OH 44714

14 Sisters

Apostolic Work: Eucharistic Adoration and contemplative prayer, music ministry.

Represented in the Diocese of Youngstown.

Vocation Directress: Sr. Marion Zeltmann, PCPA, Sancta Clara Monastery, 4200 N. Market Ave., Canton, OH 44714. (330) 492-1171. E-mail: sismomzelt@yahoo.com; Web: www.poorclares.org

POOR CLARES OF PERPETUAL ADORATION (P.C.P.A.)

Our Lady of the Angels Monastery, 3222 County Rd. #548, Hanceville, AL 35077. (256) 352-6267

41 Nuns

Perpetual adoration of the Most Blessed Sacrament.

Vocation Directress: Sr. Mary Catherine, PCPA, Vicar

POOR CLARES OF PERPETUAL ADORATION (P.C.P.A.)

3900 13th St., NE, Washington, DC 20017-2699. (202) 526-6808. Fax: (202) 526-0678. E-mail: ourpreciousgift@starpower.net

10 Sisters

Primary Apostolic Work: Perpetual Adoration of the Most Blessed Sacrament (enclosed order).

Vocation Directress: Sr. Mary Rita

POOR CLARES OF PERPETUAL ADORATION (P.C.P.A.)

Adoration Monastery, 4108 Euclid Ave., Cleveland, OH 44103

18 Sisters, 1 Postulant

Autonomous, Contemplative Community

Apostolate Work: Perpetual Eucharistic Adoration

Represented in the (Arch)dioceses of Cleveland, Washington, DC, Youngstown, OH; Columbus, OH and Birmingham, AL. Also in India, Poland, France, Germany and Austria.

Vocation Contact: Mother Mary James, P.C.P.A. (216) 361-0783

POOR CLARES OF PERPETUAL ADORATION (P.C.P.A.)

St. Joseph Adoration Monastery, 2311 Stockham Lane, Portsmouth, OH 45662-3049

6 Cloistered Nuns, 2 Postulants

Apostolic Work: Contemplative prayer, Perpetual Adoration of the Blessed Sacrament.

Contact Person: Mother Dolores Marie, P.C.P.A. (740) 353-4713

POOR HANDMAIDS OF JESUS CHRIST (P.H.J.C.)

PHJC Ministry Center, PO Box 1, Donaldson, IN 46513. (574) 936-9936

157 Sisters, 210 Associates, 5 Fiat Spiritus members in American province; worldwide in Germany, Kenya, the Netherlands, England, India, Mexico and Brazil

Apostolic Work: Attentive to the Spirit's prompting, ministries are determined by the Sisters' gifts and the needs of the people they serve. PHJC ministries include healthcare, education, parish and social services.

Represented in the (Arch)dioceses of Belleville, Chicago, Cincinnati, Fort Wayne-South Bend, Gary, Joliet, St. Cloud, Savannah, Springfield (IL), and Springfield-Cape Girardeau. Also in Brazil, Germany, Mexico and Kenya.

Director of Vocation Ministry: Sister Marybeth Martin, PHJC Ministry Center, PO Box 1, Donaldson, IN 46513. (574) 936-9936. E-mail: sistermarybeth@juno.com; Web: www.poorhandmaids.org

POOR SERVANTS OF THE MOTHER OF GOD (S.M.G.)

24 Sisters

Motherhouse: England

Apostolic Work: Health care, education, retreats, social concerns, catechetics.

Represented in the (Arch)dioceses of Philadelphia, Richmond, Charlotte and Metuchen. Also in England, Ireland, Italy, France, Scotland, Africa and South America.

Vocation Director: Sr. Elizabeth, S.M.G., Emmaus House, 101 Center St., Perth Amboy, NJ 08861. (732) 442-7783. Fax: (732) 442-7793. E-mail: ecrehan@aol.com; Web: www.poorservants.com

POOR SISTERS OF NAZARETH (P.S.N.)

See listing under "N" (Sisters of) Nazareth (C.S.N.)

POOR SISTERS OF ST. JOSEPH
US Foundations in Alexandria, VA, Bethlehem, PA, and Reading, PA
13 Sisters in US
Apostolic Work: Schools, hospitals, nursing homes.
Vocations: Mother Maria D. Gonzalez, 532 Spruce St., Reading, PA 19602. (610) 378-1947

SISTERS OF THE PRECIOUS BLOOD (C.PP.S.) Generalate: 4000 Denlinger Rd., Dayton, OH 45426-2399. (937) 837-3302
247 Sisters
Apostolic Work: Pastoral ministry, religious education, retreat work, food service, healthcare, social services, teaching (elementary, secondary, university), and Chilean and Guatemalan foreign missions.
Represented in the Archdioceses of Cincinnati, Denver and Detroit and in the Dioceses of Cleveland, Columbus, Dallas, Ft. Wayne, Lafayette, Lansing, Toledo, Phoenix, Saginaw, San Diego, Tucson and Youngstown.
Vocation Contact: Sister Carolyn Hoying, C.PP.S., Coordinator of Vocation Ministry, 4960 Salem Ave., Dayton, OH 45416. (937) 278-0871. E-mail: cppsvocations@salemheights.com; Web: www.bright.net/~cppsnews

UNION OF SISTERS OF THE PRESENTATION OF THE BLESSED VIRGIN MARY (P.B.V.M.) - UNITED STATES PROVINCE
Provincialate: 729 W. Wilshire Dr., Phoenix, AZ 85007. (602) 271-9687
85 Sisters
Apostolic Work: Teaching, religious education, adult education, nursing, social work, parish ministries.
Represented in the Archdioceses of Los Angeles, Mobile, New Orleans, San Antonio and San Francisco and in the Dioceses of Biloxi, Birmingham, Oakland, Orange, Phoenix, Sacramento, San Bernardino, Savannah and Tucson. Sisters in Africa, England, India, Ireland, New Zealand, Pakistan, Philippines and South America.
Vocation Coordinator: Sr. Consilio Buckley, PBVM, 18091 Commission Rd., Long Beach, MS 39560. (228) 864-8418. E-mail: consilioEB@aol.com

PRESENTATION SISTERS OF ABERDEEN (P.B.V.M.)
Motherhouse: Presentation Heights, Aberdeen, SD 57401-1238
125 Sisters
Apostolic Work: Education, hospital, nursing homes, parish and youth ministries and social services, ministry with Native American, Hispanic and rural people, Bolivian and Guatemalan missions, retreat work, campus ministry.
Represented primarily in South Dakota. Also in Minnesota, New Mexico, Iowa, Nebraska, Michigan, New York, Oregon, Bolivia and Guatemala.
Vocation Director: Sister Mary Thomas, P.B.V.M., Presentation Heights, 1500 N. Second, Aberdeen, SD 57401-1238. (605) 229-8401. E-mail: mthomas@presentationsisters.org; Web: www.presentationsisters.org, www.nuns2youth.org (youth site)

PRESENTATION SISTERS OF DUBUQUE (P.B.V.M.) Motherhouse and Novitiate: 2360 Carter Rd., Dubuque, IA 52001-2997
152 Sisters
Apostolic Work: College, high schools, elementary schools, religious education, pastoral ministry, campus ministry, youth ministry, home and foreign missions, spiritual direction, housing, vocation ministry, retreat work, prison ministry, social justice lobbying, massage therapy and food service.
Represented in the Archdioceses of Dubuque, Chicago, Denver, St. Paul-Minneapolis and Washington and in the Dioceses of Birmingham, Brownsville, Covington, Davenport, Jackson, Knoxville, Nashville, New Ulm, Orlando, Rapid City, Sioux City, South Bend and Winona. Also in Entre Rios, Tarija, Bolivia.
Vocation Director: Sr. Carmen Hernandez, PBVM, 2360 Carter Rd., Dubuque, IA 52001-2997. (563) 588-2008. E-mail: carmher@mwci.net; Web: dubuquepresentations.org

SISTERS OF THE PRESENTATION OF THE BLESSED VIRGIN MARY (P.B.V.M.) Motherhouse and Novitiate: 1101 32 Ave.S., Fargo, ND 58103-6036. (701) 237-4857
57 Professed
Apostolic Work: Education, pastoral ministry, health care, domestic services, social work, spirituality centers, home and foreign missions.
Represented in the (Arch)dioceses of Bismarck, Columbus, Dubuque, Fargo, Jackson, Knoxville, New York, Rapid City, and Springfield-Cape Girardeau. Also in Peru.
Vocation Director: Sr. Lois Byrne, PBVM, Presentation Ministries, 3001 11th St. S., Fargo, ND 58103. (701) 235-8246. E-mail: lbyrne@cableone.net; Web: www.presentationsistersfargo.org

PRESENTATION SISTERS OF NEW ENGLAND AND TRI-STATE AREA (P.B.V.M.) Administration Center: Mt. St. Joseph, 880 Jackson Ave., New Windsor, NY 12553. (845) 564-0513. Fax: (845) 567-0219. E-mail: mcredmond13@aol.com; Web: www.sistersofthepresentation.org
167 Sisters
Apostolic Work: High schools, elementary schools, social/pastoral ministry, health care and religious education.
Represented in the Archdioceses of Boston, Newark, New York and Washington and in the Dioceses of Brooklyn, Manchester, Metuchen, Norwich, Paterson, Providence, Rockville Center, Trenton and Worcester. Also in Tarija (Bolivia) and Cape Coast (Ghana).
Vocation Director: Sr. Mary Catherine Redmond, PBVM

SISTERS OF THE PRESENTATION OF THE BLESSED VIRGIN MARY (P.B.V.M.), SAN FRANCISCO
Motherhouse: 2340 Turk Blvd., San Francisco, CA 94118-4340. (415) 751-0406
135 Sisters
Apostolic Work: Presentation women are committed to fulfilling the mission of our foundress, Nano Nagle, by continuing to serve the poor in the ministries of education, parish ministry, community organizing, pastoral care in hospitals, literacy programs, foreign missions, immigration work, spiritual direction, retreat work, personal care facility for the poor, SafeHouse for women wanting to escape prostitution. Ministries vary according to the gifts of each Sister and the needs of the time and locale.
Represented in the Archdioceses of San Francisco and Los Angeles and in the Dioceses of Oakland, Santa Rosa, San Jose and Orange with missionaries in Guatemala.
Find out more about our history, charism, and current life on our Website: presentationsisterssf.org
Vocation Contact: Sr. Patricia Elower, PBVM, 2340 Turk Blvd., San Francisco, CA 94118. (415) 751-0406. E-mail: pelower@pbvmsf.org; Web: www.presentationsisterssf.org

PRESENTATION SISTERS OF STATEN ISLAND (P.B.V.M.)
Motherhouse: Our Lady of the Presentation, 419 Woodrow Rd., Annadale, S.I., NY 10312-1351. (718) 356-2121
19 Sisters (members of an international organization of women)
Apostolic Work: Elementary schools, high school, university, pastoral min-

istry in parish, hospital and university. Represented in the Archdioceses of New York, Philadelphia and South Dakota.

Vocation Contact: Sr. Catherine Quinn, PBVM, Congregation Leader, Our Lady of the Presentation, 419 Woodrow Rd., Annadale, S.I., NY 10312-1351. (718) 356-2121. Fax: (718) 948-4115. E-mail: cquinnpbvm @si.rr.com

PRESENTATION SISTERS OF WATERVLIET (P.B.V.M.),

St. Colman's Presentation Convent, Watervliet, NY 12189. (518) 273-4911

60 Sisters

Apostolic Work: 2 grammar schools, 1 child caring institution, 2 day nursery centers, 4 classes for pre-school handicapped, residential school for emotionally disturbed and autistic children, social work, pastoral ministry, 1 school of religion.

Represented in the Diocese of Albany.

Vocation Directress: Sr. Mary Michael, P.B.V.M.

SISTERS OF THE PRESENTATION OF MARY (P.M.) (Manchester Province) Provincial House: 495 Mammoth Rd., Manchester, NH 03104. (603) 669-1080

206 Sisters in US; 1,600 Sisters worldwide

Apostolic Work: Education at all levels: college, high school, elementary, kindergarten, preschool, day care, after-school programs, campus ministry, tutoring, substitute teaching; pastoral ministry, religious education, adult education, youth ministry, retreat ministry, spiritual direction, formation in spirituality, lay associates, house of prayer, discernment house, summer Concern program, volunteer program experiences with the poor, foreign missions, social services, counseling, ministry to immigrants, prison ministry, nursing, chaplaincy, hospital and nursing home visitation, care of the elderly.

Represented in the Dioceses of Houston, Manchester and Providence and in 18 countries.

Vocation Director: Sr. Jenny Levasseur, p.m., 495 Mammoth Rd., Manchester, NH 03104. (603) 623-0671. E-mail: srjenny@juno.com; Web: www.presentationofmary.com

SISTERS OF THE PRESENTATION OF MARY (P.M.) (Methuen Province) Provincial House: 209 Lawrence St., Methuen, MA 01844

135 Sisters

Apostolic Work: 1 high school, 5 elementary schools, 1 kindergarten, 3 Montessori day nurseries, 1 religious instruction center, pastoral care, retreat center, discernment house.

Represented in the Archdiocese of Boston and in the Dioceses of Portland (ME), Springfield and Worcester. Foreign mission areas in 18 different countries.

Vocation Director: Sr. Claire Gagnon, p.m., 10 Quincy St., Methuen, MA 01844. (978) 682-2502. E-mail: pmsistersmeth@yahoo.com; Web: presmarymethuen.org

SISTERS OF PROVIDENCE (S.P.) (Western US) (Mother Joseph Province) 506 Second Ave., Suite 1200, Seattle, WA 98104. (206) 464-3355. Fax: (206) 464-3984; 9 E. Ninth Ave., Spokane, WA 99202-1295. (509) 474-2300. Fax: (509) 474-2302

187 Sisters, 2 Temporary Vows, 1 Novice, 2 Candidates

Ministries: Varied according to the needs of the people and the gifts and creativity of each Sister. Many Sisters minister in health care, education, parish/diocesan ministries, low-income housing, shelters, prisons, pastoral care, administration, and elderly and multi cultural ministries. Opportunities for foreign mission ministry.

Sponsor/Manage: A high school, university, Montessori school, child care center; many health-care facilities from Anchorage to Burbank, Seattle to Great Falls; shelters/ housing for women and children, women in transition, those with AIDS, the elderly and handicapped.

Represented in the (Arch)dioceses of Anchorage, Boise, Great Falls, Helena, Los Angeles, Oakland, Portland (OR), Seattle, Spokane and Yakima. Also in El Salvador.

Vocation Office: Sr. Judy George, SP, Manager, 9 East Ninth Ave., Spokane, WA 99202-1295. (509) 474-2323. E-mail: vocations@ providence.org; Web: www.sisters ofprovidence.net

SISTERS OF PROVIDENCE (S.P.)

Providence Place, 5 Gamelin St., Holyoke, MA 01040-4080. (413) 536-7511

90 Members

Apostolic Work: Contemporary women grappling with many of society's most complex and serious social issues such as the plight of the poor and homeless, those who live on the edge and those who fall through the cracks. The Sisters' focus is on making all decisions in light of the impact they will have on women, the earth and the poor. Ministries include children, the sick, the elderly, holistic health, spiritual direction and presence on religious and civic boards. Being rooted in the past and open to the future gives meaning and direction to the Sisters' lives and ministries.

Represented in the Dioceses of Springfield and Worcester (MA) and Raleigh (NC).

Vocation Director: Sister Ann Horgan, SP, Genesis Spiritual Life Center, 53 Mill St., Westfield, MA 01085. (413) 562-3627. E-mail: sisters@sisofprov .org; Web: www.sisofprov.org

SISTERS OF PROVIDENCE OF SAINT MARY-OF-THE-WOODS (S.P.)

Motherhouse: Saint Mary-of-the-Woods, IN 47876-1089. (800) 860-1840, ext. 124 or (812) 535-3131, ext. 124

550 Sisters

Apostolic Work: Education ministries in colleges, universities, high schools, grade schools, parishes, adult learning centers; pastoral ministry in parishes, colleges, prisons, retirement and health-care facilities, retreat centers; health-care ministries; social service ministries including counseling, administration, justice work, eco-justice center; administrative ministries in arch/diocesan and parish offices, congregation service, national organizations; foreign missions.

Represented in the (Arch)dioceses of Belleville, Boston, Chicago, Cincinnati, Cleveland, Corpus Christi, Covington, Davenport, Evansville, Fort Wayne/South Bend, Galveston, Indianapolis, Helena, Joliet, Los Angeles, Lafayette (IN), Lafayette (LA), Lexington, Louisville, Manchester, Oklahoma City, Omaha, Orange, Owensboro, Peoria, Portland, Richmond, San Antonio, San Francisco, Santa Fe, Springfield, St. Paul, St. Petersburg, Trenton, Venice, Washington, DC and Worcester. Also in Canada, China, Taiwan and the Philippines.

Vocation Ministry Office: Sister Bernice Kuper, SP, Owens Hall, 1 Sisters of Providence, Saint Mary-of-the-Woods, IN 47876-1089. (800) 860-1840, ext. 124 or (812) 535-3131, ext. 124. E-mail: bkuper@spsmw.org; Web: www.sistersofprovidence.org

REDEMPTORISTINE NUNS (O.SS.R.) (Order of the Most Holy Redeemer)

9 Professed Sisters, 1 Postulant in this monastery, 550 members in approx. 45 monasteries worldwide

Mother of Perpetual Help Monastery, PO Box 220, Esopus, NY 12429-0220

Apostolic Work: Contemplation.

Represented in the Archdioceses of New York and St. Louis.

Vocation Director: Sr. Mary Anne Reed, O.SS.R., Redemptoristine Nuns, PO Box 220, Esopus, NY 12429-0220. (845) 384-6533. E-mail: vocdir@juno.com; Web: www.catholic.org/macc/redemptoristine

RELIGIOUS OF CHRISTIAN EDUCATION
See Christian Education, Religious of

RELIGIOUS OF THE ASSUMPTION
See Assumption, Religious of the

RELIGIOUS OF THE INCARNATE WORD (C.V.I.)
Motherhouse: Mexico City
US Vice Provincial: 153 Rainier Crt., Chula Vista, CA 91911
7 Sisters in US; 490 Sisters worldwide
Apostolic Work: Teaching, residence for students, campus ministry, catechetics, pastoral ministry, Third Order, home for aged and missions.
Represented in the Diocese of San Diego. Also in Mexico, Spain, France, Guatemala, Argentina and Africa.
Vocation Director: Sr. Camille Crabbe, C.V.I., 153 Rainier Crt., Chula Vista, CA 91911. (619) 420-0231. E-mail: ccrabbe@hotmail.com

RELIGIOUS OF JESUS AND MARY (R.J.M.) (US Province) Provincial House: 3706 Rhode Island Ave., Mt. Rainier, MD 20712. (301) 277-3794. Fax: (301) 277-8656
138 Sisters; 1,630 worldwide
Apostolic Work: Teaching at all levels, pastoral team work, catechetical instruction, health care, counseling, community social action, retreat work, nursing. Summer and long-term QUEST, lay volunteer program experiences with the poor and minority groups. Lay Associates: The Family of Jesus and Mary. Missions in seven foreign countries.
Represented in the Archdioceses of Boston, New York, Los Angeles and Washington, DC and in the Dioceses of Providence, El Paso, Manchester, Fall River and San Diego. Also in Haiti and Tijuana, Mexico.
Vocation Director: Sr. Rosemary Nicholson, RJM, 1354 Hilltop Dr., Chula Vista, CA 91911. E-mail: rosienicholson@juno.com

RELIGIOUS OF MARY IMMACULATE (R.M.I.) Villa Maria, 719 Augusta St., San Antonio, TX 78215. (210) 226-0025
Fax: (210) 226-3305; Centro Maria, 539 W. 54th St., New York, NY 10019-5017. (212) 581-5273. Fax: (212) 307-5687; 650 Jackson St. N.E., Washington, DC 20017-1424. (202) 635-1697. Fax: (202) 635-7246
28 Sisters in US; 1,700 Sisters in 21 countries
Apostolic Work: Residences for young girls of good moral conduct, away from home for work, study or both. Age 17-29 normally, of any age, creed or nationality.
Represented in the Archdioceses of New York, Washington, DC and San Antonio.
Vocation Director: Sr. Clara Echeverra, Local Superior, Centro Maria, 539 W. 54th St., New York, NY 10019-5017. (212) 581-5273. Fax: (212) 307-5687. E-mail: cenmariany@mindspring.com; Web: ww.mi-world.org

RELIGIOUS MISSIONARIES OF ST. DOMINIC (O.P.)
See "C" - Congregation of the Religious Missionaries of St. Dominic

RELIGIOUS OF THE SACRED HEART OF MARY (R.S.H.M.)
(Eastern American Province) Provincial Center, 50 Wilson Park Dr., Tarrytown, NY 10591
210 Sisters, 1,000 Sisters worldwide
Apostolic Work: Education at all levels, retreat work, parish ministry, health care, social work, law in urban, rural areas.
Represented in the Archdioceses of New York, St. Louis and Washington, DC and in the Dioceses of Arlington, Baltimore, Brooklyn, Norwich, Oakland, Palm Beach, Paterson, Richmond, Rockville Centre, Venice (FL) and Winona. Foreign Missions in Zimbabwe and Zambia, Africa. Overseas schools in London, Paris and Rome.
Vocation Directress: Sister Ann Marino, 50 Wilson Park Dr., Tarrytown, NY 10591. (914) 631-8872. E-mail: cormaria@aol.com; Web: www.rshm.org

RELIGIOUS OF THE SACRED HEART OF MARY (R.S.H.M.)
(Western American Province) 441 N. Garfield Ave., Montebello, CA 90640-2901. (323) 887-8821. E-mail: RSHMWAP@earthlink.net
85 Sisters, 1,100 Sisters worldwide
Apostolic Work: Education at all levels, parish ministry, campus ministry, hospital pastoral care, social service ministry, detention ministry.
Represented in the (Arch)dioceses of Los Angeles, San Francisco, Monterey, San Bernardino and San Diego. Also in Amacuzac, Cuernavaca and Mexico City in Mexico.
Vocation Directors: Sr. Renée Rushton, RSHM, 441 N. Garfield Ave., Montebello, CA 90640-2901. (323) 890-9912. E-mail: reneerushton@earthlink.net; Web: www.rshm.org; Hna. Arcenia Escamilla, RSCM, Sassoferrato, #136, Colonia Alfonso XIII, Delegacion Alvaro Obregon, 01460 Mexico, D.F. 011-525-563-4745

RELIGIOUS SISTERS OF CHARITY (R.S.C.) Motherhouse: Ireland
US Headquarters: 10664 St. James Dr., Culver City, CA 90230. (310) 559-0176, 838-0654. Fax: (213) 559-3530
31 Sisters in California
Apostolic Work: Education, health care, parish ministry, juvenile hall, counseling, religious education, retreat and spirituality work, campus ministry, special outreach to marginalized in all settings.
Represented in the Archdiocese of Los Angeles. Also in La Guaira, Venezuela, Ireland, England, Zambia, Ethiopia, Nigeria.
Vocation Director: Sr. Eva Bryan, RSC, 10664 St. James Dr., Culver City, CA 90230. (310) 559-0176, 838-0654. Fax: (213) 559-3530

RELIGIOUS TEACHERS FILIPPINI, M.P.F. (Filippini Sisters)
(St. Lucy Province) Motherhouse, Novitiate and Provincial House: Villa Walsh, 455 Western Ave., Morristown, NJ 07960-4928
255 Sisters
Apostolic Work: Elementary and secondary education, parish ministry, retreat ministry, child day care centers, and foreign missions.
Represented with foundations in the United States, Italy, Brazil, Eritrea, Ethiopia, India, England, Ireland and Albania. Another province in Connecticut.
Vocation Director: Sr. Jane Feltz, M.P.F., Villa Walsh, 455 Western Ave., Morristown, NJ 07960-4928. (973) 538-2886, ext. 146. E-mail: jfeltzmpf@hotmail.com; Web: www.filippiniusa.org

RELIGIOUS VENERINI SISTERS (M.P.V.)
Generalate: Rome
Provincialate: 23 Edward St., Worcester, MA 01605. (508) 754-1020
31 Sisters in the US; 405 worldwide
Apostolic Work: Teaching, religious education, parish work, social work, nursing, pastoral associate and missionary work.
Represented in the Dioceses of Albany and Worcester. Also in Albania, Brazil, Cameroon, Chile, India, Italy, Nigeria, Romania and Venezuela.
Vocation Contact: Mary Rose

Zaccari, MPV, Provincial, 23 Edward St., Worcester, MA 01605. (508) 754-1020. E-mail: zaccari@venerini.org; Web: www.venerinisisters.com

RELIGIOUS OF THE VIRGIN MARY (R.V.M.) (RVM SISTERS)

Motherhouse: Quezon City, Philippines

US Headquarters: Sacred Heart Convent, 200 Randolph Ave., South Plainfield, NJ 07080

751 Sisters worldwide

Apostolic Work: Retreats, education (early childhood, elementary, secondary, college and university), campus ministry, health care ministry, prison ministry, administration, theological formation in seminaries and institutions.

Represented in the (Arch)dioceses of Honolulu, Metuchen, Sacramento and San Francisco. Also in the Philippines, Indonesia, Italy, Papua New Guinea, Pakistan, Samoa, Africa, Taiwan, Canada and Switzerland.

Vocation Directress: Sister Maria Cornelia Ramirez, RVM, Sacred Heart Convent, 200 Randolph Ave., South Plainfield, NJ 07080. (908) 756-0633, ext. 33, 756-0631. E-mail: cramirez@diometuchen.org

SISTERS OF REPARATION OF THE CONGREGATION OF MARY (S.R.C.M.)

Motherhouse: St. Zita Villa, Monsey, NY 10952. (845) 356-2011

11 Sisters

Apostolic Work: 1 home for adult women, 1 novitiate.

Represented in the Archdiocese of New York.

Vocations: Sr. Maureen Frances, Superior, St. Zita Villa, 50 Saddle River Rd. N., Monsey, NY 10952. (845) 356-2011

SISTERS OF REPARATION OF THE SACRED WOUNDS OF JESUS (S.R.)

2120 S.E. 24th Ave., Portland, OR 97214-5504

3 Sisters, 6 Priest Associates, 116 Lay Donnes

Apostolic Work: Nursing, teaching, liturgy and worship, healing ministries, counseling, catechesis, music ministries, spiritual enrichment, ministering to the homebound and hospital visitation.

Represented in the Archdiocese of Portland (OR) and in the state of Washington.

Vocation Directress: Sister Mary Immaculate, SR, 2120 S.E. 24th Ave., Portland, OR 97214-5504. (503) 236-4207. Fax: (503) 236-3400. E-mail: repsrs@msn.com, repsrs@juno.com

SISTERS OF THE RESURRECTION (C.R.) (New York Eastern Province) Provincial House: Mt. St. Joseph, 35 Boltwood Ave., Castleton-on-Hudson, NY 12033

Apostolic Work: Education (primary and secondary), health care (nursing homes), pastoral care, campus ministry, catechetical programs.

Represented in the Archdiocese of New York and in the Dioceses of Albany and Trenton.

Vocation Directress: Sister Dolores Marie, C.R., Mt. St. Joseph, 35 Boltwood Ave., Castleton-on-Hudson, NY 12033. (518) 732-2226. E-mail: vocation@resurrectionsisters.org; Web: www.resurrectionsisters.org

SISTERS OF THE RESURRECTION (C.R.) (Chicago Western Province) 7432 W. Talcott Ave., Chicago, IL 60631

72 Sisters

Apostolic Work: Teaching and administration, nursing and health care, day care centers, retirement center, hospital pastoral care, parish pastoral ministry.

Represented in the (Arch)dioceses of Chicago and Mobile.

Vocation Directress: Sister Kathleen Ann, C.R., 7432 W. Talcott Ave., Chicago, IL 60631-3743. (773) 792-6363. E-mail: callres@hotmail.com

SACRAMENTINE NUNS (O.S.S.)

Blessed Sacrament Monastery, 86 Dromore Rd., Scarsdale, NY 10583-1706

12 Sisters

Cloistered contemplatives. Perpetual Adoration.

Represented in the Archdiocese of New York and in the Diocese of Gaylord, MI.

Vocation Directress: Sr. Mary Sygne Dyda, OSS, Blessed Sacrament Monastery, 86 Dromore Rd., Scarsdale, NY 10583-1706. (914) 722-1657. Fax: (914) 722-1665. E-mail: obsny@aol.com; Web: www.catholic.org/macc (Sacramentines)

SACRAMENTINE NUNS (O.S.S.)

Sacramentine Monastery of Perpetual Adoration, 2798 US 31 N., P.O. Box 86, Conway, MI 49722. (231) 347-0447

3 Sisters

Represented in the Diocese of Gaylord.

Vocation Contact: Sister Mary Rosalie Smith, O.S.S., Prioress

SISTERS OF THE SACRED HEART OF JESUS (S.S.C.J.)

Generalate/Motherhouse: France

(Sacred Heart Province) Provincialate Offices, 11931 Radium St., San Antonio, TX 78216-2714. (210) 344-7203

61 Sisters: 790 Sisters worldwide

Conduct: Work in education, pastoral work, nursing, social services in 3 states in US, 2 Mexican missions.

Represented in the Archdioceses of San Antonio and Santa Fe and in the Dioceses of Brownsville, Galveston-Houston and Jefferson City. Also in Mexico City.

Vocation Directress: Sr. Juana Villescas, SSCJ, 11931 Radium St., San Antonio, TX 78216-2714. (210) 344-7203. E-mail: jnlv@juno.com; Web: www.texas.net/~square1/vocation/sscj.html

SISTERS OF THE SACRED HEART OF JESUS (S.S.H.J.)

Motherhouse: Sacred Heart Villa, 5269 Lewiston Rd., Lewiston, NY 14092

650 Sisters

Apostolic Work: All areas of education, rest homes and hospitals, social service, catechetical and parish ministry and missions.

Represented in New York and Connecticut. Also in Italy, Canada, Madagascar, Poland, Philippines, Nigeria and Romania.

Vocation Contact: Sister Ambrogia Alderuccio, Sacred Heart Villa, 5269 Lewiston Rd., Lewiston, NY 14092. (716) 284-8273 (tel., fax - call first to fax). E-mail: shvschool@adelphia.net

SOCIETY OF THE SACRED HEART (R.S.C.J.) (Religious of the Sacred Heart) Provincial House: 4389 West Pine Blvd., St. Louis, MO 63108. (314) 652-1500

Nearly 3,500 Sisters in 45 countries; nearly 450 Sisters in US

Apostolic Work: Contemplatives in action, the Sisters are committed to making God's love visible in the heart of the world. Ministries include teaching and educational administration on every level, work with the poor, health care, social work, counseling; pastoral ministry in hospitals, parishes and prisions; communication; spiritual direction and retreats; law and art.

Represented in the Archdioceses of Baltimore, Boston, Chicago, Detroit, Miami, New Orleans, New York, Omaha, St. Louis, San Francisco, Seattle and Washington, DC and in the Dioceses of Albany, Bridgeport, Lafayette, Galveston-Houston, San Jose, San Diego and Trenton.

Vocation Director: Nancy Koke, RSCJ, 6142 N. Kenmore Ave. #3, Chicago, IL 60660. (888) 844-7725. Fax: (773) 856-5906. E-mail: nkoke@rscj.org; Web: www.rscj.org

SACRED HEARTS COMMUNITY–SISTERS OF SACRED HEARTS OF JESUS AND MARY (SS.CC.)
Generalate: Italy
Pacific Province:1120 5th Ave., Honolulu, HI 96816. (808) 737-5822; East Coast Region: 35 Huttleston Ave., Fairhaven, MA 02719-3154
49 Sisters in US
Apostolic Work: A variety of parish ministries, religious education, schools, hospital chaplaincy, visiting and bringing Eucharist to the elderly and the homebound, visiting prisoners, working in shelters for the homeless, education for justice and peace, intercessory prayer, home and foreign missions.
Represented in the Dioceses of Fall River and Honolulu. Also in 15 foreign countries.
Vocation Contact: Sr. Dolores Pavao, SS.CC, Regional Superior, 35 Huttleston Ave., Fairhaven, MA 02719-3154. (508) 994-9341. Fax: (508) 990-1967. E-mail: srdolores pavao@cs.com; Web: www.sscc .org/vocations.html

SISTERS OF SACRED HEARTS OF JESUS AND MARY (S.H.J.M.)
California Region: 2150 Lakeshore Ave., Oakland, CA 94606-1123. (510) 832-2935
14 Sisters US, 270 Sisters worldwide
Conduct: Pastoral care of the sick and shut-ins, campus ministry, education, nursing, refugee ministry; caring ministries to AIDS sufferers, people with special needs, women and children.
Represented in the Dioceses of Oakland, Sacramento and Stockton. Also in England, Scotland, Ireland and Wales. Foreign missions in Zambia, El Salvador, Colombia, Uganda and the Philippines.
Vocations Directress: Sr. Una Bridget Mulvey, SHJM, 2012 48th Ave., Oakland, CA 94601. (510) 536-5898. Fax: (510) 535-0509. E-mail: shjmvocation@aol.com

CONGREGATION OF ST. AGNES (C.S.A.) St. Agnes Convent, 320 County Road K, Fond du Lac, WI 54935. (920) 907-2321
363 Sisters
Apostolic Work: Work in fields of education, health care, pastoral ministry, social services, art, law and spiritual direction.
Represented in the Archdioceses of Chicago, New York, Milwaukee and St. Paul as well as 24 dioceses. Also in Nicaragua and Honduras.
Vocation Promoter: S. Deborah Walter, 320 County Road K, Fond du Lac, WI 54935. (920) 907-2310. E-mail: dwalter@csasisters.org; Web: www.csasisters.org

SISTERS OF SAINT ANN (S.S.A.)
Headquarters: Rome, Italy
Motherhouse in US: Mt. St. Ann, PO Box 328, Ebensburg, PA 15931. (814) 472-9354 (tel., fax)
6 Sisters in US, 1,500 worldwide
Apostolic Work:Teaching in elementary/high school, parish religion education, hospitals, nursing homes, orphanages and social work mainly for, and with, the poorest of the poor.
Represented in the Dioceses of Altoona-Johnstown (PA) and Corpus Christi (TX). Foreign missions in Italy, India, Switzerland, Brazil, Mexico, Philippines, Peru, Argentina, New Republic of Congo and Cameroon.
Vocation Director: Sr. Lucia D'Cunha, SSA, 2100 Morris St., Corpus Christi, TX 78405. (361) 888-4027

SISTERS OF ST. ANNE (S.S.A.)
(St. Marie Province) 720 Boston Post Rd. East, Marlborough, MA 01752. (508) 485-3791
Apostolic Work: Ministry to those with AIDS, education, parish ministry, spiritual direction, elderly care, retreats, counseling, computer work, ministry to the handicapped, religious education, music and art, prison ministry, secretarial work, chaplaincy, campus ministry, healthcare.
Represented in the Archdiocese of Boston and in several other dioceses. Also in Africa, Canada, Chile and Haiti.
Vocation Director: Sister Elaine Potvin, S.S.A., Sisters of St. Anne, 1015 Pleasant St., Worcester, MA 01602. (508) 757-6053. E-mail: selpotvin4@aol.com

SISTERS OF ST. ANNE (S.S.A.)
1550 Begbie St., Victoria, B.C., Canada V8R 1K8. (250) 592-3133
900 Sisters
Apostolic Works: Education, health care and pastoral ministry. Active in Africa, Canada, Chile, Haiti and US.
Vocation Director: Marina Smith, 929 Burdett Ave., Victoria, B.C., Canada V8V 3G6. E-mail: marinasmith2002 @yahoo.ca; Web: www.sistersof stanne.org/bc

SISTERS OF ST. BASIL THE GREAT (Byzantine Rite)
See Eastern Catholic Religious Communities for Women

SISTERS OF THE ORDER OF ST. BASIL THE GREAT (Ukrainian Byzantine Rite)
See Eastern Catholic Religious Communities for Women

CONGREGATION OF ST. BRIGID (C.S.B.) Motherhouse: Ireland; US Foundation: St. Brigid's Convent, 5118 Loma Linda Dr., San Antonio, TX 78201. (210) 733-0701. Fax: (210) 785-2820
16 Sisters
Apostolic Work: Education, pastoral work, counseling, music ministry, hospital care, campus ministry, jail ministry.
Represented in the Archdioceses of Boston and San Antonio and in the Diocese of Wilmington.
Vocation Contact: Sr. Canice Walsh, C.S.B., 5118 Loma Linda Dr., San Antonio, TX 78201. (210) 733-0701

SISTERS OF ST. CASIMIR (S.S.C.)
Motherhouse: 2601 W. Marquette Rd., Chicago, IL 60629
146 Sisters
Apostolic Work: Education in 2 high schools, 7 parishes, health care in 1 hospital and 2 homes for the aged, 2 missions in Argentina. The ministries reflect Jesus' concern for the whole person as we teach and evangelize; care for the sick, the aging, and others who are hurting; provide a sense of belonging to people of various cultures; share Christ's special love for the poor.
Represented in the Archdioceses of Chicago, Philadelphia and Washington, DC and in the Dioceses of Allentown, Joliet and Las Cruces.
Vocation Contact: Vocation Ministry Office, 2601 West Marquette Rd., Chicago, IL 60629. (773) 776-1324, ext 223. E-mail: graceKal@ssc2601 .com; Web: www.ssc2601.com

SISTERS OF ST. CHRETIENNE (S.S.Ch.) Provincial House: 297 Arnold St., Wrentham, MA 02093. (508) 384-8066
60 Sisters in US
Apostolic Work: Teaching, nursing, pastoral ministry, foreign missions, retreats, spiritual direction.
Represented in the Archdiocese of Boston and in the Dioceses of Portland (ME), Providence, St. Petersburg and Manchester. Also, in Canada, France, Austria, Africa and Hungary.
Vocation Director: Sister Lisette Michaud, SSCh, 297 Arnold St., Wrentham, MA 02093. (508) 384-8066. Fax: (508) 384-3170. E-mail: ssch@tiac.net

SISTERS OF ST. CLARE (O.S.C.)
Generalate: Ireland; Regional Residence: St. Clare's Convent, 446 South Poplar Ave., Brea, CA 92821-6649. (714) 256-1278
Conduct: Religious education, adult faith formation, diocesan administra-

tion, secretarial.
Represented in the Dioceses of Orange, San Diego, St. Petersburg and San Bernardino. Also in Albania, Australia, El Salvador, England, Ireland and Wales
Director of Vocations: Sister Eymard Flood, OSC, Marywood Center, 2811 East Villa Real Dr., Orange, CA 92867. (714) 282-3038. E-mail: sr.eflood@rcbo.org

SISTERS OF ST. CLARE (OSC) (Franciscan Spirituality within the Order of St. Clare) 446 South Popular Ave., Brea, CA 92621
Apostolic Work: Prayer-retreat ministry; education in all its forms; care of deprived children and the elderly; social and pastoral work in the local church, and evangelization in the Third World. Efforts to match the gifts of the Sister with the needs of the local community.
Represented in Great Britain, North and Central America and Albania.
Vocation Contacts: Sr. Sarah Shrewsbury, OSC, 446 South Popular Ave., Brea, CA 92621. (714) 256-1278. E-mail: osc1253@aol.com; Sr. Lucia Brady, St. Clare Convent, 14550 Apache Ave., Largo, FL 33774. (727) 517-2295. E-mail: Kiffalu@aol.com

ST. COLUMBAN SISTERS
See Missionary Sisters of St. Columban

SISTERS OF SAINTS CYRIL AND METHODIUS (SS.C.M.)
Villa Sacred Heart, Danville, PA 17821-1698
150 Sisters, 150 Lay Associates
Apostolic Work: Educational apostolate in Catholic schools from preschool/kindergarten level through university, religious education, parish and campus ministry, music conservatory, pastoral care, hearing impaired, spiritual direction, retreat ministry, ecumenism, evangelization, Coninuing Care Retirement Community and home for the aged.
Represented in the (Arch)dioceses of Allentown, Bridgeport, Charleston, Chicago, Detroit, Gary, Harrisburg, Scranton, Syracuse and Wilmington.
Director of Vocations: Sister Deborah Marie, SS.C.M., Villa Sacred Heart, Danville, PA 17821-1698. (570) 275-1093. Fax: (570) 275-5997. E-mail: debbiesscm@hotmail.com; Web: www.sscm.org

CONGREGATION OF THE SISTERS OF ST. DOROTHY (S.S.D.)
(North American Province) Provincial House: Mt. St. Joseph, 13 Monkeywrench Ln., Bristol, RI 02809
45 Sisters in US, 1,200 worldwide
Apostolic Work: Education at all levels, catechetical work, summer camps, pastoral ministry, hospital ministry, social work.
Represented in the Archdiocese of New York and in the Dioceses of Brownsville, Fall River and Providence. Also in 18 foreign lands.
Vocation Directress: Sister Mary Sardinha, S.S.D., 519 W. Walnut Ave., McAllen, TX 78501. (956) 971-8900; Mt. St. Joseph, 13 Monkeywrench Ln., Bristol, RI 02809. (401) 254-8876, 5434 (June-Sept.).
E-mail: sards@sc2000.net

SISTERS OF SAINT FRANCIS (O.S.F.)
Motherhouse: 588 N. Bluff Blvd., Clinton, IA 52732-3953. (563) 242-7611
91 Sisters, 2 Novices, 62 Associates
Conduct: 1 college, 1 retirement home/health care facility, 1 speech & hearing center.
Represented in the Archdioceses of Chicago, Dubuque, Louisville and St. Louis and in the Dioceses of Belleville, Davenport, Des Moines, Joliet, Kansas City-St. Joseph, Lexington, Oakland, Orange in California, Peoria, Phoenix, Portland, San Bernardino, San Diego and Sioux City. Also in Chulucanas, Peru, South America.
Initial Discernment Coordinator: Sister Gael Gensler, OSF, 588 N. Bluff Blvd., Clinton, IA 52732-3953. (563) 242-7611. Fax: (563) 243-0007. E-mail: sisters@clintonfranciscans.com; Web: www.clintonfranciscans.com

ST. JOAN OF ARC SISTERS (S.J.A.)
Motherhouse: 1505 rue de l'Assomption, Sillery, Quebec, G1S 4T3
187 Sisters in 30 convents
Apostolic Work: Twofold: uniting contemplation with action – through prayer and by performing ordinary household tasks in rectories, bishops' residences, homes for retired priests, etc. Also in areas of parish ministries.
Represented in the Archdioceses of Boston and in the Dioceses of Fall River, Manchester and Providence. Also in Canada.
Vocation Director: Sr. Antoinette Lord, s.j.a.,1505 rue de l'Assomption, Sillery, Quebec, G1S 4T3 Canada. (418) 527-7859

SISTERS OF ST. JOHN THE BAPTIST (C.S.JB.) General House: Rome, Italy. (US Province), Provincial Residence: 3308 Campbell Dr., Bronx, NY 10465. (718) 518-7820
126 Sisters
Apostolic Work: Education, health care for aged men and women, religious education, social work and any ministry connected with the poor and abandoned especially youth.
Represented in the Archdioceses of New York and Newark and in the Diocese of Paterson. Also, missions in Zambia, India, Canada, Chile, Brazil, Argentina, the Philippines, Poland, Korea, Italy, Mexico, Moldavia, South Africa, Malawi and Madagascar.
Vocation Director: Sr. Anne Dolores, C.S.JB., 26 Landis Ave., Staten Island, NY 10305. (718) 442-6240. Web: baptistines.home.att.net

SERVANTS OF ST. JOSEPH (S.S.J.)
8 Sisters in US; 810 Sisters worldwide
Apostolic Work: Evangelization of the poor working world through: teaching, social work, missions, group homes for young working women.
Represented in the Diocese of Arlington. Also in Spain (Motherhouse), Rome (General House), Philippines, Colombia, Argentina, Peru, Chile, Zaire (Congo), Cuba, Papua and Bolivia.
Vocations: 203 N. Spring St., Falls Church, VA 22046. (703) 534-9549, 8441

SISTERS OF ST. JOSEPH OF BADEN, PA (C.S.J.) St. Joseph's Convent, 1020 State St., Baden, PA 15005. (724) 869-2151
Apostolic Work: 1 academy, 12 grade schools, preschool-early childhood education staffing in 1 high school and universities; health care; parish social service; pastoral ministry in parishes and hospitals; prisons-chaplains; religious education; social service; retreat work; communications ministry; missionary work.
Represented in the (Arch)dioceses of Altoona-Johnstown, Baltimore, Boston, Cheyenne, Covington, Detroit, Fresno, Greensburg, Harrisburg, Hartford, Memphis, Miami, New York, Pittsburgh, Richmond, Tucson, Washington (DC) and Wheeling/Charleston.
Vocation Director: Sr. Mary Pellegrino, CSJ, Visitation House, 2114 Sarah St., Pittsburgh, PA 15203. (724) 869-2151, ext. 6285. E-mail: membrcsj@usaor.net

SISTERS OF ST. JOSEPH OF BOSTON (C.S.J.) Motherhouse: 637 Cambridge St., Brighton, MA 02135
566 Sisters
Apostolic Work: Various ministries: education, health care, social services, pastoral ministry, counselling

and retreat work.
Represented in the Archdioceses of Boston and New Mexico.
Vocation Awareness Director: Sr. Mary Ann Crowley, CSJ, 637 Cambridge St., Brighton, MA 02135. (617) 746-2045. E-mail: maccsj@aol.com; Web: www.csjboston.org

SISTERS OF ST. JOSEPH OF BRENTWOOD (C.S.J.) Motherhouse and Novitiate: St. Joseph Convent, 1725 Brentwood Rd., Brentwood, NY 11717. (631) 273-4531
990 Sisters
Apostolic Work: Primary, secondary and higher education; health care, campus ministry, religious education, social service, pastoral care, special education, prison ministry, counseling, spiritual direction, retreat work, shelters for women.
Represented in the Archdiocese of New York and in the Dioceses of Brooklyn and Rockville Centre. Also in Puerto Rico, Santo Domingo and Brazil.
Vocation Director: Mary R. Walsh, CSJ, 60 Anchor Ave., Oceanside, NY 11572. (516) 536-0551. E-mail: vocationcsj@aol.com; Web: www.csjbrentwoodny.org

SISTERS OF ST. JOSEPH OF BUFFALO (S.S.J.)
Administrative Center, 23 Agassiz Circle, Buffalo, NY 14214-2611. (716) 838-4400
129 Sisters
Apostolic Work: The Sisters live out their call to be women of unity and reconciliation through a wide range of apostolic works, with special concern for the needy. They minister in the fields of education (at all levels), health care, pastoral services, retreats, spirituality and counseling.
Represented in the (Arch)dioceses of Buffalo, Cincinnati, Detroit and Pensacola-Tallahassee.
Vocation Contact: Vocation Director: 23 Agassiz Circle, Buffalo, NY 14214-2611. (716) 838-4400, ext. 15. E-mail: voc@ssjbuffalo.org; Web: www.ssjbuffalo.org

SISTERS OF ST. JOSEPH OF CARONDELET (C.S.J.)
(Congregational Center) 2311 S. Lindbergh Blvd., St. Louis, MO 63131. (314) 966-4048. E-mail: congtrcsj@attglobal.net; Web: www.csjcongregation.org

St. Louis Province: St. Joseph Provincial House, 6400 Minnesota Ave., St. Louis, MO 63111
504 Sisters, 1 Novice

St. Paul Province: St. Joseph Administration Center, 1884 Randolph Ave., St. Paul, MN 55105
379 Sisters

Albany Province: St. Joseph Provincial House, 385 Watervliet-Shaker Rd., Latham, NY 12110
521 Sisters

Los Angeles Province: Carondelet Center, 11999 Chalon Rd., Los Angeles, CA 90049
418 Sisters

Vice Province of Hawaii: Carondelet Convent, 5311 Apo Dr., Honolulu, Oahu, HI 96821-1829
31 Sisters

Vocation Contacts:
St. Louis Province: Director of Applicants, 6400 Minnesota Ave., St. Louis, MO 63111. (314) 481-8800
St. Paul Province: Director of Applicants, 1884 Randolph Ave., St. Paul, MN 55105. (612) 690-7000
Albany Province: Director of Applicants, St. Joseph's Provincial House, Latham, NY 12110. (518) 783-3500
Los Angeles Province: Director of Applicants, Carondelet Center, 11999 Chalon Rd., Los Angeles, CA 90049. (310) 889-2117
Vice Province of Hawaii: Director of Applicants, Carondelet Convent, 5311 Apo Dr., Honolulu, Oahu, HI 96821-1829. (808) 373-2096
Apostolic Work: Teaching, nursing, pastoral care, parish work, foreign missions, campus ministry, educating the deaf, social services.
Represented in 182 dioceses in the US. Also in Peru, Japan and Chile

SISTERS OF ST. JOSEPH OF CHAMBERY (C.S.J.) (US Province)
Provincial House: Convent of Mary Immaculate, 27 Park Rd., W. Hartford, CT 06119. (860) 233-5126
155 Sisters in US; 2,000 worldwide
Apostolic Work: Higher education, secondary and elementary, religious education, special education, health care, day shelter, social services, pastoral ministry, soup kitchen, day care center, prison ministry, retreat ministry, counseling, overseas missions, legal services, AIDS ministry, ministry to the elderly, hospice.
Represented in the Archdioceses of Hartford, Miami, Mobile and San Antonio and in the Dioceses of Bridgeport, El Paso, Fairbanks, Lexington, Norwich, Oakland and Springfield. Also in 10 European countries and in Africa, Asia and South America.
Vocation Director: Sr. Susan Cunningham, C.S.J., 27 Park Rd., West Hartford, CT 06119. (860) 233-5126. E-mail: suecsj@juno.com; Web: www.sistersofsaintjoseph.org

CONGREGATION OF ST. JOSEPH OF CLEVELAND (CSJ)
Motherhouse: St. Joseph Convent, 3430 Rocky River Dr., Cleveland, OH 44111-2997
200 Sisters and Associates
Ministries: Pastoral ministry, education, spiritual direction and retreat work, counseling, social work, hospital chaplaincy, nursing, systemic advocacy for justice in church and society, campus ministry, communications, deaf apostolate, Catholic bookstore, broadcasting, prayer apostolate, holistic health, direct service to those made poor, legal aid, business management, parish administration, ministry addressing environmental concerns, community organizing, organizational facilitation, and others.
Represented in the Diocese of Cleveland with Sisters serving elsewhere, including Chicago, Florida and Washington, DC.
Director of New Members: Sr. Linda Francl, CSJ, 3430 Rocky River Dr., Cleveland, OH 44111-2997. (216) 252-0440, ext. 414. Fax: (216) 941-3430. E-mail: info@csjcleveland.org; Web: www.csjcleveland.org

SISTERS OF ST. JOSEPH OF CLUNY (S.J.C.) (American Novitiate) Mary Immaculate Queen Novitiate, 20955 Halldale Ave., Torrance, CA 90501
Provincial House: Cluny Convent, 90 Brenton Rd., Newport, RI 02840. (401) 846-4757
45 Sisters in US, 3,500 worldwide
Ministry: Engaged in every corporal work of mercy on five continents, but especially concentrated in the Third World.
Represented (in the US) in the Archdiocese of Los Angeles and in the Dioceses of Providence, Little Rock and Wheeling-Charleston (WV). Also in Canada.
Vocation Director: Sister Anne Lobsinger, St. Stephen's Convent, 122 S. Ramona Ave., Monterey Park, CA 91754. (626) 573-2417. E-mail: alobsinger@hotmail.com

SISTERS OF ST. JOSEPH OF CONCORDIA (C.S.J.)
215 Court St., Box 279, Concordia, KS 66901. (785) 243-2149
200 Sisters
Apostolic Work: Making visible the love of God in our midst through communal life and all ministry efforts to live in unity and reconciliation with

God and the "the dear neighbor". The Sisters serve in health care institutions, schools, parish ministries, centers of spirituality and social justice, domestic violence shelters and prisons.

Represented in the Diocese of Salina and in many dioceses throughout the US.

Vocation Director: Sr. Anna Marie Broxterman, C.S.J., 1924 S.W. 29th Terrace, Topeka, KS 66611. (785) 234-5305. E-mail: annacsj@idir.net; Web: www.csjkansas.org

SISTERS OF ST. JOSEPH OF ERIE (S.S.J.) Motherhouse: 5031 W. Ridge Rd., Erie, PA 16506. (814) 838-4100

160 Members

Conduct: Sisters involved in various ministries: All levels of education – preschool through college; health care, social ministries, care of the elderly, poor, shelter for women, campus ministry, pastoral ministry, liturgical ministry, spiritual directors, directors of religious education, fine arts/art, writing plus others.

Represented primarily in northwestern PA, with some in Kentucky, Florida, Ohio and Washington, DC.

Vocation Director: Sister Mary Drexler, SSJ, 2531 West 8 St., Erie, PA 16505-4493. (814) 833-6250. E-mail: marydrexler@juno.com; Web: www.ssjerie.org

THE SISTERS OF ST. JOSEPH OF LAGRANGE, ILLINOIS (C.S.J.)

1515 W. Ogden Ave., LaGrange Park, IL 60526. (708) 354-9200

102 members

Sisters of St. Joseph of LaGrange are a prophetic presence in a diverse world, constantly moving toward a more profound love of God, and serving wherever the need is greatest.

Attentive to the needs of today's world, Sisters of St. Joseph use their diverse talents and gifts as women to bring the Gospel alive to all they serve. Promoting unity and reconciliation, CSJs serve as educators, parish ministers, spiritual directors, artists, musicians, social workers, chaplains and much more.

As advocates for justice, unity and reconciliation, CSJs do all that women can do individually and jointly to alleviate the conditions which cause poverty, suffering and oppression.

Sisters of St. Joseph sponsor a traveling adult literacy ministry, a coed high school, an international art and music ministry, a hermitage retreat center, and a whole life center promoting wholeness and communion with God and all creation.

Contact Information: Vocation Director: Sister Sue Torgersen, CSJ, 1021 N. Garden, #106, New Ulm, MN 56073. (507) 359-1674. E-mail: vocations@csjlagrange.org; Motherhouse/Ministry Center,1515 W. Ogden Ave., LaGrange Park, IL 60526. (708) 354-9200. Web: www.csjlagrange.org

SISTERS OF ST. JOSEPH OF NAZARETH (S.S.J.)

3427 Gull Rd., Nazareth, MI 49074. (616) 381-6290

286 Sisters

Apostolic Work: Ministries vary according to the gifts of each sister and the needs of the times and locale "wherever people lack what is needed for the fully human life that is their right".

Represented in Michigan and other parts of the US. Also two missions in Peru.

Vocation Directors: Bernadette Dean, SSJ, Marie Hogan, SSJ, Co-Directors of Membership Development, Sisters of St. Joseph, 975 E. Gardenia, Madison Heights, MI 48071-3431. (248) 582-9163. E-mail: nazvocation@aol.com; Web: www.SSJNazareth.org

SISTERS OF ST. JOSEPH OF ORANGE (C.S.J.) 480 S. Batavia St., Orange, CA 92868. (714) 633-8121

190 Sisters

Apostolic Work: Education at all levels, education network with 22 grammar schools, health system with 10 hospitals and clinics, center for spiritual development, social justice center, foreign missions, pastoral ministries, spiritual direction, campus ministry, prison ministry, social justice ministries, Hispanic ministries and ministry with the poor.

Represented in the Archdioceses of Los Angeles and San Francisco and in the Dioceses of Colorado Springs, Las Cruces, Lubbock, Oakland, Orange, San Bernardino, Santa Rosa and San Diego. Foreign missions in: Hungary, Tijuana (Mexico), El Salvador, Australia and Peru.

Director of Vocations: Sr. Cecilia Magladry, CSJ, 480 S. Batavia St., Orange, CA 92868. (714) 633-8121, ext. 7108. Fax: (714) 744-3135. E-mail: vocationcsj@csjorange.net; Web: www.sistersofstjosephorange.org

SISTERS OF ST. JOSEPH (Lyon, France) (C.S.J.) 93 Halifax St., Winslow, ME 04901. (207) 873-4512. Fax: (207) 873-1976

45 Sisters

Apostolic Work: Catechesis, holistic care, spirituality and ecology, pastoral care, education, social work, Canon law, community building.

Represented in the (Arch)dioceses of El Paso, Los Angeles, Manchester and Portland (ME). Missions in 17 countries.

Vocation Directress: Sr. Rita Bujold, c.s.j., 372 Conrad Court, El Paso, TX 79927. (915) 851-2216, 860-1827. E-mail: rbujold@earthlink.net

SISTERS OF ST. JOSEPH OF MEDAILLE (C.S.J.)

1821 Summit Rd., #210, Cincinnati, OH 45237. (513) 761-2888

210 Sisters

Apostolic Work: The Sisters strive to bring unity and reconciliation to a world in need, serving as nurses, teachers, retreat directors, missionaries, physicians, college professors, pastoral associates, social ministers, liturgists, campus ministers, etc.

Represented in the Archdioceses of Cincinnati, New Orleans and St. Paul-Minneapolis and in the Dioceses of Baton Rouge, Crookston, Covington, Fargo and Houma-Thibodaux. Also in Managua (Nicaragua, Central America).

Vocation Director: Sister Ileana Fernandez, CSJ, 5510 Moorstone Dr., Baton Rouge, LA 70820. (800) 818-0515. E-mail: ilyfercsj@aol.com; Web: www.csjmedaille.com

SISTERS OF ST. JOSEPH OF PEACE (C.S.J.P.) (St. Joseph Province) Shalom Center, 399 Hudson Terr., Englewood Cliffs, NJ 07632

130 Sisters, 56 Associates

Conduct: Alternative high school for women, transitional housing for women and children, child development center; other efforts on behalf of the poor and the powerless, retreat house and magazine office. The Sisters are involved in various areas of health, education, social service and in pastoral and religious education. The focus for all ministry is the promotion of justice as a path to peace.

Represented in the Archdioceses of Newark, Los Angeles and Washington, DC and in the Dioceses of Camden, Paterson, Trenton, Jacksonville, Metuchen, St. Petersburg and Wilmington. Also in El Salvador, England, Scotland, Wales and Ireland.

Contact: Sister Margaret Jane Kling, CSJP, Director of Ministry/Formation, Shalom Center, 399 Hudson Terr., Englewood Cliffs, NJ 07632. (201) 568-6348, ext. 13. E-mail: mjklingcsjp@aol.com; Web: www.csjp.org/sjp

CONGREGATION OF THE SISTERS OF ST. JOSEPH OF PEACE (C.S.J.P.)
(Our Lady Province) 1663 Killarney Way, PO Box 248, Bellevue, WA 98009-0248. (425) 451-1770
90 Sisters, 30 Associate Members
Apostolic Work: Education, health and hospital services, social services, religious education, parish ministry, retreat ministry, social justice and peace ministry.
Represented in the Archdioceses of Anchorage, Los Angeles, Portland, San Francisco and Seattle and in the Dioceses of Juneau, San Diego, Reno, Yakima and Spokane. Also in British Columbia (Canada) and El Salvador.
Vocation Director: Jo-Anne Miller, CSJP, 1663 Killarney Way, PO Box 248, Bellevue, WA 98009-0248. (425) 451-1770, ext. 118. E-mail: jmiller@csjp-olp.org; Web: www.csjp.org/olp

SISTERS OF ST. JOSEPH OF PHILADELPHIA (S.S.J.)
Mount Saint Joseph Convent, 9701 Germantown Ave., Philadelphia, PA 19118-2694. (215) 248-7200
1,100 Sisters
Apostolic Work: Ministry in education at all levels from preschool to university, offering daycare and after school care, special education and ministry to the hearing impaired. A variety of social, pastoral and spiritual services in parishes, institutions, and dioceses, serving the elderly, the homeless and persons with AIDS. Also participate in lobbying efforts to effect systemic change. Works include 1 college, 4 academies, 1 retreat house, 1 spirituality center, 1 welcome center, 1 hospitality house, 3 housing projects for senior citizens, and 1 healthcare/retirement facility.
Represented in the Archdioceses of Baltimore, Newark, New York, Philadelphia, Wilmington, and Washington and in the Dioceses of Albany, Allentown, Arlington, Belleville, Camden, Charlotte, Corpus Christi, Fairbanks, Harrisburg, Jackson, Jefferson City, Las Vegas, Lexington, Metuchen, Paterson, Raleigh, Rockville Center, San Antonio, Savannah, Scranton, St. Petersburg, Trenton and Venice. Also in Puerto Rico, Haiti and Peru.
Vocation Director: Sister Charlene Diorka, S.S.J., Mount Saint Joseph Convent, 9701 Germantown Ave., Philadelphia, PA 19118-2694. (215) 248-7236. E-mail: cdiorka@ssjphila.org; Web: www.ssjphila.org

SISTERS OF ST. JOSEPH OF ROCHESTER (S.S.J.)
4095 East Ave., Rochester, NY 14618-3798
350 Sisters, 107 Associate Members
Apostolic Work: Educational ministry including elementary schools, high schools, college and graduate school, religious education, school for special children and adults, pastoral ministry, numerous health care works, homes for emotionally disturbed and learning disabled children, evangelization, social service, justice and peace office, drug dependency programs, prison ministry, spirituality ministry program.
Represented in the Archdiocese of Mobile and in the Dioceses of Albany, Greensboro, Rochester and Syracuse. Missions in Brazil.
Director of Vocations: Sr. Donna Del Santo, SSJ, 150 French Rd., Rochester, NY 14618. (585) 641-8122. E-mail: vocations@ssjrochester.org: Web: ssjrochester.org

SISTERS OF ST. JOSEPH OF ST. AUGUSTINE, FLORIDA (S.S.J.)
St. Joseph's Convent, 241 St. George St., PO Box 3506, St. Augustine, FL 32085. (904) 829-3735
99 Sisters
Apostolic Work: Ministries of "unity and reconciliation" in parishes, schools, hospitals, prison, with the poor, AIDS patients, the elderly, unwed mothers and babies, persons with disabilities, retreatants and those requesting spiritual direction. Any needed ministry for which we are prepared.
Represented throughout the Dioceses of Florida.
Contact Person: Sister Elizabeth Marie, SSJ, St. Joseph Convent, 241 St. George St., PO Box 3506, St. Augustine, FL 32085. (904) 824-1752. E-mail: ssjarc@aol.com; Web: www.ssjfl.com/

SISTERS OF ST. JOSEPH OF ST. MARK (S.J.S.M.)
(Cleveland Generalate) 21800 Chardon Rd., Euclid, OH 44117
11 Sisters
Apostolic Work: Nursing, care of the aged, technicians, social service, administrative, clerical and dietetic work.
Vocation Directress: Sister M. Raphael, 21800 Chardon Rd., Euclid, OH 44117. (216) 531-7426. Fax: (216) 531-4033

SISTERS OF ST. JOSEPH OF SPRINGFIELD (S.S.J.)
Mont Marie, 34 Lower Westfield Rd., Ste. 1, Holyoke, MA 01040-2739
370 Sisters, 81 Associates
Apostolic Work: Members of the congregation are encouraged to discern individual gifts and ministries within the framework of the community goal, to live simply and to work toward alleviating unjust structures. Ministries include educational ministry in elementary schools, high schools, college; religious education, special education, pastoral ministry, health care, social services, spiritual direction, counseling, prison ministry, campus ministry, hospital chaplaincy.
Represented in the Archdioceses of Hartford and Washington, DC and in the Dioceses of Bridgeport, Fall River, Lake Charles, Maine, Providence, Rutland, Springfield (MA), Worcester and Youngstown. Also in Uganda.
Vocation Coordinator: Kathleen Imbruno, ssj, Mont Marie, 34 Lower Westfield Rd., Ste.1, Holyoke, MA 01040-2739. (413) 536-0853, ext. 249. E-mail: kimbruno@ssjspringfield.com; Web: ssjspringfield.org

SISTERS OF ST. JOSEPH OF TIPTON (C.S.J.) 1440 W. Division Rd., Tipton, IN 46072-9574. (765) 675-7599
45 Sisters
Primary Apostolic Works: Pastoral ministry, education, health care, social service, foreign mission.
Represented in the Dioceses of Lafayette, IN, Indianapolis, IN and Baker, OR. Also in Port au Prince, Haiti.
Vocation Directress: St. Joseph Center, 1440 W. Division Rd., Tipton, IN 46072-8584. (765) 675-4146, 7599 . Fax: (765) 675-7471. E-mail: csjtip@tiptontel.com; Web: www.sistersstjo-tipton.org

SISTERS OF ST. JOSEPH OF WATERTOWN (S.S.J.)
Motherhouse: 1425 Washington St., Watertown, NY 13601. (315) 788-6574
64 Members
Apostolic Work: 2 high schools, 8 grade schools, 1 conservatory of music, social service, special education, catechetical classes, tutorial work, domestic and clerical work, pastoral ministry, hospital ministry.
Represented in the (Arch)dioceses of Ogdensburg and Fairbanks.
Vocation Director: Sister Rosemary Casaleno, SSJ, St. John in the Wilderness, PO Box 260, Rte. 30, Lake Clear, NY 12945. (518) 891-2286. E-mail: srrosessj@yahoo.com; Web: home.gisco.net/users/sisssj/

SISTERS OF SAINT JOSEPH OF WHEELING (S.S.J.) 137 Mount St. Joseph Rd., Wheeling, WV 26003
109 Sisters
Apostolic Work: Diverse ministries in education, social work, pastoral care and holistic spirituality.
Represented in the Diocese of Wheeling-Charleston (WV).
Vocations Director: Sr. Judith Minear, SSJ, 137 Mount St. Joseph Rd., Wheeling, WV 26003. (304) 232-8160, ext. 129. Fax: (304) 232-1404. E-mail: judithminearssj@aol.com; Web: ssjwhg.org

SISTERS OF ST. JOSEPH OF WICHITA (C.S.J.) 3700 E. Lincoln, Wichita, KS 67218. (316) 686-7171
175 Sisters
Apostolic Work: Many and varied ministries including education at all levels - preschool through college, religious education, adult GED programs, school administration, numerous areas of health care and social services, ministry to the disabled, parish, campus, and pastoral ministry, retreat work and spiritual direction.
Represented in the Dioceses of Wichita, Dodge City, Kansas City, Oakland, Oklahoma City and Salina. Foreign mission in Japan.
Vocation Minister: Sr. Karen Salsbery, CSJ, 1412 Leavenworth St., Manhattan, KS 66502. (785) 539-7527. E-mail: ksalsbery@csjwichita, sistersofstjoseph@csjwichita.org; Web: www.csjwichita.org

SISTERS OF ST. JOSEPH OF THE THIRD ORDER OF ST. FRANCIS (SSJ-TOSF) Central Office: PO Box 305, 1300 Maria Dr., Stevens Point, WI 54481-0305. (715) 341-8457. Fax: (715) 341-8830. E-mail: vocation@ssj-tosf.org; Web: www.ssj-tosf.org
438 Sisters, 4 Temporary Professed, 3 Novices, 3 Candidates, 3 Pre-Candidates, 81 Associates
Apostolic Work: Members of the Congregation serve in a variety of ministries with the ultimate desire to promote the spiritual and material advancement of the human family including all aspects of education, parish ministry, social work, health care, diocesan services/administration, and community services.
Represented in numerous states including Arizona, California, Colorado, Connecticut, Illinois, Indiana, Michigan, Minnesota, Mississippi, Nebraska, Ohio, Pennsylvania, Tennessee and Wisconsin. Also in Brazil, Puerto Rico, South Africa and Peru.
Vocation Minister: Sr. Debra Weina, SSJ-TOSF

SISTERS OF ST. JOSEPH THE WORKER (S.J.W.)
General Motherhouse: Saint William Convent, 1 Saint Joseph Lane, Walton, KY 41094. (859) 485-4914, 4256
15 Sisters
Represented in the Dioceses of Covington and Lexington.
Vocation Director: Mother Celeste Marie, S.J.W.

CONGREGATION OF THE SISTERS OF ST. LOUIS (S.S.L.) Regional House in US: Louisville Convent, 22300 Mulholland Dr., Woodland Hills, CA 91364-4933
70 Sisters in the US
Conduct: Several grammar schools, high schools, college, parish ministry, hospital ministry, prison ministry and social services.
Represented in the Archdiocese of Los Angeles, in several other locations in California, Utah, North Carolina, Illinois and Washington, DC. Also in Ireland, England, France, Nigeria, Ghana and Brasil.
Vocation Contact: Sr. Donna Hansen, S.S.L., 22300 Mulholland Dr., Woodland Hills, CA 91364-4933. (818) 883-1678. E-mail: sslca4@worldnet.att.net

SISTERS OF ST. MARY OF NAMUR (S.S.M.N.) (Eastern Province) 241 Lafayette Ave., Buffalo, NY 14213
110 Sisters (Eastern Province), 600 worldwide
Apostolic Work: Diversified; Primary emphasis to stand with the poor and marginalized of the earth. Commitment to missions; to refugees; to women and youth.
Represented in the (Arch)dioceses of Boston, Buffalo, Charleston and Savannah. Also in Texas, Canada, Belgium, Great Britain, Africa, Brazil and the Dominican Republic.
Vocation Contact: Sister Patricia Brady, 241 Lafayette Ave., Buffalo, NY 14213. (716) 884-8221

SISTERS OF ST. MARY OF NAMUR (S.S.M.N.) (Western Province) Our Lady of Victory, 909 West Shaw St., Fort Worth, TX 76110-4057. (817) 923-8393. Fax: (817) 923-1511. E-mail: smargm@airmail.net; Web: web2.airmail.net/ssmn
56 Sisters, 82 Associates, 2 Oblates
Apostolic Work: 2 colleges, 8 elementary schools, 3 high schools, 6 social services, 1 missionary, 3 nursing, 14 pastoral ministries, 3 diocesan offices, 3 prison ministry, 1 hospice worker
Represented in the (Arch)dioceses of Dallas, Fort Worth, Galveston-Houston, Richmond and Santa Fe. Also in Brazil, Democratic Republic of the Congo and Cameroon.
Vocation Contact: Sister Margaret Miller, S.S.M.N.

SISTERS OF ST. MARY OF OREGON (S.S.M.O.) Motherhouse: St. Mary of the Valley, 4440 S.W. 148th Ave., Beaverton, OR 97007. (503) 644-9181
89 Sisters
Apostolic Work: Education: day care, kindergarten, high school, grammar schools; health care: 1 nursing home. Also parish ministry, religious education, Hispanic ministry, NRVC office (Chicago), chaplaincy.
Represented in the (Arch)dioceses of Portland (OR), Seattle, Helena and Chicago.
Vocation Director: Sister Catherine Hertel, SSMO, 4440 S.W. 148th Ave., Beaverton, OR 97007. (503) 644-9181. E-mail: srcatherineh@ssmo.org; Web: www.ssmo.org

SISTERS OF ST. PAUL OF CHARTRES (S.P.C.)
US Province: 5313 Massachusetts Ave., Bethesda, MD 20816. (301) 229-4971
General House: 193 Via della Vignaccia, Rome, 1-00163 Italy
19 Sisters in US; 4,000 worldwide
Apostolic Work: Academic and religious education, pastoral associates, ministry to the aged, hospital chaplaincy.
Represented in the Archdiocese of Washington, DC and in the Diocese of Marquette.
Vocation Contacts: Sr. Gloria Schultz, S.P.C. 5313 Massachusetts Ave., Bethesda, MD 20816. (301) 229-4971, E-mail: gjschultz123@yahoo.com; Sr. Sally Daniel, (301) 229-4971, E-mail: DanSaldc@cs.com; Sr. Kim-Phuong Nguyen, (906) 786-0292, E-mail: knguyen456@hotmail.com; Web: usaspc.org

SISTERS OF ST. PHILIP NERI MISSIONARY TEACHERS (R.F.)
Motherhouse: Apostol Santiago 74, 28017 Madrid, Spain
US: 135 Pascus Pl., Sparks, NV 89431-3340. (775) 331-0708; 2525 S.W. 9th Ave., Fort Lauderdale, FL 33315. (954) 525-3533. E-mail: sisterr@nsn.k12.nv.us
Apostolic Work: Teaching, social work, retreat houses.
Represented in the Archdiocese of Miami and in the Diocese of Reno
Vocation Director: Sr. Ofelia Roibas, R.F., 135 Pascus Pl., Sparks, NV 89431-3340. (775) 331-0708

SISTERS OF ST. RITA (O.S.A.)
Motherhouse: Wuerzburg, Germany
US: St. Rita's Convent, 4014 N. Green Bay Rd., Racine, WI 53404. (202) 639-1766; 639-5050. E-mail: srangelica@clmail.com; Web: www.sistersofstrita.org
133 Sisters worldwide
Apostolic work: Spiritual - social family care, health care, care of the aged and poor, pastoral ministry, C.C.D., education.
Represented in the Archdiocese of Milwaukee. Also in Germany and Switzerland.
Vocation Directress: Sr. Angelica Summer, O.S.A.

SOCIETY OF ST. TERESA OF JESUS (S.T.J.) Provincial House: 18080 St. Joseph's Way, Covington, LA 70435-5624. (504) 893-1470
50 Sisters in US, 1,800 worldwide
Apostolic Work: Elementary and secondary education, catechetical work, youth groups, youth retreats, prayer groups, Hispanic ministry and foreign missions.
Represented in San Antonio (TX), New Orleans (LA) and Miami (FL). Also in Mexico, Nicaragua, Colombia, Guatemala, Venezuela, Brazil, Uruguay, Costa Rica, Paraguay, Argentina, Chile, Cuba, Portugal, Spain, France, Italy, Angola, Bolivia, Ivory Coast and Philippines.
Vocation Director: Sr. Gloria Murillo, S.T.J., Teresian Sisters, 1007 Airline Park, Metairie, LA 70003. (504) 214-3437. E-mail: gloriamstj@aol.com or teresians@aol.com; Web: www.teresians.org

CONGREGATION OF SISTERS OF ST. THOMAS OF VILLANOVA (S.S.T.V.) 76 West Rocks Rd., Norwalk, CT 06851
4 Sisters in US; 330 worldwide
Conduct: 1 convalescent home.
Represented in the Diocese of Bridgeport.
Contact: Sister Marie Lucie Monast, S.S.T.V., 76 West Rocks Rd., Norwalk, CT 06851. (203) 847-2885. Fax: (203) 847-3740. E-mail: vocationdirectorsstv@juno.com

SISTERS OF ST. URSULA (S.U.)
Motherhouse: Linwood Regional Center, Rhinebeck, NY 12572. (914) 876-2341
34 Sisters
Apostolic Work: Teaching, religious education, retreats, African missions, ministry to aged, social work, parish ministry, campus ministry, nursing, financial and secretarial service.
Represented in the Archdioceses of New York and Washington, DC and in the Dioceses of Providence and Raleigh. Also in France and the Democratic Republic of the Congo.
Director of Formation: Sr. Maureen Steeley, Linwood Regional Center, 50 Linwood Rd., Rhinebeck, NY 12572. (845) 876-2341. E-mail: mfslin@ulster.net; Web: sistersofstursula.com

SALESIAN MONASTIC COMMUNITY (SMC) Salesian Monastery, HC #1, Box 455, Frantz Rd., Brodheadsville, PA 18322-9630. (570) 992-3448 (abbot), (570) 992-0230 (monastery). E-mail: monk@epix.net; Web: www.gentlestrength.org
2 Solemnly Professed Monks, 1 Solemnly Professed Nun
Apostolic Work: Monastic life, Liturgy of the Hours, use of any gift/talent compatible with monastic life, i.e., retreats, pastoral care, nursing and manual labor.
Represented in the Diocese of Scranton.
Abbot: Brother Bernard Seif, SMC

SALESIAN SISTERS OF ST. JOHN BOSCO (FMA) (Daughters of Mary Help of Christians)
Eastern Province: 655 Belmont Ave., Haledon, NJ 07508. (973) 790-4408
250 Sisters in the US; 15,000 worldwide
Apostolic Work: We, Salesian Sisters of St. John Bosco, are an international congregation of more than 15,000 Sisters ministering *to*, and *with*, youth in 89 countries around the world. A deep prayer life, a strong community life and a youth-centered ministry give us the strength and energy we need to face the challenges of daily life. Our ministry is one: reaching out to the young through formal education, youth groups, catechesis, youth centers, summer camps, retreat centers and missionary work.
We walk with the young - making a difference in the world!
Represented in the Archdioceses of Los Angeles, Miami, Newark, New York, New Orleans, San Antonio and San Francisco and in the Dioceses of Austin, Corpus Christi, Monterey, Paterson, Phoenix and St. Petersburg.
Vocations Director Contact: Sr. Antoinette Cedrone, FMA, 655 Belmont Ave., Haledon, NJ 07508. (973) 790-4408. E-mail: fmavoc@aol.com; www.salesiansisters.org

SALESIAN SISTERS OF ST. JOHN BOSCO (F.M.A.) (Daughters of Mary Help of Christians)
(Western Province) 6019 Buena Vista St., San Antonio, TX 78237. (210) 432-0090
250 Sisters in the US; 15,000 worldwide
Apostolic Work: We, Salesian Sisters of St. John Bosco, are an international congregation of more than 15,000 Sisters ministering *to*, and *with*, youth in 89 countries around the world. A deep prayer life, a strong community life and a youth-centered ministry give us the strength and energy we need to face the challenges of daily life. Our ministry is one: reaching out to the young through formal education, youth groups, catechesis, youth centers, summer camps, retreat centers and missionary work.
We walk with the young - making a difference in the world!
Represented in the Archdioceses of Los Angeles, Miami, Newark, New York, New Orleans, San Antonio and San Francisco and in the Dioceses of Austin, Corpus Christi, Monterey, Paterson, Phoenix and St. Petersburg.
Vocations Director Contact: Sr. Carmen Botello, FMA, 9758 Foster Rd., Bellflower, CA 90706. (562) 866-0675. E-mail: fmasuovoc@aol.com; Web: wwwsalesiansisterswest.org

SALVATORIANS
(Sisters of the Divine Savior) (S.D.S.)
4311 N. 100 St., Milwaukee, WI 53222-1393. (414) 466-0810
125 Sisters in US, 1, 200 Sisters worldwide
The Salvatorians are an international religious community of sisters, priests, brothers and laity. We were founded by Fr. Francis Jordan and Blessed Mary of the Apostles in Rome in the 1880's. Our mission is to make Jesus, our Savior, known so that all may experience the fullness of life. Our apostolic works include parish ministry, social work, nursing, teaching, art, secretarial, law, and retreat ministry - wherever there is a need.
Come and See weekends are scheduled for those interested, and visits can be arranged any time. Preferred age is 19-45, with the equivalency of a high-school education.
Represented in the (Arch)dioceses of Birmingham, AL; Phoenix, Tucson, AZ: Monterey, CA; Nashville, TN; Green Bay, La Crosse, Madison, and Milwaukee, WI. Also in 27 countries worldwide.
Vocation Directress: Sister Mary Frost, S.D.S., 4311 N. 100th St., Milwaukee, WI 53222-1393. (414) 466-0810. E-mail: sistermary@salvatorian sisters.org; Web: SDSsisters.org

SCALABRINIANS
See Missionary Sisters of St. Charles Borromeo

SERVANTS OF GOD'S LOVE (S.G.L.)
4399 Ford Rd., Ann Arbor, MI 48105
16 Sisters, 1 Novice, 3 Postulants
Apostolic Work: foster care home for medically fragile babies, 2 homes for the elderly (Emmanuel Houses), teaching, nursing, campus ministry, evangelization.
Represented in the Diocese of Lansing.
Vocation Director: Sr. Mary Ann Foggin, SGL, 4399 Ford Rd., Ann Arbor, MI 48105. (734) 663-6128 (tel., fax). E-mail: mafoggin@renewalministries.net

SERVANTS OF THE HOLY HEART OF MARY (S.S.C.M.)
15 Elmwood Dr., Kankakee, IL 60901-3631
60 Sisters in US, 750 Sisters worldwide
Apostolic Work: Health care, education, pastoral ministry in hospitals, parishes and campuses as well as CCD ministries, counseling and opportunities to use business expertise in a human service system.
Represented in the Dioceses of Joliet, Rockford and Peoria and in the Archdiocese of Chicago.
Vocation Directress: Sister Myra Lambert, S.S.C.M., 717 N. Batavia Ave., Batavia, IL 60510. (630) 879-1296. E-mail: lam-bert@inil.com

SERVANTS OF THE IMMACULATE HEART OF MARY (S.C.I.M.) (also known as Good Shepherd Sisters)
Provincial Residence: 313 Seaside Ave., Saco, ME 04072
98 Sisters in US
Apostolic Work: Social work: group homes for mother/child and unwed mothers, adoption agency; education: parish and public schools; pastoral work and other special ministries; and foreign missions in South Africa, Brazil, Canada, Haiti, Lesotho and Rwanda.
Represented in the Archdiocese of Boston and in the Diocese of Portland, ME.
Vocation Contact: Sister Elaine Lachance, s.c.i.m., Director of Vocation Ministry, SCIM Vocation Office,187 Bay View Rd., Saco, ME 04072. (207) 283-3636. E-mail: elachance@gwi.net

SERVANTS OF JESUS (S.J.)
2600 Harvard Rd., Berkley, MI 48072-1578
24 Sisters
Represented in the Archdiocese of Detroit and in the Dioceses of Gaylord, Grand Rapids and Saginaw.
Vocation Contact: Sr. Barbara Celeskey, SJ, 2600 Harvard Rd., Berkley, MI 48072-1578. (248) 548-6337. Fax: (248) 541-4250

SERVANTS OF THE LORD AND THE VIRGIN OF MATARA (S.S.V.M.)
Province of the Immaculate Conception (US, Canada), 28 15th St., SE, Washington, DC 20003. (202) 543-1299, 1179. Fax: (202) 543-1677. E-mail: ssvmusaprovince@aol.com; Web: www.iveamerica.org
50 Sisters, 2 Novices, 5 Postulants
Apostolic Works: Parish work, education, missions, works of charity (orphanages, homes for the elderly, handicapped children, etc.) Charism: evangelization of the culture.
Represented in the Archdioceses of New York, Philadelphia and Washington, DC and in the Diocese of Brooklyn.
Vocation Director: Mother Mary of Charity Asensio, SSVM, Blessed Kateri Tekakwitha Novitiate, 12008 Marvel Lane, Bowie, MD 20715. (301) 809-0046. E-mail: caridusa@aol.com

SERVANTS OF MARY (O.S.M.) (Servite Sisters) 1000 College Ave. West, Ladysmith, WI 54848. (715) 532-3364
80 Sisters; (1 Hermit); 47 Associates
Apostolic Work: Worship, education, healing, social service and justice, i.e. all stages of education, health care, pastoral work, community organizing, law, counseling, and ministry to youth, elderly, unwed mothers, mentally and physically handicapped, minorities.
Represented in Arizona, California, Florida, Illinois, Kentucky, Massachusetts, Minnesota, Wisconsin.
Vocation Contact: Sr. Bonnie Alho, OSM, 334 N. Wilson Ave., Rice Lake, WI 54868. (715) 234-2032 (w), (715) 234-4732 (h). E-mail: balho@discover-net.net; Web: www.servitesisters.org

SERVANTS OF MARY (O.S.M.) (Servites) US Province: Our Lady of Sorrows, 7400 Military Ave., Omaha, NE 68134-3351
110 Sisters
Apostolic Work: Teaching, nursing, pastoral ministry, campus ministry, hospital chaplaincy, counseling, marriage tribunal, social work, religious ed, liturgy, spiritual renewal, St. Peregrine ministry to cancer and AIDS patients. Missions: Jamaica, West Indies, Kentucky and Zaire.
Represented in the (Arch)dioceses of Omaha and Grand Island, NE; Des Moines, Iowa; Tucson, AR; Denver and Pueblo, CO, Covington, KY; Detroit, MI; Ogdensburg, NY; Paterson, NJ; and Portland, OR. Also in France, England, Belgium, Austria, Canada and Zaire.
Minister of Membership: Sr. Ann Marie Petrylka, OSM, 7400 Military Ave., Omaha, NE 68134-3351. (402) 571-2547. Fax: (402) 571-4422. E-mail: sam@marian.creighton.edu; Web: www.osms.org

SERVANTS OF MARY (M.S.M.) (Mantellate Sisters) Provincialate: Mother of Sorrows Convent, 13811 S. Western Ave., Blue Island, IL 60406. (708) 385-2103
19 Sisters
Apostolic Work: Teaching: elementary, kindergarten, C.C.D., foreign mission in South Africa.
Represented in the Archdiocese of Chicago.
Vocation Director: Sr. Maria Teresa Musto, M.S.M., Mother of Sorrows Convent, 13811 S. Western Ave., Blue Island, IL 60406. (708) 532-2241. E-mail: srmaria@prodigy.net; Web: www.mantellatesistersmsm.org

SERVANTS OF MARY (O.S.M.) (Mantellate Sisters) Marian Lake Convent, 16949 S. Drauden Rd., Plainfield, IL 60544. (815) 436-5796. Fax: (815) 436-7486. E-mail: smaosm@aol.com
8 Sisters
Apostolic Work: Pastoral ministry, retreat work, counseling, St. Peregrine ministry.
Represented in the Diocese of Joliet in Illinois.
Vocation Director: Sr. Gesuina Bongiorno, O.S.M., Marian Lake Convent, 16949 S. Drauden Rd., Plainfield, IL 60544. (815) 436-5796. Fax: (815) 436-7486. E-mail: smaosm129@aol.com, Web: www.mantellatesistersms.org

SERVANTS OF THE MOST SACRED HEART OF JESUS (S.S.C.J.)
United States Province: 866 Cambria St., Cresson, PA 16630-1713
33 Sisters, 4 Novices, 2 Postulants in US; 700 Sisters worldwide
Apostolic Work: Teaching, nursing, parish work, mission, social service.
Represented in the Archdiocese of Philadelphia and in the Dioceses of Altoona-Johnstown and Metuchen.
Vocation Director: Sister Amabilis, S.S.C.J., 866 Cambria St., Cresson, PA 16630-1713. (814) 886-4223. E-mail: sscjusa@nb.net; Web: www.nb.net/~sscjusa

SERVANTS OF THE SACRED HEART OF JESUS AND OF THE POOR (S.S.H.J.P.) US Regional House: Sacred Heart Children's Home Convent, 3310 S. Zapata Hwy., Laredo, TX 78046

46 Sisters in US; 600 Sisters worldwide

Apostolic Work: Education/religious education - all levels, Children's Home.

Conduct: Elementary schools, high schools, colleges, boarding schools, children's homes, hospitals, nursing homes, dispensaries, mobile clinics.

Represented in the Dioceses of Corpus Christi, El Paso and Laredo. Also in Chile, Colombia, Guatemala, Italy, Kenya (E. Africa), Mexico, Nicaragua, Tanzania and Venezuela.

Vocation Contact: Sr. Aurora Teresa Navarro, S.S.H.J.P., Regional Superior, Sacred Heart Children's Home Convent, 3310 S. Zapata Hwy., Laredo, TX 78046. (956) 723-3343. Fax: (956) 723-3409

SISTERS ADORERS OF THE PRECIOUS BLOOD (A.P.B.)

See "A" Section

CONGREGATION, SERVANTS OF CHRIST THE KING (S.S.C.K.)

Villa Loretto, N8114 Calvary St., Mt. Calvary, WI 53057

8 Sisters

Conduct: Nursing homes, residential home, Cristo Rey Ranch (weekend respite care for children).

Represented in the Archdiocese of Milwaukee and in the Diocese of Fargo.

Vocation Director: Sr. Michael, S.S.C.K., Villa Loretto, N8114 Calvary St., Mt. Calvary, WI 53057. (920) 753-3211. Fax: (920) 753-3100. E-mail: sisterss@netscape.net

SISTERS, SERVANTS OF THE IMMACULATE HEART OF MARY (I.H.M.)1140 King Rd., P.O. Box 200, Immaculata, PA 19345-0200

1,200 Sisters

Apostolic Work: 1 university, 3 academies, 100 parish schools, Also co-staff 35 high schools, 1 Montessori school, 1 visually impaired.

Represented in the (Arch)dioceses of Allentown, Arlington, Atlanta, Camden, Harrisburg, Hartford, Metuchen, Miami, Philadelphia and Savannah. Also Lawrence (MA) and in two countries in South America.

Vocation Directress: Sister Carmen Teresa Fernandez, IHM, Villa Maria House of Studies, 1140 King Rd., P.O. Box 200, Immaculata, PA 19345-0200. (610) 647-2160. Fax: (610) 889-4874. E-mail: ihmvoc@aol.com; Web: www.ihmimmaculata.org

SISTERS, SERVANTS OF THE IMMACULATE HEART OF MARY (IHM) IHM Center, 2300 Adams Ave., Scranton, PA 18509

574 Sisters, 1 Novice, 1 Candidate

Apostolic Work: Education, health care, social service and various spiritual and pastoral ministries including 4 colleges, 2 universities, 3 campus ministry settings, 21 secondary schools, 48 elementary schools, 1 Montessori school, 1 educational enrichment center, 20 religious educational settings, 39 parish ministry settings, 1 spiritual renewal center, 3 retreat conference centers, 1 hospital, 1 peace site, multiple sites for direct service to the poor and marginalized, intermediate care centers for mentally and physically handicapped children/adults, maternity and adoption services and 2 Hispanic outreach settings.

Represented in 36 (Arch)dioceses including Baltimore, Bridgeport, Brooklyn, Jackson (MS), New York, Philadelphia, Pittsburgh, Raleigh, Rockville Centre, St. Augustine, St. Petersburg, Scranton, Syracuse, Trenton, Washington, Wheeling-Charleston and Wilmington. Also in Peru and Guatamala.

Director of Vocations: Sister Ruth Anne Harkins, IHM, IHM Center, 2300 Adams Ave., Scranton, PA 18509. (570) 346-5413. E-mail: harkir@sistersofihm.org; Web: http://ihm.marywood.edu

SISTERS, SERVANTS OF THE IMMACULATE HEART OF MARY (I.H.M.) General Motherhouse: 610 W. Elm, Monroe, MI 48162. (734) 241-3660

591 Sisters, 100 Associates

Apostolic Work: Furthering God's reign in our world through education (all levels/forms); pastoral ministry; religious education; retreat/spiritual direction ministry; health care; pastoral care of the sick and elderly; social work; counseling; prison ministry; societal ministry; action for justice/peace.

Represented in 60 Dioceses in the US and in 11 Dioceses outside of the US including Puerto Rico, Honduras, Brazil, Ontario, South Africa and Mexico.

Vocation Director: Membership Coordinator, Sisters, Servants of the Immaculate Heart of Mary, 610 W. Elm, Monroe, MI 48162-7908. (734) 240-9821. E-mail: membership@ihmsisters.org; Web: www.ihmsisters.org

SISTERS, SERVANTS OF MARY (S.M.) (Ministers to the Sick)

(US Province) Provincial House: 800 N. 18th St., Kansas City, KS 66102

260 Sisters in US; 2,000 worldwide

Apostolic Work: Nursing-private and visiting nursing in patients' homes and hospitals.

Represented in the Archdioceses of Kansas City, Los Angeles, New Orleans and New York and in France, Spain, England, Italy, Portugal, U.R. of Cameroon, Mexico, Columbia, Ecuador, Brazil, Argentina, Bolivia, Cuba, Dominican Republic, Puerto Rico, Belgium, Panama, Peru, the Philippines and Uruguay.

Vocation Director: Sister Susana Orozco, S.M., 3305 Country Club Rd., Bronx, NY 10465-1296. (718) 829-0428. Fax: (718) 829-2346

SISTERS SERVANTS OF MARY IMMACULATE (S.S.M.I.)

See Eastern Catholic Religious Communities for Women

SISTERS, SERVANTS OF MARY IMMACULATE (S.S.M.I.)

(Provincialate and Novitiate) 1220 Tugwell Drive, Catonsville, MD 21228

32 Sisters in American Province; 900 worldwide

Apostolic Work: Primarily pre-school care of children, health care and social and charitable ministry to the aged.

Represented in the Dioceses of Baltimore, Cleveland and Washington, DC. General Motherhouse in Poland. Also in Rome, Africa and Lithuania.

Vocation Director: Sister Ce Ann Sambor, S.S.M.I., 285 Panorama Dr., Seven Hills, OH 44131. (216) 441-5402

SERVITES

See Servants of Mary

SISTERS OF OUR LADY OF MERCY (MERCEDARIAN SISTERS)

See "O" section - Sisters of Our Lady of Mercy

SISTERS OF THE SICK POOR OF LOS ANGELES (S.S.P.)

1124 W. Adams Blvd., Los Angeles, CA 90007. (213) 200-2377; 3570 Brenton Ave., #E, Lynwood, CA 90262. (310) 603-1764. E-mail: salveregina@prodigy.net

3 Sisters

Apostolic Work: Ministry to the sick poor in any area of need. A multicultural community; inquiries welcomed from women age 21 and older, including women with disabilities.

Represented in the Archdiocese of

Los Angeles.
Vocation Contact: Sister Ellie Alcala, SSP, Vicar Sister Servant

SISTERS OF SOCIAL SERVICE (S.S.S.)
US Residence: 296 Summit Ave., Buffalo, NY 14214
No institutions by Constitution (Members are free to work for Church-related and secular agencies.)
17 Sisters in US
Apostolic Work: (All forms of) social work with individuals, groups and communities; health ministry, inner-city work; parish ministry; retreat work; religious education; youth ministry, political ministry and education for social justice; Spanish apostolate.
Represented in the (Arch)dioceses of Buffalo, Miami, Washington and Ponce P.R. Also in Cuba, Hungary, Rumania and Slovakia.
Vocation Director: Sr. Anna Szabados, SSS, 1022 Delaware Ave., Buffalo, NY 14209. (716) 884-0331. E-mail: annas@bluefrog.com

SISTERS OF SOCIAL SERVICE (S.S.S.)
2303 S. Figueroa Way, Los Angeles, CA 90007-2504. (213) 746-2117
115 Sisters
Apostolic Work: Primarily social workers: pastoral ministry and social work in parish settings, neighborhood centers in low-income communities, drop-in center for homeless teens, foster care, parent education for inner-city mothers, therapeutic counseling, lobby for social justice at the legislative level, summer camps for inner-city children, retreat center. Similar programs at international locations.
Represented in the Archdioceses of Los Angeles, San Francisco, Portland (OR) and Seattle and in the Dioceses of Oakland, Sacramento and San Diego. Also in Mexico, the Philippines and Taiwan.
Vocation Team: Sr. Martha Vega, S.S.S., Vocation Director, 303 S. Figueroa Way, Los Angeles, CA 90007-2504. (213) 746-2117. E-mail: Mvegasss@aol.com; Web: sistersofsocialservice.com/home.html

SISTERS OF THE SOCIETY DEVOTED TO THE SACRED HEART (S.D.S.H.)
Motherhouse: 9814 Sylvia Ave., Northridge, CA 91324
50 Sisters
Ministries: The Sisters are primarily involved in teaching the truths of the faith with their unique teaching method and in making the Father and His love known. They are sent to joyfully proclaim the Good News of Jesus in religious education, family retreats, catechetical/sacramental retreats for children, youth retreats, catechist formation, worldwide video catechesis, girls' summer camps and in music. The Holy Father appointed the Sisters as members of the International Council for Catechetics.
Represented in the Archdioceses of Los Angeles and St. Louis and in the Dioceses of San Bernardino and Orange. Foreign mission areas: Taipei, Taiwan, R.O.C., Budapest, Hungary.
Vocation Director: Sister Jane Stafford, S.D.S.H., 9814 Sylvia Ave., Northridge, CA 91324. (818) 772-9961. Fax: (818) 772-2742. Web: www.sacredheartsisters.com and www.SDSH.org

SOCIETY OF HELPERS (S.H.)
Provincialate: Helper House, 3206 So. Aberdeen, Chicago, IL 60608. (773) 523-8638
900 Sisters worldwide, 38 Sisters in US
The Helpers, an international society, are engaged in the pastoral work of the Church, especially with those who are suffering in any way.
Represented in the Archdioceses of New York, Chicago, St. Louis and San Francisco. Also in Europe, Asia, Africa and Latin America.
Contact: Vocation Director, 2043 N. Humboldt Blvd., Chicago, IL 60647. (773) 384-7707. Fax: (773) 278-6629. E-mail: jeanMK@aol.com; Web: www.helpers.org

SOCIETY OF THE HOLY CHILD JESUS
See "H" - Holy Child of Jesus

SOCIETY OF OUR MOTHER OF PEACE (SMP) Mary the Font Solitude, 6150 Antire Rd., High Ridge, MO 63049. (636) 677-3235. Fax: (636) 677-0644
19 Sisters in the US
Apostolic Work: Contemplative-apostolic balance of life in the context of simplicity and poverty; emphasis on solitary prayer; apostolates of retreat work and spiritual direction; direct evangelization especially within the African-American community and among the poor.
Represented in the Archdiocese of St. Louis and in the Diocese of Springfield-Cape Girardeau. Also in the Philippines.
Vocation Director: Sister Mary Faith, SMP, Queen of Heaven Solitude, 12494 Highway T, Marionville, MO 65705. (417) 744-2011. Web: www.cmswr.org/MemberCommunities/SMP.htm

SOCIETY OF OUR LADY OF THE MOST HOLY TRINITY (S.O.L.T.)
Motherhouse: Immaculate Conception Convent, PO Box 189, Skidmore, TX 78389. (361) 287-3570. Web: www.solt3.org
74 Professed Sisters, 13 Novices, 8 Postulants
Apostolic Work: Serving the neediest of the needy - taking them to to be in Communion with the Most Holy Trinity through Mary.
Represented in the (Arch)dioceses of Corpus Christi, Fargo, Kansas City, San Juan and Santa Fe. Foreign mission in Belize, Guatemala, Honduras, Mexico, Haiti, England, Italy, Thailand, Philippines, Macau (Chaina) and Papua New Guinea.
Vocation Servant: Sr. Mary Emmanuel Schmidt, SOLT. E-mail: smemmanuel@catholicexchange.org

SISTERS OF THE SORROWFUL MOTHER (Third Order Regular of St. Francis of Assisi) (SSM)
Our Lady of Sorrows Convent, 17600 East 51st St., Broken Arrow, OK 74012. (918) 355-5581
400 Sisters Internationally
Ministries: Teaching and healing the unserved through literacy and advocacy programs, retreat ministry, education, Native American and Hispanic ministry, nursing, art therapy, administration, hospice, accounting, social work, counseling, outreach clinics, clerical work, archives, patient advocacy, House of Discernment, hospital chaplain.
Represented in the (Arch)dioceses of Galveston-Houston, Green Bay, La Crosse, Las Cruces, Los Angeles, Milwaukee, Paterson, Superior, Tulsa, Wichita and Winona. In the Caribbean: Castries, St. Lucia; St. George, Grenada; Santiago, Dominican Republic; Port of Spain, Trinidad. Also minister in Austria, Brazil, Germany and Italy.
Vocation Counselor: Sister Theresa Gil, SSM, Our Lady of Sorrows Convent, 17600 East 51st St., Broken Arrow, OK 74012. (918) 355-5581. E-mail: ssmvoc@aol.com; Web: www.ssmfranciscans.org

COMMUNITY OF TERESIAN CARMELITES (C.T.C.)
See "C" section - Community of Teresian Carmelites

TRAPPISTINES (O.C.S.O.) (Cistercian Nuns of the Strict Observance) Santa Rita Abbey, HC1 Box 929, Sonoita, AZ 85637-9705
13 Sisters
Represented in the Diocese of

Tuscon.
Vocation Director: Sr. Victoria Murray, O.C.S.O., Santa Rita Abbey, HC1 Box 929, Sonoita, AZ 85637-9705. (520) 455-5595. Fax: (520) 455-5770. E-mail: sracommty@dakota com.net, Web: www.santaritabbey .org

TRAPPISTINES (O.C.S.O.) (Cistercian Nuns of the Strict Observance) Redwoods Monastery, 18104 Briceland Thorn Rd., Whitethorn, CA 95589. (707) 986-7419. Web: www.redwoodsabbey.org
9 Sisters
Represented in the Diocese of Santa Rosa.
Contact Person: Sr. Kathy DeVico, OCSO

TRAPPISTINES (O.C.S.O.) (Cistercian Nuns of the Strict Observance) Our Lady of the Mississippi Abbey, 8400 Abbey Hill, Dubuque, IA 52003
23 Sisters, 2 Junior Professed, 1 Novice
Contemplative monastic community
Represented in the Archdiocese of Dubuque.
Vocational Contact: Sr. Rebecca Stramoski, O.C.S.O., Our Lady of the Mississippi Abbey, 8400 Abbey Hill, Dubuque, IA 52003. (563) 582-2595. E-mail: vocations@mississippi abbey.org; Web: www.mississippi abbey.org

TRAPPISTINES (O.C.S.O.) (Cistercian Nuns of the Strict Observance) Mount Saint Mary's Abbey, 300 Arnold St., Wrentham, MA 02093-1799. (508) 528-1282. E-mail: sisters@msmabbey.org; Web: www.msmabbey.org
Contemplative Monastic Order
48 Sisters, 3 Junior Professed, 1 Novice, 3 Postulants, 1 Observer
Represented in the Archdiocese of Boston.
Vocational Contact: Sr. Evelyn McGarry, O.C.S.O. E-mail: evmc garry@juno.com

TRAPPISTINES (O.C.S.O.) (Cistercian Nuns of the Strict Observance) Monastery of Our Lady of the Angels, 3365 Monastery Dr., Crozet, VA 22932
9 Professed, 1 Novice
Apostolic Work: Contemplative monastic.
Represented in the Diocese of Richmond.
Vocations: Sister Claire Boudreau, O.C.S.O., Vocation Director, Monastery of Our Lady of the Angels, 3365 Monastery Dr., Crozet, VA 22932. (434) 823-1452. E-mail: vocations@ olamonastery.org; Web: www.ola monastery.org

TRINITY MISSIONS (M.S.B.T.) (Missionary Servants of the Most Blessed Trinity)
See "M" section - Missionary Servants of the Most Blessed Trinity

URSULINE SISTERS (O.S.U.)
(Roman Union) (Western Province) 639 Angela Dr., Santa Rosa, CA 95403-1793. (707) 528-8578
42 Sisters
Apostolic Work: Spiritual development through education: pre-school, elementary and secondary; parish ministries, retreat and conference centers; spiritual assistance for women and children, the poor, the elderly, spiritual direction.
Represented in the Archdioceses of Anchorage, Los Angeles and San Francisco and in the Dioceses of Fairbanks, Santa Rosa, Great Falls/ Billings, Juneau and San Jose.
Vocation Coordinator: Sr. Dianne Baumunk, OSU, 8730 Mill Creek Rd., Healdsburg, CA 95448. (707) 433-3136

URSULINE SISTERS OF BELLEVILLE (O.S.U.). 1026 N. Douglas Ave., Belleville, IL 62220. (618) 235-3444
15 Professed Sisters
Ministries: Elementary schools, parish ministry, retreat work, Director of Religious Education, ministry to home-bound, community service, spiritual direction, nursing, hospice.
Represented in the Diocese of Belleville.
Vocation Director: Sr. Rita Winkelmann, osu, 1026 N. Douglas Ave., Belleville, IL 62220. (618) 234-3326, 233-5010. E-mail: osubell@juno .com; Web: www.diobelle.org/reli gious_life/womenreligious/osu1.html

URSULINE SISTERS (O.S.U.) (Congregation of Paris)
Convent of Our Lady of Lourdes, 901 E. Miami St., Paola, KS 66071
30 Sisters
Apostolic Work: Elementary and secondary education, adult education and campus ministry, parish ministry, retreat work.
Represented in the Archdiocese of Kansas City (KS) and in the Diocese of Sacramento.
Contact: Sr. Pat Lynch, OSU, Convent of Our Lady of Lourdes, 901 E. Miami St., Paola, KS 66071. (913) 557-2349. E-mail: patosu@paola ursuline.org; Web: www.paola ursuline.org

URSULINE SISTERS (O.S.U.) (Congregation of Paris)
3105 Lexington Rd., Louisville, KY 40206
164 Sisters, 2 Temporary Professed, 1 Novice
Apostolic Work: Teachers and administrators in Montessori pre-school, elementary schools, secondary schools, colleges and adult and religious education, music and musical drama education, special education, among Hispanics, administrators of health and social services. Also in pastoral ministry, deaf ministry, retreat ministry and spiritual direction, ministry to the sick and elderly. Foreign mission in Peru.
Represented in the Archdioceses of Louisville, Indianapolis, Baltimore, Cincinnati, Philadelphia and San Francisco and in the Dioceses of Charleston, Covington, Davenport, Pittsburgh, Grand Island, Jackson, Lexington, Wheeling-Charleston, Callao and Cajamarca, Peru.
Vocation Director: Sister Merry Marcotte, O.S.U., 3105 Lexington Rd., Louisville, KY 40206. (502) 896-3948. E-mail: mmarcotte@ursulines lou.org; Web: www.ursulineslou.org (Vocation contact for South Carolina only: Sister Julienne Guy, O.S.U., (803) 738-1294. E-mail: julie.guyosu @juno.com)

URSULINE SISTERS OF MOUNT SAINT JOSEPH (O.S.U.) (Congregation of Paris) Mount Saint Joseph, 8001 Cummings Rd., Maple Mount, KY 42356. (270) 229-4103
190 Sisters
Apostolic Work: Through a ministry of education and Christian formation, commitment is to simplicity, hospitality, justice and service.
Represented in the Archdioceses of Boston, Louisville, Santa Fe and Washington, DC and in the Dioceses of Gallup, Gary, Kansas City-St. Joseph, Lincoln, Memphis, Owensboro, Shreveport and Springfield-Cape Girardeau. Also in Chillan, Chile.
Director of Vocation Ministry: Sr. Pam Mueller, Mount Saint Joseph, 8001 Cummings Rd., Maple Mount, KY 42356. (270) 229-4103, ext. 448. E-mail: vocations@maplemount.org; Web: www.ursulinesmsj.org

URSULINE NUNS (O.S.U.)
(Roman Union) (Northeastern Province) 45 Lowder St., Dedham, MA 02026-4200
41 Sisters
Apostolic Work: 1 high school, 1 elementary school.
Represented in the Archdiocese of

Boston and in the Diocese of Portland (ME).
Vocation Contact: Sr. Angela Krippendorf, o.s.u., Provincial, 45 Lowder St., Dedham, MA 02026-4200. (781) 326-6219. E-mail: provosu@juno.com

URSULINE SISTERS (O.S.U.)
(Roman Union, Central Province) Ursuline Provincialate, 210 Glennon Heights Rd., Crystal City, MO 63019. (636) 937-6206
164 Sisters
Apostolic Work: Education for evangelization in schools, parishes, diocesan offices, ministry to the poor, foreign mission, retreat work, counseling, pastoral care in hospitals, social work.
Represented in the (Arch)dioceses of Minneapolis-St. Paul, St. Louis, Springfield (IL), Springfield-Cape Girardeau, Dallas, San Antonio, Corpus Christi, Galveston-Houston, New Orleans, Cincinnati, Brownsville and Juneau. Also in Europe, Asia, Africa, Latin America, the Caribbean, Australia and the Middle East.
Director of Vocation Ministries: Sr. Susan Kienzler, OSU, PO Box 8, Cape Girardeau, MO 63702-0008. (573) 332-1804. E-mail: srsusan@osucentral.org; Web: www.osucentral.org

URSULINE SISTERS (O.S.U.)
(Roman Union) (Eastern Province of the U.S.), 323 E. 198th St., Bronx, NY 10458. (718) 365-7410
175 Sisters, 1 Temporary Professed
Apostolic Work: Education: primary, secondary, college, graduate levels; catechetics, pastoral ministry, social services, health-related services and retreat ministry.
Represented in the Archdioceses of New York and Washington and in the Dioceses of Ogdensburg, Orlando and Wilmington and in New Jersey and North Carolina. Three other US provinces have central offices in Archdioceses of Boston, St. Louis and San Francisco. Missions in Europe, Asia, Africa and Latin America.
Vocation Director: Sr. Pat Schifini, O.S.U., 323 E. 198th St., Bronx, NY 10458. (718) 365-7410. E-mail: patsosu@aol.com

URSULINE SISTERS OF TILDONK (O.S.U.) Provincialate: 81-15 Utopia Pkwy., Jamaica, NY 11432. (718) 591-0681
60 Sisters in the US
Apostolic Work: Grammar schools, retreat house at St. Ursula Center, Blue Point, NY, pastoral ministry, religious education, hospital chaplaincy, social work, spirituality.
Represented in the Archdioceses of New York and Hartford and in the Dioceses of Bridgeport, Brooklyn, Rockville Centre, Burlington and Cleveland. Provinces in Belgium, Canada and India. District in Democratic Republic of the Congo, Africa.
Provincial: Sister Catherine Talia, O.S.U., 81-15 Utopia Pkwy., Jamaica, NY 11432. (718) 591-0681. Web: members.tripod.com/~tressy

URSULINES OF CINCINNATI (O.S.U.) (Congregation of Paris)
St. Ursula Convent, 1339 E. McMillan St., Cincinnati, OH 45206. (513) 961-3410
21 Sisters
Apostolic Work: Teaching, adult education, parish ministry, Catholic social services, neighborhood community services, Hispanic ministry.
Represented in the Archdiocese of Cincinnati and in the Diocese of Covington, KY.
Vocation Director: Sr. Mary Jerome Buchert, O.S.U., St. Ursula Convent, 1339 E. McMillan St., Cincinnati, OH 45206. (513) 661-3410, ext. 139. E-mail: buchert@zoomtown.com

URSULINE SISTERS (O.S.U.)
Motherhouse: 2600 Lander Rd., Cleveland, OH 44124
237 Sisters
Apostolic Works: Primarily education and pastoral ministry, but also includes nursing, social service, foreign missions and retreat ministry.
Represented primarily in the Diocese of Cleveland with individual sisters serving also in Indiana, Kentucky, Massachusetts, Minnesota, Missouri, New York, Pennsylvania and Virginia. Also in El Salvador.
Vocation Directors: Sister Denise Marie Vlna, OSU, 2600 Lander Rd., Cleveland, OH 44124. (440) 884-3030. E-mail: sdmosu1@aol.com; Sister Roberta Goebel, OSU, 2600 Lander Rd., Cleveland, OH 44124. (440) 449-1200, ext. 138. Fax: (440) 449-3588. E-mail: rgoebel@ursulinesisters.org; Web: ursulinesisters.org

URSULINE SISTERS (O.S.U.) (Congregation of Paris)
Ursulines of Brown County, Ursuline Center, St. Martin, OH 45118. (513) 875-2020
Conduct: 1 academy, 1 three-year college, teaching administration, hospital, social ministry, pastoral, archdiocesan work, teaching, adult education and senior services.
Represented in the (Arch)dioceses of Cincinnati and Toledo.
Vocation Director: Sr. Lucy Schmid, OSU, 1080 Cooks Crossing #11, Milford, OH 45150. (513) 576-6606. E-mail: lucyfschmid@aol.com; Web: www.ursulinesofbc.org

URSULINE SISTERS (O.S.U.)
Ursuline Convent of the Sacred Heart, 4045 Indian Rd., Toledo, OH 43606
78 Sisters
Apostolic Ministries: Teaching, administration, hospital chaplain, D.R.E.; pastoral asssociate, spiritual direction, home health care, any work of charity, missionary work.
Represented in the (Arch)dioceses of Toledo, Fresno and Washington, DC. Foreign mission in Peru.
Vocation Director: Sister Sandy Sherman, OSU, 4045 Indian Rd., Toledo, OH 43606. (419) 536-9587. E-mail: sanjea_43606@yahoo.com; Web: toledoursulines.org

URSULINE SISTERS OF YOUNGSTOWN (O.S.U.) (Congregation of Paris) 4250 Shields Rd., Canfield, OH 44406
77 Sisters; also Companions in Mission (lay volunteer ministry), Company of Angela (lay prayer associates)
Ministries: high schools, parochial schools, own pre-school/kindergarten and adult education center, public pre-school/kindergarten, parish ministry and religious education, diocesan offices, social services, hospital services, higher education school of music, transitional housing for single homeless women with children, AIDS/HIV ministry, speech and hearing center, Potter's Wheel ministry to train women in skills and business, seminary education, Women's Well (outreach to women at risk), mission in Brownsville.
Represented in the Diocese of Youngstown.
Vocation Contact: Sr. Mary Alice Koval, Vocation Team, 4250 Shields Rd., Canfield, OH 44406. (330) 792-7636. E-mail: treerich@aol.com; Web: www.theursulines.org

VERONA MISSIONARY SISTERS
See Comboni Missionary Sisters

VINCENTIAN SISTERS OF CHARITY (V.S.C.) 8200 Midnight Rd., Pittsburgh, PA 15237
146 Sisters
Apostolic Work: Education: day care, kindergarten, elementary, high schools; health care: nursing homes, disabled children's home, clinic, interpreter for deaf; religious education; social services; hospital chap-

laincy; parish, pastoral and youth ministry.
Represented in PA, OH, FL, AL, MO, WI and Canada.
Vocation Director: Sr. Valerie Miller, V.S.C., 8200 Midnight Rd., Pittsburgh, PA 15237. (412) 364-6201. Fax: (412) 364-9055. E-mail: vmiller @vincentiansrspgh.org; Web: www. vincentiansrspgh.org

VINCENTIAN SISTERS OF CHARITY (V.S.C.) 1160 Broadway, Bedford, OH 44146-4523. (440) 232-4755
62 Sisters
Apostolic Work: Education, health care, pastoral ministry, ministry with the poor, hospice, missionaries in El Salvador, ministry with the elderly.
Represented in the Diocese of Cleveland, OH and Lexington, KY.
Contact: Sister Dorothy Ann Blatnica, (440) 232-4755. E-mail: a.vscoffice @att.net

VISITATION NUNS (V.H.M.)
Monastery of the Visitation of Georgetown, 1500 35th St., N.W., Washington, DC 20007
21 Sisters
Apostolic Work: Prayer and education (girls' high school).
Vocation Director: Sr. Mary de Sales McNabb, Monastery of the Visitation of Georgetown, 1500 35th St., N.W., Washington, DC 20007. (202) 337-0305. Fax: (202) 965-3845. E-mail: geovision@aol.com; Web: www. visi.org

VISITATION NUNS (V.H.M.)
Visitation Monastery, 200 E. Second St., Frederick, MD 21701. (301) 662-3322
6 Sisters
Apostolic Work: Contemplative order with apostolate of teaching.
Vocation Contact: Sister Marguerite Therese Leary, VHM, Superior, Visitation Monastery, 200 E. Second St., Frederick, MD 21701. (301) 662-3322. Fax: (301) 695-8549

VISITATION NUNS (V.H.M.)
Monastery of the Visitation, 2455 Visitation Dr., Mendota Heights, MN 55120
16 Sisters
Apostolic Work: Prayer and educational ministries of various forms with a variety of people.
Vocation Director: S. Bridget Marie Keefe, V.H.M., Monastery of the Visitation, 2455 Visitation Dr., Mendota Heights, MN 55120. (651) 683-1700. E-mail: brigidk@vischool.org

VISITATION NUNS (V.H.M.)
Visitation Monastery, 1527 Fremont Ave. North, Minneapolis, MN 55411
Apostolic Work: Contemplative/ monastic prayer with hospitality to inner-city neighbors.
Represented in the (Arch)diocese of St. Paul & Minneapolis.
Vocation Director: Sister Katherine Mullin, V.H.M., Visitation Monastery, 1527 Fremont Ave. North, Minneapolis, MN 55411. (612) 521-6113, 529-8215. Fax: (612) 521-4020. E-mail: mullinkf@aol.com; Web: www.visitationmonastery.org/ minneapolis

VISITATION NUNS (V.H.M.)
Visitation Monastery, 3020 N. Ballas Rd., St. Louis, MO 63131. (314) 432-5353
25 Sisters
Apostolic Work: Seeking union with God in contemplation; community life creates family bonds among the members and also with those entrusted to the sisters' apostolates of prayer, spiritual direction, and teaching (preschool through 12th grade).
Vocation Director: Sr. Catherine Brady, V.H.M., 3020 N. Ballas Rd., St. Louis, MO 63131. (314) 432-5353, ext. 3719. E-mail: srcbrady @visitation.com

VISITATION NUNS (V.H.M.)
Visitation Monastery, 8902 Ridge Blvd., Brooklyn, NY 11209-5716. (718) 745-5151. E-mail: vamon astery@aol.com
25 Sisters, 8 in Formation, 2 Associates
Apostolic Work: Primary mission: ministry of prayer in the monastic contemplative tradition. Retreatants and those discerning vocations are invited to experience monastic life with the Sisters. Religious instruction in the Sisters' private academy for girls (N-8). .
Represented in the Diocese of Brooklyn.
Vocation Directress: Sr. Marie de Chantal Mannino, V.H.M., Visitation Monastery, 8902 Ridge Blvd., Brooklyn, NY 11209-5716. (718) 745-5151. Fax: (718) 745-3680. E-mail: smdecvis@aol.com or VAMonastery @aol.com: Web: www.visitation sisters.org/mona/bro_main.asp and www.catholic.org/macc

VISITATION NUNS (V.H.M.) (Cloistered) (First Federation of North America) Monastery of the Visitation, 12221 Bienvenue Rd., Rockville, VA 23146. (804) 749-4885
120 Sisters, 7 Monasteries
Apostolic Work: Prayer is primary, limited retreats.
Monasteries: 2300 Spring Hill Ave., Mobile, AL 36607; 5820 City Ave., Philadelphia, PA 19131; 12221 Bienvenue Rd., Rockville, VA 23146; 1745 Parkside Blvd., Toledo, OH 43607; 14 Beach Rd., P.O. 432, Tyringham, MA 01264; 2055 Ridgedale Dr., Snellville, GA 30278; 200 2nd St., Frederick, MD 21701-5397.
Vocation Directress: Mother Margaret Mary McGuire, VHM, Monastery of the Visitation, 12221 Bienvenue Rd., Rockville, VA 23146. (804) 749-4885. Web: sistersofthevisitation.org

VISITATION NUNS (V.H.M.)
Monastery of the Visitation, Mt. de Chantal, 410 Washington Ave., Wheeling, WV 26003
15 Sisters
Apostolic Work: Education.
Vocations Contact: Sr. Mary Grace Flynn, Monastery of the Visitation, 410 Washington Ave., Wheeling, WV 26003. (304) 232-1283. E-mail: marygflynn@yahoo.com

SISTERS OF VISITATION OF THE CONGREGATION OF THE IMMACULATE HEART OF MARY (S.V.M.) Visitation Convent, 2950 Kaufmann Ave., Dubuque, IA 52001-1655. (563) 556-2440, ext. 3. E-mail: bcuroe@loras.edu
7 Sisters
Apostolic Work: Elementary, secondary education. Also engaged in adult education, parish ministry, college counseling.
Represented in the Archdiocese of Dubuque
Vocation Contact: Sister Bernadette Curoe, President

VOCATIONIST SISTERS (S.D.V.) (Sisters of Divine Vocations)
US Foundation: Perpetual Help Day Nursery, 172 Broad St., Newark, NJ 07104. (201) 484-3535; Sister Joanna Formation House, 88 Brooklake Rd., Florham Park, NJ 07932. (973) 966-9762
Apostolic Work: To guide and foster vocations to priesthood and religious life; teaching, parish ministry and missionary work; special emphasis is given to work with the poor and underprivileged.
Represented in the Dioceses of Newark and Paterson. Also in Italy, France, Brazil, Argentina, Philippines, India, Indonesia and Madagascar.
Vocation Contact: Sr. Anna Maria or Sr. Gelsy Mosca, 88 Brooklake Rd., Florham Park, NJ 07932. (973) 966-9762. E-mail: vocationist@yahoo .com; Web: www.vocationist.org/ sisters

XAVIER SISTERS (XS) (Catholic Mission Sisters of St. Francis Xavier) 37179 Moravian Dr., Clinton Township, MI 48036

1 Sister

Represented in the Archdiocese of Detroit.

Coordinator of Community: Sister Mary Agnes Malburg, XS, 37179 Moravian Dr., Clinton Township, MI 48036. (586) 465-5082

XAVERIAN MISSIONARY SISTERS OF MARY (X.M.M.) US Headquarters: 242 Salisbury St., Worcester, MA 01609

8 Sisters in US

Apostolic Work: Evangelization among non-Christian peoples: catechetical, medical, educational, social work.

Represented in Italy (Motherhouse), R.D. Congo, Brazil, Cameroon, Chad, Mexico, Japan and Thailand. In US: Archdiocese of New York and Diocese of Worcester.

Vocation Director: Sr. Rosa Casali, XMM, 242 Salisbury St., Worcester, MA 01609. (508) 757-0514 (tel., fax)

EASTERN CATHOLIC COMMUNITIES FOR WOMEN

ANTONINE SISTERS (MARONITE) (A.S.) Headquarters: Lebanon 2691 North Lipkey Rd., North Jackson, OH 44451

7 Sisters in US; 200 worldwide.

Apostolic Work: Education, health care, pastoral ministry and social service.

Represented in Ohio. Also in Cyprus, Australia, France, Canada.

Vocation Contact: Sr. Samia Abou-Shakra, AS, Superior, Antonine Sisters, 2691 North Lipkey Rd., North Jackson, OH 44451. (330) 538-9822 or 2567. Fax: (330) 538-9820. E-mail: sistersamia@yahoo.com

BASILIANS – NUNS OF SAINT BASIL THE GREAT, O.S.B.M.

(Sacred Heart Monastery) 209 Keasel Rd., Middletown, New York 10940-6287. (845) 343-1308

Apostolic Work: Contemplative community.

Vocation Contact: Mother M. Bernadette Reshetylo, OSBM, 209 Keasel Rd., Middletown, New York 10940-6287. (845) 343-1308

BASILIANS – SISTERS OF ST. BASIL THE GREAT (Byzantine Catholic Church) OSBM

500 W. Main St., P.O. Box 878, Uniontown, PA 15401

91 Sisters

Conduct: 3 grammar schools,1 nursing home, 1 retreat center, staff religious education offices, diocesan offices, pastoral and parochial ministry.

Represented in the Byzantine Catholic Archeparchy of Pittsburgh and in the Eparchies of Parma, Passaic and Van Nuys.

Vocation Director: Sr. Jean Marie Cihota, OSBM, Sisters of St. Basil the Great (Byzantine Catholic Church). (724) 438-8644. E-mail: srjeanmc@hotmail.com

BASILIANS – SISTERS OF THE ORDER OF ST. BASIL THE GREAT (O.S.B.M.) (Ukrainian Byzantine Rite)

65 Sisters

Apostolic Work: Education at all levels, pastoral ministry, chancery support, spiritual direction, retreats, liturgical arts.

Vocation Director: 710 Fox Chase Rd., Fox Chase Manor, PA 19046-4198. (215) 342-4222 . E-mail: basilians@aol.com; Web: www.basiliansfoxchase.org

BENEDICTINE SISTERS (BYZANTINE) (O.S.B.)

Queen of Heaven Monastery, 8640 Squires Ln. N.E., Warren, OH 44484

9 members

Apostolic Work: Teaching, religious education, pastoral care, parish ministry, office work, child care, retreat work, spiritual direction.

Vocation Director: Sister Agnes Knapik, OSB, 8640 Squires Lane NE, Warren, OH 44484. (330) 856-1813. E-mail: agnes@netdotcom.com; Web: www.benedictinebyzantine.org

BYZANTINE NUNS OF ST. CLARE (B.N.S.C.) Poor Clares in the Byzantine Rite in the Ruthenian Eparchy of Parma, OH

Monastery of Holy Protection, 6688 Cady Rd., N. Royalton, OH 44133

6 Professed

Apostolic Work: Contemplatives, Second Order of St. Francis, in Eastern Monasticism.

Vocation Director: Vocation Directress, 6688 Cady Rd., N. Royalton, OH 44133. (440) 237-6800

COMMUNITY MOTHER OF GOD TENDERNESS (C.M.G.T.)

79 Golden Hill Rd., Danbury, CT 06811

3 Sisters

Apostolic Work: Active/contemplative community.

Vocation Contact: Sister Mary Ann Socha, C.M.G.T., 79 Golden Hill Rd., Danbury, CT 06811. (203) 794-1486

DISCALCED CARMELITE NUNS OF THE BYZANTINE RITE (O.C.D.)

Holy Annunciation Monastery, 403 W. County Rd., Sugarloaf, PA 18249. (570) 788-1205. E-mail: carmel@epix.net

11 Professed Nuns, 2 Novices

Contact: Mother Marija of the Holy Spirit, OCD, Prioress

MISSIONARY SISTERS OF MOTHER OF GOD (M.S.M.G.)

111 W. North St., Stamford, CT 06902. (203) 323-1237

11 Sisters, 1 Novice

Apostolic Work: Elementary education, catechetical instructions, kindergarten and nursery schools; liturgical art distribution.

Represented in the Ukrainian Archdiocese of Philadelphia and in the Ukrainian Diocese of Stamford.

Vocation Director: Sister Yosaphata, MSMG, Motherhouse: 711 North Franklin St., Philadelphia, PA 19123. (215) 627-7808

SISTERS SERVANTS OF MARY IMMACULATE (S.S.M.I.)

(Immaculate Conception Province) Provincialate: Sisters Servants Lane, PO Box 9, Sloatsburg, NY 10974-0009. (845) 753-2840

Apostolic Work: Serves the Eastern Catholic Church (Ukrainian & Byzantine). Teaching, nursing, senior citizens, youth ministry, pilgrimages, catechizing, sewing vestments, retreats, pastoral ministries, arts, domestics, administration.

Foreign Countries: Canada, Brazil, Argentina, Italy, Poland, Slovakia (former Yugoslavia), France, England, Germany, Ukraine.

Vocation Contact: Sr. Michele Yakymovitch, SSMI, Provincial Superior, PO Box 9, Sloatsburg, NY 10974-0009. (845) 753-2840. E-mail: ssminy@aol.com

Holy Father, look upon this humanity of ours, that is taking its first steps along the path of the Third Millennium. Its life is still deeply marked by hatred, violence and oppression, but the thirst for justice, truth and grace still finds a space in the hearts of many people, who are waiting for someone to bring salvation, enacted by You through Your Son Jesus. There is the need for courageous heralds of the Gospel, for generous servants of suffering humanity. Send holy priests to Your Church, we pray, who may sanctify Your people with the tools of Your grace. Send numerous consecrated men and women, that they may show Your holiness in the midst of the world. Send holy laborers into Your vineyard, that they may labor with the fervor of charity and, moved by Your Holy Spirit, may bring the salvation of Christ to the farthest ends of the Earth. Amen

From Castel Gandolfo, 8th September 2001
IOANNES PAULUS PP. II

Volunteer Lay Ministries

The laity has a significant role in our Church today, being identified as the principle bearers of the Church's social message to civil society.

We are all called to social ministry to fulfill our baptismal responsibility.

John Paul II states, "The call is addressed to everyone." Lay people are called by the Lord to a mission on behalf of the Church and the world. "You go into my vineyard too!"

This represents the unity within our Church. The union between Christ and the disciples who were called to bear their own fruit in the world continues in the modern-day disciples called lay volunteers.

Many of our laity – young, old, married and single – fully respond to their call as Catholics. This growing number of people are leaving their jobs, money, security, and material possessions to serve for one, two or three years as lay missioners to our needy world. Daily, they are putting their faith into action.

These lay mission volunteers can be found across our own country in parishes, schools, social agencies, and hospitals. They are working with those in need in our nation's rural and urban areas. They can be found in soup kitchens and child-care centers. No area is without their presence.

They can be found in churches in Africa, Asia, Oceania, Europe, Latin and Central America. Whether teachers, construction workers, home-care aides, or accountants (and the list goes on), these lay people in mission are apostles of hope.

Challenged by Our Holy Father, these lay volunteers know that to say "CHURCH" is to say "MISSION!"

Information about volunteer mission work may be obtained by contacting one or more organizations listed in the section that follows or by contacting:

Catholic Network of Volunteer Service (CNVS)
6930 Carroll Ave., Suite 506
Takoma Park, MD 20912-4423
(800) 543-5046
(301) 270-0900
Fax: (301) 270-0901
E-mail: volunteer@cnvs.org
Web: www.cnvs.org

Note: Although these listings were carefully compiled, The Catholic News Publishing Company neither endorses or recommends the organizations in this section and the one that follows. Prospective volunteers and/or lay members should carefully screen organizations to which they intend to apply.

ADORERS OF THE BLOOD OF CHRIST VOLUNTEER PROGRAM
2 Pioneer Ln., Red Bud, IL 62278. (618) 282-3848. E-mail: newtonf@adorers.org; Web: adorers.org
Contact: Sr. Frances Newton, ASC, Director
Mission Areas: New Mexico, Texas, Arizona, Illinois, Missouri; foreign: Boliva and Guatemala
Type of Service: cathechetics, community work, education, health care, office work
Term of Service: a few weeks to 2 years or more
Basic Benefits: room/board with ASC community
Basic Requirements: M/F; single/married; Christian; 21 and up for foreign service
Affiliation: Adorers of the Blood of Christ (US Province)

AGNESIANS IN MISSION - AIM
320 County Rd. K, Fond du Lac, WI 54935. (920) 907-2319. Fax: (920) 923-4551. E-mail: khenning@csasisters.org; Web: www.csasisters.org
Contact: Karen Henning, Volunteer Coordinator
Mission Areas: various sites in US; some in Latin America
Type of Service: education, social service, parish ministries, health care
Term of Service:1 month min. (US); 6 months minimum (Latin America)
Basic Benefits: room/board (negotiable: transportation; medical insurance; stipend)
Basic Requirements: M/F; 21 and up; desire to put Gospel in action
Affiliation: Congregation of St. Agnes

ALASKA RADIO MISSION - KNOM
PO Box 988, Nome, AK 99762-0988. (907) 443-5221. Fax: (907) 443-5757. E-mail: rschmidt@knom.org; Web: www.knom.org
Contact: Ric Schmidt
Mission Areas: Nome, Alaska
Type of Service: radio announcers, news reporter, producers
Term of Service: 1 year (renewable)
Basic Benefits: rt air transportation; room/board; stipend; medical insurance; AmeriCorps placement
Basic Requirements: M/F; recent college graduates: able to read and speak aloud in unaccented English (prior broadcasting experience not necessary - training provided)
Affiliation: Diocese of Fairbanks

ALIVE (A Lay Invitation to a Visitation Experience)
890 E. 154th St., South Holland, IL 60473. (708) 333-7595. E-mail: srmm0812@aol.com; Web: www.cnd-m.com
Contact: Sr. Marilyn Medinger CND
Mission Areas: US, Canada
Type of Service: ministry to poor in educational settings
Term of Service: 1 year (renewable)
Basic Benefits: room/board, monthly stipend, health insurance, local transportation
Basic Requirements: F; single; 21-30; Catholic orientation
Affiliation: Congregation of Notre Dame

AMATE HOUSE
2601 N. Sayre, Chicago, IL 60707. (866) 262-8384. E-mail: amateh@aol.com; Web: www.amatehouse.org
Contacts: Meghan Rogers, Mark Laboe
Mission Area: Chicago
Type of Service: teaching, community work, health care, legal, social services
Term of Service: 1 year
Basic Benefits: room/board; stipend; health insurance; transportation to/from mission site
Basic Requirements: M/F; single; between 21 and 29; Catholic
Affiliation: Archdiocese of Chicago

ANDRÉ HOUSE OF ARIZONA
PO Box 2014, Phoenix, AZ 85001-2014. (602) 255-0580. Fax: (602) 254-3834. E-mail: director@andrehouseaz.org
Contact: Fr. Bill Wack, CSC
Mission Area: Phoenix
Type of Service: services to poor and homeless in houses of hospitality
Term of Service: 1 year preferred
Basic Benefits: room/board; medical insurance; stipend; AmeriCorps ed award
Basic Requirements: M/F; 21 and up; Catholic; willing to live in community
Affiliation: Holy Cross Priests (Indiana Province) Catholic Worker

ANTHONY FAMILY SHELTER-CATHOLIC CHARITIES
256 N. Ohio, Wichita, KS 67214. (316) 264-7233. Fax: (316) 267-3774. Web: www.wkscatholiccharities.org
Contact: Claudette Moore, Program Director
Mission Area: Wichita, KS
Type of Service: homeless shelter
Basic Requirements: M/F; 21 and up

ASSOCIATE MISSIONARIES OF THE ASSUMPTION
914 Main St. #5, Worcester, MA 01610. (508) 767-1356. Fax: (508) 767-1356. E-mail: ama-usa@juno.com; Web: www.assumption.edu/pastoral/volunteer/AMA/AMA.html
Contacts: Beth Fleming, Sr. Mary Ann Azanza, RA
Mission Areas: US, Ireland, Bolivia, England, Belgium, Guatemala, Italy, France, Rwanda, Scotland
Type of Service: catechetics, community work, education, health care, office work, hospice
Term of Service: 1 to 2 years (renewable)
Basic Benefits: room/board; stipend; medical expenses/insurance; travel from mission site (in some cases)
Basic Requirements: M/F; single; between 22 and 40; Catholic
Affiliation: Religious of the Assumption (Provincial House: Philadelphia, PA)

AUGUSTINIAN VOLUNTEER PROGRAM
1165 East 54th Place, Chicago, IL 60615-5109. (773) 684-6510, ext. 25. Fax: (773) 684-9830. E-mail: fredkaosa@aol.com; Web: www.midwestaugustinians.org
Contact: Br. Fred Kaiser, OSA, Director
Mission Areas: Chicago, Detroit, St. Louis
Type of Service: education, youth ministry, Hispanic outreach, inner city shelters, food programs
Term of Service: nine months minimum
Basic Benefits: room/board; medical insurance; monthly stipend; AmeriCorps award; annual retreat/days of reflection; support of the fraternal organization
Basic Requirements: M; 19-55 years old; college preferred
Affiliation: Augustinian Friars (Province of Our Lady of Good Counsel)

AUGUSTINIAN VOLUNTEERS
PO Box 340, Villanova, PA 19085-0340. (610) 527-3330, ext. 279. Fax: (610) 520-0618. E-mail: osavol@aol.com; Web: www.augustinian.org
Contact: Rev. Joseph Mostardi, OSA
Mission Areas: Bronx, Chicago, Lawrence (MA), San Diego

Type of Service: teaching on various levels, youth ministry, work with the elderly, day care and services for children, outreach to immigrants, food pantry, soup kitchen
Term of Service: 10 months (Sept.-June)
Basic Benefits: room/board; health insurance; monthly stipend; transportation to/from site
Basic Requirements: M/F; 21 years and up; college degree or equivalent work experience
Affiliation: The Augustinians

BENEDICTINE APPALACHIAN VOLUNTEERS
Mt. Tabor Benedictines, 150 Mt. Tabor Rd., Martin, KY 41649. (606) 886-9624. E-mail: mtabor150@hotmail.com; Web: www.geocities.com/athens/9871
Contact: Sr. Kathleen Weigand, O.S.B.
Mission Areas: Appalachian region of Eastern Kentucky
Type of Service: catechetics, community work, education, health care, office work, gardening, home repairs
Term of Service: 2 weeks to 3 months
Basic Benefits: room/board
Basic Requirements: M/F w/o dependents; 21 years and up.

BENEDICTINE ASSOCIATE PROGRAM
St. Scholastica Monastery, 1001 Kenwood Ave., Duluth, MN 55811-2300. (218) 723-7059. E-mail: snancyosb@yahoo.com; Web: www.DuluthBenedictines.org
Contact: Sister Nancy Flaig, OSB
Mission Area: Duluth
Type of Service: education, health care, geriatric services, parish/pastoral, domestic, maintenance, gardening
Term of Service: 3 months -1 year (renewable)
Basic Benefits: room/board
Basic Requirements: F; no dependents.

BENEDICTINE LAY VOLUNTEERS
Mother of God Monastery, 110 28th Ave. SE #302, Watertown, SD 57201. (605) 882-6631. E-mail: rosepalm85@hotmail.com; Web: www.watertownbenedictine.org
Contact: Sister Rose Palm, Director
Mission Area: South Dakota
Type of Service: community work, clerical, rural ministry, varied ministries within the monastery and in South Dakota
Term of Service: 1 month to 1 year; summer program
Basic Benefits: room/board; experience Benedictine community life
Basic Requirements: F; 21-65 (year long); M/F; 18 and up (summer program)
Affiliation: Benedictine Sisters (Watertown, SD)

BENEDICTINE SISTERS OF THE BYZANTINE RITE VOLUNTEER PROGRAM
Queen of Heaven Monastery, 8640 Squires Lane, N.E., Warren, OH 44484. (330) 856-1813. E-mail: smm@netdotcom.com; Web: www.benedictinebyzantine.org
Contact: Sr. Margaret Mary Schima, OSB
Mission Area: Warren (OH) and neighboring cities
Type of Service: clerical, religious education youth ministry, library work, outreach to the elderly, gardening, cooking, housekeeping, driver, computer work, early education
Term of Service: 2 weeks - 1 year
Basic Benefits: room/board; experience Byzantine Benedictine spirituality, community life and ministry
Basic Requirements: F; 18 and up
Affiliation: Benedictine Sisters (Byzantine)

BENEDICTINE SISTERS OF FLORIDA VOLUNTEER PROGRAM
Holy Name Monastery, PO Box 2450, St. Leo, FL 33574-2450. (352) 588-8320. Fax: (352) 588-8319. E-mail: mary.david.hydro@saintleo.edu; Web: www.floridabenedictines.com
Contact: Sister Mary David Hydro, OSB
Mission Area: Holy Name Monastery, St. Leo, FL
Type of Service: Housekeeping, gardening, cooking, hospitality, care/companionship for elderly Sisters, driving, computer work, clerical, development
Basic Benefits: room/board; shared prayer with Sisters; spiritual growth opportunities; experience of living in community
Basic Requirements: F; 25-70; no dependents; good health
Affiliation: Benedictine Sisters of Florida

BENEDICTINE SISTERS VOLUNTEER PROGRAM
840 S. Main St., Mt. Angel, OR 97362-9527. (503) 845-6141. Fax: (503) 845-6585. E-mail: smarietta@juno.com; Web: www.benedictine-srs.org
Contact: Sister Marietta Schindler, OSB
Mission Areas: rural Mt. Angel, OR
Type of Service: community work, nurse, gardening, receptionist, computer, library, shelter
Term of Service: varies - 1 week to 1 year
Basic Benefits: room/board
Basic Requirements: M/F; single/married w/o dependents; 18-65
Affiliation: Benedictine Sisters (Mt. Angel, OR)

BENEDICTINE VOLUNTEER PROGRAM (Atchison, KS)
Mount St. Scholastica, 801 South 8th., Atchison, KS 66002. (913) 360-6203. Fax: (913) 360-6190. E-mail: rbertels@mountosb.org; Web: www.mountosb.org/volunteers.html
Contact: Rosemary Bertels, OSB
Mission Areas: northeast Kansas, northwest Missouri
Type of Service: gardening, clerical, retreat support services, tutoring, library
Term of Service: several months to a year (renewable for second year)
Basic Benefits: room/board; stipend negotiable; opportunities of life in monastic community
Basic Requirements: M/F; over 21; no dependents; desire to enter into monastic life style; good health
Affiliation: Benedictine Sisters

BENEDICTINE VOLUNTEER PROGRAM (Rapid City, SD)
St. Martin Monastery, 2110-C St. Martin Dr., Rapid City, SD 57702-9660. (605) 343-8011. Fax: (605) 399-2723. E-mail: fmartin620@aol.com
Contact: Sr. Lorane Coffin, OSB, Director
Mission Area: Rapid City
Type of Service: hospitality, housekeeping, gardening, dietary assistance, care of elderly
Term of Service: several weeks to one year
Basic Benefits: room/board
Basic Requirements: F; 18 years and older; no dependents
Affiliation: Benedictine Sisters (Rapid City, SD)

BENEDICTINE VOLUNTEERS
Benedictine Monastery, 31970 State Hwy. P, Clyde, MO 64432-8100. (660) 944-2221. Fax: (660) 944-2152. E-mail: volunteer@benedictinesisters.org; Web: www.benedictinesisters.org

Contact: Director of Volunteers
Mission Areas: Arizona, Oklahoma, Wyoming
Type of Service: housekeeper, gardener, cook, altar bread production and distribution
Term of Service: short, long term
Basic Benefits: room/board
Basic Requirements: M/F; ages 20-65; in good health; commitment to celibacy during time of service; ability to live in community
Affiliation: Benedictine Sisters of Perpetual Adoration

BETHANY VOLUNTEERS - YOUNG PEOPLE WHO CARE (YPWC)
PO Box 129, Frenchville, PA 16836. (814) 263-4177, 4855. E-mail: bethanyyouth@pennswoods.net or bethanyadult@pennswoods.net; Web: www.ypwcministries.org
Contact: Volunteer Coordinator
Mission Area: Clearfield County in western PA-rural Appalachia
Type of Service: social service work in the community
Term of Service: 6 months to 1 year and longer; summer program
Basic Benefits: room/board; monthly stipend; medical insurance
Basic Requirements: M/F; single; 20 and over
Affiliation: Anawim Community of Frenchville, PA; Diocese of Erie

BON SECOURS VOLUNTEER MINISTRY PROGRAM
Bon Secours Spiritual Center, 1525 Marriottsville Rd., Marriottsville, MD 21104. (410) 442-5519. Fax: (410) 442-1394. E-mail: Eileen_Kiefer@bshsl.com
Contact: Eileen Kiefer, Director
Mission Areas: Baltimore, Arcadia (FL), Detroit, Richmond
Type of Service: health care, home health care to the poor and underserved, community organizing, social service, case management, tutoring, outreach in Hispanic ministry/urban cities
Term of Service: one year, renewable
Basis Benefits: room/board; stipend; health insurance
Basic Requirements: M/F; 21-65; Christian
Affiliation: Sisters of Bon Secours

BONA (BENEDICTINE OUTREACH TO THE NATIVE AMERICANS)
Queen of Peace Monastery, Box 370, Belcourt, ND 58316-0370. (701) 477-6167. Fax: (701) 477-5575. E-mail: qop@utma.com; Web: www.utma.com/~qop
Contact: Sr. Judith Emge, OSB
Mission Area: Turtle Mt. Indian Reservation, ND
Type of Service: cathechetics, administrative, music ministry, youth ministry, outreach to hospitals and shut-ins
Term of Service: summer; 1 month to 1 year
Basic Benefits: private room/board
Basic Requirements: F; single/divorced/widowed; 21-55
Affiliaiton: Benedictine Sisters (Belcourt, ND)

BOYS HOPE GIRLS HOPE
National Office, 12120 Bridgeton Sq. Dr., Bridgeton, MO 63044. (877) 878-4673. E-mail: hope@bhgh.org; Web: www.BoysHopeGirlsHope.org
Contact: Recruitment/Volunteer Coordinator
Mission Areas: St. Louis, New York, Chicago, New Orleans, Cincinnati, Detroit, Cleveland/Akron, Phoenix, Pittsburgh, Las Vegas, Orange County, Denver, Baton Rouge, San Antonio, San Francisco, Baltimore
Type of Service: Provide surrogate parenting services to hurt and at-risk, yet academically capable, youth in family-like settings
Term of Service: 1 year or more
Basic Benefits: room/board; stipend; medical insurance; transportation to orientation program, opportunity for full-time employment
Basic Requirements: M/F; single; 21 and up, college degree or experience working with youth
Affiliation: Jesuit traditions, private

BROTHER BENNO'S FOUNDATION
PO Box 308, Oceanside, CA 92054. (760) 439-1244, ext. 104. E-mail: brotherbenno@yahoo.com
Contact: Theresa Byrne
Mission Area: Oceanside, CA
Type of Service: day center, soup kitchen, emergency shelter staff, community work, after school tutoring program, case management, accounting, administration, warehouse, alcohol/drug recovery program
Term of Service: 1 year (or longer)
Basic Benefits: room/board (in ministry house); stipend; transportation
Basic Requirements: M/F; single; 45-68
Affiliation: Benedictine Monks (Prince of Peace Abbey)

BROTHERS OF THE SACRED HEART VOLUNTEER SERVICE COMMUNITY
1244 65th St., Brooklyn, NY 11219-5999. (718) 621-3164. E-mail: rcz@monmouth.com; Web: brothersofthesacredheart.org
Contact: Brother Robert Ziobro, SC
Mission Area: New York (Queens & Brooklyn)
Type of Service: teaching, pastoral care, youth ministry, youth counselor
Term of Service: 1-2 years
Basic Requirements: M; single; 21-28; 2 years college
Affiliation: Brothers of the Sacred Heart (New York Province)

CABRINI MISSION CORPS
610 King of Prussia Rd., Radnor, PA 19087-3698. (610) 971-0821. E-mail: cmcorps@aol.com; Web: www.cabrini-missioncorps.org
Contacts: Madeline Bialecki, Peg Barrett, Annette Villa
Mission Areas: NY, IL, CO, PA, Africa, Guatemala, Nicaragua, Philippines
Type of Service: a faith-based lay mission organization serving in the areas of education, health care, pastoral ministry, youth ministry, child care and other social services
Term of Service: 1 year (US); 2 years (overseas)
Basic Benefits: room/board; monthly stipend; medical insurance; transportation to/from mission site
Basic Requirements: M/F; 21 and up; single/married couples w/o dependents; Christian; college or work experience
Affiliation: Missionaries of the Sacred Heart of Jesus (Cabrini Sisters)

CAPUCHIN FRANCISCAN VOLUNTEER CORPS
EAST: Capuchin College, 4121 Harewood Rd. NE, Washington, DC 20017. (202) 529-3994. Fax: (202) 526-6664. E-mail: btoomey58@aol.com; Web: www.capuchin.com
MIDWEST: 301 Church St., Mt. Calvary, WI 53057. toll-free: (1-888) 297-2702. Fax: (414) 271-0637. E-mail: capcorps@juno.com; Web: www.capuchinfranciscans.org/capcorps.htm
Contacts: Br. Bob Toomey, OFM Cap. (East); Br. David Schwab, OFM Cap. (Midwest)
Mission Areas: East: Baltimore, Washington, Pittsburgh, Papua New Guinea, Puerto Rico; Midwest: Chicago, Detroit, Milwaukee, Nicaragua

Type of Service: advocacy, education, community organizing, health care, social service
Term of Service: 1 to 2 years (renewable)
Basic Benefits: room/board (in community with other volunteers); stipend; medical insurance; transportation to/from work site
Basic Requirements: M/F; single/ married w/o dependents; 21 and up
Affiliation: Capuchin Franciscan Friars

CAPUCHIN YOUTH AND FAMILY MINISTRIES
781 Rte. 9D, PO Box 192, Garrison, NY 10524. (845) 424-3609. Fax: (845) 424-4403. E-mail: cyfm@ cyfm.org; Web: www.cyfm.org
Contact: Tom Brinkmann, Director
Mission Areas: New York, Connecticut
Type of Service: community work, retreat ministry, youth and campus ministry, high school ministry
Term of Service: one year (beginning in Aug.) (renewable)
Basic Benefits: room/board; stipend; medical insurance
Basic Requirements: M/F; Catholic, 21 and older; college graduate (preferred)
Affiliation: Capuchin Franciscan Friars

CASA JUAN DIEGO
4818 Rose, P.O. Box 70113, Houston, TX 77270. (713) 869-7376. Fax: (713) 864-4994. E-mail: info@cjd.org; Web: www.cjd.org
Contacts: Mark or Louise Zwick
Mission Area: Houston, TX
Type of Service: refugee work for men and women, Spanish speaking, battered and/or homeless women and children
Term of Service: No minimum
Basic Benefits: room/board (in community); stipend; medical insurance; transportation home after 1 year of service
Basic Requirements: M/F; single/ married/widowed; 21 and up; functional Spanish; faith commitment
Affiliation: Catholic Worker

CATHOLIC CHARITIES - PROJECT SERVE
2305 N. Charles St., 3rd Floor, Baltimore, MD 21218 5128. (410) 261-6776. Fax: (410) 889-0203. E-mail: rrich@catholiccharities-md.org; Web: www.catholiccharities-md.org
Contact: (Ms.) Robin Rich, Director
Mission Area: greater Baltimore metro area
Type of Service: work with the poor, homeless, emotionally abused children, adults with mental illness; nursing homes, volunteer coordination, advocacy
Term of Service: one year (August to August)
Basic Benefits: room/board; medical insurance; monthly stipends; AmeriCorps award; student loan deferment
Basic Requirements: M/F; 21 years and older; single/married (with no dependents); college degree; ability to live in community
Affiliation: Catholic Charities, Baltimore

CATHOLIC CHARITIES VOLUNTEER CORPS
438 Main St., St. Paul, MN 55102. (800) 336-2066, (651) 298-0959. Fax: (651) 227-9914. E-mail: ccvc@ ccspm.org; Web: www.ccspm.org/ volunteer/volunteer.html
Contact: Kim Smolik
Mission Area: 12 counties of the Archdiocese of St. Paul/Minneapolis
Type of Service: community work, counseling, office work, social work/ case work, nursing, teaching, pastoral care, immigration services
Term of Service: 1 year minimum.
Basic Benefits: room/board; stipend; medical insurance; transportation stipend; AmeriCorps scholarship possible (based on placement)
Basic Requirements: M/F; single/ divorced /widowed; 21 and up; willingness/desire to live in community with other Corps members, college degree not required (some placements require a related degree)
Affiliation: Catholic Charities (Archdiocese of St. Paul & Minneapolis)

CATHOLIC MEDICAL MISSION BOARD
10 West 17th St., New York, NY 10011-5765. (212) 242-7757. Fax: (212) 242-0930. E-mail: rdecostanzo@cmmb.org; Web: www.cmmb.org
Contact: Rosemary DeCostanzo
Mission Areas: Africa, Latin America, the Caribbean, Asia
Type of Service: health care
Term of Service: 1-3 years (shorter term possibilities)
Basic Benefits: room/board; stipend; transportation; Visa; full health/ individual medical evacuation/life/ malpractice insurance
Basic Requirements: Licensed and registered to practice medicine, nursing; therapists, lab techs and most areas of health trained personnel in the United States and Canada
Affiliation: Catholic

CATHOLIC NETWORK OF VOLUNTEER SERVICE (CNVS)
6930 Carroll Ave., Suite 506, Takoma Park, MD 20912-4423. (800) 543-5046, (301) 270-0900. Fax: (301) 270-0901. E-mail: volunteer@cnvs.org; Web: www.cnvs.org
Coordinating center for volunteer/lay missioner programs serving those in need throughout the US and worldwide. Publisher of "Response", a directory of volunteer opportunities. To receive your free directory call, write, or E-mail at above numbers. (Volunteer opportunities also available at CNVS office.)
Contact: Jim Lindsay, Executive Director
Basic Benefits: room/board; stipend; medical insurance; transportation to/from mission site (varies according to program chosen)
Affiliation: Catholic, private, nonprofit

CATHOLIC VOLUNTEERS IN FLORIDA
PO Box 536476, Orlando, FL 32853-6476. (407) 660-8800. Fax: (407) 660-0033. E-mail: volunteer@cvif .org; Web: www.cvif.org
Contact: Timmy Rupeiks
Mission Area: Florida (urban, rural)
Type of Service: community work, education, health care, social work, legal, counseling, shelter and group homes.
Term of Service: 1 year (renewable)
Basic Benefits: room/board; stipend; medical insurance; AmeriCorps ed award
Basic Requirements: M/F; single/ married/no dependents; 21 and up; Christian; degree or work experience; previous part-time volunteer experience; interest in social justice; emotional maturity; flexibility
Affiliation: Sisters of St. Joseph of St. Augustine, Florida; The Bishops of Florida

CATHOLIC WORKER HOUSES
PO Box 102, Winona, MN 55987-2727. (507) 454-8094. E-mail: bethany@hbci.com; Web: www. catholicworker.org/winona
Contacts: Mike Sersch
Mission Area: Winona (SE Minnesota)
Type of Service: offer temporary shelter and hospitality for homeless in a homelike setting
Term of Service: one year or longer (preferred)

Basic Benefits: room/board; medical insurance; use of community car
Basic Requirements: M/F; 21 and older; single/married; desire to live simply and with the poor
Affiliation: Catholic Worker

CCVI INCARNATE WORD MISSIONARIES – CONGREGATION OF THE SISTERS OF CHARITY OF THE INCARNATE WORD
4503 Broadway, San Antonio, TX 78209. (210) 828-2224. Fax: (210) 828-9741. E-mail: iwg017@ccvisanantonio.org
Contact: Gloria Drews-Vallecillo
Mission Areas: US, Mexico, Guatemala, Peru
Type of Service: catechetics, community work, education, health care
Term of Service: 1 year (US); 2 years (out of US)
Basic Benefits: housing; stipend; medical insurance; transportation from mission site; two-week vacation
Basic Requirements: M/F; single/married/divorced/separated/without dependents; 21 and over; Catholic
Affiliation: Sisters of Charity of the Incarnate Word

CHANGE A HEART (Millvale Franciscan Volunteer Program)
146 Hawthorne Rd., Pittsburgh, PA 15209. (412) 821-0861. Fax: (412) 821-3318. E-mail: volunteer@millvalefranciscans.org; Web: www.millvalefranciscans.org
Contact: Sister Donna Stephenson, OSF
Mission Areas: Pittsburgh, Waynesburg (PA), Cayey (Puerto Rico)
Type of Service: education, health care, social services, parish ministry, Hispanic ministry
Term of Service: 1 to 2 years, renewable
Basic Benefits: room/board; medical insurance; stipend; transportation home at end of service; AmeriCorps ed award
Basic Requirements: M/F; 21-35 (negotiable); high-school graduate with 2 years work experience or college graduate
Affiliation: Millvale Franciscan Sisters

CHI RHO CATHOLIC SERVICE CORPS
St. Mary Rectory, 626 Willard Ave., Newington, CT 06111-2614. (860) 666-1591. Fax: (860) 666-5720. E-mail: ChiRhoCatholic@aol.com
Contact: Rev. Thomas Barry
Mission Areas: inner-city neighborhoods of Connecticut (Hartford, Waterbury)
Type of Service: teaching, tutoring, youth development, AIDS ministry, work with single mothers and their children, assisting the homeless
Term of Service: 1 year (Aug. - July) (with one additional week community service in South America)
Basic Benefits: room/board; weekly stipend; medical insurance; work-related transportation, 1 free graduate course at area college
Basic Requirements: M/F; single; Catholic; recent college graduates, ages 21-25
Affiliation: Catholic

CHRIST HOUSE
1717 Columbia Rd., N.W. Washington, DC 20009-2803. (202) 328-1100. E-mail: mroberts@christhouse.org; Web: www.christhouse.org
Contact: Mark Roberts, Coordinator of Volunteers
Mission Area: Washington, DC
Type of Service: 32-bed medical recovery facility for homeless men and women. Nurses, social workers, nursing assistants, activities coordinators, administrative assistants, cooking and maintenance assistants, and general services needed
Term of Service: to 1 year or more; 1 month minimum
Basic Benefits: room/board (in community with other volunteers); 1 year or more service is eligible for stipend, transportation; health/life insurance
Basic Requirements: M/F; short term: single/married, 18 or older; long term: single, 21 or older

CHRISTIAN BROTHERS LAY VOLUNTEERS
20 Vernon St., Norwood, MA 02062. (781) 762-1759. E-mail: christianbrothersvp@hotmail.com; Web: www.cbvp.org
Contact: Br. Jack Flaherty, CFC, Director
Mission Areas: Bonita Springs, Brownsville, New York, Lima (Peru)
Type of Service: teaching, parish youth work, retreats, campus ministry, work with migrant peoples; summer camps (short term)
Term of Service: one year, renewable; two-three months (short term)
Basic Benefits: long-term: room/board; medical insurance; stipend; transportation to and from site; student loan deferment during term of service
Basic Requirements: M /F; 18 years and older; baptized Catholic; good health; ability to live in Christian community
Affiliation: Congregation of Christian Brothers (Eastern Province)

CHRISTIAN FOUNDATION FOR CHILDREN AND AGING
One Elmwood Ave., Kansas City, KS 66103-3719. (913) 384-6500. Fax: (913) 384-2211. E-mail: volunteers@cfcausa.org; Web: www.cfcausa.org
Contact: Michelle Boudet, Volunteer Coordinator
Mission Areas: Mexico, Guatemala, Honduras, El Salvador, Nicaragua, Costa Rica, the Dominican Republic, Haiti, Colombia, Venezuela, Peru, Bolovia, Brazil, Chile, the Philippines, India, Kenya, Madagascar, Uganda, Liberia, Nigeria, Burundi, Sri Lanka and Jamaica
Type of Service: community work, education, health care
Term of Service: 1 year or more (flexible)
Basic Benefits: room/board
Basic Requirements: M/F; single/married/religious
Affiliation: Catholic/ecumenical

CLARETIAN SUMMER MINISTRY PROGRAM
205 W. Monroe St., 10th Fl., Chicago, IL 60606-5013. (312) 236-7846. Fax: (312) 236-3733. E-mail: frcarl@claret.org; Web: www.claret.org
Contact: Father Carl Quebedeaux
Mission Area: Chicago inner city
Type of Service: based on applicants' skills and interests and the needs of the communities, with opportunities including children, youth, adults, social justice, medical clinic, and legal clinic
Term of Service: Mid-June to August (one-week orientation, ongoing discernment and support)
Basic Benefits: an experience of ministry, community, and spirituality that helps deepen one's sense of vocation; an experience of a lifestyle of service. Live with other participants and Claretian Missionaries (priest, brothers, lay). Room/board; stipend; transportation to/from site
Basic Requirements: M/F; 18 or older; recommendation forms; telephone interview; app. deadline Apr. 30
Affiliation: Claretian Missionaries

CLARETIAN VOLUNTEERS
205 W. Monroe St., Chicago, IL 60606-5013. (312) 236-7782, ext. 479. Fax: (312) 236-7756. E-mail: cv_ministry@claret.org; Web: www.claretianvolunteers.org

Contact: John DiMucci, Director
Mission Areas: Atlanta, Chicago, Springfield (MO), Perth Amboy (NJ), Juarez (Mexico), Kingston (Jamaica)
Type of Service: community organizing, housing, teaching, youth/young adult/elderly/senior outreach and ministry, immigration/refugee services, Hispanic ministries, campus ministry, food pantry, soup kitchen, homeless shelter, peace and justice, legal, religious education, etc.
Term of Service: 1 year (renewable)
Basic Benefits: room/board (with other volunteers); stipend; medical insurance; transportation
Basic Requirements: M/F; single/married/widowed w/o dependents; 21 and up; Christian
Affiliation: Claretian Missionaries

COLORADO VINCENTIAN VOLUNTEERS - Companions on the Journey
PO Box 6011, Denver, CO 80206-0011. (303) 863-8141. E-mail: cvv@juno.com; Web: www.covino.org
Contacts: Bill Jaster, Mary Frances Jaster, Directors
Mission Areas: downtown Denver area
Type of Service: school/parish ministries, social services, health care; elderly/women/AIDS/ homeless ministries
Term of Service: one year (August to August)
Basic Benefits: room/board; stipend; medical insurance; AmeriCorps award; transportation
Basic Requirements: M/F; ages 22 to 30; college degree or equivalent work experience
Affiliation: The Vincentians (Midwest Province)

COLUMBAN LAY MISSION PROGRAM
5410 S. University Ave., Chicago, IL 60615. (773) 955-5044. E-mail: collaymissionus@yahoo.com;
Web: columban.org
Contact: Fr. Mike Cody
Mission Areas: Asia, Latin America, Oceania
Type of Service: community work, catechetics, youth work, workers apostolate
Term of Service: 3 years
Basic Benefits: living accommodations; health care; travel to/from mission site
Basic Requirements: M/F; single; 23 to 40 years; practicing Catholics with pastoral/social involvement
Affiliation: Columban Fathers

COMBONI LAY MISSIONARY PROGRAM
1615 East 31st St., La Grange Park, IL 60526-1377. (708) 354-2050. Fax: (708) 354-2006. E-mail: combonilmp1@qwest.net, clmpallen@qwest.net; Web: www.laymission-comboni
Contacts: Allen Scheid, Mary Ellen O'Donnell
Mission Areas: Africa, Latin America
Type of Service: doctors, nurses, teachers (secondary, special education, religious education), clerical, accountants, social service workers
Term of Service: 6 months training in Chicago, 3 years of service in mission country
Basic Benefits: room/board; stipend; medical insurance; transportation to/from mission site
Basic Requirements: M/F; 23-55 (negotiable); single/married/widowed; active Catholic
Affiliation: Comboni Missionaries

COMMUNITY LIVING AND SERVICE PROJECTS - CLASP
7712 N. Paulina #2, Chicago, IL 60626. E-mail: crfosm@aol.com; Web: www.servitesisters.org
Contact: Sr. Cecilia Fandel, OSM
Mission Areas: Ladysmith, Rice Lake (WI), St. Paul (MN), Chicago
Type of Service: tutor, ESL, homebound visits, outdoor work, hospitality, youth/child programs, clerical/receptionist, seniors, justice/peace advocacy
Term of Service: 1 week - 3 months (renewable)
Basic Benefits: room/board
Basic Requirements: M/F; 18 and older; married/single/couples
Affiliation: Servants of Mary (Ladysmith, WI)

COVENANT HOUSE FAITH COMMUNITY
346 W. 17th St., New York, NY 10011. (212) 727-4153. E-mail: faithmail@covenanthouse.org; Web: www.covenanthouse.org
Contact: Ann Hoelle, Director
Mission Areas: New York City, Ft. Lauderdale, Atlantic City; Toronto, Vancouver (Canada).
Type of Service: street outreach, crisis-intervention, case management, long-term residential programs, phone hotline, education, health care, legal, and office work. Dedicated to serve wherever and however most needed by agency
Term of Service: 13 months minimum
Basic Benefits: room/board (in community); small stipend; medical/life insurance
Basic Requirements: M/F; single/married w/o dependents/religious/divorced; over 21; commit to 1/2 hour of daily prayer together; faith background

CRISPAZ VOLUNTEERS & SUMMER INTERNS
122 DeWitt Dr., Boston, MA 02120. (617) 445-5115. Fax: (413) 723-4047. E-mail: crispaz@igc.org; Web: www.crispaz.org
Contact: Christopher Ney
Mission Area: El Salvador
Type of Service: work with women's group, youth & sports programs, education, rural communities, appropriate technology, peacemaking, cross-cultural understanding
Term of Service: 2 separate programs: 3 months or 1 year
Basic Requirements: long term: intermediate level Spanish and church or community sponsorship; short term: financial sponsorship

CRISTO REY JESUIT ALUMNI VOLUNTEERS
1852 W. 22nd Place, Chicago, IL 60608. (773) 890-6800. Fax: (773) 890-6801. E-mail: JAV@cristorey.net, ekatsfey@cristorey.net; Web: www.cristorey.net
Contact: Emily Katsfey
Mission Area: Chicago
Type of Service: social service, child care, elderly care, tutoring, prison/youth/parish ministry
Term of Service: 3 years, renewable
Basic Benefits: room/board; transportation; stipend
Basic Requirements: M/F; 21 and older; single/married - dependents possible; college education or comparable experience
Affiliation: Jesuits (Chicago Province)

CSJ SUMMER MINISTRY PROGRAM
Sisters of St. Joseph of Boston, 637 Cambridge St., Brighton, MA 02135. (617) 746-1605. E-mail: eleanor.daniels@csjboston.org
Contact: Eleanor Daniels, C.S.J.
Mission Area: Greater Boston area
Type of Service: ministry with homeless, youth, people with AIDS, new immigrants
Term of Service: mid June to mid July
Basic Benefits: room/board; transportation

Basic Requirements: F; college age to 30
Affiliation: Sisters of St. Joseph of Boston

CSJ VOLUNTEER PROGRAM OF CONCORDIA, KS
PO Box 279, Concordia, KS 66901. (785) 243-2149. Fax: (785) 267-5913 (call first). E-mail: annacsj@idir.net; Web: csjkansas.org
Contact: Anna Marie Broxterman, CSJ
Mission Areas: Southwest, Midwest
Type of Service: retreat center as gardener,hospitality person, kitchen worker; domestic violence shelter; parish work as visitor to elderly and homebound, assisting with children's liturgy; homeless shelter for men
Term of Service: long-term: 6 months - 1 year; short-term: 1- 3 months
Basic Benefits: room/board; $100 monthly stipend, $150 insurance coverage if necessary (long-term only)
Basic Requirements: M/F; single, 20+
Affiliation: Sisters of St. Joseph of Concordia

CSJ VOLUNTEERS IN MISSION
27 Park Rd., West Hartford, CT 06119. (860) 233-5126, ext. 217. Fax: (860) 232-4649. E-mail: sebcsj@hotmail.com; Web: www.sistersofsaintjoseph.org
Contact: Sr. Elaine Betoncourt, CSJ
Mission Areas: long-term: Hartford (CT), Kentucky; short-term: Hartford, Ludlow (VT), Kentucky
Type of Service: teaching, medical clinic, pre-school, rural ministry
Term of Service: long-term: 1 year minimum; short-term: college breaks, summer: 1 week-2 months
Basic Benefits: room/board; stipend; medical insurance; AmeriCorps ed award; transportation home after 1 full year of service
Basic Requirements: F; single; 18 and up
Affiliation: Sisters of St. Joseph of Chambery

DEHONIAN LAY MISSIONERS
Provincialate Offices, 6871 S Highway 100, PO Box 289, Hales Corners, WI 53130-0289. (414) 427-4265. Fax: (414) 425-2938. E-mail: scjaffiliates@worldnet.att.net; Web: www.scjvocation.org
Contact: Fr. Anthony P. Russo, SCJ
Holy Spirit Church, PO Box 424, Hernando, MS 38632. (662) 429-7851. Fax: (662) 429-7882. E-mail: cgreer1950@aol.com
St. Joseph's Indian School, North Main St., PO Box 89, Chamberlain, SD 57325-0089. (605) 734-3486, 3311. Fax: (605) 734-3390. E-mail: hrdept@stjo.org; Web: www.stjo.org
Mission Areas: South Dakota, Mississippi, Wisconsin, Florida, Illinois
Type of Service: serving African-Americans, Hispanic, Native Americans, others through: teaching/tutoring, elderly/child care, social services, abuse shelters, counseling, prison/parish/youth/deaf ministry, evangelization
Term of Service: 3 years, renewable
Basic Benefits: room/board; stipend; transportation
Basic Requirements: M/F; 21 and older; single/married - dependents ok; active Catholics: college degree/comparable experience desirable
Affiliation: Priests of the Sacred Heart

DESALES SERVICE WORKS (HEART 2 HEART)
1202 Harrison St., Philadelphia, PA 19124-2910. (215) 535-1068.
E-mail: lukefour18@hotmail.com; Web: www.2desales.com
Contact: Rev. Rick Wojnicki, OSFS
Mission Areas: Philadelphia, PA and surrounding areas
Type of Service: serving the urban poor
Term of Service: 1 year (August - July)
Basic Benefits: room/board; living expenses; medical insurance; stipend
Basic Requirements: M/F; 21 and older; Catholic
Affiliation: Oblates of St. Francis de Sales

DOMINICAN VOLUNTEERS USA
(formerly Apostolic Volunteer Program, Dominican Volunteers - Eastern Region and Southern Dominican Volunteer Program)
Dominican University, 7200 W. Division St., River Forest, IL 60305-1066. (708) 524-5985/4. Fax: (708) 714-9002. E-mail: ddodde@email.dom.edu; Web: www.dvusa.org
Contact: Donielle Dodde
Mission Areas: Throughout the US
Type of Service: community work, education, health care, office work, social service, recreational coordinator
Term of Service: 1 to 2 years
Basic Benefits: room/board; accident/medical insurance; monthly ($100) stipend
Basic Requirements: M/F; single/married; 21 or older
Affiliation: Dominicans Priests, Brothers and Sisters

EDMUNDITE MISSIONS CORPS
707 Arsenal Pl., Selma, AL 36701-4628. (334) 874-3798. Fax: (334) 872-8123. E-mail: director@edmunditemissionscorps.org; Web: www.edmunditemissionscorps.org
Contact: Dr. Jane M. LaMarche
Mission Area: Selma, New Orleans
Type of Services: rural construction, youth ministry, teaching/tutoring, social services, elder ministry
Term of Service: 10 months
Basic Benefits: room/board; stipend ($200); medical/dental insurance; transportation (airfare) to/from mission site; student loan deferment
Basic Requirements: M/F; single; 21 and up; practicing Christian
Affiliation: Edmundites

EDUCATIONAL PARTNERS IN CATHOLIC SCHOOLS - EPICS
Seton Hall University, Kozlowski Hall, 4th Fl., 400 South Orange Ave., South Orange, NJ 07079-2685. (973) 761-9668. Fax: (973) 275-2187. E-mail: toytasha@shu.edu; Web: education.shu.edu/epics
Contact: Fr. Kevin Hanbury, Director
Mission Areas: underserved elementary/secondary schools in NJ and surrounding areas
Type of Service: teaching
Term of Service: 2 years
Basic Benefits: live in community; tuition reimbursement
Basic Requirements: M/F; college degree; able to pursue master's degree in education
Affiliation: Seton Hall University, Archdiocese of Newark

EXODUS YOUTH SERVICES, INC.
16643 Bleak Hill Rd., Culpeper, VA 22701. (540) 829- 2325. Fax: (540) 829-9068. E-mail: jacksonml@erols.com, info@exodusyouth.org; Web: www.exodusyouth.org
Contact: Mary Lyman Jackson
Mission Areas: Virginia, Maryland, Washington, DC
Type of Service: homeless/runaway/refugee/latchkey/at-risk children and families
Term of Service: 1 year, also short-term, summer possible
Basic Benefits: monthly stipend; full health benefits
Basic Requirements: M/F; willingness to serve the poor; witness to Gospel; promote teachings of Catholic Church
Affiliation: Catholic, independent

FATHER CARR'S PLACE 2B
1965 Oshkosh Ave., Oshkosh, WI 54902-2600. (920) 231-2378. Fax: (920) 231-2502
Contact: Fr. Martin P. Carr
Mission Area: Oshkosh and surrounding area
Type of Service: community work, health care, soup kitchen, food pantry, domestic violence shelter, mission
Term of Service: 3 weeks to 1 year (or more)
Basic Benefits: room/board; free walk-in clinic
Basic Requirements: faith-filled, open heart; team worker; good health; able to live out Matt. 25: 31-46

FRANCIS HOUSE, INC.
2226 Maryland Ave., Baltimore, MD 21218. (410) 235-2588. Fax: (410) 243-6125. E-mail: pmcalpin@aol.com
Contact: Sr. Patricia McAlpin, OSF
Mission Area: Baltimore (MD)
Type of Service: direct service to the poor
Term of Service: 1 year
Basic Benefits: room/board; monthly stipend; medical insurance; transportation home
Basic Requirements: M/F; single; 21 and up
Affiliation: Sisters of St. Francis of Assisi

FRANCISCAN COMMON VENTURE
3390 Windsor Ave., Dubuque, IA 52001-1311. (563) 583-9786. Fax: (563) 583-3250. E-mail: goedkenr@osfdbq.org
Contact: Sr. Rita Goedken, OSF
Mission Areas: southern US: Texas, Mississippi, South Carolina, Iowa, Chicago
Type of Service: educational programs, GED, TESL, general pastoral care, children's recreation, immigration, resale store
Term of Service: 6 weeks - 1 year or longer
Basic Benefits: room/board; medical insurance; stipend; transportation to/from site
Basic Requirements: F; 21 and older; 2/4 year college degree or skills
Affiliation: Sisters of St. Francis of the Holy Family

FRANCISCAN COMPANIONS IN MISSION
Our Lady of Angels Convent, 609 S. Convent Rd., Aston, PA 19014-1207. (610) 558-7756. Fax: (610) 558-6131. E-mail: kboehm@osfphila.org; Web: www.osfphila.org
Contact: Kathy Boehm, Director
Mission Areas: Delaware Valley Area
Type of Service: education, health care, social and pastoral work
Term of Service: 1 to 2 years (renewable)
Affiliation: Sisters of St. Francis of Philadelphia

FRANCISCAN COVENANT PROGRAM
PO Box 970, San Juan Bautista, CA 95045-0970. (831) 623-1119. Fax: (831) 623-1118. E-mail: covprg@yahoo.com; Web: www.sbfranciscans.org
Contact: John & Jeanette Buege, Directors
Mission Areas: California, Arizona
Type of Service: primarily at retreat centers, administration, receptionist, bookkeeper, accountant, office work, health care, cook, maintenance, kitchen, housekeeping, gift shop, gardening, grounds, computer, nursing
Term of Service: 1-6 years (renewable annually, upon mutual agreement)
Basic Benefits: living allowance; room & board; health insurance
Basic Requirements: single/divorced/married couples w/o dependents; Catholic; 21-65; US citizenship
Affiliation: Franciscan Friars (Province of St. Barbara)

FRANCISCAN MISSION SERVICE OF NORTH AMERICA
PO Box 29034, Washington, DC 20017-0034. (202) 832-1762. Fax: (202) 832-1778. E-mail: fms5@juno.com; Web: http://franciscanmissionservice.catholic.edu
Contact: Megeen P. White, Co-Director
Mission Area: Central America, Zambia, Bolivia, Kenya, Philippines, Namibia, Brazil, Cameroon, Jamaica, Thailand and other Franciscan missions
Type of Service: health care, teachers, social workers, counselors, community developers, agriculturist, pastoral work
Term of Service: 3 months orientation plus 3 years service and 3 weeks re-entry/integration
Basic Benefits: monthly stipend; medical/life insurance; transportation to/from site, room/board
Basic Requirements: M/F; single/married; 23 to 65; Catholic

FRANCISCAN OUTREACH ASSOCIATION
1645 West Le Moyne St., Chicago, IL 60622-7120. (773) 278-6724. Fax: (773) 278-2170. E-mail: volunteer@franoutreach.org; Web: franoutreach.org
Contacts: Danielle Simonetti, Rev. Paul Gallagher, OFM
Mission Areas: greater Chicago metropolitan area
Type of Service: overnight shelter, dining room, showers/laundry
Term of Service: 1 year, 1-3 months summer, interim/holidays program
Basic Benefits: room/board (in community); small salary; medical insurance
Basic Requirements: M/F; single/married w/o dependents; college age and up
Affiliation: nonprofit, associated with Franciscan Friars (Province of the Assumption of the B.V.M.)

FRANCISCAN PARTNERS PROGRAM
PO Box 12315, Albuquerque, NM 87195. (505) 452-3270. Fax: (505) 452-1999. E-mail: bruceofm@aol.com; Web: www.hshields.com/guadalupe
Contact: Br. Bruce Michalek, OFM
Mission Areas: Navajo Reservation (AZ), New Mexico, Juarez (Mexico)
Type of Service: catechists, home visitors, teachers, doctors, nurses, office helpers, mechanics, construction, musicians, etc.
Term of Service: 1 year (shorter possible)
Basic Benefits: room; food allowance; personal stipend; commuting expenses; medical insurance, if necessary
Basic Requirements: M/F; 20 and older
Affiliation: Franciscan Friars (Province of Our Lady of Guadalupe)

FRANCISCAN VOLUNTEER MINISTRY
P.O. Box 29276, Philadelphia, PA 19125. (215) 427-3070. Fax: (215) 427-3059. E-mail: fvmpd@aol.com; Web: www.franciscanvolunteerministry.org
Contact: Katie B. Sullivan, Director
Mission Areas: Philadelphia, Wilmington (DE), Anderson (SC)
Type of Service: medical clinic assistant, ESL instructor, parish assistant, youth and elderly outreach, prison ministry, soup kitchen, teacher/teacher's aide, community organizer, other.
Term of Service: 1 year

Basic Benefits: room/board; stipend; medical insurance
Basic Requirements: M/F; single; Christian; 18 and up
Affiliation: Franciscan Friars (Province of the Most Holy Name)

FRANCISCAN VOLUNTEER PROGRAM (Cicero, IL)
4860 W. 29th St., Cicero, IL 60804-3611. (708) 656-7274. Fax: (708) 656-2708. E-mail: franvol@aol.com. Web: www.brotherfrancis.com
Contact: Cathy Miller, Director
Mission Areas: Midwestern and Southern states
Type of Service: parish work, HIV/AIDS service agencies, educational facilities, outreach to the homeless poor
Term of Service: 1 year – renewable.
Basic Benefits: room/board; small salary/stipend; medical insurance
Basic Requirements: M/F; 22 and up; college graduate
Affiliation: Franciscan Friars (Sacred Heart Province)

FRANCISCAN VOLUNTEER PROGRAM (Savannah, MO)
104 E. Park, PO Box 488, Savannah, MO 64485. E-mail: osf@ccp.com; Web: www.Sistersof stfrancis.org
Contact: Sr. Kathleen Reichert, OSF
Mission Areas: Missouri
Type of Service: Work with women in crisis, elderly, children, HIV/AIDS challenged, prisoners, and pastoral ministry
Term of Service: 1 month to 1 year
Basic Benefits: Room/board; orientation/in-service training; opportunities for daily participation in prayer/Eucharist; generally no salary, but payment for any contracted services
Basic Requirements: Regular volunteers: M/F; w/o dependents, over 21. Others: F; under 21; serve under a year (usually less than six months) modified form of program
Affiliation: Sisters of St. Francis of Savannah, MO (O.S.F.)

FRANCISCANS FOR THE POOR
60 Compton Rd., Cincinnati, OH 45215-5199. (877) 761-9040, ext. 110. Fax: (513) 761-6703. E-mail: karenhartman@voyager.net; Web: www.franforthepoor.com
Contact: Sr. Karen J. Hartman, SFP
Mission Area: Midwest US
Type of Service: inner-city ministry community work
Term of Service: (alternative spring mission break), short term (1 week or longer), long term (1 year or longer), youth groups for summers
Basic Benefits: room/board; medical insurance; stipend (long term)
Basic Requirements: M/F; single/married/widowed/divorced; 18 and up
Affiliation: Franciscan Sisters of the Poor

FRANCISCORPS (A Franciscan Lay Volunteer Experience)
Assisi Center, 800 N. Salina St., Syracuse, NY 13208. (315) 426-0481. Fax: (315) 473-0945. E-mail: francorps@aol.com. Web: www.franciscorps.org
Contact: Bro. Jim Moore, OFM Conv.
Mission Area: Syracuse
Type of Service: teaching, child care, youth programs, drop-in centers, soup programs, elderly, women's shelter, L'Arche
Term of Service: 1 year, begin early August, renewable
Basic Benefits: room/board; medical insurance; stipend; transportation to-from site; AmeriCorps ed award
Basic Requirements: M/F; single: college degree or equivalent
Affiliation: Franciscan Friars (Order of Friars Minor Conventual) (Immaculate Conception Province)

GATEWAY VINCENTIAN VOLUNTEERS
2912 Arsenal, St. Louis, MO 63118. (314) 771-1474, (1-888) 771-7220. Fax: (314) 771-2410. E-mail: gatevol@aol.com
Contact: Jim & Geri Ryan
Mission Area: St. Louis
Type of Service: social/community service, child care, criminal justice, health care assistance, parish ministry
Term of Service: 1 year, starting in August
Basic Benefits: room/board; medical insurance; stipend; transportation
Basic Requirements: M/F; 22-30; college degree or equivalent experience
Affiliation: Vincentians (Midwest Province)

GIMME A BREAK
St. Jude, 890 E. 154 St., So. Holland, IL 60473-1199. (708) 333-3550, 7595. Fax: (708) 339-3336. E-mail: srmm0812@aol.com; Web: www.cnd-m.com
Contact: Sister Marilyn Medinger, CND
Mission Areas: Many areas of the US and Canada
Type of Service: service to the poor, many in educational settings
Term of Service: one week during Christmas/spring break
Basic Benefits: room/board; community experience; possible financial aid for long distance travel
Basic Requirements: M/F; college students; $50 fee; adventurous spirit.

GLENMARY GROUP VOLUNTEER PROGRAM
Volunteer Director, PO Box 7, Vanceburg, KY 41179. (606) 796-3421. Fax: (606) 796-2606. E-mail jgrosek@glenmary.org: Web: www.glenmary.org
Contact: Joe Grosek
Mission Area: Lewis County, KY (Appalachia)
Type of Service: home repair/renovation, manual labor, health care center
Term of Service: 5-10 days (year-round)
Basic Benefits: participants pay nominal fee to cover room/board, accident insurance
Basic Requirements: groups 0f 12-20 (college, parish, high schools, etc.); M/F: 17-45; single; Catholic
Affiliation: Glenmary Home Missioners

GLENMARY PASTORAL COORDINATORS
1312 Fifth Ave. North, Nashville, TN 37208. (615) 256-4384. Fax: (615) 256-1902. E-mail: bdalton@glenmary.org; Web: www.glenmary.org
Contact: Rev. Robert Dalton, Director
Mission Areas: 10 states in Appalachia, the South and Southwest.
Type of Service: Starting new Catholic Churches in counties in the rural South where there currently is no Catholic congregation, or pastoring churches under missionary development. Emphasis on ecumenism, evangelization and justice.
Term of Service: long-term commitment desired
Basic Benefits: professional salary and benefits
Basic Requirements: master's degree in Theology; at least three years of missionary or parish experience (preferably in a rural and Southern setting).
Affiliation: Glenmary Home Missioners

GOOD SHEPHERD VOLUNTEERS
337 East 17th St., New York, NY 10003. (212) 475-4245, ext. 718; (888) 668-6GSV, ext. 780. Fax: (212) 979-8604. E-mail: gsv@

goodshepherds.org; Web: www.goodshepherdvolunteers.org
Contact: Maureen McGowan, RGS
Mission Areas: New York City, New Jersey, Washington (DC), Los Angeles, Philadelphia, Paraguay, Peru, Mexico
Type of Service: family and youth services, education, shelter for battered women, day care, economic empowerment, health care, advocacy
Term of Service: 1 to 2 years
Basic Benefits: room/board; modest stipend; medical insurance; student loan deferment
Basic Requirements: M/F; single; over 21, college or 2 years work experience
Affiliation: Sisters of the Good Shepherd

HOLY CROSS ASSOCIATES
P.O. Box 668, Moreau Seminary, Notre Dame, IN 46556. (574) 631-5521. E-mail: hca@nd.edu; Web: holycrossassociates.nd.edu
Contact: John Pinter
Mission Areas: Portland, OR; Phoenix, AZ; Coachella Valley, CA; Colorado Springs, CO; South Bend, IN; Brockton, MA; Wilkes-Barre, PA; Santiago, Chile; Pocuro, Chile
Type of Service: teaching, social work, outreach, parish ministries, general human services
Term of Service: August through following July (US), 2-1/2 years (Chile)
Basic Benefits: room/board; health insurance; AmeriCorps Education Award (US only); job assistance at end of program
Basic Requirements: M/F; single; 21 and up; Christian
Affiliation: Holy Cross Priests (Indiana Province)

HOPE HOUSE MINISTRIES
PO Box 358, Port Jefferson, NY 11777. (631) 928-2377 ext. 31. Fax: (631) 473-5210. E-mail: frfritz@aol.com; Web: montfortmissionaries.com
Contact: Father Francis Pizzarelli, smm
Mission Areas: Port Jefferson (NY)
Type of Service: residential care of 16-21 year olds, nontraditional junior/ senior high school, homeless, drug/alcohol treatment, family counseling
Term of Service: June, July, August
Basic Benefits: room/board; stipend
Basic Requirements: M; single; at least a college junior
Affiliation: Montfort Missionaries

HUMILITY OF MARY SERVICE - SEEDS OF HOPE
Humility of Mary Service, 20015 Detroit Rd., Rocky River, OH 44116-2418. (440) 333-5373. E-mail: kking19220@aol.com; Web: www.humilityofmary.org
Contact: Sr. Kathleen King, HM
Seeds of Hope, 820 W. Central Park, Davenport, IA 52804-1900. (563) 323-9466. Fax: (563) 323-5209. E-mail: seeds@chmiowa.org: Web: www.chmiowa.org
Contact: Barbara Gross, ACHM
Mission Areas: FL, WV, AZ, OH, SC, DC, TX; international: Chile (Humility of Mary Service)
Type of Service: social work, community work, nursing, parish outreach
Term of Service: 1 year (long term); short term varies
Basic Benefits: room/board; minimal stipend; need-based health insurance/transportation
Basic Requirements: M/F; 18 and up
Affiliation: Congregation /Sisters of the Humility of Mary

IDAHO MONASTIC LIVING EXPERIENCE
Monastery of St. Gertrude, HC 3 Box 121, Cottonwood, ID 83522-9408. (208) 962-3224. E-mail: vocation@stgertrudes.org; Web: www.stgertrudes.org
Contact: Sr. Janet Barnard, OSB
Mission Areas: rural Idaho
Type of Service: join in monastic life, particularly in aspects of community, prayer and outside work.
Term of Service: July 1-12, other possible dates
Basic Benefits: room/board
Basic Requirements: F; single; 18-45.

IHM VOLUNTEER PROGRAM (Monroe, WI)
610 West Elm Ave., Monroe, MI 48162. (734) 240-9820.
E-mail: membership@ihmsisters.org; Web: www.ihmsisters.org
Contact: Membership Coordinator
Mission Area: varied sites
Type of Service: summer environmental experiences, community supported agriculture
Term of Service: summer; 1 full year
Basic Benefits: room/board; stipend
Basic Requirements: M/F; single/ married w/o dependents; 21 and up; college/work experience; some connection to IHM Congregation
Affiliation; Sisters, Servants of the Immaculate Heart of Mary

IHM VOLUNTEER PROGRAM (Scranton, PA)
IHM Center, 2300 Adams Ave., Scranton, PA 18509-1598. (570) 963-2480. Fax: (570) 346-5439.
E-mail: coleme@sistersofihm.org; Web: ihm.marywood.edu
Contact: Sr. Eileen Coleman, IHM
Type of Service: catechetics, community work, education, health care, office work, migrant ministry, inner-city clinic, teen-age shelter, ministry to Native Americans, Hispanics, AIDS victims
Term of Service: 1-2 years; summer
Basic Benefits: room/board (with religious community); stipend; medical insurance
Basic Requirements: F; 21 and older (18 for summer program)
Affiliation: Sisters, Servants of the Immaculate Heart of Mary (Scranton, PA)

INNER-CITY TEACHING CORPS
3141 W. Jackson Blvd., Chicago, IL 60612. (773) 265-7240. Fax: (773) 265-7259. E-mail: teach@ictc-chicago.org, avasconcelos@ictc-chicago.org; Web: www.ictc-chicago.org
Contact: Anabela Vasconcelos
Mission Area: Chicago
Type of Service: teachers, inner-city elementary schools
Term of Service: 2 years
Basic Benefits: room/board; stipend; medical insurance; transportation; alternative teacher certification
Basic Requirements: M/F; single; 21-30; college degree
Affiliation: Catholic

INTERCOMMUNITY MINISTRY VOLUNTEER PROGRAM
1216 NE 65th St., Ste. 200, Seattle, WA 98115. (206) 442-4268. Fax: (206) 621-7046. E-mail: volunteer@imvp.org; Web: www.imvp.org
Contact: Sister Mary Medved, SNJM, Director
Mission Areas; US, some international locations
Term of Service: short/long term; summer
Type of Service: Work among Native Americans/migrant families/ Hispanic women/children, emergency affordable housing with services for families, food/clothing banks, housing for mentally handicapped people, work in orphanage, education for children living in poverty, detention ministry, adult literacy programs, peace/justice education
Basic Benefits: room/board; AmeriCorps ed award (2 or more

months of service)
Basic Requirements: M/F; 21 or older; Christian; married couples, retirees welcome
Affiliation: Nine communities of sisters: Sisters of St. Dominic of Tacoma, Sisters of Providence (Mother Joseph Province), Sisters of St. Francis of Philadelphia, Sisters of St. Joseph of Peace (Western Province), Sisters of Charity of the Blessed Virgin Mary, Sisters of the Holy Names of Jesus and Mary (California, Oregon, Washington Provinces), Adrian Dominicans

JESUIT VOLUNTEER CORPS
Contact: any office listed below or Web: www.jesuitvolunteers.org
EAST: Kate Haser, Executive Director, 801 St. Paul St., Baltimore, MD 21202. (410) 244-1744. Fax: (410) 244-1766. E-mail: jvceast @jesuitvolunteers.org
MIDWEST: Tim McCabe, Executive Director, 7333 West Seven Mile Rd., PO Box 21936, Detroit, MI 48221-0936. (313) 345-3480. Fax: (313) 345-5410. E-mail: jvcmw@jesuit volunteers.org
NORTHWEST: John Matcovich, Executive Director, PO Box 3928, Portland, OR 97208-3928. (503) 335-8202. Fax: (503) 249-1118. E-mail: jvcnw@jesuitvolunteers.org
SOUTHWEST: Yvonne Prowse, Executive Director, PO Box 40039, San Francisco, CA 94140-0039. (415) 522-1599, ext. 310. Fax: (415) 522-1633. E-mail: jvcsw @jesuitvolunteers.org
SOUTH: Pam Krinock, Executive Director, PO Box 3126, Houston, TX 77253-3126. (713) 756-5095. Fax: (713) 756-8928. E-mail: jvcsouth@ jesuitvolunteers.org
INTERNATIONAL: Dennis Heaphy, Executive Director, PO Box 3756, Washington, DC 20007. (202) 687-1132. Fax: (202) 687-5082. E-mail: jvi@jesuitvolunteers.org
Mission Areas: Throughout the US and in Belize, Boliva, Chile, Haiti, Marshall Islands, Micronesia, Nepal, Nicaragua, Peru, South Africa, Tanzania
Type of Service: Domestic ministry is in youth work, legal issues, AIDS ministry, emergency assistance, education, health care, housing issues, immigration, advocacy, etc. International ministry is primarily in education (including science and math) and social service
Term of Service: 1 year (Aug. to Aug. domestic); 2 years (international)
Basic Benefits: room/board; stipend; medical insurance; transportation home
Basic Requirements: M/F; single/ married - no dependents; over 21; Christian
Affiliation: Jesuits

JOSEPH HOUSE VOLUNTEERS
P.O. Box 1755, Salisbury, MD 21802-1755. (410) 543-1645. E-mail: lsjm@ezy.net; Web: www.thejosephhouse.org
Contacts: Sr. Patricia Lennon, Sr. Connie Ladd
Mission Areas: MD, DE, VA
Type of Service: any gifts and skills are useful
Term of Service: 1 year (renewable)
Basic Benefits: room/board; stipend; medical insurance
Basic Requirements: M/F; single/ married/widowed/divorced/religious; 21 and up; Christian
Affiliation: Little Sisters of Jesus and Mary

L'ARCHE COMMUNITIES
L'ARCHE USA
19230 Forest Park Dr., NE #H326, Seattle, WA 98155. (206) 306-1330. Fax: (206) 306-1329. E-mail: CHIMOS @aol.com; Web: www.larcheusa.org
Contact:Joan Eads, Zone Coordinator

L'ARCHE EASTERN US REGION
1101 Peach St., 2nd Fl., Erie, PA 16501. (814) 824-5130. Fax: (814) 452-4188. E-mail: vlwashek@ aol.com
Contact: Vicki Washek, Regional Coordinator

L'ARCHE CLEVELAND - Eastern Region
Box 20450, Cleveland, OH 44120. (216) 721-2614. Fax: (216) 229-2311. E-mail: office_larchecleveland @juno.com
Contact: Becky Brady, Director

L'ARCHE ERIE - Eastern Region
1101 Peach St., 2nd Fl., Erie, PA 16501. (814) 452-2065. Fax: (814) 452-4188. E-mail: office@ larcheerie.org
Contact: Lon Whitman, Director

L'ARCHE IRENICON - Eastern Region
PO Box 5034, Bradford, MA 01835. (978) 374-6928. Fax: (978) 373-9097. E-mail: office@larcheirenicon.org
Contact: Peg Newman, Director

L'ARCHE LYNCHBURG - Eastern Region
Box 2242, Lynchburg, VA 24501. (434) 384-6300. E-mail: larchebrm @ntelos.net
Contact: Mark Russell, Director

L'ARCHE SYRACUSE - Eastern Region
1232 Teall Ave., Syracuse, NY 13206. (315) 479-8088. Fax: (315) 479-8118. E-mail: larchesyracuse @aol.com
Contact: Frank Woolever, Director

L'ARCHE WASHINGTON, DC - Eastern Region
PO Box 21471, Washington, DC 20009. (202) 232-4539. Fax: (202) 387-1179. E-mail: community@ larche; Web: www.larchewashing tondc.org
Contact: John Cook, Director

L'ARCHE US CENTRAL REGION
445 1/2 5th Ave. S., Clinton, IA 52732. (563) 242-5624. E-mail: cenusa@mehsi.com
Contact: JoAnne Horstmann, Regional Coordinator
THE ARCH - Central Region
PO Box 0278, Clinton, IA 52732. (319) 243-9035 (tel, fax). E-mail: larchia@clinton.net
Contact: Maria Zeimen, Director

L'ARCHE CHICAGO
1049 S. Austin Blvd., Chicago, IL 60644. (773) 287-8249 (tel, fax). E-mail: larchechicago@hotmail.com
Contact: Deb Seles, Director

L'ARCHE HARBOR HOUSE - Central Region
700 Arlington Rd., Jacksonville, FL 32211-7306. (904) 744-4435. Fax: (904) 744-4470. E-mail: larchfl@ aol.com
Contact: Patrick Mayhew, Director

L'ARCHE HEARTLAND - Central Region
PO Box 40493, Shawnee Mission, KS 66204-4493. (913) 341-2265. Fax: (913) 648-6764. E-mail: larchkc@juno.com
Contact: Kathy Newham, Director

L'ARCHE MOBILE - Central Region
151 S. Ann St., Mobile, AL 36604. (334) 438-2094. Fax: (334) 433-5835. E-mail: larchmob@hotmail .com
Contact: Dennis O'Keefe, Director

L'ARCHE US WESTERN REGION
2382 NW Marshall St., Portland, OR 97210. (503) 227-3694. Fax: (503)

227-3157. E-mail: larchewregion@attbi.com
Contact: Joan Mahler, Regional Coordinator

L'ARCHE NEHALEM - Western Region
8501 SE Stephens, Portland, OR 97216. (503) 251-6901. Fax: (503) 251-6952. E-mail: mail@larche-portland.org
Contact: Mary Anne Ramey, Director

L'ARCHE NOAH SEALTH - Western Region
P.O. Box 22023, Seattle, WA 98122-0023. (206) 325-9434. Fax: (206) 568-0367. E-mail: gerry@larche.com
Contact: Gerry Scully, Director

L'ARCHE SPOKANE - Western Region
703 E. Nora, Spokane, WA 99207. (509) 483-0438. Fax: (509) 483-0460. E-mail: larchespokane@earthlink.net
Contact: Cathy Anderson, Director

L'ARCHE TAHOMA HOPE - Western Region
12303 36th Ave. E., Tacoma, WA 98446. (253) 535-3178. Fax: (253) 539-9208. E-mail: tahomahope@larchethc.org
Contact: Kevin Going, Director

WAVECREST-FRIENDS OF L'ARCHE
155 S. Angelina Dr. #274, Placentia, CA 92870. (714) 996 0219. E-mail: wavecrest@adelphia.net
Contact: Karen Carr, Director

Mission Areas: Alabama, California, Florida, Indiana, Illinois, Iowa, Massachusetts, Oregon, Pennsylvania, Ohio, Washington (DC), New York, Kansas, Virginia, State of Washington
Type of Service: living in communities, working and sharing life with developmentally disabled adults
Term of Service: 1 year to long term (flexible); some summer programs - 1 year preferred
Basic Benefits: room/board; generous stipend; health insurance: AmeriCorps ed award
Basic Requirements: M/F; single/married/religious; over 18; no experience required, but must be willing to commit to living in community
Affiliation: international, ecumenical, Christian

LALANNE
Center for Catholic Education, University of Dayton, Dayton, OH 45469-0531. (937) 229-3709. Fax: (937) 229-3670. E-mail: edward.brink@notes.edayton.edu; Web: www.udayton.edu/~lalanne
Contact: Br. Ed Brink, SM
Mission Areas: Cleveland, Dayton, Detroit, Indianapolis, Toledo
Type of Service: teaching in urban Catholic schools
Term of Service: 2 years
Basic Benefits: room; stipend; medical insurance; live in community; professional/spiritual development
Basic Requirements: M/F; have/be eligible for teacher certificate/license; for beginning teachers
Affiliation: Marianists (Society of Mary), University of Dayton

LAMP MINISTRIES
2704 Schurz Ave., Bronx, NY 10465. (718) 409-5062. E-mail: tscheuring@lampministries.org; Web: www.lampministries.org
Contacts: Drs. Tom and Lyn Scheuring, Marybeth and Ed Greene
Mission Areas: Metropolitan New York
Type of Service: ministries of Catholic evangelization, in materially poor parishes and with the homeless, sick and disabled
Term of Service: 1 year minimum, community living available
Basic Benefits: room/board; stipend; medical insurance; transportation to/from mission site
Basic Requirements: M/F; single/married/religious; over 24; Catholic
Affiliation: private, Catholic

LASALLIAN VOLUNTEERS
822 North Toney St., Philadelphia, PA 19130. (215) 382-9394; 4351 Garden City Drive, Suite 200, Landover, MD 20785. (301) 459-9410. Fax: (301) 459-8056; E-mail: LV@cbconf.org; Web: www.cbconf.org/ volunteers
Contact: David Kasievich
Mission Areas: California, Illinois, Missouri, Montana, New Jersey, New York, Pennsylvania, Rhode Island, Tennessee
Type of Service: education, social work, youth ministry
Term of Service: 1 year domestic (renewable)
Basic Benefits: room/board; small stipend; medical insurance; college loan deferment or forbearance; AmeriCorps ed awards; transportation to/from home/worksite/orientation/in-service sessions; spiritual growth and reflection; meaningful career experience
Basic Requirements: M/F; 21 and up; college degree or comparable work experience
Affiliation: De La Salle Christian Brothers

LAY EMD MISSIONER
Eucharistic Missionaries of St. Dominic, 3801 Canal St., Suite #400, New Orleans, LA 70119. (504) 486-1133. Fax: (504) 486-6547. E-mail: info@emdsisters.org; Web: www.emdsisters.org/membership.html
Type of Service: shares in the works of the Sisters
Term of Service: 1 year
Basic Benefits: room/board; experience ministry and community life of the Eucharistic Missionaries of St. Dominic; vocation discernment
Affiliation: Eucharistic Missionaries of St. Dominic

THE LAY MISSION – HELPERS ASSOCIATION (LMH)
3424 Wilshire Blvd., Los Angeles, CA 90010-2241. (213) 637-7222. Fax: (213) 637-6223. E-mail: lmh@la-archdiocese.org; Web: www.laymissionhelpers.org
Contact: Janice England, Coordinator
Mission Areas: Micronesia, American Samoa, Cameroon, Kenya, Central America, Marshall Islands
Type of Service: education, engineering/ construction, health care, office/computer work, finance/administration, skilled trades, computer technicians
Term of Service: 3 years
Basic Benefits: room & board; monthly stipend
Basic Requirements: M/F; single/married; over 21, Catholic
Affiliation: Archdiocese of Los Angeles

LORETTO VOLUNTEERS
Sisters of Loretto and Loretto Co-Members, Loretto Staff Office, 590 E. Lockwood Ave., St. Louis, MO 63119-3279. (314) 962-8112. Fax: (314) 962-0400. E-mail: bmecker@lorettocommunity.org; Web: www.lorettocommunity.org
Contact: Barbara Mecker, Volunteer Coordinator
Mission Areas: Denver, El Paso, Kansas City, Kentucky (rural areas) Mobile, New York, St. Louis, Thoreau (NM), Washington (DC)
Type of Service: (determined on

individual basis): community organizing, working in schools/after-school programs/day-care centers, Catholic Worker Houses, shelters for women/children, programs for children of migrant workers and their families, prison ministry, ecumenical retreat work, assisting Loretto's NGO representative at UN
Term of Service: summer, 6 months, 1 year
Basic Benefits: room/board; stipend; medical insurance
Basic Requirements: F; single; 20 or older
Affiliation: Sisters of Loretto

LSAV - FAMILY LIFELINE VOLUNTEERS, INC.
(formerly Little Sisters of the Assumption Volunteers)
132 Endicott St., Worcester, MA 01610. (508) 767-0365. Fax: (508) 791-3491. E-mail: director@familylifelinevolunteers.org; Web: www.familylifelinevolunteers.org
Contact: Tony Lorenzen, Director
Mission Areas: Massachusetts, New York, Pennsylvania
Type of Service: child care and youth workers, social workers, community health nurses, shelter staff, maintenance workers, advocacy counselors, teachers (ESL and GED), tutors, thrift shop workers, computer data entry, administrative/clerical help, van drivers, home attendants, organizers for food bank, etc.; summer youth programs seek recreational, organizational, creative talents
Term of Service: 4 months to 2 years (option to renew); priority given to 1 year commitment
Basic Benefits: room/board; 4+ months service: monthly stipend/health insurance; 2 weeks vacation for each full year of service
Basic Requirements: M/F; 20 and up; any religion
Affiliation: Little Sisters of the Assumption

MARIANIST VOLUNTARY SERVICE COMMUNITIES EAST
144 Beach 111th St., Rockaway Park, NY 11694-2592. (718) 945-2800. Fax: (718) 945-4662. E-mail: woberstersm@hotmail.com
Contact: Br. Walter Oberster, SM, Local Coordinator
Mission Area: Rockaway (Queens, NY)
Type of Service: child care, communications/public relations, education, tutoring, literacy programs, social services, counseling, recreation, coaching, youth ministry
Term of Service: 1 year, renewable
Basic Benefits: room/board; stipend; medical insurance; AmeriCorps ed award
Basic Requirements: M/F; 21 years and older; practicing Catholics
Affiliation: Marianists, Society of Mary

MARIST VOLUNTEER PROGRAM
PO Box 242, Esopus, NY 12429. (845) 384-6590. E-mail: wambliw@aol.com; Web: www.marist.net/~mvp/
Contact: Bro. Brice Byczywski, Director
Mission Area: US
Type of Service: education, community work, shelter, etc.
Term of Service: 1 year (renewable)
Basic Benefits: room/board; stipend; medical insurance; transportation to/from placement; college loan deferment; AmeriCorps ed award (possible)
Basic Requirements: M/F; single; 21 and up; Christian; college degree (for most positions)
Affiliation: Marist Fathers & Brothers, Marist Sisters, Marist Missionary Sisters, Marist Brothers of the Schools

MARYKNOLL MISSION ASSOCIATION OF THE FAITHFUL
Bethany Bldg., PO Box 307, Maryknoll, NY 10545-0307. (914) 762-6364. (800) 818-5276. Fax: (914) 762-7031. E-mail: kwright@mkl-mmaf.org, mcambier@mkl-mmaf.org; Web: www.maryknoll.org
Contacts: Kathy Wright, Margo Cambier
Mission Areas: Bolivia, Brazil, Cambodia, Chile, Kenya, Mexico, Peru, Salvador, Tanzania, Thailand, Venezuela, Vietnam, Zimbabwe
Type of Service: agriculture, communications, catechetics, education, health care, community work, pastoral, leadership training
Term of Service: 3-1/2 years
Basic Benefits: room/board; stipend; transportation to/from country of assignment
Basic Requirements: M/F; 21 or older; single/married with/without dependents, families with children no older than 8 yrs
Affiliation: Maryknoll Fathers, Brothers, Sisters

THE MATTHEW KELLY FOUNDATION
2330 Kemper Lane, Cincinnati, OH 45206. (513) 221-7700. Fax: (513) 221-7710. E-mail: julie@matthewkelly.org; Web: www.matthewkelly.org
Contact: Julie Gomez, Volunteer Coordinator
Mission Area: Cincinnati
Type of Service: assist the Foundation in its works, including managing speaking engagements; distribution of Catholic books, videos and tapes; hosting retreat in Fatima (Portugal); and help with quarterly newsletter
Basic Requirements: M/F

MERCY VOLUNTEER CORPS
1325 Sumneytown Pike, Gwynedd Valley, PA 19437-0901. (215) 641-5535. Fax: (215) 641-5503. E-mail: contactus@mercyvolunteers.org; Web: www.mercyvolunteers.org
Contact: Eileen M. Campbell, RSM
Mission Areas: throughout US; Guyana (South America)
Type of Service: catechetics, community work, education, health care, social work
Term of Service: 1 year
Basic Requirements: M/F; ages 21 and older; no dependents
Affiliation: Sisters of Mercy of the Americas (Regional Community of Erie)

MICHAELA FARM
PO Box 100, Oldenburg, IN 47036. (812) 933-0661. Fax: (812) 933-6403. E-mail: michaelafarm@seidata.com; Web: sonak.marian.edu/oldenburg/MichaelaFarm.html
Contact: Sr. Anita Brelage, OSF
Mission Area: Oldenburg
Type of Service; agricultural assistance, garden development, outdoor education
Term of Service: 9 months - 1 year
Basic Benefits: room/board; training in sustainable agriculture
Basic Requirements: 18 or over; single/married; interest in sustainable agriculture
Affiliation: Franciscan Sisters of Oldenburg

MILFORD SPIRITUAL CENTER YOUTH MINISTRY INTERNSHIP
5361 S. Milford Rd., Milford, OH 45150-9744. (513) 248-3517. Fax: (513) 248-3503. Web: milfordspiritualcenter.org
Contacts: Sarah Dodds
Mission Area: Milford, OH (Cincinnati area)
Type of Service: youth retreat team
Term of Service: 7 months (mid Sept.-mid Apr.)
Basic Benefits: health/dental insurance, stipend
Basic Requirements: M/F; single/religious
Affiliation: Jesuits (Chicago Province)

MISERICORDIA/HEART OF MERCY
6300 North Ridge, Chicago, IL 60660. (773) 273-4161. Fax: (773) 973-5214. E-mail: theresar@misericordia.com; Web: www.misericordia.com
Contact: Theresa Rooney, Director of Volunteers
Mission Area: Chicago (IL)
Type of Service: working with people with mental and/or physical disability in residential, vocational and recreational environments
Term of Service: minimum 2 to 3 hours per week for 6 months - 1 year
Basic Requirements: at least 16; desire to work with people with mental disability

MISSION DOCTORS ASSOCIATION
3424 Wilshire Blvd., Los Angeles, CA 90010. (626) 285-8868. Fax: (626) 309-1716. E-mail: missiondrs@earthlink.net; Web: www.missiondoctors.org
Contact: Mrs. Elise Frederick
Mission Areas: Africa, Latin America
Type of Service: medical
Term of Service: 3 years plus training; short-term program of less than 2 months
Basic Benefits: 3-year program; full sponsorship for physician and family; short-term program: support varies
Basic Requirements: Catholic, physician, completed 12-month residency, families welcome
Affiliation: Archdiocese of Los Angeles

MISSION OF FRIENDSHIP
St. Mark Center, 429 E. Grandview Blvd., PO Box 10397, Erie, PA 16514-0397. (814) 824-1230. Fax: (814) 824-1128. E-mail: TZoky@eriercd.org; Web: www.eriercd.org/missions4.asp
Contact: Sister Theresa Zoky, OSB
Mission Areas: Merida, Yucatan, Mexico and surrounding areas
Type of Service: nursing, public health promoter, elementary teaching in unstructured setting
Term of Service: 15 months
Basic Benefits: room/board; stipend; health Insurance; transportation to/from mission site
Basic Requirements: M/F; 23 years and up: single: ability to speak Spanish
Affiliation: Diocese of Erie

MISSIONARIES OF CHARITY BROTHERS VOLUNTEER PROGRAM
1316 S. Westlake Ave., Los Angeles, CA 90006. (213) 384-6116
Contact: Br. Bob Theis, MC
Mission Area: downtown Los Angeles
Type of Service: homeless, centers of hospitality serving handicapped and immigrants
Term of Service: 1-6 months
Basic Benefits: room/board; minimum health insurance
Basic Requirements: M; 18-45; single
Affiliation: Missionaries of Charity (Brothers) (founded by Mother Teresa)

MISSIONARY CENACLE VOLUNTEERS
Long term: Trinity Mission Center, P O Box 35105, Cleveland, OH 44135-0105. (800) 221-5740. Fax: (216) 671-2320. E-mail: cenaclevolunteer@aol.com; short term: same as above. E-mail: TrinityCtr@aol.com; Web: www.TMC3.org
Contacts: (Mr.) Shawn M. Witmer (long-term); Summer Program Coordinator (short-term)
Mission Areas: US, Mexico, Puerto Rico, Costa Rica
Type of Service: elementary school teachers, youth ministers, catechists, social workers, maintenance workers, retreat ministers, parish ministers, ministers to the homeless, the mentally challenged, youth in crisis, Native Americans, Hispanics and Appalachians
Term of Service: long-term: 1 year; short-term: 1 week-3 months
Basic Benefits: long-term: room/board; small monthly stipend; medical insurance; short-term: room/board
Basic Requirements: M/F; fluency in Spanish for long-term Hispanic ministry and some of the short-term Hispanic placements

MOUNT ST. BENEDICT MONASTERY LIVE-IN VOLUNTEER PROGRAM
Mount St. Benedict Monastery, 620 E. Summit Ave., Crookston, MN 56716-2799. (218) 281-3441. E-mail: volunteer@msb.net; Web: msb.net
Contact: Sister Eleanor Mueller, OSB
Mission Area: Crookston, MN
Type of Service: community work, education, health care, homeless, care of children
Term of Service: 1 month to 1 year (renewable)
Basic Benefits: room/board (in Benedictine community)
Basic Requirements: F; single or single again; 23 and up
Affiliation: Benedictine Sisters (Crookston, MN)

NATIVITY PREPARATORY SCHOOL
39 Lamartine St., Jamaica Plain, MA 02130. (857) 728-0031. Fax: (857) 728-0037. E-mail: lafontainesj@bchigh.edu; Web: www.nativityboston.org
Contact: Fr. James Lafontaine, SJ
Mission Area: Boston
Type of Service: middle school teachers (inner-city boys school
Term of Service: 1 year minimum, renewable
Basic Benefits: room/board; medical insurance; AmeriCorps ed award; Boston College graduate credits
Basic Requirements: M/F; college degree
Affiliation: Jesuits (New England Province)

NAZARETH COMMON VENTURE
285 Bellevue Rd., Pittsburgh, PA 15229-2195. (412) 931-4778, ext. 2281. Fax: (412) 931-9746. E-mail: innazareth@aol.com;
Web: www.csfn.org
Contact: Sr. Rose Mary Modzelewski, CSFN
Mission Areas: PA, OH, MI
Type of Service: education, health care, care for the elderly, child care, soup kitchen, parish ministry, family services, housing services
Term of Service: long-term:1 year (renewable); short-term:1 week to 6 months
Basic Benefits: room/board; small stipend; medical insurance
Basic Requirements: M/F; 21-40 (negotiable); single; 2 years work experience/education
Affiliation: Sisters of the Holy Family of Nazareth

NAZARETH FARM
Rt. 2, Box 194-3, Salem, WV 26426. (304) 782-2742. Fax: (304) 782-4358. E-mail: nazarethfarm@citynet.net; Web: www.nazarethfarm.org
Contact: Kay McCluskey
Mission Area: Doddridge County, West Virginia
Type of Service: community work, construction, housing rehabilitation, youth ministry

Term of Service: 1 year
Basic Benefits: room/board; stipend; medical insurance
Basic Requirements: M/F; single/ married/ widowed/divorced/religious; 21 years and up
Affiliation: Diocese of Wheeling/ Charleston

NAZARETH HOMES
399 NE 25th Terr., Boca Raton, FL 33431. (561) 392-9474. Fax: (561) 392-9475. E-mail: nazhomes@aol.com
Contact: Sister Rita Baum, SSJ
Mission Area: So, Florida (Boca Raton area)
Type of Service: sharing with residents: joys/sorrows, chores/ celebrations in small-group homes for adults with developmental disabilities
Term of Service: I year (renewable)
Basic Benefits: room/board; stipend; health insurance
Basic Requirements: M/F; 21 and older

NETWORK (A National Catholic Social Justice Lobby)
801 Pennsylvania Ave., SE, Ste. 460, Washington, DC 20003-2167. (202) 547-5556. Fax: (202) 547-5510. E-mail: network@networklobby.org; Web: www.networklobby.org
Contact: Linda Rich
Mission Area: Washington, DC
Type of Service: advocacy, lobbying for social justice
Term of Service: 11 months (September - July)
Basic Benefits: stipend; contribution to health plan
Basic Requirements: M/F; college graduates through retiree age
Affiliation: Catholic, independent

NEW ORLEANS VOLUNTEER SERVICE COMMUNITY
Brothers of the Sacred Heart, 4600 Elysian Fields Ave., New Orleans, LA 70122. (504) 288-7456. Fax: (504) 288-9920. E-mail: brotherhenry@hotmail.com; Web: www.novsc.org
Contact: Br. Henry Gaither, S.C.
Mission Areas: LA, MS, AL, AZ
Type of Service: work with young people (teach, tutor, coach, etc.)
Term of Service: 1 school year
Basic Benefits: room/board; small stipend; medical insurance; possible AmeriCorps award; transportation expenses negotiable
Basic Requirements: M; single; 20 to 30; Catholic
Affiliation: Brothers of the Sacred Heart

NEW YORK TEACHER VOLUNTEER PROGRAM
Archdiocese of New York, Department of Education, 1011 First Ave., New York, NY 10022. (212) 371-1011, ext. 2803. Fax: (212) 758-3018. E-mail: sr.deanna.sabetta@archny.org; Web: ny-archdiocese.org/education/volunteer
Contact: Sister Deanna Sabetta, CND
Mission Areas: NY City (Manhattan, Bronx)
Type of Service: teaching in inner-city high schools
Term of Service: 1 year
Basic Benefits: room/board; stipend; health insurance; AmeriCorps education awards
Basic Requirements: F; 21 years and older; college graduate (teaching degree/certification not required)
Affiliation: Archdiocese of New York

NEWARK BENEDICTINE VOLUNTEER PROGRAM
520 Martin Luther King Blvd., Newark, NJ 07102-1314. (973) 792-5751. Fax: (973) 643-6922. E-mail: aholtz@sbp.org; Web: www.newarkabbey.org
Contact: Fr. Albert Holtz, OSB
Mission Area: Newark
Type of Service: teaching, tutoring, sports, clerical, community outreach, catechesis, food pantry
Term of Service: September - June; summer 6 weeks: end of June - August
Basic Benefits: room/board; stipend; medical insurance; possible deferment of student loans
Basic Requirements: M; 20 - 30 years old; no dependents
Affiliation: Benedictine Monks, Newark Abbey

NOTRE DAME MISSION VOLUNTEER PROGRAM
403 Markland Ave., Baltimore, MD 21212. (410) 532-6864. Fax: (410) 532-2418. E-mail: natloffice@ndmva.org; Web: www.ndmva.org
Contact: Sr. Katherine Corr, SND, Director
Mission Area: rural, urban US
Type of Service: tutoring, literacy education, GED, ESL
Term of Service: 1 year (renewable)
Basic Benefits: community housing; monthly stipend; medical insurance; AmeriCorps ed award
Basic Requirements: M/F; single/ married w/o dependents; 21 and up; work experience and/or college education
Affiliation: Sisters of Notre Dame de Namur

OBLATE LAY MISSIONARIES
224 South DeMazenod Dr., Belleville, IL 62223-1035. (877) 361-4617. E-mail: laymissionaries@omiusa.org; Web: www.omiusa.org
Contact: Director
Mission Areas: US, Mexican border
Type of Service: community work
Term of Service: 1 year
Basic Benefits: room/board; stipend; medical insurance; transportation; annual retreat/vacation
Basic Requirements: Catholic, single/married couple w/small children; 21 or older
Affiliation: Missionary Oblates of Mary Immaculate (Priests & Brothers)

OFFICE OF LAY VOLUNTEERS (Referral Agency)
Diocese of Youngstown, 144 W. Wood St., Youngstown, OH 44503. (330) 744-8451, ext. 276. Fax: (330) 744-2848. E-mail: tadolan@dioceseofyoungstown.org
Contact: Thomas Aquinas Dolan, O.P., Director
Affiliation: Diocese of Youngstown

OUR LADY OF MERCY COMMUNITY OUTREACH
Volunteers in Ministry, PO Box 607, 1684 Brownswood Rd., Johns Island, SC 29455. (843) 559-4109. Fax: (843) 559-8819. E-mail: olmoutreach@aol.com
Contact: Sister Carol Wentworth, OLM
Mission Areas: rural communities, Sea Islands, Charleston County, SC
Type of Service: education, ESL tutors, housing, outreach to poor, home repair, tutoring
Term of Service: long-term: 9 months; short-term: 1 week to 6 months, summer program in July
Basic Benefits: room/board; living allowance; medical insurance where necessary
Basic Requirements: m/f; 21 year and older; singe/married w/o dependents
Affiliation: Sisters of Charity of Our Lady of Mercy

PASSIONIST LAY MISSIONERS
Western Province: 5700 N. Harlem Ave., Chicago, IL 60631-2342. (773) 631-6336; Fax: (773) 631-8059. E-mail: plm@visioni.com; Web: www.passionist.org/plm

Contacts: Soyun Kim, Carrie Maus
Mission Areas: Chicago, Detroit
Type of Service: education, community organizing, social work, legal advocacy, youth work, housing and homelessness issues, outreach to elderly and more
Term of Service: 1 year (renewable - begins mid-August)
Basic Benefits: room/board; monthly stipend; medical insurance; deferred student loans (up to $4,750 in loan cancellation); job training; retreats; community living
Basic Requirements: M/F; single/ married w/o dependents; 21 and up; Christian commitment; summer:18 and up;1-2 weeks: groups only
Affiliation: Passionist Priests & Brothers (Holy Cross Province)

PASSIONIST VOLUNTEERS
80 David St., South River, NJ 08882. (732) 257-7177. Fax: (732) 257-0042. E-mail: passionistvol@sr.cpprov.org; Web: www.passionistvolunteers.org
Contact: Jill Wallace, Jennifer Wiley
Mission Areas: Appalachian Mountains (WV); Brooklyn; international: Jamaica and Honduras (pending)
Type of Service: recreation, community outreach with youth and elderly, home repair, literacy, mentoring, tutoring, youth ministry
Term of Service: 2 to 10 weeks; summer; year long: Aug. - Aug.
Basic Benefits: room/board (in community with other volunteers); year long: room/board, stipend, health insurance
Basic Requirements: M/F; single/ married/families with children/ retirees; 18 and up, out of high school for at least one year; flexibility, sense of humor
Affiliation: Passionist Priests & Brothers (Province of St. Paul of the Cross)

PIARIST VOLUNTEERS
Highway 80, Box 870, Martin, KY 41649-0870. (606) 285-3950. Fax: (606) 285-3950. E-mail: piarist@ kih.net
Contact: Fr. Thomas Carroll, Sch.P.
Mission Areas: Appalachian region of Eastern Kentucky
Type of Service: education, outreach work
Term of Service: 1 year, renewable
Basic Benefits: room/board; stipend; medical insurance; transportation to/from mission site
Basic Requirements: M/F; single; college education
Affiliation: Piarist Fathers and Brothers

PIME VOLUNTEERS
17330 Quincy St., Detroit, MI 48221. (313) 342-4066. Fax: (313) 342-6816. E-mail: volunteers@ pimeusa.org
Contact: Fr. George Berendt
Mission Areas: Asia, Africa, Latin America, Papua New Guinea
Type of Service: medical, physical therapy, agriculture
Term of Service: 3 to 5 years minimum
Basic Requirements: M/F; Catholic; college graduate; useful skills

PRESENTATION MINISTRIES
3230 McHenry Ave., Cincinnati, OH 45211. (513) 662-5378. Web: www.presentationministries.com
Contact: Marianne Lander
Mission Areas: worldwide
Type of Service: Bible teaching, retreats, publishing, developing small Christian communities
Term of Service: one year (renewable)
Basic Benefits: growth in holiness, building God's kingdom
Basic Requirements: strongly committed Catholic, love for Jesus in the sacraments

PROVIDENCE HOUSE
703 Lexington Ave., P.O. Box 210529, Brooklyn, NY 11221. (718) 455-0197. Fax: (718) 455-0692. E-mail: sorensonm@providence house.org; Web: providencehouse .org
Contact: S. Marie Sorenson
Mission Areas: Brooklyn, Queens, Westchester County in New York
Type of Service: being present to the needs of homeless women and children in 6 residential settings
Term of Service: 1 week to 1 year
Basic Benefits: room/board; long term: stipend/health benefits
Basic Requirements: F; single/ married; 21 or older
Affiliation: Diocese of Brooklyn

PROVIDENCE VOLUNTEER MINISTRIES (Allison Park, PA)
9000 Babcock Blvd., Allison Park, PA 15101-2713. (412) 635-5433. Fax: (412) 635-6318. E-mail: CDProvMin@aol.com; Web: www. sistersofdivprovidence.org
Contact: Sr. Donna Tracy
Mission Area: Pennsylvania and surrounding states; Puerto Rico
Type of Service: education, human services, health care, pastoral care, summer: day camp, child day care, work w/elderly
Term of Service: 3 months to 1 year (renewable); short-term: 2-week summer program
Basic Benefits: room/board; stipend; health insurance; AmeriCorps ed award
Basic Requirements: F; Christian; 21 and older
Affiliation: Sisters of Divine Providence (St. Peter's Province)

PROVIDENCE VOLUNTEER MINISTRIES (Kingston, MA)
363 Bishops Hwy., Kingston, MA 02364-2035. (781) 585-3545. Fax: (781) 582-1596. E-mail: angelacdp@adelphia.net
Contact: Sr. Angela Provost, CDP
Mission Areas: small towns south of Boston
Type of Service: education, pastoral care of sick, handicapped, elderly; outreach to homeless and poor, as instructor, visitor, musician, caretaker, aide
Term of Service: 3 months to 1 year (renewable); three weeks in summer
Basic Benefits: room/board; monthly stipend, health insurance (long-term); transportation to ministry
Basic Requirements: F; Catholic; 18 and up (summer); 20 and up (long-term); w/o dependents
Affiliation: Sisters of Divine Providence

PROVIDENCE VOLUNTEER MINISTRY (Saint Mary-of-the-Woods, IN)
Sisters of Providence, Saint Mary-of-the-Woods, IN 47876-1095. (812) 535-3131, ext. 259. E-mail: mmontgom@spsmw.org; Web: www.sistersofprovidence.org or www.p-v-m.org
Contact: Sr. Mary Montgomery, SP
Mission Areas: CA, IN, IL, KY, Washington, DC
Type of Service: education, community services, trades
Term of Service: short term (8 wks. minimum); long term (6 months - 2 years)
Basic Benefits: room/board; long-term: stipend/medical insurance; local transportation, AmeriCorps education award
Basic Requirements: M/F; single; 20 and up
Affiliation: Sisters of Providence of Saint Mary-of-the-Woods

QUEST
3706 Rhode Island Ave., Mt. Rainier, MD 20712-2009. (301) 277-3594. Fax: (301) 277-8656. E-mail: Joanfaraone@aol.com; Web: www. quest-rjm.org
Contact: Sr. Joan Faraone, RJM

Mission Areas: Gros Morne, Jean Rabel (Haiti)
Type of Service: education, child care, community work, nurses, AIDS ministry
Term of Service: 6 weeks (summer); 1 year (renewable; Sept. to Aug.)
Basic Benefits: room/board; stipend/ medical insurance; orientation; retreats throughout year
Basic Requirements: M/F; single/ married/religious; 21 and older
Affiliation: Religious of Jesus and Mary

RED CLOUD VOLUNTEERS
Holy Rosary Mission, 100 Mission Dr., Pine Ridge, SD 57770. (605) 867-5888. E-mail: cdippold@redcloudschool.org; Web: www.redcloudschool.org
Contact: Christina Dippold
Mission Area: Pine Ridge Indian Reservation, SD
Type of Service: elementary and secondary education
Term of Service: 1 school year (renewable; 2-3 years preferred)
Basic Benefits: room/board; monthly stipend; medical insurance; travel allowance
Basic Requirements: M/F; single/ married; college degree; Christian
Affiliation: Jesuits (Wisconsin Province)

REDEEMER MINISTRY CORPS
521 Moredon Rd., Huntingdon Valley, PA 19006. (215) 914-4116. E-mail: rmcorps@aol.com; Web: www.sistersholyredeemer.org
Contact: Eileen Zebrowski
Mission Areas: Philadelphia and suburbs, South Jersey
Type of Service: health care and social services, including nursing, therapies, social work, child day care, pastoral counseling, clerical work; also homeless mothers, elder care, hospice care
Term of Service: 1 year (renewable)
Basic Benefits: room/board; monthly stipend; medical insurance; transportation home after year
Basic Requirements: M/F; single; 21 and over; Christian
Affiliation: Sisters of the Holy Redeemer

REDEMPTORIST VOLUNTEER MINISTRIES
Sarnelli House, PO Box 29303, Philadelphia, PA 19125. (215) 739-9112. Fax: (215) 739-8881. E-mail: CSSRvols@aol.com; Web: www.redemptoristvolunteerministries.org
Contact: Father Kevin Murray, C.Ss.R
Mission Areas: long-term: inner city Philadelphia; short-term: outreach to other East Coast cities and the Caribbean
Type of Service: ministries to abandoned poor
Term of Service: long-term: 6-12 months; short-term: 1-4 weeks
Basic Benefits: long-term: room/ board, full medical/dental insurance, stipend; short-term: room/board
Basic Requirements: M/F; 20-26; openness to persons who are poor/abandoned; desire to live in faith-based community.
Affiliation: Redemptorists (Baltimore Province)

RESPONSE-ABILITY
Rosemont College, Rosemont, PA 19010-1699. (610) 527-0200, 525-2186. E-mail: ra@ravolunteers.com; Web: www.ravolunteers.com
Contacts: Audrey Ruppert, Liz Eager
Mission Areas: Philadelphia, Los Angeles, Washington (DC), Dominican Republic, Chile
Type of Service: education; other opportunities in Dominican Republic and Chile.
Term of Service: 1 or 2 year programs
Basic Benefits: room/board; stipend/ medical insurance: long term
Basic Requirements: M/F; single; bachelor's degree
Affiliation: Society of the Holy Child Jesus

ST. ANN'S CATHOLIC SCHOOL
PO Box 2020, Belcourt, ND 58316. (701) 477-2667. Fax: (701) 477-0602. E-mail: annschl@utma.com; Web: solt3.org
Contact: Fr. Dan Estes, SOLT
Mission Area: Turtle Mt. Indian Reservation (ND)
Type of Service: certified elementary teachers, teachers' aides, administrative staff, religious education (school); staff/mentors for camp (Hearts United)
Term of Service: August - May (school); June-July (camp)
Basic Benefits: room/board; monthly stipend; health insurance (negotiable)
Basic Requirements: M/F; 18 and up; single/married/families; loyal to Catholic Church
Affiliation: Society of Our Lady of the Most Holy Trinity (Priests, Sisters)

ST. FRANCIS CATHOLIC MISSION SCHOOL
P.O. Box 1028, Gallup, NM 87305. (505) 863-3563. Fax: (505) 863-8150
Contact: Fr. Thomas Maikowski
Mission Area: northern New Mexico
Type of Service: teachers: P-6
Term of Service: school year, Aug. - June
Basic Benefits: room/board (in community); monthly stipend; medical insurance
Basic Requirements: M/F; single; 21 and up; college degree, Catholic
Affiliation: Diocese of Gallup

ST. JOSEPH'S CATHOLIC WORKER HOUSE
402 South Ave., PO Box 31062, Rochester, NY 14603. (585) 232-3262. E-mail: cathworker@frontiernet.net
Contact: George McVey, Volunteer Coordinator
Mission Area: Rochester
Type of Service: work with poor and homeless of Rochester, NY in soup kitchen, shelter and outreach
Term of Service: 1 year or longer
Basic Benefits: housing with other volunteers; stipend; medical insurance
Basic Requirements: M/F; ability to get along with others in a diverse Catholic worker community setting
Affiliation: Catholic Worker

SAINT JUDE'S MISSION CENTER
Rt. 5, Box 1083, Louisa, KY 41230. (606) 638-0219. E-mail: jimh1@lycomonline.com
Contact: Fr. Ralph Beiting
Mission Areas: Appalachian counties of Lawrence, Martin, Floyd (Kentucky)
Type of Service: mobilizing rural communities, community resource centers, warehouses, rummage stores
Term of Service: long-term: 1 year (renewable); short-term: 3-8 months; 1 week for groups
Basic Benefits: long-term: room/ board, stipend, medical insurance; short-term: room/board
Basic Requirements: long-term: M/F; single/married/widowed/ divorced w/o dependents; 21 years and older; short-term: 18 years and older; groups: 7th grade and older
Affiliation: Diocese of Lexington

SAINT MICHAEL INDIAN SCHOOL
PO Box 650, St. Michaels, AZ 86511. Elementary: (928) 871-4636, e-mail: skksbs@aol.com; high

school: (928) 871-4443, e-mail: kries@schoolaccess.net
Type of Service: teachers, counselors, coaching
Term of Service: academic year (early August - early June)
Basic Benefits: housing; stipend; medical insurance
Basic Requirements: M/F; teachers: college degree, (preferably ed major)
Affiliation: Sisters of the Blessed Sacrament

ST. VINCENT PALLOTTI CENTER FOR APOSTOLIC DEVELOPMENT
(Clearinghouse/long-term/short-term volunteer - Referral agency)
NATIONAL OFFICE: Terrace Level, 415 Michigan Ave. N.E., Washington, DC 20017. 877-VOL-LINK (877-865-5465). E-mail: pallotti@pallotticenter.org; Web: www.pallotticenter.org
Contacts: Andrew Thompson, National Director; Dani Clark Scano, Program Director; Kaela M. Volkmer, Volunteer Contact
REGIONAL OFFICES:
BOSTON, MA
St. Vincent Pallotti Center, 159 Washington St., Brighton, MA 02135. (617) 783-3924. E-mail: volservice@aol.com
Contact: Kristelle Angelli, Director
PATERSON, NJ
St. Vincent Pallotti Center, 476 17th Ave., Paterson, NJ 07504. (973) 523-1544. E-mail: pallotti03@aol.com
Contact: Anita Saira Morawski, Director
SACRAMENTO, CA
St. Vincent Pallotti Center, 5890 Newman Court, Rm. 14, Sacramento, CA 95819. (916) 454-4320. E-mail: pallotti02@aol.com
Contact: Sally Quinn Reed, Director
ST. LOUIS, MO
St. Vincent Pallotti Center, 4532 Lindell Blvd., St. Louis, MO 63108. (314) 367-5500. E-mail: jsmith@archstl.org
Contact: Maureen Cunningham, Director

SALESIAN LAY MISSIONERS
2 LeFevre Lane, PO Box 30, New Rochelle, NY 10802. (914) 633-8344. Fax: (914) 633-7404. E-mail: slm@salesianmissions.org
Contact: Marie Carr
Mission Areas: Mexico, Bolivia, China, Ecuador, Papua New Guinea, Philippines, Sierra Leone, Thailand, Alabama, California, Florida, New York, New Jersey, Ohio, Texas
Type of Service: youth minister, religious education, staff for recreation/camp services, rural life ministry, counselor, pastoral/parish minister, building tradesman, Hispanic ministry, teaching in schools
Term of Service: 1-2 years ordinarily; shorter term by arrangement (e.g. camps)
Basic Benefits: room/board; medical insurance; transportation to/from mission site
Basic Requirements: M/F; single/married w/o dependents; 20 to 60; college education or work experience; Christian commitment; US citizen
Affiliation: Salesians of Don Bosco (Priests, Brothers and Sisters)

SALESIAN SISTERS VOLUNTEER PROGRAM
659 Belmont Ave., North Haledon, NJ 07508. (973) 790-6202. Fax: (973) 790-6125. E-mail: volunteersvides@hotmail.com; Web: www.fmausa.org
Contact: Michelle Geiger, Program Coordinator
Mission Area: Newton, NJ
Type of Service: summer camps: group counselor, recreational activities, arts/crafts
Term of Service: 3-7 weeks (summer)
Basic Benefits: room/board
Basic Requirements: F; 18-30 years; good health; desire to work with youth
Affiliation: Salesian Sisters of St. John Bosco (Eastern Province)

SAN MIGUEL SCHOOL
1949 W. 48th St., Chicago, IL 60609-4145. (773) 890-1481. Fax: (773) 254-3382. E-mail: manderer@juno.com; Web: www.san-miguel.org
Contact: Mike Anderer-McClelland
Mission Area: inner city Chicago
Type of Service: education (grades 6-8, all subjects) for low-income, at-risk youth
Term of Service: 1 year minimum (2 years preferred)
Basic Benefits: room/board; stipend; medical insurance; AmeriCorps ed award; travel to and from site
Basic Requirements: M/F; teaching skills (preferred); experience with/love for early adolescents
Affiliation: DeLaSalle Christian Brothers (Midwest Province)

SCALABRINIAN VOLUNTEER PROGRAM
PO Box 77, El Paso, TX 79941-0077. 011-52-16-870676. Fax: 011-52-16-870677. E-mail: progvoluntariado@hotmail.com; Web: www.migrante.com.mx
Contact: Fr. Francisco Pellizzari, c.s.
Mission Areas: urban parishes in Chicago, Los Angeles, Houston; border shelters: Tijuana, Tapachula, Ciudad Juarez (Mexico); Tecun-Uman (Guatemala)
Type of Service: migrant worker ministry, immigration/refugee services
Term of Service: one year, renewable
Basic Benefits: room/board; health insurance; monthly allowance
Basic Requirements: M/F; single/married w/o dependents; 21-35

SERVICE IN THE CITY
3058 N. Mango Ave., Chicago, IL 60634-5216. (888) 827-1724 (toll free); (773) 237-6367; E-mail: bolzan@sndden.org; Web: www.sndden.org
Contact: Gerry Bolzan, SNDdeN
Mission Areas: various - in East/West/Midwest
Type of Service: education and social services among poor families, children, homeless people and/or recent immigrants in collaboration with the Sisters of Notre Dame de Namur
Term of Service: 1 week - dates vary by site
Basic Benefits: room and board
Basic Requirements: F; single; own health insurance; 18 - 40
Affiliation: Sisters of Notre Dame de Namur

SHARED HORIZONS
912 Market St., La Crosse, WI 54601-8800. (608) 791-5290. Fax: (608) 782-6301. E-mail: affiliation@fspa.org
Contact: Karen Neuser
Mission Areas: US, Cameroon, Africa
Type of Service: varies
Term of Service: 10 months - 1 year
Basic Benefits: room/board; stipend; medical insurance (in some cases)
Basic Requirements: M/F; single/married w/o dependents; 23 and older; college and/or work experience
Affiliation: Franciscan Sisters of Perpetual Adoration

SIDE BY SIDE LAY VOLUNTEER PROGRAM
5625 Isleta Blvd., SW, Albuquerque, NM 87105. (505) 873-2059; Fax: (505) 877-2571; E-mail: sbsvolunteers@aol.com

Contact: Sr. Liz Chambers, fdcc
Mission Areas: New Mexico, Mexico, Africa, Asia, Latin America
Type of Service: pastoral ministry, health care, education, social work, community work
Term of Service: 18 months; 1 year
Basic Benefits: room/board; stipend; medical insurance
Basic Requirements: F; single; Catholic
Affiliation: Canossian Daughters of Charity

SISTERS OF CHARITY OF CINCINNATI: ASSOCIATES IN VOLUNTEER MINISTRY
5900 Delhi Rd., Mt. St. Joseph, OH 45051. (513) 347-5473. Fax: (513) 347-5467. E-mail: associates@srcharitycinti.org; Web: www.srcharitycinti.org
Contact: Mary Jo Borgman
Mission Areas: Ohio, Texas, New Mexico and Colorado
Type of Service: education, health care, pastoral ministry, social service
Term of Service: short, long-term options
Basic Benefits: varies
Basic Requirements: M/F; single/married; no dependents; 20 and older
Affiliation: Sisters of Charity of Cincinnati

SISTERS OF ST. JOSEPH - COMPANIONS IN MISSION
975 E. Gardenia, Madison Heights, MI 48071-3431. (248) 582-9163. E-mail: nazvocation@aol.com; Web: www.SSJNazareth.org
Contacts: Bernadette Dean, SSJ, Marie Hogan, SSJ
Mission Area: Kalamazoo (MI)
Type of Service: soup kitchen, Meals on Wheels, youth and elderly programs, ecological work, migrant camps
Term of Service: 1 week (6/20 to 6/26/2004)
Basic Requirements: F; single/married; 18 or older

SISTERS OF SAINT JOSEPH VOLUNTEER CORPS
891 Jay St., Rochester, NY 14611-1219. (585) 529-5689. Fax: (585) 529-9989. E-mail: ssjvol@juno.com; Web: www.ssjvolunteers.org
Contact: Sr. Donna Del Santo, SSJ
Mission Areas: long-term: Rochester; short-term: Rochester, Pine Apple (AL
Type of Service: teachers, teachers aides, child care, elderly, social/outreach workers
Term of Service: long-term: 6-12 months; short-term: 1-2 weeks, summer
Basic Benefits: long-term: room/board, stipend, health benefits, AmeriCorps ed grants; short-term: room/board
Basic Requirements: M/F; 21 years and older (long-term), 18 years and older (short-term)
Affiliation: Sisters of St. Joseph of Rochester

SISTERS OF THE BLESSED SACRAMENT LAY VOLUNTEERS
1663 Bristol Pike, Bensalem, PA 19020-5796. (215) 244-9900, ext. 383. E-mail: soulliardm@aol.com or sbs@libertynet.org
Contact: Sr. Mary John Soulliard, SBS
Mission Area: St. Michaels on Navajo Reservation, AZ
Type of Service: education, house staff, nurse or nurse's aide
Term of Service: 10 months to 1 year (renewable)
Basic Benefits: room/board; stipend; medical insurance; transportation to/from mission site
Basic Requirements: M/F; single/married w/o dependents/widowed/religious; 21 and over; Catholic.

SISTERS OF THE DIVINE SAVIOR SALVATORIAN SUMMER SERVICE PROGRAM
4311 North 100 St., Milwaukee, WI 53222-1393. (414) 466-0810. E-mail: SrMary@SDSvocations.com; Web: www.SDSvocations.com
Contact: Sr. Mary Frost
Mission Area: Wisconsin
Type of Service: poverty relief services, elderly outreach, parish/pastoral ministries, homeless shelters
Term of Service: summer: extended weekend; 1 week
Basic Requirements: F; single; Catholic; interested in religious life; 18 and up.

S.M.A. LAY MISSIONARIES
256 North Manor Circle, Takoma Park, MD 20912-4561. (301) 891-2037. Fax: (301) 270-6370. E-mail: smausa-v@smafathers.org
Contact: Theresa Hicks
Mission Areas: Liberia, Ghana, Cote d'Ivoire, Kenya
Type of Service: education, health, development, agriculture, pastoral ministries, catechetics, social work, etc.
Term of Service: Formation: Sept.-April in Takoma Park (MD); 3 months language training in country, followed by 3 years service with a 6 week break in US midway
Basic Benefits: room/board; stipend; medical insurance; transportation to/from mission site
Basic Requirements: M/F; single or married w/o dependents; college degree; at least 2 years work experience; 23-50 years; Catholic
Affiliation: Society of African Missions

SOCIETY OF OUR LADY OF THE MOST HOLY TRINITY
PO Box 152, Robstown, TX 78380-0152. (361) 767-2079; (361) 387-8090. Fax: (361) 387-3818. E-mail: soltlaity@yahoo.com
Contacts: Jennifer Knebel, Deacon Wayne Lickteig
Mission Areas: Native, Hispanic & Afro Americans throughout the US; Belize; Guatemala; Thailand; the Philippines; Mexico, Haiti, New Guinea, Africa (lay volunteers not in all areas)
Type of Service: catechetics, health care, evangelization, addictions, orphanage, pastoral ministries, community work, education, construction, mechanic, crafts, housekeeper, cook
Term of Service: orientation, 1 year minimum; society members: 3 year commitment
Basic Benefits: room/board
Basic Requirements: M/F; single/married/widowed with or w/o dependents; 22 and over; college degree needed for some; Catholic
Affiliation: Society of Our Lady of the Most Holy Trinity (Priests, Sisters)

SOCIETY OF OUR MOTHER OF PEACE
Queen of Heaven Solitude, 12494 Hwy. T, Marionville, MO 65705. (417) 744-2011
Contact: Sister Mary Faith
Mission Areas: St. Louis (MO), Springfield (MO), the Philippines
Type of Service: person-to-person evangelization especially within the black community; manual and domestic work at the monastery: cooking, maintenance, carpentry, plumbing, etc.
Term of Service: Negotiable/but at least 2 years for manual and domestic service/long term preferred for evangelization service
Basic Benefits: room/board; stipend; prayer with the religious community
Basic Requirements: M/F; single/married/divorced/separated (w/o dependents); 22 to 55; Catholic
Affiliation: Society of Our Mother of

Peace (Priests, Brothers, Sisters)

SOJOURNERS MAGAZINE
2401 15th. St. NW, Washington, DC 20009. (202) 328-8842. Fax: (202) 328-8757
Contact: Robin Fillmore
Mission Area: Washington, DC
Type of Service: administrative, Internet support, development, marketing, editorial assignments
Term of Service: 1 month to 1 year
Basic Requirements: commitment to social justice

SPIRITAN ASSOCIATES
Laval House, Duquesne University, Pittsburgh, PA 15282. (412) 765-3755. Fax: (412) 765-1983. E-mail: DonMcEachin@aol.com; Web: www.spiritans.org
Contact: Fr. Don McEachin
Mission Areas: Haiti, Tanzania, Ghana, US
Type of Service: education, administration, crafts, tradesman, agriculture, mechanic, pilot, administrator
Term of Service: 3 years
Basic Benefits: room/board; stipend; medical insurance; transportation to/from mission site; relocation allowance
Basic Requirements: M/F; 22 or older; college education plus a few years of professional experience.

STARCROSS COMMUNITY
34500 Annapolis Rd., Annapolis, CA 95412. (707) 886-1919. E-mail: community@starcross.org; Web: www.starcross.org
Contact: Sr. Julie De Rossi
Mission Area: Sonoma County (CA)
Type of Service: office work, housework, farm maintenance
Term of Service: 6 months to 1 year (renewable)
Basic Benefits: room/board
Basic Requirements: M/F; single/married/divorced/separated/religious; 21 years and up

SU CASA CATHOLIC WORKER
Central American Martyrs Center, 5045 S. Laflin St., Chicago, IL 60609. (773) 376-9263. Fax: (773) 376-9291
Contact: Volunteer Coordinator
Mission Area: inner-city Chicago
Type of Service: work among homeless Latino families: community activities, neighborhood gardens, soup kitchen, etc.
Term of Service: 1 year minimum (summer, college break also)
Basic Benefits: room/board; stipend; medical insurance; AmeriCorps ed awards
Basic Requirements: M/F; single/married/religious; 10 and older; Spanish helpful
Affiliation: Catholic Worker

URBAN CATHOLIC TEACHER CORPS
Boston College, Campion Hall, 140 Commonwealth Ave., Chestnut Hill, MA 02467. (617) 552-0602. Fax: (617) 552-2499. E-mail: gervaism@bc.edu; Web: www.bc.edu/bc_org/avp/soe/urbcathteach.html
Contact: Madeleine Gervais
Mission Area: Boston area inner-city schools
Type of Service: teaching
Term of Service: 2 years
Basic Benefits: room/board; stipend; medical/dental benefits; loan forgiveness/deferment
Basic Requirements: M/F; single; 21 and older; college grads with student teaching experience
Affiliation: Archdiocese of Boston, Boston College

URSULINE COMPANIONS IN MISSION, CENTRAL REGION
Ursuline Center, 210 Glennon Heights Rd., Crystal City, MO 63019-1199. (314) 937-6206. Fax: (314) 937-7627. E-mail: fulgenzi@osucentral.org; Web: www.ursulinecompanions.org
Contact: Sister Diane Fulgenzi, osu
Mission Areas: IL, LA, MN, TX, MO
Type of Service: education, child care, social work, pastoral ministries, youth ministry, poverty relief services, ministry to the elderly, Hispanic ministry
Term of Service: academic and calendar year (renewable); short term, esp. summer
Basic Benefits: room/board; stipend; long-term: medical insurance; transportation to/from mission site
Basic Requirements: Christian men and women, single/married w/o dependents
Affiliation: Ursuline Sisters (Roman Union, Central Province)

VIDES WEST USA
(International volunteer organization for the development/education of at-risk young people/women)
632 Filbert St., San Francisco, CA 94133. (415) 433-1588. Fax: (415) 421-6049. E-mail: videswusa@prodigy.net; Web: www.vides.org, www.fmausa.org
Contact: Sister Rachel Crotti, FMA
Mission Areas: TX, LA, AZ, CA; over 90 nations worldwide
Type of Service: community outreach benefiting at-risk women and children; youth ministry; education; social services and healthcare in mission regions.
Term of Service: 2 months - 2 years
Basic Benefits: room/board; basic medical insurance
Basic Requirements: M/F; 18-35; single/married; US citizen/resident
Affiliation: Salesian Sisters of St. John Bosco (Western Province)

VINCENTIAN SERVICE CORPS (VSC)
VSC EAST: St. John's University-Annex 31, 8000 Utopia Pkwy., Jamaica, NY 11439. (718) 990-6266. Fax: (718) 990-2307. E-mail: vsceast@stjohns.edu; Web: www.vscorps.org
Contact: Sr. Kathleen Kull, Director
VSC CENTRAL: 7800 Natural Bridge Rd., St. Louis, MO 63121-4694. (314) 382-2800, ext 249. Fax: (314) 382-8392. E-mail: vcscentral@juno.com; Web: see above
Contact: Sr. Mary Catherine Dunn, DC, Director
Mission Areas: Urban and rural areas throughout the US
Type of Service: Adult literacy teachers, advocacy workers, case workers for shelters and/or mentally ill, child care workers, community organizers, computer programmers, volunteer coordinators, crisis counselors, day care workers, fund raisers, health care professionals (RN, LPN, CNA, therapists), immigration/refugee counselors, legal aides, maintenance workers, nursing home assistants, outreach workers to the homebound elderly, parish ministers, pastoral care ministers, skilled laborers, social workers, teachers and teachers' aides (grade and middle schools), youth ministers.
Term of Service: 1 to 2 years (renewable).
Basic Benefits: room/board; monthly stipend; medical insurance; loan deferment; AmeriCorps education award
Basic Requirements: M/F; single, married/widowed; 20 years and up; college degree or significant life/work experience; persons with disabilities possible; Christian; desire for challenge and ability to be flexible
Affiliation: VSC: EAST: Vincentian Priests & Brothers, Daughters of Charity (Albany, Convent Station, Emmitsburg, Halifax)
VSC CENTRAL: Daughters of Charity (West Central Province)

VISITATION NEIGHBORS
Visitation Monastery, 1527 Fremont Ave. N, Minneapolis, MN 55411-3232. (612) 521-6113. Fax: (612) 521-4020. E-mail: vmonastery@aol.com
Contacts: Sr. Mary Virginia Schmidt, Sr. Suzanne Homeyer
Mission Area: Minneapolis inner-city neighborhood
Type of Service: building relationships with the neighborhood through day care, social services, support groups, etc.
Term of Service: 1 year minimum (renewable for another year)
Basic Benefits: shared households; medical insurance
Basic Requirements: M/F; 20 years and older; single/married/retired; college and/or work experience
Affiliation: Visitation Sisters (Visitation Monastery of Minneapolis)

VOLUNTEER MISSIONARY MOVEMENT
5980 W. Loomis Rd., Greendale, WI 53129. (414) 423-8660. E-mail: vmm@vmmusa.org; Web: www.vmmusa.org
Contact: Gregory W. Smith
Mission Areas: Africa, Central America, central cities in US
Type of Service: health care, agriculture, community work, education, labor, pastoral ministry, social work
Term of Service: 2 years
Basic Benefits: vary according to project
Basic Requirements: M/F; single/married/widowed; 23 and over; Christian commitment
Affiliation: private, Catholic tradition

VOLUNTEERS FOR LIFE
2900 Sunset Place #109, Los Angeles, CA 90005. (213) 382-2707. E-mail: Vforlife@aol.com, mmount@aol.com; Web: www.volunteersforlife.org
Contacts: Sr. Paula Vandegaer, SSS, Joan M. Mount
Mission Area: greater Los Angeles area
Type of Service: direct service/administration in pro-life agencies, Respect Life offices, maternity homes, day care centers, etc.;
Term of Service: 1-2 years
Basic Benefits: room/board; stipend; medical insurance; transportation to and from place of work
Basic Requirements: M/F; 21 years and older; single/married w/o dependents; college education or work experience
Affiliation: Sisters of Social Service

VOLUNTEERS IN AN ACT OF HOPE
519 East 118th St., New York, NY 10035. (212) 410-3465. Web: www.rscj.org/volunteers
Contact: Natalie Runfola, RSCJ
Mission Areas: East Harlem (NY), Houston
Type of Service: literacy programs/teaching, work with homeless, health care, family counseling
Term of Service: 11 months (renewable)
Basic Benefits: room/board; medical insurance; stipend; transportation to/from site; AmeriCorps ed award
Basic Requirements: F; 21 and older; sincere desire to work with the poor
Affiliation: Society of the Sacred Heart (Religious of the Sacred Heart)

VOLUNTEERS IN MISSION
137 Mt. St. Joseph Rd., Wheeling, WV 26003. (304) 232-8160, ext. 126. Fax: (304) 232-1404. Web: ssjwhg.org
Contact: Sister Judith Minear, SSJ
Type of Service: community work, education, health care, spiritual growth/development, retreat work
Basic Requirements: F; 19-40
Affiliation: Sisters of Saint Joseph of Wheeling

VOLUNTEERS WITH THE SISTERS OF THE HOLY NAMES OF JESUS AND MARY
P O Box 907, Los Gatos, CA 95031. (408) 287-3145, 395-5150. Fax: (408) 354-8305. E-mail: everettsnjm@earthlink.net; Web: www.imvp.org, www.holynames.net
Contact: Rosemary Everett, snjm
Mission Areas: US, Canada, Nicaragua, Haiti, Mexico
Type of Service: Available in many of the sponsored works of the Sisters, also with IMVP (Intercommunity Ministry Volunteer Program)
Term of Service: short/long term; ongoing
Basic Requirements: M/F
Affiliaiton: Sisters of the Holy Names of Jesus and Mary (California Province)

WOMEN IN SERVICE TO APPALACHIAN SUMMER PROGRAM
77 Garfield, Woburn, MA 01801. (781) 933-1367. E-mail: barbara jstygies@attloi.com; Web: www.womeninservice.org
Contact: Barbara Stygies
Mission Area: Rural Eastern Kentucky
Type of Service; home repair, parish visiting, recreation with school-age children, visiting elderly
Term of Service: 1 week
Basic Benefits: training in Appalachian culture: $150 fee covers room/board, insurance, transportation to/from Cincinnati
Basic Requirements: F; 18 and up: good health
Affiliation: Glenmary Home Missioners

XAVERIAN VOLUNTEER CORPS
Xaverian Brothers Generalate, 4409 Frederick Ave., Baltimore, MD 21229. (410) 644-0034. E-mail: mmccarthy@xaverianbrothers.org
Contact: Bro. Michael McCarthy, CFX
Mission Area: Haiti
Type of Service: sharing of one's self and gifts. Possibilities include tutoring, athletics, community formation, religious education, English as a second language, and working with youth, elderly, the sick, the poor and marginalized
Term of Service: 1 year
Basic Benefits: strong community/spiritual life with live-in Xaverian Brothers; room/board; stipend; health insurance; travel to/from mission area
Basic Requirements: M; Christian (preferably Catholic); 21 and up; college or work experience; flexibility; desire for community and service; sense of humor
Affiliation: Xaverian Brothers

YOUTH SERVICE OPPORTUNITIES PROJECT (YSOP)
15 Rutherford Place, New York, NY 10003. (212) 598-0973, ext. 105. E-mail: ysopnyc@ysop.org; Web: www.ysop.org
Contact: Paul Nelson
Mission Area: throughout New York City, Washington, DC
Type of Service: ongoing programs at service agencies helping homeless and hungry people, typically: soup kitchens, drop-in centers, clothing and food banks and recreational programs for children living in family shelters.
Term of Service: single day, overnight, weeklong workcamps; internships in YSOP office - minimum of 6 weeks
Basic Requirements: M/F; hs/college students; nondenominational

Associates, Oblates, Secular Institutes and Other Communities

APOSTOLIC OBLATES
(Secular Institute for Women)
For information contact: Teresa Monaghen, AO, 11002 N. 204th St., Elkhorn, NE 68022. (402) 289-2670. E-mail: psm@mitec.net; 205 S. Pine Dr., Fullerton, CA 92833; 739 E. 87th St., Brooklyn, NY 11236. Web: www.secularinstitutes.org or www.prosanctity.org

APOSTOLIC SODALES
(Secular Institute for Diocesan Priests)
For information contact: Rev. Michael F. Murphy, 672 B Ave., Coronado, CA 92118-2299. (619) 435-3167. E-mail: pastor@sacred heartcor.org; Web: www.secular institutes.org/as.htm

BLESSED TRINITY MISSIONARY INSTITUTE
(An Association of the Faithful for Men and Women)
For information contact: Margaret Hayes, 198 Bartholdi Ave., Jersey City, NJ 07305. (908) 647-5311. Web: www.tmc3.org/NewFrameset .htm

CARITAS CHRISTI
(Secular Institute for Women)
For information contact: Caritas Christi, New Member Coordinator; PO Box 5162, River Forest, IL 60305-1900. E-mail: vocations@ ccinfo.org; Web: www.ccinfo.org

CATECHISTS OF SACRED HEART OF JESUS [Ukrainian]
(Secular Institute for Women)
Contact: Cecelia Daciuk, 161 Glenbrook Rd., Stamford, CT 06902. (203) 327-6374

COMPANY OF ST. PAUL
(Secular Institute for Lay People and Priests)
For information contact: Rev. Stuart Sandberg, 52 Davis Ave., White Plains, NY 10605. (914) 946-1019. Web: www.secularinstitutes.org

CRUSADERS OF ST. MARY
(Secular Institute for Men)
For information contact: Antonio Pérez Alcalá, 2001 Great Falls St., McLean, VA 22101 . (703) 536-3546. Web: www.secularinstitutes .org/csm.htm

DIOCESAN LABORER PRIESTS
(Secular Institute)
For information contact: Rev. Rutilio J. del Riego, 5250 Central Ave., Riverside, CA 92504. (909) 689-8921. Fax: (909) 689-3619. E-mail: rutiliodelriego@aol.com; Web: www.secularinstitutes.org

DON BOSCO INSTITUTE
(Association of the Faithful for Celibate Men)
For information contact: Fr. John Puntino, SDB, Salesian Center, 80 S. Sixth St., Columbus, OH 43215-4784. (614) 224-8000, ext. 405. Fax: (614) 224-8000, ext. 7. E-mail: puntinosdb@juno.com; Web: www.secularinstitutes.org

DON BOSCO VOLUNTEERS
(Secular Institute for Women)
For information contact: Coordinator, PO Box 588, Hawthorne, NJ 07506. (973) 238-0797. E-mail: dockatie@ aol.com; Web: www.secularinstitutes .org/dbv.htm

FR. KOLBE MISSIONARIES OF THE IMMACULATA
(Secular Institute for Women)
For information contact: Ada Locatelli, Anna Brizzi, 531 E. Merced Ave., West Covina, CA 91790-5025. (626) 917-0040; Fax: (626) 917-0900. E-mail: FKMincal@ aol.com; Web: www.kolbemission .org or www.secularinstitutes.org

FRANCISCAN MISSIONARIES OF JESUS CRUCIFIED
(Association of the Faithful for Men and Women. Persons with disabilities most welcome.)
For information contact: Louise D. Principe, FMJC, 400 Central Ave., Apt. 3D, Albany, NY 12206-2207. (518) 438-5887. Web: www.secular institutes.org/a-fmjc.htm

HANDMAIDS OF DIVINE MERCY
(Secular Institute for Women)
For information contact: Elaine Gagilano, 2410 Hughes Ave., Bronx, NY 10458. (718) 409-2153. Web: www.secularinstitutes.org

INSTITUTE OF THE HEART OF JESUS
(Secular Institute for Diocesan Priests and Lay Women; Association of the Faithful for Lay Men)
priests: Rev. William S. Whelan, Conception Seminary, Conception, MO 64433. E-mail: bwhelan@ conception.edu; men: David Bland, PO Box 17310, Los Angeles, CA 90017. (213) 385-406); women: Diana Bland, 1112 N. Naomi St., Burbank, CA 91505. (818) 558-6624. E-mail: PTL4E@msn.com: Web: www.secularinstitutes.org

LAY MISSIONARIES OF THE PASSION
(Secular Institute)
For information in Tri-State Area contact: Constance Leist, 311 Leonard St., Brooklyn, NY 11211. (718) 387-3619. E-mail: Leo311c@ aol.com; Web: www.secular institutes.org

MISSION OF OUR LADY OF BETHANY
(Secular Institute for Women)
For information contact: Estelle Nichols, 7 Locksley St., Jamaica Plain, MA 02130. (617) 522-1961 or PO Box 807, Boston, MA 02130. Web: www.secularinstitutes.org/ mlb.htm

MISSIONARIES OF THE KINGSHIP OF CHRIST
(Based on Franciscan spirituality: one Institute for Women, one for Men)
For information contact: Charles Dahlin, President, PO Box 34513, Bethesda, MD 20827 (women); Fr. Dominic Monti, OFM, St. Bonaventure Friary, St. Bonaventure, NY. (716) 375-2532 (men). Web: www. simkc.org, www.secularInstitutes .org/mkcm.htm

OBLATE MISSIONARIES OF MARY IMMACULATE
(Secular Institute for Women)
For information contact: Theresa Cademartori, 1015 Grand St., #5-D, Hoboken, NJ 07030-2156. E-mail: demartori@aol.com; Web: www. ommi-is.org

OPUS SPIRITUS SANCTI
(Apostolic Life Community for Sisters; Secular Institute for Diocesan Priests; Secular Institute for Single Women; Community of Apostolic Christians; Apostolic Life Community for Priests)

For information contact: Rev. James McCormick, Midwest Coordinator, Holy Spirit Church, 421 E. Bluff St., Carroll, IA 51401-3099. (712) 792-4386. Fax: (712) 792-8038. E-mail: frjim@pionet.net; Web: www.secular institutes.org

PIUS X
(Secular Institute for Men)
For information contact: Rev. Gerald C. Lacroix, P.O. Box 7731, Charlesbourg, Quebec, Canada G1G 5W6. E-mail: lafamille_ispx@yahoo.com: Web: www.ispx.org or www.secularinstitutes.org

REGNUM CHRISTI MOVEMENT
(Association for the promotion of the Christian vocation. For lay men/women, deacons and priests.)
For information, contact: Fr. Anthony Bannon, LC, 393 Derby Ave., Orange, CT 06477. (203) 795-2800

SECULAR INSTITUTE OF ST. FRANCIS DE SALES
(Secular Institute composed of two groups: professed women; associates-men and women, married and single)
For information contact: (CT area): Therese C. Keyes, 87 Gerrish Ave. T2, East Haven, CT 06512. (203) 469-3277. Fax: (203) 469-2094. E-mail: tkyes03e@aol.com. (DE area): Mary Robinson, 3127 Charing Cross, Wilmington, DE 19808. (302) 234-8616. E-mail: geegaugh@aol .com. (MD area): Janet Miller, 3440 Aldino Rd., Churchville, MD 21028. (410) 734-6240. (VA area): Nancy Prizio, 3503 Jean St., Fairfax, VA 22030. (703) 591-5196. E-mail: jbereswill@cox.rr.com; Web: www. secularinstitutes.org/sfs.htm

SECULAR INSTITUTE OF THE SCHOENSTATT SISTERS OF MARY
(Secular Institute for Women)
W284 N 404 Cherry Lane, Waukesha, WI 53188-9416. (262) 542-4384. Fax: (262) 542-5730. E-mail: vocation@schsrsmary.org or schoenstattsisters@schsrsmary; Web: www.schsrsmary.org or www.schoenstatt-texas.org

SERVITIUM CHRISTI
(Secular Institute for Women)
For information contact: Olympia Panagatos, 1540 York Ave., Apt. 16R, New York, NY 10028. (212) 734-9748. Web: www.secular institutes.org/sc.htm

SOCIETY OF OUR LADY OF THE WAY
(Secular Institute for Women)
2339 N. Catalina St., Los Angeles, CA 90027-1128; 1925 Eastman Ave., Green Bay, WI 54302; 584 Capitol Ave., Bridgeport, CT 06606; 1064 Oxford Rd., Cleveland Heights, OH 44121. Web: www.secular institutes.org/slw.htm

VOLUNTAS DEI INSTITUTE
(Secular Institute of Pontifical Right for priests, celibate laymen and married couples)
For information contact: Rev. George Hazler, 615 Palm Ave., Los Altos, CA 94022 or Rev. Michael Craig, 4257 Tazewell Terrace, Burtonsville, MD 20866. (301) 549-3286. E-mail: ivdusa@cs.com; Web: www.voluntasdeiusa.org or www.secularinstitutes.org

MISCELLANEOUS

ANAWIM COMMUNITY
(Corning, NY) (For Priests, Single Lay People and Married Couples)
Contacts: Fr. Daniel Healy, Director; Barbara Brennan, Co-Director, Anawim Community, 122 East First St., Corning, NY 14830. (607) 936-4965. Fax: (607) 936-0207. E-mail: corning@anawim.com; Web: www. anawim.com

ANAWIM COMMUNITY
(Frenchville, PA) (For Priests, Single Lay People and Married Couples)
Contact: Sister Therese Dush, PO Box 186, Frenchville, PA 16836. (814) 263-4518. E-mail: anawimco @pennswoods.net

APOSTOLATE FOR FAMILY CONSECRATION
(Mission: To transform families, parishes and neighborhoods)
3375 County Rd. 36, Bloomingdale, OH 43910-7903. (740) 765-5500, 1-800-77-FAMILY. Fax: (740) 765-5561. E-mail: info@familyland.org; Web: www.familyland.org

CONSECRATED WIDOWS AND WIDOWERS
Casa San Jose, 109 W. Avenue F, Robstown, TX 78380. (361) 387-2754. Web: www.solt3.org/widows .htm
Purpose: Prayer and service of the Church, through a vow of perpetual chastity as a sign of the kingdom of God. (Pope John Paul 11, Post-Synodal Apostolic Exhortation Vita Consecrata, No. 7)
For: M/F
Affiliation: The Society of Our Lady of the Most Holy Trinity (Priests and Sisters)

MAGNIFICAT
(A Ministry to Catholic Women)
1629 Metairie Rd., Suite 3, Metairie, LA 70005-3926. (504) 828-6279. Fax: (504) 828-1060. E-mail: magnificatcst@aol.com; Web: www.magnificat-ministry.org
Purpose: To evangelize and to encourage Catholic women to grow in holiness through opening more fully to the gifts of the Holy Spirit
For: Catholic women
Contact: Magnificat Chapter Information

SERRA INTERNATIONAL
220 S. State St., Ste. 1703, Chicago, IL 60604. (800) 488-4008. Fax: (800) 377-7877. E-mail: jwoodward @serrainternational.org; Web: www.serra@serrainternational.org
Purpose: To foster vocations to the religious life through prayers, meetings, vocation awareness programs; to help its members (laity and permanent deacons) to live their own Christian vocations to service
For: M/F, all ages, all walks of life
Contact: John W. Woodward, Executive Director

US ASSOCIATION OF CONSECRATED VIRGINS
(An association of persons in the United States who have received the Consecration of Virgins for women living in the world, according to Canon 604 of the New Code of Canon Law.)
PO Box 1212, Oregon City, OR 97045-0091. (503) 656-7828. Fax: (503) 656-5361. E-mail: info@ consecratedvirgins.org; Web: www. consecratedvirgins.org
For: Women
Contact: Loretta Matulich

ASSOCIATES, THIRD ORDERS, OBLATES

Note: If you are interested in a community not listed here, contact them directly to find out if they have an associate, oblate, etc. program.

ACJ ASSOCIATES
8141 NW 11 Court, Pembroke Pines, FL 33024
Contact: Evelyn Quinones
Affiliation: Handmaids of the Sacred

Heart of Jesus (acj) (2796 Galahad Dr. NE, Atlanta, GA 30345. (404) 636-5970. Web: www.acjusa.org)

ACSCO ASSOCIATES (ASSOCIATES OF THE SISTERS OF CHARITY OF OTTAWA)
St. Joseph Province, 559 Fletcher St., Lowell, MA 01854-3434. (978) 441-1452. E-mail: pmalo@attbi.com
Contact: Sr. Claire Cayer, s.c.o.
Affiliation: Sisters of Charity of Ottawa (S.C.O.) (Grey Nuns of the Cross)

AFFILIATES - SISTERS OF THE HOLY SPIRIT (S.H.S.)
5246 Clarwin Ave., Pittsburgh, PA 15229. (412) 931-1917. E-mail: srshs@aol.com
Contact: Sister Patricia Eleanor Myers, SHS
Affiliation: Sisters of the Holy Spirit (S.H.S.)

ALAM (ASSOCIATION OF LAITY IN MINISTRY OF MERCY)
Villa Rossello, 1009 Main Rd., Newfield, NJ 08344-5203. (856) 697-2983. E-mail: dmnewfield@yahoo.com
Contact: Sister Mary Grace
Affiliation: Daughters of Our Lady of Mercy
For women

APOSTLES OF THE RESURRECTION (Chicago Western Province)
7432 W. Talcott Ave., Chicago, IL 60631-3743. (773) 792-6363. E-mail: callres@hotmail.com
Contact: Director of Associates
Affiliation: Sisters of the Resurrection (C.R.)

APOSTLES OF THE RESURRECTION (New York Eastern Province)
35 Boltwood Ave., Castleton-on-Hudson, NY 12033. (518) 732-2226. E-mail: crsister@resurrectionsisters.org; Web: www.resurrectionsisters.org
Contact: Sister Dolores Marie, C.R.
Affiliation: Sisters of the Resurrection (C.R.)

ASSOCIATE COMMUNITY OF DIVINE PROVIDENCE
St. Anne Convent, 1000 St. Anne Dr., Melbourne, KY 41059. (859) 441-0700, ext. 308. E-mail: vaolfzorn@hotmail.com; Web: www.cdpkentucky.org
Contact: Sr. Virginia Ann Wolfzorn, CDP
Affiliation: Sisters of Divine Providence (Melbourne, KY)

ASSOCIATE MEMBERS OF THE SOCIETY OF OUR MOTHER OF PEACE (SMP)
Mary the Font Solitude, 6150 Antire Rd., High Ridge, MO 63049. (636) 677-0644
Contact: Sr. Anne Marie
Affiliation: Society of Our Mother of Peace (SMP); Third Order

ASSOCIATE PROGRAM (Sisters of Charity of Leavenworth)
4200 S. 4th St., Leavenworth, KS 66048-5054. (913) 758-6522. E-mail: ssmith@scls.org; Web: www.scls.org
Contact: Sister Sharon Smith, SCL
Affiliation: Sisters of Charity of Leavenworth

ASSOCIATE PROGRAM OF THE DAUGHTERS OF THE HOLY SPIRIT
4 Ravine St., Putnam, CT 06260-1818. (860) 928-6163. E-mail: lindabdhs@juno.com
Contact: Sr. Linda Babineau, DHS
Affiliation: Daughters of the Holy Spirit, Holy Spirit Provincial House, 72 Church St., Putnam, CT 06260. (860) 928-0891

ASSOCIATE PROGRAM (Sisters of St. Joseph of LaGrange - CSJ)
1515 W. Ogden Ave., LaGrange Park, IL 60526. (708) 354-9200. E-mail: pbergen@csjlagrange.org; Web: www.csjlagrange.org
Contact: Pat Bergen, CSJ
Affiliation: The Sisters of St. Joseph of LaGrange, IL (CSJ)

ASSOCIATE PROGRAM OF THE VISITATION NUNS
Visitation Monastery, 8902 Ridge Blvd., Brooklyn, NY 11209-5716. (718) 745-5151. Fax: (718) 745-3680. E-mail: vamonastery@aol.com; Web: www.visitationsisters.org/mona/bro_main.asp
Contact: Sr. Aimee Franklin, V.H.M.
Affiliation: Visitation Nuns (Brooklyn, NY)

ASSOCIATE PROGRAM TO THE F.C.S.C.J.
226 Grove St., Littleton, NH 03561-4210. (603) 444-5346. Fax: (603) 444-5348. E-mail: wnddr.jed@verizon.net; Web: www.daughters-fcscj-charity-sacredheart.org
Contact: Sister Theresa Faurnier
Affiliation: Daughters of the Charity of the Sacred Heart of Jesus (F.C.S.C.J.)

ASSOCIATE RELATIONSHIP PROGRAM (Sisters of St. Francis of Assisi, Milwaukee, WI)
St. Francis Convent, 3221 South Lake Dr., Milwaukee, WI 53235-3799. (414) 744-1160. E-mail: oarel@lakeosfs.org; Web: www.lakeosfs.org
Contact; Sister Valerie Sepenski, OSF
Affiliation: Sisters of St. Francis of Assisi

ASSOCIATES - CONGREGATION OF THE HUMILITY OF MARY
820 W. Central Park, Davenport, IA 52804-1900. E-mail: joannk@chmiowa.org; Web: www.sisters@chmiowa
Contact: Sister Joann Kuebrich, C.H.M.
Affiliation: Congregation of the Humility of Mary (C.H.M.)

ASSOCIATES OF ASSUMPTION ABBEY
Assumption Abbey, Rte. 5, Box 1056, Ava, MO 65608. E-mail: tobiashan@yahoo.com, maschultz@stlnet.com, Web: www.assumptionabbey.org/friends.html
Contacts: Br. Tobias Shanahan, ocso, Marilyn Schultz
Affiliation: Trappists

ASSOCIATES OF BLESSED EDMUND RICE
33 Pryer Terrace, New Rochelle, NY 10804. (914) 636-6194, ext. 25. Web: www.iona.edu/about/CFC/Associates.htm
Contact: Br. J. J. McCarthy, CFC
Affiliation: Congregation of the Christian Brothers (Eastern American Province)

ASSOCIATES (Sisters of the Assumption of the B.V.)
18 Harbor St., Salem, MA 01970. (978) 744-0581
Contact: Sr. Estelle Grenier, S.A.S.V.
Affiliation: Sisters of the Assumption of the B.V.

ASSOCIATES OF THE HOLY FAMILY (Monroe, CT)
Marian Heights, 1428 Monroe Tnpk., Monroe, CT 06468. (203) 459-8286. E-mail: sisters-holy@snet.net; Web: www.ct-csfn.org
Contact: Sr. Victoria Czajkowski, CSFN
Affiliation: Sisters of the Holy Family of Nazareth (C.S.F.N.)

ASSOCIATES OF THE HOLY FAMILY (Philadelphia, PA)
2755 Holme Ave., Philadelphia, PA 19152. (215) 338-8992. E-mail: partykar2001@yahoo.com; Web: csfn.org then phila-csfn.org
Contact: Sr. M. Rita Partyka, CSFN
Affiliation: Sisters of the Holy Family of Nazareth (C.S.F.N.)

ASSOCIATES (Sisters of the Holy Names of Jesus and Mary)
1061 New Scotland Ave., Albany, NY 12208. (518) 489-5469. Fax: (518) 489-5804. E-mail: brennanpv @aol.com; Web: www.snjm.org
Contact: Sister Patricia Brennan,SNJM
Affiliation: Sisters of the Holy Names of Jesus and Mary (SNJM)

ASSOCIATES OF THE INCARNATE WORD (Parma Heights, OH)
6618 Pearl Rd., Parma Heights, OH 44130-3808. (440) 886-6440. E-mail: smrksiw@yahoo.com
Contact: Sister Mary Rose Kocab, SIW
Affiliation: Sisters of the Incarnate Word and Blessed Sacrament (S.I.W.)

ASSOCIATES OF THE INCARNATE WORD (Victoria, TX)
1101 N.E. Water St., Victoria, TX 77901. (361) 575-7111. E-mail: srmemiliana@yahoo.com; Web: www.rsbp.org or www.catholic-forum.com/iwbsvictoria
Contact: Sister Emiliana Grafe, IWBS
Affiliation: Congregation of the Incarnate Word and Blessed Sacrament (IWBS)

ASSOCIATES OF NOTRE DAME
701 E. Columbia Ave., Cincinnati, OH 45215. (513) 761-7636
Contact: Sister Claire Foley, SNDdeN
Affiliation: Sisters of Notre Dame de Namur (SNDdeN)

ASSOCIATES OF THE POOR SERVANTS OF THE MOTHER OF GOD
Emmaus House, 101 Center St., Perth Amboy, NJ 08861. (732) 442-7783. Fax: (732) 442-7793. E-mail: ecrehan@aol.com; Web: www.poor servants.com
Contact: Sr. Elizabeth Crehan, S.M.G.
Affiliation: Poor Servants of the Mother of God

ASSOCIATES OF THE SISTERS OF CHARITY OF ST. HYACINTHE
1137 Washington Ave., Portland, ME 04103-3624. (207) 797-8607. E-mail: jacquiep@juno.com
Contact: Sister Jacqueline Peloquin, SCSH
Affiliation: Sisters of Charity of St. Hyacinthe (S.C.S.H.) (Grey Nuns)

ASSOCIATES OF THE SISTERS OF THE LIVING WORD
800 N. Fernandez Ave.-B, Arlington Heights, IL 60004. (847) 577-5972. E-mail: tibspsslw@yahoo.com; Web: www.slw.org
Contact: Sister Barbara Mass, SLW
Affiliation: Sisters of the Living Word

ASSOCIATES OF THE SISTERS OF ST. JOSEPH OF BUFFALO
23 Agassiz Circle, Buffalo, NY 14214-2611. (716) 838-4400. E-mail: buffssjvoc@ronconet.org; Web: www.ssjbuffalo.org
Contact: Associate Team: Karen Shaver, SSJ, Sally Tower, SSJA
Affiliation: Sisters of St. Joseph of Buffalo

ASSOCIATES OF THE SISTERS OF ST. JOSEPH OF NORTHWESTERN PA
5031 West Ridge Rd., Erie, PA 16506-1249. (814) 836-4199. E-mail: associates@ssjerie.org; Web: www.sssjerie.org
Contact: Sr. Ann Marie Cappello, SSJ
Affiliation: Sisters of St. Joseph of Northwestern Pennsylvania (SSJ)

ASSOCIATES OF THE SISTERS OF ST. JOSEPH (Holyoke, MA)
Mont Marie, 34 Lower Westfield Rd., Ste.1, Holyoke, MA 01040-2739. (413) 536-0853, ext. 249. E-mail: kimbruno@ssjspringfield.com; Web: ssjspringfield.org
Contact: Kathleen Imbruno, ssj
Affiliation: Sisters of St. Joseph of Springfield (S.S.J.)

ASSOCIATES OF THE SOCIETY OF THE HOLY CHILD JESUS
460 Shadeland Ave., Drexel Hill, PA 19026-2312. (610) 626-1400. E-mail: cquinn@shcj.org; Web: www.shcj.org
Contact: Catherine Quinn, SHCJ
Affiliation: Society of the Holy Child Jesus (SHCJ)

ASSOCIATION OF THE HOLY FAMILY (Pittsburgh, PA)
285 Bellevue Rd., Pittsburgh, PA 15229. (412) 931-4778, ext. 2090. E-mail: jblados@mtnazarethcenter .org
Contact: Sr. Janice Marie Blados, CSFN
Affiliation: Sisters of the Holy Family of Nazareth (C.S.F.N.)

AUXILIARY OBLATES
St. Aloysius Novitiate, Beekman Rd., PO Box 98, Hopewell Junction, NY 12533. (845) 226-5671. Web: www.Staloysius-NY.org
Contact: Sister Julia Berdugo
Affiliation: Sisters Oblates to the Blessed Trinity

BASILIAN ASSOCIATES (Fox Chase Manor, PA)
710 Fox Chase Rd., Fox Chase Manor, PA 19046-4198. (215) 663-9153. E-mail: basilians@aol.com; Web: www.basiliansfoxchase.org
Contact: Sister Elizabeth, OSBM
Affiliation: Basilian - Sisters of the Order of St. Basil the Great (Ukrainian Byzantine Rite)

BASILIAN ASSOCIATES (Uniontown, PA)
500 W. Main St., Box 878, Uniontown, PA 15401. (724) 438-8644
Contact: Sr. Melita M. Penchalk, OSBM
Affiliation: Basilians - Sisters of St. Basil the Great (Byzantine Catholic Church)

BENEDICTINE OBLATES (Atchison, KS)
Mount St. Scholastica, 801 S. 8th St., Atchison, KS 66002. (913) 360-6200. E-mail: colson@mountosb .org; Web: www.mountosb.org
Contact: Sr. Cecilia Olson, OSB
Affiliation: Benedictine Sisters (Atchison, KS)

BENEDICTINE OBLATES (Beech Grove, IN)
Our Lady of Grace Monastery, 1402 Southern Ave., Beech Grove, IN 46107-1160. (317) 787-3287. Fax: (317) 780-2368. E-mail: olgmoblate @msn.com; Web: www.benedictine .com
Contact: Sr. Antoinette Purcell, OSB
Affiliation: Sisters of St. Benedict (Beech Grove, IN)

BENEDICTINE OBLATES (Bismarck, ND)
Annunciation Monastery, 7520 University Dr., Bismarck, ND 58504. (701) 255-1520. E-mail: sslosb@ hotmail.com; Web: www.annuncia tionmonastery.org
Contact: Sr. Susan Lardy, osb
Affiliation: Benedictine Sisters (Bismarck, ND)

BENEDICTINE OBLATES (Byzantine)
8640 Squires Lane NE, Warren, OH 44484. (330) 856-1813. E-mail: agnes@netdotcom.com; Web: www.benedictinebyzantine.org
Contact: Sister Agnes Knapik, OSB
Affiliation: Benedictine Sisters (Byzantine)

BENEDICTINE OBLATES (Canyon, TX)
St. Benedict Monastery, 17825 South Western St., Canyon, TX 79015. (806) 655-9317. E-mail: nuns@osbcanyontx.org; Web: www.osbcanyontx.org
Contact: Sister Marcella Schmalz, OSB
Affiliation: Benedictine Sisters (Canyon, TX)

BENEDICTINE OBLATES (Chicago, IL)
St. Scholastica Monastery, 7430 N. Ridge Blvd., Chicago, IL 60645. (773) 764-2413, ext. 231. Web: www.benedictine-sisters.org
Contact: Benita Coffey, OSB
Affiliation: Benedictine Sisters (Chicago, IL)

BENEDICTINE OBLATES (Cleveland, OH)
St. Andrew Svorad Abbey, 10510 Buckeye Rd., Cleveland, OH 44104. (216) 721-5300, ext. 268. E-mail: mpb1993@msn.com; Web: www.bocohio.org
Contact: Rev. Michael Brunovsky, OSB
Affiliation: Benedictine Monks

BENEDICTINE OBLATES (Clyde, MO)
Benedictine Monastery, 31970 State Highway P, Clyde, MO 64432-8100. (660) 944-2221. E-mail: jeanfr@benedictinesisters.org
Contact: Oblate Director
Affiliation: Benedictine Sisters of Perpetual Adoration

BENEDICTINE OBLATES (Colorado Springs, CO)
Benet Hill Monastery, 2555 N. Chelton Rd., Colorado Springs, CO 80909-1399. (719) 633-0655. Fax: (719) 471-0403. E-mail: benet@qwest.net; Web: www.benethillmonastery.org/monastic-life/oblate.html
Contact: Sister Joseph Marie Jacobsen, O.S.B.
Affiliation: Benedictine Sisters

BENEDICTINE OBLATES (Columbia, MO)
Our Lady of Peace Monastery, 3710 W. Broadway, Columbia, MO 65203-0116. (573) 446-2300. E-mail: oblates@benedictinesister.org; Web: www.benedictinesister.org/oblates.htm
Contact: Director of Oblates
Affiliation: Benedictine Sisters (Columbia, MO)

BENEDICTINE OBLATES (Conception, MO)
Conception Abbey, PO Box 501, 37174 State Hwy. V V, Conception, MO 64433-0501. (660) 944-3165. Fax: (660) 944-2800. E-mail: oblates@conception.edu; Web: www.ConceptionAbbey.org
Contact: Fr. Kenneth Reichert, O.S.B.
Affiliation: Benedictine Monks (Conception, MO)

BENEDICTINE OBLATES (Cottonwood, ID)
Monastery of St. Gertrude, HC 3 Box 121, Cottonwood, ID 83522-9408. (208) 962-3224. E-mail: gemsass@juno.com; Web: www.StGertrudes.org
Contact: Sr. Meg Sass, OSB
Affiliation: Benedictine Sisters

BENEDICTINE OBLATES (Cullman, AL)
Saint Bernard Abbey, Cullman, AL 35055. (256) 734-8291, ext. 133
Contact: Fr. Thomas O'Connor, OSB
Affiliation: Benedictine Monks

BENEDICTINE OBLATES (Elkhorn, NE)
Mount Michael Abbey, 22520 Mount Michael Rd., Elkhorn, NE 68022-3400. (402) 289-2541, ext. 1111. E-mail: hagemann_john@hotmail.com; Web: www.mountmichael.org/vocation.htm
Contact: Fr. John Hagemann, OSB
Affiliation: Benedictine Monks (Elkhorn, NE)

BENEDICTINE OBLATES (Emmaus, PA)
Transfiguration Monastery, 526 Fairview St., Emmaus, PA 18049-3837. (610) 965-6818. E-mail: smartina@entermail.net; Web: www.emmausosb.org
Contact: Sister Martina Revak, O.S.B
Affiliation: Benedictine Sisters (Emmaus, PA)

BENEDICTINE OBLATES (Ferdinard, IN)
Monastery Immaculate Conception, 802 E. 10th St., Ferdinand, IN 47532-9239. (812) 367-1411. E-mail: sylviag@thedome.org, mvictor@thedome.org
Contacts: Sister Sylvia Gehlhausen, O.S.B., Sister Mary Victor Kercher, O.S.B., Oblate Team
Affiliation: Benedictine Sisters (Ferdinard, IN)

BENEDICTINE OBLATES (Fort Smith, AR)
St. Scholastica Monastery, P.O. Box 3489, 1301 S. Albert Pike, Fort Smith, AR 72913-3489. (479) 783-4147. E-mail: magdalen@scholasticafortsmith.org; Web: www.scholasticafortsmith.org
Contact: Sr. Magdalen Stanton, O.S.B.
Affiliation: Benedictine Sisters

BENEDICTINE OBLATES (Grand Terrace, CA)
Holy Spirit Monastery, 22791 Pico St., Grand Terrace, CA 92313. (909) 783-4446. Fax: (909) 783-3525. E-mail: hsmonastery@prodigy.net; Web: www.rc.net/sanbernardino.hsmonastery
Contact: Sr. Deanna O'Neill, OSB
Affiliation: Benedictine Sisters

BENEDICTINE OBLATES (Jonesboro, AR)
Holy Angels Convent, Olivetan Benedictines, 1699 CR766/P.O. Drawer 130, Jonesboro, AR 72403-0130. (870) 935-5810. E-mail: srseyler@olivben.org
Contact: Sister Mary John Seyler, OSB
Affiliation: Benedictine Sisters (Jonesboro, AR)

BENEDICTINE OBLATES (Lacey, WA)
Saint Martin's Abbey, 5300 Pacific Ave. SE, Lacey, WA 98503-1297. (360) 491-4700. Fax: (360) 438-4441. E-mail: oblates@stmartin.edu; Web: www.stmartin.edu/abbey/newsletter.htm
Contact: Br. Edmund Ebbers, O.S.B.
Affiliation: Benedictine Monks

BENEDICTINE OBLATES (Lacey, WA)
St. Placid Priory, 500 College St., N.E., Lacey, WA 98516. (360) 438-1771. E-mail: lwynkoop@stplacid.org; Web: www.stplacid.org
Contact: Sister Lucy Wynkoop, OSB
Affiliation: Benedictine Sisters (Lacey, WA)

BENEDICTINE OBLATES (Latrobe, PA)
Saint Vincent Archabbey, 300 Fraser Purchase Rd., Latrobe, PA 15650-2690. (724) 532-6655 or 6686. E-mail: vocations@stvincent.edu; Web: benedictine.stvincent.edu/archabbey
Contact: Fr. Justin Matro, OSB
Affiliation: Benedictine Monks (Latrobe, PA)

BENEDICTINE OBLATES (Martin, KY)
150 Mt. Tabor Rd., Martin, KY 41649. (606) 886-9624. E-mail: mtabor@hotmail.com; Web: www.geocities.com/athens/9871
Contact: Sr. Judy Yunker
Affiliation: Benedictine Sisters (Mt. Tabor)

BENEDICTINE OBLATES (Marvin, SD)
Blue Cloud Abbey, 46561 147th St., P.O. Box 98, Marvin, SD 57251-0098. (605) 398-9200. Fax: (605) 398-9201. E-mail: vocation@bluecloud.org; Web: www.bluecloud.org/assoc-cand.html
Contact: Fr. Denis Quinkert, O.S.B.
Affiliation: Benedictine Monks (Marvin, SD)

BENEDICTINE OBLATES (Morristown, NJ)
St. Mary's Abbey, 230 Mendham Rd., Morristown, NJ 07960. (973) 538-3231, ext. 2019. E-mail: osbmonks@delbarton.org; Web: www.osbmonks.org
Contact: Fr. Hilary O'Leary, OSB
Affiliation: Benedictine Monks

BENEDICTINE OBLATES (Mt. Angel, OR)
Queen of Angels Monastery, 840 S. Main St., Mt. Angel, OR 97362. (503) 845-6141. Fax: (503) 845-6585. Web: www.benedictine-srs.org
Contact: Sr. Antoinette, OSB
Affiliation: Benedictine Sisters

BENEDICTINE OBLATES (Rock Island, IL)
St. Mary Monastery, 2200 88th Ave. W., Rock Island, IL 61201. (309) 283-2107, 2108. E-mail: ccleary@stmarymonastery.org; Web: www.stmarymonastery.org
Contact: Sr. Catherine Cleary, O.S.B.
Affiliation: Benedictine Sisters (Rock Island, IL)

BENEDICTINE OBLATES (Newark Abbey Oblates)
Newark Abbey, 528 Dr. Martin Luther King Jr. Blvd., Newark, NJ 07102-1314. (973) 792-5751. E-mail: aholtz@sbp.org; Web: www.newarkabbey.org
Contact: Rev. Albert T. Holtz, OSB
Affiliation: Benedictine Monks (Newark Abbey)

BENEDICTINE OBLATES (Petersham, MA)
St. Scholastica Priory, Box 606, 271 N. Main St., Petersham, MA 01366-0606. (978) 724-3213
Contact: Sr. Mary Angela Kloss, O.S.B.
Affiliation: Benedictine Nuns

BENEDICTINE OBLATES (Pittsburgh, PA)
Oblates Program: Sr. Raphael Frank, OSB, 4530 Perrysville Ave., Pittsburgh, PA 15229-2296. (412) 931-2844, ext. 164. Fax: (412) 931-8970. E-mail: raphfrank@yahoo.com; Web: www.osbpgh.org
Associates Program: Sister Donna Wojtyna, O.S.B. (412) 931-2844, ext. 103. E-mail: djwoodreed@hotmail.com
Affiliation: Benedictine Sisters of Pittsburgh

BENEDICTINE OBLATES (Rapid City, SD)
Benedictine Convent of St. Martin, 2110-C St. Martin's Dr., Rapid City, SD 57702-9660. (605) 343-8011, 2688. E-mail: srmarmion@aol.com; Web: www.catholic-church.org/stmartins
Contact: Sr. Marmion Howe, OSB
Affiliation: Benedictine Sisters (Rapid City, SD)

BENEDICTINE OBLATES (St. Benedict, LA: St. Joseph Abbey)
St. Joseph Abbey, St. Benedict, LA 70457. (985) 892-1800
Contact: Fr. Dominic Braud, OSB
Affiliation: Benedictine Monks

BENEDICTINE OBLATES (St. Benedict, OR)
Mount Angel Abbey, 1 Abbey Dr., St. Benedict, OR 97373. (503) 845-3225. Web: www.mtangel.edu
Contact: Fr. Bernard Sander, OSB
Affiliation: Benedictine Monks

BENEDICTINE OBLATES (St. David, AZ)
Holy Trinity Monastery, PO Box 298, St. David, AZ 85630. (520) 720-4016, (520) 720-4642, ext. 17. Fax: (520) 720-4202. E-mail: guestmaster@theriver.com; Web: http://personal.riverusers.com/~trinitylib/associates.htm
Contact: Guest Coordinator
Affiliation: Benedictine Monks and Nuns (Olivetan Benedictines)

BENEDICTINE OBLATES (St. Joseph, MN)
Saint Benedict's Monastery, 104 Chapel Lane, St. Joseph, MN 56374-0220. (320) 363-7144. E-mail: hmercier@csbsjo.edu; Web: www.sbm.osb.org
Contact: S. Hélène Mercier, OSB
Affiliation: Benedictine Sisters (St. Joseph, MN)

BENEDICTINE OBLATES (St. Leo, FL)
Holy Name Monastery, P.O. Box 2450, St. Leo, FL 33574-2450. (352) 588-8320. E-mail: mary.david.hydro@saintleo.edu; Web: www.floridabenedictines.com
Contact: S. Mary David Hydro, OSB
Affiliation: Benedictine Sisters (St. Leo, FL)

BENEDICTINE OBLATES (Saint Leo, FL)
Saint Leo Abbey, PO Box 2040, Saint Leo, FL 33574-2350. English: (352) 588-8183, Español: (352) 588-5151. Fax: (352) 588-5217. (Respuestas correspondencia en Español). E-mail: monksvocations@saintleoabbey.org
Contact: Br. Mukasa Theodore, O.S.B.
Affiliation: Benedictine Monks

BENEDICTINE OBLATES (St. Paul, MN)
St. Paul's Monastery, 2675 Larpenteur Ave. E., St. Paul, MN 55109-5097. (651) 777-8181. Web: www.osb.org/spm
Contact: Director of Oblates
Affiliation: Benedictine Sisters

BENEDICTINE OBLATES (Schuyler, NE)
Christ the King Priory-Benedictine Mission House, PO Box 528, Schuyler, NE 68661-0528. (402) 352-2177. E-mail: volker.schuyler@dtnspeed.net; Web: www.megavision.net/benedict
Contact: Fr. Volker Futter, OSB
Affiliation: Benedictine Monks (O.S.B.) (Congregation of St. Ottilien for Foreign Missions)

BENEDICTINE OBLATES (Valyermo, CA)
St. Andrew's Abbey, P.O. Box 40, Valyermo, CA 93563-0040. (661) 944-2178. Fax: (661) 944-1076. Web: www.valyermo.com
Contact: Abbot Francis Benedict, OSB
Affiliation: Benedictine Monks

BENEDICTINE ASSOCIATES (Villa Hills, KY)
St. Walburg Monastery, 2500 Amsterdam Rd., Villa Hills, KY 41017. (859) 331-6324. Web: www.stwalburg.org
Contact: Sr. Mary Tewes, O.S.B.
Affiliation: Benedictine Sisters (Villa Hills, KY)

BENEDICTINE OBLATES (Washington, DC)
St. Anselm's Abbey, 4501 S. Dakota Ave. N.E., Washington, DC 20017. (202) 269-2300. E-mail: dcabbey@erols.com; Web: www.stanselms.org/oblate.htm
Contact: Abbot Aidan Shea, O.S.B.
Affiliation: Benedictine Monks (St. Anselm's Abbey, Washington, DC)

BENEDICTINE OBLATES (Watertown, SD)
Mother of God Monastery, 110 28th Ave. SE # 201, Watertown, SD 57201. (605) 882-6650. E-mail: monastery@dailypost.com; Web: www.watertownbenedictines.org
Contact: S. Jeanne Giese, OSB
Affiliation: Benedictine Sisters (Watertown, SD)

BENEDICTINE OBLATES (Westfield, VT)
Benedictine Monastery, Immaculate Heart of Mary, 4103 VT Rte. 100, Westfield, VT 05874. (802) 744-6525
Contact: Sr. Marie-Catherine Lavallee, O.S.B.
Affiliation: Benedictine Nuns of the Congregation of Solesmes

BENEDICTINE OBLATES (Yankton, SD)
Sacred Heart Monastery, 1005 West 8th, Yankton, SD 57078-3389. (605) 668-6169. E-mail: akessler@mtmc.edu; Web: www.yanktonbenedictines.org
Contact: S. Ann Kessler
Affiliation: Benedictine Sisters (Yankton, SD)

BENEDICTINE OBLATES-CLAUSTRAL OBLATE PROGRAM
650 Benet Hill Rd., Oceanside, CA 92054-1246. (760) 430-1305. E-mail: VocationDr@aol.com
Contact: Br. Daniel Sokol, OSB
Affiliation: Benedictine Monks

BENEDICTINE OBLATES OF JESUS CRUCIFIED
Monastery of the Glorious Cross, 61 Burban Dr., Branford, CT 06405-4003. (203) 315-9964. Fax: (203) 483-5829. E-mail: monasterygc@juno.com
Contact: Director of Oblates
Affiliation: Congregation of the Benedictines of Jesus Crucified

BERNARDINE FRANCISCAN ASSOCIATES
460 Saint Bernardine St., Reading, PA 19607. (610) 796-8971. E-mail: associates@bfranciscan.org; Web: www.bfranciscan.org
Contact: Sr. Jean Jacobchik, OSF
Affiliation: Bernardine Franciscan Sisters

BON SECOURS ASSOCIATES
1525 Marriottsville Rd., Marriottsville, MD 21104. (410) 442-2115. E-mail: Jean_Sonnenberg@bshsi.com
Contact: Jean Sonnenberg
Affiliation: Sisters of Bon Secours

CABRINI ASSOCIATES
610 King of Prussia Rd., Founders Hall-Basement, Radnor, PA 19087. (610) 995-2385. E-mail: ecurrie45@aol.com; Web: www.cabrinivocation.org
Contact: Sr. Eileen Currie, MSC
Affiliation: Missionaries of the Sacred Heart of Jesus (M.S.C.) (Cabrini Sisters)

CAMALDOLESE OBLATES
New Camaldoli Hermitage, 62475 Coast Hwy. 1, Big Sur, CA 93920. (831) 667-2456. E-mail: camoblates@contemplation.com; Web: www.contemplation.com
Contact: Rev. Michael Fish, OSB Cam.
Affiliation: Camaldolese Monks

CCVI LAY ASSOCIATES
6510 Lawndale Ave., P.O. Box 230969, Houston, TX 77223-0969. (713) 928-6053. E-mail: zbarkey@ccvi-vdm.org; Web: www.ccvi-vdm.org
Contact: Zita Barkey
Affiliation: Sisters of Charity of the Incarnate Word - Houston

CDP ASSOCIATE COMMITMENT (Congregation of Divine Providence (CDP) San Antonio, TX)
Our Lady of the Lake Convent, 515 S.W. 24th St., San Antonio, TX 78207-4619. (210) 434-1866, ext. 1105. Fax: (210) 431-9965. Web: www.cdptexas.org/associates.htm
Contact: Florence Carvajal
Affiliation: Congregation of Divine Providence (CDP) San Antonio, TX

CENACLE AFFILIATES/ COMPANIONS & AUXILIARIES
Cenacle Formation Community, PO Box 797, Warrenville, IL 60555-0797. (630) 393-1085. Fax: (630) 393-1729. E-mail: sr.janice.m.bemowski@usa.net; Web: www.cenaclesisters.org
Contact: Sr. Janice Bemowski, r.c.
Affiliation: Religious of the Cenacle

COJOURNER
1001 14th St. NW, Suite 100, Rochester, MN 55901. (507) 282-7441. E-mail: RFCojourn@aol.com; Web: www.rfvocations.org
Contact: Central Minister, Rochester Franciscan Life Teams
Affiliation: Franciscan Sisters of Rochester, MN

COJOURNERS
Presentation Heights, 1500 N. Second, Aberdeen, SD 57401-1238. (605) 229-8494
Contact: Sister Pam Donelan, PBVM, Co-Director, E-mail: pdonelan@presentationsisters.org
PO Box 476, Eagle Butte, SD 57625
Contact: Sister Marilyn Dunn, PBVM, Co-Director, E-mail: dunnm@presentation.edu
Web: www.presentationsisters.org
Affiliation: Presentation Sisters of Aberdeen, SD

COMMUNITY OF PASSIONIST PARTNERS
700 Sunnyside, Sierra Madre, CA 91024. (626) 355-5298. Web: www.passionist.org/partners
Contact: Elaine Mickle
Affiliation: Passionists

COMMUNITY OF TERESIAN CARMELITES
Box 826, Worcester, MA 01613-0826. (508) 752-5734. E-mail: danthony@assumption.edu; Web: www.teresiancarmelites.org
Contact: Arlene Wyrzykowski, c.t.c.s.
Affiliation: Community of Teresian Carmelites

CPPS COMPANIONS
2800 Milvia St., Berkeley, CA 94703-2209. (510) 841-2777. E-mail: SloanCPPS@aol.com

Contact: Fr. James Sloan
Affiliation: Society of the Precious Blood (C.PP.S.)

CSA ASSOCIATE RELATIONSHIP
320 County Rd. K, Fond du Lac, WI 54935. (920) 907-2318. E-mail: jparker@csasisters.org; Web: www.csasisters.org
Contact: Jan Parker
Affiliation: Congregation of St. Agnes (C.S.A.)

CSA ASSOCIATES
Mt. Augustine, 5232 Broadview Rd., Richfield, OH 44286-9608. (330) 659-5100. E-mail: srs@srsofcharit y.org; Web: www.srsofcharity.org
Contact: Jeanne Burrige
Affiliation: Sisters of Charity of St. Augustine

CSJ ASSOCIATES
(Sisters of St. Joseph of Brentwood)
St. Joseph Convent, 1725 Brentwood Rd., Brentwood, NY 11717. (631) 273-4531. E-mail: vocationcsj@aol.com; Web: www.csjbrentwoodny.org
Contact: CSJ Associates Co-Directors
Affiliation: Sisters of St. Joseph of Brentwood

CSJ ASSOCIATES
(Congregation of St. Joseph of Cleveland)
3430 Rocky River Dr., Cleveland, OH 44111. (216) 252-0440. E-mail: info@csjcleveland.org; Web: www.csjcleveland.org
Contact: Sr. Linda Francl, CSJ
Affiliation: Congregation of St. Joseph of Cleveland

CSJ ASSOCIATES
(Sisters of St. Joseph of Medaille (C.S.J.)
1821 Summit Rd., #210, Cincinnati, OH 45237. (513) 761-2888. E-mail: anne@sistersofstjoseph.org; Web: www.csjmedaille.com
Contact: S. Anne Meridier
Affiliation: Sisters of St. Joseph of Medaille (C.S.J.)

CSJ ASSOCIATES
(Sisters of St. Joseph of Wichita)
3700 E. Lincoln, Wichita, KS 67218. (316) 686-7171. E-mail: sistersof stjoseph@csjwichita.org; Web: www.csjwichita.org
Contact: Sister Josephine O'Gorman, CSJ
Affiliation: Sisters of St. Joseph of Wichita (CSJ)

CSJP ASSOCIATES
(Sisters of St. Joseph of Peace (C.S.J.P.) (Bellevue, WA)
1663 Killarney Way, PO Box 248, Bellevue, WA 98009. (425) 451-1770. E-mail: sdewitt@csjp-olp.org; Web: www.csjp.org/olp
Contact: Susan Dewitt, csjp
Affiliation: Congregation of the Sisters of St. Joseph of Peace (C.S.J.P.)

CSJP ASSOCIATES
(Sisters of St. Joseph of Peace (C.S.J.P.) (Englewood Cliffs, NJ)
Shalom Center, 399 Hudson Terr., Englewood Cliffs, NJ 07632. (201) 568-6348, ext. 23. E-mail: Anna cwagner@earthlink.net, srann@juno.com; Web: www.csjp.org/sjp
Contacts: Ann Wagner, CSJP Associate, Sister Ann Jordan, CSJP
Affiliation: Sisters of St. Joseph of Peace (C.S.J.P.)

DMJ ASSOCIATES
5300 Crest Rd., Rancho Palos Verdes, CA 90275-5004. (310) 377-4867, ext. 400. E-mail: dmjca@earthlink .net; Web: home.earth link.net/dmjca
Contact: Sister Renee Bauerly
Affiliation: Daughters of Mary and Joseph

DOMINICAN ASSOCIATES
(Adrian, MI)
1257 E. Siena Heights Dr., Adrian, MI 49221-1793. (517) 266-3531. E-mail: ADAssoc@adriansisters.org: Web: www.adriansisters.org
Contact: Mary Ellen Youngblood, OP
Affiliation: Dominican Sisters of Adrian

DOMINICAN ASSOCIATES
(Columbus/Akron, OH)
2320 Airport Dr., Columbus, OH 43229-2098. (614) 416-1054. Web: www.columbusdominicans.org
Contact: Anita Davidson
Affiliations: Dominican Sisters of St. Mary of the Springs, Dominican Sisters of Akron

DOMINICAN ASSOCIATES
(Blauvelt, NY)
496 Western Hwy., Blauvelt, NY 10913. (845) 359-7800, ext. 334. E-mail: beryl.herdt@dc.edu
Contact: Sister Theresa Lardner, O.P.
Affiliation: Dominican Sisters of Blauvelt (NY)

DOMINICAN ASSOCIATES
(Caldwell, NJ)
1 Ryerson Ave., Caldwell, NJ 07006. Web: www.caldwellop.org
Contacts: Sister Ann Murtha, O.P., (732) 842-3963; Sister Carol Van Billiard, O.P., (201) 433-3303; Louis Squitieri, (201) 333-8001
Affiliation: Dominican Sisters of Caldwell, NJ

DOMINICAN ASSOCIATES
(Dighton, MA)
3012 Elm St., Dighton, MA 02715. (508) 669-5425. E-mail: srfaye@netscape.net; Web: www.Dominican Sistersofthepresentation.org
Contact: Sr. Faye Medina, O.P.
Affiliation: Dominican Sisters of Charity of the Presentation of the Blessed Virgin

DOMINICAN ASSOCIATES
(Edmonds, WA)
PO Box 280, Edmonds, WA 98020-0280. (206) 542-8167. E-mail: verso@opedmonds.org; Web: www.opedmonds.org
Contact: Sister Carolyn Roeber, OP
Affiliation: Dominican Sisters of Edmonds/Adrian

DOMINICAN ASSOCIATES
(Elkins Park, PA)
750 Ashbourne Rd., Elkins Park, PA 19027-2596. (215) 635-6027, ext. 14
Contact: Sr. Carolyn Krebs, OP
Affiliation: Dominican Sisters of St. Catherine de Ricci

DOMINICAN ASSOCIATES
(Grand Rapids, MI)
Marywood, 2025 E. Fulton St., Grand Rapids, MI 49503-3895. (800) 253-7343, (616) 459-2910, ext. 144. Fax: (616) 454-6105. E-mail: jbarkwell@grdominicans.org; Web: www.GRDominicans.org
Contact: Joellen Barkwell, op
Affiliation: Dominican Sisters (Grand Rapids, MI)

DOMINICAN ASSOCIATES
(Great Bend, KS)
3600 Broadway, Great Bend, KS 67530. (620) 792-1232. Fax: (620) 792-1746. E-mail: kathy@ksdom .org; Web: www.ksdom.org
Contact: Kathy Goetz, OP
Affiliation: Dominican Sisters of Great Bend

DOMINICAN LAITY
(Lancaster, PA)
Monastery of the Immaculate Heart of Mary, 1834 Lititz Pike, Lancaster, PA 17601-6585. (717) 569-2104. E-mail: mon1hm@juno.com
Contact: Genevieve Liebl
Affiliation: Dominican Nuns of the Perpetual Rosary

DOMINICAN ASSOCIATES (Lewiston, ME)
123 Dumont Ave., Apt. 2, Lewiston, ME 04240-6107. (207) 786-5058. E-mail: tldemers@megalink.net
Contact: Sr. Therese Demers, OP
Affiliation: Dominican Sisters of the Roman Congregation

DOMINICAN ASSOCIATES (Menlo Park, CA)
215 Oak Grove Ave., Menlo Park, CA 94025-3249. (650) 853-0729; 807 Foothill Dr., San Mateo, CA 94402-3321. (650) 341-4348. E-mail: nunsmenlo@aol.com; Web: www.op.org/nunsmenlo
Contacts: Fr. Dominic de Domenico, OP, (Mrs.) Earlene V. Billing
Affiliation: Dominican Nuns (Menlo Park, CA)

DOMINICAN ASSOCIATES (Mission San Jose)
PO Box 3908, Mission San Jose, CA 94539. (510) 657-2468. Web: www.msjdominicans.org
Contact: Sr. Charlotte O'Shea, OP
Affiliation: Dominican Sisters of Mission San Jose

DOMINICAN ASSOCIATES (Racine, WI)
Siena Center, 5635 Erie St., Racine, WI 53402-1900. E-mail: rdassoc@miliserv.net; Web: www.racinedominicans.org/associate_pages/associates.html
Contact: Barbara Sharp, Associate Director
Affiliation: Dominican Sisters of Racine

DOMINICAN ASSOCIATES (St. Catharine, KY)
1437 Central Ave. #917, Memphis, TN 38104-4832. (901) 726-5611. E-mail: cgalaski@cbu.edu, bettypate@hotmail.com; Web: www.opkentucky.org
Contacts: Sr. Cathy Galaskiewicz, OP, Betty Pate
Affiliation: Dominican Sisters of St. Catharine of Siena

DOMINICAN ASSOCIATES (Sinsinawa, WI)
1355 Challenge Dr., Batavia, IL 60510. (630) 761-3524. E-mail: jana31341@aol.com; 1114 Green Pine Blvd. G2, West Palm Beach, FL 3409. (561) 684-9895. E-mail: jdrea@bellsouth.net; Web: www.sinsinawa.org
Contacts: Jana Minor, Jeanne Drea, OP
Affiliation: Dominican Sisters of Sinsinawa

DOMINICAN ASSOCIATES (Springfield, IL)
Sacred Heart Convent, 1237 W. Monroe St., Springfield, IL 62704. (217) 787-0481. E-mail: smmccormick@spdom.org
Contact: Sr. Margaret McCormick, OP
Affiliation: Dominican Sisters of Springfield (IL)

DOMINICAN ASSOCIATES (Summit, NJ)
Monastery of Our Lady of the Rosary, 543 Springfield Ave., Summit, NJ 07901-4498. (908) 273-1228. E-mail: nunsop@att.net; Web: www.op.org/nunsopsummit
Affiliation: Dominican Nuns (Summit, NJ)

DOMINICAN ASSOCIATES (Tacoma, WA)
935 Fawcett Ave. So., Tacoma, WA 98402. (253) 272-9688. E-mail: marypmurphy@tacoma op.org; Web: www.tacoma-op.org
Contact: Mary Pat Murphy, OP
Affiliation: Dominican Sisters of Tacoma

DOMINICAN ASSOCIATES (Youngstown, OH)
St. Dominic Priory, 77 E. Lucius Ave., Youngstown, OH 44507-1898. (330) 783-1901. Fax: (330) 783-2396. E-mail: allenop@juno.com
Contact: Fr. Joseph P. Allen, O.P.
Affiliation: Dominicans (Priests and Sisters)

DOMINICAN LAITY (Canadian Province)
2715 Ch. Cote-Ste-Catherine, Montreal, QC, Canada H3T 1B6. (514) 341-2244. Web: www.op.org/oplaity/laycat.htm#canada
Contact: Fr. Lionel Picard, O.P., Promoter
Affiliation: Dominicans Sisters & Friars

DOMINICAN LAITY (Central Province)
Dominican Laity Office, PO Box 08545, Racine, WI 53408-5451. Web: www.op.org/oplaity/laycat.htm#central
Contact: Fr. James Motl, O.P.
Affiliation: Dominicans Sisters & Friars

DOMINICAN LAITY (Eastern Province)
487 Michigan Ave., NE, Washington, DC 20017-1584. (202) 636-4459. Fax: (202) 636-4460
Contact: Fr. James M. Sullivan, O.P., 201 Seminary Ave., Yonkers, NY 10704-1896. (303) 783-1901. E-mail: jmsullivan@op.org; Web: www.op-stjoseph.org/third-order/index.htm
Affiliation: Dominicans Sisters & Friars

DOMINICAN LAITY (Southern Province)
1701 Windsor Dr. Orange, TX 77632- 0555. (409) 746-3264. E-mail: DChauffe@aol.com; Web: www.op.org/oplaity/laycat.htm#south
Contact: Druscilla Chauffe, Provincial Moderator
Affiliation: Dominicans Sisters & Friars

DOMINICAN LAITY (Western Province)
2619 E. Orange St., Tempe, AZ 85281. (480) 833-8599. Fax: (480) 833-0994. E-mail: kwl@juno.com; Web: www.op.org/oplaity/laycat.htm#west
Contact: Karen Woods, O.P.L.
Affiliation: Dominicans Sisters & Friars

DONNES OF REPARATION
2120 S.E. 24th Ave., Portland, OR 97214-5504. (503) 236-4207. Fax: (503) 236-3400. E-mail: repsrs@juno.com, repsrs@msn.com
Contact: Sister Mary Immaculate, SR
Affiliation: Sisters of Reparation of the Sacred Wounds of Jesus (S.R.)

EMD ASSOCIATES
3801 Canal St., Suite #100, New Orleans, LA 70119. (504) 486-1133. Fax: (504) 486-6547. E-mail: info@emdsisters.org; www.emdsisters.org/associates.html
Contact: Associates Coordinator
Affiliation: Eucharistic Missionaries of St. Dominic

FAUSTINUM ASSOCIATION OF APOSTLES OF THE DIVINE MERCY
241 Neponset Ave., Dorchester, MA 02122. (617) 288-1202. Fax: (617) 265-9405. E-mail: mercy@sisterfaustina.org; Web: www.sisterfaustina.org
Contact: Sr. M. Caterina Esselen, O.L.M.
Affiliation: The Congregation of the Sisters of Our Lady of Mercy

FELICIAN ASSOCIATES (Buffalo, NY)
Villa Maria, 600 Doat St., Buffalo, NY 14211. (716) 892-4141, ext. 161. Fax: (716) 892-4177. E-mail: smkush@yahoo.com

Contact: Sister Suzanne Marie Kush, CSSF
Affiliation: Felician Sisters (Buffalo, NY)

FELICIAN ASSOCIATES (Chicago, IL)
739 N. Armour St., Chicago, IL 60622. (312) 226-4160. E-mail: holyinnocents739@yahoo.com; Web: www.feliciansisters.org/pages/collaborate.cfm
Contact: Sister Carole Mary Capoun, C.S.S.F.
Affiliation: Felican Sisters

FELICIAN ASSOCIATES (Coraopolis, PA)
1500 Woodcrest Ave., Coraopolis, PA 15108-3099. (412) 431-1356. Fax: (412) 264-7047. E-mail: slouisemo@hotmail.com; Web: www.felicianspa.org
Contact: Sister Louise Marie Olsofka, C.S.S.F.
Affiliation: Felician Sisters

FELICIAN ASSOCIATES (Livonia, MI)
Presentation of the B.V.M. Convent, 36800 Schoolcraft Rd., Livonia, MI 48150. (734) 591-1730. E-mail: cssf@felicianslivonia.org
Contact: Sister Mary De Sales Herman, CSSF
Affiliation: Felician Sisters (Presentation of the Blessed Virgin Mary Province)

FRANCISCAN AFFILIATES (Franciscan Sisters of Perpetual Adoration, La Crosse, WI)
912 Market St., La Crosse, WI 54601-8800. (608) 791-5290, 5610. E-mail: affiliation@fspa.org; Web: www.fspa.org
Contact: Sister Karen Neuser
Affiliation: Franciscan Sisters of Perpetual Adoration, (FSPA) (La Crosse, WI)

FRANCISCAN ASSOCIATES (Franciscan Sisters of Allegany)
38151 Archer Ave., Zephyrhills, FL 33541. E-mail: judyradell@aol.com or fsaassoc@aol.com; Web: www.franciscansister.com
Contact: Judy Radell, Associate Co-Director
Affiliation: Franciscan Sisters of Allegany

FRANCISCAN ASSOCIATES (Clinton, IA)
588 N. Bluff Blvd., Clinton, IA 52732-3953. (563) 242-7611. Fax: (563) 243-0007. E-mail: sisters@clintonfranciscans.com; web: www.clintonfranciscans.com
Affiliation: Sisters of Saint Francis (Clinton, IA)

FRANCISCAN ASSOCIATES (Dubuque, IA)
Mount St. Francis, Dubuque, IA 52001. (563) 583-9786. E-mail: helenenelson@mcshi.com; Web: www.osfdbq.org
Contact: Helen Nelson, osf
Affiliation: Sisters of St. Francis of the Holy Family

FRANCISCAN ASSOCIATES (Frankfort, IL)
St. Francis Woods, 9201 W. St. Francis Rd., Frankfort, IL 60423-8335. (815) 469-4895. E-mail: elaineateders@provenahealth.com; Web: www.fssh.com
Contact: Sr. Elaine Teders, OSF
Affiliation: Franciscan Sisters of the Sacred Heart (Frankfort, IL)

FRANCISCAN ASSOCIATES (Green Bay, WI)
3025 Bay Settlement Rd., Green Bay, WI 54311-7301. (920) 468-1828. E-mail: Sr.Fran@gbfranciscans.org; Web: www.gbfranciscans.org
Contact: Sr. Francis Bangert
Affiliation: Sisters of St. Francis of the Holy Cross

FRANCISCAN ASSOCIATES (Little Falls, MN)
St. Francis Convent, 116 8th Ave. SE, Little Falls, MN 56345-3597. (320) 631-0693. E-mail: associates@fslf.org; Web: www.fslf.org/associat.htm
Contact: Sister Pat Imdieke
Affiliation: Franciscan Sisters of Little Falls, MN

FRANCISCAN ASSOCIATES (Franciscan Sisters of Oldenburg)
P.O. Box 100, Oldenburg, IN 47036-0100. Web: oldenburgfranciscans.org
Contacts: Judy Hillman (812-933-6457. E-mail: jhillman@oldenburgosf.com); Sr. Joan Laughlin, OSF (812-933-6439. E-mail: jlaughlin@oldenburgosf.com)
Affiliation: Franciscan Sisters of Oldenburg, IN

FRANCISCAN ASSOCIATES (St. Louis, MO)
335 South Kirkwood Rd., St. Louis, MO 63122-6117. (314) 965-3700, ext. 3054. Fax: (314) 965-3710. E-mail: srmarcy@fsolph.org; Web: www.franciscansisters-olph.org
Contact: Marcy Romine, OSF
Affiliation: Franciscan Sisters of Our Lady of Perpetual Help (OSF)

FRANCISCAN ASSOCIATES (Sylvania, OH)
6832 Convent Blvd., Sylvania, OH 43560. (419) 824-3635. E-mail: mgoretti@sistersosf.org
Contacts: Sr. Maria Goretti Sodd, Vincenz Marie Meyer, Associate Co-Directors
Affiliation: Sisters of St. Francis (Sylvania, OH) (Congregation of Our Lady of Lourdes)

FRANCISCAN ASSOCIATES (Syracuse, NY)
7770 Green Lakes Rd., Fayetteville, NY 13066. (315) 637-6661. E-mail: marise@aiusa.com
Contact: Sr. Marise Maye
Affiliation: Franciscan Sisters of Syracuse (1118A Court St., Syracuse, NY 13208)

FRANCISCAN ASSOCIATES (Tiffin, OH)
St. Francis Convent, 200 St. Francis Ave., Tiffin, OH 44883. (419) 447-0435. E-mail: jbrodman@tiffinfranciscans.org; Web: www.tiffinfranciscans.org
Contact: Sr. Joann Brodman
Affiliation: Sister of St. Francis, Tiffin, OH

FRANCISCAN ASSOCIATES (West Peoria, IL)
Immaculate Conception Convent, 2408 W. Heading Ave., West Peoria, IL 61604. (309) 674-6168. Fax: (309) 674-2006. Web: www.osfsisterswpeoria.org
Contact: Sister Betty Jean Haverback, O.S.F.
Affiliation: Franciscan Sisters of the Immaculate Conception (O.S.F.)

FRANCISCAN ASSOCIATES (Wheaton, IL)
PO Box 667, Wheaton, IL 60189-0667. (630) 462-7422. E-mail: adrewek@wheatonfranciscan.org; Web: www.wheatonfranciscan.org
Contact: Sr. Alice Drewek, OSF
Affiliation: Franciscan Sisters, Daughter of the Sacred Hearts of Jesus and Mary (Wheaton Franciscans) (O.S.F.)

FRANCISCAN ASSOCIATES (Williamsville, NY)
142 Laverack Ave., Lancaster, NY 14086-1849. (716) 683-4380. E-mail: roseclara@juno.com
Contact: Sr. Rose Therese DiGregorio
Affiliation: Sisters of St. Francis of Williamsville

FRANCISCAN ASSOCIATES (School Sisters of the Third Order of St. Francis [Bethlehem])
395 Bridle Path Rd., Bethlehem, PA 18017. (610) 866-2597. E-mail: peace@enter.net
Contact: Sister M. Barbara DeStefano, OSF
Affiliation: School Sisters of the Third Order of St. Francis (Bethlehem)

FRANCISCAN ASSOCIATES (School Sisters of the Third Order of St. Francis) (Pittsburgh)
Mount Assisi Convent, 934 Forest Ave., Pittsburgh, PA 15202. (412) 766-0758. Web: www.franciscansisters-pa.org
Contact: Sister Lois Jean DiFalco, OSF
Affiliation: School Sisters of the Third Order of St. Francis (Pittsburgh)

FRANCISCAN ASSOCIATES (Sisters of St. Francis of Penance and Christian Charity)
4421 Lower River Rd., Stella Niagara, NY 14144 1001. (716) 754-4312, ext. 701. Fax: (716) 754-7657. E-mail: annmcd@miamiarch.org; 2615 Roosevelt St., Hollywood, FL 33020. (305) 762-1182. Fax: (305) 762-1298. Web: www.franciscans-stella-niagara.org/assoc.htm
Contacts: Sister Ann McDermott, OSF, Zoila Diaz
Affiliation: Sisters of St. Francis of Penance and Christian Charity

FRANCISCAN ASSOCIATES (Sisters of St. Francis of Penance and Christian Charity)
P.O. Box 1028, Redwood City, CA 94064. (650) 369-1725
Contact: Margie Will, OSF
Affiliation: Sisters of St. Francis of Penance and Christian Charity

FRANCISCAN ASSOCIATES (Sisters of St. Francis of the Providence of God) (Pittsburgh)
3603 McRoberts Rd., Pittsburgh, PA 15234-2398. (412) 885-7228. E-mail: usaprovosf@aol.com
Contact: S. Maria Rainaldi, OSF
Affiliation: (Sisters of St. Francis of the Providence of God) (Pittsburgh)

FSSJ ASSOCIATE PROGRAM
5286 S. Park Ave., Hamburg, NY 14075. (716) 649-1205. E-mail: ahudzina@fssj.org
Contact: Sr. Ann Marie Hudzina, Judith Slon, Co-Directors
Affiliation: Franciscan Sisters of St. Joseph (FSSJ)

GENESEE LAY CONTEMPLATIVES
Abbey of the Genesee, Piffard, NY 14533. (585) 243-0660, ext. 18. E-mail: FrancisSteger@GeneseeAbbey.org; Web: www.geneseeabbey.org
Contact; Fr. Francis Steger, O.C.S.O.
Affiliation: Trappists

GOOD SHEPHERD AFFILIATION
187 Bay View Rd., Saco, ME 04072. (207) 283-3636. E-mail: elachance@gwi.net
Contact: Sister Elaine Lachance, s.c.i.m.
Affiliation: Servants of the Immaculate Heart of Mary (S.C.I.M.) (also known as Good Shepherd Sisters)

GREY NUN ASSOCIATES
24 Shoshone St., Buffalo, NY 14214. (716) 515-0629. E-mail: espangnsh@aol.com
Contact: Sr. Eileen Spanier, GNSH
Affiliation: Grey Nuns of the Sacred Heart

HM ASSOCIATE PROGRAM
20015 Detroit Rd., Rocky River, OH 44116-2418. (440) 356-6560. E-mail: maspangler@hmministry.org; Web: www.humilityofmary.org
Contact: Sr. Mary Ann Spangler, HM
Affiliation. Sisters of the Humility of Mary (H.M.)

HOLY CROSS ASSOCIATES
PO Box 668, Notre Dame, IN 46556. (574) 631-5521. E-mail: hca@nd.edu; Web: http://holycrossassociates.nd.edu
Contact: John Pinter
Affiliation: Holy Cross Priests and Brothers

HOLY CROSS ASSOCIATES
60 Riverbank Rd., Manchester, NH 03103. (603) 627-2079. E-mail: rondalla@attbi.com
Contact: Shirley H. Brien, Director
Affiliation: Sisters of Holy Cross

HOLY CROSS ASSOCIATES
501 S. Center Ave., Merrill, WI 54452. (715) 539-5000. E-mail: info@holycrosssisters.org; Web: www.holycrosssisters.org
Contact: Sister Linda Songy
Affiliation: Holy Cross Sisters

HOLY FAMILY ASSOCIATES
PO Box 3248, Fremont, CA 94539. (510) 624-4511. E-mail: ruthfaisca@aol.com; Web: www.holyfamilysisters.com
Contact: Sr. Ruth Faisca, SHF
Affiliation: Sisters of the Holy Family

HOLY UNION ASSOCIATES
528 Hanover St., Fall River, MA 02720. (508) 678-1348. E-mail: medonohue1234@aol.com; Web: www.holyunionsisters.org
Contact: Sister Mary Ellen Donohue
Affiliation: Holy Union Sisters (SUSC) (US Province)

HOME VISITORS OF MARY ASSOCIATES
121 E. Boston Blvd., Detroit, MI 48202-1318. (313) 869-2160. E-mail: homevisitors@myexcel.net
Contact: Sr. Mary Frances Roberts, HVM
Affiliation: Home Visitors of Mary (H.V.M.)

IBVM AFFILIATE RELATIONSHIP
101 Mason Blvd., Toronto, Ontario M5M 3E2 Canada. (416) 483-2238. E-mail: ibvmjed@rogers.com; Web: www.ibvm.org
Contact: Johanna D'Agostino, IBVM
Affiliation: Institute of the Blessed Virgin Mary (IBVM)

IDENTE FAMILY
143-48 84th Dr., Briarwood, NY 11435-2232. (718) 526-3595. Fax: (718) 526-9632. E-mail: dolores.sanchez4@verizon.net
Contact: Dolores Sanchez, M.Id.
Affiliation: Idente Missionaries of Christ Crucified

IGNATIAN ASSOCIATES
731 W. Washington St., Milwaukee, WI 53204. (414) 389-9540. E-mail: joan.shrout@jesuitswisprov.org; Web: www.ignatianassociates.com
Contact: Joan Shrout
Affiliation: Jesuits (Wisconsin Province)

IHM ASSOCIATES
610 W. Elm, Monroe, MI 48162. (734) 240-9821. Web: www.ihmsisters.org
Contact: Associate Coordinator
Affiliation: Sisters, Servants of the Immaculate Heart of Mary (IHM)

INCARNATE WORD ASSOCIATES
2930 S. Alameda St., Corpus Christi, TX 78404-2798. (361) 882-5413. Fax: (361) 880-4152
Contact: Annette Wagner, IWBS
Affiliation: Congregation of the Incarnate Word and Blessed Sacrament (I.W.B.S.)

INCARNATE WORD ASSOCIATES (C.V.I.)
3400 Bradford Pl., Houston, TX 77025-3668. (713) 668-0423. Web:

falcon.incarnateword.org/cvi
Contact: Sr. Anastasia, C.V.I.
Affiliation: Congregation of the Incarnate Word and Blessed Sacrament (C.V.I.)

LAY ASSOCIATES
Mt. St. Francis, 474 Sloatsburg Rd., Ringwood, NJ 07456. (973) 962-7411. Fax: (973) 962-0445. E-mail: Mt.St.Francis@juno.com
Contact: Sr. Clare Agnes Conforti
Affiliation: Franciscan Sisters of Ringwood

LAY ASSOCIATES (SISTERS OF ST. JOHN THE BAPTIST (C.S.JB.)
3304 Waterbury Ave., Bronx, NY 10465. (718) 931-3000, ext. 3116. E-mail: smichele50@aol.com; Web: baptistines.home.att.net
Contact: Sr. Michele, C.S.JB.
Affiliation: Sisters of St. John the Baptist (C.S. JB.)

LAY CANOSSIANS
PO Box 173, Pine Grove, CA 95665. (209) 223-3553. E-mail: helena@volcano.net; Web: www.fdcc.org/in/missionariesec/missiona.htm
Contact: Helena Anderson
Affiliation: Canossian Daughters of Charity, 5625 Isleta Blvd., SW, Albuquerque, NM 87105. (505) 873-2854

LAY CARMELITES - THIRD ORDER SECULAR (Darien, IL)
8501 Bailey Rd., Darien, IL 60561-8418. (630) 969-5050. E-mail: laycarmelites@carmelnet.org; Web: www.carmelites.org/laycarmelites.htm
Contact: Fr. Patrick McMahon, O.Carm.
Affiliation: Carmelites (Darien, IL)

LAY CARMELITES - THIRD ORDER SECULAR (St. Elias Province, NY)
St. Eliseus Priory, PO Box 27, 100 Kings Hwy., Tappan, NY 10983-0027. (845) 359-0535
Contact: Provincial Director, Office of Lay Carmelites
Affiliation: Carmelite Friars (Middletown, NY)

LAY CLARETIANS
205 W. Monroe St., Room 2106, Chicago, IL 60606. (1-800) 328-6515, (312) 236-7846. E-mail: frcarlweb@claret.org; Web: www.claretians.org
Contact: Father Carl Quebedeaux, C.M.F.
Affiliation: The Claretian Missionaries (Priests and Brothers)

LAY MISSIONARIES OF THE SACRED HEART (LAY MSC)
2811 Moyers Lane, Reading, PA 19605. (610) 929-5944. E-mail: lorrainemsc@aol.com; Web: www.hometown.aol.com/mscvocdir/usa.html
Contact: Sr. Lorraine Molchanow, MSC
Affiliation: Missionary Sisters of the Most Sacred Heart of Jesus (M.S.C.)

LAY SALVATORIANS
128 Clearview Dr., McMinnville, TN 37110-1615. (931) 474-8186. E-mail: LaySalvatorians@sdsvocations.com; Web: sdsvocations.com/sds-l.htm
Contact: Ms. Judy Davis SDS, National Director of Lay Salvatorians
Affiliation: The Salvatorians (Priests, Brothers, Sisters)

L.C.M. ASSOCIATES
9350 So. California Ave., Evergreen Pk., IL 60805. (708) 229-5797. E-mail: vocations@lcmh.org; Web: www.lcmh.org
Contact: Sister Jean Stickney, L.C.M.
Affiliation: Little Company of Mary Sisters

LORETTO CO-MEMBERS
300 E. Hampden Ave. #400, Englewood, CO 80110. (877) LORETTO (toll-free, outside Colorado); (303) 783-0450 (Colorado). Fax: (303) 783-0611. E-mail: annakoop@lorettocommunity.org; Web: www.lorettocommunity.org
Contact: Anna Koop, SL
Affiliation: Sisters of Loretto (S.L.)

MARIANIST LAY NETWORK OF NORTH AMERICA
618A N. Tazewell St., Arlington, VA 22203. E-mail: jcavana@verizon.net
Contact: Margaret Cavanaugh
Affiliation: Marianists, Society of Mary

MARIE RIVIER ASSOCIATION
186 Lowell Rd., Hudson, NH 03051. (603) 883-5899. E-mail: srestelle@juno.com; Web: www.presentationofmary.com
Contact: Sr. Estelle Leveillee
Affiliation: Sisters of the Presentation of Mary (p.m.)

MARIST LAITY
Notre Dame des Victoires School, 659 Pine St., San Francisco, CA 94108-3696. (415) 421-0069
Contact: Mary Ghisolfo
Affiliation: Marist Fathers and Brothers (Atlanta Province)

MARYKNOLL AFFILIATES
Maryknoll Affiliates, PO Box 311, Box 528, Maryknoll, NY 10545-0311. (877) 897-2386 (tel., fax). E-mail: inquiries@maryknollaffiliates.org; Web: www.maryknoll.org/MARYKNOLL/AFFILIATES/welcom_ma.htm
Contacts: Fred Goddard, Sr. Janet Srebalus, MM, Fr. Jack Sullivan, MM
Affiliation: Maryknoll Fathers, Brothers, Sisters and Lay Missioners

MERCEDARIAN THIRD ORDER
6398 Drexel Rd., Philadelphia, PA 19151-2596. (215) 879-0594. Web: www.orderofmercy.org
Contact: Rev. Gene A. Costa, O.de M.
Affiliation: Order of the Blessed Virgin Mary of Mercy (Mercedarian Friars)

MERCY ASSOCIATES (Regional Community of Baltimore)
1322 E. Northern Pkwy., Baltimore, MD 21239. (410) 435-4400. E-mail: somfran@qis.net; Web: www.mercysistersbalt.com
Contact: Sister Fran DeMarco, RSM
Affiliation: Sisters of Mercy of the Americas (R.S.M.) (Regional Community of Baltimore)

MERCY ASSOCIATES (Buffalo, NY)
625 Abbott Rd., Buffalo, NY 14020. (716) 825-5531, ext. 424
Contact: Sister Marilyn Brewer, R.S.M.
Affiliation: Sisters of Mercy of the Americas (R.S.M.) (Regional Community of Buffalo)

MERCY ASSOCIATES (Regional Community of Burlingame)
2300 Adeline Dr., Burlingame, CA 94010-5599. (1-877) 50-MERCY or (650) 340-7458. E-mail: dlnice@worldnet.att.net; Web: www.sistersofmercy.org
Contact: Dolores L. Nice, Co-Director
Affiliation: Sisters of Mercy of the Americas (R.S.M.) (Regional Community of Burlingame)

MERCY ASSOCIATES (Regional Community of Cedar Rapids)
1125 Prairie Dr. NE, Cedar Rapids, IA 52404. (319) 364-5196
Contacts: Sheila Kielly, Rose Marie Martensen, RSM
Affiliation: Sisters of Mercy of the Americas (R.S.M.) (Regional Community of Cedar Rapids)

MERCY ASSOCIATES (Regional Community of Cincinnati)
2335 Grandview Ave., Cincinnati, OH 45206-2280. (513) 221-1800. E-mail: srcarren@cinci.rr.com; Web: www.mercycincinnati.org
Contact: Sr. Carren Herring
Affiliation: Sisters of Mercy of the Americas (R.S.M.) (Regional Community of Cincinnati)

MERCY ASSOCIATES (Regional Community of Detroit)
29000 Eleven Mile Rd., Farmington Hills, MI 48336-1405. (248) 476-8000. E-mail: associates@mercy detroit.org; Web: www.sistersof mercy.org
Contact: Ann Dillon
Affiliation: Sisters of Mercy of the Americas (R.S.M.) (Regional Community of Detroit)

MERCY ASSOCIATES (North Carolina)
100 Mercy Dr., Belmont, NC 28012. (704) 829-5260. E-mail: cabrini@ mercync.org; Web: www.sistersof mercy.org/connections/associates .html
Contact: Sister M. Cabrini Taitano, RSM
Affiliation: Sisters of Mercy of the Americas (R.S.M.) (Regional Community of North Carolina)

MERCY ASSOCIATES (Regional Community of Omaha)
7262 Mercy Rd., Omaha, NE 68124. (402) 558-8873, 393-8145. E-mail: srmcamprsm@aol.com
Contact: Sister Anne Pellegrino, RSM
Affiliation: Sisters of Mercy of the Americas (R.S.M.) (Regional Community of Omaha)

MERCY ASSOCIATES (Regional Community of Providence)
15 Highland View Rd., Cumberland, RI 02864-1124. (401) 333-6333. E-mail: associate@mercyri.org; Web: www.mercyri.org/associates .htm
Contact: Associate Office
Affiliation: Sisters of Mercy of the Americas (R.S.M.) (Regional Community of Providence)

MERCY ASSOCIATES (Regional Community of Rochester)
1437 Blossom Rd., Rochester, NY 14610. (716) 288-2710, ext. 252. E-mail: nancy@mercyrochester.org
Contact: Sister Nancy Whitley, RSM
Affiliation: Sisters of Mercy of the Americas (R.S.M.) (Regional Community of Rochester)

MISSIONARY BENEDICTINE OBLATES
Immaculata Monastery, 300 N. 18th St., Norfolk, NE 68701-3687. (402) 371-3438. Fax: (402) 379-2877. E-mail: rosann@conpoint.com; Web: www.norfolkosb.org
Contact: Sister Rosann Ocken, OSB
Affiliation: Missionary Benedictine Sisters

MISSIONARY CENACLE APOSTOLATE
1602 E. Helmick St., Carson, CA 90745. (310) 632-0641. E-mail: josiemorales@juno.com; 460 Bancroft Way, Baton Rouge, LA 70808-4805. (225) 766-5987. E-mail: poboln@lsu.edu; Web: www.mcenacle.org/mca/mca.htm
Contacts: Josie Morales, James Bolner, Sr.
Affiliation: Trinity Missions Missionary Servant of the Most Blessed Trinity

MISSIONARY SISTERS ASSOCIATES
PO Box 3026, 779 Broadway, Paterson, NJ 07509. (973) 279-3790. E-mail: vocationteam@ aol.com
Contact: Maria Gonzalez
Affiliation: Missionary Sisters of the Immaculate Conception of the Mother of God (S.M.I.C.)

MSC LAY ASSOCIATES
305 S. Lake St., P.O. Box 270, Aurora, IL 60507-0270. (630) 892-2371. E-mail: info@misacor-usa .org; Web: www.misacor-usa.org
Contact: Kathy Marsala
Affiliation: Missionaries of the Sacred Heart (MSC)

NORBERTINES ASSOCIATES/ OBLATES
Daylesford Abbey, 220 S. Valley Rd., Paoli, PA 19301-1999. (610) 647-2530, ext. 21. Fax: (610) 651-0219. E-mail: salbero@daylesford.org; Web: www.Daylesford.org
Contact: Fr. Steven J. Albero, O. Praem.
Affiliation: Norbertines

NORTH AMERICAN CONFERENCE OF ASSOCIATES AND RELIGIOUS
NACAR, 1720 Metropolitan Ave., Bronx, NY 10462. (718) 918-9420. Fax: (718) 918-9421. E-mail: eocsc @aol.com and nacar@erols.com; Web: www.catholic-church.org/ nacar
Contacts: Sr. Ellen Rose O'Connell, SC, Jean Sonnenberg, ACBS
Clearinghouse for all US and Canadian Associates

NOTRE DAME ASSOCIATES
3501 State St., Omaha, NE 68112. (402) 738-9952. E-mail: meagher@ creighton.edu; Web: www.notre damesisters.org/becomeassociate .htm
Contact: Sr. Mary Kay Meagher, N.D.
Affiliation: Notre Dame Sisters (N.D.)

OBLATE ASSOCIATE PROGRAM
721 Lawrence St., NE, Washington, DC 20017. (202) 526-5651. Fax: (202) 526-5653. E-mail: knadolski@ oblates.org; Web: www.oblates.org/ vocations/associate.html
Contact: Fr. Kevin Nadolski, OSFS
Affliation: Oblates of St. Francis de Sales

OBLATE ASSOCIATE PROGRAM
2056 Parkwood Ave., Toledo, OH 43620. (419) 243-5105. E-mail: mlosfs@aol.com; Web: www. oblates.org/vocations/associate .html
Contact: Fr. Martin Lukas, OSFS
Affiliation: Oblates of St. Francis de Sales (Toledo/Detroit Province)

OBLATES OF ST. PAUL
231 Morden Rd., Oakville, Ontario, Canada L6K 2S2. (905) 845-3603. E-mail: michael_mancusi@ sympatico.ca
Contact: Rev. Michael M. Mancusi, CRSP
Affiliation: Barnabite Fathers and Brothers (1023 Swann Rd., Youngstown, NY 14174. (716) 754-7489)

O.C.D.S.
Our Lady of Mt. Carmel Monastery, 1628 Ridge Rd., Munster, IN 46321. (219) 838-7111. Fax: (219) 838-7214. E-mail: karmel@netnitco.net
Contact: O.C.D.S. Director
Affiliation: Discaled Carmelite Fathers

PASSIONIST SISTERS LAY ASSOCIATE PROGRAM
Our Lady of Calvary Retreat House, 31 Colton St., Farmington, CT 06032. (860) 677-8519. E-mail: annrodgers@snet.net
Contact: Sister Ann Rodgers, C.P.
Affiliation: Passionist Sisters (Sisters of the Cross and Passion)

PHJC ASSOCIATE PARTNERSHIP
PHJC Ministry Center, P.O. Box 1, Donaldson, IN 46513. (574) 936-9936. E-mail: fiwek@poorhand maids.org; Web: www.poorhand maids.org
Contact: Gayle Fiwek
Affiliation: Poor Handmaids of Jesus Christ (PHJC)

PFM ASSOCIATES
2 Dupont St., Worcester, MA 01604. (508) 756-0978. E-mail: PRHUSA EAST@prodigy.net
Contact: Sr. Irma Gendreau, p.f.m.
Affiliation: Little Franciscans of Mary (P.F.M.)

PRECIOUS BLOOD COMPANIONS
5401 S. Cornell Ave., Chicago, IL 60615-5664. (773) 684-7959. E-mail: djkinderman@aol.com
Contact: Fr. Denny Kinderman, Director (Kansas City Province)
2130 Hughes Rd., Liberty, MO 64068. (816) 781-4344. Fax: (816) 781-3639. E-mail: KCCPPS Vocations@aol.com
Contact: Marie Trout, Assistant Director (Kansas City Province)
225 W. Wayne St., Celina, OH 45822. (419) 586-2857. E-mail: jzg@bright.net
Contact: Mark Giesige, Assistant Director (Cincinnati Province)
Affiliation: Missionaries of the Precious Blood (C.PP.S.)

PRESENTATION ASSOCIATES
281 Masonic Ave., San Francisco, CA 94118-4416. (415) 422-5017. E-mail: jromero@pbvmsf.org
Contact: Sister Judy Romero, Associate Director
Affiliation: Sisters of the Presentation of the Blessed Virgin Mary (San Francisco)

PRESENTATION ASSOCIATES
2360 Carter Rd., Dubuque, IA 52001-2997. (563) 588-2008. Fax: (563) 588-4463. E-mail: mls@ ststephenuni.org; Web: www. dubuquepresentations.org/New_ Site/Associate_Membership.html
Contact: Mary Lou Specha, PBVM, Charlotte McCoy, Co-Coordinators of Presentation Associates
Affiliation: Presentation Sisters of Dubuque

PRESENTATION ASSOCIATES
Sacred Heart Convent, 1101 32nd Ave., South Fargo, ND 58103-6036. (701) 237-4857. E-mail: fjanousek@ juno.com; Web: www.presentation sistersfargo.com
Contact: Sr. Francine Janousek, PBVM
Affiliation: Sisters of the Presentation of the Blessed Virgin Mary (Fargo) (PBVM)

PROVIDENCE ASSOCIATES (Western US)
9 E. Ninth Ave., Spokane, WA 99202. (509) 325-9074. E-mail: srpwhte@msn.com
Contact: Pam White, SP
Affiliation: Sisters of Providence (S.P.) (Western US)

REDEMPTORISTINE ASSOCIATE PROGRAM
Mother of Perpetual Help Monastery, PO Box 220, Esopus, NY 12429-0220. (845) 384-6533. Web: www.catholic.org/macc
Contact: Sr. Paula Schmidt, O.Ss.R.
Affiliation: Redemptoristine Nuns (O.Ss.R.)

ROSSELLIAN FAMILY OUTREACH
Villa Rossello, 1009 Main Rd., Newfield, NJ 08344-5203. (856) 697-2983. E-mail: dmnewfield@yahoo .com; Web: www.blessings-catalog .com/Special%20Orders/sp059.html
Contact: Sister Mary Grace
Affiliation: Daughters of Our Lady of Mercy
(For families)

SACRED HEART ASSOCIATES (US EAST- SECULAR BRANCH)
10 Lawrence St., New Bedford, MA 02745. (508) 998-3703
Contact: Mrs. Theodora Gomes
Affiliation: Sacred Hearts Community, Priests and Brothers-Eastern Province (77 Adams St., P.O. Box 111, Fairhaven, MA 02719-0111. (508) 993-2442)

ST. JOSEPH CHRISTIAN COMMUNITY
975 E. Gardenia, Madison Heights, MI 48071-3431. (248) 582-9163. E-mail: nazvocation@aol.com; Web: www.SSJNazareth.org
Contacts: Bernadette Dean, SSJ, Marie Hogan, SSJ
Affiliation: Sisters of St. Joseph of Nazareth (S.S.J.)

ST. LEONARD'S FAMILY
4076 Case Rd., Avon, OH 44011. (440) 934-6270. E-mail: FrGiam pietro@aol.com; Web: www. stleonard-yrc.org
Contact: Fr. Giampietro Gasparin, C.S.J.
Affiliation: Congregation of St. Joseph

ST. PASCHAL BAYLON SECULAR FRANCISCAN FRATERNITY, S.F.O.
789 Parker St., Mission Hill (Boston), MA 02120-3021. (617) 442-2556
Contact: Formation Director
Affiliation: Little Brothers of Saint Francis (L.B.S.F.)

SECULAR FRANCISCAN ORDER (Formerly Third Order of St. Francis)
1615 Vine St., Cincinnati, OH 45210. 1-800-FRANCIS. E-mail: sfowicks@ aol.com; Web (regional fraternities listed): www.nafra-sfo.org/regions .html
Contact: William Wicks, SFO, National Minister
Affiliation: Franciscan Friars, Brothers and Sisters

SECULAR FRANCISCAN ORDER (Brooklyn, NY)
Franciscan Brothers, 275 Wolf Hill Rd., South Huntington, NY 11747. (631) 271-7415. E-mail: JMcVOSF @aol.com; Web: www.franciscan brothers.org
Contact: Brother James McVeigh, O.S.F.
Affiliation: Franciscan Brothers, 135 Remsen St., Brooklyn, NY 11201

SECULAR OBLATES OF HOLY TRINITY ABBEY
Holy Trinity Abbey, 1250 South 9500 East, Huntsville, UT 84317. (801) 745-3784. E-mail: hta@xmission .com; Web: www.xmission.com/~hta
Contact: Fr. Leander Dosch, ocso
Affiliation: Trappists

SECULAR ORDER OF DISCALCED CARMELITES (O.C.D.S.) (Loretto, PA)
239 Church St., Indiana, PA 15701. (412) 349-1476
Contact: Gertrude Moshier, O.C.D.S.
Affiliation: Carmelite Nuns, Discalced (Carmel of St. Therese of Lisieux, Loretto, PA)

SECULAR ORDER OF DISCALCED CARMELITES (O.C.D.S.) (Salt Lake City)
1605 S. Orchard Dr., Bountiful, UT 84010. (801) 295-7719; 933 East 1700 St., Salt Lake City, UT 84105. (801) 467-1898
Contacts: Maria Cruz F. Gray, Honey Campos
Affiliation: Carmelite Nuns, Discalced, Carmel of the Immaculate Heart of Mary, 5714 Holladay Blvd., Salt Lake City, UT 84121. (801) 277-6075. Web: www.carmelslc.org

SECULAR ORDER OF DISCALCED CARMELITES (O.C.D.S.) (San Diego, CA)
1601 Sunburst Dr., El Cajon, CA 92021. (619) 444-4971
Contact: Jeanette Curran
Affiliation: Carmelite Nuns, Discalced, Carmelite Monastery of the Trinity, 5158 Hawley Blvd., San Diego, CA 92116-1934

SECULAR ORDER OF DISCALCED CARMELITES (O.C.D.S.) (Schenectady, NY)
1097 Alheim Dr., Schenectady, NY 12304-4226. (518) 355-4914
Contact: Director
Affiliation: Carmelite Nuns, Discalced (St. Teresa of Jesus Monastery, Schenectady, NY)

SECULAR SERVITES
3121 W. Jackson Blvd., Chicago, IL 60612-2729. (773) 533-0360. Web: www.servite.org
Contact: Rev. Vidal Martinez, O.S.M.
Affiliation: Servite Friars

SETON FAMILY
Caritas Christi, Mt. Thor Rd., Greensburg, PA 15601. (724) 853-7948, ext. 194. E-mail: setonfa@scsh.org
Contact: Sister Mary Price, SC
Affiliation: Sisters of Charity of Seton HIll

SFP ASSOCIATE PROGRAM
60 Compton Rd., Cincinnati, OH 45215-5199. E-mail: karenhartman @voyager.net
Contact: Sr. Karen Hartman, SFP
Affiliation: Franciscan Sisters of the Poor (SFP)

SION ASSOCIATES
160 Marion St., Toronto, Ontario, Canada M6R 1E8. (416) 533-7734. E-mail: Aamgerwing@aol.com
Contact: Audrey Gerwing, nds
Affiliation: Notre Dame de Sion (Sisters of Sion)

SISTERS OF CHARITY OF THE INCARNATE WORD ASSOCIATES (San Antonio, TX)
3724A Candlewyck Club Dr., Florissant, MO 63034-2576. (800) 259-0587. E-mail: ccviassoc@aol.com
Contact: Lois Atnip
Affiliation: Sisters of Charity of the Incarnate Word (San Antonio, TX)

SISTERS OF DIVINE PROVIDENCE ASSOCIATES
49 N. Sprague Ave., Pittsburgh, PA 15202. (412) 761-0913. E-mail: jschaff6@juno.com; Web: www. sistersofdivprovidence.org/
Contact: Sr. Janet Schaffran, C.D.P.
Affiliation: Sisters of Divine Providence (Pittsburgh, PA)

SISTERS OF THE DIVINE COMPASSION ASSOCIATE MEMBERSHIP
37 Sherwood, Valhalla, NY 10595. (914) 686-4472. E-mail: mccarthy pate@aol.com; Web: www.divine compassion.org
Contact: Patricia McCarthy
Affiliation: Sisters of the Divine Compassion

SISTERS OF THE HOLY NAMES ASSOCIATES (Province of California)
PO Box 907, Los Gatos, CA 95031. (408) 873-7858. E-mail: everettsnjm @earthlink.net; Web: www.snjm.org /joinus/join_us.htm
Contact: Rosemary Everett, snjm
Affiliation: Sisters of the Holy Names of Jesus and Mary (SNJM) (Province of California)

SISTERS OF THE HOLY NAMES ASSOCIATES (Spokane, WA)
2911 West Fort Wright Dr., Spokane, WA 99224. (509) 328-7470. Fax: (509) 328-9824. E-mail: bmclellan@ snjmwa.org; Web: www. snjm.org
Contact: Sister Betty McLellan
Affiliation: Sisters of the Holy Names of Jesus and Mary (SNJM) (Spokane, WA)

SISTERS OF SAINTS CYRIL AND METHODIUS ASSOCIATES
Villa Sacred Heart, Danville, PA 17821-1698. (570) 275-1093.
E-mail: Associates@sscm.org; Web: www.sscm.org
Contact: Sister Maria Goretti, SSCM
Affiliation: Sisters of Saints Cyril and Methodius

SISTERS OF ST. FRANCIS OF MARY IMMACULATE ASSOCIATE RELATIONSHIP
801 N. Larkin Ave., Ste. 101, Joliet, IL 60435. (815) 725-8735. (815) 727-3686. E-mail: sfrederick@ stfrancis.edu
Contact: Sister Sharon Frederick, OSF
Affiliation: Sisters of St. Francis of Mary Immaculate

SISTERS OF ST. MARY ASSOCIATES
3000 Lansing Blvd., Wichita Falls, TX 76309. (940) 692-9770. E-mail: mercycom@aol.com; Web: web2 .airmail.net/ssmn/
Contact: Sister Patricia Ste. Marie
Affiliation: Sisters of St. Mary of Namur (S.S.M.N.)

SISTERS OF SOCIAL SERVICE ASSOCIATES
303 S. Figueroa Way, Los Angeles, CA 90007-2504. (619) 295-1896. E-mail: ssssd@juno.com; Web: www.socialservicesisters.org
Contact: Sr. Merita Dekat
Affiliation: Sisters of Social Service

SPIRITAN ASSOCIATES
6230 Brush Run Rd., Bethel Park, PA 15102. (412) 835-3510. E-mail: bevancssp@cs.com; Web: www. spiritans.org
Contact: Rev. Norm Bevan, C.S.Sp.
Affiliation: Holy Ghost Fathers and Brothers (Spiritans)

SSJ AGREGES
Contacts: Joan M. Doeblin, 163 Pulteney St., Geneva, NY 14456. (315) 789-8090; Sr. Anne, 118 William St., Geneva, NY 14456. Sr. Dorothy Mulcahy, 3388 Hopkins Rd., Canandaigua, NY 14424. Web: www. ssjvolunteers.org/assocmem.htm
Affiliation: Sisters of St. Joseph of Rochester

SSM ASSOCIATES
9056 North Deerbrook Trail, Brown Deer, WI 53223-2454. (414) 357-8940. E-mail: ssmassoc@aol.com; Web: www.ssmfranciscans.org
Contact: Sister M. Raphael Narcisi
Affiliation: Sisters of the Sorrowful Mother (Third Order Regular of St. Francis of Assisi) (SSM)

SSMO ASSOCIATES
4440 S.W. 148th Ave., Beaverton, OR 97007. (503) 644-9181.
E-mail: srcatherineh@ssmo.org; Web: www.ssmo.org
Contact: Sister Catherine Hertel, SSMO
Affiliation: Sisters of St. Mary of Oregon (S.S.M.O.)

SSND ASSOCIATES (Milwaukee Province)
Notre Dame Hall, 13105 Watertown Plank Rd., Elm Grove, WI 53122-2291. (262) 782-9850, ext. 717. Fax: (262) 207-0051. E-mail: lfox@ssnd-milw.org
Contact: Linda Fox, SSND Associate
Affilliation: School Sisters of Notre Dame

STIGMATINE LAY ASSOCIATES
554 Lexington St., Waltham, MA 02452. (781) 209-3100
Contact: Rev. Robert Masciocchi, C.S.S.
Affiliation: Stigmatine Fathers and Brothers

THIRD ORDER OF THE INSTITUTE OF THE INCARNATE WORD
Saint Paul the Apostle Church, 113 E. 117th St., New York, NY 10035. (212) 534-5257. E-mail: prov .immaculate.conception@ive.org; Web: www.iveamerica.org/3_order /english/third_order_index.asp
Affiliation: Institute of the Incarnate Word (Priests)

THIRD ORDER OF MARY
Northeast US (6 New England states, NY, MI, WI): Fr. Albert Dianni, S.M., Our Lady of Victories Rectory, 27 Isabella St., Boston, MA 02116-5216. (617) 426-4448. E-mail: rlajoie@aol.com; Southern, Western US: Fr. Ed Keel, SM, Marist Community, 1706 Jackson Ave., New Orleans, LA 70113-1510. (504) 524-5192. Fax: (504) 524-9796. E-mail: edwink@bellsouth.net; Web: www.maristsociety.org
Affiliation: Marist Fathers and Brothers (Boston Province)

URSULINE SISTERS AFFILIATES (Cleveland, OH)
2600 Lander Rd., Pepper Pike (Cleveland), OH 44124. (440) 449-1200, ext. 138. E-mail: rgoebel@ursulinesisters.org; Web: ursulinesisters.org
Contact: Sister Roberta Goebel, OSU
Affiliation: Ursuline Sisters (Cleveland, OH)

URSULINE ASSOCIATES (Dedham, MA)
142 Western Ave., Waterville, ME 04901. (207) 873-3515
Contact: Sr. Mae Doucette, osu
Affiliation: Ursuline Nuns (Dedham, MA)

URSULINE ASSOCIATES (Paola, KS)
7021 W. 227th Terr., Bucyrus, KS 66013. (913) 533-4116. Web: www.paolaursuline.org/obl.htm
Contact: Sr. Marie William Blyth, O.S.U.
Affiliation: Ursuline Sisters (osu) (Congregation of Paris)

URSULINE ASSOCIATES (St. Martin, OH)
1080 Cooks Crossing #11, Milford, OH 45150. (513) 576-6606. Web: www.ursulinesofbc.org
Contact: Sr. Lucy Schmid, osu
Affiliation: Ursuline Sisters

URSULINE ASSOCIATES (Ursuline Sisters of Tildonk)
399 Miller Ave., Freeport, NY 11520
Contact: Linda A. Siani
Affiliation: Ursuline Sisters of Tildonk, 81-15 Utopia Pkwy., Jamaica, NY 11432. (718) 591-0681

URSULINE ASSOCIATES (Toledo, OH)
4045 Indian Rd., Toledo, OH 43606. (419) 536-9587. E-mail: ursulines@accesstoledo.com; Web: toledoursulines.org
Contact: Director
Affiliation: Ursuline Sisters (Toledo, OH)

VEDRUNA FRIENDS
1222 Monroe St. NE, Washington, DC 20017-2507. (202) 832-2114, 265-1349; E-mail: fuertes@american.edu
Contact: Sr. Covadonga Fuertes, ccv
Affiliation: Carmelite Sisters of Charity

VENERINI ASSOCIATES
23 Edward St., Worcester, MA 01605. (508) 754-1020. E-mail: MPV31@aol.com; Web: www.venerinisisters.com
Affiliation: Religious Venerini Sisters (M.P.V.)

VINCENTIAN ASSOCIATES
8200 McKnight Rd., Pittsburgh, PA 15237. (412) 364-3000. E-mail: mabehary@vincentiansrspgh.org; Web: www.vincentiansrspgh.org
Contact: Sr. Mary Ann Behary
Affiliation: Vincentian Sisters of Charity (V.S.C.)

VOCATIONIST FATHERS ASSOCIATES
90 Brooklake Rd., Florham Park, NJ 07932. (973) 966-6262 E-mail: info@vocationist.org; Web: www.vocationist.org
Contact: Fr. Ezio Antunes, S.D.V.
Affiliation: Vocationist Fathers (S.D.V.) (Society of the Divine Vocations)

Retreat Centers

More than 650 locations offering workshops, spiritual formation, spiritual direction, and silent/nondirected retreats as well as "directed" retreats.

ALABAMA

Benedictine Spirituality & Conference Center
PO Box 2040, Cullman, AL 35056-2040. 256-734-8302, fax: 256-734-8302 (phone first), e-mail: shmon@hiwaay.net, web: www.shmon.org
Contact: Gloria Garrison, OSB
Affiliation: Benedictine Sisters

Blessed Trinity Shrine Retreat
107 Holy Trinity Rd., Fort Mitchell, AL 36856. 334-855-4474, fax: 334-855-4525, e-mail: btsr107@juno.com, web: www.msbt.org/mis_btsr.htm
Contact: Sister Gerry
Affiliation: Missionary Servants of the Blessed Trinity

Casa Maria Retreat House
3721 Belmont Rd., Birmingham, AL 35210. 205-956-6760
Contact: Mother Mary Gabriel, S.S.E.W.
Affiliation: Sister Servants of the Eternal Word

St. Bernard Retreat & Conference Center
1600 St. Bernard Dr. SE, Cullman, AL 35055. 256-734-8291, 3946, fax: 256-734-3885, e-mail: andre35055@yahoo.com, web: www.stbernardabbey.com
Contact: Bro. André, OSB
Affiliation: Benedictine Monks

Visitation Sacred Heart Retreat House
2300 Spring Hill Ave., Mobile, AL 36607. Fax: 251-476-9761
Contact: Mother Superior
Affiliation: Visitation Nuns

ALASKA

Holy Spirit Center
10980 Hillside Dr., Anchorage, AK 99507. 907-346-2343, fax: 907-346 2140, e-mail: hsrh@alaska.com, web: home.gci.net/~hsrh
Contact: Fr. Paul B. Macke, S.J.
Affiliation: Archdiocese of Anchorage, Jesuits (Oregon Province)

St. Marys Conference Center
PO Box 172, Nome, AK 99658. 907-438-2712, fax: 907-438-2823, e-mail: weingarth@juno.com
Contact: Erik Weingarth, Administrator

Shrine of St. Therese
5933 Lund St., Juneau, AK 99801. 907-780-6112, fax: 907-780-6112, e-mail: fitterer@gci.net, web: www.shrineofsainttherese.org/
Contact: Thomas P. Fitterer
Affiliation: Diocese of Juneau

House of Prayer
1316 Peger Rd., Fairbanks, AK 99709. 907-474-9379
Contact: Fr. Normand A. Pepin, S.J.

ARIZONA

Desert House of Prayer
7350 W. Picture Rocks Rd., PO Box 569, Cortaro, AZ 85652. 520-744-3825, fax: 520-744-0774, e-mail: paulcssr@aol.com, web: www.desertrenewal.org/DHOP_Main.asp
Contact: Rev. Paul Curtin, C.Ss.R.

Franciscan Renewal Center
5802 East Lincoln Dr., Scottsdale, AZ 85253. 800-356-3247, fax: 480-948-2325, e-mail: casa@thecasa.org, web: www.thecasa.org
Affiliation: Franciscan Friars (Province of St. Barbara)

Joshua Retreat Center
1530 23rd St., Douglas, AZ 85607. 520-364-4411, fax: 520-364-2397
Contact: Janet E. Fullen

Mt. Claret Center
4633 N. 54th St., Phoenix, AZ 85018. 602-840-5066, fax: 602-840-5732
Contact: Msgr. John J. McMahon

Our Lady of Solitude House of Prayer
PO Box 1140, Black Canyon City, AZ 85324. 623-374-9204, web: www.laycontemplative.org/ols.htm
Contact: Sr. Mary Therese Sedlock, O.S.F.
Affiliation: Diocese of Phoenix

Redemptorist Renewal Center
7101 W Picture Rocks Rd., Tucson, AZ 85743, 520-744-3400, fax: 520-744-8021, e-mail: tmscssr@cs.com, web: www.desertrenewal.org
Contact: Rev. Thomas M. Santa, CSsR
Affiliation: Redemptorists (Denver Province)

Tolomei Retreat House
Holy Trinity Monastery, PO Box 298, St. David, AZ 85630-0298. 520-720-4016, 520-720-4642 ext.17, fax: 520-720-4202, e-mail: guestmaster@theriver.com, web: www.holytrinitymonastery.org
Contact: Guest Coordinator
Affiliation: Benedictine Monks (Olivetan Benedictines)

ARKANSAS

Coury House Retreat Center of Subiaco Abbey
340 N. Subiaco Ave., Subiaco, AR 72865. 479-934-4411,1290, fax: 845-424-2162, e-mail: couryhouse@subi.org, web: www.subi.org/couryhouse.htm
Affiliation: Benedictine Monks

Hesychia House of Prayer
204 St. Scholastica Rd., New Blaine, AR 72851. 479-938-7375, web: www.scholasticafortsmith.org/hesychia.html
Contact: Sr. Louise Sharum, OSB
Affiliation: Benedictine Sisters (St. Scholastica Monastery, Fort Smith, AR)

Little Portion Retreat/Training Center
171 Hummingbird Lane, Eureka Springs, AR 72632, 479-253-7710, 7379, fax: 479-253-6640, e-mail: retreats@littleportion.org, web: www.littleportion.org
Contact: Kathy Mitchell
Affiliation: The Brothers and Sisters at Little Portion Hermitage

St. Scholastica Center
1205 South Albert Pike, Fort Smith, AR 72913-3489, 479-783-1135, fax: 479-782-4352, e-mail: retreats@scholasticafortsmith.org, web: www.scholasticafortsmith.org
Contact: Sister Hilary Decker, OSB
Affiliation: Benedictine Sisters

CALIFORNIA

Angela Center
535 Angela Dr., Santa Rosa, CA 95403. 707-528-8578, fax: 707-528-0114, e-mail: angelacenter@juno.com, web: www.angelacenter.com
Contact: Sr. Christine van Swearingen, O.S.U.
Affiliation: Ursuline Sisters (Roman Union - Western Province)

Camp Mariastella
2303 S. Figueroa Way, Los Angeles, CA 90007. 213-745-7870, fax: 213-745-7871
Affiliation: Sisters of Social Service

Camp Oliver
PO Box 712525, 2202 Comstock St., Ste. 2, San Diego, CA 92171. 858-492-9171, fax: 858-874-2939, e-mail: camp_oliver@yahoo.com, web: www.campoliver.com
(summer, residential, girls/boys, ages 6-16)
Affiliation: Sisters of Social Service

Camp St. Francis
2320 Sumner Ave., Aptos, CA 95003. 831-763-4486
Affiliation: Salesians of St. John Bosco

Cardinal Newman Retreat Center
24 A Ursuline Rd., Santa Rosa, CA 95403. 707-568-6822, fax: 707-566-3360, web: www.santarosacatholic.org/cardinal.htm
Contact: Richard Boyer
Affiliation: Diocese of Santa Rosa

Carmelite House of Prayer
PO Box 347, Oakville, CA 94562. 707-944-2454, fax: 707-944-8533,e-mail: carmeloakville@aol.com
Contact: Rev. John Reginald McSweeney, O.C.D.
Affiliation: Discalced Carmelite Friars (California-Arizona Province)

Center for Spiritual Development
434 South Batavia St., Orange, CA 92868. 714-744-3175, ext. 4421, fax: 714-744-3176, e-mail: csdinfo@csjorange.org
Contact: MaryAnne Huepper, CSJ
Affiliation: Sisters of St. Joseph of Orange

Christ the King Retreat Center
6520 Van Maren Lane, Citrus Heights, CA 95621. 916-725-4720, fax: 916-725-4812, e-mail: christtheking@passionist.org, web: www.passionist.org./christtheking/
Contact: Fr. Ron Corl, C.P.
Affiliation: Passionists (Holy Cross Province)
(also Spiritual Life Institute [Contact: Sr. Marcella Fabing, C.S.J.])

Christian Brothers Retreat/ Conference Center
4401 Redwood Rd., PO Box 3720, Napa, CA 94558. 707-252-3810, 3811, fax: 707-252-3818, e-mail: lbausch@dlsi.org, web: www.christianbrosretreat.com
Contact: Ronald Tapper

Claretian Retreat Center
1119 Westchester Pl., Los Angeles, CA 90019. 323-737-8464, fax: 323-733-6201
Contact: Fr. Frank J. Ferrante, C.M.F.
Affiliation: Claretian Missionaries

DePaul Center
1105 Bluff Rd., Montebello, CA 90640-6198. 323-721-6060, fax: 323-887-0765, e-mail: DePaulCenter@att.net
Contact: Fr. Jim Osendorf, C.M.
Affiliation: Vincentian Fathers (Congregation of the Mission)

Diocese of Oakland Youth Retreat Center
PO Box 1505, 1977 Reliez Valley Rd., Lafayette, CA 94549. 925-934-5802, fax: 925-934-0642, e-mail: oakdiocythrtr@aol.com, web: www.oakdiocese.org/youthretreat
Affiliation: Diocese of Oakland

Divine Word Retreat Center
11316 Cypress Ave., Riverside, CA 92505. 909-689-4858
Affiliation: Divine Word Missionaries

El Carmelo Retreat Center
926 E. Highland Ave., Redlands, CA 92376. 909-792-1047, fax: 909-798-3497, e-mail: elcarmelo@juno.com
Contact: Fr. Fernando Pinto, O.C.D.
Affiliation: Discalced Carmelite Friars (Province of St. Joseph of the Western US)

El Retiro San Inigo-Jesuit Retreat House of Los Altos
300 Manresa Way, Los Altos, CA 94022. 650-948-4491, fax: 650-948-0640, e-mail: retreat@elretiro.org, web: www.elretiro.org
Affiliation: Jesuits (California Province)

Heart of Jesus Retreat Center
2927 S. Greenville St., Santa Ana, CA 92704. 714-557-4538, fax: 714-668-9780, e-mail: sdshretreatcenter@juno.com, web: www.sacredheartsisters.com
Contact: Sister Adriane Torrisi, SDSH
Affiliation: Society Devoted to the Sacred Heart of Jesus (SDSH)

Holy Family Center
2059 Pleasant Hill Rd., Pleasant Hill, CA 94523. 925-935-6151, fax: 925-935-1394, e-mail: holyfamcen@aol.com

Holy Redeemer Center
8945 Golf Links Rd., PO Box 5427, Oakland, CA 94605. 510-635-6341, fax: 510-635-6342, e-mail: HRCoakland@aol.com, web: www.holyredeemercenter.org
Contact: Kevin Dwyer
Affiliation: Redemptorists (Denver Province)

Holy Spirit Retreat Center
4316 Lanai Rd., Encino, CA 91436. 818-784-4515, fax: 818-784-0409, e-mail: HSRCenter@earthlink.net, web: www.HSRCenter.com
Contact: Sr. Rochelle Mitchell, SSS
Affiliation: Sisters of Social Service

Holy Transfiguration Monastery
Monks of Mt. Tabor, 17001 Tomki Rd., PO Box 217, Redwood Valley, CA 95470-0217. 707-485-8959, fax: 707-485-1122, e-mail: mttabor@pacific.net
Affiliation: Monks of Mt. Tabor

House of Prayer for Priests
7734 Santiago Canyon Rd., Orange, CA 92869. 714-639-9740, fax: 714-639-9313
Contact: Fr. J. Gordon Moreland, S.J.

Immaculate Heart Center for Spiritual Renewal
888 San Ysidro Lane, Santa Barbara, CA 93108. 805-969-2474, fax: 805-565-2156, e-mail: ihccenter@aol.com, web: www.immaculateheartcenter.org
Contact: Sr. Carol Carrig, IHM

Immaculate Heart Retreat House
3431 Waverly Dr., Los Angeles, CA 90027-2526. 323-664-1126, fax: 323-664-2215, e-mail: laihm@aol.com; web: www.retreats@sistersihm.org
Contact: Sr. Rita Callanan, I.H.M.
Affiliation: Sisters of the Immaculate Heart
(days of recollection only)

La Casa de Maria
800 El Bosque Rd., Santa Barbara, CA 93108. 805-969-5031, fax: 805-969-2759, e-mail: glatt@lacasademaria.org, web: www.lacasademaria.org
Contact: Stephanie Glatt, IHM
Affiliation: The Sisters of The Immaculate Heart (Lay Community)

La Providencia Spiritual Renewal Center
1510 Peutz Valley Rd., Alpine, CA 91901-1223. 619-445-4570. Fax: 619-445-8289. E-mail: laprovda@adnc.com, Web: www.geocities.com/laprov
Contacts: Patricia Hanson, CSJO, Millicent Peaslee, OLVM, Co-Directors
Affiliation: Sisters of St. Joseph of Orange, Our Lady of Victory Missionary Sisters

Madonna of Peace Renewal Center
2010 Hunt Rd., PO Box 71, Copperopolis, CA 95228. 209-785-2157 (youth facility)

Marianist Center
22622 Marianist Way, Cupertino, CA 95014. 408-253-6279, fax: 408-253-1834, e-mail: marcenter@aol.com, web: www.marianistcenter.org
Contact: Kevin Dincher
Affiliation: Marianists, Society of Mary

Mary & Joseph Retreat Center
5300 Crest Rd., Rancho Palos Verdes, CA 90275. 310-377-4867, ext. 222, fax: 310-541-1176, e-mail: registrar@maryjoseph.org, web: www.maryjoseph.org
Contact: Mary Kaighan
Affiliation: Daughters of Mary and Joseph

Marywood Retreat Center
2811 E. Villa Real Dr., Orange, CA 92867. 714-282-3099, fax: 714-282-3029, e-mail: sr.concetta@rcbo.org, web: www.rcbo.org/offices/retreatcenter.htm
Contact: Sr. M. Concetta Banez, S.P.

Mater Dolorosa Retreat Center
700 North Sunnyside Ave., Sierra Madre, CA 91024. 626-355-7188, fax: 626-355-0485, e-mail: materdolorosa@compuserve.com, web: www.materdolorosa.org
Contact: Rev. Patrick Brennan, c.p.
Affiliation: Passionists (Holy Cross Province)

Mercy Center
2300 Adeline Dr., Burlingame, CA 94010. 650-340-7474, fax: 650-340-1299, e-mail: mc@mercyburl.org, web: www.mercy-center.org
Affiliation: Sisters of Mercy of the Americas (Regional Community of Burlingame)

Mercy Center Auburn
535 Sacramento St., Auburn, CA 95603. 530-887-2019, fax: 530-887-1154, e-mail: mercycenter@mercyauburn.com, web: www.mercyauburn.org
Affiliation: Sisters of Mercy of the Americas (Regional Community of Auburn)

Mission San Luis Rey Retreat Center
4050 Mission Ave., Oceanside, CA 92057-6402. 760-757-3659, ext. 113, fax: 760-757-8025, e-mail: slretreat@sanluisrey.org, ben@sanluisrey.org, web: www.sanluisrey.org
Contact: Fr. Ben Innes, OFM
Affiliation: Franciscan Friars (Province of St. Barbara)

Mount Alverno Conference and Retreat Center
3910 Bret Harte Dr., Redwood City, CA 94061. 650-369-0798, fax: 650-361-9672, e-mail: reservations@mountalverno.com, web: www.mountalverno.com
Contact: Laurie Landis
Affiliation: Sisters of St. Francis of Penance and Christian Charity (O.S.F.) (Redwood City Franciscans)

New Camaldoli Retreat House/Hermitage
62475 Hwy. 1, Big Sur, CA 93920. (831) 667-2456, web: www.contemplation.com/Hermitage/retreat.html
Affiliation: Camaldolese Monks

Our Lady of the Oaks Villa
PO Box 128, Applegate, CA 95703. 530-878-2776, fax: 530-878-1615, e-mail: appvilla@pacbell.net
Contact: Fr. Gerald H. Robinson, S.J. (available for retreats Sept. 1- May 15)

Pala Rey Youth Camp/Retreat Center
10779 Pala Rd., Pala, CA 92059. 760-742-8767
Contact: Roy Alvarado

Pendola Center
2110 Broadway, Sacramento, CA 95818-2541. 916-733-0123, 916-PEN-DOLA, fax: 916-733-0195, e-mail: campendola@aol.com, web: www.pendola.org
Contact: Stephen Tholcko
Affiliation: Diocese of Sacramento (teenage, youth adult, school midweek retreats)

Poverello of Assisi Retreat House
1519 Woodworth St., San Fernando, CA 91340-4153. 818-365-1071, fax: 818-361-2751
Contact: Sr. Mary Jesus, O.S.F.
Affiliation: Franciscan Missionary Sisters of the Immaculate Conception

Presentation Center
19480 Bear Creek Rd., Los Gatos, CA 95033. 408-354-2346, fax: 408-354-5226, web: www.prescenter.org
Contact: Sr. Patricia Marie Mulpeters, P.B.V.M.
Affiliation: Sisters of the Presentation of the Blessed Virgin Mary (San Francisco)

Prince of Peace Abbey
650 Benet Hill Rd., Oceanside, CA 92054. 760-430-1305, fax: 760-967-8711, e-mail: princeabby@aol.com
Contact: Guest Master
Affiliation: Benedictine Monks

Pro Sanctity Spirituality Center
205 S. Pine Dr., Fullerton, CA 92833. 714-956-1020, fax: 714-525-8948, e-mail: apostolico@aol.com, web: www.prosanctity.org/retreats.php
Contact: Agnes Rus
Affiliation: Apostolic Oblates

Sacred Heart Retreat Camp
896 Cienga Rd., PO Box 1795, Big Bear Lake, CA 92315. 909-866-5696, fax: 909-866-5650, web: sacredheartsisters.com
Contact: Sister Doreen Reinke, SDSH
Affiliation: Sisters of the Society Devoted to the Sacred Heart of Jesus

Sacred Heart Retreat House
920 East Alhambra Rd., Alhambra, CA 91801. 626-289-1353, fax: 626-281-3546, e-mail: shrhrd@pacbell.net, web: www.shretreathouse.org
Contact: Sister Marisa, ocd
Affiliation: Carmelite Sisters of the Most Sacred Heart of Los Angeles

St. Andrew's Abbey Retreat House
31001 N. Valyermo Rd., PO Box 40, Valyermo, CA 93563. 661-944-1076, e-mail: retreats@valyermo.com, web: www.valyermo.com

Contact: Sr. Karen Wilhelmy, C.S.J.
Affiliation: Benedictine Monks (Congregation of the Annunciation)

St. Anthony Retreat Center
PO Box 249, Three Rivers, CA 93271. 559-561-4595, fax: 559-561-4493, e-mail: stanthonyretreat center_ francis@yahoo.com, web: www.homestead.com/ stanthony retreatcenter/stanthonyhome.html
Contact: Fr. Richard Juzix, O. F. M.
Affiliation: Franciscan Friars (Province of St. Barbara)

St. Clare's Retreat
2381 Laurel Glen Rd., Soquel, CA 95073. 831-423-8093, fax: 831-423-1541, e-mail: stclaresretreat@juno .com, web: www.infoteam.com/ nonprofit/stclaresretreat/index.html
Affiliation: Franciscan Friars, Franciscan Missionary Sisters

St. Francis Retreat Center
549 Mission Vineyard Rd., San Juan Bautista, CA 95045-0970. 831-623-4234, fax: 831-623-9046, e-mail: info@stfrancisretreat.com, www.stfrancisretreat.com
Affiliation: Franciscan Friars (Province of St. Barbara)

St. Joachim & St. Anne Retreat Center
PO Box 1760, Running Springs, CA 92382. 909-867-7362

St. Mary Seminary Retreat Center
1964 Las Canoas Rd., Santa Barbara, CA 93105. 805-966-4829, fax: 805-564-1662, e-mail: stmarys seminary@cox.net; web: home .CatholicWeb.com/stmaryseminary retreatcenter
Contact: Fr. Patrick Mullin, C.M.
Affiliation: Vincentians (Congregation of the Mission) (Province of the West)

St. Joseph's Salesian Youth Renewal Center
8301 Arroyo Dr., PO Box 1639, Rosemead, CA 91770-0986. 626-280-8622, fax: 626-280-0545, e-mail: stjosephrc@aol.com
Contact: Fr. Bill Bolton, S.D.B.
Affiliation: Salesians of St. John Bosco

San Damiano Retreat
PO Box 767, 710 Highland Dr., Danville, CA 94526-0767. 925-837-9141, fax: 925-837-0522, e-mail: maryp@sandamiano.org, web: www.sandamiano.org
Contact: Fr. Raymond Bucher, OFM
Affiliation: Franciscan Friars (Province of St. Barbara)

San Miguel Retreat House
PO Box 69, San Miguel, CA 93451. 805-467-3256, fax: 805-467-2448
Contact: Br. Bill Short, O.F.M.

Santa Sabina Center
25 Magnolia Ave., San Rafael, CA 94901. 415-457-7727, fax: 415-457-2310, e-mail: sntasabina@aol.com; web: www.retreatsonline.net/ santasabina
Affiliation: Dominican Sisters of San Rafael

Serra Retreat
3401 Serra Rd., PO Box 127, Malibu, CA 90265. 310-456-6631, fax: 310-456-6051, e-mail: frwarren @serraretreat.com, web: serra retreat.com
Contact: Fr. Warren Rouse, O.F.M.
Affiliation: Franciscan Friars

Servants of the Paraclete Guadalupe Retreat Center
39100 Orchard Ave., Cherry Valley, CA 92223. 909-845-7777, fax: 909-845-6271

Silver Penny Farm Retreat Center
5215 Old Lakeville Rd., No. 1, Petaluma, CA 94954. 707-762-1498
Contact: Fr. Raymond K. Smith

Spiritual Ministry Center
4822 Del Mar Ave., San Diego, CA 92107-3407. 619-224-9444, fax: 619-224-1082, e-mail: spiritmin@ aol.com, web: spiritmin.org
Affiliation: Society of the Sacred Heart (R.S.C.J.) (Religious of the Sacred Heart)

Spirituality Center - Archdiocese of Los Angeles
10 Chester Place, Los Angeles, CA 90007. 213-747-6508, e-mail: tbernard@msmc.la.edu
Affiliation: Archdiocese of Los Angeles

Vallombrosa Retreat Center
250 Oak Grove Ave., Menlo Park, CA 94025. 650-325-5614, fax: 650-325-0908, e-mail: host@vallom brosa.org, web: www.vallombrosa .org
Affiliation: Archdiocese of San Francisco

Villa Holy Names
82 Prospect Ave., Los Gatos, CA 95030-7026. 408-354-2312, fax: 408-354-8305, e-mail: jmvillalg@ yahoo.com, web: www.holynames .net
Contact: Sr. Dorothy Clare Klingler, S.N.J.M.
Affiliation: Sisters of the Holy Names of Jesus and Mary

Villa Maria del Mar
2-1918 E. Cliff Dr., Santa Cruz, CA 95062. 831-475-1236, fax: 831-475-8867, e-mail: villamariadelmar@ earthlink.net
Contact: Patricia Doyle, SNJM
Affiliation: Sisters of the Holy Names of Jesus and Mary

Villa Maria House of Prayer
1252 N. Citrus Dr., La Habra, CA 90631. 562-691-5838, fax: 562-691-2572
Affiliation: Sisters of St. Joseph of Carondelet

Vina de Lestonnac Spirituality Center
39300 De Portola Rd., Temecula, CA 92592-8758. 909-302-5571, fax: 909-302-2830, web: vinalestonnac .com
Contacts: Patricia Garcia, Sr. Maria Elena
Affiliation: Company of Mary

Whispering Winds Catholic Conference Center
8186 Commercial St., La Mesa, CA 91942-2926. 619-464-1479, 760-765-1600, fax: 619-464-4491, e-mail: wwccc@aol.com, web: www. whisperingwinds.org/index.html
Contact: Don Kojis

COLORADO

Abbey of St. Walburga
32109 North US Hwy. 287, Virginia Dale, CO 80536-8942. tel., fax: 970-472-0612, e-mail: retreats@ walburga.org, web: www.walburga .org
Contact: Sister Hildegard, OSB
Affiliation: Benedictine Nuns

Benet Pines Retreat Center
15780 Hwy. 83, Colorado Springs, CO 80921. 719-495-2574, fax: 719-471-0403, e-mail: bpinescs@ hotmail.com, web: www.benethill monastery.org
Contact: Sr. Marian Bellotti, OSB
Affiliation: Benedictine Sisters

Center at Benet Hill Monastery
2577 N. Chelton Rd., Colorado Springs, CO 80909. 719-473-6184, e-mail: benet@qwest.net, web: www.benethillmonastery.org
Contact: Sister Marian Bellotti, OSB
Affiliation: Benedictine Sisters

Franciscan Retreat Center at Mount Saint Francis
7740 Deer Hill Grove, Colorado Springs, CO 80919. 719-955-7025, fax: 719-260-8044, e-mail: frc@stfrancis.org, web: www.franciscanretreatcenter.org
Contact: Sister Joanne Moeller, FSPA
Affiliation: Sisters of Saint Francis of Perpetual Adoration (Mount Saint Francis, Colorado Springs, CO)

Jesus Our Hope Hermitage
10519 S. Deer Creek Rd., Littleton, CO 80127. Fax: 303-697-7539, e-mail: srmariejoann@att.net
Contact: Sister Marie Joann Rekart, S.L.
Affiliation: Sisters of Loretto at the Foot of the Cross (Nerinx, KY)

Marycrest Retreat & Conference Center
2851 W. 52nd Ave., Denver, CO 80221-1259. 303-458-6270, ext. 123, fax: 303-433-5865, e-mail: maryjoy@marycrest.org, web: www.marycrest.org
Contact: Sr. Mary Joy Peter
Affiliation: Sisters of St. Francis (Sacred Heart Province)

Mercy Center for Healing the Whole Person
520 W. Buena Ventura St., Colorado Springs, CO 80907. 717-633-2302, fax: 719-633-1031, e-mail: info@mercycenter.com, web: www.mercycenter.com
Contact: Timothy J. Fogle
Affiliation: Society of Missionaries of Mercy (Association of the Faithful)

Nada Hermitage
Box 219, Crestone, CO 81131. 719-256-4778, fax: 719-256-4719, e-mail: nada@fone.net, web: spirituallifeinstitute.org/nretreats.html
Affiliation: Spiritual Life Institute

Sacred Heart Jesuit Retreat House
PO Box 185, Sedalia, CO 80135-0185. 303-688-4198, fax: 303-688-9633, e-mail: shjesrh@aol.com, web: www.sacredheartretreat.org
Affiliation: Jesuits (Missouri Province)

St. Malo Religious Retreat & Conference Center
10758 Hwy. 7, Allenspark, CO 80510. 303-747-0201, fax: 303-747-2892, e-mail: malo@webaccess.net, web: www.saintmalo.org
Contact: Jose Ambrozic
Affiliation: Archdiocese of Denver

Spes in Deo Franciscan Family Retreat Center
21661 Hwy. 550, Montrose, CO 81401-8713. 970-249-3526, e-mail: joyce@spesindeoretreat.com, web: www.spesindeoretreat.com
Contact: M. Joyce Martin, S.F.O.
Affiliation: Franciscan (SFO, OFM, OFM Cap.)

CONNECTICUT

Emmaus Spiritual Life Center
24 Maple Ave., Uncasville, CT 06382-2314. 860-848-3427, fax: 860-848-0755, e-mail: EmmausSLC@aol.com
Contact: Sr. Barbara Hobbs
Affiliation: Diocese of Norwich

Holy Family Passionist Retreat Center
303 Tunxis Rd., West Hartford, CT 06107. 860-521-0440, fax: 860-521-1929, e-mail: holyfamilyretreat@cpprov.org, web: www.holyfamilyretreat.org
Contact: Fr. David Cinquegrani, C.P.
Affiliation: Passionists (Province of St. Paul of the Cross)

Immaculata Retreat House
289 Windham Rd., PO Box 55, Willimantic, CT 06226-0055. 860-423-8484, fax: 860-423-5285, e-mail: immact@ntplx.net, web: http://users.ntplx.net/~omict
Contact: Fr. Daniel Nassaney, OMI
Affiliation: Missionary Oblates of Mary Immaculate

Mercy Center at Madison
PO Box 191, Madison, CT 06443-0191. 203-245-0401, e-mail: mercymad@aol.com, web: www.mercyctrmadison.com
Contact: Eugenie Guterch, RSM
Affiliation: Sisters of Mercy of the Americas (Regional Community of Connecticut)

Monastery of the Glorious Cross
61 Burban Dr., Branford, CT 06405-4003. 203-315-9964, fax: 203-481-4059, e-mail: monasterygc@juno.com
Contact: Sr. M. Zita Wenker, OSB
Affiliation: Congregation of the Benedictines of Jesus Crucified (O.S.B.)

Montfort House
PO Box 667, Rt. 118, Litchfield, CT 06759. 860-567-8434, fax: 860-567-9670, e-mail: information@montforthouse.com, web: www.montforthouse.com
Affiliation: Montfort Missionaries

My Father's House Spiritual Retreat Center
PO Box 22, 39 North Moodus Rd., Moodus, CT 06469. 860-873-1581, fax: 860-873-2357, e-mail: Info@myfathershouse.com, web: www.myfathershouse.com
Contacts: Fr. Bill McCarthy, Sr. Bernadette Sheldon

Our Lady of Calvary Retreat
31 Colton St., Farmington, CT 06032. 860-677-8519, fax: 860-677-2873, e-mail: olcret@mindspring.com, web: www.ourladyofcalvary.com
Contact: Ann Rogers, C.P.
Affiliation: Sisters of the Cross and Passion

Queen of Saints Retreat Center
238 Jewett Ave., Bridgeport, CT 06606. 203-372-4301, ext. 217

St. Edmund's Retreat
PO Box 399, Mystic, CT 06355-0399. 860-536-0565, fax: 860-572-7655, e-mail: programs@endersisland.com, web: www.endersisland.com
Contact: Fr. Thomas F.X. Hoar, S.S.E.
Affiliation: Society of St. Edmund

Trinita Retreat Center
Trinita Retreat Center, 595 Town Hill Rd., New Hartford, CT 06057. 860-379-4329, fax: 860-379-4329, e-mail: amgmsbt@juno.com
Contact: Sr. Ann Miriam Gallagher, MSBT
Affiliation: Missionary Servants of the Most Blessed Trinity

Vikingsborg Spiritual Center
Convent of St. Birgitta, 4 Runkenhage Rd., Darien, CT 06820. 203-655-1068, fax: 203-655-3496, e-mail: convent@birgittines-us.com, web: www.birgittines-us.com
Affiliation: Brigittine Sisters

Wisdom House Retreat and Conference Center
229 E Litchfield Rd., Litchfield, CT 06759-3002. 860-567-3163, fax: 860-567-3163, e-mail: rg@wisdomhouse.org, web: www.wisdomhouse.org
Contact: Sr. Rosemarie Greco, DW
Affiliation: Daughters of Wisdom

DELAWARE

St. Francis Renewal Center
St. Francis Renewal Center, 1901 Prior Rd., Wilmington, DE 19809. 302-798-1454
Contact: Fr. Cyprian Rosen, ofm Cap
Affiliation: Capuchin Franciscan

Friars (Province of the Stigmata of St. Francis)

DISTRICT OF COLUMBIA

Washington Retreat House
4000 Harewood Rd., NE, Washington,DC 20017-1595. 202-529-1111, fax: 202-529-2102, e-mail: washretreat@juno.com
Contact: Sr. Margaret Mullin, S.A.
Affiliation: Franciscan Sisters of the Atonement

FLORIDA

Campo San Jose
PO Box 899, Lake Placid, FL 33862-0899; 70 Sun "n" Lake Blvd., Lake Placid, FL 33852. 863-385-6762, fax: 863-699-1561, e-mail: antonio@digital.net, web: www.camposanjose.com
Contact: Rev. Jose Gonzalez

Carmelite Fathers House of Prayer
141 Carmelite Dr., Bunnell, FL 32010. 386-437-2910, fax: 386-437-5125. E-mail: saintjoseph1988@aol.com
Affiliation: Discalced Carmelite Fathers

Casa Stella Maris
7650 Clark St., Navarre, FL 32566. 850-932-6807
Contact: Very Rev. Steven J. O'Connor

Cenacle Spiritual Life Center
1400 S. Dixie Hwy., Lantana, FL 33462-5492. 561-582-2534, fax: 561-582-8070, e-mail: cenaclefl@aol.com, web: www.cenaclesisters.org/lantana.htm
Contact: Sr. Peg Lane, r.c.
Affiliation: Religious of the Cenacle (Sisters)

Dominican Retreat House
7275 SW 124 St., Miami, FL 33156. 305-238-2711, fax: 305-238-2717, e-mail: drhmia@bellsouth.net
Contact: Sr. June M. Fitzgerald, OP
Affiliation: Dominican Sisters of St. Catherine de Ricci (Elkins Park, PA)

Encuentros Familiares
12190 S.W. 56th St. (Miller Dr.), Miami, FL 33265. 305-596-0001, web: www.efjc.com
Contact: Florentino Azcoitia, S.J.
Affiliation: Jesuits

Franciscan Center
3010 Perry Ave., Tampa, FL 33603. 813-229-2695, fax: 813-228-0748, e-mail: francntr@tampabayrr.com, web: www.alleganyfranciscans.org/franciscancenter.htm
Affiliation: Franciscan Sisters of Allegany, NY

Holy Name Monastery
PO Box 2450, St. Leo, FL 33574-2450. 352-588-8320, fax: 352-588-8319, e-mail: dianne.wansley@saintleo.edu, web: www.floridabenedictines.org
Contact: Sr. Dianne Wansley, OSB
Affiliation: Benedictine Sisters of Florida

John Paul II Retreat House
720 NE 27th St., Miami, FL 33137-4697. 305-576-2748, 573-1418, fax: 305-576-2748, e-mail: webmaster@acu-adsum.org, web: www.acu-adsum.org
Contact: Fr. Amando Llorente, S.J.
Affiliation: Jesuits (Province of the Antilles)

Marywood Center for Spirituality/ Ministry Formation
1714-5 State Rd.13, Jacksonville, FL 32259-9253. (888) 287-2539, 904-287-2525, fax: 904-287-9738, e-mail: info@marywoodcenter.org, web: www.marywoodcenter.org
Affiliation: Diocese of St. Augustine

Mother of God House of Prayer
17880 Cypress Creek Rd., Alva, FL 33905. 239-728-3614, fax: 239-728-3760, e-mail: moghop@earthlink.net, web: www.moghop.com
Contacts: Sr. Jamesine Riley, SSJ, Patricia Ross, Co-Directors
Affiliation: Sister of St. Joseph of Rochester, NY

Our Lady of Florida Spiritual Center
1300 U S Hwy. #1, North Palm Beach, FL 33408. 561-626-1300, fax: 561-627-3956, e-mail: ourladyofflorida@cpprov.org, web: www.ourladyofflorida.org
Contact: Fr. Francis Finnigan, C.P.
Affiliation: Passionists

Our Lady of Perpetual Help Retreat/ Spirituality Center
3989 S. Moon Dr., Venice, FL 34292. 941-486-0233, fax: 941-486-1524, e-mail: olphsct@aol.com
Contact: Fr. Charles Mallen, C.Ss.R.

The Saint John Neumann Spiritual Renewal Center
685 Miccosukee Rd., Tallahassee, FL 32308. 850-224-2971
Contact: Sr.Christine Kelly, S.S.J.

Saint Leo Abbey Retreat Center
PO Box 2350, Saint Leo, FL 33574. 352-588-8182, fax: 352-588-5217, e-mail: donna.cooper@saintleo.edu, web: www.saintleoabbey.org/retreat.htm
Affiliation: Benedictine Monks (Saint Leo Abbey)

San Pedro Spiritual Development Center
2400 Dike Rd., Winter Park, FL 32792. 407-671-6322, fax: 407-671-3992, e-mail: info@sanpedrocenter.org, web: sanpedrocenter.org
Contact: Alice Gill
Affiliation: Franciscan Friars (T.O.R) (Province of the Immaculate Conception)

Zacchaeus Retreat House
St. Joseph Parish, 2704- 33rd Ave. West, Bradenton, FL 34205. Fax: 941-753-4095

GEORGIA

Cedar Hill Enrichment Center
5735 Dawsonville Hwy., Gainesville, GA 30506. 770-887-0051, fax: 770-844-1371, e-mail: cedarhillenrichment@juno.com, web: www.cedarhillenrichment.org
Contacts: June Racicot, OP, Kathryn Cliatt, OP, Co-Directors

Dominican Friars Retreat House
112 Palmetto Dr., Wilmington Island, Savannah, GA 31410, e-mail: HGrooverOP@aol.com
Contact: Rev. Henry B. Groover, O.P.
Affiliation: Dominican Fathers (Miami, FL)

Ignatius Retreat Center
6700 Riverside Dr., N.W. Atlanta, GA 30328-2710. 404-255-0503, fax: 404-256-0776, e-mail: ijesuit@bellsouth.net, web: www.ignatiushouse.org
Contact: Bob Fitzgerald
Affiliation: Jesuits

Maisha House of Prayer
520 Parkway Dr. NE, Atlanta, GA 30308. 404-872-0096, fax: 404-872-7925, e-mail: maishahouse@earthlink.net; web: www.archatl.com/gabulletin/1999/990325d.html
Contact: Sr. Loretta McCarthy
Affiliation: Sisters of the Blessed Sacrament

Monastery of the Holy Spirit
2625 Hwy. 212, SW, Conyers, GA 30094. 770-760-0959, fax: 770-760-0989, e-mail: rhouse@trappist.net, web: www.trappist.net
Affiliation: Trappists (Cistercians of the Strict Observance)

Sisters of the Cenacle
5913 Jackson Trail Rd., Hoschton, GA 30548. 706-654-3460, fax: 706-654-1459, web: www.cenacle sisters.org
Contact: Sr. Susan Arcaro, r.c.
Affiliation: Religious of the Cenacle (Sisters)

HAWAII

Benedictine Monastery of Hawaii Retreat Center
67-290 Farrington Hwy., PO Box 490, Waialua, Oahu, HI 96791. 808-637-7887, fax: 808-637-8601, e-mail: benedicthi@aol.com, web: www.catholichawaii.com/religious/benedictine
Contact: Sr. Mary Jo McEnany
Affiliation: Benedictine Congregation of Our Lady of Mounte Oliveto

Marianist Center of Hawaii
3140 Waialae Ave., Honolulu, HI 96816. 808-739-4738 fax; 808-732-3374, web: www.chaminade.edu/general.php3?articleno=422

St. Anthony Retreat Center
3351 Kalihi St., Honolulu, HI 96819. 808-845-4353, fax: 808-848-2696

St. Stephen Diocesan Center
6301 Pali Hwy., Kaneohe, HI 96744. 808-263-8844, ext. 324, fax: 808-261-8966, web: catholichawaii.com/ssdc
Affiliation: Diocese of Honolulu

IDAHO

Nazareth Retreat
4450 N. Five Mile Rd., Boise, ID 83173. 208-375-2932, fax: 208-376-5787, e-mail: nazrtctr@aol.com, web: www.alban.org/RetreatDetails.asp?ID=84
Contacts: Dorothy Anderson, Sr. Grayce Ross, SNJM
Affiliation: Diocese of Boise

St. Gertrude's Retreat Center
Monastery of St. Gertrude, HC 3 Box 121, Cottonwood, ID 83522-9408. 208-962-3224, fax: 208-962-7213, e-mail: retreat@stgertrudes.org, web: www.stgertrudes.org
Contacts: Sr. Lillian Englert, OSB, Kathy McFaul
Affiliation: Benedictine Sisters

ILLINOIS

Bellarmine Jesuit Retreat House
175 West County Line Rd., Barrington, IL 60010. 847-381-1261, fax: 847-381-4695, e-mail: bellarmine_jesuits@hotmail.com
Contact: John T. Dillon, S.J.
Affiliation: Jesuits (Chicago Province)

Bishop Lane Retreat Center
7708 East McGregor Rd., Rockford, IL 61102. 815-965-5011, fax: 815-965-5811, web: www.rockford diocese.org/ministries/index.htm#BISHOPLANE
Contacts: Don and Lorrie Gramer
Affiliation: Diocese of Rockford

Cabrini Retreat Center
9430 Golf Rd., Des Plaines, IL 60016. 847-297-6530, fax: 847-297-6544, e-mail: cabriniretreat@aol.com
Contact: Robert Moynihan
Affiliation: Missionary Sisters of the Most Sacred Heart of Jesus

Cardinal Stritch Retreat House
1000 E. Maple, PO Box 455, Mundelein, IL 60060. 847-566-6060, fax: 847-566-6082, e-mail: csrhouse@aol.com
Contact: Fr. Edmund J. Siedlecki, Administrator
Affiliation: Archdiocese of Chicago (For priests only)

Carmelite Spiritual Center
8433 Bailey Rd., Darien, IL 60561. 630-969-4141, fax: 630-969-3376, e-mail: cscretreat@aol.com, web: www.carmelnet.org
Affiliation: Carmelite Priests & Brothers (Province of the Most Pure Heart of Mary, Darien, IL)

Cenacle Retreat & Conference Center
513 Fullerton Pkwy., Chicago, IL 60614-5999. 773-528-6300, fax: 773-528-0361, e-mail: crcc@cenaclechicago.org, web: www.cenaclechicago.org
Contact: Robert J. Raccuglia
Affiliation: Religious of the Cenacle (Sisters)

Cenacle Retreat House
29 W. 012 Batavia Rd., PO Box 797, Warrenville IL 60555. 630-393-1231, fax: 630-393-2646, e-mail: ministry@cenacle.org, web: www.cenacle.org
Affiliation: Religious of the Cenacle (Sisters)

Christ in the Wilderness
7500 S. Randecker Rd., Stockton, IL 61085. 815-947-2476, fax: 815-947-2095, e-mail: citw@aeroinc.net, web: www.citwretreat.com
Contact: Julia Marie Bathon, OSF

Christ the King Retreat Center
Box 165, Henry, IL 61537. 309-364-3084
Contact: Deacon Frederick J. Kruse
Affiliation: Diocese of Peoria

Conference Center at University of St. Mary of the Lake/Mundelein Seminary
1000 E. Maple, Mundelein, IL 60060. 847-566-8290, fax: 847-566-7971, e-mail: center@usml.edu, web: www.usml.edu
Affiliation: Archdiocese of Chicago, The University of St. Mary of the Lake/Mundelein Seminary

Divine Word International
2001 Waukegan Rd., PO Box 176, Techny, IL 60082-0176. 847-272-1100, fax: 84 7-272-9363, e-mail: jjldwi@netzero.net, web: www.divineword.org/divineword.asp
Contact: Bro. Patrick Hogan, S.V.D.
Affiliation: Society of the Divine Word

Fiat House
113 N. Ottawa St., Joliet, IL 60432. E-mail: frjohnr@aol.com, web: www.vocations.com
Contact: Fr. John Rogan
Affiliation: Diocese of Joliet
(Annual day of discovery [vocation discernment])

The John Henry Newman Institute of Catholic Thought
1007 1/2 South Wright St., Champaign, IL 61820. 217-384-5961, fax: 217-384-5974

King's House Retreat and Renewal Center
700 N. 66th St., Belleville, IL 62223. 618-397-0584, fax: 618-397-5123, e-mail: knghsebv@peaknet.net
Affiliation: Missionary Oblates of Mary Immaculate

LaSalette Missionaries Retreat Center
5065 Olivet Rd., Georgetown, IL 61846. 217-662-6671
Contact: Fr. John Paninski

Lasalle Manor Retreat Center
12480 Galena Rd., Plano, IL 60545. 630-552-3224, fax: 630-552-9160, e-mail: lsmanor@aol.com, web: www.lasallemanor.org
Contact: Robert Dressel
Affiliation: De La Salle Christian Brothers

Loretto Center
1600 Somerset Lane, Wheaton, IL 60187. 630-653-7918, fax: 630-653-

0845, e-mail: ibvmlc@aol.com, web: www.lorettocenter.org
Contact: Arlene Ashack, IBVM

Mariapolis Center
5001 S. Greenwood Ave., Chicago, IL 60615. 773-285-2746

Marytown Retreat & Conference Center
1600 W Park Ave., Libertyville, IL 60048847-367-7800, fax: 847-367-7831, e-mail: mail@marytown.com, web: www.marytown.com
Affiliation: Franciscan Friars (O.F.M.Conv.) (St. Bonventure Province)

Mayslake Ministries
760 Pasquinelli Dr., Ste. 304, Westmont, IL 60559. 630-323-1620, fax: 630-323-1621, e-mail: info@mayslakeministries.org, web: mayslakeministries.org
Contact: David E. Nowak
Adult spiritual formation programs

Monastery of the Holy Cross
3111 S. Aberdeen St., Chicago, IL 60608-6503. 773-927-7424, fax: 773-927-5734, e-mail: porter@chicagomonk.org, web: www.chicagomonk.org
Contact: Br. Edward Glanzmann, OSB
Affiliation: Benedictine Monks

Our Lady of the Angels House of Prayer
13820 Main St., Lemont, IL 60439. 630-257-8368, fax: 630-257-8959

Portiuncula Center for Prayer
9263 West St. Francis Rd., Frankfort, IL 60423-8330. 815-464-3880, fax: 815-469-4880, e-mail: portc4p@aol.com, web: www.portc4p.com
Contact: Sister Elaine Teders
Affiliation: Franciscan Sisters of the Sacred Heart

Resurrection Center
2710 S. Country Club Rd., Woodstock, IL 60098. 815-338-1032, fax: 815-338-1017, e-mail: info@resurrectioncenter.org, web: www.resurrectioncenter.org
Affiliation: Congregation of the Resurrection (priests and brothers)

St. Mary's Retreat House
14230 Main St., PO Box 608, Lemont, IL 60439. 630-257-5102, fax: 630-257-6432
Contact: Fr. Blase Chemazar, O.F.M.

San Damiano Conference/Retreat Center
Rt.,1, Box 106, Golconda, IL 62938. 618-385-3507, fax: 618-285-3508
Contact: Fr. Robert Vonnahmen

Villa Redeemer
1111 N. Milwaukee Ave., Box 6, Glenview, IL 60025. 847-724-7804, fax: 847-724-7816
Contact: Fr. Raymond Maiser, C. Ss. R.
Affiliation: Redemptorists

INDIANA

Angela House Retreat & Prayer Center
412 West Tenth St., Michigan City, IN 46360. 219-873-1324, e-mail: angela@adsnet.com
Contact: Anna C. O'Connor, CSC
Affiliation: Sisters of the Holy Cross

Archabbey Guest House
Saint Meinrad Archabbey, St. Meinrad, IN 47577. 812-357-6585, fax: 812-357-6325, e-mail: mzoeller@saintmeinrad.edu, web: www.saintmeinrad.edu/abbey/retreats.htm
Affiliation: Benedictine Monks (Saint Meinrad Archabbey)

Benedict Inn Retreat & Conference Center
1402 Southern Ave., Beech Grove IN 46107-1197. 317-788-7581, fax: 317-782-3142, e-mail: benedict@indy.net, web: www.benedictinn.org
Contact: Sister Mary Luke Jones, OSB
Affiliation: Benedictine Sisters of Our Lady of Grace Monastery

Bethany Retreat House
2202 Lituanica Ave., East Chicago, IN 46312. 219-398-5047, fax: 219-398-9329, e-mail: bethanyrh@sprynet.com, web: www.bethanyretreathouse.org
Contact: Joyce Diltz, PHJC
Affiliation: Poor Handmaids of Jesus Christ

Elizabeth House of Prayer
808 W. Wayne St., Fort Wayne, IN 46802. 260-424-4989, e-mail: butlerjoan@msn.com, web: www.olvm.org/elizabeth_house.html
Contact: Sr. Rita Musante

Fatima Retreat Center
PO Box 929, Notre Dame, IN 46556-0929. 574-631-8288, fax: 574-631-5239, e-mail: nd.fatima.1@nd.edu, web: www.nd.edu/~fatima
Contact: Jim Kavanagh
Affiliation: Holy Cross Priests

Fatima Retreat House
5353 E 56th St., Indianapolis, IN 46226. 317-545-7681, fax: 317-545-0095, e-mail: fatima@archindy.org, web: www.archindy.org/fatima

John XXIII Center
407 W. Mc Donald St., Hartford City, IN 47348. 765-348-4008, fax: 765-348-5819, e-mail: john23rd@netusa1.net, web: www.netusa1.net/~john23rd
Contacts: Fr. Patrick Keith Hosey, Sr. Maureen Mangen, C.P.P.S.

Kordes Retreat Center
841 E 14th St., Ferdinand, IN 47532. 800-880-2777, 812-367-2777, fax: 812-367-2313, e-mail: kordes@thedome.org, web: www.thedome.org/kordes/
Contact: Sr. Barbara C. Schmitz, OSB
Affiliation: Benedictine Sisters (Ferdinand, IN)

Lindenwood Conference & Retreat Center
9601 Union Rd., PO Box 1, Donaldson, IN 46513. 574-935-1780, fax: 574-935-1728, e-mail: lw@lindenwood.org, web: www.lindenwood.org

Little Noddfa
1440 W. Division Rd., Tipton, IN 46072. 765-675-4146, 3950, fax: 765-675-7471, e-mail: wwetli@tiptontel.com, web: www.sistersstjo-tipton.org/ssj_nodfa.htm
Contact: Sister Wanda
Afiliaition: Sisters of St. Joseph of Tipton

Mary's Solitude
100 Lourdes Hall, Saint Mary's, Notre Dame IN 46556-5014. 574-284-5599, fax: 574-284-5701, e-mail: msolitude@cscsisters.org

Mt. St. Francis Retreat Center
101 St. Anthony Dr., Mt. St. Francis, IN 47146. 812-923-8817, fax: 812-923-0177, e-mail: mtstfran@cris.com, web: www.cris.com/~mtstfran
Contact: Bro. Ambrose
Affiliation: Conventual Franciscan Friars (O.F.M. Conv.) (Our Lady of Consolation Province)

Our Lady of Lourdes Retreat House
12915 Parrish Ave., PO Box 156, Cedar Lake, IN 46303, 219-374-5931
Contact: Rev. Bert Pepowski, OFM
Affiliaiton: Diocese of Gary

Providence Center
1 Sisters of Providence, Saint Mary-of-the-Woods, IN 47876-1092. 812-535-4531, ext. 140, fax: 812-535-3765, e-mail: bdonaghu@spsmw.org, provctr@spsmw.org, web: www.provcenter.org
Contact: Barry Donaghue
Affiliation: Sisters of Providence

St. Joseph Conference Center
1440 West Division Rd., Tipton, IN 46072. 765-675-4121, fax: 765-675-7471, e-mail: betty@csjtipton.org, web: www.sistersstjo-tipton.org/ssj_conference.htm
Affiliation: Sisters of St. Joseph of Tipton

Sarto Retreat Center
4200 N. Kentucky Ave., Evansville, IN 47711. 800-637-1731, 812-424-5536, fax: 812-421-1334, e-mail: gryder@evansville-diocese.org, web: www.evansville-diocese.org/activities/sartotour.htm
Contacts: George, Anne Ryder, Directors
Affiliation: Diocese of Evansville

Spiritual Life Center
1441 Hoffman St., Hammond, IN 46327-1782. 219-398-5047
Affiliation: Jesuits

IOWA

American Martyrs Retreat House
2209 N Union Rd. Box 605, Cedar Falls, IA 50613-0428. 319-266-3543, fax: 319-266-3543, e-mail: dbqamrh@arch.pvt.k12.ia.us, web: http://americanmartyrs.tripod.com/
Contact: Sister Jeanine Kuhn, PBVM

Beacon House, House of Prayer
915 N. Third, Burlington, IA 52601. 319-752-2121
Contact: Br. Mark Gastel, C.F.P.

Covenant Monastery Spirituality Center
1128 - 1100th St., Harlan, IA 51537-4900. 712-755-2004, e-mail: benedictines@fmctc.com, web: www.mountosb.org/Covenant/retreats.html
Contact: Sr. Linda Zahner, OSB
Affiliation: Benedictine Sisters

Creighton University Retreat Center
16493 Contrail Ave., Griswold, IA 51535-9406. (712) 778-2466, fax: (712) 778-2467, e-mail: curc@netins.net, Web: www.creighton.edu/CURC/curc.html
Contact: Fr. David Smith, S.J.
Affiliation: Creighton University (Jesuits)

Nazareth
4450 N. Five Mile Rd., Boise, IA 83713-2709. 208-375-2932, fax: 208-376-5787
Contact: Sr. Grayce E. Ross, S.N.J.M.

New Melleray Guest House
6500 Melleray Circle, Dubuque, IA 52068. 563-588-2319, fax: 563-588-4117, e-mail: melleray@mwci.net, web: www.osb.org/cist/melleray
Affiliation: Trappists (New Melleray Abbey)

Our Lady of the Prairie Retreat
2664 145th St., Wheatland, IA 52777. 319-374-1092, fax: 319-323-5209, e-mail: joannk@chmiowa

Prairiewoods Franciscan Spirituality Center
120 E. Boyson Rd., Hiawatha, IA 52233-1277. 319-395-6700, fax: 319-395-6703, e-mail: ecospirit@prairiewoods.org, web: www.prairiewoods.org
Contact: Helen Elsbernd, F.S.P.A.
Affiliation: Congregation of the Sisters of the Third Order of St. Francis of Perpetual Adoration

Prayer and Spirituality Center
518 W. Locust St., Davenport, IA 52803. 563-333-6189, fax: 563-333-6234, e-mail: clearyaudrey@sau.edu
Contact: Sr. Audrey Cleary, O.S.B.
Affiliation: St. Ambrose University (ecumenical in scope)

Shalom Retreat Center
1001 Davis St., Dubuque, IA 52001-1398. 563-582-3592, fax: 563-582-5872, e-mail: shalommj@aol.com, web: members.aol.com/DBQShalom
Contact: Margaret Jungers
Affiliation: Sisters of St. Francis of Dubuque

St. Thomas More Center
6177 Panorama Rd., Panora, IA 50216. 641-755-3164, fax: 641-755-4157, e-mail: stmg@netins.net, web: www.stmcenter.com
Contact: Bob Perron
(TEC, Confirmation,Quest retreats)

Wakonda Prayer House
Box 370, Griswold, IA 51535. 712-784-3797

KANSAS

Benedictine Retreat Ministry
St. Benedict's Abbey, 1020 N. Second St., Atchison, KS 66002. 913-367-5340, ext. 2842, e-mail: matth@benedictine.edu, web: www.kansasmonks.org/fr_abbey.html
Contact: Fr. Matthew Habiger, OSB
Affiliation: Benedictine Monks

Capuchin Center for Spiritual Life
900 Cathedral Ave., Victoria, KS 67671. 913-735-9393, fax: 913-735-9455, e-mail: ccsl@ruraltel.net

Heartland Center for Spirituality
3600 Broadway, Great Bend, KS 67530. 620-792-1232, fax: 620-792-1746, e-mail: office@heartlandspirituality.org, web: www.heartlandspirituality.org
Contact: Louise Hageman, OP
Affiliation: Dominican Sisters of Great Bend

Heartland Farm
RR1, Box 37, Pawnee Rock, KS 67567-9602. 316-923-4585, e-mail: hfarm@ruraltel.net
Contact: Sr. Mary Terence Wasinger, O.P.
Affiliation: Dominican Sisters of Great Bend

Manna House of Prayer
323 E. Fifth St., Box 675, Concordia, KS 66901. 785-243-4428, e-mail: mannahse@dustdevil.com, www.mannahouse.org
Contact: Sr. Bette Suther, C.S.J.

Sophia Center
751 South Eighth St., Atchison, KS 66002. 913-360-6160. Fax: 913-360-6162, e-mail: jkputnam@benedictine.edu, web: www.mountosb.org/sophia.html
Contact: Sr. Johnette Putman, OSB
Affiliation: Benedictine Sisters of Mount St. Scholastica

Spiritual Life Center
7100 E. 45th N., Wichita, KS 67226. 316-744-0167, fax: 314-744-8072, e-mail: spiritlife@feist.com, web: www.spirituallifecenterwichita.org/cover.html
Contact: Fr. Joseph M. Gile, C.Ss.R.

Ursuline Retreat Center
Convent of Our Lady of Lourdes, 901 E. Miami St., Paola, KS 66071-

1879. 913-557-2349, fax: 913-294-2233, e-mail: jlucas@paolaursuline.org, web: www.paolaursuline.org
Contact: JoAnn Lucas
Affiliation: Ursuline Sisters

KENTUCKY

Bethany Spring
Bethany Spring,115 Dee Head Rd., New Haven, KY 40051. 502-549-8277, fax: 502-549-8270, e-mail: morningstar@bardstown.com, web: www.scnazarethky.org/retreat.htm
Contact: Mary Luken
Affiliation: Sisters of Charity of Nazareth

Catherine Spalding Retreat/ Conference Center
PO Box 24, Nazareth, KY 40048. 502-348-1516, fax: 502-348-1518, e-mail: sreasbeck@scnazarethky.org, web: www.scnazarethky.org
Contact: Suzanne Reasbeck
Affiliation: Sisters of Charity of Nazareth

Catholic Charismatic Renewal
Maloney Center, 1200 S.Shelby St., Louisville, KY 40203-2600. 502-636-0296, fax: 502-636-2379
Contact: Marti Jewell

Cliffview Center for Renewal
789 Bryant's Camp Rd., Lancaster, KY 40444, 877-792-3330, 859-792-3333, fax: 859-792-1223, e-mail: cliffctr@cdlex.org, web: www.cliffview.org
Contacts: Joe and Judy Schueneman
Affiliaition: Diocese of Lexington

Father Farrell Spiritual Life Center
329 Poplar at Cedar, Hazard, KY 41701. 606-436-2533, fax: 606-435-0171
Contact: Fr. Michael Chowning, O.F.M.

Flaget Center
1935 Lewiston Dr., Louisville, KY 40216-2523. 502-448-8581, fax: 502-448-5518, e-mail: dmc@archlou.org, web: www.archlou.org/agency.htm
Contact: Donna McHugh, Facility Coordinator
Affiliation: Archdiocese of Louisville

Gethsemani Retreat House
Abbey of Gethsemani, Trappist, KY 40051. 502-549-4133, fax: 502-549-4124, web: www.monks.org
Contact: Guestmaster
Affiliation: Trappists

Knobs Haven
515 Nerinx Rd., Nerinx, KY 40049. 270-865-2621, e-mail: knobshaven@yahoo.com
Contacts: Mary Gutzwiller, S.L., Peg Jacobs
Affiliation: Sisters of Loretto

Lake St. Joseph Center
5800 Old LaGrange Rd., Crestwood, KY 40014. 502-241-4469

Marydale Retreat Center
945 Donaldson Hwy., Erlanger, KY 41018-1093. 800-995-4863, fax: 859-647-5682
Contact: Deacon Paul Yancey
Affiliation: Diocese of Covington

Mount Saint Joseph Retreat and Conference Center
8001 Cummings Rd., Maple Mount, KY 42356. 270-229-0200, fax: 270-229-0279, e-mail: msjcenter@maplemount.org, web: www.msjcenter.org
Contact: Sr. Amelia

Mt. Tabor Retreat Center
150 Mt. Tabor Rd., Martin, KY 41649. 606-886-9624, fax: 606-886-7070, e-mail: mtabor150@hotmail.com
Contact: Sr. Jan Barthel, OSB
Affiliation: Benedictine Sisters

Moye Spiritual Life Center
1000 St. Anne Dr., Melbourne, KY 41059-9603. 859-441-0700, ext. 327, fax: 859-441-1510, e-mail: mjhummeldorf@cdpkentucky.org, web: www.cdpkentucky.org/retreatcenter.htm
Affiliation: Congregation of Divine Providence

LOUISIANA

Abbey Christian Life Center
St. Joseph Abbey, St. Benedict, LA 70457. 985-892-3473, fax: 985-892-3448, web: www.stjosephabbey.org
Contact: Rev. Thomas Perrier, OSB
Affiliation: Benedictine Monks

Archdiocesan Spirituality Center
2901 S. Carrollton Ave., New Orleans, LA 70118-4391. 504-8681-3254
Contact: Sr. Noel Toomey, O.P.

Ave Maria Retreat House
8089 Barataria Blvd., Crown Point, LA 70072. 504-689-3837, fax: 504-689-2785, e-mail: avemariarh@cox.net
Affiliation: Archdiocese of New Orleans/Missionary Oblates of Mary Immaculate

Bishop Robert E. Tracy Center
PO Box 2028, Baton Rouge, LA 70821-2028. 225-242-0222, fax: 225-242-0134, e-mail: tracycenter@diobr.org
Contact: Charles Jumonville, Administrator

The Blessing Place
PO Box 130, Lacombe, LA 70445. 504-882-7579, fax: 504-882-3619, e-mail: barbara@blessingplace.org
Contact: Sr. Barbara Breaud, O.Carm.

Cenacle Retreat House
5500 St. Mary St., PO Box 8115, Metairie, LA 70011-8115. 504-887-1420, fax: 504-887-6624, e-mail: cenacle2@aol.com, web: www.cenaclesisters.org/metairie.htm
Contact: Sr. Kathy Dunne, r.c.
Affiliation: Religious of the Cenacle (Sisters)

Center of Jesus the Lord
1236 N. Rampart St., New Orleans, LA 70116-2497. 504-529-1636, fax: 504-529-5003, e-mail: CCRCNO@aol.com, web: www.members.aol.com/CCRCNO
Affiliation: Catholic Charismatic Renewal of New Orleans

Dominican Conference Center
540 Broadway, New Orleans, LA 70118-3593, 504-861-8711, fax: 504-861-8718, e-mail: dcc15@juno.com
Contact: Charlotte Fenerty Ewing

Holy City Community
5611 Welcome Rd., Lake Charles, LA 70611. 337-855-2871
Contact: Deacon Ed McNally

Jesuit Spirituality Center
St. Charles College, PO Box C, Grand Coteau, LA 70541-1003. 337-662-5251, fax: 337-662-3187, e-mail: jespirtcen@aol.com, web: http://home.centurytel.net/spiritualitycenter
Contact: Warren Broussard, S.J.
Affiliation: Jesuits (New Orleans Province)

Lumen Christi Retreat Center
100 Lumen Christi Lane, Schriever, LA 70395. 985-868-1523, fax: 985-868-1525

Magnificat Center of the Holy Spirit
23629 Faith Rd., Ponchatoula, LA 70454. 800-531-9710, 225-386-5815, fax: 504-200-7771
Contact: Fr. Harry J. Adams, Jr., S.C.

Manresa on the Mississippi
PO Box 89, 5858 Louisiana Hwy. 44, Convent, LA 70723-0089. 800-782-9431, 225-562-3596, fax 225-562-3147, e-mail: ostini@stargazer.net, web: bsd.leonce.com/manresa
Contact: Fr. Anthony H. Ostini, S.J.
Affiliation: Jesuits

Maryhill Renewal Center
600 Maryhill Rd., Pineville, LA 71360. 318-640-1378, fax: 318-640-8604, e-mail: maryhill@iamerica.net
Contact: Todd J. Marye
Affiliation: Diocese of Alexandria

Our Lady of the Oaks Retreat House
PO Drawer D, Grand Coteau, LA 70541-1004. 337-662-5410, fax: 337-662-5331, e-mail: olorhgcla@centurytel.net
Contact: Kenneth Buddendorff, S.J.

Regina Coeli Retreat Center
17225 Regina Coeli Rd., Covington, LA 70435-9156. 985-982-4110 (tel, fax)
Contacts: June and Earl Magner

Rosaryville Spirit Life Center
39003 Rosaryville Rd., Ponchatoula, LA 70454. 800-627-9183, 225-294-5039, fax: 225-294-3510, e-mail: dsslc@i55.com, web: http://rosaryville.org/index1.htm
Contact: Sister Mary Edmund

Saint Charles Center
2151 Sam Houston Jones Pkwy., Lake Charles, LA 70601. 337-855-1232, fax: 337-855-9062, e-mail: cgscc@juno.com, web: http://lcdiocese.org
Affiliation: Diocese of Lake Charles

Sophie Barat House
1719 Napoleon Ave., New Orleans, LA 70115-4809. 504-899-6027, fax: 504-899-6210, e-mail: jmckinlay@rscj.org
Contact: Sr. Jane McKinlay, R.S.C.J.

MAINE

Bay View Villa
187 Bay View Rd., Saco, ME 04072. (207) 286-8762, e-mail: bvv@gwi.net
Affiliation: Servants of the Immaculate Heart of Mary

Christian Life Center
PO Box 530, Frenchville, ME 04745-0530. 207-543-6193, fax: 207-543-6193, e-mail: clc@ainop.com
Contact: Don Clavette

Divine Mercy Hermitage
57 Bryant Rd., St. Albans, ME 04971. 207-938-3730 (tel, fax), e-mail: srmm@somtel.com
Contact: Sr. Margaret Mary Cuddleback

Living Water Spiritual Center
93 Halifax St., Winslow, ME 04901. 207-872-2370, fax: 207-873-1976, e-mail: info@e-livingwater.org, web: www.e-livingwater.org
Contact: Angela Fortier, csj
affilaition: Sisters of St. Joseph (Lyon, France)

Marie Joseph Spiritual Center
10 Evans Rd., Biddeford, ME 04005. 207-284-5671, fax: 207-286-1371, e-mail: mariejosephcenter@yahoo.com, web: www.presmarymethuen.org/english/mariejo/htm
Contact: Sr. Claire Vanasse, pm
Affiliation: Sisters of the Presentation of Mary

Notre Dame Spiritual Center
Shaker Hill Rd., PO Box 159, Alfred, ME 04002-0159. 207-324-6160, 6612, fax: 207-324-5044, e-mail: spiritualcenter2002@yahoo.com
Contact: Rev. Theodore Letendre, F.I.C.
Affiliation: Brothers of Christian Instruction

St. Joseph by the Sea Retreat House
203 Pleasant Ave., Peaks Island, ME 04108. 207-766-2284
Affiliation: Augustinian Friars

St. Paul Center
136 State St., PO Box 2028, Augusta, ME 04338-2028. 877-621-8520 (statewide), (207) 621-8520, e-mail: stpaulinfo@ccmaine.org, web: www.ccmaine.org/stpaulcenter.html
Contact: Steve Letourneau, Program Director

Sky-Arch Hermitage
47 Byrant Rd., St. Albans, ME 04971. 207-938-3458, e-mail: srhermit@somtel.com
Contact: Sr. B. Emmanuel Bryant

Transfiguration Hermitage
548 Files Hill Rd.,Thorndike, ME 04986-9709. 207-568-3731, e-mail: srewagner@uninets.net
Contact: Sr. Elizabeth Wagner
Affiliation: Benedictine

MARYLAND

Berg Retreat Center
Saint Gertrude Monastery, 14259 Benedictine Lane, Ridgely, MD 21660. 410-634-2497, fax: 410-634-1410, e-mail: smp52@juno.com; web: www.ridgelybenedictines.org
Affiliation: Benedictine Sisters

Bon Secours Spiritual Center
1525 Marriottsville Rd., Marriotsville, MD 21104. 410-442-1320, ext. 304, fax: 410-442-8219, e-mail: carol_marozzi@bshsi.com, web: www.bonsecours.org/bssc
Contact: Carol Marozzi, SSJ
Affiliation: Sisters of Bon Secours

Camp Maria Retreat Center
41290 Camp Maria Rd., Leonardtown, MD 20650. 301-475-8330, fax: 301-475-8782, e-mail: campmaria@erols.com, web: www.erols.com/campmaria
Contact: Carol McKean, SCN
Sisters of Charity of Nazareth, KY

Christian Brothers Spiritual Center
2535 Buckeystown Pike, PO Box 29, Adamstown, MD 21710. 301-874-5180, fax: 301-874-3757
Contact: Bro. Richard W. Breese, F.S.C.
Affiliation: De La Salle Christian Brothers (Baltimore Province)

De Sales Spirituality Centre
1120 Blue Ball Rd., Childs, MD 21916-0043. 410-398-3040, ext 237, fax: 410-398-0116, e-mail: mmurray@osfs.org, web: www.oblates.org/spirituality
Contact: Michael S. Murray, OSFS
Affiliation: Oblates of St. Francis de Sales

Holy Trinity Spiritual Center
8400 Park Hgts. Ave., Box 5742, Baltimore, MD 21282. 410-486-5171, fax: 410-486-0614, e-mail: teamcat@trinitarians.org
Affiliation: The Trinitarian Friars

Loyola Retreat House
PO Box 9, 9270 Loyola Retreat Rd., Faulkner, MD 20632-0009. 301-870-3515, 301-934-8862, fax: 301-392-0808, e-mail: director@loyolaretreat.org, web: www.loyolaretreat.org
Contact: Fr. Timothy J. Stephens, S.J.
Affiliation: Jesuits (Maryland Province)

Msgr. Clare J. O'Dwyer Retreat House
15523 York Rd., Sparks, MD 21152. 410-666-2400, fax: 410-472-3281, e-mail: odwyer@clark.net
Contact: Fr. J. Kevin Farmer

Our Lady of Guadalupe Renewal Center
1903 Norhurst Way N., Catonsville, MD 21228. 410-788-8821
Contact: Sr. Anne Colette Potthast, S.N.D.

Our Lady of Mattaponi Youth Retreat/Conference Center
11000 Mattaponi Rd., Upper Marlboro, MD 20772. 301-952-9074, fax: 301-952-0609, e-mail: Mattaponi@adw.org.
Contact: Rev. Robert Mordino
Affiliation: Washington (DC) CYO

St. Mary's Spiritual Center
600 N. Paca St., Baltimore, MD 21201-1995. 410-728-6464, fax: 410-669-8140, e-mail: SMSCBalto@aol.com
Contact: Rev. John E. McMurry, S.S.
Affiliation: Sulpician Fathers

Seton Retreat Center
333 S. Seton Ave., Emmitsburg, MD 21727. 310-447-3121, fax: 301-447-6038, e-mail: dcvdc@atlantech.net, web: www.daughtersofcharity-emmitsburg.org
Contact: Sr. JoAnne Goecke, D.C.
Affiliation: Daughters of Charity

MASSACHUSETTS

Calvary Retreat Center
59 South St., PO Box 219, Shrewsbury, MA 01545-0219. 508-842-8821, fax: 508-842-5356, e-mail: erivard@ccprov.org, web: www.calvaryretreat.org
Contact: Fr. John Powers, C.P.
Affiliation: Passionists (St. Paul of the Cross Province)

Campion Renewal Center
319 Concord Rd., Weston, MA 02493-1398. 781-788-6810, fax: 781-894-5864, e-mail: acopponi@campioncenter.org, web: www.campioncenter.org
Contact: John W. Michalowski, S.J.
Affiliation: Jesuits (New England Province)

Cathedral Camp Retreat Center
167 Middleboro Rd., PO Box 428, East Freetown, MA 02717-0428. 508-763-3994, fax: 508-763-3768, e-mail: joseph_marie2@juno.com, web: www.cathedralcamp.com
Contact: Sr. Joseph Marie Levesque, O.P.
Affiliation: Diocese of Fall River

Center for Spiritual Development
Memorial House, Mercy Hospital, PO Box 9012, Springfield, MA 01102-9012. 413-734-8843, fax: 413-788-0195

Don Orione Center
Old Groveland Rd., PO Box 205, Haverhill, MA 01835. 508-373-0461
Contact: Fr. Gino Marchesani, F.D.P.

Eastern Point Retreat House
37 Niles Pond Rd., Gloucester, MA 01930-4499. 978-283-0013, fax: 978-282-1989, e-mail: gonzaga@cove.com, web: www.easternpoint.org
Contact: James M. Keegan, S.J.
Affiliation: Jesuits

Espousal Retreat House
554 Lexington St., Waltham, MA 02452. 781-209-3101, fax: 781-209-2091
Contact: Fr. Robert Mascicchi, C.S.S.
Affiliation: Stigmatine Fathers and Brothers

Foyer of Charity
74 Hollett St., Scituate, MA 02066. 781-545-1080, fax: 240-332-5826, e-mail: info@foyerofcharity.com, web: www.foyerofcharity.com
Contact: Fr. Matthew Bradley
Affiliation: Association of the Faithful

Franciscan Center - Retreat House
459 River Rd., Andover, MA 01810. 978-851-3391, fax: 978-858-0675, e-mail: franretc@aol.com, web: www.franrcent.org
Contact: Fr. John D. Bavaro, O.F.M.
Affiliation: Order of Friars Minor

Genesis Spiritual Life Center
53 Mill St., Westfield, MA 01085. 413-562-3627, fax: 413-572-1060, e-mail: genretc@exit3.com, web: www.westfield-ma.com/genesis
Contact: Sr. Catherine M. Walsh, RSM
Affiliation: Sisters of Providence/Diocese of Springfield

Glastonbury Abbey Retreat & Spirituality Center
16 Hull St., Hingham, MA 02043. 781-749-2155, fax: 781-749-6236, e-mail: office@glastonburyabbey.org, web: www.glastonburyabbey.org
Contact: Fr. John Kelleher, OSB
Affiliation: Benedictine Monks

Holy Cross Fathers Retreat House
490 Washington St., North Easton, MA 02356-1294. 508-238-2051, fax: 508-238-0164, e-mail: jfcal@hotmail.com
Contact: Fr. Joseph F. Callahan, C.S.C.
Affiliation: Priests of the Congregation of the Holy Cross

La Salette Center for Christian Living
947 Park St., Attleboro, MA 02703. 508-222-8530, fax: 508-236-9089, e-mail: lasalett@rcn.com
Contact: Anna Marie Kane, SSJ
Affiliation: Missionaries of Our Lady of La Salette

LaSalette Retreat House
Newman Hall, 251 Topsfield Rd., Ipswich, MA 01938. 508-356-3151

Marian Center
1365 Northampton St., Holyoke, MA 01040-1900. 413-532-7406
Affiliation: Daughters of the Heart of Mary

The Marist House
518 Pleasant St., Framingham, MA 01701. 508-879-1620, fax: 508-879-1132, e-mail: retreats@themarists.org, web: www.themarists.org/TheMaristHouse
Contact: Fr. James G. Strasz, S.M.
Affiliation: Marist Fathers and Brothers

Mary House
186 N. Spencer Rd. (Rte. 31), PO Box 20, Spencer, MA 01562. 508-885-5450
Contact: Joyce Thomasmeyer
Affiliation: Diocese of Worcester

Miramar Retreat Center
121 Parks St., PO Box M, Duxbury, MA 02331-0614. 781-585-2460, fax: 781-585-3770, e-mail: miramarma@aol.com
Contact: Fr. Robert M. Jones, SVD
Affiliation: Divine Word Missionaries

Mont Marie Conference Center
34 Lower Westfield Rd., Holyoke, MA 01040. 413-536-0853, fax: 413-532-0285, e-mail: montconf@ssjspringfield.com, web: www.ssjspringfield.org/conference.htm
Contact: Agnes Fleming

Mount Carmel Retreat Center
Oblong Rd., PO Box 613, Williamstown, MA 01267. 413-458-3164, fax: 413-458-9420
Contact: Rev. Maurice Cummings, O. Carm.
Affiliation: Carmelite Friars - Province of St. Elias

Notre Dame Mission Center
30 Jeffreys Neck Rd., Ipswich, MA 01938. 978-356-9759, e-mail: ndmcips@aol.com, web: www.sndden.org/ndmcips
Contact: Sr. Kathleen Walsh, SND
Affiliation: Sisters of Notre Dame de Namur

Sacred Hearts Retreat Center
226 Great Neck Rd., Wareham, MA 02571. 508-295-0100, fax: 508-291-2624, e-mail: retreat@sscc.org, web: www.sscc.org/wareham
Contact: Deacon Frank Tremblay
Affiliation: Congregation of the Sacred Hearts

St. Basil's Salvatorian Center
30 East St., Methuen, MA 01844. 978-683-2952, fax: 978-683-2471, web: www.parishesonline.com/scripts/dbgetParishRecord.asp?ID=904
Contact: Fr. Martin Hyatt
Affiliation: Basilian Salvatorian Fathers

St. Benedict Abbey
252 Still River Rd., PO Box 67, Still River, MA 01467. 978-456-3221, e-mail: abbeyretreats@aol.com
Contact: Fr. James
Affiliation: Benedictine Monks

St. Joseph Abbey
167 N. Spencer Rd., Spencer, MA 01562-1233. 508-885-8710, fax: 508-885-8701, e-mail: spenabbey@spencerabbey.org, web: www.spencerabbey.org
Contact: Rev. Matthew Flynn, O.C.S.O.

St. Joseph Villa Retreat Center
339 Jerusalem Rd., Cohasset, MA 02025-1139. 781-383-6024, e-mail: retreat.center@csjboston.org
Affiliation: Sisters of St. Joseph of Boston

St. Stephen Priory Retreat and Renewal Center
20 Glen Street Box 370, Dover, MA 02030-0370. 508-785-0124, fax: 508-785-1020, e-mail: thepriory@aol.com, web: www.ststephenpriory.org
Affiliation: Dominican Friars (Province of Saint Joseph - Eastern Province)

MICHIGAN

Augustine Center
2798 US 31 North, PO Box 84, Conway, MI 49722-0084. 231-347-3657, fax: 231-347-9502, e-mail: hubenyop@freeway.net, web: www.dioceseofgaylord.org
Contact: Sr. Barbara Hubeny, O.P.
Affiliation: Diocese of Gaylord

Bethany House (Spiritual Life Center for Youth)
St. Francis Retreat Center, 703 E. Main St., De Witt, MI 48820. 517-669-8321
Contact: Fr. Gerald Vincke

Camp Sancta Maria
PO Box 338, Gaylord, MI 49734. 231-546-3878, fax: 231-546-3171, e-mail: office@campsanctamaria.org, web: www.campsanctamaria.org
Contact: James Berigan

Capuchin Retreat
62460 Mt. Vernon Rd., PO Box 396, Washington (Detroit), MI 48094. 248-651-4826, fax: 248-650-4910, e-mail: capuchinretreat@msn.com, web: www.capuchinfranciscans.org/washington.htm
Contact: Fr. Randy Knauf, ofm Cap.
Affiliation: Capuchin Franciscans (Province of St. Joseph)

Center for Ministry
5802 Weiss, Saginaw, MI 48603. 989-797-6607, 6608, fax: 989-797-6648, e-mail: roberta@dioceseofsaginaw.org, web: www.saginaw.org/cfm
Contact: Roberta Kolasa, SJ
Affiliation: Diocese of Saginaw

Colombiere Retreat Center
9075 Big Lake Rd., PO Box 139, Clarkston, MI 48347-0139. 248-625-5611, fax: 248-620-2534, e-mail: colombiere@colombiere.com, web: www.colombiere.com
Contact: Peggy Desrosier
Affiliation: Jesuits (Detroit Province)

De Sales Center
1124 Ventura, Brooklyn, MI 49230-9078. 517-592-8218, fax: 517-592-8218, e-mail: mckenna@desales.org, web: www.desales.org
Contact: Fr. Kenneth N. McKenna, O.S.F.S.
Affiliation: Oblates of St. Francis de Sales
(For clergy only)

Dominican Center at Marywood
2025 E. Fulton St., Grand Rapids, MI 49503-2861. 616-454-1241, fax: 616-454-2861, e-mail: mclarke@dominicancenter.com, web: www.dominicancenter.com
Affiliation: Dominican Sisters of Grand Rapids

Emmaus House
733 S. 14th St., Saginaw, MI 48601. 517-755-7538 (tel, fax)
Contact: Sr. Marietta Fritz, S.N.D. deN.

Emmaus Monastery
10154 Pine Grove Rd., Vestaburg, MI 48891-9555. 989-268-5494, fax: 989-268-5373, e-mail: about@emmausmonastery.org, web: www.emmausmonastery.org
Affiliation: The Emmaus Community (canonical community in the Diocese of Grand Rapids)

Manresa Jesuit Retreat House
1390 Quarton Rd., Bloomfield Hills, MI 48304-3554. 248-644-4933, fax: 248-644-8291, e-mail: jserrick@manresa-sj.org, web: www.manresa-sj.org
Affiliation: Jesuits (Detroit Province)

Marianhill Retreat Center
23715 Ann Arbor Trail, Dearborn Heights, MI 48127. 313-278-9461
Contact: Fr. Al Dennis Kupla

Marygrove Retreat Center
6411 State St., Garden, MI 49835. 906-644-2771, fax: 906-644-2463, e-mail: mgc@up.net, web: www.marygrove.org
Contact: Msgr. Timothy Desrochers
Affiliation: Diocese of Marquette

Queen of Angels Retreat Center
3400 S. Washington Rd., PO Box 2026, Saginaw, MI 48605. 989-755-2149, fax: 989-755-1640, web: www.rc.net/saginaw/retreat
Contact: Fr. Robert Malloy, OFM Cap.
Affiliation: Capuchin Franciscans Friars (Province of St. Joseph)

St. Francis Retreat Center
703 E. Main St., Dewitt, MI 48820. 866-669-8321, fax: 517-669-2708, e-mail: information@stfrancis.ws, web: www.stfrancis.ws
Affiliation: Diocese of Lansing

St. John Center
44011 Five Mile Rd., Plymouth, MI 48170-2555. 734-414-1111, fax: 734-414-1150
Contact: Fr. John H. West

St. Joseph Home Retreat and Conference Center
1000 E Porter St., Jackson, MI 49202. 517-787-3320, fax: 517-787-3704
Contact: Sr. Mary Catherine
Affiliation: Felician Sisters

St. Lazare Retreat House
18600 W. Spring Lake Rd., Spring Lake, MI 49456-0462. 616-842-3370, fax: 616-842-6815, e-mail: mjs_stlazare@triton.net
Contact: Fr. Michael J. Shea, C.M.

St. Mary's Retreat House
775 W. Drahner Rd., Oxford, MI 48371-4866. 248-628-3894, fax: 248-628-9755, web: www.stmarys retreathouse.org
Contact: Sister Audrey Rash, OP

St. Paul of the Cross Retreat Center
23333 Schoolcraft, Detroit, MI 48223. 313-535-9563, fax: 313-535-9207, e-mail: stpauls@passionist .org, web: www.passionist.org./ stpauls
Affiliation: Passionist Priests & Brothers (Holy Cross Province)

Transformations SSJ Spirituality Center
3427 Gull Rd., PO Box 02, Nazareth, MI 49074. 269-381-6290, ext. 310, fax: 269-381-4616, e-mail: ssjnaza reth@voyager.net, web: www.ssj nazareth.org, www.findthedivine.com
Contact: Michele Gossman
Affiliation: Sisters of St. Joseph of Nazareth

Visitation Spirituality Center
529 Stewart Rd., Monroe, MI 48162. 734-242-5520, fax: 734-242-5530, e-mail: visitation@teleweb.net; web: www.ihmsisters.org
Contact: Margaret Gaffney, I.H.M.
Affiliation: Sisters, Servants of the Immaculate Heart of Mary

Weber Retreat Center
1257 E. Siena Heights Dr., Adrian, MI 49221. 517-266-4000, fax: 517-266-4004, e-mail: webercenter@ adriansisters.org, web: www.adrian sisters.org/weber
Contact: Linda Braman
Affiliation: Dominican Sisters of Adrian

MINNESOTA

Assisi Community Center
Assisi Heights, 1001 14th St. NW Suite 200, Rochester, MN 55901-2511. 507-280-2180, fax: 507-282-7762, e-mail: acomc@aol.com, web: www.acomc.org
Contact: S. Alice Thraen, OSF
Affiliation: Franciscan Sisters of Rochester, MN

Benedictine Center of St. Paul's Monastery
2675 E Larpenteur Ave. East, St. Paul, MN 55109. 651-777-7251, fax: 651-773-5124, e-mail: info@ benedictctr.org, web: www.osb.org/ spm
Affiliation: Benedictine Sisters (St. Paul's Monastery)

Carondelet Center
1890 Randolph Ave., St. Paul, MN 55105. 651-696-2750, fax: 651-696-2742, e-mail: sbcarondelet@aol .com, web: www.csjstpaul.org
Contacts: Sally Bandt, Susan Wagner, Co-Directors
Affiliation: Sisters of St. Joseph

Center for Spiritual Development
211 S. 10th St., Box 538, Bird Island, MN 55310-0538. 320-365-3644, fax: 320-365-4042, e-mail: centerbi@ willmar.com, web: www.centerbi .com
Contact: Sr. Janet Mallak, S.S.N.D.

Christ the King Retreat Center
621 South First Ave., Buffalo, MN 55313. 763-682-1394, fax: 763-682-3453, e-mail: christheking@kings house.com, web: www.kingshouse .com
Contact: Fr. John E. Hensohn, OMI
Affiliation: Missionary Oblates of Mary Immaculate

Christian Brothers Retreat Center
15525 St. Croix Tr. N., Marine on St. Croix, MN 55047. 651-433-2846, fax: 651-433-5755, e-mail: dunrovin cbrc@juno.com, web: www.dunrovin .org
Contact: Jerome Meeds
Affiliation: Christian Brothers

The Dwelling In the Woods Hermitage Retreat
14044 220th St., McGrath, MN 56350. 218-658-4612, fax: 320-592-3838, web: www.thedwellinginthe woods.org
Contact: Jeanne Stodola, CSJ

Franciscan Retreats
16385 St. Francis Lane, Prior Lake, MN 55372-2220. 952-447-2182, fax: 952-447-2170, e-mail: director@ franciscanretreats.net, web: www. franciscanretreats.net

Good Counsel Education Center
151 Good Counsel Dr., Mankato, MN 56002. 507-389-4287, fax: 507-389-4119
Contact: Sr. Lois Wickenhauser, S.S.N.D.

Holy Spirit Retreat Center
3864 420th Ave., Janesville, MN 56048. 507-234-5712, fax: 507-234-6188, e-mail: retreat@frontier net.net, web: www.rochesterfrancis can.org
Affiliation: Franciscan Sisters of Rochester, MN

Jesuit Retreat House
8243 N. Demontreville Trail, Lake Elmo, MN 55042-9546. 651-777-1311, fax: 651-777-1312
Contact: Fr. Doetz, S.J.
Affiliation: Jesuits

Loyola
389 N. Oxford St., St. Paul, MN 55104. 612-641-0008, fax: 651-641-0554, e-mail: loyolasrr@aol.com, web: loyolasp.faithweb.com
Contact: Sr. Elizabeth Kerwin, C.S.J.
Affiliation: Archdiocese of St. Paul/ Minneapolis

Maryhill
1988 Summit Ave., St. Paul, MN 55105. 651-696-2970, fax: 651-696-1190, e-mail: maryhillsd@earthlink .net
Affiliation: Daughters of the Heart of Mary

McCabe Renewal Center
2125 Abbotsford Ave., Duluth, MN 55803. 218-724-5266, fax: 218-724-7138, e-mail: McCabeRenCtr@aol .com, web: www.DuluthBenedic tines.org/McCabe.html
Contact: Sr. Lois Eckes, OSB
Affiliation: Benedictine Sisters (Duluth, MN)

Mount St. Benedict Center
620 Summit Ave., Crookston, MN 56716. Fax: 218-281-6966, e-mail: msbcenter@msb.net
Contact: Sr. Lorraine Kraft, OSB
Affiliation: Benedictine Sisters

Pacem in Terris Center for Spirituality
Hermitage Retreats, PO Box 418, St. Francis, MN 55070. 763-444-6408, fax: 763-444-9649, e-mail: jeffrey@ paceminterris.org
Contact: Jeffrey Wanchena

Queen of Angels Hermitage
1009 Oakland Ave. E., Austin, MN 55912. 507-437-4015
Contact: Fr. Jon Moore
Affiliation: Monastic Fraternity of St. Joseph

Schoenstatt Sisters of Mary
27762 County Rd. 27, Sleepy Eye, MN 56085-9801. 507-794-7727 (tel, fax)
Contact: Sr. Marie Day
Affiliation: Schoenstatt Sisters of Mary (Waukesha, WI)

Spiritual Life Programs
Saint John's Abbey, Collegeville, MN 56321-2015. 320-363-3929, fax: 320-363-2504, e-mail: SpirLife@csbsju.edu, web: www.saintjohnsabbey.org/slp/
Contact: Fr. Don Tauscher, OSB
Affiliation: Benedictine Monks

Spirituality Center
Saint Benedict's Monastery, 104 Chapel Lane, St. Joseph, MN 56374-0220. fax: 320-363-7173, e-mail: dmanuel@csbsju.edu, web: www.sbm.osb.org/ben spirituality.html
Contact : S. Dorothy Manuel, OSB
Affiliation: Benedictine Sisters

Tau Center
511 Hilbert St., Winowa, MN 55987. 507-454-2993, e-mail: taucenter@luminet.net, web: www.winonanet.com/orgs/taucenter
Contact: L. Susan Althoff

Villa Maria Center
29847 County 2 Blvd., Frontenac, MN 55026. 651-345-4582, fax: 651-345-3457, e-mail: villamaria_retreats@yahoo.com, web: www.villamariaretreats.org

MISSISSIPPI

St. Mary of the Pines Retreat Center
PO Box 38, Chatawa, MS 39632. 601-783-3494, fax: 601-783-3984, e-mail: retcenter@telapex.com
Contact: Sister Joan Schaefer, SSND

The Dwelling Place
2824 Dwelling Place Rd., Brooksville, MS 39739-9537. 662-738-5348, fax: 662-738-5345, e-mail: dwellpl@crawdat.com, web: www.dwellingplace.com
Contact: Clare Van Lent
Affiliation: Sisters of St. Francis of the Holy Family

MISSOURI

Abbey Center for Prayer & Ministry
Conception Abbey, Conception, MO 64433. 660-944-2809, fax: 660-944-2885, e-mail: abbeycenter@conception.edu, web: www.conceptionabbey.org/AbbeyCenter/retreats.htm
Affiliation: Benedictine Monks (Conception, MO)

Assumption Abbey
Rte. 5, Box 1056, Ava, MO 65608. 417-683-5110, fax: 417-683-5658, e-mail: assumptionabbey@usa.net, web: assumptionabbey.org
Contact: Fr. Mark Scott, O.C.S.O.
Affiliation: Trappists

Cordis House
648 S. Assisi Way, Republic, MO 65738-2190. 417-732-8602
Contacts: Fr. Eric Kahn, O.F.M., Sr. Coletta Wrasman, P.H.J.C.

Franciscan Prayer Center
2100 N. Noland Rd., Independence, MO 64050. 816-252-1673, fax: 816-252-5574, e-mail: stfran2100@aol.com
Contact: Sister Connie Boulch, OSF
Affiliation: Sisters of St. Francis of the Holy Eucharist

IL Ritiro-The Little Retreat
Eime Rd., PO Box 38, Dittmer, MO 63023. 636-285-3759, fax: 636-274-3380, e-mail: gpeter@nightowl.net
Contact: Fr. Nathan McNally
Affiliation: Franciscan Friars

Immaculata Retreat Center
300 E. 36th St., PO Box 419037, Kansas City, MO 64141-6037. 816-756-1850

La Salle Institute-Retreat/ Conference Center
2101 Rue de La Salle, Wildwood, MO 63038-2299. 636-938-5374, fax: 636-587-9792, e-mail: cblasalle@aol.com
Contact: Br. Joseph Zastrow, F.S.C.
Affiliation: De La Salle Christian Brothers

Little Portion Retreat Center
645 S. Assisi Way, Republic, MO 65738. 417-732-6684
Contact: Sr. Lorraine Biebel, O.S.F., Coordinator

Maria Center
336 Ripa Ave., St. Louis, MO 63125. 314-544-0455, ext. 220, fax: 314-544-6754
Contact: Sr. Marie Ambrose
Affiliation: School Sisters of Notre Dame

Marianist Retreat & Conference Center
1280 Highway 109, PO Box 718, Eureka, MO 63025. 636-938-5390, fax: 636-938-3493, e-mail: macmrcc@aol.com
Affiliation: Marianists, Society of Mary

Mary the Font Solitude
6150 Antire Rd., High Ridge, MO 63049-2135. 636-677-3235, Fax: 636-677-0644, e-mail: motherofpeace@netzero.net
Contact: Sr. Anne Marie, S.M.P.
Affiliation: Society of Our Mother of Peace

Mercy Center
2039 N. Geyer Rd., St. Louis, MO 63131-3399. 314-966-4686, fax: 314-909-4631, e-mail: retreats@corp.mercy.net
Contact: Miriam Nolan, RSM
Affiliation: Sisters of Mercy of the Americas (Regional Community of St. Louis)

Pallottine Renewal Center
15270 Old Halls Ferry Rd., Florissant, MO 63034. 314-837-7100, fax: 314-837-1041, e-mail: pall4@juno.com, web: www.geocities.com/pallottinerenewal
Contact: Sr. Bernadita Peterson
Affiliation: Pallottine Sisters

Queen of Heaven Solitude
12494 State Hwy. T, Marionville, MO 65705-7121. 417-744-2011
Contact: Sister Mary Emmanuel, SMP
Affiliation: Society of Our Mother of Peace

St. Charles Lwanga Center
5021 Northland Ave., St. Louis, MO 63113-1014. 314-367-7929, fax: 314-367-4134

Vianney Renewal Center
6476 Eime Rd., PO Box 130, Dittmer, MO 63023. 636-274-5226, fax: 636-274-1430, www:theservants.org
Contact: Fr. Peter Lechner, s.P.
Affiliation: Servants of the Paraclete

Vision of Peace Hermitages
P.O. Box 69, Pevely, MO 63070-0069. 636-475-3697, fax: 636-475-3697, e-mail: visofpeace@juno.com, web: www.dogbird.com/vision_of_peace

White House Retreat
Suite 204, Jesuit Hall, 3601 Lindell Blvd., St. Louis, MO 63108-3301. 800-643-1003, 314-533-8903, fax: 314-533-8428, e-mail: reservations@whretreat.org, web: whretreat.org
Contact: Rev. Richard O. Buhler, S.J.
Affiliation: Jesuits (Missouri Province)

MONTANA

Sacred Heart Renewal Center
PO Box 153, Billings, MT 59103. 406-252-0322, fax: 406-252-0322, e-mail: shrc@mcn.net
Contact: Kathleen O'Neal
Affiliation: Diocese of Great Falls-Billings

Ursuline Retreat Centre
2300 Central Ave., Great Falls, MT 59401. 406-452-8585, fax: 406-452-8586, e-mail: ursuline@in-tch.com
Contact: Harry J. Tholen
Affiliation: Ursuline Nuns (Santa Rosa, CA)

NEBRASKA

Archdiocesan Retreat & Conference Centers
3330 N. 60th St., Omaha, NE 68104. 402-558-1442, fax: 402-551-1482, e-mail: cmfinocchiaro@archomaha.org; web: www.archomaha.com
Contact: Christine M. Finocchiaro
Affiliation: Archdiocese of Omaha

Knowles Mercy Spirituality Center
2304 Campanile Rd., Waterloo, NE 68069-6838. 402-359-4288, fax: 402-359-4843 (call ahead), e-mail: rosiev@mercyoma.org, web: kmscenter.org
Contact: Peg O'Malley
Affiliation: Sisters of Mercy

Niobrara Valley House of Renewal
PO Box 167, Lynch, NE 68746. 402-569-2421, e-mail: marypmin@threeriver.net, web: www.threeriver.net /retreat
Contact: Mary Hildman
Affiliation: Archdiocese of Omaha

Our Lady of Good Counsel Retreat House
7303 N. 112th St., RR. No. 1, Box 110, Waverly, NE 68462. 402-786-2705, fax: 402-786-7211, web: www.goodcounselretreat.com
Contact: Fr. Lawrence Stoley

Sacred Heart House of Prayer
89574 545th Ave., Crofton, NE 68730-3238. 402-388-2472 (tel, fax), e-mail: sfhop@bloomnet.com
Contact: Dr. Joseph Kelly
Affiliation: Brothers and Sisters of Charity

St. Benedict Center
St. Benedict Rd., PO Box 528, Schuyler, NE 68661. 402-352-8819, fax: 402-352-8884, e-mail: benedict.center@alltel.net, web: www.megavision.net/benedict
Contact: Fr. Thomas A. Leitner, OSB
Affiliation: Benedictine Monks (Congregation of St. Ottilien for Foreign Missions)

St. Columban's Center
PO Box #10, St. Columbans, NE 68056-0010. 402-291-1920, fax: 402-291-4984, e-mail: cgmo@aol.com
Affiliation: Columban Fathers

NEVADA

Monastery of Christ in the Mountains
PO Box 708, Caliente, NV 89008. 775-726-3669 (tel, fax)

NEW HAMPSHIRE

Emmaus House
286 Concord St., Manchester, NH 03104. 603-624-1173
Contact: Sr. Bernadette Turgeon, S.N.D.deN.

Joseph House Contemplative Retreat Center
279 Cartier St., Manchester, NH 03102-3702. 603-627-9493, e-mail: srmaryannl@aol.com
Contact: Sister Mary Anne Laughlin, Director
Affiliation: Sisters of Notre Dame de Namur (Boston Province)

La Salette Retreat Center
417 N.H. Rte. 4A, PO Box 420, Enfield, NH 03748. 603-632-7087, fax: 603-632-7648
Contact: Retreat Center Director

NEW JERSEY

Benedictine Center for Spirituality
Saint Walburga Monastery, 851 N. Broad St., Elizabeth, NJ 07208. 908-353-3028, e-mail: maritaosb@aol.com, web: www.catholic-forum.com/bensisnj
Contact: S. Marita Funke, OSB
Affiliation: Benedictine Sisters

Bethany Ridge
PO Box 241, Little York, NJ 08834. 908-995-9758, fax: 908-995-7299 (for clergy only)

Bethlehem Hermitage
82 Pleasant Hill Rd., Chester, NJ 07930, 908-879-7059 (tel, fax)
Contact: Rev. Eugene C. Romano

Carmel Retreat
1071 Ramapo Valley Rd., Mahwah, NJ 07430-2406. 201-327-7090, fax: 201-327-9133, e-mail: mwastag@carmelnet.org
Contact: Mike Wastag

Emmaus House
101 Center St., Perth Amboy, NJ 08861. 908-442-7688, fax: 732-442-5510, e-mail: emmaushouse@juno.com
Affiliation: Poor Servants of the Mother of God

Father Judge Apostolic Center
1292 Long Hill Rd., Stirling, NJ 07980. 908-647-7112, fax: 908-647-6045, email: fjac3@aol.com, web: www.fjac.org/

Felician Retreat House
35 Windemere Ave., Mount Arlington, NJ 07856. 973-398-9806
Contact: Sr. Mary Gilbert Szaroleta, C.S.S.F.

Francis House of Prayer
PO Box 392, Rancocas, NJ 08073. 609-877-0509, fax: 609-877-5810, e-mail: fhop@pics.com, web: www.francishouseofprayer.org
Contact: Sister Marcy Springer, S.S.J.
Affiliation: Diocese of Trenton

Loyola Retreat House
161 James St., Morristown, NJ 07960. 973-539-0740, fax: 973-898-9839, e-mail: retreathouse@loyola.org, web: www.loyola.org
Contact: Rev. Patrick J. Sullivan, S.J.
Affiliation: Jesuits (New York Province)

Marianist Family Retreat Center
417 Yale Ave., PO Box 488, Cape May Point, NJ 08212. 609-884-3829, fax: 609-884-0545, e-mail: mfrc@capemaymarianists.org, web: www.capemaymarianists.org
Contact: Anthony Fucci
Affiliation: Marianists, Society of Mary

Maris Stella
PO Box 3135, Harvey Cedars, NJ 08008. 609-361-8863 (tel, fax), e-mail: stmsalerno@aol.com
Contact: Sister Thomas Mary Salerno, S.C.
Affiliation: Sisters of Charity of Saint Elizabeth

Morning Star House of Prayer
312 W. Upper Ferry Rd., Trenton, NJ 08628. 609-882-2766, web: www.morningstarprayerhouse.org
Contact: Sister Geraldine Calabrese, MPF, Coordinator
Affiliation: Religious Teachers Filippini

Mount Paul Retreat Center
243 Mount Paul Rd., Oak Ridge, NJ 07438-9512. 973-697-6341, e-mail: mountpaulnj@cs.com
Contact: Fr. John J. Foley, C.S.P., J.C.D., Director of Ministries
Affiliation: Paulist Fathers (for groups only)

Mount Saint Francis Retreat Center
474 Sloatsburg Rd., Ringwood, NJ 07456. 973-962-9778, fax: 973-962-0445. E-mail: msfretreat@aol.com
Contact: Sr. Rosemary Napolitano, OSF
Affiliation: Sisters of St. Francis of Philadelphia

Mount Saint Mary House of Prayer
1651 U.S. Highway 22, Watchung, NJ 07069-6567. 908-753-2091, e-mail: msmhope@juno.com, web: www.msmhope.com
Contact: Eileen P. Smith, RSM
Affiliation: Sisters of Mercy of the Americas (Regional Community of New Jersey)

Our Lady of Providence
31 Britton Dr., Flemington, NJ 08822. 908-782-4495
Contact: Sr. Jean of St. Peter, L.S.P.
Affiliation: Little Sisters of the Poor

Pope John Paul II Retreat Center
414 S. 8th St., Vineland, NJ 08360. 856-691-2299, fax: 856-691-5522, e-mail: sccpjllrc@aol.com
Contact: Msgr. Victor Muro

Queen of Peace Retreat House
St. Paul's Abbey, PO Box 7, Newton, NJ 07860. 973-383-2470, ext. 123, fax: 973-383-5782, e-mail: nt-retreat @catholic.or.kr, web: www.osb newton.org
Contact: Fr. Odilo Yi, OSB
Affiliation: Benedictine Monks, Congregation of St. Ottilien

Sacred Heart Renewal Center
PO Box 68, Belvidere, NJ 07823. 908-475-4694
Contact: Br. Eric Gougen, S.C.

Sacred Heart Retreat Center
20 Old Swartswood Rd., Newton, NJ 07860. 973-383-2620, fax: 973-383-3083, e-mail: shcenter@juno.com
Affiliation: Salesian Sisters of St. John Bosco

St. Joseph By the Sea
400 Rte. 35 North, South Mantoloking, NJ 08738. 732-892-8494, fax: 732-892-9905, web: www.filippiniusa .org
Contact: Sr. Frances Lauretti, M.P.F.
Affiliation: Religious Teachers Filippini

St. Mary's Abbey Retreat Center
230 Mendham Rd., Morristown, NJ 07960. 973-538-3231, ext. 2100, fax: 973-538-7109, e-mail: abbeyretreat @juno.com
Affiliation: Benedictine Monks

St. Pius X Retreat House
1840 Peter Cheeseman Rd., Blackwood NJ 08012. 856-227-1436, fax: 856-277-2907, e-mail: staff@stpius 10th.org, web: www.stpius10th.org
Contact: Fr. Thomas Barcellona
Affiliation: Diocese of Camden

San Alfonso Retreat House
755 Ocean Ave., Long Branch, NJ 07740. 732-222-2731, fax: 732-870-8892, e-mail: sanalfonso755@aol .com, web: www.sanalfonsoretreats .org
Contact: Rev. John McGowan, CSsR
Affiliation: Redemptorists (Baltimore Province)

Sanctuary of Mary - Our Lady of the Holy Spirit
252 Wantage Ave., Branchville, NJ 07826. 973-875-7625
Contact: Fr. Silvester J. Livolsi

Stella Maris Retreat Center
981 Ocean Ave., Elberon, NJ 07740. 732-229-0602, fax: 732-229-8960, e-mail: smreservation@mycomcast .com, web: www.stellamarisretreat center.org
Contact: Sister Clare McNerney, CSJP
Affiliation: Sisters of St. Joseph of Peace (CSJP) (St. Joseph Province)

Upper Room Spiritual Center
W. Banks Ave., & Rte. 33, PO Box 1104, Neptune, NJ 07754-1104. 732-922-0550, fax: 732-922-3904, e-mail: upperroom@bytheshore .com, web: www.theupper-room.org
Contacts: Sr. Maureen Conroy, RSM, Sr. Maureen Christensen, RSM, Sr. Trudy Ahern, SSJ, Co-Directors
Affiliation: Diocese of Trenton

Villa Pauline
Mallinckrodt Convent, 352 Bernardsville Rd., Mendham, NJ 07945. 973-543-6528, fax: 973-543-9459, e-mail: socc@nac.net, web: scceast .org
Contact: Sister Mary Irene Sorber
Affiliation: Sisters of Christian Charity

Vincentian Renewal Center
75 Mapleton Rd., Princeton, NJ 08540-9614. 609-520-9626, ext. 2, fax: 609-520-0593, e-mail: vrc@ vincentianfamilycenter.com, web: www.vincentianfamilycenter.com
Contact: Fr. Joseph A. Morris, C.M.
Affiliation: Vincentian Priests & Brothers (Eastern Province)

Vocationist Fathers Retreat Center
90 Brooklake Rd., Florham Park, NJ 07932. 973-966-6262, fax: 973-593-8381, e-mail: vocationist@aol.com, web: www.vocationist.org
Contact: Fr. Michael M. Reardon, S.D.V.
Affiliation: Vocationist Fathers

Xavier Center
PO Box 211, 2 Convent Rd., Convent Station, NJ 07961-0211. 973-290-5100, fax: 973-290-5121, e-mail: xaviercnt@aol.com, web: www.xaviercenter.org
Affiliation: Sisters of Charity of Saint Elizabeth

NEW MEXICO

Canossian Spirituality Center
5625 Isleta Blvd. SW, Albuquerque, NM 87105. 505-452-9402, fax: 505-877-2571, e-mail: fdccspirituality@ aol.com, web: www.geocities.com/ fdccspirituality
Contact: Sr. Necy Guan, FdCC
Affiliation: Canossian Daughters of Charity

Center for Action and Contemplation
PO Box 12464, Albuquerque, NM 87195. 505-242-9588, fax: 505-242-9518, e-mail: cacforprophet@juno .com, web: www.cacradical grace.org
Contact: Kathleen O'Malley

Holy Cross Retreat Center
PO Box 158, Mesilla Park, NM 88047. 505-524-3688, fax: 505-524-3811, e-mail: Franciscan@zianet .com, web: www.zianet.com/ franciscan
Contact: Fr. Sebastian Cunningham, O.F.M. Conv.

Immaculate Heart of Mary Retreat/Conference Center
Mt. Carmel Rd., Santa Fe, NM 87501. 505-988-1975, fax: 505-988-3963
Contact: Ben Armijo

LifeWay Glorieta Conference Center
PO Box 8, I-25 North Exit 299, Glorieta, NM 87535. 888-366-5676, ext. 4270, fax: 505-757-4385, web: www.glorieta.com

Madonna Retreat/Conference Center
4040 St. Joseph PL., N.W., Albuquerque, NM 87120. 505-831-8196, fax: 505-831-8103, e-mail: asfmod @flesh.net, web: www. archdiocese santafe.org

Nazareth House
PO Box 1531, Deming, NM 88031. 505-546-7599, e-mail: nazhouse@swnm.com
Contact: Jacqueline Sailer, DHM
Affiliation: Daughters of the Heart of Mary

Our Lady of Guadalupe Abbey
PO Box 1080, Pecos, NM 87552-1080. 505-757-6415, fax: 505-757-2285, e-mail: guestmaster@pecos-nm.com, web: www.pecosabbey.org
Contact: Rev. Andrew Miles, OSB
Affiliation: Benedictine Monks of Our Lady of Guadalupe Abbey, Benedictine Sisters of Mother of Mercy and Peace

Sacred Heart Retreat & Conference Center
PO Box 1338, Gallup, NM 87305. 505-722-6755, fax: 505-722-6755, e-mail: smmward@cnetco.com, web: dioceseof gallup.org
Contact: Sr. Mary Matthias Ward, O.S.U.

Spiritual Renewal Center
6400 Coors Blvd. NW, Albuquerque, NM 87120. 505-877-4211, fax: 505-890-4110, e-mail: domreths@juno.com, web: www.christdesert.org/dominican/index.htm
Affiliation: Dominican Sisters (Elkins Park, PA)

NEW YORK

Abba House of Prayer
647 Western Ave., Albany, NY 12203. 518-438-8320 (tel, fax: call first), e-mail: abba.house@verizon.net
Contact: Sister Rosemary J. Sgroi, RSM

Anawim Community Center
122 E. First St., Corning, NY 14830. 607-936-4965, fax: 607-936-0207, e-mail: corning@anawim.com, web: www.anawim.com
Contact: Fr. Daniel Healy
Affiliation: Diocese of Metuchen

Bethany Ministries
176 Mill Ln., PO Box 420, Middleburgh, NY 12212. 518-827-4699, e-mail: bethmin@midtel.net, web: www.midtel.net/~bethmin
Contact: Friar Peter Chepaitis, O.F.M.
Affiliation: Franciscan Friars (Province of the Most Holy Name)

Bethany Retreat House
202 County Rd., PO Box 1003, Highland Mills, NY 10930-1003. 845-928-2213, fax: 845-928-9437, e-mail: thevenet@frontiernet.net, web: www.rc.net/newyork/bethany
Contact: Sr. Catherine McIntyre, R.J.M.
Affiliation: Religious of Jesus and Mary

Bishop Molloy Passionist Retreat House
86-45 Edgerton Blvd., Jamaica, NY 11432. 718-739-1229, fax: 718-739-3421, e-mail: Roseannq@aol.com, web: www.bishopmolloy.org
Contact: Fr. Jim Price, C.P., Director
Affiliation: Passionists

Blessed Kateri Guest House
Rte. 5, PO Box 627, Fonda, NY 12068. 518-853-3646, fax: 518-853-3371, e-mail: kkenny@nycap.rr.com, web: katerishrine.com
Contact: Rev. Kevin Kenny, O.F.M. Conv. Affiliation: Conventual Franciscan Friars

Blessed Sacrament Center of Eucharist Worship
15 University Ave., Buffalo, NY 14214. 716-834-6290, fax: 716-834-6290, e-mail: sacramentines.buffalony@worldnet.att.net
Contacts: Sr. Mary of the Rosary, O.S.S., Sr. Maria Christi, O.S.S.

Borromeo Prayer Center
3011 Dewey Ave., Rochester, NY 14616. 585-663-5856, fax: 585-663-8055, e-mail: bpc98@juno.com, web: www.frontiernet.net/~stcharls
Contact: Patricia Scouten, Administrator
Affiliation: Diocese of Rochester

Cenacle Center for Spiritual Renewal
154-27 Horace Harding Expwy., Flushing, NY 11367-1296. 718-463-2073, fax: 718-353-3514, e-mail: cenflushing@juno.com, web: www.cenaclesisters.org/flushing.htm
Contact: Sr. Judith Osterburg
Affiliation: Religious of the Cenacle (Sisters)

Cenacle Retreat House
PO Box 4005, Lake Ronkonkoma, NY 11779-0430. 631-588-8366, fax: 631-585-8485, e-mail: retreat@cenaclesisters.org, web: www.cenaclesisters.org/ronkonkoma.htm
Contact: Mary Spratt, r.c.
Affiliation: Religious of the Cenacle (Sisters)

Center of Renewal
4421 Lower River Rd., Stella Niagara, NY 14144-1001, 716-754-7376, e-mail: Hospitality@Center-of-Renewal.org, web: www.center-of-renewal.org
Contact: Tom Delonghry
Affiliation: Sisters of St. Francis at Stella Niagara

Christ the King Retreat House
500 Brookford Rd., Syracuse, NY 13224. 315-446-2680, fax: 315-446-2689, web; retreats@christtheking retreat.com
Contact: Fr. Michael J. Carmola

Corazon
Villa St. Dominic, PO Box 189, Glasco, NY 12432. 845-246-8941, fax: 845-246-5610, e-mail: kgbcor@ulster.org
Contact: Katherine Gaffney, OP
Affiliation: Dominican Sisters of Sparkill

Cormaria Retreat House
Bay St., PO Box 1993, Sag Harbor, NY 11963. 631-725-4206, fax: 631-725-1837, e-mail: cormaria@aol.com web: www.cormaria.org

Divine Compassion Center for Spiritual Renewal
52 N. Broadway, White Plains, NY 10603-3710. 914-948-4086, fax: 914-949-5169, e-mail: dccsr@bestweb.net, web: www.bestweb.net/~dccsr/
Contact: Corita Clarke, R.D.C.
Affiliation: Sisters of the Divine Compassion

Dominican Center
Dominican Convent, 175 Rte. 340, Sparkill, NY 10976-1047. 845-359-6400, ext. 215, fax: 845-359-7204, e-mail: dominican.center@sparkill.org, web: www.sparkill.org/spiritual opportunities
Contact: Mary Reynolds, OP
Affiliation: Dominican Sisters of Sparkill, NY

Dominican Retreat and Conference Center
1945 Union St., Niskayuna (Schenectady), NY 12309. 518-393-4169, fax: 518-393-4525, e-mail: dslcny@nycap.rr.com, web: www.dslcny.org
Contact: Jeanne Qualters
Affiliation: Dominican Sisters of St. Catherine de' Ricci

Don Bosco Retreat Center - The Marian Shrine
174 Filors Lane, Stony Point, NY 10980-2645. 845-947-2200, fax: 845-947-2203, e-mail: DBretreats@aol.com, web: www.MarianShrine.org
Contact: Fr. Richard Alejunas, SDB
Affiliation: Salesians of Don Bosco

Gilead
1011 State Hwy. 7, Unadilla, NY 13849. 607-563-3713, e-mail: tngilead@aol.com, web: www.gilead.org

Graymoor Spiritual Life Center
Rt. 9, PO Box 300, Garrison, NY 10524-0300. 845-424-2111, fax: 845-424-2162, e-mail: graymoor center@atonementfriars.org, web: www.atonementfriars.org (click on "retreats")
Contact: Rev. James J. Gardinar, SA
Affiliation: Atonement Friars (Franciscan Friars of the Atonement)

Jogues Retreat
PO Box F, Cornwall, NY 12518-0522. 845-534-7570
Contact: Rev. Herbert T. Kane, S.J.
Affiliation: Jesuits

Linwood Spiritual Center
50 Linwood Rd., Rhinebeck, NY 12572. 845-876-4178, fax: 845-876-1920, e-mail: linwood@ulster.net
Contact: Mary Callaghan, S.U.
Affiliation: Society of St. Ursula

Mariandale Retreat & Conference Center
299 North Highland Ave., Ossining, NY 10562-2327. 914-941-4455, fax: 914-941-8480, e-mail: jmcgorry@ophope.com, web: www.ophope.org/Mariandale/Mariandale.html
Contact: Jeanne McGorry, CSJ, Program Director
Affiliation: DominicanSisters of Hope

Marydell Faith & Life Center
640 N. Midland Ave., Nyack, NY 10960. 845-358-5399, fax: 845-358-1671, e-mail: marydell@netzero.net, web: www.sistersrcd.org
Contact: Sr. Marie de Lourdes, RCD
Affiliation: Sisters of Our Lady of Christian Doctrine

Mercy Prayer Center
65 Highland Ave., Rochester, NY 14620. 585-473-6893, fax: 585-473-6414
Contact: Chris McGraw
Affiliation: Sisters of Mercy of the Americas (Regional Community of Rochester)

Mount Alvernia Reteat Center
158 Delavergne Ave., PO Box 858, Wappinger Falls, NY 12590-0858. (845) 297-5706, ext. 12, fax: 845-298-0309, web: www.mtalvernia.org
Contact: Fr. Roch Ciandella, O.F.M.
Affiliation: Franciscan Friars (Immaculate Conception Province)

Mount Alvernia Retreat and Conference Center
PO Box 301,105 Prospect Rd., Centerport, NY 11721. 631-261-5730, fax 631-754-4204, e-mail: alvernia@juno.com, web: www.alvernia.org/MOUNT.html
Contact: Br. Bryan Murphy, OSF
Affiliation: Franciscan Brothers

Mount Irenaeus
Mt. Irenaeus, West Clarksville, NY 14786-1000. 585-973-2470, fax: 585-973-2400, e-mail: jkotula7@yahoo.com, web: www.mounti.com
Contact: Br. Joseph A. Kotula, O.F.M.
Affiliation: Order of Friars Minor (Holy Name Province)

Mount Manresa
239 Fingerboard Rd., Staten Island, NY 10305. 718-727-3844, fax: 718-727-4881, e-mail: mountmanresa@si.rr.com, web: www.manresasi.org
Affiliation: Jesuits (New York Province)

Mount St. Francis Hermitage
PO Box 236, Maine, NY 13802. 607-754-0001 (tel. fax), e-mail: ffimaine@marymediatrix.com, web: www.mary mediatrix.com
Contact: Fr. Maximilian Mary, F.I.
Affiliation: Franciscans of the Immaculate

Mount Saviour Monastery
231 Monastery Rd., Pine City, NY 14871-9787. 607-734-1688, fax: 607-734-1689, e-mail: guest@msaviour.org, web: www.msaviour.org
Contact: Br. James Cronen, OSB
Affiliation: Benedictine Monks

Mt. St. Alphonsus Retreat Center
PO Box 219, Esopus, NY 12429. 845-384-8000, fax: 845-384-8088, e-mail: mailbag@msaretreat.org, web: www.msaretreat.org
Contact: Fr. George Geaveney
Affiliation: Redemptorists

Notre Dame Retreat House
Box 342, 5151 Foster Rd., Canandaigua, NY 14424. 585-394-5700, fax: 585-394-9215, web: notredame retreathouse.org
Contact: Rev. John Kingsbury, C.Ss.R.
Affiliation: Redemptorists (Baltimore Province)

Our Lady of Grace Center
29 Shelter Rock Road, Manhasset, NY 11030. 516-627-9255, fax: 516-365-9329, e-mail: info@olgcenter.com, web: olgcenter.com
Contacts: Sr. Mary Dawson, IHM, Sr. Maria Wittenborn, SC
Affiliation: Sisters, Servants of the Immaculate Heart of Mary (IHM), Scranton, PA

Our Lady of Hope Spiritual Life Center
532 River Rd., Newburgh, NY 12550. 845-561-0685, fax: 845-561-7956
Affiliation: Dominican Sisters of Hope

The Passionist Spiritual Center
5801 Palisade Ave., Bronx NY 10471. 718-549-6500, fax: 718-884-9732, e-mail: passSpiritctr@cpprov.org, web: www.passionists.org, www.preacherman.org
Contact: Fr. Paul R. Fagen, C.P.
Affiliation: Passionist Community

Priory Retreat House
135 Priory Rd. PO Box 336, Chestertown, NY 12817. 518-494-3733, fax: 518-494-3733, e-mail: priory retreat@aol.com, web: www.priory retreathouse.com/page2.html
Affiliation: Sisters of St. Joseph of Carondelet

Pyramid Life Center
Albany, NY 12858. 518-585-7545. E-mail: monphy@juno.com, Web: pyramidlife.com
Affiliation: Albany CYA

Regina Maria Spiritual Life Center
77 Brinkerhoff St., Plattsburgh, NY 12901-2703. 518-561-3421, fax: 518-561-3816, e-mail: reginamh@westelcom.com
Contact: Mary Curran
Affiliation: Daughters of the Heart of Mary

St. Andrew's Retreat House
257 St. Andrew's Rd., Walden, NY 12586. 845-778-5941. Fax: 845-778-5099. E-mail: olcwald@frontier.net
Contact: Sister Martha Hernandez
Affiliation: Sisters of Our Lady of Charity (North American Union)

St. Columban Center
6892 Lake Shore Rd., PO Box 816, Derby, NY 14047-0816. 716-947-4708, fax: 716-947-5759, e-mail: columban@buffnet.net, web: www.stcolumbancenter.org
Contact: Rev. Msgr. James E. Wall
Affiliation: Diocese of Buffalo

St. Francis Center
1365 Planting Fields Rd., Oyster Bay, NY 11771-1302. 516-922-3708, fax: 516-922-9649
Contact: Br. Roman Morris. O.S.F.
Affiliation: Franciscan Brothers of Brooklyn

St. Francis Retreat/Trinity Retreat
1 Pryer Manor Rd., Larchmont, NY 10538. 914-235-6839, fax: 914-576-6540

St. Gabriel's Youth House
64 Burns Rd., Shelter Island, NY 11965. 631-749-0032, e-mail: st.gabes@aol.com, web: www.drvc.org/youngadult/retreatcenters1.htm
Affiliation: Passionists

St. Ignatius Retreat House
251 Searingtown Rd., Manhasset, NY 11030. 516-621-8300, fax: 516-621-7201, e-mail: inisfada@inisfada.net, web: www.inisfada.net
Contact: Rev. Joseph Costantino, S.J.
Affiliation: Jesuits (New York Province)

St. Joseph Spiritual Life Center
495 Maple Ln., Valatie, NY 12184. 518-784-9481, fax: 518-784-9494, web: bpmcsc.berk.com
Contact: Bro. Francis Feeley

St. Joseph's
167 Wolf Hill Rd., Melville, NY 11747. 516-421-3369

St. Joseph's Center for Spirituality
4875 Strickler Rd., Clarence, NY 14031, web: www.wnyreligion.net
Contact: Sr. Joan Wagner, SSJ
Affiliation: Sisters of St. Joseph of Buffalo

St. Joseph's Center (Spanish Cursillo Center)
(Spanish Cursillo Center) 275 W. 230th St., Bronx, NY 10463. 718-796-4340

St. Joseph's Prayer Center
312 Maple Ave., Patchogue, NY 11772. 631-207-3751, fax: 631-764-3316
Contact: Suzanne Reilly

St. Josephats Retreat House
East Beach Dr., Glen Cove, NY 11542. (516) 671-8980. Web: www.the-finest.com/rcn/retreatcenters/home.htm
Contact: Peggy Stanchfield

St. Mary's Villa
150 Sisters Servants Lane, PO Box 9, Sloatsburg, NY 10974-0009. 845-753-5100, fax: 845-753-5100, e-mail: ssminy@aol.com
Contact: Sr. Albina Gregory
Affiliation: Sisters Servants of Mary Immaculate

St. Paul Center
21-35 Crescent St., Astoria, NY 11105. 718-932-0752, fax: 718-721-9391
Contact: Fr. James Fitzpatrick
Affiliation: Center for Lay Spirituality

Nolasco Spiritual Center
7758 E. Main St., LeRoy, NY 14482. 585-768-7110, 8971, fax: 585-768-4803, e-mail: mercygrove@aol.com, Web: www.orderofmercy.org
Contact: Rev. Paul J. Pietrzyk, O.de.M.
Affiliation: Mercedarian Friars (Order of the Blessed Virgin Mary of Mercy)

St. Ursula Retreat Center
PO Box 86, Middle Rd., Blue Point, NY 11715. 631-363-2422, fax: 631-363-0319, e-mail: retreatcenter@ursulinesofbluepoint.org
Contact: Sr. Mary Elizabeth Preston, OSU
Affiliation: Ursuline Sisters of Tildonk

Siena Spirituality Center
615 Montauk Hwy., Water Mill, NY 11976. 631-726-4740, fax: 631-726-1930, e-mail: nora@sienawatermill.com, web: www.sienawatermill.com
Contact: Sr. Linda Rivers
Affiliation: Dominican Sisters of Amityville

Sisters of Mary Reparatrix
287 Hayward St., Yonkers, NY 10704

Sisters of St. Joseph Spirituality Center
402 Rogers Pkwy., Rochester, NY 14617. 585-336-4370, fax: 585-336-4373, e-mail: mlhssj@juno.com
Contact: Mary Louise Heffernan, SSJ
Affiliation: Sisters of St. Joseph of Rochester (S.S.J.)

Spirit Life Center
300 Washington Ave., Plainview, NY 11803. 516-938-7119, fax: 516-938-7225, e-mail: spiritlifecenter@yahoo.com
Contact: Fr. Robert A. McGuire, S.J.
Affiliation: Jesuits

Stella Maris Retreat Center
130 East Genesee St., Skaneateles, NY 13154. 315-685-6836, fax: 315-685-7008, e-mail: info@stellamarisretreat.org, web: www.stellamarisretreat.org
Contact: Sister Rose Raymond Wagner, O.S.F.
Affiliation: Sisters of the Third Franciscan Order of Syracuse

Still Point House of Prayer
Rte. 423, Box 53, Stillwater, NY 12170. 518-587-4967 (tel, fax), e-mail: stillpt423@aol.com

Tabor Retreat Center
60 Anchor Ave., Oceanside, NY 11572. 516-536-3004, fax: 516-536-0214, e-mail: taborretreats@juno.com, web: www.taborretreatcenter.org
Contact: Sr. Helen Chasse, O.S.U.

Wellsprings
93 Maple St., Glens Fall, NY 12801. 518-792-3183, fax: 518-792-3184, e-mail: info@wsprings.org, web: www.wsprings.org

NORTH CAROLINA

A Place for Women to Gather
6512 Six Forks Rd., Suite 401-A, Raleigh, NC 27615-2840. 919-846-3601, 919-846-3578, e-mail: womengather@earthlink.net, web: www.womengather.org
Contacts: Sr. Patricia Cornell, CSC, Sr. Mary Margaret Weber, CSC
Affiliation: Sisters of the Holy Cross
(Offers educational programs, as well as retreat days)

Avila Retreat Center
711 Mason Rd., Durham, NC 27712. 919-477-1285, fax: 919-477-9485, e-mail: avila@raldioc.org, web: www.raldioc.org
Contact: Sr. Damian Marie Jackson, OSF
Affiliation: Diocese of Raleigh

Catholic Conference Center
1551 Trinity Lane, Hickory, NC 28602-9049. 888-536-7441, e-mail: info@catholicconference.org, web: www.catholicconference.org/Catalog.asp?Collection=16

Christian Family Living Center
2006 Wicker St., North Topsail Beach, NC 28460. 910-328-1584, fax: 910-328-1584, e-mail: cflcentertopsail@aol.com, web: www.christianfamilyliving.org
Contacts: Fr. Rich Kuhn, S.M., Br. Ray McQuade, S.M., (Mr.) Joseph DiCostanzo
Affiliation: Marianists Priests and Brothers

Jesuit House of Prayer
289 Hwy. 25/70, PO Box 7, Hot Springs, NC 28743. 828-622-7366, tel, fax, e-mail: vpaul@madison.main.nc.us, web: www.geocities

.com/ ~jesuit_housenc
Contact: Sr. Peggy Verstege, RSM
Affiliation: Jesuits

Living Waters Catholic Reflection Center
103 Living Waters Lane, Maggie Valley, NC 28751. 828-926-3833, fax: 828-926-1997, e-mail: lwcrc@main.nc.us, web: www.catholicretreat.org
Contact: Fr. Terry Hyland, OSA

McCauley Center
100 Mercy Dr., Belmont, NC 28012. 704-829-5260
Affiliation: Sisters of Mercy of the Americas (Regional Community of North Carolina)

NORTH DAKOTA

Benedictine Spirituality Center
8969 Hwy. 10, PO Box 364, Richardton, ND 58652. 701-974-2121, fax: 701-974-2124, web: www.sacredheartmonastery.com
Contact: Sr. Ruth Fox, OSB
Affiliation: Benedictine Sisters (Richardton, ND)

Maryvale Spiritual Life Center
11550 River Rd., Valley City, ND 58072. 701-845-2864, fax: 701-845-0805, e-mail: srdorothy@fargodiocese.org, web: www.sistersofmarypresentation.com
Contact: Sister Dorothy Bunce
Affiliation: Sisters of Mary of the Presentation

Presentation Prayer Center
1101 32nd Ave. S., Fargo, ND 58103. 701-237-4857, fax: 701-237-9822, e-mail: presprayerctr@cableone.net, web: www.presentationsistersfargo.com
Contact: S. Andrea Arendt, PBVM
Affiliation: Sisters of the Presentation of the Blessed Virgin Mary

Queen of Peace Retreat Center
1310 Broadway, Fargo, ND 58102. 701-293-9286, fax: 701-235-0296, e-mail: george@fargodiocese, web: www.fargodiocese.org
Affiliation: Diocese of Fargo

OHIO

Bergamo Center for Lifelong Learning
4400 Shakertown Rd., Dayton OH 45430-1075. 937-426-2363, fax: 937-426-1090, e-mail: info@bergamocenter.org, www.bergamocenter.org
Contact: Dick Flack
Affiliation: Marianists, Society of Mary

Chiara Center
6832 Convent Blvd., Sylvania, OH 43560. 419-824-3602
Affiliation: Sisters of St. Francis

Friarhurst Retreat Center
8136 Wooster Pike, Cincinnati, OH 45227. 513-561-2270, fax: 513-561-0367
Contact: Fr. Lambert Dannenfelser, O.F.M.

Jesuit Retreat House of Cleveland
5629 State Rd., Parma (Cleveland), OH 44134-2292. 440-884-9300, fax: 440-885-1055, e-mail: jrhcleve@worldnet.att.net
Contact: Clem Metzger, S.J.
Affiliation: Jesuits (Detroit Province)

Lial Renewal Center
5900 Davis Rd., Whitehouse OH 43571. 419-474-5485, fax: 419-474-1336, e-mail: jmfrania@toledosnd.org, web: sndtoledo.org
Contact: Sister Joanne Mary Frania, SND
Affiliation: Sisters of Notre Dame

Loyola of the Lakes Jesuit Retreat House
700 Killinger Rd., Clinton, OH 44216-9653. 330-896-2315, fax: 330-896-0858, e-mail: lotljrh@aol.com, web: www.loyolaofthelakes.com
Contact: Fr. Paul Panaretos, S.J.
Affiliation: Jesuits (Detroit Province)

Milford Spiritual Center
5361 S. Milford Rd., Milford, OH 45150. 513-248-3500, fax: 513-248-3503, e-mail: milfordspiritualcenter@zoomtown.com, web: www.milfordspiritualcenter.org
Contact: Dan Roche
Affiliation: Jesuits

Our Lady of Consolation Retreat House
321 Clay St., Carey, OH 43316. 419-396-7970, fax: 419-396-3355, e-mail: olcretreathouse@aol.com, web: www.olcshrine.com
Contact: Lucy Pahl
Affiliation: Diocese of Toledo

Our Lady of the Holy Spirit Center
5440 Moeller Ave., Norwood, OH 45212. 513-351-9800, fax 513-351-9885, e-mail: info@olhsc.org, web: www.olhsc.org
Contact: Fr. Joseph A. Bruemmer

Our Lady of the Pines Retreat Center
1250 Tiffin St., Fremont, OH 43420. 419-332-6522, e-mail: olprc@ezworks .net, web: www.pinesretreat.org
Contact: Sr. Marianne Longo, RSM

Sacred Heart Retreat & Renewal Center
3128 Logan Way, PO Box 6074, Youngstown, OH 44501. 330-759-9539, fax: 330-759-8239, e-mail: mscyng@aol.com
Contact: Rev. Vincent T. Freeh, MSC
Affiliation: Missionaries of the Sacred Heart

St. Joseph Christian Life Center
18485 Lake Shore Blvd., Cleveland, OH 44119-1244. 216-531-7370, fax: 216-531-0629, e-mail: cjauch@stjosephchristianlife.org, web: www.stjosephchristianlife.org
Contact: Fr. Wally Hyclak
Affiliation: Diocese of Cleveland

St. Francis Spirituality Center
200 St Francis Ave., Tiffin OH 44883. 419-443-1485, fax: 419-443-1478, e-mail: retreats@stfrancisspiritualitycenter.org, web: www.stfrancisspiritualitycenter.org
Contact: Carol Theis
Affiliation: Sisters of St. Francis

St. Leonard Youth Retreat Center
4076 Case Rd., Avon, OH 44011. 440-934-6735, e-mail: FrLeoDechant@aol.com, web: www.murialdo.it/youthretreat
Contact: Fr. Leo Dechant, C.S.J.

St. Therese's Retreat Center
5277 E. Broad St., Columbus, OH 43213. 614-866-1611, fax: 614-863-9091, e-mail: mstthereses@aol.com, web: www.st-therese-retreat .org
Contact: Mary E. Murphy
Affiliation: Diocese of Columbus

Sisters of Charity Spirituality Center
5900 Delhi Rd., Mount Saint Joseph, OH 45051. 513-347-5456, 5453, fax: 513-347-5467, e-mail: spirituality.center@srcharitycinti.org, web: srcharitycinti.org/spirit.htm
Contact: Carol Brenner, SC, Esther Marie Humbert, SC
Affiliation: Sisters of Charity of Cincinnati

Spiritual Center of Maria Stein
2365 St. John Rd., PO Box 95, Maria Stein, OH 45860. 877-925-7625, 419-925-7625, fax: 419-925-6516, e-mail: spiritualcenterms@bright.net, web: www.spiritualcenter.net
Contact: Larry Reichley

Tabor Center
1160 Broadway, Bedford, OH 44146-4523. 440-232-4755, fax: 440-232-7832, e-mail: a.vscoffice@att.net
Contact: Judy Kendrick
Affiliation: Vincentian Sisters of Charity

OKLAHOMA

Benedictine Spirituality Center
Red Plains Monastery, 728 Richland Rd. SW, Piedmont, OK 73078. 405-373-4565, fax: 405-373-3392, e-mail: osbokc@ionet.net, web: www.geocities.com/redplains
Contact: Sister Marie Ballmann, OSB
Affiliation: Benedictine Sisters (Red Plains Monastery)

Catholic Pastoral Center
7501 Northwest Expressway, PO Box 32180, Oklahoma City, OK 73123-0380. 405-721-5651, fax: 405-721-5210, web: www.diocese ofpueblo.com
Affiliation: Diocese of Pueblo

St. Gregory's Abbey Office
1900 W. MacArthur Dr., Shawnee, OK 74804-2499, 405-878-5491, e-mail: mtbrooks@sgc.edu, web: www.monksok.org/guestroom.htm
Contact: Attn: Guest Master

OREGON

The Grotto
NE 85th and Sandy Blvd., PO Box 20008, Portland, OR 97294-0008. 503-254-7371, fax: 503-254-7948, web: www.thegrotto.org/contacting .htm
Affiliation: The Servants of Mary

Mt. Angel Abbey Retreat
Mount Angel Abbey, One Abbey Dr., St. Benedict, OR 97373. 503-845-3025, fax: 503-845-3027, e-mail: retreat@mtangel.edu, web: www.mtangel.edu/GuestHouse/retreatport al.htm
Affiliation: Benedictine Monks

Our Lady of Peace Retreat
3600 SW 170th Ave., Beaverton, OR 97006-5099. 503-649-7127, fax: 503-649-8382
Contact: Sr. Anne Marie Warren, OSF
Affiliation: Franciscan Missionary Sisters of Our Lady of Sorrows

Shalom Prayer Center
Queen of Angels Monastery, 840 S. Main St., Mt. Angel, OR 97362. 503-845-6773, fax: 503-845-6585, e-mail: shalom@open.org, web: www.open.org/shalom
Contact: Sr. Joan Pokorny OSB
Affiliation: Benedictine Sisters

St. Benedict Lodge- Dominican Retreat/Conference Center
56630 N. Bank Rd., McKenzie Bridge, OR 97413-9614. 541-822-3572, fax: 541-822-6151, 3631, web: www.op.org/stbenedicts
Contact: Br. Daniel Thomas, O.P.

St. Rita's Retreat Center
PO Box 310, Gold Hill, OR 97525. 514-855-1333
Contact: Fr. Edward D. Altstock

PENNSYLVANIA

Avila Retreat Center
61 E. High St., Union City, PA 16438. 814-438-7020
Contact: Larry Pline

Basilian Spirituality Center
710 Fox Chase Rd., Fox Chase Manor, PA 19046. 215-342-8381
Contact: Sr. Marina Bochnewich, O.S.B.M.
Affiliation: Sisters of the Order of St. Basil the Great

Bethany Retreat Center
PO Box 129 - Germania Rd., Frenchville, PA 16836. 814-263-4855, fax: 814-263-7106, e-mail: bethanyadult@pennswoods.net, web: www.ypwcministries.org
Contact: Sr. Therese Dush
Affiliation: Anawim Community

The Burning Bush: Franciscan House of Prayer
32-40 Pius St., Pittsburgh, PA 15203-1617. 412-381-3819, fax: 412-381-1585, e-mail: burnbush @nb.net
Contact: Fred Koerner, L.F.A.
Affiliation: Franciscan-oriented (Lay Franciscans of Adoration)

Bethany Youth Center
PO Box 129 - Germania Rd., Frenchville, PA 16836. 814-263-4177, e-mail: bethanyyouth@ pennswoods.net, web: www. ypwcministries.org
Contact: Sr. Suzanne Thibault, C.A.
Affiliation: Young People Who Care, Inc.

Center for Marianist Spirituality & Communities (CMSC)
1341 N. Delaware Ave., Ste. 308, Philadelphia, PA 19125-4300. 610-634-4116, fax: 610-634-4955, e-mail: info@marianist-cmsc.org, web: www.marianist-cmsc.org
Contact: Bro. Jack Ventura, S.M.
Affiliation: Marianist Priests and Brothers

Clare House
608 B. Legion Rd., Aston, PA 19014. 610-459-4077. Fax: 610-558-6122. E-mail: jeanu@osfphila.org; Web: www.fscaston.org/CH.htm
Contact: Sr. Jean Ustasiewski, O.S.F.
Affiliation: Sisters of St. Francis of Philadelphia

Daylesford Abbey
220 S. Valley Rd., Paoli, PA 19301-1999. (610) 647-2530, ext. 11, fax: 610-651-0219, web: www.Daylesford .org
Affiliation: Norbertines

Dominican Retreat House
750 Ashbourne Rd., Elkins Park, PA 19027. 215-782-8520, fax: 215-782-1744, e-mail: info@elkinspark retreats.org, web: www.elkinspark retreats.org

Ecclesia Center/Renewal Center
9101 Ridge Rd., Erie, PA 16417-9625. 814-774-9691, fax: 814-774-4893, e-mail: ecclesia@adelphia .net, web: www.ecclesiacenter.org
Contact: Kathleen A. Kutz
Affiliation: Diocese of Erie

Franciscan Spirit and Life Center
3605 McRoberts Rd., Pittsburgh, PA 15234-2340. 412-881-9207, fax: 412-885-7247, e-mail: fslccom@ aol.com
Contact: Fr. Bernard Tickerhoof, T.O.R.
Affiliation: Sisters of St. Francis of the Providence of God

Franciscan Spiritual Center
609 S. Convent Rd., Aston, PA 19014. 610-558-6152, fax: 610-558-6122, e-mail: fsc@osfphila.org, web: www.fscaston.org
Affiliation: Sisters of St. Francis of Philadelphia

Gilmary Diocesan Center
601 Flaugherty Run Rd., Coraopolis, PA 15108-3899. 412-264-8400, fax: 412-264-8415, e-mail: gilmary@ diopitt.org, web: www.gilmarycenter .org
Contact: Ronald W. Ragan
Affiliation: Diocese of Pittsburgh

Glinodo Center
6270 E. Lake Rd., Erie, PA 16511. 814-899-4584, fax: 814-899-0253, e-mail: glindo@glindo.org, web: www.glindo.org
Contact: Sr. Annette Marshall, O.S.B.
Affiliation: Benedictine Sisters of Erie

Holy Ghost Animation Center
6230 Bush Run Rd., Bethel Park, PA 15102. 412-835-3510, fax: 412-835-3541, e-mail: bethel41@juno.com
Contact: Rev. Norman E. Bevan, C.S.Sp
Affiliation: Holy Ghost Fathers (Eastern Province)

IHM Spiritual Renewal Center
Box 1781 RR, Cresco, PA 18326. 570-595-7548, fax: 570-595-9698, e-mail: ihmcreso@yahoo.com, web: http://ihm.marywood.edu
Contact: Sr. Anne Mary Boslett, IHM

Jesuit Center for Spiritual Growth
501 N Church Rd., Box 223, Wernersville, PA 19565-0223. 610-670-3640, fax: 610-670-3650, e-mail: jescntbus@talon.net, web: www.jesuitspiritualcenter.org
Contact: Rev. Lucien Longtin, S.J.
Affiliation: Jesuits

Kearns Spirituality Center
9000 Babcock Blvd., Allison Park, PA 15101. 412-366-1124, fax: 412-635-6318, e-mail: kearnssc1@aol .com, web: www.sistersofdiv providence.org
Contact: Sister Agnes Raible
Affiliation: Sisters of Divine Providence

Malvern Retreat House
St Joseph's-in-the-Hills, 313 S. Warren Ave., PO Box 315, Malvern, PA 19355-0315. 610-644-0400, fax: 610-644-4363, e-mail: mail@ malvernretreat.com, web: malvern retreat.com
Contact: Chuck Burgy

Mariawald Renewal Center
1094 Welsh Rd., PO Box 97, Reading, PA 19607. 610-777-0135, fax: 610-777-3359, e-mail: mariawald@ aol.com, web: http://hometown.aol .com/mariawald
Contacts: Diane Ross, Sr. Magdalena Vogt, C.P.S.
Affiliation: Missionary Sisters of the Precious Blood

Martina Spiritual Renewal Center
5244 Clarwin Ave., Pittsburgh, PA 15229-2208. 412-931-9766, fax: 412-931-1823, e-mail: martina5244 @worldnet.att.net
Contact: Sister Cindy Ann Kibler, SHS
Affiliation: Sisters of the Holy Spirit

Mary Immaculate Center
300 Cherryville Rd., Northampyon, PA 18067-9548. 610-262-7866, fax: 610-262-6766, e-mail: bkefer@ adphila.org
Contact: Bill Kefer, Administrator
Affiliation: Archdiocese of Philadelphia

Mother Boniface Spirituality Center
3501 Solly Ave., Philadelphia, PA 19136. (215) 335-7541, e-mail: vimormsbt@juno.com, web: www. msbt.org
Contacts: Sr. Virginia Morris, M.S.B.T., Sr. Becky Betz, M.S.B.T.
Affiliation: Missionary Servants of the Most Blessed Trinity

Mount St. Benedict Monastery
6101 East Lake Rd., Erie, PA 16511. 814-899-0614, ext. 402, fax 814-898-4004, e-mail: spirituality@mtst benedict.org, web: www.eriebene dictines.org
Contact: Sr. Carolyn Gorny-Kopkowski, OSB
Affiliation: Benedictine Sisters

Mt. St. Macrina Retreat Center
510 W. Main St., PO Box 878, Uniontown, PA 15401-0878. 724-438-7149 (tel, fax), e-mail: macrina @sgi.net
Contact: Sr. Carol Petrasovich, OSBM
Affiliation: Sisters of St. Basil the Great (Byzantine Catholic)

Precious Blood Spiritual Center
3950 Columbia Ave., Columbia, PA 17512-9714. 717-285-2215, fax: 717-285-4415, e-mail: pbsc@ adorers.org, web: www.pbspiritual center.org

Providence Center
1750 Quarry Rd., Yardley, PA 19067-3998. 215-968-4236, fax: 215-968-6656, e-mail: tmckittrick@greynun .org
Contact: Tom McKittrick
Affiliation: Grey Nuns of the Sacred Heart

Providence Villa
10745 Babcock Blvd., Gibsonia (Pittsburgh), PA 15044-6094. 724 444-8055, fax: 724-444-8058, e-mail: providencevilla@yahoo.com, web: www.sistersofdivprovidence .org
Contacts: Sr. Maura Luffy, Sr. Marilyn Seidel
Affiliation: Sisters of Divine Providence

St. Cyril Academy Spiritual Center
Villa Sacred Heart, Danville, PA 17821-1698. 570-275-0910, fax: 570-275-5997, e-mail: jeanholupsscm@hotmail.com, web: www.sscm.org
Contact: Sr. Jean Marie Holup, SSCM

St. Emma Retreat House
1001 Harvey Ave., Greensburg, PA 15601. 724-834-3060, fax: 724-834-5772, e-mail: benedictinenuns@ stemma.org, web: www.stemma.org
Contact: Mother Mary Anne Noll, OSB
Affiliation: Benedictine Nuns, St. Emma Monastery

St. Francis Center
Adult & Youth Retreats, 900 W. Market St., Orwigsburg, PA 17961-1006. 570-366-1405, fax: 570-366-1426, e-mail: oyyak@ptbprolog.net
Contact: Deacon Alex Maggitti
Affiliation: Diocese of Allentown

St. Francis Center for Renewal
395 Bridle Path Rd., Bethlehem, PA 18017. 610-867-8890, fax: 610-861-7478, e-mail: peace@enter.net, web: www.catholic-church.org/ stfrancis-cfn
Contact: Sr. M. Anita Kuchera
Affiliation: School Sisters of Saint Francis

St. Francis Retreat House
0010 Chipman Rd., Easton, PA 18045-3014. 610-258-3053, fax: 610-258-2412, e-mail: stfranrh@ localnet.com, web: www.catholic-church.org/stfran-retreat
Contact: James W. McElrone
Affiliation: Franciscan Friars (Province of St. John the Baptist, Cincinnati, OH)

St. Gabriel's Retreat Center
631 Griffin Pond Rd., Clarks Summit, PA 18411. 570-586-4957, fax: 570-586-8210, e-mail: cpnuns @intiques.com, web: www.intiques .com/cpnuns
Affiliation: Passionist Nuns (contemplative)

St. John the Baptist Retreat Center
PO Box 10, New Baltimore, PA 15553. 814-733-2210, fax: 814-733-2966

St. Joseph Center
2900 Seminary Dr., Rte. 30 East, Greensburg, PA 15601. 724-834-

7350, fax: 724-834-7351, e-mail: jbertig@dioceseofgreensburg.org, web: www.saintjosephcenter.org
Contact: Gerald R. Bertig
Affiliation: Diocese of Greensburg

St. Mary's House of Greater Solitude
Passinist Community, 2970 Imlertown Rd., Bedford, PA 15522-8101. 814-623-1796, fax: 814-623-2457
Affiliation: Passionists

St. Paul of the Cross Retreat Center
148 Monastery Ave., Pittsburgh, PA 15203. 412-381-7676, fax: 412-431-3044, e-mail: stpaulrcpa@cpprov.org, web: trfn.clpgh.org/stpaulrc
Contact: Fr. Tom (Eugene) Bonacci, C.P.
Affiliation: Passionists

St. Raphaela Center
616 Coopertown Rd., Haverford, PA 19041-1135. 610-642-5715, fax: 610-642-6788, e-mail: acihaverford @juno.com
Contact: Dorothy Beck, acj
Affiliation: Handmaids of the Sacred Heart of Jesus(a.c.j.)

Special Ministries
PO Box 10682, Erie, PA 16514. 814-456-0891
Contact: Msgr. James W. Paterson

Theophilus
Theophilus House, 4115 Royal Ave., Erie, PA 16509-1428. 814-866-6891, e-mail: theoprayer@aol.com

Trinity Spiritual Center
603 N. 2nd St., Harrisburg, PA 17101

Urban House of Prayer
1919 Cambridge St., Philadelphia, PA 19130. 215-236-8328
Affiliation: Sisters of Notre Dame de Namur

Villa Maria Retreat Center
Box 424, Villa Maria, PA 16155-0424. 724-964-8861, fax: 724-964-8071, e-mail: mmarszal@humilityofmary.org, web: http://villamaria .tripod.com
Contact: Margaret J. Marszal, HM
Affiliation: Sisters of the Humility of Mary

Villa of Our Lady Retreat House
HCR 1 Box 41, Mount Pocono, PA 18344-9714. 570-839-7217, fax: 570-839-7553, e-mail: sbonaventa @villaourlady.com, web: www.villaourlady.com/home.htm

RHODE ISLAND

Bethany Renewal Center
397 Fruit Hill Ave., North Providence, RI 02911. 401-353-5860, e-mail: bethanyfmm@aol.com, web: www.fmmusa.org
Contacts: Joyce Gardella, fmm, Yvette Hubert, fmm
Affiliation: Franciscan Missionaries of Mary

Father Marot Center
53 Federal St., PO Box 518, Woonsocket, RI 02895
Affiliation: CYO

Mt. St. Joseph Spiritual Life Center
13 Monkeywrench Lane, Bristol, RI 02809-2916. 401-253-4630
Affiliation: Sisters of St. Dorothy

Our Lady of Peace Spiritual Life
PO Box 507, Narragansett, RI 02882. 401-783-2871 or 884-7676, fax: 401-792-8682, e-mail: jeanmmcgee@juno.com
Contact: Jean Marie McGee, RSM
Affiliation: Diocese of Providence

St. Dominic Savio Youth Center
60 St. Dominic Rd., Peacedale, RI 02883. 401-783-4055

St. Paul Priory Guest House
61 Narragansett Ave., Newport, RI 02840-4099. 401-847-2423
Contact: Guest Master
Affiliaiton: Benedictine Monks

SOUTH CAROLINA

Emmanuel House
1916 N. Pleasantburg Dr., Greenville, SC 29609, 864-268-5065, fax: 864-268-9379, e-mail: cforgette@juno.com, web: pages.prodigy.net/abrgreenville
Contact: Sr. Carolyn Forgette, OSC
Affiliation: Poor Clare Nuns, Greenville

Oratory: Center for Spirituality
PO Box 11586, Rock Hill, SC 29731-1586. 803-327-2097, fax: 803-327-6264, e-mail: oratoryctrforsp@cetlink .net, web: www.rockhilloratory .com

Sea of Peace House of Prayer
59 Palmetto Pointe Rd., Edisto Island, SC 29438. 843-869-0513 (tel, fax), e-mail: econdon@awod.com
Contacts: Sr. Elizabeth Condon, O.P., Sr. Barbara Hubbard, O.P.
Affiliation: Dominican Sisters of Adrian

Springbank Center for Eco-Spirituality and the Arts
1345 Springbank Rd., Kingstree, SC 29556. 800-671-0361, fax: 843-382-5340, e-mail: springbank@mind spring .com, web: www.springbank spirit.org
Contact: Ursula Ording, OP
Affiliation: Dominican/Franciscan

SOUTH DAKOTA

Benedictine Peace Center
1005 West 8th St., Yankton, SD 57078. 605-668-6024, fax: 605-668-6033, e-mail: jranek@mtmc.edu, web: www.yanktonbenedictines.org
Contact: Jeanne Ranek, OSB
Affiliation: Benedictine Sisters (Sacred Heart Monastery)

Blue Cloud Abbey Retreat Center
PO Box 98, Marvin, SD 57251. 605-398-9200, fax: 605-398-9201, e-mail: Abbey@bluecloud.org, web: www.bluecloud.org
Contact: Fr. Thomas Roznowski, OSB
Affiliation: Benedictine Monks

Mother of God Monastery
110 28th Ave. SE, Watertown, SD 57201. 605-886-4188, e-mail: leonagauer@hotmail.com, sisteremily@hotmail.com, web: www.dailypost.com/monastery
Contacts: Sister Leona Gauer, OSB, Sister Emily Meisel, OSB
Affiliation: Benedictine Sisters

Sacred Heart Center
121 Landmark St., PO Box 2000, Eagle Butte, SD 57625-2000. 605-964-6062, fax: 605-964-6060, e-mail: shc@rapidnet.com
Contact: Br. Francis J. Presto, S.C.J.
Affiliation: Congregation of the Priests and Brothers of the Sacred Heart

Sioux Spiritual Center
20100 Center Rd., Howes, SD. 57748-7703. 605-985-5906, fax: 605-985-5908, e-mail: ssc@gwtc .net, web: www.jesuit.org/resources/retreat.html#NC
Contact: Rev. George Winzenburg, S.J.
Affiliation: Diocese of Rapid City, Jesuits
(Center located in Plainview, SD)

TENNESSEE

Carmel Center of Spirituality
610 Bluff Rd., PO Box 117, Liberty, TN 37095. 615-536-5177, fax: 615-536-5499
Contact: Fr. Zachary Payikat, C.M.I.

The Mountaincrest Spiritual Center
1310 Luttrell St., Knoxville, TN 37917. 865-524-0068
Contact: Dr. Joanna Humphrey

TEXAS

Benedictine Retreat Center
HC#2, Box 6300, Sandia, TX 78383-9989. 512-547-9797, fax: 512-547-9599, e-mail: ccabbey retreat@juno.com
Contact: Bro. Aelred Guerra, O.S.B.
Affiliation: Benedictine Monks (Corpus Christi Abbey)

Bishop DeFalco Retreat Center
2100 North Spring St., Amarillo, TX 79107. 806-383-1811, fax: 806-383-6919, e-mail: bdrc@1s.net, web: www.bdrc.org
Contact: Sr. M. Theresa Rozga
Affiliation: Diocese of Amarillo

Bishop Rene H. Gracida Retreat House
3036 Saratoga Blvd., Corpus Christi, TX 78415. 361-851-1443, fax: 361-851-1552, e-mail: CatholicCenter@interconnect.net
Contact: Fr. Bradley A. Barber

Catholic Renewal Center
4503 Bridge St., Fort Worth, TX 76103. 817-429-2920, fax: 817-492-8668, e-mail: crcwomen@aol.com, web: www.catholiccrc.org
Contact: Gail Schatzman

Cedarbrake Renewal Center
5508 N. Hwy. 317 PO Box 58, Belton, TX 76513. 254-780-2436, fax: 254-780-2684, e-mail: cedar brake@austindiocese.org, web: www.austindiocese.org
Contact: Abigail Jimenez
Affiliation: Diocese of Austin

Cenacle Retreat House
420 North Kirkwood, Houston, TX 77079. 281-497-3131, ext. 50, fax: 281-497-7632, e-mail: ministry@ cenacleretreathouse.org, web: www.cenacleretreathouse.org
Contact: Sue Ellen Ruggles
Affiliation: Religious of the Cenacle (Sisters)

Christ the King Retreat Center
802 Ford St., San Angelo, TX 76905. 915-651-5352, fax: 915-651-5667, e-mail: ckrd@wcc.net
Contact: Rev. Dr. John G. Castro, OMI
Affiliation: Diocese of San Angelo

Christian Renewal Center
PO Box 699 1515 Hughes Rd., Dickinson, TX 77539. 281-337-1312, fax: 281-337-2615, e-mail: crc1515@wt.net, web: www.retreat centercrc.org
Affiliation: Missionary Oblates of Mary Immaculate

El Convento at Loretto
1400 Hardaway St., El Paso, TX 79903. 915-566-1628, fax: 915-566-5127, e-mail: elconvento@whc.net
Affiliation: Sisters of Loretto

Hermitage
Rte. 3, Box 3575, Palestine, TX 75801. E-mail: dhpvcsl@hotmail .com
Contact: Rev. Denis Walsh, C.S.C.

Holy Family Retreat Center
9920 North Major Dr., Beaumont, TX 77713-7618. 409-899-5617, fax: 409-899-3161, e-mail: retreatcenter @dioceseofbmt.org, web: www. dioceseofbmt.org/HFRC/HFRC.htm
Affiliation: Diocese of Beaumont

Holy Name Retreat Center
430 Bunker Hill Rd., Houston, TX 77024-6399. 713-464-0211, fax: 713-464-0671, e-mail: holynamerc @yahoo.com, web: www.passion ist.org/holyname
Affiliation: Passionists (Holy Cross Province)

Holy Spirit Retreat and Conference Center
501 S. Century Dr., Laredo, TX 78046. 956-726-4352, fax: 956-726-4363, e-mail: stjohn@border.net, web: www.stjean.com/laredo/hsrc/ holy.htm
Contact: Br. John Crawley, F. J., Guest Master
Affiliation: Congregation of St. John

Lebh Shomea (Listening Heart) House of Prayer
La Parra Ranch, Sarita, TX 78385-0009. 361-294-5369, fax: 361-294-5791, e-mail: admin@lebhshomea .org, web: www.lebhshomea.org
Contact: Francis Kelly Nemeck, OMI
Affiliation: Missionary Oblates of Mary Immaculate

Montserrat Retreat House
PO Box 1390, Lake Dallas, TX 75065. (Metro) 940-321-6020, 6030, fax: 940-321-6040, e-mail: retreat1@airmail.net, web: www. montserratretreat.org
Contact: Fr. George Wiltz, S.J.
Affiliation: Jesuits (New Orleans Province)

Mt. Carmel Center
4600 W. Davis St., Dallas, TX 75211. 214-331-6224, fax: 214-330-0844, e-mail: mtc@professional webs.net; web: www.mtcarmel dallas.org
Contact: Rev. John Svenram, O.C.D.
Affiliation: Discalced Carmelite Fathers and Brothers (Oklahoma Province of St. Therese)

Mt. Carmel House of Prayer
9600 Deer Trail Dr., Houston, TX 77038-3902.281-931-1698, fax: 281-445-5748, web: www. diocese-gal-hou.org/RetreatCenter-MtCarmelHouseOfPrayer.htm
Contact: Sr. Brigida Rivera, C.M.S.T
Affiliation: Carmelite Missionaries of St. Teresa (CMST)

Mount St. Michael Spiritual Life Center
4500 W. Davis St., Dallas, TX 75211. 214-331-1754, fax: 214-333-1659, e-mail: mmc4500@airmail.net
Affiliation: Sisters of Our Lady of Charity

Moye Center
600 London St., Castroville, TX 78009. 830-931-2233, fax: 830-931-2227, e-mail: moyecenter@aol.com, web: www.moyecenter.org
Affiliation: Sisters of Divine Providence, San Antonio

Oblate Renewal Center
5700 Blanco Rd., San Antonio, TX 78216-6615. 210-349-4173, fax: 210-349-4281, e-mail: orc@ost.edu, web: www.ost.edu/oblate_ renewal_ center.htm
Contact: Rev. Patrick M. McGee, O.M.I.
Affiliation: Missionary Oblates of Mary Immaculate

Omega Retreat Center
216 W. Highland, Boerne, TX 78006. 830-816-8470, e-mail: omegactr@boernenet.com, web: www.boernebenedictines.com
Contact: Andrew Anderson
Affiliation: Benedictine Sisters

Our Lady of Mercy Retreat Center
1225 W. Division St., PO Box 744, Slaton, TX 79364-0744. 806-828-6428, fax: 806-828-3856, e-mail: mercy@door.net, web: www. door.net/mercycenter
Contact: Msgr. Joseph W. James

Prayer Mountain Hermitage
Rte. 3, Box 3574, Palestine, TX 75801
Contact: Sr. Mary Vogel, H.S.S.R.

Prayer Town Emmanuel Retreat House
PO Box 17, Channing, TX. 806-534-2312, fax: 806-534-2223
Contact: Sr. Joan Rodriguez
Affiliation: Disciples of the Lord Jesus Christ

St. Eugene de Mazenod Christian Renewal Center
PO Box 747, San Juan, TX 78589. 956-787-0033
Contact: Retreat Director

The Seton Cove
3708 Crawford St., Austin, TX 78731. 512-451-0272, fax: 512-451-0784, e-mail; setoncove@seton.org, web: www.setoncove.net
Contact: Patricia Speier
Affiliation: Daughters of Charity

Spiritual Renewal Center
718 Gussie Schmidt Rd., Victoria, TX 77905. 361-572-0836, web: www.victoriadiocese.org/renctr/renewalctr.htm
Contact: Connie Amador
Affiliation: Diocese of Victoria

UTAH

Our Lady of the Mountains Retreat House
1794 Lake St., Ogden, UT 84401-3016. 801-392-9231, fax: 801-612-9619, e-mail: olmrh@juno.com
Affiliation: Diocese of Salt Lake City

VERMONT

Blessed Rafka Retreat Center
6420 Rte. 116, Shelbourne, VT 05482-7191. 802-660-2528, fax: 802-863-8456
Contact: Rev. Anthony Weiler

Lumen Christi Retreat House
56 Howard Hill Rd., Benson, VT 05743. 802-537-4531, 846-7084
Contact: Sr. Judy Fortune, R.S.M.

Weston Priory
58 Priory Hill Rd., Weston, VT 05161-6400. 802-824-5409, fax: 802-824-3573, e-mail: brothers@westonpriory.org, web: westonpriory.org
Affiliation: Benedictine Monks

VIRGINIA

Dominican Retreat
7103 Old Dominion Dr., Mc Lean, VA 22101-2799. 703-356-4243, fax: 703-893-4502, e-mail: aggiebop@juno.com, web: www.dominicanretreat.org
Contact: Sr. Agnes B. Gott, O.P.

The Dwelling Place
601 Holly Grove Ln., Richmond, VA 23235. 804-323-3360
Contact: Patricia Carreras

Holy Family Retreat House
1414 N. Mallory St., Hampton, VA 23663. 757-722-3997, fax: 757-723-2478, e-mail: holyfretreat@aol.com
Contact: Fr. Vincent Douglass, C.Ss.R.
Affiliation: Diocese of Richmond

Jubilee House Retreat Center
822 East Main St., Abingdon, VA 24210-4415. 276-619-0919, fax: 276-739-7753, e-mail: info@jubileeretreat.com, web: www.jubileeretreat.com
Contact: Sister Stephanie Ward
Affiliation: Diocese of Richmond

Madonna House
828 Campbell Ave., SW, Roanoke, VA 24016-3551. 540-343-8464, web: www.madonnahouse.org
Contact: Patricia M. Lawton
Affiliation: Diocese of Richmond

Mary Mother of the Church Retreat Center
12829 River Rd., Richmond, VA 23233. (804) 784-3508, ext. 125, fax: 804-784-2214, e-mail: brjeffery@mmotcva.org, web: www.richmondmonks.org
Contact: Br. Jeffrey Williams, OSB
Affiliation: Benedictine Monks

Missionhurst Mission Center
4651 N. 25th St., Arlington, VA 22207. 703-525-6557

Retreat House, Holy Cross Abbey
Rte. 2, Box 3870, Berryville, VA 22611. 540-955-3124, fax: 540-955-1356
Contact: Bro. Stephen Maguire, O.C.S.O., Guest Master
Affiliation:Trappists (Cistercians of the Strict Observance)

Richmond Hill
Ecumenical Center, 2209 E. Grace St., Richmond, VA 23235. 804-783-7903
Contact: Fr. Benjamin Campbell

Shalom House
PO Box 196, Montpelier, VA 23192. 804-883-6149, e-mail: ccawley@richmonddiocese.org
Contact: Catherine Cawley
Affiliation: Diocese of Richmond

Tabor Retreat Center
2125 Langhorne Rd., Lynchburg, VA 24501. 804-846-6475
Contact: Deacon Gordon Cartwright

Well Retreat Center
18047 Quiet Way, Smithfield, VA 23430-6411. 757-255-2366, (tel., fax-call first), e-mail: staff@thewellretreatcenter.org, web: www.thewellretreatcenter.org
Contacts: Sr. Nancy Healy, SFCC, Diane D. Weymouth
Affiliation: Diocese of Richmond

WASHINGTON

Camp Don Bosco
CYO, 814 N.E. 85th St., Seattle, WA 98115. 206-382-4350, fax: 206-903-4627, e-mail: cyo@seattlearch.org
Affiliation: Catholic Youth Organization

Camp Hamilton
25405 Lake Fontal Rd., Monroe, WA 98272.
Contact: CYO, 814 N.E. 85th St., Seattle, WA 98115. 206-382-4350, fax: 206-903-4627, e-mail: cyo@seattlearch.org
Affiliation: Catholic Youth Organization

Dominican Reflection Center
23120 Woodway Park Rd., PO Box 280, Edmonds, WA 98020. 206-542-3740, fax: 206-546-9490, e-mail: drc@netos.com
Contact: Sr. Mary White, O.P.

House of the Lord Retreat Center
PO Box 1034, Tum Tum, WA 99034. 509-276-2219
Contact: Ramona Salvatore, Retreat Director

Ignatian Resource Center
732 18th Ave. East, Seattle, WA 98112. 206-329-4824, fax: 206 726-6179, e-mail: ignatianctr@juno.com, web: www.montserratretreat.org/montserrat/index.html
Affiliation: Jesuits (Oregon Province)

Immaculate Heart Retreat Center
6910 S. Ben Burr Rd., Spokane, WA 99223. 509-448-1224, fax: 509-448-1623
Contact: Deacon John Ruscheinsky, Executive Director

Kairos House of Prayer
1714 W. Stearns Rd., Spokane, WA 99208. 509-466-2187
Contact: Sr. M. Florence Leone, O.S.F.

Palisades Retreat Center
4700 SW Dash Point Rd., Federal Way, WA 98023. 206-748-7991, 253-927-9621, fax: 206-382-3482, e-mail: davej@seattlearch.org, web: www.seattle.org/FormationAndEducation/Palisades+Retreat+Center/
Contact: Dave Jones
Affiliation: Archdiocese of Seattle

Priory Spirituality Center
500 College St. NE, Lacey, WA 98516-5339. 360-438-2595, fax: 360-438-9236, e-mail: spiritualityctr@stplacid.org, web: www.stplacid.org
Contact: Theresa Scott
Affiliation: Benedictine Sisters

St. Mary Conference Center
107 Spencer Rd., Toledo, WA 98591. 360-864-6464, fax: 360- 864-6465, e-mail: sstmarys@ toledotel.com, web: toledotel.com/ ~stmarys

St. Peter the Apostle Retreat Center
15880 Summitview Rd., Cowiche, WA 98923. 509-678-4935, fax: 509-678-8758, e-mail: stpetersretreat@juno.com
Contact: William D. Hudson

Spiritual Exercise in Everyday Life (SEEL)
330 E. Boone, Spokena, WA 99202
Contact: Sr. Sheila McEvoy, S.N.J.M.

Still Point
1111 Harvard Ave., Seattle, WA 98122-4205. 206-322-8006, fax: 209-322-9266, e-mail: stillpt@nwnexus.com
Contact: Donna Kamos

WEST VIRGINIA

Bishop Hodges Pastoral Center
Rte. 1, Box 9D, Huttonsville, WV 26273. 304-335-2165 (tel, fax), e-mail: bhpc@sunlitsurf.com, web: www.neumedia.net/~bhpc
Contact: Deacon Louis J. Belldina

Holy Spirit Hermitage
H.C. 66, Box 20, Old Fields, WV 26845-9201
Contact: Fr. Richard B. Hite, M.S.A.

John XXIII Pastoral Center
100 Hodges Rd., Charleston, WV 25314. 304-342-0507, fax: 304-342 4786, e-mail: johnxxiii@newwave.net
Contact: Deacon John J. Lynch

Maryhill Hermitage
PO Box 230, 2264 Marshall Ave., Wheeling, WV 26003. 304-233-0880, fax: 304-233-0890, e-mail: jelerick@dwc.org

Our Lady of Good Counsel Franciscan Friary
493 Tyrone Rd., Morgantown, WV 26508-2960. 304-594-1714, fax: 304-594-9247
Contact: Fr. Jude J. Mili, O.F.M.
Affiliation: Order of Friars Minor (O.F.M.)

Paul VI Pastoral Center
667 Stone & Shannon Rd., Wheeling, WV 26003. 304-277-3300, fax: 304-277-4320, e-mail: paulvi@hgo.net

Priest Field Pastoral Center
Box 133, State Rte. 51, Kearneysville, WV 25430. 304-725-1435, fax: 304-725-1437, e-mail: PriestFieldPC@ aol.com
Contact: Rev. William P. Linhares, T.O.R.

Saint Joseph Center
137 Mount St. Joseph Rd., Wheeling, WV 26003. 304-232-8160, ext.126, fax: 304-232-1404, e-mail: srmclark@aol.com, web: www.ssjwhg.org/ministries.htm#SSJ Center
Contact: Sr. Mary Clark

St. Thomas More Center
PO Box 230, 2264 Marshall Ave., Wheeling, WV 26003. 304-233-0880, fax: 304-233-0890, e-mail: jelerick@dwc.org

WISCONSIN

Archbishop Cousins Catholic Center
3501 S. Lake Dr., Milwaukee, WI 53207. 414-769-3440, e-mail: nohlr@archmil.org, web: www.archmil.org
Contact: Randy Nohl
Affiliation: Archdiocese of Milwaukee

The Bridge-Between
4471 Flaherty Lane, Denmark, WI 54208. 920-864-7230, fax: 920-864-7044, e-mail: bridgebetween@itol.com, web: www.bridge-between.com
Contact: Sr. Caroline Sullivan, O.P.
Affiliation: Dominicans Sisters of Sinsinawa

Cardoner Retreat Center
1501 S. Layton Blvd., Milwaukee, WI 53215. 414-384-2120
Contact: Fr. James E. Mauel, S.J.
Affiliation: Jesuits (Wisconsin Province)

Cedar Valley Center
5349 Hwy. D, West Bend, WI 53090. 262-629-9202, fax: 262-629-9962, e-mail: skolb@cedarcommunity.org
Contact: Susan Kolb

The Dwelling Place
1704 E. Norwich St., Milwaukee, WI 53207. 414-489-9444. E-mail: jskap@hotmail.com
Contact: Fr. Francis J. Dombrowski, O.F.M. Cap.

Epiphany House
444 W. Bradley Rd., Milwaukee, WI 53217-2614. 414-352-0108, fax: 414-357-8950, e-mail: ssmassoc@aol.com
Contact: Sister M. Raphael Narcisi
Affiliation: Sisters of the Sorrowful Mother

Franciscan Spirituality Center
Franciscan Spirituality Center, 920 Market St., La Crosse, WI 54601-8809. 608-791-5295, fax: 608-782-6301, e-mail: fscenter@fspa.org; www.franciscanspiritualitycenter.org
Contact: Vincent J. Hatt
Affiliation: Franciscan Sisters of Perpetual Adoration

Holy Name Retreat House
PO Box 23825, Green Bay, WI 54305-1506. 877-500-3580, ext. 8296, 920-437-7531, ext. 8296, fax: 920-437-0694, e-mail: HNRH@gbdioc.org, web: www.gbdioc.org/pg/spiritualityRetreatHouse.tpl
Affiliation: Diocese of Green Bay

Jesuit Retreat House
4800 Fahrnwald Rd., Oshkosh, WI 54902-7598. 920-231-9060, fax: 920-231-9094, e-mail: office@jesuitretreathouse.org, web: www.jesuitretreathouse.org
Contact: Rev. Michael Morrison, S.J.
Affiliation: Jesuits (Wisconsin Province)

Marywood Franciscan Spirituality Center
3560 Hwy. 51 N., Arbor Vitae, WI 54568-9538. 715-385-3750, fax: 715-385-9118, e-mail: marywood@newnorth.net
Contact: Jolynn Ann Brehm, FSPA

Monte Alverno Retreat Center
1000 N Ballard Rd., Appleton, WI 54911-5198. 920-733-8526, fax: 920-733-7562, e-mail: montealverno@juno.com

Mount Carmel Hermitage
897 US Hwy. 8, Amery, WI 54001-2541. 715-268-9313, fax: 715-268-7495
Contact: Sr. Kristine Haugen, O.C.D.H., Coordinator

Mount Carmel Hermitage
4270 Cedar Creek Rd., Slinger, WI 53086-9795. E-mail: jmjose@catholic.org; Web: www.carmelitehermit.homestead.com, www.carmelitehermit.org
Contact: Sr. Joseph Marie, C.H.T.
Affiliation: Carmelite Hermit of the Trinity

Mount Tabor Center
522 2nd St., Menasha, WI 54952-3112. 920-722-8918, fax: 920-722-8918
Contact: Eden Foord

Norbertine Center for Spirituality
1016 N. Broadway, De Pere, WI 54115. 920-337-4315, fax: 920-337-4328, e-mail: norbertinecenter@yahoo.com, web: www.norbertines.org
Contact: Fr. John Bostwick, O. Praem.
Affiliation: Norbertine Fathers

Redemptorist Retreat Center
1800 N. Timber Trail Ln., Oconomowoc, WI 53066-4897. 262-567-6900, fax: 262-567-0134, e-mail: phrc@globaldialog.com, web: www.redemptoristretreat.org
Contact: Fr. John A. Broker, C.Ss.R.
Affiliation: Redemptorist Fathers

St. Anthony Retreat Center
300 E. 4th St., Marathon, WI 54448-9602. 715-443-2236, fax: 715-443-2235, e-mail: info@sarcenter.com, web: www.sarcenter.com
Leadership Team: Fr. Dan Crosby, OFM Cap., Ron & Barb Burclaff

Saint Bede Retreat Center
1190 Priory Rd., PO Box 66, Eau Claire, WI 54702-0066. 715-834-8642, fax: 715-834-4292, e-mail: sisters@saintbede.org
Contact: Sr. Hildegarde Geraets, OSB
Affiliation: Benedictine Sisters (St. Bede Monastery)

St. Benedict's Abbey and Retreat Center
12605 244 Ave., Benet Lake, WI 53102-0333. 847-395-8360, fax: 262-396-4365, e-mail: benetlake@msn.com, web: www.benetlake.org
Contact: Bro. Michael O'Brien, OSB
Affiliation: Benedictine Monks

Saint Benedict Center
Box 5070, Madison, WI 53705-0070. 608-831-9305, ext.139, fax: 608-836-5586, e-mail: monastery@sbcenter.org, web: www.sbcenter.org
Affiliation: Benedictine Sisters, ecumenical

St. Clare Center for Spirituality
7381 Church St., Custer, WI 54423. 715-592-4099, e-mail: stclare@coredcs.com

St. Joseph Retreat Center
3035 O'Brien Rd., Baileys Harbor, WI 54202-9132. 920-839-2391, fax: 920-839-2391, e-mail: malbert@ital.com
Contact: Sr. Mary Anne Albert, S.S.S.F.
Affiliation: Priests of the Sacred Heart

St. Vincent Pallotti Center
N. 6409 Bowers Rd., Elkhorn, WI 53121. 262-723-2108, fax: 262-723-8608, e-mail: vpallelk@elknet.net, web: www.vpallelk@elknet.net
Affiliation: Pallotine Fathers

Schoenstatt Retreat Center
W284 N698 Cherry Ln., Waukesha, WI 53188-9402. 262-547-7733, fax: 262-547-7749, e-mail: intlcenter@schsrsmary.org, web: schsrsmary.org
Contact: Sr. M. Jacinta Brunner
Affiliation: Schoenstatt Sisters of Mary

Servite Center for Life
1000 College Ave. W., Ladysmith, WI 54848. 715-532-9611(tel, fax), e-mail: info@servitecenter.org, web: www.servitecenter.org
Contact: Nancy Wheeler
Affiliation: Servants of Mary (Ladysmith, WI)

Siena Center
5635 Erie St., Racine, WI 53402. 262-639-4100, fax: 262-639-9702, e-mail: rdrp@miliserv.net, web: www.racinedominicans.org
Contact: Sr. Rita Lui, O.P.
Affiliation: Dominican Sisters of Racine

Sinsinawa Mound Center
585 County Rd. Z, Sinsinawa, WI 53824-9700. 608-748-4411, fax: 608-748-4491, e-mail: center@sinsinawa.org, web: www.sinsinawa.org
Contact: Sheila Heim
Affiliation: Sinsinawa Dominican Sisters

Tyme Out Youth Center
W. 332 N6786 County Rd. C, Nashotah, WI 53058. 262-966-1800, fax: 262-966-1815, e-mail: youth@tymeout.org, web: www.tymeout.org
Contact: Kieran Sawyer, SSND
Affiliation: Archdiocese of Milwaukee

WYOMING

San Benito Monastery
PO Box 510, Dayton, WY 82836. 307-655-9013, e-mail: sanbenit@fiberpipe.net, web: www.benedictinesisters.org
Affiliation: Benedictine Sisters

NATIONWIDE

Mid-Life Directions/Long Life Directions
4 Palm Ave., Brick, NJ 08723. (732) 255-1239 (tel, fax)
Contacts: Janice Brewi, csj, Anne Brennan, csj, Directors
Personal and spiritual growth, ages 40- 95+, retreats, workshops

GUAM

Our Lady of the Waters Retreat Center
PO Box 163, Agana, GU 96932. 671-477-3122, fax: 671-477-3766
Contact: Rev. Patrick K.G. Garcia

PUERTO RICO

Casa Charlie Rodriguez
PO Box 1190, San Lorenzo, PR 00754. 787-736-5750
Contact: Rev. Edward Santana, J.C.D.

Casa Cristo Redentor
PO Box 8, Aguas Buenas, PR 00703-0008. 787-732-5161, fax: 787-732-1115, web: www.redcatolica.org/caguas/casas.htm
Contact: P. Marcos Wise, CSSR

Casa Cursillos de Cristiandad of Caguas
Salida de Juncos Carretera 919, PO Box 1761, Juncos, PR 00777. 787-734-7068

Casa Manresa
Box 1319, Albonito, PR 00705. 787-735-8016, 8017, fax: 787-735-2421
Contact: Rev. Aurelio Adan

VIRGIN ISLANDS

COR (Christ in Others) Retreat
PO Box 547, Frederiksted, St. Croix, VI 00841. 340-772-0138, fax: 340-772-0142
Contact: Rev. Kenneth Gaddy., C.Ss.R.
Affiliation: Redemptorist Fathers

Religious Study Opportunities

Studying about God and all that is of the Spirit is not just for those first discerning their vocation. It is, indeed, part of the essence of what it means to be Christian. Catholic colleges, retreat centers, diocesan and religious communities offer a variety of opportunities, ranging from one-day workshops to semester-long courses.

ALABAMA

SPRING HILL COLLEGE

Graduate Studies/Summer Institute of Christian Spirituality, 4000 Dauphin St., Mobile, AL 36608-1791. (334) 380-3094. Fax: (334) 460-2190. E-mail: grad@shc.edu; Web: www.shc.edu/grad

Contact: (Mrs.) Pat Warren

Affiliation: Jesuits

Lay/religious women/men; year-round, including summers; non-credit/undergraduate/graduate credit; workshops

ARIZONA

KINO INSTITUTE

1224 E. Northern Ave., Phoenix, AZ 85020-4295. (602) 997-7397. Fax: (602) 870-8871 . Web: www.kino institute.org

CALIFORNIA

THE DOMINICAN SCHOOL OF PHILOSPHY & THEOLOGY

2401 Ridge Rd., Berkeley, CA 94709. (510) 849-2030. Web: www.dspt.edu

DOMINICAN UNIVERSITY OF CALIFORNIA

Department of Religion, 50 Acacia Ave., San Rafael, CA 94901-2298. (415) 457-4440. Fax: (415) 485-3205. E-mail: enroll@dominican .edu; Web: www.dominican.edu

FRANCISCAN SCHOOL OF THEOLOGY

1712 Euclid Ave., Berkeley, CA 94709. (510) 848-5232; (800) 793-1378, ext. 36. Fax: (510) 549-9466. E-mail: info@fst.edu; Web: www.fst.edu

Contact: Jonathan Diaz, Director of Recruitment

Lay/religious women/men; year-round including summers; noncredit/graduate credit

HOLY NAMES COLLEGES

3500 Mountain Blvd., Oakland, CA 94619. (510) 436-1000. Fax: (510) 436-1199. Web: www.hnc.edu

Affiliation: Sisters of the Holy Names of Jesus and Mary

INSTITUTE FOR LEADERSHIP IN MINISTRY

900 Lafayette St., Suite 301, Santa Clara, CA 95050-4966. (408) 983-0110

Contact: Anne E. Grycz

Affiliation: Diocese of San Jose

Lay/religious women/men; year-round; noncredit

JESUIT SCHOOL OF THEOLOGY AT BERKELEY (JSTB)

1735 LeRoy Ave., Berkeley, CA 94709. (510) 549-5000, (800) 824-0122. Fax: (510) 841-8536. E-mail: admissions@jstb.edu; Web: www.jstb.edu

Lay/religious women/men; year-round; noncredit/graduate credit; workshops

LOYOLA MARYMOUNT UNIVERSITY

Department of Theological Studies, One LMU Dr., Ste. 3700, Los Angeles, CA 90045-2659. (310) 338-7772. Fax: (310) 338-1947. E-mail: lschultz @lmu.edu; Web: www.lmu.edu

Contact: Linda Schultz

Lay/religious women/men; year-round including summers; noncredit/undergraduate/graduate credit; workshops

MARYMOUNT COLLEGE

Department of Religious Studies, 30800 Palos Verdes Dr. East, Rancho Palos Verdes, CA 90275-6299. (310) 377-5501. Web: www.marymountpv.edu

MOUNT ST. MARY'S COLLEGE

Doheny Campus, 10 Chester Place, Los Angeles, CA 90007. (213) 477-2640. E-mail: anavarro@msmc.la .edu

Contact: Dr. Alexis Navarro, IHM

Lay/religious women/men; year-round; noncredit/undergraduate/graduate credit; workshops

NOTRE DAME DE NAMUR UNIVERSITY

Department of Philosophy and Religious Studies, 1500 Ralston Ave., Ralston Hall, Second Floor, Belmont, CA 94002. (800) 263-0545, (650) 508-3600, Fax: (650) 508-3426. E-mail: admissions@ ndnu.edu; Web: www.ndnu.edu/

Affiliation: Sisters of Notre Dame de Namur

QUEEN OF THE HOLY ROSARY COLLEGE

PO Box 3908, 43326 Mission Blvd., Mission San Jose, CA 94539. (510) 657-2468. Fax: (510) 657-1734. Web: www.msjdominicans. org/college.html

Contact: Sister Mary Paul, Dean

Affiliation: Dominican Sisters of Mission San Jose

Lay/religious women/men; year-round, including summers; undergraduate/graduate credit; workshops

ST. MARY'S COLLEGE

Department of Religious Studies, Morega, CA 94575. (510) 631-4000. Fax: (925) 376-1847. Web: www. stmarys-ca.edu

Contact: Dr. Thomas Poundstone, Associate Professor

Affiliation: Brothers of the Christian Schools

SCHOOL FOR PASTORAL LEADERSHIP

One Peter Yorice Way, San Francisco, CA 94109. (415) 614-5500

Contact: Joni Gallagher

Affiliation: Archdiocese of San Francisco

SCHOOL OF APPLIED THEOLOGY (SAT)

Graduate Theological Union-Berkeley, 5890 Birch Court, Oak-

land, CA 94618. (800) 831-0555, (510) 652-1651. Fax: (510) 420-0542. E-mail: satgtu@aol.com; Web: www.satgtu.org
Contact: Maureen-Therese McGroddy, RSHM, Dean of Admissions
Affiliation: Graduate Theological Union
Lay/religious women/men, clergy; year-round; noncredit (sabbatical/renewal program)

SANTA CLARA UNIVERSITY
Graduate Program in Pastoral Ministries, Santa Clara, CA 95053. (408) 554-4831. Fax: (408) 554-2387. E-mail: ampineda@scu.edu; Web. www.scu.edu/Pastoral Ministries
Contact: Ana Maria Pineda, RSM
Lay/religious women/men, clergy; year-round including summers; graduate credit; workshops

UNIVERSITY OF SAN DIEGO
Graduate Programs in Practical Theology & Pastoral Care and Counseling, Center for Christian Spirituality, 5998 Alcala Park, San Diego, CA 92110-2492. (619) 260-4784 (Center). (800) 248-4873 (Graduate Admissions). Web: www.sandiego.edu/theo
Contacts: Sr. Barbara Quinn (Center); Fr. Ron Pachence (Graduate Admissions)
Affiliation: University of San Diego
Lay/religious women/men, clergy; year-round; graduate credit/workshops

UNIVERSITY OF SAN FRANCISCO
The Department of Theology and Religious Studies, 2130 Fulton St., San Francisco, CA 94117-1080. (415) 422-5555. Fax: (415) 422-2303. Web: www.usfca.edu/theology
Affiliation: Jesuits
Branch campuses in CA: North Bay, Oakland, Sacrament, San Ramon, South Bay and Phoenix, AZ

CONNECTICUT

ALBERTUS MAGNUS COLLEGE
Department of Philosophy and Religion, Division of Continuing Education, 700 Prospect St., New Haven, CT 06511-1189. (203) 773-8550. Fax: (203) 773-8652. E-mail: ce_info@albertus.edu; Web: www.albertus.edu
Affiliation: Dominican Sisters of St. Mary of the Springs

FAIRFIELD UNIVERSITY
Department of Religious Studies, College of Arts and Sciences, 1073 North Benson Rd., Fairfield, CT 06824. (203) 254-4000. Web: www.fairfield.edu/academic/artsci/majors/religiou/relicrse.htm
Affiliation: Jesuits

SACRED HEART UNIVERSITY
University College, 5151 Park Ave., Fairfield, CT 06825-1000. (203) 371-7832. E-mail: sidotin@sacredheart.edu; Web: www.sacredheart.edu
Contact: Nancy Sidoti, Interim Dean
Master of Arts in Religious Studies, 5151 Park Ave., Fairfield, CT 06825-1000. (203) 365-7619. Fax: (203) 365-4732. E-mail: gradstudies@sacredheart.edu; Web: www.sacredheart.edu/graduate
Contact: Alexis Haakonsen, Dean of Graduate Admissions
Lay/religious women/men, clergy; year-round, including summers; graduate credit
REAPS
5151 Park Ave., Fairfield, CT 06432-1000. (203) 371-7867. Fax: (203) 365-4798. E-mail: reaps@sacredheart.edu; Web: http://reaps.sacredheart.edu
Contact: Rev. Barry C. Meehan, SJ
Affiliation: Sacred Heart University
Lay/religious women/men, clergy; year-round, including summers; noncredit, workshops

SAINT JOSEPH COLLEGE CONNECTICUT
Department of Religious Studies, 1678 Asylum Ave., West Hartford, CT 06117-2791. (860) 231-5299. E-mail: jthompson@sjc.edu; Web: www.sjc.edu
Contact: Dr. J. Milburn Thompson, Chair

DELAWARE

MINISTRY FORMATION INSTITUTE
1626 N. Union St., Wilmington, DE 19806. (302) 472-4142
Contact: Fr. Paul Mast
Affiliation: Diocese of Wilmington

DISTRICT OF COLUMBIA

THE CATHOLIC UNIVERSITY OF AMERICA
School of Religious Studies, Caldwell Hall, Washington, DC 20064. (202) 319-5683. E-mail: cua-deansrs@cua.edu; Web: religiousstudies.cua.edu/opport.cfm

GEORGETOWN UNIVERSITY
Department of Theology, 120 New North, 37th & O Sts. NW, Washington, DC 20057-1135. (202) 687-5945, 5846. Fax: (202) 687-8000. E-mail: mcmahonk@georgetown.edu; Web: www.georgetown.edu/departments/theology
Contact: Kathryn McMahon-Sowerwine
Woodstock Theological Center, Box 571137, Washington, DC 20057-1137. (202) 687-3532. E-mail: wtc@gusun.georgetown.edu: Web: www.georgetown.edu/centers/woodstock/index.html#About%20Woodstock
Contact: Gasper F. Lo Biondo, S.J., Director
Affiliation: Jesuits

TRINITY COLLEGE
Department of Religious Studies and Theology, College of Arts and Sciences, 125 Michigan Ave. NE; Washington, DC 20017. (202) 884-9000. Web: www.trinitydc.edu/academics/catalog/programs/religious_st.html
Affiliation: Sisters of Notre Dame de Namur

WASHINGTON THEOLOGICAL UNION
Office of Enrollment Services, 6896 Laurel St. NW, Washington, DC 20012-2016. (202) 726-8800, ext. 5213; (800) 334-9922, ext. 5213. Fax: (202) 726-1716. E-mail: admissions@wtu.edu; Web: www.wtu.edu
Lay/religious women/men, clergy; year-round; noncredit/graduate credit; workshops

FLORIDA

BARRY UNIVERSITY
Department of Theology and Philosophy, School of Arts and Sciences, 11300 N.E. Second Ave., Miami Shores, FL 33161-6695. (1-800) 756-6000, ext. 3469(305) 899-3469. E-mail: mwedig@mail.barry.edu; Web: www.barry.edu/TheologyPhilosophy
Affiliation: Dominican Sisters of Adrian

LAY MINISTRY DEVELOPMENT
421 E. Robinson St., PO Box 1800, Orlando, FL 32802. (407) 246-4880. E-mail: layminore@juno.com

LAY PASTORAL MINISTRY INSTITUTE
PO Box 40200, St. Petersburg, FL 33710. (727) 812-4837. E-mail: amw@dosp.org
Contact: Dr. Ann Marie Winter, Director
Affiliation: Diocese of St. Petersburg

SAINT LEO UNIVERSITY

Department of Religion, College of Arts and Sciences, 33701 State Rd. 52, Saint Leo, FL 33574. (352) 588-8295. E-mail: robert.imperato@saintleo.edu; Web: www.saintleo.edu/academics/Schools/dept.cfm?MajorID=REL&schoolid=A

Contact: Professor Robert Imperato, Coordinator

The Center for Catholic-Jewish Studies, P.O. Box 6665, Saint Leo, FL 33574-6665. (352) 588-8356, 8597. Fax: (352) 588-8885. E-mail: catholic.jewish.center@saintleo.edu; Web: www.centerforcatholicjewishstudies.org/

Contacts: Father Michael Cooper, S.J., Director; Jane Bracken, Coordinator

ST. THOMAS UNIVERSITY

Department of Religious Studies and History, 16400 NW 32nd Ave., Miami, FL 33054-6459. In FL: (1-800) 367-9006, outside FL (1-800) 367-9010, (305) 625-6000. Fax: (305) 628-6591. E-mail: tryan@stu.edu; Web: www.stu.edu/relph

Contact: Dr. Thomas F. Ryan

SCHOOL OF LAY MINISTRY

9401 Biscayne Blvd., Miami Shores, Fl 33138. (305) 762-1184. E-mail: laymin@miamiarch.org

Contact: Sr. Ann E. McDermott

Affiliation: Archdiocese of Miami

Lay women/men

HAWAII

CHAMINADE UNIVERSITY OF HONOLULU

Department of Religion, 3140 Waialae Ave., Honolulu, HI 96816. (800) 735-3733, (808) 735-4866 Fax: (808) 739-4647. E-mail admissions@chaminade.edu; Web: www.chaminade.edu/academic.php3?articleno=406

Contact: Dr. David Coleman, Program Advisor

Master of Arts in Pastoral Leadership (MAPL) Program, 3140 Waialae Ave., Honolulu, HI 96816. (800) 735-3733, (808) 735-4866 Fax: (808) 739-4647. E-mail admissions@chaminade.edu; Web: www.chaminade.edu/general.php3?articleno=421

Contact: Dr. David Coleman, Program Advisor

ILLINOIS

BENEDICTINE UNIVERSITY

Department of Religious Studies, College of Arts and Sciences, Benedictine Hall Room 360, 5700 College Rd., Lisle, IL 60532. (630) 829-6266, 6250. Fax: (630) 960-4805. E-mail: ptimko@ben.edu; Web: www.ben.edu

Contact: Dr. Philip Timko, O.S.B.

Affiliation: Benedictine Monks of St. Procopius Abbey

CATHOLIC THEOLOGICAL UNION

5401 South Carroll Ave., Chicago, IL 60615-5698. (773) 324-5316. Fax: (773) 324-4360. E-mail: admissions@ctu.edu; Web: www.ctu.edu

Contact: Terance Stadler

Lay/religious women/men; summers; graduate credit; workshops

CENTER FOR ONGOING FORMATION IN MINISTRY

419 North Kedzie Ave., Chicago, IL 60625. (773) 478-7543. Fax: (773) 583-8130. E-mail: ofim@archchicago.org; Web: www.ofim.org

Contact: Sr. Judy Vallimont (Director)

Related programs: Office of Lay Ecclesial Ministry [includes P.A.A.C. - Pastoral Associates: Archdiocese of Chicago](847) 837-4556; Office for Catechesis (312) 243-3700; Office of Catholic Schools [courses for Catholic school teachers]: (773) 478-7543

Affiliation: Archdiocese of Chicago

DEPAUL UNIVERSITY

Department of Religious Studies, College of Liberal Arts and Sciences, One E. Jackson, Chicago, IL 60604. (1-800) 4DEPAUL (outside Illinois), (312) 362-8000. Web: http://condor.depaul.edu/~religion/

DOMINICAN UNIVERSITY

Department of Theology/Pastoral Ministries, College of Arts and Sciences, 7900 W. Division St., River Forest, IL 60305. (1-800) 828-8475, (708) 524-6800. E-mail: domadmis@dom.edu; Web: www.dom.edu/rosary/majors/theology.html

Affiliation: Dominican Sisters of Sinsinawa, WI

INSTITUTE FOR SPIRITUAL LEADERSHIP

PO Box 53147, Chicago, IL 60653-0147. (877) 844-9440, (773) 752-5962. Fax: (773) 752-5964. E-mail: islusa@aol.com; Web: www.spiritleader.org

Contact: Patricia Bombard, Executive Director

Lay/religious women/men; year-round; noncredit/graduate* credit (*through affiliated institutions); workshops

LEWIS UNIVERSITY

Department of Theology, College of Arts and Sciences, One University Pkwy., Romeoville, IL 60446. (815) 838-0500. Web: www.lewisu.edu/academics/religion

Undergraduate credit

Master of Arts in Leadership Studies (MALS), Pastoral Leadership Certificate, Advanced Catechetical Certificate, One University Pkwy., Romeoville, IL 60446. (815) 838-0500. Web: www.lewisu.edu/academics/religion

Graduate credit

Affiliation: De La Salle Christian Brothers

LOYOLA UNIVERSITY CHICAGO

Department of Theology, Crown Center 323, 6525 North Sheridan Rd., Chicago, IL 60626. (773) 508-2368. Fax: (773) 508-2386. E-mail: pjung@luc.edu; Web: www.luc.edu/depts/theology/academics/grad/index.html

Contact: Dr. Patricia Beattie Jung, Graduate Programs Director

Lay/religious women/men, clergy; year-round; undergraduate/graduate credit; workshops

The Religion, Culture, & Society Program, Center for Interdisciplinary Programs, Lake Shore Campus, 6525 North Sheridan Road, Damen Hall 105, Chicago, IL 60626. (773) 508-2372. Fax: (773) 508-2940. Web: www.luc.edu/depts/rel_cul_soc/

Director: Dr. Tracy Pintchman

Undergraduate credit/minors in Catholic Studies/Peace Studies

Institute for Pastoral Studies (IPS), 6525 N. Sheridan Rd., Chicago, IL 60626. (800) 424-1238, Fax: (773) 508-2319. E-mail: ckempne@luc.edu; Web: www.luc.edu/depts/ips

Contact: Carita Kempner

Lay/religious women/men; year-round including summers; non-credit/graduate credit; workshops

Affiliation: Jesuits

QUINCY UNIVERSITY

Theology & Religious Studies Program, 1800 College, Quincy, IL 62301. E-mail: biallas@quincy.edu; Web: www.quincy.edu/colleges/programs/theology

Contact: Dr. Leonard Biallas

SAINT XAVIER UNIVERSITY

Department of Religious Studies, 3700 West 103rd. St., Chicago, IL 60655. (773) 298-3441. Web: www.sxu.edu/religious_studies

Undergraduate/graduate credit

Affiliation: Sisters of Mercy of the Americas

Pastoral Ministry Institute, 3700 West 103rd. St., Chicago, IL 60655. (773) 298-3900. E-mail: cahill@sxu.edu; Web: www.sxu.edu
Contact: Cathleen Cahill, RSM, Director
Affiliation: Sisters of Mercy of the Americas
Lay/religious women/men; year-round, clergy; noncredit/undergraduate/graduate credit; workshops

SPRINGFIELD COLLEGE IN ILLINOIS
Department of Religious Studies, 1500 North Fifth St., Springfield, IL 62702. (217) 525-1420
Undergraduate credit (two-year college)
Affiliation: Ursuline Sisters

UNIVERSITY OF ST. FRANCIS
Department of Theology and Philosophy, 500 Wilcox St., Joliet, IL 60435. (800) 735-7500. Web: http://admissions.stfrancis.edu/academics/philo.cfm
Undergraduate credit
Affiliation: Franciscans

UNIVERSITY OF SAINT MARY-OF-THE-LAKE
The Liturgical Institute, 1000 East Maple Ave., Mundelein, IL 60060-1174. (847) 837-4524. Fax: (847) 837-4545. E-mail: fmannion@usml.edu; Web: www.vocations.org/liturgicalinstitute
Contact: Msgr. M. Francis Mannion, Director
Graduate credit
Affiliation: University of Saint Mary of the Lake/Mundelein Seminary

INDIANA

ANCILLA COLLEGE
Department of Religion, Division of Humanities, Donaldson, IN 46513. (574) 936-8898, ext. 305. Web: www.ancilla.edu
Contact: Dr. Charles E. Bayless, Chair
Undergraduate credit (two-year college)
Affiliation: Poor Handmaids of Jesus Christ

CALUMET COLLEGE OF ST. JOSEPH
Religious Studies Program, 2400 New York Ave., Whiting, IN 46394. Web: www.ccsj.edu/academics/programs/rst/index.html
Contact: Dr. Eugene Finnegan, Program Director
Undergraduate credit; distance learning (online) courses

HOLY CROSS COLLEGE
Department of Philosophy and Religion, PO Box 308, Vincent 196, 54515 State Rd. 933 North, Notre Dame, IN 46556. (574) 239-8308. E-mail: mamen@hcc-nd.edu; Web: www.hcc-nd.edu/Academics/BA/CourseDescriptions.htm
Contact: Fr. Maurice Amen, CSC
Affiliation: Holy Cross Priests & Brothers

INSTITUTE FOR ADULT SPIRITUAL RENEWAL
Retreats International, Box 1067, Notre Dame, IN 46556. (1-800) 556-4532, (219) 631-5320. Fax: (219) 631-4546, 4463. E-mail: retreats.retreats.1@nd.edu; Web: www.retreatsintl.org
Contact: Anne M. Luther, Executive Director
Affiliation: Retreats International

MARIAN COLLEGE
Department of Theology and Philosophy, 3200 Cold Spring Rd., Indianapolis, IN 46222-1997, (317) 955-6448. E-mail: ahohman@marian.edu; Web: www.marian.edu/departments_theology.asp
Contact: Andrew P. Hohman, Chair

SAINT JOSEPH'S COLLEGE
Department of Religion, Division of Humanities, US Highway 231, PO Box 870, Rensselaer, IN 47978. (219) 866-6000. Web: www.saintjoe.edu/programs
Undergraduate credit
Department of Lay Ecclesial Ministry, Division of Humanities, US Highway 231, PO Box 870, Rensselaer, IN 47978. (219) 866-6000. Web: www.saintjoe.edu/programs
Undergraduate credit
Department of Graduate Music, Church Music and Liturgy, Pastoral Liturgy and Music, Division of Humanities, US Highway 231, PO Box 870, Rensselaer, IN 47978. (219) 866-6000. Web: www.saintjoe.edu/programs
Contact: Fr. James Challancin
Affiliation: Missionaries of the Precious Blood (C.PP.S.)

SAINT MARY-OF-THE-WOODS COLLEGE
Department of Theology, Saint Mary-of-the-Woods, IN 47876. (812) 535-5151. Fax: (812) 535-5241. E-mail: mmilano@smwc.edu; Web: www.smwc.edu/acad/theo
Contact: Mary Lucille Milano
Undergraduate credit: distance learning (online) courses
Graduate Program in Pastoral Theology, 226 Guerin Hall, Saint Mary-of-the-Woods, IN 47876-0068. (812) 535-5206. Fax: (812) 535-5177. E-mail: mapt@smwc.edu; Web: www.smwc.edu
Contact: Virginia Unverzagt, Director
Lay/religious women/men, clergy; year-round, including summers; graduate credit; workshops; distance learning (online) courses
Affiliation: Sisters of Providence

SAINT MARY'S COLLEGE
Department of Religious Studies, Notre Dame, IN 46556. (574) 284-5000. E-mail: kaminski@saintmarys.edu; Web: www.saintmarys.edu/~incandel/majorreq.html
Contact: Phyllis Kaminski, Chairperson
Lay/religious women; undergraduate credit
Affiliation: Sisters of the Holy Cross

UNIVERSITY OF NOTRE DAME
Department of Theology, 130 Malloy Hall, Notre Dame, IN 46556. (574) 631-6662, 7811. E-mail: Cavadini.1@nd.edu; Web: www.nd.edu/~theo
Contact: Professor John Cavadini, Chair
Undergraduate credit
Graduate Studies, Department of Theology, Notre Dame, IN 46556. (219) 631-4254 (MA); (219) 631-5732 (Ph.D.). Web: www.nd.edu~theo/
Contact: Director of Graduate Studies
Graduate credit
Notre Dame Center for Pastoral Liturgy, 1224 Hesburgh Library, Notre Dame, IN 46556. (574) 631-5435. Fax: (574) 631-6968. E-mail: ndcpl.1@nd.edu; Web: www.nd.edu/~ndcpl
Satellite Theological Education Program (STEP), The Institute for Church Life, 1201 Hesburgh Library, Notre Dame, IN 46556. (1-866) 425-STEP. E-mail: icl@nd.edu, cummings.8@nd.edu; Web: http://step.nd.edu
Contact: Thomas C. Cummings III, Director, STEP
distance learning (online) courses
Affiliation: University of Notre Dame

UNIVERSITY OF SAINT FRANCIS
Department of Philosophy and Theology, 2701 Spring St., Fort Wayne, IN 46808-3994. (219) 434-3100. Web: www.sf.edu/philosophy
Affiliation: Sisters of St. Francis of Perpetual Adoration

IOWA

BRIAR CLIFF UNIVERSITY

Theology/Philosophy Department, H-317, 3303 Rebecca St., Sioux City, IA 51104. (712) 279-1702. E-mail: cooney@briarcliff.edu; Web: www.briarcliff.edu/theology/index.htm

Contact: Dr. William Cooney, Chair

CHURCH MINISTRIES PROGRAM/ PRE-DIACONATE FORMATION

2605 S. Magnolia St., Sioux City, IA 51106. (712) 276-6486. E-mail: deke@willinet.net

Contact: Deacon Ron Forrest

Affiliation: Diocese of Sioux City

CLARKE COLLEGE

Department of Religious Studies, 105 MJ, 1550 Clarke Dr., Dubuque, IA 52001. (1-800) 383-2345, (563) 588-6604. E-mail: admissions@clarke.edu; Web: www.clarke.edu/academics/departments/religiousstudies/index.htm

Contact: Professor Janet O'Meara, Chair

Music Ministry Degree, Department of Music,1550 Clarke Dr., Dubuque, IA 52001. (1-800) 383-2345, (563) 588-6604. E-mail: admissions@clarke.edu; Web: www.clarke.edu/academics

Affiliation: Sisters of Charity of the Blessed Virgin Mary

DIVINE WORD COLLEGE

102 Jacoby Dr., Epworth IA 52045-0380. (1-800) 553-3321, (319) 876-3353. E-mail: dwm@mwci.net; Web. www.dwci.edu

Contact: Director of Admissions

Affiliation: Divine Word Missionaries

Lay men; year round; undergraduate credit; seminary

THE FRANCISCAN UNIVERSITY

Franciscan Studies, Department of Psychology (Social Justice), 400 North Bluff Blvd., Clinton, IA 52732. (1- 800) 242-4153, (563) 242-4023

Affiliation: Sisters of St. Francis of Clinton

LORAS COLLEGE

Department of Religious Studies, 1450 Alta Vista St., Dubuque, IA 52004-0178. (1-800) 245-6727, (563) 557-7106. E-mail: dwathier@loras.edu; Web: http://depts.loras.edu/academics

Contact: Rev. Doug Wathier, Chair

Graduate Program in Religious Studies, 1450 Alta Vista St., Dubuque, IA 52004-0178. (1-800) 245-6727, ext. 1, (563) 557-7106. E-mail: bharring@loras.edu; Web: www.loras.edu

Contact: Barb Harrington, Admissions

MOUNT MERCY COLLEGE

Religious Studies Program, 1330 Elmhurst Dr. NE, Cedar Rapids, IA 52402. (1-800) 248-4504, (319) 363-1323. Web: www2.mtmercy.edu/current/relstudies.htm

Affiliation: Sisters of Mercy of the Americas (Regional Community of Cedar Rapids)

ST. AMBROSE UNIVERSITY

Theology Department, 518 W. Locust St., Davenport, IA 52803. (563) 333-6442, 6188. E-mail: jdefrano@sau.edu; Web: www.sau.edu/academic/theology/Default.htm

Contact: Fr. Joe DeFrancisco

Undergraduate credit; seminary

Department of Pastoral Studies, 518 W. Locust St., Davenport, IA 52803. (563) 333-6442. E-mail: cwinter@saunix.sau.edu; Web: www.sau.edu/academic/mps/Default.htm

Contact: Dr. Corinne Winter, Chair

Graduate credit/certificate in Pastoral Studies

KANSAS

BENEDICTINE COLLEGE

The Religious Studies Department, 1020 North Second St., Atchison, KS 66002. (1-800) 467-5340. Web: www.benedictine.edu/departments/rs/rsindex.html

Undergraduate credit

Institute for Religious Studies, 1020 North Second St., Atchison, KS 66002. (913) 367-5340, ext. 2562. E-mail: suthere@benedictine.edu; Web: www.benedictine.edu

Contact: Sister Eleanor Suther, O.S.B.

Affiliation: Benedictine College and the Archdiocese of Kansas City in Kansas

NEWMAN UNIVERSITY

Department of Theology, 3100 McCormick Ave., Wichita, KS 67213-2097. (1-877) NEWMANU, (316) 942-4291, ext. 144. E-mail: admissions@newmanu.edu; Web: www.newmanu.edu/Degrees/BS/theo.pdf

Undergraduate credit

UNIVERSITY OF SAINT MARY

Department of Theology and Pastoral Ministry, 4100 South 4th St., Leavenworth, KS 66048-5082. (1- 800) 752-7043, (913) 758-4332. E-mail: woodk@stmary.edu; Web: www.stmary.edu

Contact: Sister Kathleen Wood, SCL, Chair

Affiliation: Sisters of Charity of Leavenworth

Lay/religious women/men, clergy; year-round; undergraduate credit; workshops

KENTUCKY

BELLARMINE UNIVERSITY

Department of Theology, Bellarmine College, 2001 Newburg Rd., Louisville, KY 40205-0671. Outside Louisville: (1-800) 274-4723, ext. 8131, (502) 452-8131. Web: www.bellarmine.edu/cas/departments/theology/index.asp

BRESCIA UNIVERSITY

Ministry Formation Program, 717 Frederica St., Owensboro, KY 42301. (270) 686-4262. E-mail: josephm@brescia.edu; Web: www.brescia.edu/academics/ministry/default.htm

Contact: Coordinator

Lay/religious women/men; noncredit/undergraduate credit

Theology Program, Division of Humanities, 717 Frederica St., Owensboro, KY 42301. (270) 686-4221. E-mail: ellend@brescia.edu; Web: www.brescia.edu/academics/humanities/religion.htm

CLIFFVIEW CENTER

777 Bryants Camp Rd., Lancaster, KY 40444. (1-877) 792-3330

Affiliation: Diocese of Lexington

MINISTRY FORMATION PROGRAM

1200 S. Shelby St., Louisville, KY 40203-2600. (502) 636-0296. E-mail: sdb@archlou.org

Contact: Sal Della Bella, Director

Lay/religious women/men; year-round; workshops

ST. CATHARINE COLLEGE

2735 Bardstown Rd., St. Catharine, KY 40061. (859) 336-5082. Web: www.sccky.edu

SPALDING UNIVERSITY

Russell Institute of Religion & Ministry, 51 South Fourth St., Louisville, KY 40203. (502) 585-7126. Fax: (502) 992-2407. E-mail: russellinstitute@spalding.edu; Web: www.spalding.edu

Affiliation: Sisters of Charity of Nazareth

THOMAS MORE COLLEGE

Department of Theology, 333 Thomas More Pkwy., Crestview

Hills, KY 41017. (859) 344-3375. Web: www.thomasmore.edu/academics/study/theology.asp

LOUISIANA

CATHOLIC LEADERSHIP FORMATION

3500 Fairfield Ave., Shreveport, LA 71104. (1-800) 256-1542; (318) 868-4441, Fax: (318) 868-4605. E-mail: pmadden@dioshpt.org; Web: www.grecoinstitute.org

Contact: Rev. Patrick J. Madden, Ph.D.

Lay/religious women/men; year-round; undergraduate credit

LOYOLA UNIVERSITY NEW ORLEANS

Department of Religious Studies, 408 Bobet Hall, Box 81, 6363 St. Charles Ave., New Orleans, LA 70118. (504) 865-3943. Fax: (504) 865-3179. E-mail: kkeulman@loyno.edu; Web: www.loyno.edu/religious.studies

Contact: Kenneth Keulman, Department Chair

Undergraduate credit; noncredit

Catholic Studies Program, Bobet Hall, 6363 St. Charles Ave., New Orleans, LA 70118. (1-800) LOYOLA, (504) 865-3240. E-mail: bernardi@loyno.edu; Web: www.loyno.edu/catholicstudies

Contact: Rev. Peter Bernardi, S.J.

Graduate Studies, Religious Studies Department, 6363 St. Charles Ave., New Orleans, LA 70118. (504) 865-3060. E-mail: sjduffy@loyno.edu; Web: www.loyno.edu/~religion/graduate/index.html

Contact: Stephen Duffy, Director of Graduate Studies

Loyola Institute for Ministry, Campus Box 67, 6363 St. Charles Ave., New Orleans, LA 70118. (504) 865-3728, (800) 777-5469. Fax: (504) 865-2066. E-mail: lim@loyno.edu; Web: www.loyno.edu/lim

Contact: Butch Ekstrom, Associate Director of Student Services

Lay/religious women/men; year-round including summers; noncredit/graduate credit; workshops

OUR LADY OF HOLY CROSS COLLEGE

Department of Theology, 4123 Woodland Dr., New Orleans, LA 70131-7399. (504) 394-7744.

E-mail: smcneely@olhcc.edu; Web: www.olhcc.edu/olhcc/Academics/academic_programs/Theology.htm

Affiliation: Marianites of the Holy Cross (Sisters)

XAVIER UNIVERSITY OF LOUISIANA

Department of Theology, 1 Drexel Dr., Box 81-A, New Orleans, LA 70125-1098. (504) 482-5457. E-mail: mstachow@xula.edu; Web: www.xula.edu/Academic/as_college/theo_dept/index.htm

Undergraduate credit

Institute for Black Catholic Studies (IBCS), 1 Drexel Dr., Box 81-A, New Orleans, LA 70125-1098. (504) 483-7691. Fax: (504) 485-7921. E-mail: mstachow@xula.edu; Web: www.xula.edu/IBCS.html

Graduate,credit/certificate/noncredit

MAINE

SAINT JOSEPH'S COLLEGE OF MAINE

Department of Theology, 278 Whites Bridge Rd., Standish, ME 04084. (1-800) 752-4723, (207) 892-7841. E-mail: info@sjcme.edu; Web: www.sjcme.edu/gpsnew/prospective/theology

Lay Ministry Foundation Program, 278 Whites Bridge Rd., Standish, ME 04084. (1-800) 752-4723. Web: www.sjcme.edu

Undergradute credit/noncredit

MARYLAND

THE COLLEGE OF NOTRE DAME OF MARYLAND

Religious Studies Program, 4701 North Charles St., Baltimore, MD 21210. E-mail: cmacleod@ndm.edu; Web: www.ndm.edu/academics/departments/nd_aca_religiousStudies.cfm

Contact: Dr. Catriona M. K. MacLeod, Chairperson

Affiliation: The School Sisters of Notre Dame

LOYOLA COLLEGE IN MARYLAND

Department of Theology, College of Arts and Sciences, 4501 N. Charles St., Baltimore, MD 21210. (410) 617-2000, ext. 5012. Web: www.loyola.edu/theology

Graduate Programs - Pastoral Counseling and Spiritual Care, 215 Knott Humanities Center, 4501 N. Charles St., Baltimore, MD 21210-2699. (1-800) 221-9107, ext. 5020, (410) 617-5020. Fax: (410) 617-2002. E-mail: graduate@loyola.edu; Web: http://graduate.loyola.edu

MOUNT ST. MARY'S COLLEGE

Department of Theology, 16300 Old Emmitsburg Rd., Emmitsburg, MD 21727. (301) 447-6122. E-mail: mcdonald@msmary.edu; Web: www.msmary.edu/college/html/undergraduate/theology.htm

Contact: Patricia M. McDonald, Chair

MASSACHUSETTS

ANNA MARIA COLLEGE

Department of Catholic Studies, 50 Sunset Lane, Paxton, MA 01612. (1-800) 344-4586, (508) 849-3300. Web: www.annamaria.edu

Undergraduate credit

ASSUMPTION COLLEGE

Department of Theology, 500 Salisbury St., Worcester, MA 01615-0005. (508) 767-7000. Fax: (508) 756-1780. E-mail: info@ave.assumption.edu; Web: www.assumption.edu/dept/theology

Contact: Professor Marc LePain

Affiliation: Augustinians of the Assumption

BOSTON COLLEGE

Theology Department, College of Arts and Sciences, 417 Carney Hall, 140 Commonwealth Ave., Chestnut Hill, MA 02467. (617) 552-3892. E-mail: theology@bc.edu, popest@bc.edu; Web: www.bc.edu/schools/cas/theology

Contact: Stephen J. Pope, Department Chair

Institute of Religious Education/ Pastoral Ministry, 31 Lawrence Ave., Chestnut Hill, MA 02167. (800) 487-1167, (617) 552-8440. Fax: (617) 552-0811. E-mail: irepm@bc.edu; Web: www.bc.edu/irepm.html

Contact: Dr. Thomas H. Groome, Director

Lay/religious women/men; year-round, including summers; noncredit/graduate credit; workshops

Affiliation: Jesuits

COLLEGE OF THE HOLY CROSS

Department of Religious Studies, Smith 405, 1 College St., Worcester, MA 01610. (508) 793-3411. Fax: (508) 793-3840. E-mail: aavery@holycross.edu; Web: www.holycross.edu/departments/religiousstudies/website/index.html

Contact: Alan Avery-Peck, Chair

Undergraduate credit

Affiliation: Jesuits

CRYSTAL SPRING CENTER

76 Everett Skinner Rd., Plainville, MA 02762. (508) 699-7167

Contact: Carole Rossi

Affiliation: Dominican Sisters of Kentucky

ELMS COLLEGE

Department of Religious Studies, Division of Humanities and Fine Arts, 291 Springfield St., Chicopee, MA 01013. (413) 594-2761, ext. 380. Web: www.elms.edu

Contacts: Dr. Marty Pion, Sr. Eleanor Dooley
Undergraduate credit; distance learning (online) courses
Master of Arts in Applied Theology Program (MAAT), 291 Springfield St., Chicopee, MA 01013. (413) 557-6924. Fax: (413) 594-8173. E-mail: pionm@elms .edu; Web: www.elms.edu/ Academic/graduate/progdiscript .htm#maat
Contact: Martin Pion, Director of MAAT Program
Affiliation: Sisters of St. Joseph

EMMANUEL COLLEGE
Department of Religious Studies, 400 The Fenway, Boston, MA 02115. (617) 264-7754. Web: www.emman uel.edu/academic/departments/ religiousstudies
Contact: Dr. Mary E. Hines, Chair

MERRIMACK COLLEGE
Department of Religious Studies, Room 107, Cushing Hall, PO Box C-2, 315 Turnpike St., North Andover, MA 01845 (978) 837-5000, ext. 4522. E-mail: Warren.Kay@ merrimack.edu; Web: www.merri mack.edu/generator.php?id=195
Contact: Warren Kay, Chair
The Center for Augustinian Study, Sul 101, 315 Turnpike St., North Andover, MA 01845. (978) 837-5000, ext. 5218. E-mail: Joseph. Kelley@merrimack.edu; Web: www. merrimack.edu/generator.php?id=80
Contact: Joseph Kelley, Vice President

REGIS COLLEGE
Religious Studies, Center for Humanities and Social Sciences, 235 Wellesley St., Weston MA 02493. (781) 768-7000. Web: http:// regisnet.regiscollege.edu/rel_studies
Center for Graduate and Continuing Studies, 235 Wellesley St., Weston, MA 02493. (781) 768-7400. Web: www.regiscollege. edu/acad/cen_grad_cs
Contact: Edward Mulholland, Director of Continuing Studies

STONEHILL COLLEGE
Religious Studies Department, Duffy 220B, 320 Washington St., Easton, MA 02357. (508) 565-1355. Fax: (508) 565-1444. Web: www. stonehill.edu/religious_studies/index. htm
Contact: Gregory J. Shaw, Chair
Affiliation: Congregation of the Holy Cross (Fathers)

WESTON JESUIT SCHOOL OF THEOLOGY
Office of Admissions, 3 Phillips Place, Cambridge, MA 02138-3495. (617) 492-1960. Fax: (617) 492-5833. E-mail: admissionsinfo@ wjst.edu; Web: www.wjst.edu
Contact: Karen McLennan, Director of Admissions
Lay/religious women/men; year-round; noncredit/graduate credit

MICHIGAN

AQUINAS COLLEGE
Department of Theology, 1607 Robinson Rd. S.E., Grand Rapids, MI 49506-1799. (616) 459-8281, ext. 4493. E-mail: fabbrama@aquinas .edu; Web: www.aquinas.edu/ theology/index.html
Contact: Dr. Amata Fabbro, O.P.
Lay/religious women/men, clergy; year-round, including summers; undergraduate credit

AVE MARIA UNIVERSITY
Aquinas Center for Theological Renewal, 300 West Forest Ave., Ypsilanti, MI 48197. (734) 337-4605. E-mail: mlevering@avemaria.edu; Web: www.aquinas.avemaria.edu
Institute for Pastoral Theology, 300 W. Forest Ave., Ypsilanti, MI 48197. (1-866) 866-1100, (734) 337-4180. Fax: (734) 337-4199. E-mail: ipt@avemaria.edu; Web: www.ipt.avemaria.edu
Lay/religious women/men; graduate credit
Pre-Theologate Program, 300 W. Forest Ave., Ypsilanti, MI 48197. (1-866) 866-1100, (734) 337-4189. Web: www.avemaria.edu/Pretheo/ index.asp
Contact: Fr. Francis X. McGerity
Affiliation: Ave Maria University
Lay men

MADONNA UNIVERSITY
Department of Pastoral Ministry and Religious Studies, 36600 Schoolcraft Rd., Livonia, MI 48150. (1-800) 852-4951. E-mail: stamm @madonna.edu; Web: http:// madonna2.siteobjects.com/pages/pa storalministry.cfm
Contact: Sr. Ann Stamm, Chair
Distance learning (online) courses

MARYGROVE COLLEGE
Department of Religious Studies, Madame Cadillac Bldg., Room 350, 8425 West McNichols Rd., Detroit, MI 48221-2599. (313) 927-1351. E-mail: galcser@marygrove.edu; Web: www.marygrove.edu/ programs/undergrad/religion /index.htm
Contact: George P. Alcser
Lay/religious women/men, clergy; year-round, including summers; undergraduate/graduate credit
Graduate Program in Pastoral Ministry, Madame Cadillac Bldg., Rooms 348 and 349, 8425 West McNichols Rd., Detroit, MI 48221-2599. (313) 927-1461,1462. E-mail: asinnott@marygrove.edu; Web: www.marygrove.edu/programs/grad/ programs/pminis.htm
Contact: Dr. Anneliese Sinnott, O.P., Director
Lay/religious women/men, clergy; year-round, including summers; noncredit/graduate credit

MINISTRY FORMATION PROGRAM
300 W. Ottawa St., Lansing, MI 48933. (517) 342- 2512. Fax: (517) 342-2515. E-mail: mtardi@diocese oflansing.org
Contact: Mary Tardif
Lay/religious women/men; year-round, including summers; undergraduate/graduate credit

SAINT MARY'S COLLEGE (MICHIGAN)
Department of Theology, 3535 Indian Trail, Orchard Lake, MI 48324. (248) 683-1757. E-mail: Contact@gosaintmarys.edu; Web: www.saintmarys.edu

SIENA HEIGHTS UNIVERSITY
Department of Religious/ Theological Studies, Division of Humanities, 1247 E. Siena Heights Dr., Adrian, MI 49221. (517) 263-0731. E-mail: mbarnett@sienahts .edu; Web: www.sienahts.edu/ acdiv.html
Contact: Marilyn Barnett, Coordinator
Affiliation: Adrian Dominican Sisters

UNIVERSITY OF DETROIT MERCY
Department of Religious Studies, 4001 W. McNichols Rd., PO Box 19900, Detroit, MI 48219-0900. (313) 993-6156. Web: http:// liberalarts.udmercy.edu/religion
Contact: Dr. James Tubbs

MINNESOTA

COLLEGE OF SAINT BENEDICT/ SAINT JOHN'S UNIVERSITY
Theology Department, Collegeville, MN 56321. (320) 363-5059, 2114. E-mail: mpatella@csbsju.edu; Web: www.csbsju.edu/theology
Contact: John Merkle, Acting Chairperson

Companions on a Journey: Listening to the Voice of a Vocation, Collegeville, MN 56321. (320) 363-5059, 2114. E-mail: dmillis@csbsju.edu; Web: www.csbsju.edu/journey/
Contact: Dr. Diane M. Millis

THE COLLEGE OF ST. CATHERINE
Department of Theology, St. Paul Campus: 2004 Randolph Ave., St. Paul, MN 55105. (1-800) 945-4599, ext. 6000, (651) 690-6000; Minneapolis Campus: 601 25th Ave., South Minneapolis, MN 55454. (1-800) 945-4599, ext. 7700, (651) 690-7700. E-mail: pmwiegand@stkate.edu; Web: http://minerva.stkate.edu/offices/academic/theology.nsf
Contact: Dr. Russell Connors [(651) 690-6017]
Affiliation: Sisters of St. Joseph of Carondelet

THE COLLEGE OF ST. SCHOLASTICA
Department of Religious Studies,1200 Kenwood Ave., Duluth, MN 55811. (1-800) 249-6412, (218) 723-6046. Fax: (218) 723-6290. E-mail: admissions@css.edu; Web: http://admissions.css.edu/factsheets/religstudies.shtml
Contact: Dr. Katherine A. McLaughlin, CSJ
Affiliation: Benedictine Sisters

INSTITUTE OF LAY MINISTRIES
PO Box 588, Winona, MN 55987. (507) 454-4643. Fax: (507) 454-8106. E-mail: tgraff@dow.org; Web: www.dow.org/ilm.htm
Contact: Todd Graff, Director of Ministry Formation
Lay women/men; Sept. - May; noncredit/undergraduate*/graduate* credit (* through participating institutions)
Affiliation: Diocese of Winona

LITURGY IN A FORMATIVE ENVIRONMENT (L.I.F.E.)
The Liturgical Press, St. John's Abbey, PO Box 7500, Collegeville, MN 56321-7500. (800) 858-5450, ext. 3152, 3096. Fax: (800) 445-5899. Web: www.litpress.org/life.html
Lay/religious women/men, clergy; year-round, including summers; noncredit/undergraduate/graduate credit; workshops

PASTORAL LEADERSHIP PROGRAM - DIOCESE OF CROOKSTON
Box 610, Crookston, MN 56716. (218) 281-4533. Fax: (218) 281-5991. E-mail: pmurphy@crookston.org, Web: www.crookston.org
Contact: Sr. Pat Murphy, CSJ, Executive Director
Lay women/men, religious women; year-round; noncredit; workshops
Affiliation: Diocese of Crookston

SAINT JOHN'S SCHOOL OF THEOLOGY AND SEMINARY
Collegeville, MN 56321-7288. (320) 363-2102. Fax: (320) 363-3145. E-mail: mbanken@csbsju.edu; Web: www.csbsju.edu/sot
Contact: Mary Beth Banken, OSB
Affiliation: College of Saint Benedict/Saint John's University

SAINT MARY'S UNIVERSITY OF MINNESOTA
Department of Theology, 700 Terrace Heights #22, Winoma, MN 55987-1399. (1-800) 635-5987.
E-mail: rsmith@smumn.edu; Web: www.smumn.edu
Contact: Br. Robert Smith, FSC, Chair
Institute in Pastoral Ministries, 700 Terrace Heights #79, Winoma, MN 55987-1399. (1-800) 635-5987, ext. 1767. E-mail: gsobolew@smumn.edu; Web: www.smumn.edu/ipm
Contact: Dr. Gregory Sobolewski, Director
Affiliation: De La Salle Christian Brothers

UNIVERSITY OF ST. THOMAS
Department of Catholic Studies, 2115 Summit Ave. Mail 55-S, St. Paul, MN 55105. (1-800) 328-6819, (651) 962-5704. E-mail: cjthompson@stthomas.edu; Web: www.stthomas.edu/cathstudies
Contact: Dr. Christopher Thompson, Chair

WOMANWELL
1784 La Crosse Ave., Saint Paul, MN 55119-4808. (651) 739-7953. Fax: (651) 739-7475. E-mail: seeking@WomanWell.org; Web: www.WomanWell.org
Contact: Delmarie Gibney, FSPA, Director
Religious/lay women
Affiliation: Franciscan Sisters of Perpetual Adoration

MISSOURI

AVILA UNIVERSITY
Department of Theology, 11901 Wornall Rd., Kansas City, MO 64145-1698. (816) 942-8400. Web: www.avila.edu/catalog/degrees/theology.htm
Undergraduate credit

CENTER FOR PASTORAL LIFE AND MINISTRY
PO Box 419037, 300 E. 36th St., Kansas City, MO 64141. (816) 756-1850. E-mail: simeone@diocesekcsj.org; Web: www.cplm.org
Contact: Denise Simeone
Lay/religious women/men; year-round; noncredit; workshops

FONTBONNE UNIVERSITY
Department of Philosophy, Religion and Social Sciences, 6800 Wydown Blvd., St Louis, MO 63105. (314) 862-3456. Web: www.fontbonne.edu/department.php?DepartmentID=31
Affiliation: Sisters of St. Joseph of Carondelet

ROCKHURST UNIVERSITY
Department of Theology and Religious Studies, College of Arts and Sciences, 1100 Rockhurst Rd., Kansas City, MO 64110. (1-800) 842-6776. E-mail: jennifer.liebnitz@rockhurst.edu; Web: www.rockhurst.edu/academic/theology/index.html
Affiliation: Jesuits

SAINT LOUIS UNIVERSITY
Department of Theological Studies, College of Arts and Sciences,3800 Lindell Blvd., Humanities Building #124, St. Louis, MO 63108-3414. (314) 977-2878. Fax: (314) 977-2947. E-mail: theology@slu.edu; Web: www.slu.edu/colleges/AS/theology
Aquinas Institute of Theology, 3642 Lindell Blvd., St. Louis, MO 63108. (1-888) 656-3646, (314) 977-3889. Fax: (314) 977-7225. E-mail: aquinas2@slu.edu; Web: www.ai.edu
Contact: Ronald Knapp, Director
Lay/religious women/men, clergy; year-round including summers; noncredit/graduate credit
Affiliation: Jesuits

MONTANA

CARROLL COLLEGE
Department of Theology, 1601 North Benton Ave., Helena, MT 59625. (406) 447-4332. E-mail: amoran@carroll.edu; Web: www.carroll.edu
Contact: Sr. Annette Moran, C.S.J.

PROGRAM OF FORMATION FOR LAY MINISTERS
PO Box 1729, Helena, MT 59624-1729. (406) 442-5820. Fax: (406) 442-5191. E-mail: jtucker@diocesehelena.org; Web: www.diocesehelena.org
Contact: Jim Tucker
Lay/religious women/men; noncredit/undergraduate credit; workshops

UNIVERSITY OF GREAT FALLS

Department of Theology and Religion, 1301 20th St. South, Great Falls, MT 59405-4996. (1-800) 856-9544, (406) 761-8210. Web: www.ugf.edu/academic programs/undergrad/Religion.html#theo1

Undergraduate credit; distance education (online) courses

Affiliation: Sisters of Providence

NEBRASKA

COLLEGE OF ST. MARY

Department of Theology, College of Arts and Sciences, 1901 S. 72nd St., Theology 333, Omaha, NE 68124-2377. (1-800) 926-5534, (402) 399-2414. E-mail: jphillips@csm.edu; Web: www.csm.edu/home/theology.htm

Contact: Jack Phillips, Assistant Professor of Theology

CREIGHTON UNIVERSITY

Theology Department, 2500 California St., Omaha, NE 68178. (1-800) 637-4279, (402) 280-2700. Web: moses.creighton.edu/dept/index.html

Contact: Dr. John J. O'Keefe, Theology Chair

Master's of Arts in Christian Spirituality, 2500 California St., Omaha, NE 68178. (1-800) 637-4279, (402) 280-2669. Fax: (402) 280-2423. E-mail: univcol@creighton.edu, hausersj@creighton.edu; Web: http://moses.creighton.edu/dept/graduate.html

Contacts: Fr. Richard J. Hauser S.J., Director, Christian Spirituality Program; Dr. Susan Calef, Director, Graduate Program in Theology

Center for the Study of Religion and Society, Omaha, NE 68178. (402) 280-2504. E-mail: rsmkns@creighton.edu: Web: moses.creighton.edu/CSRS/

Contact: Ronald A. Simkins, Director

Affiliation: Creighton University

NEVADA

GENESIS

290 South Arlington Ave., Ste. 200, Reno, NV 89501. (775) 326-9431

Contact: Dr. Mary Margaret Swogger

Affiliation: Diocese of Reno

NEW HAMPSHIRE

REGIS COLLEGE

Ministry Institute, 1800 Elm St., Manchester, NH 03104. (603) 222-2202. Fax: (603) 222-9168. E-mail: ministry.institute@regiscollege.edu; Web: http://regisnet.regiscollege.edu/ministryinst/

Contact: Dr. Barbara Anne Radtke, Director

RIVIER COLLEGE

Department of Religious Studies, 420 Main St., St. Joseph's Annex, Nashua, NH 03060-5086. (603) 897-8485. E-mail: akubick@rivier.edu; Web: www.rivier.edu/academics/religious_studies/default.asp

Contact: Art Kubick

Lay/religious women/men; undergraduatae credit

Center for Peace and Social Justice, see above

Lay/religious women/men; summer institute

SAINT ANSELM COLLEGE

Department of Theology, Saint Anselm College, 100 Saint Anselm Dr., Manchester, NH 03102. (603) 641-7000. Web: www.anselm.edu/general/courses/theocat.html

Contact: James McGhee, Chairperson

NEW JERSEY

ASSUMPTION COLLEGE FOR SISTERS

350 Bernardsville Rd., Mendham, NJ 07945-2923. (973) 543-6528, ext. 230. Fax: (973)543-1738. E-mail: acs@scceast.org; Web: www.acscollegeforsisters.org

Contact: Sister Mary Joseph Schultz, President

Affiliation: Diocese of Paterson

Religious women, lay men/women; year-round, including summers; noncredit/undergraduate/graduate credit; workshops

CALDWELL COLLEGE

Department of Theology and Philosophy, 9 Ryerson Ave., Caldwell, NJ 07006. (973) 618-3000

Contact: Sister Barbara C. Krug, Chair

Undergraduate credit/certificate; distance education (online) courses

Pastoral Ministry Program, Graduate Admissions, 9 Ryerson Ave., Caldwell, NJ 07006. (973) 618-3000

Graduate credit

COLLEGE OF SAINT ELIZABETH

Department of Theology, 2 Convent Rd., Morristown, NJ 07960-6989. (973) 290-4112. Web: www.cse.edu

Graduate Program in Theology, 2 Convent Rd., Morristown, NJ 07960-6989. (973) 290-4337. E-mail: ejoyce@cse.edu; Web: www.cse.edu/cgi-any/majors.dll/detail?sitename=CSE&id=94

Contact: Sister Ellen Joyce, Director

Center for Theological/Spiritual Development, 2 Convent Rd., Morristown, NJ 07960. (973) 290-4364, 4300. Fax: (973) 290-4312. Web: www.csespirit.org

Contact: Fr. Anthony Ciorra, Director

Lay/religious women/men; year-round, including summers; non-credit/undergraduate/graduate credit; workshops

FELICIAN COLLEGE

Department of Religious Studies, 262 South Main St., Lodi, NJ 07644-2117. (Rutherford Campus: 223 Montross Ave., Rutherford, NJ 07070-1612.) (201) 559-6000. Fax: (201) 559-6188. Web: www.felician.edu

Lay/religious women/men, clergy; year-round; undergraduate credit (certificate program)

Department of Online Religious Education, 262 South Main St., Lodi, NJ 07644-2117. (Rutherford Campus: 223 Montross Ave., Rutherford, NJ 07070-1612.) (201) 559-6053. E-mail: henchyd@felician.edu; Web: www.felician.edu

Contact: Dr. Dolores Henchy, Chairperson, Online Religious Education

Lay/religious women/men, clergy; year-round; graduate credit; distance learning (online) courses

GEORGIAN COURT COLLEGE

Department of Religion, 900 Lakewood Ave., Lakewood, NJ 08701. (732) 364-2200, ext. 354. E-mail: schubert@georgian.edu; Web: www.georgian.edu/religion/index.html

Contact: Sister Judith Schubert, Chairperson

Undergraduate/graduate credit/certificate

Institute for Lay Ecclesial Ministry, 900 Lakewood Ave., Lakewood, NJ 08701. (732) 364-2200. Web: www.georgian.edu

SAINT PETER'S COLLEGE

Department of Theology, 2641 Kennedy Blvd., Jersey City, NJ 07306. (201) 915-9000. Web: www.spc.edu/departments/theology/index.shtml

Contact: Robert E. Kennedy, S.J., Chairperson

SETON HALL UNIVERSITY

Department of Religious Studies, College of Arts and Sciences, 400 South Orange Ave., South Orange, NJ 07079. (973) 761-9000. Web: www.shu.edu/

Contact: Rev. John Morley

Center for Catholic Studies, 400 South Orange Ave., South Orange, NJ 07079. E-mail: liddyric@shu .edu; Web: www.shu.edu

Contact: Msgr. Dick Liddy

School of Theology, Immaculate Conception Seminary, 400 South Orange Ave., South Orange, NJ 07079. (973) 761-9575. Fax: (973) 761-9577. E-mail: theology@shu .edu; Web: www.shu.edu

Contact: Rev. Msgr. Robert F. Coleman, Dean

Lay/religious women/men, clergy; year-round, including summers; graduate credit; noncredit

VINCENTIAN RENEWAL CENTER

St. Joseph Seminary, 75 Mapleton Rd., Princeton, NJ 08540. (609) 520-9626 . E-mail: smfrate@ vincentianfamilycenter.com; Web: www.sjseminary.org

Contact: Sr. Mary Frate, Program Director

Workshops/seminars

Affiliation: Vincentian Community of the Eastern Province

NEW MEXICO

CENTER FOR ACTION AND CONTEMPLATION

PO Box 12464, Albuquerque, NM 87195. (505) 242-9588. Fax: (505) 242-9518. E-mail: info@cacradical grace.org; Web: www.cacradical grace.org

COLLEGE OF SANTA FE

Department of Humanities - Religious Studies, 1600 St. Michael's Dr., Santa Fe NM 87505. (1- 800) 456-2673, (505) 473-6011. Web: www.csf.edu/pr/viewbook/ hum_degree_programs.htm

NEW YORK

CANISIUS COLLEGE

Department of Religious Studies, Churchill Tower 1003, 2001 Main St., Buffalo, NY 14208-1098.(716) 888-2824. E-mail: wadkins@ canisius.edu, Web: www.canisius .edu/rst/

Contact: Dr. Timothy Wadkins

The Center for the Global Study of Religion, 2001 Main St., Buffalo, NY 14208-1098

CENTER FOR MISSION RESEARCH AND STUDY

Box 305, Maryknoll, NY 10545-0305. (914) 941-7590. Fax: (914) 941-5753. E-mail: cmrsm@mary knoll.org; Web: www.maryknoll.org

Contact: Dr. Anne Reissner

COLLEGE OF MOUNT SAINT VINCENT

Department of Religious Studies, 6301 Riverdale Ave., Riverdale, NY 10471-1093. (1-800) 665-CMSV, (718) 405-3267. Fax: (718) 549-7945. E-mail: admissns@mount saintvincent.edu; Web: www.cmsv .edu

Undergraduate credit

THE COLLEGE OF NEW ROCHELLE

School of Arts & Sciences, Department of Religious Studies, Office of Admission, 29 Castle Place, New Rochelle, NY 10805. (1-800) 933-5923. Fax: (914) 654-5464. E-mail: admission@cnr.edu; Web: www.cnr.edu

THE COLLEGE OF SAINT ROSE

Department of Religious Studies, School of Arts and Humanities, 432 Western Ave., Albany, NY 12203. (1-800) 637-8556. Web: www.strose .edu

CROSS-CULTURAL SERVICES AT MARYKNOLL

Box 305, Maryknoll, NY 10545-0305. (914) 941-7590, ext. 2371. Fax: (914) 941-5753. E-mail: kpierce@mary knoll.org; Web: www.maryknoll.org

Contact: Kathryn Pierce, IHM

Lay/religious women/men, clergy; year-round, including summers; workshops (discernment/preparation program, lay missionary orientation, reentry/debriefing of mission experience, acculturation for foreign-born missionaries)

DOMINICAN COLLEGE

Department of Religious Studies, 470 Western Hwy., Orangeburg, NY 10962. (845) 359-7800. Web: www. dc.edu/liberal/religion.html

FORDHAM UNIVERSITY

Department of Religious Studies, Fordham Rd., Collins 110, Bronx, NY 10458. (718) 817-3248. E-mail: dathompson@fordham.edu; Web: www.fordham/edu

Contact: Dr. Daniel Speed Thompson

Lay/religious women/men, clergy; year-round, including summers: undergraduate/graduate credit

Department of Theology, 441 E. Fordham Rd., Collins 103, Bronx, NY 10458-9993. (718) 817-3240. Fax: (718) 817-5787. E-mail: fordhamtheology@yahoo.com; Web: www.fordham/edu

Contact: Thomas R. Kopfensteiner, Dean

Lay/religious women/men, clergy; year-round, including summers: undergraduate/graduate credit

Graduate School of Religion and Religious Education (GSRRE), Bronx, NY 10458-5163. (718) 817-4800. Fax: (718) 817-3352. Web: www.fordham.edu

Contact: Dean Vincent Novak, S.J.

Lay/religious women/men; year-round including summers; noncredit/ graduate credit

Affiliation: Jesuits

FORMATION FOR MINISTRY (ALBANY, NY)

40 N. Main Ave., Albany, NY 12203. (518) 453-6670. E-mail: betsy.rowe @rcda.org

Contact: C. Elizabeth Rowe

Affiliation: Diocese of Albany

Lay/religious women/men; year-round; noncredit

FORMATION FOR MINISTRY (OGDENSBURG, NY)

622 Washington St., PO Box 369, Ogdensburg, NY 13669. (315) 393-2920. Fax: (315) 394-7401.E-mail: jbaumert@dioogdensburg.org; Web: www.dioogdensburg.org/formation

Contact: Sister Judith Baumert, SSJ

Lay/religious women/men; year-round; noncredit; workshops

HILBERT COLLEGE

Religious Studies, Arts and Sciences Department, 5200 S. Park Ave., Hamburg, NY 14075. (716) 649-7900. Fax: (716) 649-0702. E-mail: cernst@hilbert.edu; Web: www.hilbert.edu/academics/liberal_ arts/default.asp

Contact: Dr. Charles Ernst, Chairperson

IONA COLLEGE

Department of Religious Studies, School of Arts and Sciences, 715 North Ave., New Rochelle, NY 10801. (914) 633-2682, fax: (914) 633-2248. E-mail: bsrozenski@ iona.edu; Web: www.iona.edu/ academic/arts_sci/departments/relig ion/index.htm

Contact: Sr. Barbara Srozenski

Iona Spirituality Institute, 715 North Ave., New Rochelle, NY 10801. (1-800) 231-IONA. E-mail: KDeignan@iona.edu; Web: www. iona.edu

Contact: Kathleen P. Deignan, CND, Ph.D.

Affiliation: Iona College

Lay women/men; year-round; noncredit; workshops

LE MOYNE COLLEGE
Department of Religious Studies, 1419 Salt Springs Rd., Syracuse, NY 13214-1399. (315) 445-4345. Fax: (315) 445-4540. E-mail: glennon@lemoyne.edu; Web: www.lemoyne.edu/religious_studies/index.htm
Contact: Dr. Fred Glennon, Department Chair

LEGION OF CHRIST COLLEGE
584 Columbus Ave., Thornwood, NY 10594. (914) 773-1368. Fax: (914) 773-1438
Contact: Br. Scott Madgey, LC

MANHATTAN COLLEGE
Department of Religious Studies, Manhattan College Parkway, Riverdale, NY 10471. (1-800) MC2-XCEL. (718) 862-7113. Fax: (718) 862-8044. E-mail: stephen.kaplan@manhattan.edu; Web: www.manhattan.edu/arts/rls/ index.html
Contact: Stephen Kaplan, Chairperson

MARIST COLLEGE
Department of Religious Studies, School of Liberal Arts. Marist College, 3399 North Rd., Poughkeepsie, NY 12601. (845) 575-3295. E-mail: thomas.wermuth@marist.edu; Web: www.marist.ecu
Contact: Thomas Wermuth, Dean

MARIA COLLEGE
Religious Studies/Philosophy, Liberal Arts Department, 700 New Scotland Ave., Albany, NY 12208. (518) 438-3111. E-mail: anned@mariacollege.org
Contact: Anne Devlin, Liberal Arts Department Chairperson

MARYMOUNT COLLEGE
Department of Philosophy and Religious Studies, 100 Marymount Ave., Tarrytown, NY 10591. (914) 631-3200. E-mail: thomasg@mmc.marymt.edu; Web: www.marymt.edu
Contact: Philosophy and Religious Studies Facilitator
Affiliation: Religious of the Sacred Heart of Mary

MARYMOUNT MANHATTAN COLLEGE
Department of Religious Studies, 221 East 71st St., New York, NY 10021. (212) 517-0641. E-mail: ebazzini@mmm.edu; Web: marymount.mmm.edu/home.htm
Contact: Elanor Bazzini

MOLLOY COLLEGE
Theology Certificate Program, Division of Continuing Education and Professional Development (CEPD), 1000 Hempstead Ave., Rockville Centre, NY 11571-5002. 888-4-MOLLOY. Web: www.molloy.edu/ce/theology/index.htm
Contacts: Division of Continuing Education or Timothy Carroll, Diocese of Rockville Centre, (516) 678-5800, ext. 542.

MOUNT SAINT MARY COLLEGE
Department of Philosophy and Religious Studies, 330 Powell Ave., Newburgh, NY 12550. (845) 561-0800. Web: www.msmc.edu

NIAGARA UNIVERSITY
Department of Religious Studies, Niagara University, NY 14109-2015. (716) 285-1212. Web: www.niagara.edu/rs
Affiliation: Congregation of the Mission (Vincentian Fathers and Brothers)

ST. BERNARD'S SCHOOL OF THEOLOGY AND MINISTRY
120 French Rd., Rochester, NY 14618. (585) 271-3657, ext. 289. Fax: (585) 271 2045. E-mail: tmcdadeclay@stbernards.edu; Web: www.stbernards.edu
Contact: Tom McDade Clay, Director of Admissions
(Extension program: Albany: 40 North Main Ave., Albany, NY 12203. (518) 453-6760. Fax: (518) 453-6793. Contact: Dr. Joseph Piccolino, Director of Albany Extension)
Lay/religious women/men; year round, including summers; noncredit/undergraduate/graduate credit; workshops; distance learning (online) courses

ST. BONAVENTURE UNIVERSITY
Department of Theology, D8 Plassmann, St. Bonaventure, NY 14778. (716) 375-2105, ext. 2137, (1-800) 541-2525. E-mail: XSEUBERT@sbu.edu; Web: www.sbu.edu
Contact: Xavier Seubert
The Franciscan Institute, St. Bonaventure, NY 14778. (716) 375-2105. E-mail: franinst@sbu.edu; Web: http://franinst.sbu.edu

ST. JOHN'S UNIVERSITY
Department of Theology and Religious Studies, SJH B26, 8000 Utopia Pkwy., Jamaica, NY 11439. (718) 990-6424. Fax: (718) 990-1907. E-mail: ruizj@stjohns.edu; Web: www.stjohns.edu
Contact: Patrick D. Primeaux, S.M., Chair
Affiliation: Vincentian Priests and Brothers (Eastern Province)
Lay/religious women/men, clergy; year-round, including summers; noncredit/undergraduate/graduate credit
Evening Theological Education Program (ETEP)

ST. JOSEPH'S COLLEGE
Department of Religious Studies, School of Arts & Sciences, 245 Clinton Ave., Brooklyn, NY 11205. (718) 636–6868. E-mail: brooklynas@sjcny.edu; Web: www.sjcny.edu/brooklyn/artscience/programs/index.html

ST. JOSEPH'S COLLEGE, NEW YORK
Religious Studies/Religious Leadership Studies, School of Arts and Sciences, Suffolk Campus: 155 W. Roe Blvd., Patchogue, NY 11772. (631) 447–3219: Brooklyn Campus: 245 Clinton Ave., Brooklyn 11205. (718) 636–6800. Web: www.sjcny.edu

ST. THOMAS AQUINAS COLLEGE
Department of Philosophy and Religious Studies, Division of Humanities, 125 Route 340, Sparkill, NY 10976-1050. (845) 398-4000. Web: www.stac.edu/humanities/Phil%20and%20Rel/philpage.html

SEMINARY OF THE IMMACULATE CONCEPTION
M.A. Program, Academic Office, 440 West Neck Rd., Huntington, NY 11743. (631) 423-0483, ext. 147, 112
Contact: Bro. Jeffrey Pedersen, O.S.F., Associate Dean
Affiliation: Seminary of the Immaculate Conception
Lay/religious women/men, clergy; year-round, including summers; undergraduate/graduate credit/workshops

SIENA COLLEGE
Department of Religious Studies, 515 Loudon Rd., Loudonville, NY 12211-1462. (518) 783-2300. Web: www.siena.edu/relstudy

VILLA MARIA COLLEGE
Religious Studies, 240 Pine Ridge Rd., Buffalo, NY 14225-3999. (716) 896-0700. Fax: (716) 896-0705. E-mail: mwendzikowski@villa.edu; Web: www.villa.edu
Contact: Sister Marcella Anne Wendzikowski, Program Coordinator
Lay women/men; year-round; undergraduate credit

WELLSPRINGS - PROGRAMS IN HOLISTIC SPIRITUALITY
93 Maple St., Glens Falls, NY 12801 (518) 792-3183. Fax: (518)792-3184. E-mail: info@wsprings.org; Web: www.wsprings.org

NORTH CAROLINA

BELMONT ABBEY COLLEGE
Department of Theology, 100 Belmont-Mt.Holly Rd., Belmont, NC 28012. (1-888) BAC-0110. Web: www.belmontabbeycollege.edu/Academics/programs.asp#theology

NORTH DAKOTA

UNIVERSITY OF MARY
Division of Philosophy and Theology, 7500 University Dr., Bismarck, ND 58504. (701) 255-7500. Fax: (701) 255-7687. E-mail: sjoann@umary.edu; Web: www.umary.edu/AcadInfo/PhiTheoDiv
Contact: Sister JoAnn Krebsbach, OSB

OHIO

CHATFIELD COLLEGE
Religious Studies, 20918 State Rte. 251, St. Martin, OH 45118. (513) 875-3344. Fax: (513) 875-3912. E-mail: chatfield@chatfield.edu; Web: www.chatfield.edu (http://66.162.52.87)
Undergraduate credit
Affiliation: The Ursulines of Brown County

COLLEGE OF MOUNT ST. JOSEPH
Department of Religious and Pastoral Studies, 5701 Delhi Rd., Cincinnati, OH 45233-1670. (513) 244-4272. E-mail: john_trokan@mail.msj.edu; Web: www.msj.edu/academics/Religion/index.htm
Contact: Dr. John Trokan, Chair
Lay/religious women/men, clergy; year-round, including summers; noncredit/undergraduate/graduate credit; workshops; distance learning (online) courses

FRANCISCAN UNIVERSITY OF STEUBENVILLE
Department of Theology, 1235 University Blvd., Steubenville, OH 43952. (740) 283-6495. Fax: (740) 283-6377. E-mail: pretheo@franciscan.edu; Web: http://developer.franuniv.edu/Admissions/majors/theology.htm
Contact: Dr. Alan Schreck, Chair
Pre-Theologate Program, 1235 University Blvd., Steubenville, OH 43952. (740) 283-6495. Fax: (740) 283-6377. E-mail: pretheo@franciscan.edu; Web: www.franuniv.edu/home2/Content/PreTheologate/main.aspx?id=303
Contact: Fr. John R. Cody, C.Ss.R.

JOHN CARROLL UNIVERSITY
Department of Religious Studies, 20700 North Park Blvd., Suite B250-Administration Bldg., University Heights, OH 44118-4581. (216) 397-4708. E-mail: plauritzen@jcu.edu; Web: www.jcu.edu/religion
Contact: Paul Lauritzen, Chairperson
The Walter and Mary Tuohy Chair of Interreligious Studies
The Ignatian Spirituality Institute

LAY PASTORAL MINISTRY PROGRAM
6616 Beechmont Ave., Cincinnati, OH 45230. (513) 231-1200. E-mail: modonnel@mtsm.org
Contact: Mary Sue O'Donnell
Lay/religious men/women; year-round; noncredit/graduate credit; workshops

LOURDES COLLEGE
Department of Religious Studies, 6832 Convent Blvd., Learning Center Hall (LCH) - Room 289, Sylvania, OH 43560. (419) 824-3819. E-mail: sschrein@lourdes.edu; Web: www.lourdes.edu/Religious/index.htm
Contact: Dr. Shannon Schrein, O.S.F.
Affiliation: Sisters of St. Francis

MINISTRY FORMATION PROGRAM
197 E. Gay St., Columbus, OH 43215. (614) 241-2544. E-mail: lyoung@colsdioc.org
Contact: Leslie Young
Affiliation: Diocese of Columbus

NOTRE DAME COLLEGE
Theology Department, Administration Building - Rm. 430, 4545 College Rd., South Euclid, OH 44121-4293. (1-877) NDC-OHIO, (216)373-5348. Fax: (216) 381-3802. E-mail: emehok@ndc.edu; Web: www.notredamecollege.edu/academics/theology/index.html
Contact: Dr. Edward E. Mehok
The Center for Pastoral Theology and Ministry, 4545 College Rd., Administration Building, South Euclid, OH 44121-4293. (1-877) NDC-OHIO, (216) 373-5389. Fax: (216) 381-3802. E-mail: mbaran@ndc.edu; Web: www.notredamecollege.edu/academics/pastoralMinistry/faculty2.htm
Contact: Sister Mary Ann Baran, S.N.D., Assistant Professor of Theology
Lay/women/men; fall,spring; undergraduate credit

OHIO DOMINICAN UNIVERSITY
The Division of Philosophy and Theology, 1216 Sunbury Rd., Columbus, OH 43219. (614) 253-2741. E-mail: Finanb@ohiodominican.edu; Web: www.ohiodominican.edu/majors/theology/default.shtml
Contact: Dr. Barbara Finan, Division Chair

PASTORAL FORMATION PROGRAM
Pastoral Ministry Office, 28700 Euclid Ave., Wickliffe, OH 44092. (440) 943-7670. Fax: (440) 943-7577. E-mail: pastoralministry@dioceseofcleveland.org
Contact: Kathleen Haase-Falbo, Director
Lay/religious women/men; year-round; noncredit/undergraduate/graduate credit; workshops

UNIVERSITY OF DAYTON
Department of Religious Studies, 300 College Park Ave., Dayton, OH 45469-1530. (937) 229-4321. Fax: (937) 229-4330. E-mail: relstudy@notes.udayton.edu; Web: www.udayton.edu/~relstudy
Contact: Dr. Sandra Yocum Mize, Chair
Lay/religious women/men, clergy; year-round, including summers; noncredit/undergraduate/graduate credit; workshops; distance learning (online) courses
The Program for Christian Leadership (to explore vocation), College of Arts and Sciences, 300 College Park, Jesse Phillips Humanities Center, Room 123, Dayton, OH 45469-1530. (937) 229-4592. Web: artssciences.udayton.edu/askus/askus.asp?strLocationName=Christian+Leadership&SelectedArea=117.
Contact: Dr. Maura Skill, Director

URSULINE COLLEGE
Religious Studies Department, 2550 Lander Rd., Besse Library, Second Floor - Faculty Carrel E, Pepper Pike, OH 44124-4398. (1-888) URSULINE, (440) 646-8196.E-mail: dblatnica@ursuline.edu; Web: www.ursuline.edu/acadaff/religious_studies/#graduate_programs
Contact: Dr. Dorothy Ann Blatnica
Affiliation: Ursuline Sisters of Cleveland
Undergraduate credit; Cleveland Diocesan Lay Pastoral Ministry Certification

WALSH UNIVERSITY
Department of Theology, Division of Humanities, 116 Science Center, 2020 Easton Street NW, North Canton, OH 44720. (1-800) 362-

9846, ext. 7042. E-mail: jtrapani@walsh.edu; Web: www.walsh.edu/maincategory.php?cid=11
Contact: Dr. John Trapani

XAVIER UNIVERSITY

Department of Theology, 3800 Victory Pkwy. 318 Hinkle Hall, Cincinnati, OH 45207. (513) 745-3026. E-mail: madges@xu.edu; Web: www.xu.edu/theology
Contact: Dr. William Madges, Chair
Affiliation: Jesuits
Undergraduate/graduate credit

The Brueggeman Center for Interreligious Dialogue, 3800 Victory Pkwy., Cincinnati, OH 45207. (1-800) 344-4698, (513) 745-3000. Web: www.xu.edu/brueggeman_center
Affiliation: Jesuits

OKLAHOMA

ST. GREGORY'S UNIVERSITY

Theology Division, 1900 West Macarthur Dr., AD011, Shawnee, OK 74804. (405) 878-5380. E-mail: ljgarry@sgc.edu; Web: www.stgregorys.edu/academics/theology.htm
Contact: Dr. Laurie Wright Garry, Chair

OREGON

MARYLHURST UNIVERSITY

Department of Religious Studies, 17600 Pacific Highway (Hwy. 43), PO Box 261, Marylhurst, OR 97036-0261. (1-800) 634-9982, (503) 636-8141. Fax: (503) 636-9526. Web: www.marylhurst.edu/attend/undergrad/ls-religious.html
Undergraduate credit

Religious Studies Department, 17600 Pacific Hwy. (Hwy. 43), PO Box 261, Marylhurst, OR 97036-0261. (800) 634-9982, (503) 699-6305. Web: www.marylhurst.edu/attend/undergrad/ls-religious.html
Contact: Dr. Jerry Roussell, Jr.
Lay/religious women/men, clergy; year-round, including summers; graduate credit

THE UNIVERSITY OF PORTLAND

Department of Theology, College of Arts and Sciences, 5000 N. Willamette Blvd., Portland, OR 97203-5798. (503) 943-7274. Web: www.up.edu
Theology, B.A., Pastoral Ministry, M.A.
Affiliation: Congregation of Holy Cross

PENNSYLVANIA

ALVERNIA COLLEGE

Theology Program, Humanities Department, Reading, PA 19607. (610) 796-8200. Web: www.alvernia.edu/academics/depts.htm

CABRINI COLLEGE

Department of Religious Studies, 610 King of Prussia Rd., Radnor, PA 19087-3698. (610) 902-8100. Fax: (610) 902-8309. Web: www.cabrini.edu
Affiliation: Missionary Sisters of the Sacred Heart

CARLOW COLLEGE

Department of Theology and Ministry, 3333 Fifth Ave., Pittsburgh, PA 15213. (1-800) 333-CARLOW. Web: www.carlow.edu/academic/theology.html#ministry

CHESTNUT HILL COLLEGE

Department of Religious Studies, 9601 Germantown Ave., Philadelphia, PA 19118-2693. (215) 248-7000. Web: www.chc.edu

Division of Holistic Spirituality, School of Graduate Studies, 9601 Germantown Ave., Philadelphia, PA 19118-2693. (215) 248-7170. E-mail: graddiv@chc.edu; Web: www.chc.edu
Contact: Dr. Catherine Nerney, SSJ, Chair
Graduate credit; workshops

COLLEGE MISERICORDIA

Department of Religious Studies, Division of Humanities, 301 Lake St., Dallas, PA 18612. (570) 674-6400. Web: www.misericordia.edu/templates/alltemps.cfm?cat_id=304&pg=1

Center for Professional Development, 301 Lake St., Dallas, PA 18612-1098. (570) 674-6161. Fax: (570) 674-6232. E-mail: conted@miseri.edu; Web: www.miseri.edu/adult_ed
Affiliation: College Misericordia

DE SALES UNIVERSITY

Department of Philosophy & Theology, 2755 Station Ave., Center Valley, PA 18034-9568. (610) 282-1100. Fax: (610) 282-2255. Web: www4.desales.edu/~philtheo/academic.htm

De Sales C.E.N.T.R.E. (Continuing Education Network for Teachers and Religious Educators), 2755 Station Ave., Center Valley, PA 18034-9568. (610) 282-1100. Fax: (610) 282-2255. Web: www4.desales.edu/~philtheo/continuing.htm

The Salesian Center for Faith and Culture, 2755 Station Ave., Center Valley, PA 18034-9568. (610) 282-1100. Fax: (610) 282-2255. Web: www4.desales.edu/~philtheo/salesian.htm
Affiliation: Oblates of St. Francis de Sales

DUQUESNE UNIVERSITY

Department of Theology/Religious Studies, College of Liberal Arts, 600 Forbes Ave., Pittsburgh, PA 15282. (412) 396-6000. Web: www.duq.edu
Contact: Fr. Michael Slusser, Chair
Lay/religious women/men, clergy; year-round, including summers; noncredit/undergraduate/graduate credit; distance learning (online) courses

ECCLESIAL LAY MINISTRY FORMATION

PO Box 355, Harrisburg, PA 17105-3557. (717) 657-4804, ext. 319. E-mail: modonnell@hbgdiocese.org
Contact: Mary Ann O'Donnell
Affiliation: Diocese of Harrisburg

GANNON UNIVERSITY

University Square, PAC 3206 (Peach and 9th), Erie, PA 16541. (814) 871-7544, 1-800-GannonU. E-mail: orbanek@gannon.edu; Web: www.gannon.edu/PROGRAMS/UNDER/theology.ihtml
Contact: Msgr. Gerald Orbanek, Chair

GWYNEDD-MERCY COLLEGE

Religious Studies, School of Arts and Sciences, 1025 Sumneytown Pike, PO Box 901, Gwynedd Valley, PA 19437-0901. (1-800) DIAL-GMC, (215) 646-7300. E-mail: miller.e@gmc.edu; Web: www.gmc.edu/academic/programs.html#Arts
Contact: Prof. Edward Jeremy Miller

HOLY FAMILY UNIVERSITY

Department of Religious Studies, School of Arts & Sciences, Grant & Frankford Aves., Philadelphia, PA 19114. (215) 637-7700. E-mail: sjgedaka@holyfamily.edu; Web: www.holyfamily.edu
Contact: Dr. Johanna Gedaka, SSJ
Affiliation: Sisters of the Holy Family of Nazareth
Lay/religious women/men, clergy; year-round, including summers; undergraduate credit

IMMACULATA UNIVERSITY

Department of Theology, 1145 King Rd., Immaculata, PA 19345. (1-877) ICTODAY, (610) 647-4400. Web: www.immaculata.edu/theology

Contact: Sr. John Sheila Galligan
Affiliation: Sisters, Servants of the Immaculate Heart of Mary
Lay women/men; year-round; undergraduate credit; distance learning (online) courses

KING'S COLLEGE

Department of Religious Studies, 133 N. River St., Wilkes-Barre, PA 18711. (570) 208-5900. Web: www.kings.edu/frames/tb_frames/academics.html

LA ROCHE COLLEGE

Department of Religious Studies, School of Humanities, La Roche College, 9000 Babcock Blvd., Pittsburgh, PA 15237. (412) 536-1796. E-mail: leblanp1@LaRoche.edu; Web: www.laroche.edu
Contact: Dr. Paul LeBlanc, Division Chair of Humanities
Pacem in Terris Institute

LA SALLE UNIVERSITY

The Department of Religion, School of Arts and Sciences, 1900 W. Olney Ave., Philadelphia, PA 19141-1199. (215) 951-1042. E-mail: mcmanus@lasalle.edu; Web: www.lasalle.edu
Contact: Undergraduate Director of Admissions
Lay/religious women/men, clergy; year-round, including summers; undergraduate credit
Graduate Program in Theology and Ministry, Graduate Religion Office, 1900 W. Olney Ave., Philadelphia, PA 19141-1199. (215) 951-1335. E-mail: berna@lasalle.edu; Web: www.lasalle.edu
Contact: Fr. Frank Berna, OFM, Ph.D., Director
Lay/religious women/men, clergy; year-round, including summers; graduate credit

MANOR COLLEGE

Catechist/Educator Development Certificate, 700 Fox Chase Rd., Jenkintown, PA 19046. (215) 885-2360. E-mail: webmaster@manor.edu; Web: www.manor.edu/certificateprogram.htm
Affiliation: Sisters of St. Basil the Great

MARYWOOD UNIVERSITY

Department of Religious Studies, Scranton, PA 18509. (570) 348-6211, ext. 2490. E-mail: zaums@es.marywood.edu; Web: www.marywood.edu/ug_cat/departments/relstu.stm
Contact: Dr. John R. Zaums, Chair
Undergraduate credit
Affiliation: Servants of the Immaculate Heart of Mary

MERCYHURST COLLEGE

Department of Religious Studies, 501 East 38th, PRES 204, Erie, PA 16546. (814) 824-2532. E-mail: msnyder@mercyhurst.edu; Web: www.mercyhurst.edu/Academics/religious_studies.htm
Contact: Dr. Mary Hembrow Snyder, Director
Undergraduate program
Mercy Institute for Religious Education and Lay Ministry, 501 East 38th St., Erie, PA 16546. (814) 824-2572. E-mail: kleap@mercyhurst.edu; Web: www.mercyhurst.edu/ Academics/AC_06_01.htm
Contact: Sister Kathleen Marie Leap, RSM

MOUNT ALOYSIUS COLLEGE

Department of Religious Studies/Theology, 7373 Admiral Peary Highway, Cresson, PA 16630-1999. (1-888) 823-2220. Web: www.mtaloy.edu/minors.htm#religious
Undergraduate credit
Affiliation: Religious Sisters of Mercy of the Americas

NEUMANN COLLEGE

The Religious Education Institute, One Neumann Dr., Aston, PA 19014-1298. (610) 558-5616 or (1-800) 9-NEUMAN. E-mail: neumann @ neumann.edu; Web: www.neumann.edu
(two locations: Neumann College campus, Aston; St. Maria Goretti HS in South Philadelphia)
Undergraduate credit
Neumann Institute for Franciscan Studies, One Neumann Dr., Aston, PA 19014-1298. (610) 361-5407. Fax: (610) 361-5277. E-mail: hutchisp@neumann.edu; Web: www.neumann.edu/about/nifs.html
Contact: Sr. Patricia Hutchison, OSF, Director
Lay/religious women/men, clergy; year-round, including summers; noncredit/undergraduate/graduate credit; workshops; distance learning (online) courses
Pastoral Care & Counseling Graduate Program, One Neumann Dr., Aston, PA 19014-1298. (610) 558-5616 or (1-800) 9-NEUMAN. E-mail: neumann@neumann.edu; Web: www.neumann.edu
Lay/religious women/men, clergy; year-round, including summers; graduate credit
Affiliation: Sisters of St. Francis of Philadelphia

ROSEMONT COLLEGE

Department of Religious Studies, 1400 Montgomery Ave., Lawrence Hall, Rosemont, PA 19010. (610) 527-0200, ext. 2351. Web: www.rosemont.edu
Contact: Professor Virginia Ratigan
Affiliation: Society of the Holy Child Jesus

ST. CHARLES BORROMEO SEMINARY

Department of Religious Studies, 100 East Wynnewood Rd., Wynnewood, PA 19096. (610) 785-6287. Fax: (610) 667-4122. E-mail: relstudiescs@adphila.org; Web: www.scs.edu/div/relstudy/relstudy.html
Contact: Rev. Anthony J. Costa, Academic Dean
Affiliation: Archdiocese of Philadelphia
Lay/religious women/men, clergy; year-round, including summers; noncredit/undergraduate/graduate credit

SAINT FRANCIS UNIVERSITY

Department of Religious Studies, PO Box 600, Loretto, PA 15940. (814) 472-3000. Web: www.francis.edu

SAINT JOSEPH'S UNIVERSITY

Department of Theology, School of Arts and Sciences, 5600 City Ave., BL 115, Philadelphia, PA 19131. (610) 660-1282. E-mail: csuchars@sju.edu; Web: www.sju.edu
Contact: Caryn Sucharski, Office of the Dean
Faith-Justice Institute, 5600 City Ave., Philadelphia, PA 19131. (610) 660-1765. E-mail: nfox@sju.edu; Web: www.sju.edu/cas/faith-justice/
Contact: Dr. Nancy Fox, Academic Program Director
Affiliation: Jesuits

ST. PAUL SEMINARY

Institute for Ministries, 2900 Noblestown Rd., Pittsburgh, PA 15205. (412) 921-5800, ext. 15. Fax: (412) 928-5921. E-mail: progan@diopitt.org; Web: www.diopitt.org
Contact: Sr. Patricia Rogan, OSF
Lay/religious women/men; year-round; noncredit; workshops

SAINT VINCENT COLLEGE

Department of Religious Studies, 300 Fraser Purchase Rd., Latrobe, PA 15650-2690. (1-800) 782-5549. E-mail: admission@stvincent.edu; Web: www.stvincent.edu/academics/ majors.html

SETON HILL UNIVERSITY

Department of Religious Studies/ Theology, Division of Humanities, Greensburg, PA 15601-1599. E-mail: jacko@setonhill.edu; Web: maura.setonhill.edu/~human/religion /religious.htm

Contact: Dr. Dorothy Jacko, S.C., Associate Professor of Religious Studies/Theology

Certificate in Ministry Program, Office of Graduate and Adult Studies, Greensburg, PA 15601-1599. (724) 838-4208. Fax: (724) 830-1294. E-mail: adultstudies@ setonhill.edu; http://maura.setonhill .edu/~conted/

Contact: Mary Kay Cooper, Director of Admissions/Adult Student Services

Lay/religious women/men, clergy; year-round; undergraduate credit (certificate in ministry)

Affiliation: Sisters of Charity of Seton Hill

UNIVERSITY OF SCRANTON

Department of Theology/ Religious Studies, College of Arts and Sciences, Scranton, PA 18510-4660. (570) 941-6309. Fax: (570) 941-4309. E-mail: gaughanm1 @uofs.edu; Web: http://academic .scranton.edu/department/theology/

Contact: E. Springs Steele, Chair of Theology Department

VILLANOVA UNIVERSITY

Department of Theology & Religious Studies, College of Liberal Arts & Sciences, Villanova, PA 19085. (610) 519-4730. E-mail: peggy.duffy@villanova.edu; Web: www.theology.villanova.edu

Contact: Peggy Duffy

Affiliation: Augustinians, Province of St. Thomas of Villanova

PUERTO RICO

PONTIFICAL CATHOLIC UNIVERSITY OF PUERTO RICO

Departamento de Teología, Colegio de Artes y Humanidades, 2250 Avenidade las Americas, Ponce, PR 00717-0777. (787) 841-2000. Web: www.pucpr.edu

Contact: Revdo. P. Eduardo Torres, Director

RHODE ISLAND

PROVIDENCE COLLEGE

Department of Theology, 549 River Ave., Providence, RI 02918-0001. (401) 865-1000. Web: www. providence.edu/college-relations/ onlincat/onlinecatalog.html

Undergraduate credit

Graduate Studies, The Department of Theology, 549 River Ave., Providence, RI 02918-0001. (401) 865-2247. Fax: (401) 865-1147. E-mail: graduate@providence .edu; Web: www.providence.edu/grad/rel.html

Contact: Terence J. Keegan, O.P.

Graduate credit

Affiliation: Dominican Friars

SALVE REGINA UNIVERSITY

Department of Religious Studies, 100 Ochre Point Ave., Newport, RI 02840-4192. (401) 847-6650. Web: www.salve.edu/catalogs/undergrad/ ugragcatalog_rst.html

SOUTH DAKOTA

MINISTRY FORMATION PROGRAM

HC 77 Box 271, Howes, SD 57748-9505. (605) 985-5906. E-mail: smitten@basec.net

Contact: Fr. Steve Mitten, SJ

Affiliation: Diocese of Rapid City

MOUNT MARTY COLLEGE

Department of Religious Studies and Philosophy, Division of Humanities,1105 West 8th St., Corby 113, Yankton, SD 57078. (1-800) 658-4552, (605) 668-1605. Fax: (605) 668-1607. E-mail: dfleischacker@mtmc.edu; Web: www.mtmc.edu

Contact: David Fleischacker, Director

Undergraduate/graduate credit-Master of Arts in Pastoral Ministries (MAPM)

Affiliation: Benedictine

PRESENTATION COLLEGE

Religious Studies, Department of Arts and Science, 1500 N. Main St., Aberdeen, SD 57401. (605) 225-1634. E-mail: admit@presentation .edu; Web: www.presentation.edu/ artssciences/index.htm

Contact: Dr. Martin Albl

Affiliation: Sisters of the Presentation of the Blessed Virgin Mary

TENNESSEE

CHRISTIAN BROTHERS UNIVERSITY

Department of Religion and Philosophy, 650 E. Parkway South, Memphis, TN 38104. (901) 321-3000. E-mail: pgathje@cbu.edu; Web: www.cbu.edu/arts/phil

Contact: Professor Peter Gathje, Department Chair

Undergraduate credit

TEXAS

CATHOLIC EDUCATION AND MINISTRY INSTITUTE (CEMI)

PO Box 3948, Beaumont, TX 77704. (409) 838-0451, ext. 144. E-mail: ldeluca@dioceseofbmt.org; Web: www.dioceseofbmt.org

Contact: Dr. Lorraine S. DeLuca, Director

Affiliation: Diocese of Beaumont

Lay women/men; year-round; noncredit; workshops

OBLATE SCHOOL OF THEOLOGY

285 Oblate Dr., San Antonio, TX 78216. (210) 341-1366. Fax: (210) 341-4519. E-mail: dean@ost.edu, registrar@ost.edu; Web: www.ost .edu

Contacts: Dean, Registrar

Lay/religious women/men, clergy; year-round, including summers; noncredit/undergraduate/graduate credit; workshops

OUR LADY OF THE LAKE UNIVERSITY

Department of Religious Studies, College of Arts and Sciences, 411 SW 24th St., San Antonio, TX 78207-4689. (1-800) 436-6558, (210) 431-3961. Fax: (210) 431-4036. Web: www.ollusa.edu

ST. EDWARD'S UNIVERSITY

Religious Studies Program, The School of Humanities, Mang House 110, Campus Mail Box 936, 3001 South Congress Ave., Austin, TX 78704. (512) 448- 8573, 8400. E-mail: eds@admin.stedwards.edu, seu.admit@admin.stedwards.edu; Web: www.stedwards.edu/hum/ rels/index.html

Contact: Dr. Ed Shirley, Coordinator

ST. MARY'S UNIVERSITY OF SAN ANTONIO

Department of Theology, School of Humanities, 1 Camino Santa Maria, San Antonio TX 78228. (210) 436-3011. E-mail: uadm@stmarytx.edu; Web: www.stmarytx.edu

UNITED COLLEGES OF SAN ANTONIO

(**Oblate School of Theology,** Our Lady of the Lake University, St. Mary's University and the University of the Incarnate Word), 285 Oblate Dr., San Antonio, TX 78216-6693. (210) 341-1366

Contact: Christiane B. Scheel

Lay/religious women/men, clergy; year-round, including summers; noncredit/undergraduate/graduate credit; workshops

UNIVERSITY OF DALLAS

Department of Theology, 845 E. Northgate Dr., Irving TX 75062. (972) 721-5219. Fax: (972) 265-5760. E-mail: wlcrawfo@udallas.edu; Web: http://acad.udallas.edu/theology

Contact: Dr. John Norris, Chairman

Undergraduate/graduate credit

The Institute for Religious and Pastoral Studies, 1845 E. Northgate Dr., Irving, TX 75062. (1-888) 447-4777, (972) 721-5105. E-mail: irps@udallas.edu; Web: www.udallas.edu/irps

Contact: Dr. Brian Schmisek

Lay/religious women/men, clergy; year-round, including summers; noncredit/undergraduate/graduate credit; workshops

UNIVERSITY OF THE INCARNATE WORD

Department of Religious Studies, College of Humanities, Arts & Social Sciences, UPO #8, 4301 Broadway, San Antonio, TX 78209. (1-800) 749-WORD. (210) 829-6005. E-mail: lozada@universe.uiwtx.edu; Web: www.uiw.edu/rstudies

Contact: Dr. Francisco Lozada Jr., Chair

Department of Pastoral Ministries, 4301 Broadway, San Antonio, TX 78209. (1-800) 749-WORD, (210) 829-3871. Fax: (210) 829-3880. E-mail: eryan@universe.uiwtx.edu; Web: www.uiw.edu/pastoral/

Contact: Dr. Eilish Ryan, c.c.v.i., Director

Lay/religious women/men; year-round including summers; noncredit/graduate credit; workshops

UNIVERSITY OF ST. THOMAS

Department of Theology: Catholic Studies, Theology, Pastoral Studies, 3800 Montrose Blvd., Houston, TX 77006. (713) 525-3529. E-mail: mac@stthom.edu, grace@stthom.edu; Web: www.stthom.edu/theology/index.html

Contact: Sr. Madeleine Grace, CVI

Lay/religious women/men, clergy; year-round, including summers; undergraduate/graduate credit

Center for Faith & Culture, 9845 Memorial Dr., Houston, TX 77024-3498. (713) 686-6844, ext. 229. Fax: (713) 957-3174. E-mail: cfc@stthom.edu; Web: www.stthom.edu/cfc

Contact: Donald S. Nesti, C.S.Sp., Director

Lay/religious women/men, clergy; year-round; noncredit/undergraduate/ graduate credit; workshops

Center for Thomistic Studies, 3800 Montrose Blvd., Houston, TX 77006. (713) 522-7911. Web: www.stthom.edu/cts

Contact: Rev. Victor B. Brezik, CSB

School of Theology at St. Mary's Seminary, 9845 Memorial Dr., Houston, TX 77024-3498. (713) 686-4345, ext. 231, 242. E-mail: sms@stthom.edu; Web: www.stthom.edu/stmary

Contact: Dr. Sandra Magie, Dean

Graduate credit

Affiliation: Basilian Fathers

VERMONT

MINISTERIAL FORMATION

PO Box 27, Stowe, VT 05672. (802) 253-7536. E-mail: blessac@together.net

Contact: Fr. Bernard Gaudreau

Affiliation: Diocese of Burlington

SAINT MICHAEL'S COLLEGE VERMONT

Department of Religious Studies, 1 Winooski Park, Colchester, VT 05439. (802) 654-2000. E-mail: jtrumbower@smcvt.edu; Web: www.smcvt.edu

Contact: Dr. Jeffrey Trumbower, Department Chair

Undergraduate credit

The Graduate Theology and Pastoral Ministry Program, One Winooski Park, Colchester, VT 05439. (802) 654-2347. E-mail: emahoney@smcvt.edu; Web: www.smcvt.edu/gradprograms

Contact: Dr. Edward Mahoney, Director

Graduate credit

Affiliation: Society of Saint Edmund

VIRGINIA

CHRISTIAN FORMATION

811 Cathedral Place, Richmond, VA 23220. (804) 359-5661. Web: www.richmonddiocese.org/ocf (see Services)

Contact: Dennis Beeman, Director of Christian Formation

Affiliation: Diocese of Richmond (liaison to Loyola University (New Orleans) extension program; University of Dayton Online Theology (virtual learning courses) and University of Notre Dame Online Theology (STEP program)

Lay/religious women/men, clergy; year-round; noncredit/undergraduate/graduate credit; distance learning (online) courses

CHRISTENDOM COLLEGE

Department of Theology, 134 Christendom Dr., Front Royal, VA 22630. (1-800) 877-5456. E-mail: info@christendom.edu; Web: www.christendom.edu/academics/bulletin/theol.shtml

MARYMOUNT UNIVERSITY

Department of Philosophy, Theology & Religious Studies, North Glebe Rd., Arlington, VA 22207-4299. (703) 526-6861. E-mail: rdraghi@marymount.edu; Web: www.marymount.edu

Contact: Dr. Robert A. Draghi, Chairperson

Undergraduate credit

Graduate Programs: Pastoral Counseling, Pastoral and Spiritual Care, North Glebe Rd., Arlington, VA 22207-4299. (703) 522-5600. E-mail: admissions@marymount.edu; Web: www.marymount.edu

Graduate credit

NOTRE DAME GRADUATE SCHOOL OF CHRISTENDOM COLLEGE (NDGS)

4407 Sano St., Alexandria, VA 22312. (703) 658-4304. Fax: (703) 658-2318. E-mail: krisburns@juno.com; Web: www.christendom.edu/grad/acad/curric.shtml

Contact: Dr. Kristin P. Burns

Affiliation: Christendom College

Lay/religious women/men, clergy; year-round, including summers; noncredit/graduate credit (certificate in ministry)

WASHINGTON

GONZAGA UNIVERSITY

Department of Religious Studies, College of Arts and Sciences, 502 East Boone Ave., Spokane, WA 99258-0001. (509) 323-6787. E-mail: dallen@gonzaga.edu; Web: www.gonzaga.edu

Contact: Fr. James Dallen

Undergraduate/graduate credit

Department of Catholic Studies, College of Arts and Sciences, 502 East Boone Ave., Spokane, WA 99258-0001. (509) 323-6720. E-mail: kries@gem.gonzaga.edu; Web: www.gonzaga.edu

Contact: Douglas Kries

Affiliation: Jesuits

The Ministry Institute at Mater Dei, 405 East Sinto, Spokane, WA 99202-1849, (1-800) 986-9585, ext. 6012. Fax: (509) 325-4011. E-mail: ministers@qwest.net; Web: www.gonzaga.edu/materdei

Contact: Dr. Bob Troman

Affiliation: Gonzaga University

Lay/religious women/men; year-round; noncredit/undergraduate/graduate credit; workshops; sabbaticals

SAINT MARTIN'S COLLEGE

Department of Religious Studies, Humanities Division, Room # 361, 5300 Pacific Ave. SE, Lacey, WA 98503. (360) 438-4342. E-mail: smead@stmartin.edu; Web: www.stmartin.edu/humanities/Religious_Studies/index.htm

Contact: Kilian J. Malvey, O.S.B.

Undergraduate credit; summer Spiritual Life Institute

SEATTLE UNIVERSITY

Department of Theology and Religious Studies, College of Arts and Sciences, Casey 2/E, 900 Broadway, Seattle, WA 98122-4460. (206) 296-5327. E-mail: damhsoir@seattleu.edu; Web: www.seattleu.edu/artsci/theology

Lay/religious women/men, clergy; year-round, including summer; noncredit/undergraduate credit; workshops

School of Theology and Ministry, 900 Broadway, Seattle, WA 98122-4340. (206) 296-5330. Fax: (206) 296-5329. E-mail: stm@seattleu.edu; Web: www.seattleu.edu/theomin

Lay/religious women/men; year-round including summers; noncredit/graduate credit; workshops

Affiliation: Jesuits

WEST VIRGINIA

WHEELING JESUIT UNIVERSITY

Department of Theology and Religious Studies, 316 Washington Ave., Wheeling, WV 26003. (1-800) 624-6992. E-mail: mfs@wju.edu; Web: www.wju.edu/academics/departments/theology/main.asp

Contact: Dr. Michael F. Steltenkamp, S.J., Chair

Master of Arts in Applied Theology, 316 Washington Ave., Wheeling, WV 26003. (1-800) 624-6992. E-mail: Kristw@wju.edu, mfs@wju.edu; Web: www.wju.edu/academics/departments/theology/maat.asp

Director: Dr. Kristopher Willumsen

Graduate credit

Affiliation: Jesuits

WISCONSIN

ALVERNO COLLEGE

Department of Religious Studies, 3400 South 43rd St., PO Box 343922, Milwaukee, WI 53234-3922. (1-800) 933-3401, (414) 382-6100. Fax: (414) 362-6354. E-mail: admissions@alverno.edu; Web: www.alverno.edu/academics/religious_studies.html

Certificate in Youth Ministry Studies, 3400 South 43rd St., PO Box 343922, Milwaukee, WI 53234-3922. (414) 382-6218, (1-800) 933-3401. Fax: (414) 362-6354. E-mail profed@alverno.edu; Web: www.alverno.edu/community_friends/continuing_prof_ministry.html

CARDINAL STRITCH UNIVERSITY

Religious Studies, College of Arts and Sciences, 6801 N. Yates Rd., Milwaukee, WI 53217-3985. (414) 410-4000. Fax: (414) 410-4239. Web: www.stritch.edu

Contact: Sr. Colette Dunn, OSF, Ph.D.

Lay/religious women/men clergy; year-round; noncredit/undergraduate/graduate credit

Certificate in Urban Ministry, 6801 N. Yates Rd., Milwaukee, WI 53217-3985. (414) 410-4000. Fax: (414) 410-4239. Web: www.stritch.edu

Master of Arts in Religious Studies, Office of Graduate Admissions, 6801 N. Yates Rd., Milwaukee, WI 53217-3985. (1-800) 347-8822, ext. 4042, (414) 410-4042. Fax: (414) 410-4239. E-mail: gradadm@stritch.edu; Web: www.stritch.edu

Contact: Pat Eckerstonfer, Director, Graduate Admissions

Lay/religious women/men, clergy; year-round, including summers; noncredit/undergraduate/graduate credit

Affiliation: Sisters of St. Francis of Assisi

DIOCESAN INSTITUTE FOR LAY & DIACONATE FORMATION

3577 High Point Rd., Madison, WI 53744. (608) 821-3083. E-mail: pastoral@straphael.org

Contact: Kate Wiskus, Director

Affiliation: Diocese of Madison

EDGEWOOD COLLEGE

Department of Religious Studies, Office of Admissions, 207 DeRicci Hall, 1000 Edgewood College Dr., Madison, WI 53711-1997. (1-800) 444-4861, (608) 663-2282. Fax: (608) 663-2214. E-mail: admissions@edgewood.edu; Web: www.edgewood.edu/academicsundergrad/rel_stud/majors/religious_studies.htm

Masters of Arts in Religious Studies, Office of Admissions, 207 DeRicci Hall, 1000 Edgewood College Dr., Madison, WI 53711-1997. (1-800) 444-4861, (608) 663-2282, Fax: (608) 663-2214. E-mail: admissions@edgewood.edu; Web: www.edgewood.edu/academics/graduate/programs/Grad_Rel.htm

LAY FORMATION INSTITUTE

Box 4004, 3710 East Ave. S., La Crosse, WI 54602-4004. (608) 788-7700. E-mail: cruff@dioceseoflacrosse.com

Contact: Christopher Ruff

Lay/religious women/men; Sept. - May; noncredit; workshops

MARIAN COLLEGE OF FOND DU LAC

Theology Studies, School of Arts and Humanities, 45 S. National Ave., Fond du Lac, WI 54935-4699. (1-800) 2-MARIAN. Fax: (920) 923-8755 Web: www.mariancollege.edu/Academics/AcademicDivisions/ArtsHumanities/theology.htm

Undergraduate credit

Affiliation: Congregation of Sisters of St. Agnes

MARQUETTE UNIVERSITY

Department of Theology, 100 Coughlin Hall, Box 1881, Milwaukee, WI, 53201-1881. (414) 288-7170. Fax: (414) 288-5548. E-mail: gale.prusinski@marquette.edu; Web: www.mu.edu/pages/home/student/undergrad/studyingatmu/majors/theology

Contact: Gale Prusinski

Affiliation: Jesuits

MOUNT MARY COLLEGE

Theology Department, 2900 N. Menomonee River Pkwy., Milwaukee, WI 53222-4597. (414) 258-4810, ext. 482. E-mail: rapped@mtmary.edu; Web: www.mtmary.edu/dept_theology.html

Contact: Dr. Donald Rappe

Affiliation: School Sisters of Notre Dame

Undergraduate/graduate credit; adult spirituality sessions

SACRED HEART SCHOOL OF THEOLOGY

7335 S. Hwy. 100, PO Box 429, Hales Corners, WI 53130-0429. (414) 425-8300. Fax: (414) 529-6999. E-mail: tknoebel@shst.edu; Web: www.shst.edu

Contact: Rev. Thomas Knoebel, Director of Admissions

Lay/religious men/women; second-career- vocations; year-round, including summers; noncredit/graduate credit; workshops

SAINT FRANCIS SEMINARY

Lay Formation Program, 3257 S Lake Dr., St. Francis, WI 53235. (414) 747-6432. Fax: (414) 747-6442. E-mail: gpokorny@sfs.edu; Web: www.sfs.edu

Contact: Gary Pokorny, Director

Lay/religious women/men; year-round, including summers; non-credit/graduate credit

ST. NORBERT COLLEGE

Religious Studies, Humanities and Fine Arts Division, 100 Grant St., De Pere, WI 54115-2099. (920) 403-3949. Fax: (920) 403-4096. E-mail: acaddean@snc.edu; Web: www.snc.edu/catalog/religion.htm
Contact: Associate Academic Dean

Master in Theological Studies Program, 100 Grant St., De Pere, WI 54115-2099. (920) 403-3741. Fax: (920) 403-4086. E-mail: theolstudy@snc.edu; Web: www.snc.edu/mts

SILVER LAKE COLLEGE

Department of Religious Studies and Philosophy, 2406 South Alverno Rd., Manitowoc, WI 54220. (920) 686-6228. E-mail: acanales@silver.sl.edu; Web: www.sl.edu/rlsphl/default.htm
Contact: Dr. Art Canales
Undergraduate/graduate credit; "Only Catholic Undergraduate Ministry & Spirituality Programs in US"
Affiliation: Franciscan Sisters of Christian Charity

VITERBO UNIVERSITY

Department of Religious Studies, School of Letters and Sciences, 815 Ninth St. South, La Crosse, WI 54601. (608) 796-3000. Web: www.viterbo.edu/academic/ug/sls/majors/philosophy/index.htm

Master of Arts in Servant Leadership, 815 Ninth St. South, La Crosse, WI 54601. (608) 796-3000. E-mail: cjkoch@viterbo.edu; Web: www.viterbo.edu/academic/gr/servlead
Contact: Carl Koch
Affiliation: Franciscan Sisters of Perpetual Adoration

Pastoral Education, 815 Ninth St. South, La Crosse, WI 54601. (608) 788-7700, 796-3705. Web: www.viterbo.edu/academic/ug/sls/majors/pastoral/index.htm
Contact: Tom Thibodeau, Coordinator
Affiliation: Diocese of La Crosse and Viterbo University

NATIONWIDE

NATIONAL PASTORAL LIFE CENTER

18 Bleecker St., New York, NY 10012-2404. (212) 431-7825. Fax: (212) 274-9786. E-mail: conferences@nplc.org; Web: www.nplc.org
Contact: Sr. Donna L. Ciangio, OP
For clergy
Affiliation: National, Catholic

Web Sites for Discerning a Religious Vocation

www.religiousministries.com

A comprehensive database of more than 3,000 Catholic organizations nationwide. The site contains in-depth information about men's and women's communities active in the United States plus many part time opportunities. Visitors to the Online Guide can search for Men's Communities, Women's Communities, Diocesan Vocation Directors, Secular Institutes, Lay Ministry Organizations , Retreat Centers and Religious Study Opportunities.

www.nccv-vocations.org

This site, maintained by NCCV (National Coalition for Church Vocations), provides resources for vocation ministry, awareness, education and discernment and includes an extensive glossary of vocation-related terms.

www.visionguide.org

This is the site for "Vision", an annual publication for vocation discernment produced by the National Religious Vocation Conference through Claretian Publications. This site includes articles on vocations as well as links to other vocation resources, including vocation discernment sites of numerous archdiocesan / diocesan vocation offices.

www.vocations.com

This site, from Fr. John Regan, Vocation Director, Diocese of Joliet (Illinois) Vocation Office, contains links to "Vocation Frequently Asked Questions", a list of other sites pertinent to vocations, a link to discovering your talents and discerning a religious vocation, as well as a link to resources for vocation directors.

www.geocities.com/Wellesley/1114/index.html

SisterSite - of interest to women religious and those interested in religious vocations - contains links to vocations; a listing of periodicals, publishers, best-sellers and services, etc. of interest to sisters; and a link to history / research of religious life, theology, scripture studies and religious studies.

members.aol.com/decide2b/home.html

"Who 2 Be" will help you discern your vocation in life, and whether that vocation is to the religious life. Links are given to "Making Choices", "Decisions, Decisions, Decisions", "Frequently Asked Questions About Vocations" and "Frequently Asked Questions About Older Priestly Vocations" as well as general vocation discernment, including "The Enneagram Inventory" and the "Myers-Briggs Personality Inventory."

www.vocations.com/priest/faqolder.html

This site, by the faculty of Sacred Heart of Theology (Hales Corner, WI) answers the following questions about becoming a priest later on in one's life: Does my age make a difference?, Will I be accepted simply because I want to be a priest?, Will I be treated like a "20 something" in the seminary?, What kind of education is needed?, What if I have been married?, What if I have made mistakes in my life?, Who will pay for the seminary education?, Do I have to sell my house?, How important is my work background?, What options in priesthood are available?, What options outside of priesthood are available?, What's the next step?

www.sistersholyredeemer.org/regform.html

Weekly chat room to meet other woman discerning a call to religious life.

www.chicagopriest.org

This site from the Archdiocese of Chicago discusses discernment questions on the calling, education and training of priests such as: Why be a priest?, Is it easy to become a priest?, What qualities does the Church look for in a candidate?, Am I holy enough to be a priest? and If I decide to go to seminary, am I committed for life?

www.vocationsplacement.org

This site can help turn your concept of religious life into an experience by arranging for you to attend a free "Live-in Experience" retreat at a community that interests you most.

www.religiouslife.com/mpd01.phtml

Take the *Ministry Potential Discerner (MPD) Self-Assessment Survey*. The *MPD* is a comprehensive spiritual evaluation tool consisting of 39 simple questions designed to measure one's vocational potential in serving the Lord and His Church as a priest, religious or consecrated person. It points out many areas of strengths, insight and Catholic values when taken honestly and conscientiously.

B-215

A Letter to God

I write this to you
And I write this to myself
In the hopes of bringing back
The peace I once felt.

It feels like years since we've last spoken
Though I heard you the other day
My ears were barely open
But I'm sure I heard you say:

"Everything will be just fine
Have faith in Me, Your friend
All things pass in time
There is no beginning and no end.

The pain you feel is fleeting
And soon it will fade away
I will give you strength for tomorrow
When you let go of yesterday."

Your words filled me with hope
And I felt as if I could fly
Overcome with happiness
Tears of joy came to my eyes.

Soon these feelings began to disappear
The Connection was no more.
Into my thoughts crept doubts and fears
Returning the pain I'd felt before.

Confusion raged inside of me but
As I fell deeper into the night
The torment was slowly lifted
And all black gave way to white.

I fell to my knees in prayer
Thanking You for all I'd been given
I offered You my life
And that is when I began living.

B-216

All are Called

"All the faithful of Christ - of whatever rank or status - are called to the fullness of the Christian life and to the perfection of charity."

(Vatican ll, *On the Church*, #40)

There are many ways in which the faithful of Christ follow the call to fullness of life - and the contemplative religious life is one way. It is a unique way, with a long and treasured history in the Church. Members of contemplative communities give themselves to God alone in solitude, silence and through continual prayer and self-denial. The entire atmosphere of a monastery - the place, the schedule, and the people - all are directed toward making it possible to experience God and His love.

By choosing contemplative life, members decide to direct all their energies to deepening the "God Life" within their hearts: by an attentive listening to the Spirit, an awareness of the Divine presence and activity in the world, and an ever deepening communion with God. The study of Scripture and other important writings of the Church helps to further develop spiritual understanding and values. Private and liturgical prayer, spiritual reading, and Lectio Divina nourish and deepen this goal.

Contemplative communities experience a number of essential elements:

- community life fully shared
- prayer and solitude
- Eucharist and Liturgy of the Hours
- sacred reading
- public vows
- work in the monastic setting
- meals in common

Also fundamental are interior discipline, silence, simplicity of life, hospitality and a readiness to pray with, and for, others. Community works, within the monastery setting, may include: spiritual direction, retreats, catechetics, publications, counseling the marginalized, baking and distributing altar breads, and making liturgical vestments.

By daily labor, members support the Community, develop their gifts and unite with their sisters and brothers all over the world who must also work.

Monastic contemplative life is centered around the communal celebration of the Liturgy of the Hours and the Eucharistic Liturgy, which gives primary meaning to the life of each member. All contemplative communities have a rhythm of prayer, work and leisure within their monastery. Throughout the centuries, the Church has promoted various expressions of the contemplative life. Individual communities reflect and share the charism and spirit of their founders in a particular way. "Come and See!"

A typical day might consist of

- Early rising with morning prayers and meditation
- Mass
- Work time (e.g., vestments, altar breads, clerical work)
- Midday prayers followed by dinner
- Afternoon work time with some free time
- Evening prayers and evening meditation
- Evening meal
- Recreation
- Free time before retiring
- Night prayers